ADVANCED
ENGINEERING
MATHEMATICS

*International Student
Edition*

ADVANCED ENGINEERING MATHEMATICS

International Student Edition

PETER V. O'NEIL

*University of Alabama
at Birmingham*

Australia   Canada   Mexico   Singapore   Spain   United Kingdom   United States

THOMSON
™

Advanced Engineering Mathematics, International Student Edition
by Peter V. O'Neil

Associate Vice-President and Editorial Director:
Evelyn Veitch

Publisher:
Chris Carson

Developmental Editor:
Kamilah Reid Burrell/
Hilda Gowaus

Permissions Coordinator:
Vicki Gould

Production Services:
RPK Editorial Services

Copy Editor:
Shelly Gerger-Knechtl/
Harlan James

Proofreader:
Erin Wagner/Harlan James

Indexer:
RPK Editorial Services

Production Manager:
Renate McCloy

Creative Director:
Angela Cluer

Interior Design:
Terri Wright

Cover Design:
Andrew Adams

Compositor:
Integra

Printer:
Quebecor World

North America
Nelson
1120 Birchmount Road
Toronto, Ontario M1K 5G4
Canada

Asia
Thomson Learning
5 Shenton Way #01-01
UIC Building
Singapore 068808

Australia/New Zealand
Thomson Learning
102 Dodds Street
Southbank, Victoria
Australia 3006

Europe/Middle East/Africa
Thomson Learning
High Holborn House
50/51 Bedford Row
London WC1R 4LR
United Kingdom

Latin America
Thomson Learning
Seneca, 53
Colonia Polanco
11560 Mexico D.F.
Mexico

Spain
Paraninfo
Calle/Magallanes, 25
28015 Madrid, Spain

Contents

PART 2 Vectors and Linear Algebra 201

PART 3   Systems of Differential Equations and Qualitative Methods   359

PART 4   Vector Analysis   473

PART 5   Fourier Analysis, Orthogonal Expansions, and Wavelets   581

PART 6 Partial Differential Equations   779

Chapter 17 The Wave Equation   781

Chapter 18 The Heat Equation   841

PART 7 Complex Analysis 911

PART 8   Probability and Statistics   1097

Preface

This Sixth Edition of *Advanced Engineering Mathematics* maintains the primary goal of previous editions—to engage much of the post-calculus mathematics needed and used by scientists, engineers, and applied mathematicians, in a setting that is helpful to both students and faculty. The format used throughout begins with the correct developments of concepts such as Fourier series and integrals, conformal mappings, and special functions. These ideas are then brought to bear on applications and models of important phenomena, such as wave and heat propagation and filtering of signals.

This edition differs from the previous one primarily in the inclusion of statistics and numerical methods. The statistics part treats random variables, normally distributed data, bell curves, the binomial, Poisson, and student t-distributions, the central limit theorem, confidence intervals, correlation, and regression. This is preceded by prerequisite topics from probability and techniques of enumeration.

The numerical methods are applied to initial value problems in ordinary differential equations, including a proposal for radioactive waste disposal, and to boundary value problems involving the heat and wave equations.

Finally, in order to include these topics without lengthening the book, some items from the fifth edition have been moved to a website, located at http://engineering.thomsonlearning.com. I hope that this provides convenient accessibility. Material selected for this move includes some biographies and historical notes, predator/prey and competing species models, the theory underlying the efficiency of the FFT, and some selected examples and problems.

The chart on the following page offers a complete organizational overview.

Acknowledgments

This book is the result of a team effort involving much more than an author. Among those to whom I owe a debt of appreciation are Chris Carson, Joanne Woods, Hilda Gowans and Kamilah Reid-Burrell of Thomson Engineering, and Rose Kernan and the professionals at RPK Editorial Services, Inc. I also want to thank Dr. Thomas O'Neil of the California Polytechnic State University for material he contributed, and Rich Jones, who had the vision for the first edition of this book many years ago.

Finally, I want to acknowledge the reviewers, whose suggestions for improvements and clarifications are much appreciated:

Preliminary Review

Panagiotis Dimitrakopoulos, University of Maryland
Mohamed M. Hafez, University of California, Davis
Jennifer Hopwood, University of Western Australia
Nun Kwan Yip, Purdue University

Organizational Overview

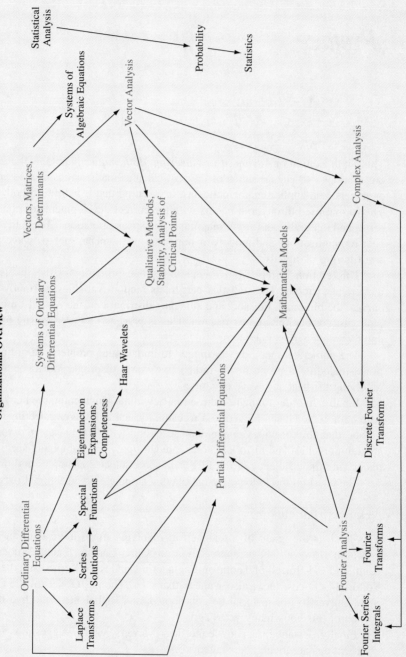

Draft Review

Sabri Abou-Ward, University of Toronto
Craig Hildebrand, California State University – Fresno
Seiichi Nomura, University of Texas, Arlington
David L. Russell, Virginia Polytechnic Institute and State University
Y.Q. Sheng, McMaster University

PETER V. O'NEIL
University of Alabama at Birmingham

PART 1

Ordinary Differential Equations

A *differential equation* is an equation that contains one or more derivatives. For example,

$$y''(x) + y(x) = 4 \ \sin(3x)$$

and

$$\frac{d^4 w}{dt^4} - (w(t))^2 = e^{-t}$$

are differential equations. These are *ordinary* differential equations because they involve only total derivatives, rather than partial derivatives.

Differential equations are interesting and important because they express relationships involving rates of change. Such relationships form the basis for developing ideas and studying phenomena in the sciences, engineering, economics, and increasingly in other areas, such as the business world and the stock market. We will see examples of applications as we learn more about differential equations.

1

The *order* of a differential equation is the order of its highest derivative. The first example given above is of second order, while the second is of fourth order. The equation

$$xy' - y^2 = e^x$$

is of first order.

A *solution* of a differential equation is any function that satisfies it. A solution may be defined on the entire real line, or on only part of it, often an interval. For example,

$$y = \sin(2x)$$

is a solution of

$$y'' + 4y = 0,$$

because, by direct differentiation,

$$y'' + 4y = -4\sin(2x) + 4\sin(2x) = 0.$$

This solution is defined for all x (that is, on the whole real line).

By contrast,

$$y = x\ln(x) - x$$

is a solution of

$$y' = \frac{y}{x} + 1,$$

but this solution is defined only for $x > 0$. Indeed, the coefficient $1/x$ of y in this equation means that $x = 0$ is disallowed from the start.

We now begin a systematic development of ordinary differential equations, starting with the first order case.

CHAPTER 1

First-Order Differential Equations

1.1   Preliminary Concepts

Before developing techniques for solving various kinds of differential equations, we will develop some terminology and geometric insight.

1.1.1   General and Particular Solutions

A first-order differential equation is any equation involving a first derivative, but no higher derivative. In its most general form, it has the appearance

$$F(x, y, y') = 0, \tag{1.1}$$

in which $y(x)$ is the function of interest and x is the independent variable. Examples are

$$y' - y^2 - e^y = 0,$$

$$y' - 2 = 0,$$

and

$$y' - \cos(x) = 0.$$

Note that y' must be present for an equation to qualify as a first-order differential equation, but x and/or y need not occur explicitly.

A *solution* of equation (1.1) on an interval I is a function φ that satisfies the equation for all x in I. That is,

$$F(x, \varphi(x), \varphi'(x)) = 0 \quad \text{for all } x \text{ in } I.$$

For example,

$$\varphi(x) = 2 + ke^{-x}$$

3

is a solution of

$$y' + y = 2$$

for all real x, and for any number k. Here I can be chosen as the entire real line. And

$$\varphi(x) = x \ln(x) + cx$$

is a solution of

$$y' = \frac{y}{x} + 1$$

for all $x > 0$, and for any number c.

In both of these examples, the solution contained an arbitrary constant. This is a symbol independent of x and y that can be assigned any numerical value. Such a solution is called the *general solution* of the differential equation. Thus

$$\varphi(x) = 2 + ke^{-x}$$

is the general solution of $y' + y = 2$.

Each choice of the constant in the general solution yields a *particular solution*. For example,

$$f(x) = 2 + e^{-x}, \quad g(x) = 2 - e^{-x}$$

and

$$h(x) = 2 - \sqrt{53}e^{-x}$$

are all particular solutions of $y' + y = 2$, obtained by choosing, respectively, $k = 1$, -1 and $-\sqrt{53}$ in the general solution.

1.1.2 Implicitly Defined Solutions

Sometimes we can write a solution explicitly giving y as a function of x. For example,

$$y = ke^{-x}$$

is the general solution of

$$y' = -y,$$

as can be verified by substitution. This general solution is explicit, with y isolated on one side of an equation, and a function of x on the other.

By contrast, consider

$$y' = -\frac{2xy^3 + 2}{3x^2y^2 + 8e^{4y}}.$$

We claim that the general solution is the function $y(x)$ implicitly defined by the equation

$$x^2y^3 + 2x + 2e^{4y} = k, \tag{1.2}$$

in which k can be any number. To verify this, implicitly differentiate equation (1.2) with respect to x, remembering that y is a function of x. We obtain

$$2xy^3 + 3x^2y^2y' + 2 + 8e^{4y}y' = 0,$$

and solving for y' yields the differential equation.

In this example we are unable to solve equation (1.2) explicitly for y as a function of x, isolating y on one side. Equation (1.2), implicitly defining the general solution, was obtained by a technique we will develop shortly, but this technique cannot guarantee an explicit solution.

1.1.3   Integral Curves

A graph of a solution of a first-order differential equation is called an *integral curve* of the equation. If we know the general solution, we obtain an infinite family of integral curves, one for each choice of the arbitrary constant.

EXAMPLE 1.1

We have seen that the general solution of

$$y' + y = 2$$

is

$$y = 2 + ke^{-x}$$

for all x. The integral curves of $y' + y = 2$ are graphs of $y = 2 + ke^{-x}$ for different choices of k. Some of these are shown in Figure 1.1. ∎

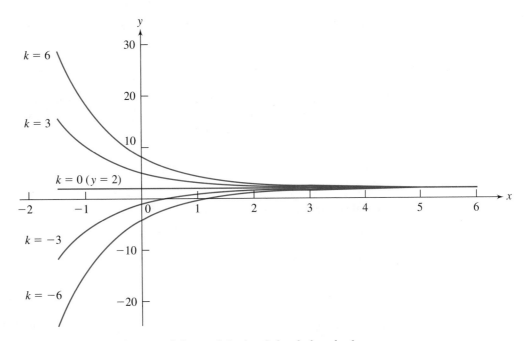

FIGURE 1.1   *Integral curves of $y' + y = 2$ for $k = 0, 3, -3, 6,$ and -6.*

EXAMPLE 1.2

It is routine to verify that the general solution of

$$y' + \frac{y}{x} = e^x$$

is

$$y = \frac{1}{x}(xe^x - e^x + c)$$

for $x \neq 0$. Graphs of some of these integral curves, obtained by making choices for c, are shown in Figure 1.2. ■

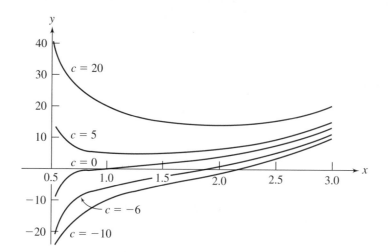

FIGURE 1.2   *Integral curves of $y' + \frac{1}{x}y = e^x$ for $c = 0, 5, 20, -6$, and -10.*

We will see shortly how these general solutions are obtained. For the moment, we simply want to illustrate integral curves.

Although in simple cases integral curves can be sketched by hand, generally we need computer assistance. Computer packages such as MAPLE, MATHEMATICA and MATLAB are widely available. Here is an example in which the need for computing assistance is clear.

EXAMPLE 1.3

The differential equation

$$y' + xy = 2$$

has general solution

$$y(x) = e^{-x^2/2} \int_0^x 2e^{\xi^2/2}\, d\xi + ke^{-x^2/2}.$$

Figure 1.3 shows computer-generated integral curves corresponding to $k = 0$, 4, 13, -7, -15 and -11. ■

1.1.4   The Initial Value Problem

The general solution of a first-order differential equation $F(x, y, y') = 0$ contains an arbitrary constant, hence there is an infinite family of integral curves, one for each choice of the constant. If we specify that a solution is to pass through a particular point (x_0, y_0), then we must find that particular integral curve (or curves) passing through this point. This is called an *initial value problem*. Thus, a first order initial value problem has the form

$$F(x, y, y') = 0; \quad y(x_0) = y_0,$$

in which x_0 and y_0 are given numbers. The condition $y(x_0) = y_0$ is called an *initial condition*.

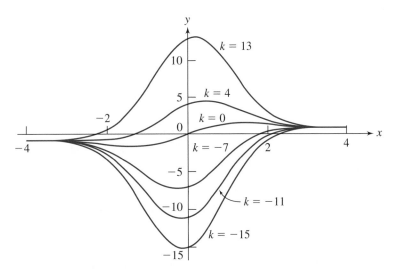

FIGURE 1.3 *Integral curves of $y' + xy = 2$ for $k = 0, 4, 13, -7, -15,$ and* $-11.$

EXAMPLE 1.4

Consider the initial value problem

$$y' + y = 2; \quad y(1) = -5.$$

From Example 1.1, the general solution of $y' + y = 2$ is

$$y = 2 + ke^{-x}.$$

Graphs of this equation are the integral curves. We want the one passing through $(1, -5)$. Solve for k so that

$$y(1) = 2 + ke^{-1} = -5,$$

obtaining

$$k = -7e.$$

The solution of this initial value problem is

$$y = 2 - 7ee^{-x} = 2 - 7e^{-(x-1)}.$$

As a check, $y(1) = 2 - 7 = -5.$ ∎

The effect of the initial condition in this example was to pick out one special integral curve as the solution sought. This suggests that an initial value problem may be expected to have a unique solution. We will see later that this is the case, under mild conditions on the coefficients in the differential equation.

1.1.5 Direction Fields

Imagine a curve, as in Figure 1.4. If we choose some points on the curve and, at each point, draw a segment of the tangent to the curve there, then these segments give a rough outline of the shape of the curve. This simple observation is the key to a powerful device for envisioning integral curves of a differential equation.

FIGURE 1.4 *Short tangent segments suggest the shape of the curve.*

The general first-order differential equation has the form

$$F(x, y, y') = 0.$$

Suppose we can solve for y' and write the differential equation as

$$y' = f(x, y).$$

Here f is a known function. Suppose $f(x, y)$ is defined for all points (x, y) in some region R of the plane. The slope of the integral curve through a given point (x_0, y_0) of R is $y'(x_0)$, which equals $f(x_0, y_0)$. If we compute $f(x, y)$ at selected points in R, and draw a small line segment having slope $f(x, y)$ at each (x, y), we obtain a collection of segments which trace out the shapes of the integral curves. This enables us to obtain important insight into the behavior of the solutions (such as where solutions are increasing or decreasing, limits they might have at various points, or behavior as x increases).

A drawing of the plane, with short line segments of slope $f(x, y)$ drawn at selected points (x, y), is called a *direction field* of the differential equation $y' = f(x, y)$. The name derives from the fact that at each point the line segment gives the direction of the integral curve through that point. The line segments are called *lineal elements*.

EXAMPLE 1.5

Consider the equation

$$y' = y^2.$$

Here $f(x, y) = y^2$, so the slope of the integral curve through (x, y) is y^2. Select some points and, through each, draw a short line segment having slope y^2. A computer generated direction field is shown in Figure 1.5(a). The lineal elements form a profile of some integral curves and give us some insight into the behavior of solutions, at least in this part of the plane. Figure 1.5(b) reproduces this direction field, with graphs of the integral curves through $(0, 1)$, $(0, 2)$, $(0, 3)$, $(0, -1)$, $(0, -2)$ and $(0, -3)$.

By a method we will develop, the general solution of $y' = y^2$ is

$$y = -\frac{1}{x + k},$$

so the integral curves form a family of hyperbolas, as suggested by the curves sketched in Figure 1.5(b). ■

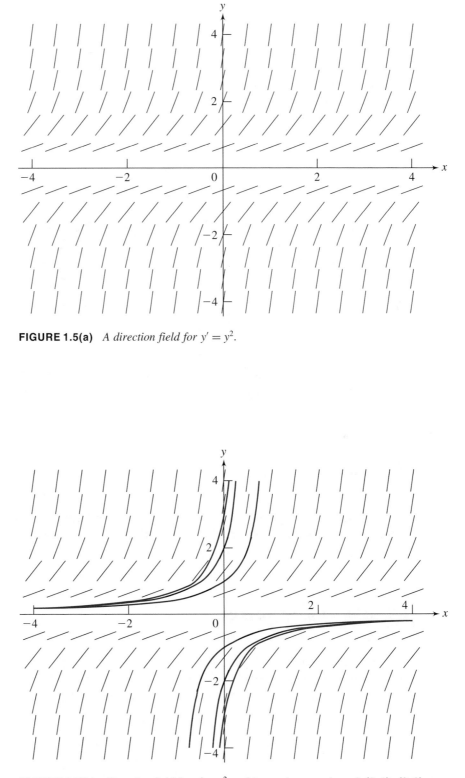

FIGURE 1.5(a) *A direction field for* $y' = y^2$.

FIGURE 1.5(b) *Direction field for* $y' = y^2$ *and integral curves through* $(0, 1)$, $(0, 2)$, $(0, 3)(0, -1)$, $(0, -2)$, *and* $(0, -3)$.

EXAMPLE 1.6

Figure 1.6 shows a direction field for

$$y' = \sin(xy),$$

together with the integral curves through $(0,1)$, $(0,2)$, $(0,3)$, $(0,-1)$, $(0,-2)$ and $(0,-3)$. In this case, we cannot write a simple expression for the general solution, and the direction field provides information about the behavior of solutions that is not otherwise readily apparent. ∎

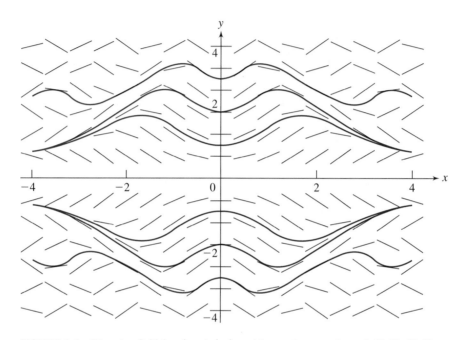

FIGURE 1.6 *Direction field for* $y' = \sin(xy)$ *and integral curves through* $(0,1)$, $(0,2)$, $(0,3)$, $(0,-1)$, $(0,-2)$, *and* $(0,-3)$.

With this as background, we will begin a program of identifying special classes of first-order differential equations for which there are techniques for writing the general solution. This will occupy the next five sections.

SECTION 1.1   PROBLEMS

In each of Problems 1 through 6, determine whether the given function is a solution of the differential equation.

1. $2yy' = 1$; $\varphi(x) = \sqrt{x-1}$ for $x > 1$

2. $y' + y = 0$; $\varphi(x) = Ce^{-x}$

3. $y' = -\dfrac{2y + e^x}{2x}$ for $x > 0$; $\varphi(x) = \dfrac{C - e^x}{2x}$

4. $y' = \dfrac{2xy}{2 - x^2}$ for $x \neq \pm\sqrt{2}$; $\varphi(x) = \dfrac{C}{x^2 - 2}$

5. $xy' = x - y$; $\varphi(x) = \dfrac{x^2 - 3}{2x}$ for $x \neq 0$

6. $y' + y = 1$; $\varphi(x) = 1 + Ce^{-x}$

In each of Problems 7 through 11, verify by implicit differentiation that the given equation implicitly defines a solution of the differential equation.

7. $y^2 + xy - 2x^2 - 3x - 2y = C$;

$$y - 4x - 2 + (x + 2y - 2)y' = 0$$

8. $xy^3 - y = C; \ y^3 + (3xy^2 - 1)y' = 0$

9. $y^2 - 4x^2 + e^{xy} = C; \ 8x - ye^{xy} - (2y + xe^{xy})y' = 0$

10. $8\ln|x - 2y + 4| - 2x + 6y = C;$

$$y' = \frac{x - 2y}{3x - 6y + 4}$$

11. $\tan^{-1}(y/x) + x^2 = C; \ \dfrac{2x^3 + 2xy^2 - y}{x^2 + y^2} + \dfrac{x}{x^2 + y^2}y' = 0$

In each of Problems 12 through 16, solve the initial value problem and graph the solution. *Hint:* Each of these differential equations can be solved by direct integration. Use the initial condition to solve for the constant of integration.

12. $y' = 2x; \ y(2) = 1$

13. $y' = e^{-x}; \ y(0) = 2$

14. $y' = 2x + 2; \ y(-1) = 1$

15. $y' = 4\cos(x)\sin(x); \ y(\pi/2) = 0$

16. $y' = 8x + \cos(2x); \ y(0) = -3$

In each of Problems 17 through 20 draw some lineal elements of the differential equation for $-4 \le x \le 4$, $-4 \le y \le 4$. Use the resulting direction field to sketch a graph of the solution of the initial value problem. (These problems can be done by hand.)

17. $y' = x + y; \ y(2) = 2$

18. $y' = x - xy; \ y(0) = -1$

19. $y' = xy; \ y(0) = 2$

20. $y' = x - y + 1; \ y(0) = 1$

In each of Problems 21 through 26, generate a direction field and some integral curves for the differential equation. Also draw the integral curve representing the solution of the initial value problem. These problems should be done by a software package.

21. $y' = \sin(y); \ y(1) = \pi/2$

22. $y' = x\cos(2x) - y; \ y(1) = 0$

23. $y' = y\sin(x) - 3x^2; \ y(0) = 1$

24. $y' = e^x - y; \ y(-2) = 1$

25. $y' - y\cos(x) = 1 - x^2; \ y(2) = 2$

26. $y' = 2y + 3; \ y(0) = 1$

27. Show that, for the differential equation $y' + p(x)y = q(x)$, the lineal elements on any vertical line $x = x_0$, with $p(x_0) \ne 0$, all pass through the single point (ξ, η), where

$$\xi = x_0 + \frac{1}{p(x_0)} \quad \text{and} \quad \eta = \frac{q(x_0)}{p(x_0)}.$$

1.2   Separable Equations

DEFINITION 1.1   *Separable Differential Equation*

A differential equation is called separable if it can be written

$$y' = A(x)B(y).$$

In this event, we can separate the variables and write, in differential form,

$$\frac{1}{B(y)} \, dy = A(x) \, dx$$

wherever $B(y) \ne 0$. We attempt to integrate this equation, writing

$$\int \frac{1}{B(y)} \, dy = \int A(x) \, dx.$$

This yields an equation in x, y, and a constant of integration. This equation implicitly defines the general solution $y(x)$. It may or may not be possible to solve explicitly for $y(x)$.

EXAMPLE 1.7

$y' = y^2 e^{-x}$ is separable. Write

$$\frac{dy}{dx} = y^2 e^{-x}$$

as

$$\frac{1}{y^2}\,dx = e^{-x}\,dx$$

for $y \neq 0$. Integrate this equation to obtain

$$-\frac{1}{y} = -e^{-x} + k,$$

an equation that implicitly defines the general solution. In this example we can explicitly solve for y, obtaining the general solution

$$y = \frac{1}{e^{-x} - k}.$$

Now recall that we required that $y \neq 0$ in order to separate the variables by dividing by y^2. In fact, the zero function $y(x) = 0$ is a solution of $y' = y^2 e^x$, although it cannot be obtained from the general solution by any choice of k. For this reason, $y(x) = 0$ is called a singular solution of this equation.

Figure 1.7 shows graphs of particular solutions obtained by choosing k as 0, 3, −3, 6 and −6. ∎

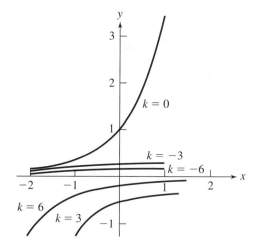

FIGURE 1.7 *Integral curves of $y' = y^2 e^{-x}$ for $k = 0, 3, -3, 6,$ and -6.*

Whenever we use separation of variables, we must be alert to solutions potentially lost through conditions imposed by the algebra used to make the separation.

EXAMPLE 1.8

$x^2 y' = 1 + y$ is separable, and we can write

$$\frac{1}{1+y}\, dy = \frac{1}{x^2}\, dx.$$

The algebra of separation has required that $x \neq 0$ and $y \neq -1$, even though we can put $x = 0$ and $y = -1$ into the differential equation to obtain the correct equation $0 = 0$.

Now integrate the separated equation to obtain

$$\ln|1 + y| = -\frac{1}{x} + k.$$

This implicitly defines the general solution. In this case, we can solve for $y(x)$ explicitly. Begin by taking the exponential of both sides to obtain

$$|1 + y| = e^k e^{-1/x} = A e^{-1/x},$$

in which we have written $A = e^k$. Since k could be any number, A can be any positive number. Then

$$1 + y = \pm A e^{-1/x} = B e^{-1/x},$$

in which $B = \pm A$ can be any nonzero number. The general solution is

$$y = -1 + B e^{-1/x},$$

in which B is any nonzero number.

Now revisit the assumption that $x \neq 0$ and $y \neq -1$. In the general solution, we actually obtain $y = -1$ if we allow $B = 0$. Further, the constant function $y(x) = -1$ does satisfy $x^2 y' = 1 + y$. Thus, by allowing B to be any number, including 0, the general solution

$$y(x) = -1 + B e^{-1/x}$$

contains all the solutions we have found. In this example, $y = -1$ is a solution, but not a singular solution, since it occurs as a special case of the general solution.

Figure 1.8 shows graphs of solutions corresponding to $B = -8, -5, 0, 4$ and 7. ■

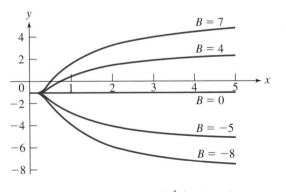

FIGURE 1.8 *Integral curves of $x^2 y' = 1 + y$ for $B = 0, 4, 7, -5,$ and -8.*

We often solve an initial value problem by finding the general solution of the differential equation, then solving for the appropriate choice of the constant.

EXAMPLE 1.9

Solve the initial value problem

$$y' = y^2 e^{-x}; \; y(1) = 4.$$

We know from Example 1.7 that the general solution of $y' = y^2 e^{-x}$ is

$$y(x) = \frac{1}{e^{-x} - k}.$$

Now we need to choose k so that

$$y(1) = \frac{1}{e^{-1} - k} = 4,$$

from which we get

$$k = e^{-1} - \frac{1}{4}.$$

The solution of the initial value problem is

$$y(x) = \frac{1}{e^{-x} + \frac{1}{4} - e^{-1}}. \; \blacksquare$$

EXAMPLE 1.10

The general solution of

$$y' = y \frac{(x-1)^2}{y+3}$$

is implicitly defined by

$$y + 3 \ln|y| = \frac{1}{3}(x-1)^3 + k. \tag{1.3}$$

To obtain the solution satisfying $y(3) = -1$, put $x = 3$ and $y = -1$ into equation (1.3) to obtain

$$-1 = \frac{1}{3}(2)^3 + k,$$

hence

$$k = -\frac{11}{3}.$$

The solution of this initial value problem is implicitly defined by

$$y + 3 \ln|y| = \frac{1}{3}(x-1)^3 - \frac{11}{3}. \; \blacksquare$$

1.2.1   Some Applications of Separable Differential Equations

Separable equations arise in many contexts, of which we will discuss three.

EXAMPLE 1.11

(The Mathematical Policewoman) A murder victim is discovered, and a lieutenant from the forensic science laboratory is summoned to estimate the time of death.

The body is located in a room that is kept at a constant 68 degrees Fahrenheit. For some time after the death, the body will radiate heat into the cooler room, causing the body's temperature to decrease. Assuming (for want of better information) that the victim's temperature was a "normal" 98.6 at the time of death, the lieutenant will try to estimate this time by observing the body's current temperature and calculating how long it would have had to lose heat to reach this point.

According to Newton's law of cooling, the body will radiate heat energy into the room at a rate proportional to the difference in temperature between the body and the room. If $T(t)$ is the body temperature at time t, then for some constant of proportionality k,

$$T'(t) = k[T(t) - 68].$$

The lieutenant recognizes this as a separable differential equation and writes

$$\frac{1}{T - 68} \, dT = k \, dt.$$

Upon integrating, she gets

$$\ln|T - 68| = kt + C.$$

Taking exponentials, she gets

$$|T - 68| = e^{kt+C} = Ae^{kt},$$

in which $A = e^C$. Then

$$T - 68 = \pm Ae^{kt} = Be^{kt}.$$

Then

$$T(t) = 68 + Be^{kt}.$$

Now the constants k and B must be determined, and this requires information. The lieutenant arrived at 9:40 p.m. and immediately measured the body temperature, obtaining 94.4 degrees. Letting 9:40 be time zero for convenience, this means that

$$T(0) = 94.4 = 68 + B,$$

and so $B = 26.4$. Thus far,

$$T(t) = 68 + 26.4e^{kt}.$$

To determine k, the lieutenant makes another measurement. At 11:00 she finds that the body temperature is 89.2 degrees. Since 11:00 is 80 minutes past 9:40, this means that

$$T(80) = 89.2 = 68 + 26.4e^{80k}.$$

Then

$$e^{80k} = \frac{21.2}{26.4},$$

so

$$80k = \ln\left(\frac{21.2}{26.4}\right)$$

and

$$k = \frac{1}{80} \ln\left(\frac{21.2}{26.4}\right).$$

The lieutenant now has the temperature function:

$$T(t) = 68 + 26.4e^{\ln(21.2/26.4)t/80}.$$

In order to find when last time when the body was 98.6 (presumably the time of death), solve for the time in

$$T(t) = 98.6 = 68 + 26.4e^{\ln(21.2/26.4)t/80}.$$

To do this, the lieutenant writes

$$\frac{30.6}{26.4} = e^{\ln(21.2/26.4)t/80}$$

and takes the logarithm of both sides to obtain

$$\ln\left(\frac{30.6}{26.4}\right) = \frac{t}{80} \ln\left(\frac{21.2}{26.4}\right).$$

Therefore the time of death, according to this mathematical model, was

$$t = \frac{80 \ln(30.6/26.4)}{\ln(21.2/26.4)},$$

which is approximately -53.8 minutes. Death occurred approximately 53.8 minutes before (because of the negative sign) the first measurement at 9:40, which was chosen as time zero. This puts the murder at about 8:46 p.m. ∎

EXAMPLE 1.12

(Radioactive Decay and Carbon Dating) In radioactive decay, mass is converted to energy by radiation. It has been observed that the rate of change of the mass of a radioactive substance is proportional to the mass itself. This means that, if $m(t)$ is the mass at time t, then for some constant of proportionality k that depends on the substance,

$$\frac{dm}{dt} = km.$$

This is a separable differential equation. Write it as

$$\frac{1}{m} dm = k\, dt$$

and integrate to obtain

$$\ln|m| = kt + c.$$

Since mass is positive, $|m| = m$ and

$$\ln(m) = kt + c.$$

Then

$$m(t) = e^{kt+c} = Ae^{kt},$$

in which A can be any positive number.

Determination of A and k for a given element requires two measurements. Suppose at some time, designated as time zero, there are M grams present. This is called the initial mass. Then

$$m(0) = A = M,$$

so

$$m(t) = Me^{kt}.$$

If at some later time T we find that there are M_T grams, then

$$m(T) = M_T = Me^{kT}.$$

Then

$$\ln\left(\frac{M_T}{M}\right) = kT,$$

hence

$$k = \frac{1}{T}\ln\left(\frac{M_T}{M}\right).$$

This gives us k and determines the mass at any time:

$$m(t) = Me^{\ln(M_T/M)t/T}.$$

We obtain a more convenient formula for the mass if we choose the time of the second measurement more carefully. Suppose we make the second measurement at that time $T = H$ at which exactly half of the mass has radiated away. At this time, half of the mass remains, so $M_T = M/2$ and $M_T/M = 1/2$. Now the expression for the mass becomes

$$m(t) = Me^{\ln(1/2)t/H},$$

or

$$m(t) = Me^{-\ln(2)t/H}. \tag{1.4}$$

This number H is called the half-life of the element. Although we took it to be the time needed for half of the original amount M to decay, in fact, between any times t_1 and $t_1 + H$, exactly half of the mass of the element present at t_1 will radiate away. To see this, write

$$m(t_1 + H) = Me^{-\ln(2)(t_1+H)/H}$$

$$= Me^{-\ln(2)t_1/H}e^{-\ln(2)H/H} = e^{-\ln(2)}m(t_1)$$

$$= \tfrac{1}{2}m(t_1).$$

Equation (1.4) is the basis for an important technique used to estimate the ages of certain ancient artifacts. The earth's upper atmosphere is constantly bombarded by high-energy cosmic rays, producing large numbers of neutrons, which collide with nitrogen in the air, changing some of it into radioactive carbon-14, or ^{14}C. This element has a half-life of about 5,730 years. Over the relatively recent period of the history of this planet in which life has evolved, the fraction of ^{14}C in the atmosphere, compared to regular carbon, has been essentially constant. This means that living matter (plant or animal) has injested ^{14}C at about the same rate over a long historical period, and objects living, say, two million years ago would have had the same ratio of carbon-14 to carbon in their bodies as objects alive today. When an organism dies, it ceases its intake of ^{14}C, which then begins to decay. By measuring the ratio of ^{14}C to carbon in an artifact, we can estimate the amount of the decay, and hence the time it took, giving an estimate of the time the organism was alive. This process of estimating the age of an artifact is called *carbon dating*. Of course, in reality the ratio of ^{14}C in the atmosphere has only been approximately constant, and in addition a sample may have been contaminated by exposure to other living organisms, or even to the air, so carbon dating is a sensitive process that can lead to controversial results. Nevertheless, when applied rigorously and combined with other tests and information, it has proved a valuable tool in historical and archeological studies.

To apply equation (1.4) to carbon dating, use $H = 5730$ and compute

$$\frac{\ln(2)}{H} = \frac{\ln(2)}{5730} \approx 0.000120968$$

in which $\approx$ means "approximately equal" (not all decimal places are listed). Equation (1.4) becomes

$$m(t) = Me^{-0.000120968t}.$$

Now suppose we have an artifact, say a piece of fossilized wood, and measurements show that the ratio of ^{14}C to carbon in the sample is 37 percent of the current ratio. If we say that the wood died at time 0, then we want to compute the time T it would take for one gram of the radioactive carbon to decay this amount. Thus, solve for T in

$$0.37 = e^{-0.000120968T}.$$

We find that

$$T = -\frac{\ln(0.37)}{0.000120968} \approx 8{,}219$$

years. This is a little less than one and one-half half-lives, a reasonable estimate if nearly $\frac{2}{3}$ of the ^{14}C has decayed. ∎

EXAMPLE 1.13

(Torricelli's Law) Suppose we want to estimate how long it will take for a container to empty by discharging fluid through a drain hole. This is a simple enough problem for, say, a soda can, but not quite so easy for a large oil storage tank or chemical facility.

We need two principles from physics. The first is that the rate of discharge of a fluid flowing through an opening at the bottom of a container is given by

$$\frac{dV}{dt} = -kAv,$$

in which $V(t)$ is the volume of fluid in the container at time t, $v(t)$ is the discharge velocity of fluid through the opening, A is the cross sectional area of the opening (assumed constant), and k is a constant determined by the viscosity of the fluid, the shape of the opening, and the fact that the cross-sectional area of fluid pouring out of the opening is slightly less than that of the opening itself. In practice, k must be determined for the particular fluid, container, and opening, and is a number between 0 and 1.

We also need Torricelli's law, which states that $v(t)$ is equal to the velocity of a free-falling particle released from a height equal to the depth of the fluid at time t. (Free-falling means that the particle is influenced by gravity only). Now the work done by gravity in moving the particle from its initial point by a distance $h(t)$ is $mgh(t)$, and this must equal the change in the kinetic energy, $(\frac{1}{2})mv^2$. Therefore,

$$v(t) = \sqrt{2gh(t)}.$$

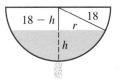

FIGURE 1.9

Putting these two equations together yields

$$\frac{dV}{dt} = -kA\sqrt{2gh(t)}. \tag{1.5}$$

We will apply equation (1.5) to a specific case to illustrate its use. Suppose we have a hemispherical tank of water, as in Figure 1.9. The tank has radius 18 feet, and water drains through a circular hole of radius 3 inches at the bottom. How long will it take the tank to empty?

Equation (1.5) contains two unknown functions, $V(t)$ and $h(t)$, so one must be eliminated. Let $r(t)$ be the radius of the surface of the fluid at time t and consider an interval of time from t_0 to $t_1 = t_0 + \Delta t$. The volume ΔV of water draining from the tank in this time equals the volume of a disk of thickness Δh (the change in depth) and radius $r(t^*)$, for some t^* between t_0 and t_1. Therefore

$$\Delta V = \pi \left[r(t^*) \right]^2 \Delta h$$

so

$$\frac{\Delta V}{\Delta t} = \pi \left[r(t^*) \right]^2 \frac{\Delta h}{\Delta t}.$$

In the limit as $t \to 0$,

$$\frac{dV}{dt} = \pi r^2 \frac{dh}{dt}.$$

Putting this into equation (1.5) yields

$$\pi r^2 \frac{dh}{dt} = -kA\sqrt{2gh}.$$

Now V has been eliminated, but at the cost of introducing $r(t)$. However, from Figure 1.9,

$$r^2 = 18^2 - (18 - h)^2 = 36h - h^2$$

so

$$\pi \left(36h - h^2 \right) \frac{dh}{dt} = -kA\sqrt{2gh}.$$

This is a separable differential equation, which we write as

$$\pi \frac{36h - h^2}{h^{1/2}} \, dh = -kA\sqrt{2g} \, dt.$$

Take g to be 32 feet per second per second. The radius of the circular opening is 3 inches, or $\frac{1}{4}$ feet, so its area is $A = \pi/16$ square feet. For water, and an opening of this shape and size, the experiment gives $k = 0.8$. The last equation becomes

$$\left(36h^{1/2} - h^{3/2} \right) dh = -(0.8)\left(\frac{1}{16} \right) \sqrt{64} \, dt,$$

or

$$\left(36h^{1/2} - h^{3/2}\right) dh = -0.4\, dt.$$

A routine integration yields

$$24h^{3/2} - \frac{2}{5}h^{5/2} = -\frac{2}{5}t + c,$$

or

$$60h^{3/2} - h^{5/2} = -t + k.$$

Now $h(0) = 18$, so

$$60(18)^{3/2} - (18)^{5/2} = k.$$

Thus $k = 2268\sqrt{2}$ and $h(t)$ is implicitly determined by the equation

$$60h^{3/2} - h^{5/2} = 2268\sqrt{2} - t.$$

The tank is empty when $h = 0$, and this occurs when $t = 2268\sqrt{2}$ seconds, or about 53 minutes, 28 seconds. ■

The last three examples contain an important message. Differential equations can be used to solve a variety of problems, but a problem usually does not present itself as a differential equation. Normally we have some event or process, and we must use whatever information we have about it to derive a differential equation and initial conditions. This process is called *mathematical modeling*. The model consists of the differential equation and other relevant information, such as initial conditions. We look for a function satisfying the differential equation and the other information, in the hope of being able to predict future behavior, or perhaps better understand the process being considered.

SECTION 1.2   PROBLEMS

In each of Problems 1 through 10, determine if the differential equation is separable. If it is, find the general solution (perhaps implicitly defined). If it is not separable, do not attempt a solution at this time.

1. $3y' = 4x/y^2$

2. $y + xy' = 0$

3. $\cos(y)y' = \sin(x + y)$

4. $e^{x+y}y' = 3x$

5. $xy' + y = y^2$

6. $y' = \dfrac{(x+1)^2 - 2y}{2y}$

7. $x\sin(y)y' = \cos(y)$

8. $\dfrac{x}{y}y' = \dfrac{2y^2 + 1}{x + 1}$

9. $y + y' = e^x - \sin(y)$

10. $[\cos(x+y) + \sin(x-y)]y' = \cos(2x)$

In each of Problems 11 through 15, solve the initial value problem.

11. $xy^2y' = y + 1;\ y(3e^2) = 2$

12. $y' = 3x^2(y+2);\ y(2) = 8$

13. $\ln(y^x)y' = 3x^2y;\ y(2) = e^3$

14. $2yy' = e^{x-y^2};\ y(4) = -2$

15. $yy' = 2x\sec(3y);\ y(2/3) = \pi/3$

16. An object having a temperature of 90 degrees Fahrenheit is placed into an environment kept at 60 degrees. Ten minutes later the object has cooled to 88 degrees. What will be the temperature of the object after it has been in this environment for 20 minutes? How long will it take for the object to cool to 65 degrees?

17. A thermometer is carried outside a house whose ambient temperature is 70 degrees Fahrenheit. After five minutes the thermometer reads 60 degrees, and fifteen minutes after this, 50.4 degrees. What is the outside temperature (which is assumed to be constant)?

18. Assume that the population of bacteria in a petri dish changes at a rate proportional to the population at that time. This means that, if $P(t)$ is the population at time t, then

$$\frac{dP}{dt} = kP$$

for some constant k. A particular culture has a population density of 100,000 bacteria per square inch. A culture that covered an area of 1 square inch at 10:00 a.m. on Tuesday was found to have grown to cover 3 square inches by noon the following Thursday. How many bacteria will be present at 3:00 p.m. the following Sunday? How many will be present on Monday at 4:00 p.m.? When will the world be overrun by these bacteria, assuming that they can live anywhere on the earth's surface? (Here you need to look up the land area of the earth.)

19. Assume that a sphere of ice melts at a rate proportional to its surface area, retaining a spherical shape. Interpret melting as a reduction of volume with respect to time. Determine an expression for the volume of the ice at any time t.

20. A radioactive element has a half-life of $\ln(2)$ weeks. If e^3 tons are present at a given time, how much will be left 3 weeks later?

21. The half-life of uranium-238 is approximately $4.5 \cdot 10^9$ years. How much of a 10-kilogram block of U-238 will be present 1 billion years from now?

22. Given that 12 grams of a radioactive element decays to 9.1 grams in 4 minutes, what is the half-life of this element?

23. Evaluate

$$\int_0^\infty e^{-t^2 - 9/t^2} \, dt.$$

Hint: Let

$$I(x) = \int_0^\infty e^{-t^2 - (x/t)^2} \, dt.$$

Calculate $I'(x)$ by differentiating under the integral sign, then let $u = x/t$. Show that $I'(x) = -2I(x)$ and solve for $I(x)$. Evaluate the constant by using the standard result that $\int_0^\infty e^{-t^2} dt = \sqrt{\pi}/2$. Finally, evaluate $I(3)$.

24. Derive the fact used in Example 1.13 that $v(t) = \sqrt{2gh(t)}$. *Hint:* Consider a free-falling particle having height $h(t)$ at time t. The work done by gravity in moving the particle from its starting point to a given point is $mgh(t)$, and this must equal the change in the kinetic energy, which is $(1/2)mv^2$.

25. Calculate the time required to empty the hemispherical tank of Example 1.13 if the tank is positioned with its flat side down.

26. (Draining a Hot Tub) Consider a cylindrical hot tub with a 5-foot radius and height of 4 feet, placed on one of its circular ends. Water is draining from the tub through a circular hole $\frac{5}{8}$ inches in diameter located in the base of the tub.

(a) Assume a value $k = 0.6$ to determine the rate at which the depth of the water is changing. Here it is useful to write

$$\frac{dh}{dt} = \frac{dh}{dV} \frac{dV}{dt} = \frac{dV/dt}{dV/dh}.$$

(b) Calculate the time T required to drain the hot tub if it is initially full. *Hint:* One way to do this is to write

$$T = \int_H^0 \frac{dt}{dh} \, dh.$$

(c) Determine how much longer it takes to drain the lower half than the upper half of the tub. *Hint:* Use the integral suggested in (b), with different limits for the two halves.

27. (Draining a Cone) A tank shaped like a right circular cone, with its vertex down, is 9 feet high and has a diameter of 8 feet. It is initially full of water.

(a) Determine the time required to drain the tank through a circular hole of diameter 2 inches at the vertex. Take $k = 0.6$.

(b) Determine the time it takes to drain the tank if it is inverted and the drain hole is of the same size and shape as in (a), but now located in the new base.

28. (Drain Hole at Unknown Depth) Determine the rate of change of the depth of water in the tank of Problem 27 (vertex at the bottom) if the drain hole is located in the side of the cone 2 feet above the bottom of the tank. What is the rate of change in the depth of the water when the drain hole is located in the bottom of the tank? Is it possible to determine the location of the drain hole if we are told the rate of change of the depth and the depth of the water in the tank? Can this be done without knowing the size of the drain opening?

29. Suppose the conical tank of Problem 27, vertex at the bottom, is initially empty and water is added at the constant rate of $\pi/10$ cubic feet per second. Does the tank ever overflow?

30. (Draining a Sphere) Determine the time it takes to completely drain a spherical tank of radius 18 feet if it is initially full of water and the water drains through a circular hole of radius 3 inches located in the bottom of the tank. Use $k = 0.8$.

1.3 Linear Differential Equations

DEFINITION 1.2 *Linear Differential Equation*

A first-order differential equation is linear if it has the form

$$y'(x) + p(x)y = q(x).$$

Assume that p and q are continuous on an interval I (possibly the whole real line). Because of the special form of the linear equation, we can obtain the general solution on I by a clever observation. Multiply the differential equation by $e^{\int p(x)\,dx}$ to get

$$e^{\int p(x)\,dx}y'(x) + p(x)e^{\int p(x)\,dx}y = q(x)e^{\int p(x)\,dx}.$$

The left side of this equation is the derivative of the product $y(x)e^{\int p(x)\,dx}$, enabling us to write

$$\frac{d}{dx}\left(y(x)e^{\int p(x)\,dx}\right) = q(x)e^{\int p(x)\,dx}.$$

Now integrate to obtain

$$y(x)e^{\int p(x)\,dx} = \int \left(q(x)e^{\int p(x)\,dx}\right)dx + C.$$

Finally, solve for $y(x)$:

$$y(x) = e^{-\int p(x)\,dx}\int\left(q(x)e^{\int p(x)\,dx}\right)dx + Ce^{-\int p(x)\,dx}. \tag{1.6}$$

The function $e^{\int p(x)\,dx}$ is called an *integrating factor* for the differential equation, because multiplication of the differential equation by this factor results in an equation that can be integrated to obtain the general solution. We do not recommend memorizing equation (1.6). Instead, recognize the form of the linear equation and understand the technique of solving it by multiplying by $e^{\int p(x)\,dx}$.

EXAMPLE 1.14

The equation $y' + y = \sin(x)$ is linear. Here $p(x) = 1$ and $q(x) = \sin(x)$, both continuous for all x. An integrating factor is

$$e^{\int dx},$$

or e^x. Multiply the differential equation by e^x to get

$$y'e^x + ye^x = e^x\sin(x),$$

or

$$(ye^x)' = e^x\sin(x).$$

Integrate to get

$$ye^x = \int e^x\sin(x)\,dx = \frac{1}{2}e^x[\sin(x) - \cos(x)] + C.$$

The general solution is

$$y(x) = \frac{1}{2}[\sin(x) - \cos(x)] + Ce^{-x}. \quad\blacksquare$$

EXAMPLE 1.15

Solve the initial value problem

$$y' = 3x^2 - \frac{y}{x}; \quad y(1) = 5.$$

First recognize that the differential equation can be written in linear form:

$$y' + \frac{1}{x}y = 3x^2.$$

An integrating factor is $e^{\int(1/x)\,dx} = e^{\ln(x)} = x$, for $x > 0$. Multiply the differential equation by x to get

$$xy' + y = 3x^3,$$

or

$$(xy)' = 3x^3.$$

Integrate to get

$$xy = \frac{3}{4}x^4 + C.$$

Then

$$y(x) = \frac{3}{4}x^3 + \frac{C}{x}$$

for $x > 0$. For the initial condition, we need

$$y(1) = 5 = \frac{3}{4} + C$$

so $C = 17/4$ and the solution of the initial value problem is

$$y(x) = \frac{3}{4}x^3 + \frac{17}{4x}$$

for $x > 0$. ■

Depending on p and q, it may not be possible to evaluate all of the integrals in the general solution 1.6 in closed form (as a finite algebraic combination of elementary functions). This occurs with

$$y' + xy = 2.$$

whose general solution is

$$y(x) = 2e^{-x^2/2} \int e^{x^2/2}\, dx + Ce^{-x^2/2}.$$

We cannot write $\int e^{x^2/2}\, dx$ in elementary terms. However, we could still use a software package to generate a direction field and integral curves, as is done in Figure 1.10. This provides some idea of the behavior of solutions, at least within the range of the diagram.

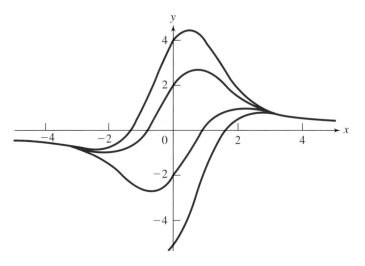

FIGURE 1.10 *Integral curves of $y' + xy = 2$ passing through $(0, 2)$, $(0, 4)$, $(0, -2)$, and $(0, -5)$.*

Linear differential equations arise in many contexts. Example 1.11, involving estimation of time of death, involved a separable differential equation which is also linear and could have been solved using an integrating factor.

EXAMPLE 1.16

(A Mixing Problem) Sometimes we want to know how much of a given substance is present in a container in which various substances are being added, mixed, and removed. Such problems are called *mixing problems*, and they are frequently encountered in the chemical industry and in manufacturing processes.

As an example, suppose a tank contains 200 gallons of brine (salt mixed with water), in which 100 pounds of salt are dissolved. A mixture consisting of $\frac{1}{8}$ pound of salt per gallon is flowing into the tank at a rate of 3 gallons per minute, and the mixture is continuously stirred. Meanwhile, brine is allowed to empty out of the tank at the same rate of 3 gallons per minute (Figure 1.11). How much salt is in the tank at any time?

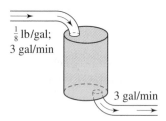

$\frac{1}{8}$ lb/gal;
3 gal/min

3 gal/min

FIGURE 1.11

Before constructing a mathematical model, notice that the initial ratio of salt to brine in the tank is 100 pounds per 200 gallons, or $\frac{1}{2}$ pound per gallon. Since the mixture pumped in has a constant ratio of $\frac{1}{8}$ pound per gallon, we expect the brine mixture to dilute toward the incoming ratio, with a "terminal" amount of salt in the tank of $\frac{1}{8}$ pound per gallon, times 200 gallons. This leads to the expectation that in the long term (as $t \to \infty$) the amount of salt in the tank should approach 25 pounds.

Now let $Q(t)$ be the amount of salt in the tank at time t. The rate of change of $Q(t)$ with time must equal the rate at which salt is pumped in, minus the rate at which it is pumped out. Thus

$$\frac{dQ}{dt} = (\text{rate in}) - (\text{rate out})$$

$$= \left(\frac{1}{8}\frac{\text{pounds}}{\text{gallon}}\right)\left(3\frac{\text{gallons}}{\text{minute}}\right) - \left(\frac{Q(t)}{200}\frac{\text{pounds}}{\text{gallon}}\right)\left(3\frac{\text{gallons}}{\text{minute}}\right)$$

$$= \frac{3}{8} - \frac{3}{200}Q(t).$$

This is the linear equation

$$Q'(t) + \frac{3}{200}Q = \frac{3}{8}.$$

An integrating factor is $e^{\int (3/200)\,dt} = e^{3t/200}$. Multiply the differential equation by this factor to obtain

$$Q'e^{3t/200} + \frac{3}{200}e^{3t/200}Q = \frac{3}{8}e^{3t/200},$$

or

$$\left(Qe^{3t/200}\right)' = \frac{3}{8}e^{3t/200}.$$

Then

$$Qe^{3t/200} = \frac{3}{8}\frac{200}{3}e^{3t/200} + C,$$

so

$$Q(t) = 25 + Ce^{-3t/200}.$$

Now

$$Q(0) = 100 = 25 + C$$

so $C = 75$ and

$$Q(t) = 25 + 75e^{-3t/200}.$$

As we expected, as t increases, the amount of salt approaches the limiting value of 25 pounds. From the derivation of the differential equation for $Q(t)$, it is apparent that this limiting value depends on the rate at which salt is poured into the tank, but not on the initial amount of salt in the tank. The term 25 in the solution is called the steady-state part of the solution because it is independent of time, and the term $75e^{-3t/200}$ is the transient part. As t increases, the transient part exerts less influence on the amount of salt in the tank, and in the limit the solution approaches its steady-state part. ■

In each of Problems 1 through 8, find the general solution. Not all integrals can be done in closed form.

1. $y' - \dfrac{3}{x}y = 2x^2$

2. $y' - y = \sinh(x)$

3. $y' + 2y = x$

4. $\sin(2x)y' + 2y\sin^2(x) = 2\sin(x)$

5. $y' - 2y = -8x^2$

6. $(x^2 - x - 2)y' + 3xy = x^2 - 4x + 4$

7. $y' + y = \dfrac{x-1}{x^2}$

8. $y' + \sec(x)y = \cos(x)$

In each of Problems 9 through 14, solve the initial value problem.

9. $y' + \dfrac{1}{x-2}y = 3x; \ y(3) = 4$

10. $y' + 3y = 5e^{2x} - 6; \ y(0) = 2$

11. $y' + \dfrac{2}{x+1}y = 3; \ y(0) = 5$

12. $(x^2 - 2x)y' + (x^2 - 5x + 4)y = (x^4 - 2x^3)e^{-x}; \ y(3) = 18e^{-3}$

13. $y' - y = 2e^{4x}; \ y(0) = -3$

14. $y' + \dfrac{5y}{9x} = 3x^3 + x; \ y(-1) = 4$

15. Find all functions with the property that the y-intercept of the tangent to the graph at (x, y) is $2x^2$.

16. A 500-gallon tank initially contains 50 gallons of brine solution in which 28 pounds of salt have been dissolved. Beginning at time zero, brine containing 2 pounds of salt per gallon is added at the rate of 3 gallons per minute, and the mixture is poured out of the tank at the rate of 2 gallons per minute. How much salt is in the tank when it contains 100 gallons of brine? *Hint:* The amount of brine in the tank at time t is $50 + t$.

17. Two tanks are cascaded as in Figure 1.12. Tank 1 initially contains 20 pounds of salt dissolved in 100 gallons of brine, while tank 2 contains 150 gallons of brine in which 90 pounds of salt are dissolved. At time zero a brine solution containing $\frac{1}{2}$ pound of salt per gallon is added to tank 1 at the rate of 5 gallons per minute. Tank 1 has an output that discharges brine into tank 2 at the rate of 5 gallons per minute, and tank 2 also has an output of 5 gallons per minute. Determine the amount of salt in each tank at any time t. Also determine when the concentration of salt in tank 2 is a minimum and how much salt is in the tank at that time. *Hint:* Solve for the amount of salt in tank 1 at time t first and then use this solution to determine the amount in tank 2.

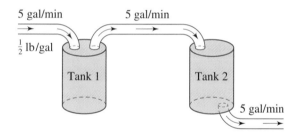

FIGURE 1.12 *Mixing between tanks in Problem 17.*

1.4 Exact Differential Equations

We continue the theme of identifying certain kinds of first-order differential equations for which there is a method leading to a solution.

We can write any first order equation $y' = f(x, y)$ in the form

$$M(x, y) + N(x, y)y' = 0.$$

For example, put $M(x, y) = -f(x, y)$ and $N(x, y) = 1$. An interesting thing happens if there is a function φ such that

$$\frac{\partial \varphi}{\partial x} = M(x, y) \quad \text{and} \quad \frac{\partial \varphi}{\partial y} = N(x, y). \tag{1.7}$$

In this event, the differential equation becomes

$$\frac{\partial \varphi}{\partial x} + \frac{\partial \varphi}{\partial y} \frac{dy}{dx} = 0,$$

which, by the chain rule, is the same as

$$\frac{d}{dx} \varphi(x, y(x)) = 0.$$

But this means that

$$\varphi(x, y(x)) = C,$$

with C constant. If we now read this argument from the last line back to the first, the conclusion is that the equation

$$\varphi(x, y) = C$$

implicitly defines a function $y(x)$ that is the general solution of the differential equation. Thus, finding a function that satisfies equation (1.7) is equivalent to solving the differential equation.

Before taking this further, consider an example.

EXAMPLE 1.17

The differential equation

$$y' = -\frac{2xy^3 + 2}{3x^2 y^2 + 8e^{4y}}$$

is neither separable nor linear. Write it in the form

$$M + Ny' = 2xy^3 + 2 + \left(3x^2 y^2 + 8e^{4y}\right) y' = 0, \tag{1.8}$$

with

$$M(x, y) = 2xy^3 + 2 \quad \text{and} \quad N(x, y) = 3x^2 y^2 + 8e^{4y}.$$

Equation (1.8) can in turn be written

$$M \, dx + N \, dy = (2xy^3 + 2) \, dx + (3x^2 y^2 + 8e^{4y}) \, dy = 0. \tag{1.9}$$

Now let

$$\varphi(x, y) = x^2 y^3 + 2x + 2e^{4y}.$$

Soon we will see where this came from, but for now, observe that

$$\frac{\partial \varphi}{\partial x} = 2xy^3 + 2 = M \quad \text{and} \quad \frac{\partial \varphi}{\partial y} = 3x^2 y^2 + 8e^{4y} = N.$$

With this choice of $\varphi(x, y)$, equation (1.9) becomes

$$\frac{\partial \varphi}{\partial x} \, dx + \frac{\partial \varphi}{\partial y} \, dy = 0,$$

or

$$d\varphi \, (x, y) = 0.$$

The general solution of this equation is

$$\varphi(x, y) = C,$$

or, in this example,

$$x^2 y^3 + 2x + 2e^{4y} = C.$$

This implicitly defines the general solution of the differential equation (1.8).

To verify this, differentiate the last equation implicitly with respect to x:

$$2xy^3 + 3x^2 y^2 y' + 2 + 8e^{4y} y' = 0,$$

or

$$2xy^3 + 2 + (3x^2 y^2 + 8e^{4y}) y' = 0.$$

This is equivalent to the original differential equation

$$y' = -\frac{2xy^3 + 2}{3x^2 y^2 + 8e^{4y}}. \quad \blacksquare$$

With this as background, we will make the following definitions.

DEFINITION 1.3   *Potential Function*

A function φ is a potential function for the differential equation $M(x, y) + N(x, y)y' = 0$ on a region R of the plane if, for each (x, y) in R,

$$\frac{\partial \varphi}{\partial x} = M(x, y) \quad \text{and} \quad \frac{\partial \varphi}{\partial y} = N(x, y).$$

DEFINITION 1.4   *Exact Differential Equation*

When a potential function exists on a region R for the differential equation $M + Ny' = 0$, then this equation is said to be exact on R.

The differential equation of Example 1.17 is exact (over the entire plane), because we exhibited a potential function for it, defined for all (x, y). Once a potential function is found, we can write an equation implicitly defining the general solution. Sometimes we can explicitly solve for the general solution, and sometimes we cannot.

Now go back to Example 1.17. We want to explore how the potential function that materialized there was found. Recall we required that

$$\frac{\partial \varphi}{\partial x} = 2xy^3 + 2 = M \quad \text{and} \quad \frac{\partial \varphi}{\partial y} = 3x^2 y^2 + 8e^{4y} = N.$$

Pick either of these equations to begin and integrate it. Say we begin with the first. Then integrate with respect to x:

$$\varphi(x, y) = \int \frac{\partial \varphi}{\partial x} \, dx = \int \left(2xy^3 + 2\right) \, dx$$
$$= x^2 y^3 + 2x + g(y).$$

In this integration with respect to x we held y fixed, hence we must allow that y appears in the "constant" of integration. If we calculate $\partial \varphi / \partial x$, we get $2xy^2 + 2$ for any function $g(y)$.

Now we know φ to within this function g. Use the fact that we know $\partial \varphi / \partial y$ to write

$$\frac{\partial \varphi}{\partial y} = 3x^2 y^2 + 8e^{4y}$$

$$= \frac{\partial}{\partial y}(x^2 y^3 + 2x + g(y)) = 3x^2 y^2 + g'(y).$$

This equation holds if $g'(y) = 8e^{4y}$, hence we may choose $g(y) = 2e^{4y}$. This gives the potential function

$$\varphi(x, y) = x^2 y^3 + 2x + 2e^{4y}.$$

If we had chosen to integrate $\partial \varphi / \partial y$ first, we would have gotten

$$\varphi(x, y) = \int \left(3x^2 y^2 + 8e^{4y}\right) dy$$
$$= x^2 y^3 + 2e^{4y} + h(x).$$

Here h can be any function of one variable, because no matter how $h(x)$ is chosen,

$$\frac{\partial}{\partial y}\left(x^2 y^3 + 2e^{4y} + h(x)\right) = 3x^2 y^2 + 8e^{4y},$$

as required. Now we have two expressions for $\partial \varphi / \partial x$:

$$\frac{\partial \varphi}{\partial x} = 2xy^3 + 2$$

$$= \frac{\partial}{\partial x}\left(x^2 y^3 + 2e^{4y} + h(x)\right) = 2xy^3 + h'(x).$$

This equation forces us to choose h so that $h'(x) = 2$, and we may therefore set $h(x) = 2x$. This gives

$$\varphi(x, y) = x^2 y^3 + 2e^{4y} + 2x,$$

as we got before.

Not every first-order differential equation is exact. For example, consider

$$y + y' = 0.$$

If there were a potential function φ, then we would have

$$\frac{\partial \varphi}{\partial x} = y, \quad \frac{\partial \varphi}{\partial y} = 1.$$

Integrate $\partial \varphi / \partial x = y$ with respect to x to get $\varphi(x, y) = xy + g(y)$. Substitute this into $\partial \varphi / \partial y = 1$ to get

$$\frac{\partial}{\partial y}(xy + g(y)) = x + g'(y) = 1.$$

But this can hold only if $g'(y) = 1 - x$, an impossibility if g is to be independent of x. Therefore, $y + y' = 0$ has no potential function. This differential equation is not exact (even though it is easily solved either as a separable or as a linear equation).

This example suggests the need for a convenient test for exactness. This is provided by the following theorem, in which a "rectangle in the plane" refers to the set of points on or inside any rectangle having sides parallel to the axes.

THEOREM 1.1   *Test for Exactness*

Suppose $M(x, y)$, $N(x, y)$, $\partial M / \partial y$, and $\partial N / \partial x$ are continuous for all (x, y) within a rectangle R in the plane. Then,

$$M(x, y) + N(x, y)y' = 0$$

is exact on R if and only if, for each (x, y) in R,

$$\frac{\partial M}{\partial y} = \frac{\partial N}{\partial x}.$$

Proof   If $M + Ny' = 0$ is exact, then there is a potential function φ and

$$\frac{\partial \varphi}{\partial x} = M(x, y) \quad \text{and} \quad \frac{\partial \varphi}{\partial y} = N(x, y).$$

Then, for (x, y) in R,

$$\frac{\partial M}{\partial y} = \frac{\partial}{\partial y}\left(\frac{\partial \varphi}{\partial x}\right) = \frac{\partial^2 \varphi}{\partial y \partial x} = \frac{\partial^2 \varphi}{\partial x \partial y} = \frac{\partial}{\partial x}\left(\frac{\partial \varphi}{\partial y}\right) = \frac{\partial N}{\partial x}.$$

Conversely, suppose $\partial M / \partial y$ and $\partial N / \partial x$ are continuous on R. Choose any (x_0, y_0) in R and define, for (x, y) in R,

$$\varphi(x, y) = \int_{x_0}^{x} M(\xi, y_0) \, d\xi + \int_{y_0}^{y} N(x, \eta) \, d\eta. \tag{1.10}$$

Immediately we have, from the fundamental theorem of calculus,

$$\frac{\partial \varphi}{\partial y} = N(x, y),$$

since the first integral in equation (1.10) is independent of y. Next, compute

$$\frac{\partial \varphi}{\partial x} = \frac{\partial}{\partial x} \int_{x_0}^x M(\xi, y_0)\, d\xi + \frac{\partial}{\partial x} \int_{y_0}^y N(x, \eta)\, d\eta$$

$$= M(x, y_0) + \int_{y_0}^y \frac{\partial N}{\partial x}(x, \eta)\, d\eta$$

$$= M(x, y_0) + \int_{y_0}^y \frac{\partial M}{\partial y}(x, \eta)\, d\eta$$

$$= M(x, y_0) + M(x, y) - M(x, y_0) = M(x, y),$$

and the proof is complete. ■

For example, consider again $y + y' = 0$. Here $M(x, y) = y$ and $N(x, y) = 1$, so

$$\frac{\partial N}{\partial x} = 0 \quad \text{and} \quad \frac{\partial M}{\partial y} = 1$$

throughout the entire plane. Thus, $y + y' = 0$ cannot be exact on any rectangle in the plane. We saw this previously by showing that this differential equation can have no potential function.

EXAMPLE 1.18

Consider

$$x^2 + 3xy + (4xy + 2x)y' = 0.$$

Here $M(x, y) = x^2 + 3xy$ and $N(x, y) = 4xy + 2x$. Now

$$\frac{\partial N}{\partial x} = 4y + 2 \quad \text{and} \quad \frac{\partial M}{\partial y} = 3x,$$

and

$$3x = 4y + 2$$

is satisfied by all (x, y) on a straight line. However, $\partial N/\partial x = \partial M/\partial y$ cannot hold for all (x, y) in an entire rectangle in the plane. Hence this differential equation is not exact on any rectangle. ■

EXAMPLE 1.19

Consider

$$e^x \sin(y) - 2x + (e^x \cos(y) + 1)\, y' = 0.$$

With $M(x, y) = e^x \sin(y) - 2x$ and $N(x, y) = e^x \cos(y) + 1$, we have

$$\frac{\partial N}{\partial x} = e^x \cos(y) = \frac{\partial M}{\partial y}$$

for all (x, y). Therefore this differential equation is exact. To find a potential function, set

$$\frac{\partial \varphi}{\partial x} = e^x \sin(y) - 2x \quad \text{and} \quad \frac{\partial \varphi}{\partial y} = e^x \cos(y) + 1.$$

Choose one of these equations and integrate it. Integrate the second equation with respect to y:

$$\varphi(x, y) = \int (e^x \cos(y) + 1) \, dy$$

$$= e^x \sin(y) + y + h(x).$$

Then we must have

$$\frac{\partial \varphi}{\partial x} = e^x \sin(y) - 2x$$

$$= \frac{\partial}{\partial x} (e^x \sin(y) + y + h(x)) = e^x \sin(y) + h'(x).$$

Then $h'(x) = -2x$ and we may choose $h(x) = -x^2$. A potential function is

$$\varphi(x, y) = e^x \sin(y) + y - x^2.$$

The general solution of the differential equation is defined implicitly by

$$e^x \sin(y) + y - x^2 = C. \quad \blacksquare$$

Note of Caution: If φ is a potential function for $M + Ny' = 0$, φ itself is not the solution. The general solution is defined implicitly by the equation $\varphi(x, y) = C$.

SECTION 1.4   PROBLEMS

In each of Problems 1 through 8, determine where (if anywhere) in the plane the differential equation is exact. If it is exact, find a potential function and the general solution, perhaps implicitly defined. If the equation is not exact, do not attempt a solution at this time.

1. $2y^2 + ye^{xy} + (4xy + xe^{xy} + 2y)y' = 0$

2. $4xy + 2x + (2x^2 + 3y^2)y' = 0$

3. $4xy + 2x^2y + (2x^2 + 3y^2)y' = 0$

4. $2\cos(x+y) - 2x\sin(x+y) - 2x\sin(x+y)y' = 0$

5. $\dfrac{1}{x} + y + (3y^2 + x)y' = 0$

6. $e^x \sin(y^2) + xe^x \sin(y^2) + (2xye^x \sin(y^2) + e^y)y' = 0$

7. $\sinh(x)\sinh(y) + \cosh(x)\cosh(y)y' = 0$

8. $4y^4 + 3\cos(x) + (16y^3x - 3\cos(y))y' = 0$

In each of Problems 9 through 14, determine if the differential equation is exact in some rectangle containing in its interior the point where the initial condition is given. If so, solve the initial value problem. This solution may be implicitly defined. If the differential equation is not exact, do not attempt a solution.

9. $3y^4 - 1 + 12xy^3y' = 0; \ y(1) = 2$

10. $2y - y^2 \sec^2(xy^2) + (2x - 2xy \sec^2(xy^2))y' = 0; \ y(1) = 2$

11. $x\cos(2y - x) - \sin(2y - x) - 2x\cos(2y - x)y' = 0; \ y(\pi/12) = \pi/8$

12. $1 + e^{y/x} - \dfrac{y}{x}e^{y/x} + e^{y/x}y' = 0; \ y(1) = -5$

13. $y\sinh(y - x) - \cosh(y - x) + y\sinh(y - x)y' = 0; \ y(4) = 4$

14. $e^y + (xe^y - 1)y' = 0; \ y(5) = 0$

In Problems 15 and 16, choose a constant α so that the differential equation is exact, then produce a potential function and obtain the general solution.

15. $2xy^3 - 3y - (3x + \alpha x^2 y^2 - 2\alpha y)y' = 0$

16. $3x^2 + xy^\alpha - x^2 y^{\alpha-1} y' = 0$

17. Let φ be a potential function for $M + Ny' = 0$ in some region R of the plane. Show that for any constant c, $\varphi + c$ is also a potential function. How does the general solution of $M + Ny' = 0$ obtained by using φ differ from that obtained using $\varphi + c$?

1.5 Integrating Factors

"Most" differential equations are not exact on any rectangle. But sometimes we can multiply the differential equation by a nonzero function $\mu(x, y)$ to obtain an exact equation. Here is an example that suggests why this might be useful.

EXAMPLE 1.20

The equation

$$y^2 - 6xy + (3xy - 6x^2)y' = 0 \tag{1.11}$$

is not exact on any rectangle. Multiply it by $\mu(x, y) = y$ to get

$$y^3 - 6xy^2 + (3xy^2 - 6x^2y)y' = 0. \tag{1.12}$$

Wherever $y \neq 0$, equations (1.11) and (1.12) have the same solution. The reason for this is that equation (1.12) is just

$$y\left[y^2 - 6xy + (3xy - 6x^2)y'\right] = 0,$$

and if $y \neq 0$, then necessarily $y^2 - 6xy + (3xy - 6x^2)y' = 0$.

Now notice that equation (1.12) is exact (over the entire plane), having potential function

$$\varphi(x, y) = xy^3 - 3x^2y^2.$$

Thus the general solution of equation (1.12) is defined implicitly by

$$xy^3 - 3x^2y^2 = C,$$

and, wherever $y \neq 0$, this defines the general solution of equation (1.11) as well. ∎

To review what has just occurred, we began with a nonexact differential equation. We multiplied it by a function μ chosen so that the new equation was exact. We solved this exact equation, then found that this solution also worked for the original, nonexact equation. The function μ therefore enabled us to solve a nonexact equation by solving an exact one. This idea is worth pursuing, and we begin by giving a name to μ.

DEFINITION 1.5

Let $M(x, y)$ and $N(x, y)$ be defined on a region R of the plane. Then $\mu(x, y)$ is an integrating factor for $M + Ny' = 0$ if $\mu(x, y) \neq 0$ for all (x, y) in R, and $\mu M + \mu Ny' = 0$ is exact on R.

How do we find an integrating factor for $M + Ny' = 0$? For μ to be an integrating factor, $\mu M + \mu Ny' = 0$ must be exact (in some region of the plane), hence

$$\frac{\partial}{\partial x}(\mu N) = \frac{\partial}{\partial y}(\mu M) \tag{1.13}$$

in this region. This is a starting point. Depending on M and N, we may be able to determine μ from this equation.

Sometimes equation (1.13) becomes simple enough to solve if we try μ as a function of just x or just y.

EXAMPLE 1.21

The differential equation $x - xy - y' = 0$ is not exact. Here $M = x - xy$ and $N = -1$ and equation (1.13) is

$$\frac{\partial}{\partial x}(-\mu) = \frac{\partial}{\partial y}(\mu(x - xy)).$$

Write this as

$$-\frac{\partial \mu}{\partial x} = (x - xy)\frac{\partial \mu}{\partial y} - x\mu.$$

Now observe that this equation is simplified if we try to find μ as just a function of x, because in this event $\partial \mu / \partial y = 0$ and we are left with just

$$\frac{\partial \mu}{\partial x} = x\mu.$$

This is separable. Write

$$\frac{1}{\mu}\,d\mu = x\,dx$$

and integrate to obtain

$$\ln|\mu| = \tfrac{1}{2}x^2.$$

Here we let the constant of integration be zero because we need only one integrating factor. From the last equation, choose

$$\mu(x) = e^{x^2/2},$$

a nonzero function. Multiply the original differential equation by $e^{x^2/2}$ to obtain

$$(x - xy)e^{x^2/2} - e^{x^2/2}y' = 0.$$

This equation is exact over the entire plane, and we find the potential function $\varphi(x, y) = (1 - y)e^{x^2/2}$. The general solution of this exact equation is implicitly defined by

$$(1 - y)e^{x^2/2} = C.$$

In this case, we can explicitly solve for y to get

$$y(x) = 1 - Ce^{-x^2/2},$$

and this is also the general solution of the original equation $x - xy - y' = 0$. ■

If we cannot find an integrating factor that is a function of just x or just y, then we must try something else. There is no template to follow, and often we must start with equation (1.13) and be observant.

EXAMPLE 1.22

Consider $2y^2 - 9xy + (3xy - 6x^2)y' = 0$. This is not exact. With $M = 2y^2 - 9xy$ and $N = 3xy - 6x^2$, begin looking for an integrating factor by writing equation (1.13):

$$\frac{\partial}{\partial x}\left[\mu(3xy - 6x^2)\right] = \frac{\partial}{\partial y}\left[\mu(2y^2 - 9xy)\right].$$

This is

$$(3xy - 6x^2)\,\frac{\partial \mu}{\partial x} + \mu(3y - 12x) = (2y^2 - 9xy)\,\frac{\partial \mu}{\partial y} + \mu(4y - 9x). \tag{1.14}$$

If we attempt $\mu = \mu(x)$, then $\partial \mu/\partial y = 0$ and we obtain

$$(3xy - 6x^2)\,\frac{\partial \mu}{\partial x} + \mu(3y - 12x) = \mu(4y - 9x)$$

which cannot be solved for μ as just a function of x. Similarly, if we try $\mu = \mu(y)$, so $\partial \mu/\partial x = 0$, we obtain an equation we cannot solve. We must try something else. Notice that equation (1.14) involves only integer powers of x and y. This suggests that we try $\mu(x, y) = x^a y^b$. Substitute this into equation (1.14) and attempt to choose a and b. The substitution gives us

$$3ax^a y^{b+1} - 6ax^{a+1}y^b + 3x^a y^{b+1} - 12x^{a+1}y^b = 2bx^a y^{b+1} - 9bx^{a+1}y^b + 4x^a y^{b+1} - 9x^{a+1}y^b.$$

Assume that $x \neq 0$ and $y \neq 0$. Then we can divide by $x^a y^b$ to get

$$3ay - 6ax + 3y - 12x = 2by - 9bx + 4y - 9x.$$

Rearrange terms to write

$$(1 + 2b - 3a)y = (-3 + 9b - 6a)x.$$

Since x and y are independent, this equation can hold for all x and y only if

$$1 + 2b - 3a = 0 \quad \text{and} \quad -3 + 9b - 6a = 0.$$

Solve these equations to obtain $a = b = 1$. An integrating factor is $\mu(x, y) = xy$. Multiply the differential equation by xy to get

$$2xy^3 - 9x^2 y^2 + (3x^2 y^2 - 6x^3 y)y' = 0.$$

This is exact with potential function $\varphi(x, y) = x^2 y^3 - 3x^3 y^2$. For $x \neq 0$ and $y \neq 0$, the solution of the original differential equation is given implicitly by

$$x^2 y^3 - 3x^3 y^2 = C. \quad \blacksquare$$

The manipulations used to find an integrating factor may fail to find some solutions, as we saw with singular solutions of separable equations. Here are two examples in which this occurs.

EXAMPLE 1.23

Consider

$$\frac{2xy}{y - 1} - y' = 0. \tag{1.15}$$

We can solve this as a separable equation, but here we want to make a point about integrating factors. Equation (1.15) is not exact, but $\mu(x, y) = (y-1)/y$ is an integrating factor for $y \neq 0$, a condition not required by the differential equation itself. Multiplying the differential equation by $\mu(x, y)$ yields the exact equation

$$2x - \frac{y-1}{y}y' = 0,$$

with potential function $\varphi(x, y) = x^2 - y + \ln|y|$ and general solution defined by

$$x^2 - y + \ln|y| = C \quad \text{for } y \neq 0.$$

This is also the general solution of equation (1.15), but the method used has required that $y \neq 0$. However, we see immediately that $y = 0$ is also a solution of equation (1.15). This singular solution is not contained in the expression for the general solution for any choice of C. ∎

EXAMPLE 1.24

The equation

$$y - 3 - xy' = 0 \tag{1.16}$$

is not exact, but $\mu(x, y) = 1/x(y-3)$ is an integrating factor for $x \neq 0$ and $y \neq 3$, conditions not required by the differential equation itself. Multiplying equation (1.16) by $\mu(x, y)$ yields the exact equation

$$\frac{1}{x} - \frac{1}{y-3}y' = 0,$$

with general solution defined by

$$\ln|x| + C = \ln|y - 3|.$$

This is also the general solution of equation (1.16) in any region of the plane not containing the lines $x = 0$ or $y = 3$.

This general solution can be solved for y explicitly in terms of x. First, any real number is the natural logarithm of some positive number, so write the arbitrary constant as $C = \ln(k)$, in which k can be any positive number. The equation for the general solution becomes

$$\ln|x| + \ln(k) = \ln|y - 3|,$$

or

$$\ln|kx| = \ln|y - 3|.$$

But then $y - 3 = \pm kx$. Replacing $\pm k$ with K, which can now be any nonzero real number, we obtain

$$y = 3 + Kx$$

as the general solution of equation (1.16). Now observe that $y = 3$ is a solution of equation (1.16). This solution was "lost", or at least not found, in using the integrating factor as a method of solution. However, $y = 3$ is not a singular solution because we can include it in the expression $y = 3 + Kx$ by allowing $K = 0$. Thus the general solution of equation (1.16) is $y = 3 + Kx$, with K any real number. ∎

1.5.1 Separable Equations and Integrating Factors

We will point out a connection between separable equations and integrating factors.

The separable equation $y' = A(x)B(y)$ is in general not exact. To see this, write it as

$$A(x)B(y) - y' = 0,$$

so in the present context we have $M(x, y) = A(x)B(y)$ and $N(x, y) = -1$. Now

$$\frac{\partial}{\partial x}(-1) = 0 \quad \text{and} \quad \frac{\partial}{\partial y}[A(x)B(y)] = A(x)B'(y),$$

and in general $A(x)B'(y) \neq 0$.

However, $\mu(y) = 1/B(y)$ is an integrating factor for the separable equation. If we multiply the differential equation by $1/B(y)$, we get

$$A(x) - \frac{1}{B(y)}y' = 0,$$

an exact equation because

$$\frac{\partial}{\partial x}\left[-\frac{1}{B(y)}\right] = \frac{\partial}{\partial y}[A(x)] = 0.$$

The act of separating the variables is the same as multiplying by the integrating factor $1/B(y)$.

1.5.2 Linear Equations and Integrating Factors

Consider the linear equation $y' + p(x)y = q(x)$. We can write this as $[p(x)y - q(x)] + y' = 0$, so in the present context, $M(x, y) = p(x)y - q(x)$ and $N(x, y) = 1$. Now

$$\frac{\partial}{\partial x}[1] = 0 \quad \text{and} \quad \frac{\partial}{\partial y}[p(x)y - q(x)] = p(x),$$

so the linear equation is not exact unless $p(x)$ is identically zero. However, $\mu(x, y) = e^{\int p(x)\,dx}$ is an integrating factor. Upon multiplying the linear equation by μ, we get

$$[p(x)y - q(x)]e^{\int p(x)\,dx} + e^{\int p(x)\,dx}y' = 0,$$

and this is exact because

$$\frac{\partial}{\partial x}e^{\int p(x)\,dx} = p(x)e^{\int p(x)\,dx} = \frac{\partial}{\partial y}\left[[p(x)y - q(x)]e^{\int p(x)\,dx}\right].$$

SECTION 1.5   PROBLEMS

1. Determine a test involving M and N to tell when $M + Ny' = 0$ has an integrating factor that is a function of y only.

2. Determine a test to determine when $M + Ny' = 0$ has an integrating factor of the form $\mu(x, y) = x^a y^b$ for some constants a and b.

3. Consider $y - xy' = 0$.

    (a) Show that this equation is not exact on any rectangle.

    (b) Find an integrating factor $\mu(x)$ that is a function of x alone.

    (c) Find an integrating factor $\nu(y)$ that is a function of y alone.

    (d) Show that there is also an integrating factor $\eta(x, y) = x^a y^b$ for some constants a and b. Find all such integrating factors.

In each of Problems 4 through 12, (a) show that the differential equation is not exact, (b) find an integrating factor, (c) find the general solution (perhaps implicitly defined), and (d) determine any singular solutions the differential equation might have.

4. $xy' - 3y = 2x^3$

5. $1 + (3x - e^{-2y})y' = 0$

6. $6x^2y + 12xy + y^2 + (6x^2 + 2y)y' = 0$

7. $4xy + 6y^2 + (2x^2 + 6xy)y' = 0$

8. $y^2 + y - xy' = 0$

9. $2xy^2 + 2xy + (x^2y + x^2)y' = 0$

10. $2y^2 - 9xy + (3xy - 6x^2)y' = 0$ (*Hint:* try $\mu(x, y) = x^a y^b$)

11. $y' + y = y^4$ (*Hint:* try $\mu(x, y) = e^{ax}y^b$)

12. $x^2y' + xy = -y^{-3/2}$ (*Hint:* try $\mu(x, y) = x^a y^b$)

In each of Problems 13 through 20, find an integrating factor, use it to find the general solution of the differential equation, and then obtain the solution of the initial value problem.

13. $1 + xy' = 0;\ y(e^4) = 0$

14. $3y + 4xy' = 0;\ y(1) = 6$

15. $2(y^3 - 2) + 3xy^2y' = 0;\ y(3) = 1$

16. $y(1 + x) + 2xy' = 0;\ y(4) = 6$

17. $2xy + 3y' = 0;\ y(0) = 4$ (*Hint:* try $\mu = y^a e^{bx^2}$)

18. $2y(1 + x^2) + xy' = 0;\ y(2) = 3$ (*Hint:* try $\mu = x^a e^{bx^2}$)

19. $\sin(x - y) + \cos(x - y) - \cos(x - y)y' = 0;$
$y(0) = 7\pi/6$

20. $3x^2y + y^3 + 2xy^2y' = 0;\ y(2) = 1$

21. Show that any nonzero constant multiple of an integrating factor for $M + Ny' = 0$ is also an integrating factor.

22. Let $\mu(x, y)$ be an integrating factor for $M + Ny' = 0$ and suppose that the general solution is defined by $\varphi(x, y) = C$. Show that $\mu(x, y)G(\varphi(x, y))$ is also an integrating factor, for any differentiable function G of one variable.

1.6 Homogeneous, Bernoulli, and Riccati Equations

In this section we will consider three additional kinds of first-order differential equations for which techniques for finding solutions are available.

1.6.1 Homogeneous Differential Equations

DEFINITION 1.6 *Homogeneous Equation*

A first-order differential equation is homogeneous if it has the form

$$y' = f\left(\frac{y}{x}\right).$$

In a homogeneous equation, y' is isolated on one side, and the other side is some expression in which y and x must always appear in the combination y/x. For example,

$$y' = \frac{x}{y} \sin\left(\frac{y}{x}\right)$$

is homogeneous, while $y' = x^2 y$ is not.

Sometimes algebraic manipulation will put a first order equation into the form of the homogeneous equation. For example,

$$y' = \frac{y}{x+y} \tag{1.17}$$

is not homogeneous. However, if $x \neq 0$, we can write this as

$$y' = \frac{y/x}{1+y/x}, \tag{1.18}$$

a homogeneous equation. Any technique we develop for homogeneous equations can therefore be used on equation (1.18). However, this solution assumes that $x \neq 0$, which is not required in equation (1.17). Thus, as we have seen before, when we perform manipulations on a differential equation, we must be careful that solutions have not been overlooked. A solution of equation (1.18) will also satisfy (1.17), but equation (1.17) may have other solutions as well.

Now to the point. A homogeneous equation is always transformed into a separable one by the transformation

$$y = ux.$$

To see this, compute $y' = u'x + x'u = u'x + u$ and write $u = y/x$. Then $y' = f(y/x)$ becomes

$$u'x + u = f(u).$$

We can write this as

$$\frac{1}{f(u) - u} \frac{du}{dx} = \frac{1}{x},$$

or, in differential form,

$$\frac{1}{f(u) - u} \, du = \frac{1}{x} \, dx,$$

and the variables (now x and u) have been separated. Upon integrating this equation, we obtain the general solution of the transformed equation. Substituting $u = y/x$ then gives the general solution of the original homogeneous equation.

EXAMPLE 1.25

Consider

$$xy' = \frac{y^2}{x} + y.$$

Write this as

$$y' = \left(\frac{y}{x}\right)^2 + \frac{y}{x}.$$

Let $y = ux$. Then

$$u'x + u = u^2 + u,$$

or

$$u'x = u^2.$$

Write this as

$$\frac{1}{u^2} \, du = \frac{1}{x} \, dx$$

and integrate to obtain

$$-\frac{1}{u} = \ln|x| + C.$$

Then

$$u(x) = \frac{-1}{\ln|x| + C},$$

the general solution of the transformed equation. The general solution of the original equation is

$$y = \frac{-x}{\ln|x| + C}. \quad \blacksquare$$

EXAMPLE 1.26   A Pursuit Problem

A pursuit problem is one of determining a trajectory so that one object intercepts another. Examples involving pursuit problems are missiles fired at airplanes and a rendezvous of a shuttle with a space station. These are complex problems that require numerical approximation techniques. We will consider a simple pursuit problem that can be solved explicitly.

Suppose a person jumps into a canal of constant width w and swims toward a fixed point directly opposite the point of entry into the canal. The person's speed is v and the water current's speed is s. Assume that, as the swimmer makes his way across, he always orients to point toward the target. We want to determine the swimmer's trajectory.

Figure 1.13 shows a coordinate system drawn so that the swimmer's destination is the origin and the point of entry into the water is $(w, 0)$. At time t the swimmer is at the point $(x(t), y(t))$. The horizontal and vertical components of his velocity are, respectively,

$$x'(t) = -v\cos(\alpha) \quad \text{and} \quad y'(t) = s - v\sin(\alpha),$$

with α the angle between the positive x axis and $(x(t), y(t))$ at time t. From these equations,

$$\frac{dy}{dx} = \frac{y'(t)}{x'(t)} = \frac{s - v\sin(\alpha)}{-v\cos(\alpha)} = \tan(\alpha) - \frac{s}{v}\sec(\alpha).$$

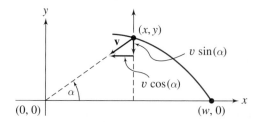

FIGURE 1.13   *The swimmer's path.*

From Figure 1.13,

$$\tan(\alpha) = \frac{y}{x} \quad \text{and} \quad \sec(\alpha) = \frac{1}{x}\sqrt{x^2 + y^2}.$$

Therefore

$$\frac{dy}{dx} = \frac{y}{x} - \frac{s}{v}\frac{1}{x}\sqrt{x^2 + y^2}.$$

Write this as the homogeneous equation

$$\frac{dy}{dx} = \frac{y}{x} - \frac{s}{v}\sqrt{1 + \left(\frac{y}{x}\right)^2}$$

and put $y = uv$ to obtain

$$\frac{1}{\sqrt{1 + u^2}}\,du = -\frac{s}{v}\frac{1}{x}\,dx.$$

Integrate to get

$$\ln\left|u + \sqrt{1 + u^2}\right| = -\frac{s}{v}\ln|x| + C.$$

Take the exponential of both sides of this equation:

$$\left|u + \sqrt{1 + u^2}\right| = e^C e^{-(s\ln|x|)/v}.$$

We can write this as

$$u + \sqrt{1 + u^2} = Kx^{-s/v}.$$

This equation can be solved for u. First write

$$\sqrt{1 + u^2} = Kx^{-s/v} - u$$

and square both sides to get

$$1 + u^2 = K^2 e^{-2s/v} - 2Kue^{-s/v} + u^2.$$

Now u^2 cancels and we can solve for u:

$$u(x) = \frac{1}{2}Kx^{-s/v} - \frac{1}{2}\frac{1}{K}x^{s/v}.$$

Finally, put $u = y/x$ to get

$$y(x) = \frac{1}{2}Kx^{1-s/v} - \frac{1}{2}\frac{1}{K}x^{1+s/v}.$$

To determine K, notice that $y(w) = 0$, since we put the origin at the point of destination. Thus,

$$\frac{1}{2}Kw^{1-s/v} - \frac{1}{2}\frac{1}{K}w^{1+s/v} = 0$$

and we obtain

$$K = w^{s/v}.$$

Therefore,

$$y(x) = \frac{w}{2}\left[\left(\frac{x}{w}\right)^{1-s/v} - \left(\frac{x}{w}\right)^{1+s/v}\right].$$

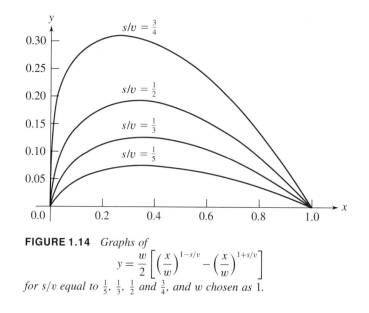

FIGURE 1.14   *Graphs of*

$$y = \frac{w}{2}\left[\left(\frac{x}{w}\right)^{1-s/v} - \left(\frac{x}{w}\right)^{1+s/v}\right]$$

for s/v equal to $\frac{1}{5}$, $\frac{1}{3}$, $\frac{1}{2}$ and $\frac{3}{4}$, and w chosen as 1.

As might be expected, the path the swimmer takes depends on the width of the canal, the speed of the swimmer, and the speed of the current. Figure 1.14 shows trajectories corresponding to s/v equal to $\frac{1}{5}$, $\frac{1}{3}$, $\frac{1}{2}$ and $\frac{3}{4}$, with $w = 1$. ∎

1.6.2   The Bernoulli Equation

DEFINITION 1.7

A *Bernoulli equation* is a first order equation,

$$y' + P(x)y = R(x)y^{\alpha},$$

in which α is a real number. ∎

A Bernoulli equation is separable if $\alpha = 0$ and linear if $\alpha = 1$. About 1696, Leibniz showed that a Bernoulli equation with $\alpha \neq 1$ transforms to a linear equation under the change of variables:

$$v = y^{1-\alpha}.$$

This is routine to verify. Here is an example.

EXAMPLE 1.27

Consider the equation

$$y' + \frac{1}{x}y = 3x^2y^3,$$

which is Bernoulli with $P(x) = 1/x$, $R(x) = 3x^2$, and $\alpha = 3$. Make the change of variables

$$v = y^{-2}.$$

Then $y = v^{-1/2}$ and

$$y'(x) = -\frac{1}{2}v^{-3/2}v'(x),$$

so the differential equation becomes

$$-\frac{1}{2}v^{-3/2}v'(x) + \frac{1}{x}v^{-1/2} = 3x^2 v^{-3/2},$$

or, upon multiplying by $-2v^{3/2}$,

$$v' - \frac{2}{x}v = -6x^2,$$

a linear equation. An integrating factor is $e^{-\int(2/x)\,dx} = x^{-2}$. Multiply the last equation by this factor to get

$$x^{-2}v' - 2x^{-3}v = -6,$$

which is

$$(x^{-2}v)' = -6.$$

Integrate to get

$$x^{-2}v = -6x + C,$$

so

$$v = -6x^3 + Cx^2.$$

The general solution of the Bernoulli equation is

$$y(x) = \frac{1}{\sqrt{v(x)}} = \frac{1}{\sqrt{Cx^2 - 6x^3}}. \quad \blacksquare$$

1.6.3 The Riccati Equation

A differential equation of the form

$$y' = P(x)y^2 + Q(x)y + R(x)$$

is called a *Riccati equation*.

A Riccati equation is linear exactly when $P(x)$ is identically zero. If we can somehow obtain one solution $S(x)$ of a Riccati equation, then the change of variables

$$y = S(x) + \frac{1}{z}$$

transforms the Riccati equation to a linear equation. The strategy is to find the general solution of this linear equation and from it produce the general solution of the original Riccati equation.

EXAMPLE 1.28

Consider the Riccati equation

$$y' = \frac{1}{x}y^2 + \frac{1}{x}y - \frac{2}{x}.$$

By inspection, $y = S(x) = 1$ is one solution. Define a new variable z by putting

$$y = 1 + \frac{1}{z}.$$

Then

$$y' = -\frac{1}{z^2}z'.$$

Substitute these into the Riccati equation to get

$$-\frac{1}{z^2}z' = \frac{1}{x}\left(1 + \frac{1}{z}\right)^2 + \frac{1}{x}\left(1 + \frac{1}{z}\right) - \frac{2}{x},$$

or

$$z' + \frac{3}{x}z = -\frac{1}{x}.$$

This is linear. An integrating factor is $e^{\int (3/x)\,dx} = x^3$. Multiply by x^3 to get

$$x^3z' + 3x^2z = (x^3z)' = -x^2.$$

Integrate to get

$$x^3z = -\frac{1}{3}x^3 + C,$$

so

$$z(x) = -\frac{1}{3} + \frac{C}{x^3}.$$

The general solution of the Riccati equation is

$$y(x) = 1 + \frac{1}{z(x)} = 1 + \frac{1}{-1/3 + C/x^3}.$$

This solution can also be written

$$y(x) = \frac{K + 2x^3}{K - x^3},$$

in which $K = 3C$ is an arbitrary constant. ∎

SECTION 1.6   PROBLEMS

In each of Problems 1 through 14, find the general solution. These problems include all types considered in this section.

1. $y' = \dfrac{1}{x^2}y^2 - \dfrac{1}{x}y + 1$

2. $y' + \dfrac{1}{x}y = \dfrac{2}{x^3}y^{-4/3}$

3. $y' + xy = xy^2$

4. $y' = \dfrac{x}{y} + \dfrac{y}{x}$

5. $y' = \dfrac{y}{x+y}$

6. $y' = \dfrac{1}{2x}y^2 - \dfrac{1}{x}y - \dfrac{4}{x}$

7. $(x - 2y)y' = 2x - y$

8. $xy' = x\cos(y/x) + y$

9. $y' + \dfrac{1}{x}y = \dfrac{1}{x^4}y^{-3/4}$

10. $x^2 y' = x^2 + y^2$

11. $y' = -\dfrac{1}{x}y^2 + \dfrac{2}{x}y$

12. $x^3 y' = x^2 y - y^3$

13. $y' = -e^{-x}y^2 + y + e^x$

14. $y' + \dfrac{2}{x}y = \dfrac{3}{x}y^2$

15. Consider the differential equation

$$y' = F\left(\dfrac{ax + by + c}{dx + ey + r}\right),$$

in which a, b, c, d, e, and r are constants and F is a differentiable function of one variable.

(a) Show that this equation is homogeneous if and only if $c = r = 0$.

(b) If c and/or r is not zero, this equation is called *nearly homogeneous*. Assuming that $ae - bd \neq 0$, show that it is possible to choose constants h and k so that the transformation $X = x + h$, $Y = y + k$ converts this nearly homogeneous equation into a homogeneous one. *Hint:* Put $x = X - h$, $y = Y - k$ into the differential equation and obtain a differential equation in X and Y. Use the conclusion of (a) to choose h and k so that this equation is homogeneous.

In each of Problems 16 through 19, use the idea of Problem 15 to find the general solution.

16. $y' = \dfrac{y - 3}{x + y - 1}$

17. $y' = \dfrac{3x - y - 9}{x + y + 1}$

18. $y' = \dfrac{x + 2y + 7}{-2x + y - 9}$

19. $y' = \dfrac{2x - 5y - 9}{-4x + y + 9}$

20. Continuing from Problem 15, consider the case that $ae - bd = 0$. Now let $u = (ax + by)/a$, assuming that $a \neq 0$. Show that this transforms the differential equation of Problem 15 into the separable equation

$$\dfrac{du}{dx} = 1 + \dfrac{b}{a}F\left(\dfrac{au + c}{du + r}\right).$$

In each of Problems 21 through 24, use the method of Problem 20 to find the general solution.

21. $y' = \dfrac{x - y + 2}{x - y + 3}$

22. $y' = \dfrac{3x + y - 1}{6x + 2y - 3}$

23. $y' = \dfrac{x - 2y}{3x - 6y + 4}$

24. $y' = \dfrac{x - y + 6}{3x - 3y + 4}$

25. (*The Pursuing Dog*) A man stands at the junction of two perpendicular roads and his dog is watching him from one of the roads at a distance A feet away. At a given instant the man starts to walk with constant speed v along the other road, and at the same time the dog begins to run toward the man with speed $2v$. Determine the path the dog will take, assuming that it always moves so that it is facing the man. Also determine when the dog will eventually catch the man. (This is *American Mathematical Monthly* problem 3942, 1941).

26. (*Pursuing Bugs*) One bug is located at each corner of a square table of side length a. At a given time they begin moving at constant speed v, each pursuing its neighbor to the right.

(a) Determine the curve of pursuit of each bug. *Hint:* Use polar coordinates with the origin at the center of the table and the polar axis containing one of the corners. When a bug is at $(f(\theta), \theta)$, its target is at $(f(\theta), \theta + \pi/2)$. Use the chain rule to write

$$\frac{dy}{dx} = \frac{dy/d\theta}{dx/d\theta},$$

where $y(\theta) = f(\theta)\sin(\theta)$ and $x(\theta) = f(\theta)\cos(\theta)$.

(b) Determine the distance traveled by each bug.

(c) Does any bug actually catch its quarry?

27. (The Spinning Bug) A bug steps onto the edge of a disk of radius a that is spinning at a constant angular speed ω. The bug moves toward the center of the disk at constant speed v.

(a) Derive a differential equation for the path of the bug, using polar coordinates.

(b) How many revolutions will the disk make before the bug reaches the center? (The solution will be in terms of the angular speed and radius of the disk.)

(c) Referring to (b), what is the total distance the bug will travel, taking into account the motion of the disk?

1.7 Applications to Mechanics, Electrical Circuits, and Orthogonal Trajectories

1.7.1 Mechanics

Before applying first-order differential equations to problems in mechanics, we will review some background.

Newton's second law of motion states that the rate of change of momentum (mass times velocity) of a body is proportional to the resultant force acting on the body. This is a vector equation, but we will for now consider only motion along a straight line. In this case Newton's law is

$$F = k \frac{d}{dt}(mv).$$

We will take $k = 1$, consistent with certain units of measurement, such as the English, MKS, or gcs systems.

The mass of a moving object need not be constant. For example, an airplane consumes fuel as it moves. If m is constant, then Newton's law is

$$F = m \frac{dv}{dt} = ma,$$

in which a is the acceleration of the object along the line of motion. If m is not constant, then

$$F = m \frac{dv}{dt} + v \frac{dm}{dt}.$$

Newton's law of gravitational attraction states that if two objects have masses m_1 and m_2, and they (or their center of masses) are at distance r from each other, then each attracts the other with a gravitational force of magnitude

$$F = G \frac{m_1 m_2}{r^2}.$$

This force is directed along the line between the centers of mass. G is the universal gravitational constant.

If one of the objects is the earth, then

$$F = G \frac{mM}{(R+x)^2},$$

where M is the mass of the earth, R is its radius (about 3,960 miles), m is the mass of the second object, and x is its distance from the surface of the earth. This assumes that the earth is spherical and that its center of mass is at the center of this sphere, a good enough approximation for some purposes. If x is small compared to R, then $R + x$ is approximately R and the force on the object is approximately

$$\frac{GM}{R^2} m,$$

which is often written as mg. Here $g = GM/R^2$ is approximately 32 feet per second per second or 9.8 meters per second per second.

We are now ready to analyze some problems in mechanics.

Terminal Velocity Consider an object that is falling under the influence of gravity, in a medium such as water, air or oil. This medium retards the downward motion of the object. Think, for example, of a brick dropped in a swimming pool or a ball bearing dropped in a tank of oil. We, want to analyze the object's motion.

Let $v(t)$ be the velocity at time t. The force of gravity pulls the object down and has magnitude mg. The medium retards the motion. The magnitude of this retarding force is not obvious, but experiment has shown that its magnitude is proportional to the square of the velocity. If we choose downward as the positive direction and upward as negative, then Newton's law tells us that, for some constant α,

$$F = mg - \alpha v^2 = m \frac{dv}{dt}.$$

If we assume that the object begins its motion from rest (dropped, not thrown) and if we start the clock at this instant, then $v(0) = 0$. We now have an initial value problem for the velocity:

$$v' = g - \frac{\alpha}{m} v^2; \quad v(0) = 0.$$

This differential equation is separable. In differential form,

$$\frac{1}{g - (\alpha/m)v^2} \, dv = dt.$$

Integrate to get

$$\sqrt{\frac{m}{\alpha g}} \tanh^{-1}\left(\sqrt{\frac{\alpha}{mg}} v \right) = t + C.$$

Solve for the velocity, obtaining

$$v(t) = \sqrt{\frac{mg}{\alpha}} \tanh\left(\sqrt{\frac{\alpha g}{m}}(t + C) \right).$$

Now use the initial condition to solve for the integration constant:

$$v(0) = \sqrt{\frac{mg}{\alpha}} \tanh\left(C \sqrt{\frac{\alpha g}{m}} \right) = 0.$$

Since $\tanh(\xi) = 0$ only if $\xi = 0$, this requires that $C = 0$ and the solution for the velocity is

$$v(t) = \sqrt{\frac{mg}{\alpha}} \tanh\left(\sqrt{\frac{\alpha g}{m}} t \right).$$

Even in this generality, we can draw an important conclusion about the motion. As t increases, $\tanh(\sqrt{\alpha g/m} t)$ approaches 1. This means that

$$\lim_{t \to \infty} v(t) = \sqrt{\frac{mg}{\alpha}}.$$

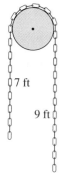

This means that an object falling under the influence of gravity, through a retarding medium (with force proportional to the square of the velocity), will not increase in velocity indefinitely. Instead, the object's velocity approaches the limiting value $\sqrt{mg/\alpha}$. If the medium is deep enough, the object will settle into a descent of approximately constant velocity. This number $\sqrt{mg/\alpha}$ is called the *terminal velocity* of the object. Skydivers experience this phenomenon.

Motion of a Chain on a Pulley   A 16 foot long chain weighing ρ pounds per foot hangs over a small pulley, which is 20 feet above the floor. Initially, the chain is held at rest with 7 feet on one side and 9 on the other, as in Figure 1.15. How long after the chain is released, and with what velocity, will it leave the pulley?

When 8 feet of chain hang on each side of the pulley, the chain is in equilibrium. Call this position $x = 0$ and let $x(t)$ be the distance the chain has fallen below this point at time t. The net force acting on the chain is $2x\rho$ and the mass of the chain is $16\rho/32$, or $\rho/2$ slugs. The ends of the chain have the same speed as its center of mass, so the acceleration of the chain at its center of mass is the same as it is at its ends. The equation of motion is

$$\frac{\rho}{2}\frac{dv}{dt} = 2x\rho,$$

FIGURE 1.15
Chain on a pulley.

from which ρ cancels to yield

$$\frac{dv}{dt} = 4x.$$

A chain rule differentiation enables us to write this equation in terms of v as a function of x. Write

$$\frac{dv}{dt} = \frac{dv}{dx}\frac{dx}{dt} = v\frac{dv}{dx}.$$

Then

$$v\frac{dv}{dx} = 4x.$$

This is a separable equation, which we solve to get

$$v^2 = 4x^2 + K.$$

Now, $x = 1$ when $v = 0$, so $K = -4$ and

$$v^2 = 4x^2 - 4.$$

The chain leaves the pulley when $x = 8$. Whenever this occurs, $v^2 = 4(63) = 252$, so $v = \sqrt{252} = 6\sqrt{7}$ feet per second (about 15.87 feet per second).

To calculate the time t_f required for the chain to leave the pulley, compute

$$t_f = \int_0^{t_f} dt = \int_0^{6\sqrt{7}} \frac{dt}{dv}\,dv$$

$$= \int_1^8 \frac{dt}{dx}\,dx = \int_1^8 \frac{1}{v}\,dv.$$

Since $v(x) = 2\sqrt{x^2 - 1}$,

$$t_f = \frac{1}{2} \int_1^8 \frac{1}{\sqrt{x^2 - 1}} \, dx = \left[\frac{1}{2} \ln \left| x + \sqrt{x^2 - 1} \right| \right]_1^8$$

$$= \frac{1}{2} \ln(8 + \sqrt{63}),$$

about 1.38 seconds.

In this example the mass was constant, so $dm/dt = 0$ in Newton's law of motion. Next is an example in which the mass varies with time.

Chain Piling on the Floor   Suppose a 40 foot long chain weighing ρ pounds per foot is supported in a pile several feet above the floor, and begins to unwind when released from rest with 10 feet already played out. Determine the velocity with which the chain leaves the support.

The amount of chain that is actually in motion changes with time. Let $x(t)$ denote the length of that part of the chain that has left the support by time t and is currently in motion. The equation of motion is

$$m \frac{dv}{dt} + v \frac{dm}{dt} = F, \tag{1.19}$$

where F is the total external force acting on the chain. Now $F = x\rho = mg$, so $m = x\rho/g = x\rho/32$. Then

$$\frac{dm}{dt} = \frac{\rho}{32} \frac{dx}{dt} = \frac{\rho}{32} v.$$

Further,

$$\frac{dv}{dt} = v \frac{dv}{dx},$$

as in the preceding example. Put this information into equation (1.19) to get

$$\frac{x\rho}{32} v \frac{dv}{dx} + \frac{\rho}{32} v^2 = x\rho.$$

If we multiply this equation by $32/x\rho v$, we get

$$\frac{dv}{dx} + \frac{1}{x} v = \frac{32}{v}, \tag{1.20}$$

which we recognize as a Bernoulli equation with $\alpha = -1$. Make the transformation $w = v^{1-\alpha} = v^2$. Then $v = w^{1/2}$ and

$$\frac{dv}{dx} = \frac{1}{2} w^{-1/2} \frac{dw}{dx}.$$

Substitute these into equation (1.20) to get

$$\frac{1}{2} w^{-1/2} \frac{dw}{dx} + \frac{1}{x} w^{1/2} = 32 w^{-1/2}.$$

Upon multiplying this equation by $2w^{1/2}$, we get

$$w' + \frac{2}{x} w = 64,$$

a linear equation for $w(x)$. Solve this to get

$$w(x) = v(x)^2 = \frac{64}{3} x + \frac{C}{x^2}.$$

Since $v = 0$ when $x = 10$, $0 = (64/3)(10) + C/100$, so $C = -64,000/3$. Therefore,

$$v(x)^2 = \frac{64}{3}\left[x - \frac{1000}{x^2}\right].$$

The chain leaves the support when $x = 40$. At this time,

$$v^2 = \frac{64}{3}\left[40 - \frac{1000}{1600}\right] = 4(210)$$

so, the velocity is $v = 2\sqrt{210}$, or about 29 feet per second.

In these models involving chains, air resistance was neglected as having no significant impact on the outcome. This was quite different from the analysis of terminal velocity, in which air resistance is a key factor. Without it, skydivers dive only once!

Motion of a Block Sliding on an Inclined Plane   A block weighing 96 pounds is released from rest at the top of an inclined plane of slope length 50 feet, and making an angle $\pi/6$ radians with the horizontal. Assume a coefficient of friction of $\mu = \sqrt{3}/4$. Assume also that air resistance acts to retard the block's descent down the ramp, with a force of magnitude equal to one half the block's velocity. We want to determine the velocity $v(t)$ of the block at any time t.

Figure 1.16 shows the forces acting on the block. Gravity acts downward with magnitude $mg\sin(\theta)$, which is $96\sin(\pi/6)$, or 48 pounds. Here $mg = 96$ is the weight of the block. The drag due to friction acts in the reverse direction and is, in pounds,

$$-\mu N = -\mu mg\cos(\theta) = -\frac{\sqrt{3}}{4}(96)\cos\left(\frac{\pi}{6}\right) = -36.$$

The drag force due to air resistance is $-v/2$, the negative sign indicating that this is a retarding force. The total external force on the block is

$$F = 48 - 36 - \tfrac{1}{2}v = 12 - \tfrac{1}{2}v.$$

Since the block weighs 96 pounds, it has a mass of 96/32 slugs, or 3 slugs. From Newton's second law,

$$3\frac{dv}{dt} = 12 - \frac{1}{2}v.$$

This is a linear equation, which we write as

$$v' + \frac{1}{6}v = 4.$$

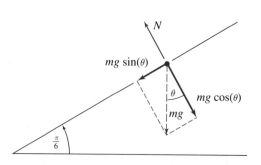

FIGURE 1.16   *Forces acting on a block on an inclined plane.*

An integrating factor is $e^{\int (1/6)\, dt} = e^{t/6}$. Multiply the differential equation by this factor to obtain

$$v'e^{t/6} + \tfrac{1}{6}e^{t/6}v = \left(ve^{t/6}\right)' = 4e^{t/6}$$

and integrate to get

$$ve^{t/6} = 24e^{t/6} + C.$$

The velocity is

$$v(t) = 24 + Ce^{-t/6}.$$

Since the block starts from rest at time zero, $v(0) = 0 = 24 + C$, so $C = -24$ and

$$v(t) = 24\left(1 - e^{-t/6}\right).$$

Let $x(t)$ be the position of the block at any time, measured from the top of the plane. Since $v(t) = x'(t)$, we get

$$x(t) = \int v(t)\, dt = 24t + 144e^{-t/6} + K.$$

If we let the top of the block be the origin along the inclined plane, then $x(0) = 0 = 144 + K$, so

$$K = -144.$$

The position function is

$$x(t) = 24t + 144\left(e^{-t/6} - 1\right).$$

We can now determine the block's position and velocity at any time.

Suppose, for example, we want to know when the block reaches the bottom of the ramp. This happens when the block has gone 50 feet. If this occurs at time T, then

$$x(T) = 50 = 24T + 144\left(e^{-T/6} - 1\right).$$

This transcendental equation cannot be solved algebraically for T, but a computer approximation yields $T \approx 5.8$ seconds.

Notice that

$$\lim_{t \to \infty} v(t) = 24,$$

which means that the block sliding down the ramp has a terminal velocity. If the ramp is long enough, the block will eventually settle into a slide of approximately constant velocity.

The mathematical model we have constructed for the sliding block can be used to analyze the motion of the block under a variety of conditions. For example, we can solve the equations leaving θ arbitrary, and determine the influence of the slope angle of the ramp on position and velocity. Or we could leave μ unspecified and study the influence of friction on the motion.

1.7.2 Electrical Circuits

Electrical engineers often use differential equations to model circuits. The mathematical model is used to analyze the behavior of circuits under various conditions, and aids in the design of circuits having specific characteristics.

We will look at simple circuits having only resistors, inductors and capacitors. A capacitor is a storage device consisting of two plates of conducting material isolated from one another by an insulating material, or dielectric. Electrons can be transferred from one plate to another via external circuitry by applying an electromotive force to the circuit. The charge on a capacitor is essentially a count of the difference between the numbers of electrons on the two plates. This charge is proportional to the applied electromotive force, and the constant of proportionality is the capacitance. Capacitance is usually a very small number, given in micro (10^{-6}) or pico (10^{-12}) farads. To simplify examples and problems, some of the capacitors in this book are assigned numerical values that would actually make them occupy large buildings.

An inductor is made by winding a conductor such as wire around a core of magnetic material. When a current is passed through the wire, a magnetic field is created in the core and around the inductor. The voltage drop across an inductor is proportional to the change in the current flow, and this constant of proportionality is the inductance of the inductor, measured in henrys.

Current is measured in amperes, with one amp equivalent to a rate of electron flow of one coulomb per second. Charge $q(t)$ and current $i(t)$ are related by

$$i(t) = q'(t).$$

The voltage drop across a resistor having resistance R is iR. The drop across a capacitor having capacitance C is q/C. And the voltage drop across an inductor having inductance L is $Li'(t)$.

We construct equations for a circuit by using Kirchhoff's current and voltage laws. Kirchhoff's current law states that the algebraic sum of the currents at any juncture of a circuit is zero. This means that the total current entering the junction must balance the current leaving (conservation of energy). Kirchhoff's voltage law states that the algebraic sum of the potential rises and drops around any closed loop in a circuit is zero.

As an example of modeling a circuit mathematically, consider the circuit of Figure 1.17. Starting at point A, move clockwise around the circuit, first crossing the battery, where there is an increase in potential of E volts. Next there is a decrease in potential of iR volts across the resistor. Finally, there is a decrease of $Li'(t)$ across the inductor, after which we return to point A. By Kirchhoff's voltage law,

$$E - iR - Li' = 0,$$

which is the linear equation

$$i' + \frac{E}{R}i = \frac{E}{L}.$$

Solve this to obtain

$$i(t) = \frac{E}{R} + Ke^{-Rt/L}.$$

To determine the constant K, we need to be given the current at some time. Even without this, we can tell from this equation that as $t \to \infty$, the current approaches the limiting value E/R. This is the steady-state value of the current in the circuit.

Another way to derive the differential equation of this circuit is to designate one of the components as a source, then set the voltage drop across that component equal to the sum of the voltage drops across the other components. To see this approach, consider the circuit of Figure 1.18. Suppose the switch is initially open so that no current flows, and that the charge

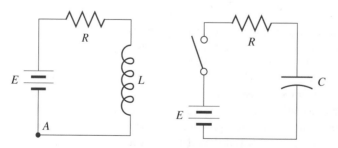

FIGURE 1.17   *RL Circuit.*   **FIGURE 1.18**   *RC circuit.*

on the capacitor is zero. At time zero, close the switch. We want the charge on the capacitor. Notice that we have to close the switch before there is a loop. Using the battery as a source, write

$$iR + \frac{1}{C}q = E,$$

or

$$Rq' + \frac{1}{C}q = E.$$

This leads to the linear equation

$$q' + \frac{1}{RC}q = \frac{E}{R},$$

with solution

$$q(t) = EC\left(1 - e^{-t/RC}\right)$$

satisfying $q(0) = 0$. This equation provides a good deal information about the circuit. Since the voltage on the capacitor at time t is $q(t)/C$, or $E(1 - e^{-t/RC})$, we can see that the voltage approaches E as $t \to \infty$. Since E is the battery potential, the difference between battery and capacitor voltages becomes negligible as time increases, indicating a very small voltage drop across the resistor.

The current in this circuit can be computed as

$$i(t) = q'(t) = \frac{E}{R}e^{-t/RC}$$

after the circuit is switched on. Thus $i(t) \to E/R$ as $t \to \infty$.

Often we encounter discontinuous currents and potential functions in dealing with circuits. These can be treated using Laplace transform techniques, which we will discuss in Chapter 3.

1.7.3   Orthogonal Trajectories

Two curves intersecting at a point P are said to be *orthogonal* if their tangents are perpendicular (orthogonal) at P. Two families of curves, or trajectories, are orthogonal if each curve of the first family is orthogonal to each curve of the second family, wherever an intersection occurs. Orthogonal families occur in many contexts. Parallels and meridians on a globe are orthogonal, as are equipotential and electric lines of force.

A problem that occupied Newton and other early developers of the calculus was the determination of the family of orthogonal trajectories of a given family of curves. Suppose we are given a family $\mathfrak{F}$ of curves in the plane. We want to construct a second family $\mathfrak{G}$ of curves so that every curve in $\mathfrak{F}$ is orthogonal to every curve in $\mathfrak{G}$ wherever an intersection occurs. As a simple example, suppose $\mathfrak{F}$ consists of all circles about the origin. Then $\mathfrak{G}$ consists of all straight lines through the origin (Figure 1.19). It is clear that each straight line is orthogonal to each circle wherever the two intersect.

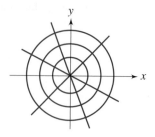

FIGURE 1.19   *Orthogonal families: circles and lines.*

In general, suppose we are given a family $\mathfrak{F}$ of curves. These must be described in some way, say by an equation

$$F(x, y, k) = 0,$$

giving a different curve for each choice of the constant k. Think of these curves as integral curves of a differential equation

$$y' = f(x, y),$$

which we determine from the equation $F(x, y, k) = 0$ by differentiation. At a point (x_0, y_0), the slope of the curve C in $\mathfrak{F}$ through this point is $f(x_0, y_0)$. Assuming that this is nonzero, any curve through (x_0, y_0) and orthogonal to C at this point, must have slope $-1/f(x_0, y_0)$. (Here we use the fact that two lines are orthogonal if and only if their slopes are negative reciprocals.) The family $\mathfrak{G}$ of orthogonal trajectories of $\mathfrak{F}$ therefore consists of the integral curves of the differential equation

$$y' = -\frac{1}{f(x, y)}.$$

Solve this differential equation for the curves in $\mathfrak{G}$.

EXAMPLE 1.29

Consider the family $\mathfrak{F}$ of curves that are graphs of

$$F(x, y, k) = y - kx^2 = 0.$$

This is a family of parabolas. We want the family of orthogonal trajectories.

First obtain the differential equation of $\mathfrak{F}$. Differentiate $y - kx^2 = 0$ to get

$$y' - 2kx = 0.$$

To eliminate k, use the equation $y - kx^2 = 0$ to write

$$k = \frac{y}{x^2}.$$

Then

$$y' - 2\left(\frac{y}{x^2}\right)x = 0,$$

or

$$y' = 2\frac{y}{x} = f(x, y).$$

This is the differential equation of the family $\mathfrak{F}$. Curves in $\mathfrak{F}$ are integral curves of this differential equation, which is of the form $y' = f(x, y)$, with $f(x, y) = 2y/x$. The family $\mathfrak{G}$ of orthogonal trajectories therefore has differential equation

$$y' = -\frac{1}{f(x, y)} = -\frac{x}{2y}.$$

This equation is separable, since

$$2y \, dy = -x \, dx.$$

Integrate to get

$$y^2 = -\tfrac{1}{2}x^2 + C.$$

This is a family of ellipses

$$\tfrac{1}{2}x^2 + y^2 = C.$$

Some of the parabolas and ellipses from $\mathfrak{F}$ and $\mathfrak{G}$ are shown in Figure 1.20. Each parabola in $\mathfrak{F}$ is orthogonal to each ellipse in $\mathfrak{G}$ wherever these curves intersect. ■

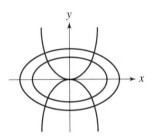

FIGURE 1.20 *Orthogonal families: parabolas and ellipses.*

SECTION 1.7   PROBLEMS

Mechanical Systems

1. Suppose that the pulley described in this section is only 9 feet above the floor. Assuming the same initial conditions as in the discussion, determine the velocity with which the chain leaves the pulley. *Hint:* The mass of the part of the chain that is in motion is $(16 - x)\rho/32$.

2. Determine the time it takes for the chain in Problem 1 to leave the pulley.

3. Suppose the support is only 10 feet above the floor in the discussion of the chain piling on the floor. Calculate the velocity of the moving part of the chain as it leaves the support. (Note the hint to Problem 1.)

4. (Chain and Weight on a Pulley) An 8ρ-pound weight is attached to one end of a 40-foot chain that weighs ρ pounds per foot. The chain is supported by a small frictionless pulley located more than 40 feet above the floor. Initially, the chain is held at rest with 23 feet hanging on one side of the pulley with the remainder of the chain, along with the weight, on the other side. How long after the chain is released, and with what velocity, will it leave the pulley?

5. (Chain on a Table) A 24-foot chain weighing ρ pounds per foot is stretched out on a very tall, frictionless table with 6 feet hanging off the edge. If the chain is released from rest, determine the time it takes for the end of the chain to fall off the table, and also the velocity of the chain at this instant.

6. (Variable Mass Chain on a Low Table) Suppose the chain in Problem 5 is placed on a table that is only

4 feet high, so that the chain accumulates on the floor as it slides off the table. Two feet of chain are already piled up on the floor at the time that the rest of the chain is released. Determine the velocity of the moving end of the chain at the instant it leaves the table top. *Hint:* The mass of that part of the chain that is moving changes with time. Newton's law applies to the center of mass of the moving system.

7. Determine the time it takes for the chain to leave the support in the discussion of the chain piling on the floor.

8. Use the conservation of energy principle (potential energy plus kinetic energy of a conservative system is a constant of the motion) to obtain the velocity of the chain in the discussion involving the chain on the pulley.

9. Use the conservation of energy principle to give an alternate derivation of the conclusion of the discussion of the chain piling on the floor.

10. (Paraboloid of Revolution) Determine the shape assumed by the surface of a liquid being spun in a circular bowl at constant angular velocity ω. *Hint:* Consider a particle of liquid located at (x, y) on the surface of the liquid, as in Figure 1.21. The forces acting on the particle are the horizontal force having magnitude $m\omega^2 x$ and a vertical force of magnitude mg. Since the particle is in radial equilibrium, the resultant vector is normal to the curve.

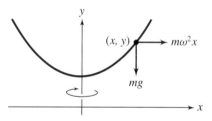

FIGURE 1.21 *Particle on the surface of a spinning liquid.*

   Properties of spinning liquids have found application in astronomy. A Canadian astronomer has constructed a telescope by spinning a bowl of mercury, creating a reflective surface free of the defects obtained by the usual grinding of a solid lens. He claims that the idea was probably known to Newton, but that he is the first to carry it out in practice. Roger Angel, a University of Arizona astronomer, has developed this idea into a technique for producing telescope mirrors called *spin casting*. As reported in *Time* (April 27, 1992), "... a complex ceramic mold is assembled inside the furnace and filled with glittering chunks of Pyrex-type glass. Once the furnace lid is sealed,

the temperature will slowly ratchet up over a period of several days, at times rising no more than 2 degrees Centigrade in an hour. At 750 degrees C (1382 degrees Fahrenheit), when the glass is a smooth, shiny lake, the furnace starts to whirl like a merry-go-round, an innovation that automatically spins the glass into the parabolic shape traditionally achieved by grinding." The result is a parabolic surface requiring little or no grinding before a reflective coat is applied. Professor Angel believes that the method will allow the construction of much larger mirrors than are possible by conventional techniques. Supporting this claim is his recent production of one of the world's largest telescope mirrors, a 6.5 meter (about 21 feet) to be placed in an observatory atop Mount Hopkins in Arizona.

11. A 10-pound ballast bag is dropped from a hot air balloon which is at an altitude of 342 feet and ascending at a rate of 4 feet per second. Assuming that air resistance is not a factor, determine the maximum height attained by the bag, how long it remains aloft, and the speed with which it strikes the ground.

12. A 48-pound box is given an initial push of 16 feet per second down an inclined plane that has a gradient of $\frac{7}{24}$. If there is a coefficient of friction of $\frac{1}{3}$ between the box and the plane, and an air resistance equal to $\frac{3}{2}$ the velocity of the box, determine how far the box will travel before coming to rest.

13. A skydiver and her equipment together weigh 192 pounds. Before the parachute is opened, there is an air drag equal to six times her velocity. Four seconds after stepping from the plane, the skydiver opens the parachute, producing a drag equal to three times the square of the velocity. Determine the velocity and how far the skydiver has fallen at time t. What is the terminal velocity?

14. Archimedes' principle of buoyancy states that an object submerged in a fluid is buoyed up by a force equal to the weight of the fluid that is displaced by the object. A rectangular box, 1 by 2 by 3 feet, and weighing 384 pounds, is dropped into a 100-foot-deep freshwater lake. The box begins to sink with a drag due to the water having magnitude equal to $\frac{1}{2}$ the velocity. Calculate the terminal velocity of the box. Will the box have achieved a velocity of 10 feet per second by the time it reaches bottom? Assume that the density of the water is 62.5 pounds per cubic foot.

15. Suppose the box in Problem 14 cracks open upon hitting the bottom of the lake, and 32 pounds of its contents fall out. Approximate the velocity with which the box surfaces.

16. The acceleration due to gravity inside the earth is proportional to the distance from the center of the

earth. An object is dropped from the surface of the earth into a hole extending through the earth's center. Calculate the speed the object achieves by the time it reaches the center.

17. A particle starts from rest at the highest point of a vertical circle and slides under only the influence of gravity along a chord to another point on the circle. Show that the time taken is independent of the choice of the terminal point. What is this common time?

Circuits

18. Determine each of the currents in the circuit of Figure 1.22.

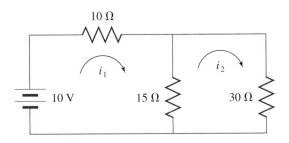

FIGURE 1.22

19. In the circuit of Figure 1.23, the capacitor is initially discharged. How long after the switch is closed will the capacitor voltage be 76 volts? Determine the current in the resistor at that time. (Here $k\Omega$ denotes 1000 ohms and μF denotes 10^{-6} farads.)

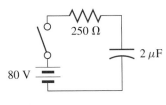

FIGURE 1.23

20. Suppose, in Problem 19, the capacitor had a potential of 50 volts when the switch was closed. How long would it take for the capacitor voltage to reach 76 volts?

21. For the circuit of Figure 1.24, find all currents immediately after the switch is closed, assuming that all of these currents and the charges on the capacitors are zero just prior to closing the switch.

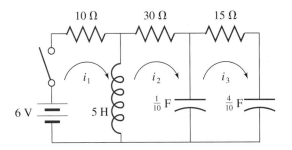

FIGURE 1.24

22. In a constant electromotive force RL circuit, we find that the current is given by

$$i(t) = \frac{E}{R}\left(1 - e^{-Rt/L}\right) + i(0)e^{-Rt/L}.$$

Let $i(0) = 0$.

(a) Show that the current increases with time.

(b) Find a time t_0 at which the current is 63% of E/R. This time is called the *inductive time constant* of the circuit.

(c) Does the inductive time constant depend on $i(0)$? If so, in what way?

23. Recall that the charge $q(t)$ in an RC circuit satisfies the linear differential equation

$$q' + \frac{1}{RC}q = \frac{1}{R}E(t).$$

(a) Solve for the charge in the case that $E(t) = E$, constant. Evaluate the constant of integration by using the condition $q(0) = q_0$.

(b) Determine $\lim_{t\to\infty} q(t)$ and show that this limit is independent of q_0.

(c) Graph $q(t)$. Determine when the charge has its maximum and minimum values.

(d) Determine at what time $q(t)$ is within 1% of its steady-state value (the limiting value requested in (b)).

Orthogonal Trajectories

In each of Problems 24 through 29, find the family of orthogonal trajectories of the given family of curves. If software is available, graph some curves in the given family and some curves in the family of orthogonal trajectories.

24. $x + 2y = K$

25. $2x^2 - 3y = K$

26. $x^2 + 2y^2 = K$

27. $y = Kx^2 + 1$

28. $x^2 - Ky^2 = 1$

29. $y = e^{kx}$

1.8 Existence and Uniqueness for Solutions of Initial Value Problems

We have solved several initial value problems

$$y' = f(x, y); \quad y(x_0) = y_0,$$

and have always found that there is just one solution. That is, the solution existed, and it was unique. Can either existence or uniqueness fail to occur? The answer is yes, as the following examples show.

EXAMPLE 1.30

Consider the initial value problem

$$y' = 2y^{1/2}; \quad y(0) = -1.$$

The differential equation is separable and has general solution

$$y(x) = (x + C)^2.$$

To satisfy the initial condition, we must choose C so that

$$y(0) = C^2 = -1,$$

and this is impossible if C is to be a real number. This initial value problem has no real-valued solution. ∎

EXAMPLE 1.31

Consider the problem

$$y' = 2y^{1/2}; \quad y(2) = 0.$$

One solution is the trivial function

$$y = \varphi(x) = 0 \quad \text{for all } x.$$

But there is another solution. Define

$$\psi(x) = \begin{cases} 0 & \text{for } x \leq 2 \\ (x-2)^2 & \text{for } x \geq 2. \end{cases}$$

Graphs of both solutions are shown in Figure 1.25. Uniqueness fails in this example. ∎

Because of examples such as these, we look for conditions that ensure that an initial value problem has a unique solution. The following theorem provides a convenient set of conditions.

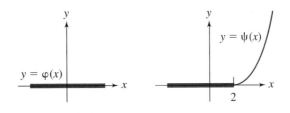

FIGURE 1.25 *Graphs of solutions of* $y' = 2\sqrt{y}$; $y(2) = 0$.

THEOREM 1.2 *Existence and Uniqueness*

Let f and $\partial f/\partial y$ be continuous for all (x, y) in a closed rectangle R centered at (x_0, y_0). Then there exists a positive number h such that the initial value problem

$$y' = f(x, y); \quad y(x_0) = y_0$$

has a unique solution defined over the interval $(x_0 - h, x_0 + h)$. ∎

As with the test for exactness (Theorem 1.1), by a closed rectangle we mean all points on or inside a rectangle in the plane, having sides parallel to the axes. Geometrically, existence of a solution of the initial value problem means that there is an integral curve of the differential equation passing through (x_0, y_0). Uniqueness means that there is only one such curve.

This is an example of a *local theorem*, in the following sense. The theorem guarantees existence of a unique solution that is defined on some interval of width $2h$, but it says nothing about how large h is. Depending on f and x_0, h may be small, giving us existence and uniqueness "near" x_0. This is dramatically demonstrated by the initial value problem

$$y' = y^2; \quad y(0) = n,$$

in which n is any positive integer. Here $f(x, y) = y^2$ and $\partial f/\partial y = 2y$, both continuous over the entire plane, hence on any closed rectangle about $(0, n)$. The theorem tells us that there is a unique solution of this initial value problem in *some* interval $(-h, h)$.

In this case we can solve the initial value problem explicitly, obtaining

$$y(x) = -\frac{1}{x - \frac{1}{n}}.$$

This solution is valid for $-1/n < x < 1/n$, so we can take $h = 1/n$ in this example. This means that the size of n in the initial value controls the size of the interval for the solution. The larger n is, the smaller this interval must be. This fact is certainly not apparent from the initial value problem itself!

In the special case that the differential equation is linear, we can improve considerably on the existence/uniqueness theorem.

THEOREM 1.3

Let p and q be continuous on an open interval I and let x_0 be in I. Let y_0 be any number. Then the initial value problem

$$y' + p(x)y = q(x); \quad y(x_0) = y_0$$

has a unique solution defined for all x in I. ∎

In particular, if p and q are continuous for all x, then there is a unique solution defined over the entire real line.

Proof Equation (1.6) of Section 1.3 gives the general solution of the linear equation. Using this, we can write the solution of the initial value problem:

$$y(x) = e^{-\int_{x_0}^x p(\xi)\,d\xi} \left[\int_{x_0}^x q(\xi) e^{\int_{x_0}^x p(\xi)\,d\xi}\,d\xi + y_0 \right].$$

Because p and q are continuous on I, this solution is defined for all x in I. ∎

Therefore, in the case that the differential equation is linear, the initial value problem has a unique solution in the largest open interval containing x_0, in which both p and q are continuous.

SECTION 1.8   PROBLEMS

In each of Problems 1 through 5, show that the conditions of Theorem 1.2 are satisfied by the initial value problem. Assume familiar facts from the calculus about continuity of real functions of one and two variables.

1. $y' = 2y^2 + 3xe^y \sin(xy); \; y(2) = 4$

2. $y' = 4xy + \cosh(x); \; y(1) = -1$

3. $y' = (xy)^3 - \sin(y); \; y(2) = 2$

4. $y' = x^5 - y^5 + 2xe^y; \; y(3) = \pi$

5. $y' = x^2 y e^{-2x} + y^2; \; y(3) = 8$

6. Consider the initial value problem $|y'| = 2y; \; y(x_0) = y_0$.

(a) Find two solutions, assuming that $y_0 > 0$.

(b) Explain why part (a) does not violate Theorem 1.2.

Theorem 1.2 can be proved using Picard iterates, which we will discuss briefly. Suppose f and $\partial f/\partial y$ are continuous in a closed rectangle R having (x_0, y_0) in its interior and sides parallel to the axes. Consider the initial value problem $y' = f(x, y); \; y(x_0) = y_0$. For each positive integer n, define

$$y_n(x) = y_0 + \int_{x_0}^x f(t, y_{n-1}(t))\,dt.$$

This is a recursive definition, giving $y_1(x)$ in terms of y_0, then $y_2(x)$ in terms of $y_1(x)$, and so on. The functions $y_n(x)$ for $n = 1, 2, \ldots$ are called *Picard iterates* for the initial value problem. Under the assumptions made on f, the sequence $\{y_n(x)\}$ converges for all x in some interval about x_0, and the limit of this sequence is the solution of the initial value problem on this interval.

In each of Problems 7 through 10, (a) use Theorem 1.2 to show that the problem has a solution in some interval about x_0, (b) find this solution, (c) compute Picard iterates $y_1(x)$ through $y_6(x)$, and from these guess $y_n(x)$ in general, and (d) find the Taylor series of the solution from (b) about x_0. You should find that the iterates computed in (c) are partial sums of the series of (d). Conclude that in these examples the Picard iterates converge to the solution.

7. $y' = 2 - y; \; y(0) = 1$

8. $y' = 4 + y; \; y(0) = 3$

9. $y' = 2x^2; \; y(1) = 3$

10. $y' = \cos(x); \; y(\pi) = 1$

REDUCTION OF ORDER CONSTANT COEFFICIENT HO
MOGENEOUS LINEAR EQUATION EULER'S EQUATION
NONHOMOGENEOUS EQUATION $y'' + p(x)y' + q(x)y =$
$f(x)$ APPLICATION OF SECOND ORDER DIFFERENTIAL

CHAPTER 2

Second-Order Differential Equations

2.1   Preliminary Concepts

A *second-order differential equation* is an equation that contains a second derivative, but no higher derivative. Most generally, it has the form

$$F(x, y, y', y'') = 0,$$

although only a term involving y'' need appear explicitly. For example,

$$y'' = x^3,$$

$$xy'' - \cos(y) = e^x$$

and

$$y'' - 4xy' + y = 2$$

are second-order differential equations.

A *solution* of $F(x, y, y', y'') = 0$ on an interval I (perhaps the whole real line) is a function φ that satisfies the differential equation at each point of I:

$$F(x, \varphi(x), \varphi'(x), \varphi''(x)) = 0 \quad \text{for } x \text{ in } I.$$

For example, $\varphi(x) = 6\cos(4x) - 17\sin(4x)$ is a solution of

$$y'' + 16y = 0$$

for all real x. And $\varphi(x) = x^3 \cos(\ln(x))$ is a solution of

$$x^2 y'' - 5xy' + 10y = 0$$

for $x > 0$. These can be checked by substitution into the differential equation.

The *linear second-order differential equation* has the form

$$R(x)y'' + P(x)y' + Q(x)y = S(x),$$

in which R, P, Q, and S are continuous in some interval. On any interval where $R(x) \neq 0$, we can divide this equation by $R(x)$ and obtain the special linear equation

$$y'' + p(x)y' + q(x)y = f(x). \qquad (2.1)$$

For the remainder of this chapter, we will concentrate on this equation. We want to know:

1. What can we expect in the way of existence and uniqueness of solutions of equation (2.1)?

2. How can we produce all solutions of equation (2.1), at least in some cases that occur frequently and have important applications?

We begin with the underlying theory that will guide us in developing techniques for explicitly producing solutions of equation (2.1).

2.2   Theory of Solutions of $y'' + p(x)y' + q(x)y = f(x)$

To get some feeling for what we are dealing with, and what we should be looking for, consider the simple linear second-order equation

$$y'' - 12x = 0.$$

We can write this as

$$y'' = 12x$$

and integrate to obtain

$$y' = \int y''(x)\, dx = \int 12x\, dx = 6x^2 + C.$$

Integrate again:

$$y(x) = \int y'(x)\, dx = \int (6x^2 + C)\, dx = 2x^3 + Cx + K.$$

This solution is defined for all x, and contains two arbitrary constants. If we recall that the general solution of a first order equation contained one arbitrary constant, it seems natural that the solution of a second-order equation, involving two integrations, should contain two arbitrary constants.

For any choices of C and K, we can graph the integral curves $y = 2x^3 + Cx + K$ as curves in the plane. Figure 2.1 shows some of these curves for different choices of these constants.

Unlike the first-order case, there are many integral curves through each point in the plane. For example, suppose we want a solution satisfying the initial condition

$$y(0) = 3.$$

Then we need

$$y(0) = K = 3,$$

but are still free to choose C as any number. All solutions

$$y(x) = 2x^3 + Cx + 3$$

pass through $(0, 3)$. Some of these curves are shown in Figure 2.2.

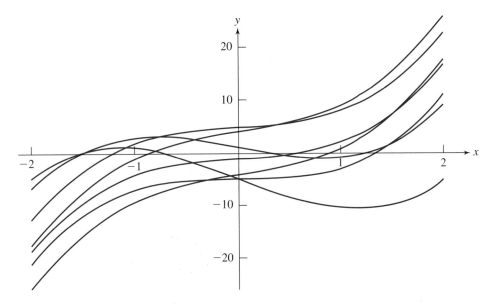

FIGURE 2.1 *Graphs of $y = 2x^3 + Cx + K$ for various values of C and K.*

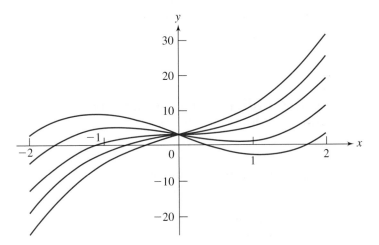

FIGURE 2.2 *Graphs of $y = 2x^3 + Cx + 3$ for various values of C.*

We single out exactly one of these curves if we specify its slope at $(0, 3)$. Suppose, for example, we also specify the initial condition

$$y'(0) = -1.$$

Since $y'(x) = 6x^2 + C$, this requires that $C = -1$. There is exactly one solution satisfying both initial conditions (going through a given point with given slope), and it is

$$y(x) = 6x^2 - x + 3.$$

A graph of this solution is given in Figure 2.3.

To sum up, at least in this example, the general solution of the differential equation involved two arbitrary constants. An initial condition $y(0) = 3$, specifying that the solution curve must pass through $(0, 3)$, determined one of these constants. However, that left infinitely many

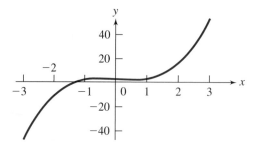

FIGURE 2.3 *Graph of $y = 2x^3 - x + 3$.*

solution curves passing through $(0, 3)$. The other initial condition, $y'(0) = -1$, picked out that solution curve through $(0, 3)$ having slope -1 and gave a unique solution of this problem.

This suggests that we define the initial value problem for equation (2.1) to be the differential equation, defined on some interval, together with two initial conditions, one specifying a point lying on the solution curve, and the other its slope at that point. This problem has the form

$$y'' + p(x)y' + q(x)y = f(x); \quad y(x_0) = A, \, y'(x_0) = B,$$

in which A and B are given real numbers.

The main theorem on existence and uniqueness of solutions for this problem is the second-order analogue of Theorem 1.3 in Chapter 1.

THEOREM 2.1

Let p, q, and f be continuous on an open interval I. Let x_0 be in I and let A and B be any real numbers. Then the initial value problem

$$y'' + p(x)y' + q(x)y = f(x); \quad y(x_0) = A, \, y'(x_0) = B$$

has a unique solution defined for all x in I. ∎

This gives us an idea of the kind of information needed to specify a unique solution of equation (2.1). Now we need a framework in which to proceed in finding solutions. We will provide this in two steps, beginning with the case that $f(x)$ is identically zero.

2.2.1 The Homogeneous Equation $y'' + p(x)y' + q(x) = 0$

When $f(x)$ is identically zero in equation (2.1), the resulting equation

$$y'' + p(x)y' + q(x) = 0 \tag{2.2}$$

is called *homogeneous*. This term was used in a different context with first-order equations, and its use here is unrelated to that. Here it simply means that the right side of equation (2.1) is zero.

A *linear combination* of solutions $y_1(x)$ and $y_2(x)$ of equation (2.2) is a sum of constant multiples of these functions:

$$c_1 y_1(x) + c_2 y_2(x)$$

with c_1 and c_2 real numbers. It is an important property of the homogeneous linear equation that linear combinations of solutions are again solutions.

THEOREM 2.2

Let y_1 and y_2 be solutions of $y'' + p(x)y' + q(x)y = 0$ on an interval I. Then any linear combination of these solutions is also a solution.

Proof   Let c_1 and c_2 be real numbers. Substituting $y(x) = c_1 y_1(x) + c_2 y_2(x)$ into the differential equation, we obtain

$$(c_1 y_1 + c_2 y_2)'' + p(x)(c_1 y_1 + c_2 y_2)' + q(x)(c_1 y_1 + c_2 y_2)$$
$$= c_1 y_1'' + c_2 y_2'' + c_1 p(x)y_1' + c_2 p(x)y_2' + c_1 q(x)y_1 + c_2 q(x)y_2$$
$$= c_1[y_1'' + p(x)y_1' + q(x)y_1] + c_2[y_2'' + p(x)y_2' + q(x)y_2]$$
$$= 0 + 0 = 0,$$

because of the assumption that y_1 and y_2 are both solutions. ∎

Of course, as a special case $(c_2 = 0)$, this theorem tells us also that, for the homogeneous equation, a constant multiple of a solution is a solution. Even this special case of the theorem fails for a nonhomogeneous equation. For example, $y_1(x) = 4e^{2x}/5$ is a solution of

$$y'' + 2y' - 3y = 4e^{2x},$$

but $5y_1(x) = 4e^{2x}$ is not.

The point to taking linear combinations $c_1 y_1 + c_2 y_2$ is to obtain more solutions from just two solutions of equation (2.2). However, if y_2 is already a constant multiple of y_1, then

$$c_1 y_1 + c_2 y_2 = c_1 y_1 + c_2 k y_1 = (c_1 + kc_2)y_1,$$

just another constant multiple of y_1. In this event, y_2 is superfluous, providing us nothing we did not know from just y_1. This leads us to distinguish the case in which one solution is a constant multiple of another, from the case in which the two solutions are not multiples of each other.

DEFINITION 2.1   Linear Dependence, Independence

Two functions f and g are linearly dependent on an open interval I if, for some constant c, either $f(x) = cg(x)$ for all x in I, or $g(x) = cf(x)$ for all x in I.

If f and g are not linearly dependent on I, then they are said to be linearly independent on the interval.

EXAMPLE 2.1

$y_1(x) = \cos(x)$ and $y_2(x) = \sin(x)$ are solutions of $y'' + y = 0$, over the real line. Neither of these functions is a constant multiple of the other. Indeed, if $\cos(x) = k\sin(x)$ for all x, then in particular

$$\cos\left(\frac{\pi}{4}\right) = \frac{\sqrt{2}}{2} = k\sin\left(\frac{\pi}{4}\right) = k\frac{\sqrt{2}}{2},$$

so k must be 1. But then $\cos(x) = \sin(x)$ for all x, a clear absurdity (for example, let $x = 0$). These solutions are linearly independent. Now we know from Theorem 2.2 that

$$a\cos(x) + b\sin(x)$$

is a solution for any numbers a and b. Because $\cos(x)$ and $\sin(x)$ are linearly independent, this linear combination provides an infinity of new solutions, instead of just constant multiples of one we already know. ∎

There is a simple test to tell whether two solutions of equation (2.2) are linearly independent on an interval. Define the *Wronskian* of solutions y_1 and y_2 to be

$$W(x) = y_1(x)y_2'(x) - y_1'(x)y_2(x).$$

This is the 2×2 determinant

$$W(x) = \begin{vmatrix} y_1(x) & y_2(x) \\ y_1'(x) & y_2'(x) \end{vmatrix}.$$

THEOREM 2.3   *Wronskian Test*

Let y_1 and y_2 be solutions of $y'' + p(x)y' + q(x)y = 0$ on an open interval I. Then,

1. Either $W(x) = 0$ for all x in I, or $W(x) \neq 0$ for all x in I.

2. y_1 and y_2 are linearly independent on I if and only if $W(x) \neq 0$ on I. ∎

Conclusion (1) means that the Wronskian of two solutions cannot be nonzero at some points of I and zero at others. Either the Wronskian vanishes over the entire interval, or it is nonzero at every point of the interval. Conclusion (2) states that nonvanishing of the Wronskian is equivalent to linear independence of the solutions. Putting both conclusions together, it is therefore enough to test $W(x)$ at just one point of I to determine linear dependence or independence of these solutions. This gives us great latitude to choose a point at which the Wronskian is easy to evaluate.

EXAMPLE 2.2

In Example 2.1, we considered the solutions $y_1(x) = \cos(x)$ and $y_2(x) = \sin(x)$ of $y'' + y = 0$, for all x. In this case, linear independence was obvious. The Wronskian of these solutions is

$$W(x) = \begin{vmatrix} \cos(x) & \sin(x) \\ -\sin(x) & \cos(x) \end{vmatrix}$$

$$= \cos^2(x) + \sin^2(x) = 1 \neq 0. \quad ∎$$

EXAMPLE 2.3

It is not always obvious whether two solutions are linearly independent or dependent on an interval. Consider the equation $y'' + xy = 0$. This equation appears simple but is not easy to solve. By a power series method we will develop later, we can write two solutions

$$y_1(x) = 1 - \frac{1}{6}x^3 + \frac{1}{180}x^6 - \frac{1}{12{,}960}x^9 + \cdots$$

and

$$y_2(x) = x - \frac{1}{12}x^4 + \frac{1}{504}x^7 - \frac{1}{45{,}360}x^{10} + \cdots,$$

with both series converging for all x. Here I is the entire real line. The Wronskian of these solutions at any nonzero x would be difficult to evaluate, but at $x = 0$ we easily obtain

$$W(0) = y_1(0)y_2'(0) - y_1'(0)y_2(0) = (1)(1) - (0)(0) = 1.$$

Nonvanishing of the Wronskian at this one point is enough to conclude linear independence of these solutions. ■

We are now ready to use the machinery we have built up to determine what is needed to find all solutions of $y'' + p(x)y' + q(x) = 0$.

THEOREM 2.4

Let y_1 and y_2 be linearly independent solutions of $y'' + p(x)y' + q(x)y = 0$ on an open interval I. Then, every solution of this differential equation on I is a linear combination of y_1 and y_2. ■

This fundamental theorem provides a strategy for finding all solutions of $y'' + p(x)y' + q(x)y = 0$ on I. Find two linearly independent solutions. Depending on p and q, this may be difficult, but at least we have a specific goal. If necessary, use the Wronskian to test for independence. The general linear combination $c_1y_1 + c_2y_2$, with c_1 and c_2 arbitrary constants, then contains all possible solutions.

We will prove the theorem following introduction of some standard terminology.

DEFINITION 2.2

Let y_1 and y_2 be solutions of $y'' + p(x)y' + q(x)y = 0$ on an open interval I.

1. y_1 and y_2 form a *fundamental set of solutions* on I if y_1 and y_2 are linearly independent on I.

2. When y_1 and y_2 form a fundamental set of solutions, we call $c_1y_1 + c_2y_2$, with c_1 and c_2 arbitrary constants, the *general solution* of the differential equation on I.

In these terms, we find the general solution by finding a fundamental set of solutions. Here is a proof of Theorem 2.4.

Proof Let φ be any solution of $y'' + p(x)y' + q(x)y = 0$ on I. We want to show that there must be numbers c_1 and c_2 such that

$$\varphi(x) = c_1y_1(x) + c_2y_2(x).$$

Choose any x_0 in I. Let $\varphi(x_0) = A$ and $\varphi'(x_0) = B$. By Theorem 2.1, φ is the unique solution on I of the initial value problem

$$y'' + p(x)y' + q(x)y = 0; \quad y(x_0) = A, y'(x_0) = B.$$

Now consider the system of two algebraic equations in two unknowns:

$$y_1(x_0)c_1 + y_2(x_0)c_2 = A$$
$$y_1'(x_0)c_1 + y_2'(x_0)c_2 = B.$$

It is routine to solve these algebraic equations. Assuming that $W(x_0) \neq 0$, we find that

$$c_1 = \frac{Ay_2'(x_0) - By_2(x_0)}{W(x_0)}, \quad c_2 = \frac{By_1(x_0) - Ay_1'(x_0)}{W(x_0)}.$$

With this choice of c_1 and c_2, the function $c_1y_1 + c_2y_2$ is a solution of the initial value problem. By uniqueness of the solution of this problem, $\varphi(x) = c_1y_1(x) + c_2y_2(x)$ on I, and the proof is complete. ∎

The proof reinforces the importance of having a fundamental set of solutions, since the nonvanishing of the Wronskian plays a vital role in showing that an arbitrary solution must be a linear combination of the fundamental solutions.

2.2.2 The Nonhomogeneous Equation $y'' + p(x)y' + q(x)y = f(x)$

The ideas just developed for the homogeneous equation (2.2) also provide the key to solving the nonhomogeneous equation

$$y'' + p(x)y' + q(x)y = f(x). \tag{2.3}$$

THEOREM 2.5

Let y_1 and y_2 be a fundamental set of solutions of $y'' + p(x)y' + q(x)y = 0$ on an open interval I. Let y_p be any solution of equation (2.3) on I. Then, for any solution φ of equation (2.3), there exist numbers c_1 and c_2 such that

$$\varphi = c_1y_1 + c_2y_2 + y_p. \ ∎$$

This conclusion leads us to call $c_1y_1 + c_2y_2 + y_p$ the *general solution* of equation (2.3) and suggests the following strategy.

To solve $y'' + p(x)y' + q(x)y = f(x)$:

1. find the general solution $c_1y_1 + c_2y_2$ of the associated homogeneous equation $y'' + p(x)y' + q(x)y = 0$,
2. find *any* solution y_p of $y'' + p(x)y' + q(x)y = f(x)$, and
3. write the general solution $c_1y_1 + c_2y_2 + y_p$. This expression contains all possible solutions of equation (2.3) on the interval.

Again, depending on p, q, and f, the first two steps may be formidable. Nevertheless, the theorem tells us what to look for and provides a clear way to proceed.

Here is a proof of the theorem.

Proof Since φ and y_p are both solutions of equation (2.3), then

$$(\varphi - y_p)'' + p(\varphi - y_p)' + q(\varphi - y_p) = \varphi'' + p\varphi' + q\varphi - (y_p'' + py_p' + qy_p)$$
$$= f - f = 0.$$

Therefore, $\varphi - y_p$ is a solution of $y'' + py' + qy = 0$. Since y_1 and y_2 form a fundamental set of solutions for this homogeneous equation, there are constants c_1 and c_2 such that

$$\varphi - y_p = c_1y_1 + c_2y_2,$$

and this is what we wanted to show. ∎

The remainder of this chapter is devoted to techniques for carrying out the strategies just developed. For the general solution of the homogeneous equation (2.2) we must produce a fundamental set of solutions. And for the nonhomogeneous equation (2.3) we need to find one particular solution, together with a fundamental set of solutions of the associated homogeneous equation (2.2).

SECTION 2.2   **PROBLEMS**

In each of Problems 1 through 6, (a) verify that y_1 and y_2 are solutions of the differential equation, (b) show that their Wronskian is not zero, (c) write the general solution of the differential equation, and (d) find the solution of the initial value problem.

1. $y'' - 4y = 0;\ y(0) = 1,\ y'(0) = 0$
   $y_1(x) = \cosh(2x),\ y_2(x) = \sinh(2x)$

2. $y'' + 9y = 0;\ y(\pi/3) = 0,\ y'(\pi/3) = 1$
   $y_1(x) = \cos(3x),\ y_2(x) = \sin(3x)$

3. $y'' + 11y' + 24y = 0;\ y(0) = 1,\ y'(0) = 4$
   $y_1(x) = e^{-3x},\ y_2(x) = e^{-8x}$

4. $y'' + 2y' + 8y = 0;\ y(0) = 2,\ y'(0) = 0$
   $y_1(x) = e^{-x}\cos(\sqrt{7}x),\ y_2(x) = e^{-x}\sin(\sqrt{7}x)$

5. $y'' - \dfrac{7}{x}y' + \dfrac{16}{x^2}y = 0;\ y(1) = 2,\ y'(1) = 4$
   $y_1(x) = x^4,\ y_2(x) = x^4\ln(x)$

6. $y'' + \dfrac{1}{x}y' + \left(1 - \dfrac{1}{4x^2}\right)y = 0;\ y(\pi) = -5,\ y'(\pi) = 8$
   $y_1(x) = \sqrt{\dfrac{2}{\pi x}}\cos(x),\ y_2(x) = \sqrt{\dfrac{2}{\pi x}}\sin(x)$

7. Let $y_1(x) = x^2$ and $y_2(x) = x^3$. Show that $W(x) = x^4$ for all real x. Then $W(0) = 0$, but $W(x)$ is not identically zero. Why does this not contradict Theorem 2.3.1, with the interval I chosen as the entire real line?

8. Show that $y_1(x) = x$ and $y_2(x) = x^2$ are linearly independent solutions of $x^2y'' - 2xy' + 2y = 0$ on $[-1, 1]$, but that $W(0) = 0$. Why does this not contradict Theorem 2.3.1 on this interval?

9. Give an example to show that the product of two solutions of $y'' + p(x)y' + q(x)y = 0$ need not be a solution.

10. Show that $y_1(x) = 3e^{2x} - 1$ and $y_2(x) = e^{-x} + 2$ are solutions of $yy'' + 2y' - (y')^2 = 0$, but that neither $2y_1$ nor $y_1 + y_2$ is a solution. Why does this not contradict Theorem 2.2?

11. Suppose y_1 and y_2 are solutions of $y'' + p(x)y' + q(x)y = 0$ on $[a, b]$, and that p and q are continuous on this interval. Suppose y_1 and y_2 both have a relative extremum at x_0 in (a, b). Prove that y_1 and y_2 are linearly dependent on $[a, b]$.

12. Let φ be a solution of $y'' + p(x)y' + q(x)y = 0$ on an open interval I, and suppose $\varphi(x_0) = 0$ for some x_0 in I. Suppose $\varphi(x)$ is not identically zero. Prove that $\varphi'(x_0) \neq 0$.

13. Let y_1 and y_2 be distinct solutions of $y'' + p(x)y' + q(x)y = 0$ on an open interval I. Let x_0 be in I and suppose $y_1(x_0) = y_2(x_0) = 0$. Prove that y_1 and y_2 are linearly dependent on I. Thus linearly independent solutions cannot share a common zero.

2.3   Reduction of Order

Given $y'' + p(x)y' + q(x)y = 0$, we want two independent solutions. Reduction of order is a technique for finding a second solution, if we can somehow produce a first solution.

Suppose we know a solution y_1, which is not identically zero. We will look for a second solution of the form $y_2(x) = u(x)y_1(x)$. Compute

$$y_2' = u'y_1 + uy_1', \quad y_2'' = u''y_1 + 2u'y_1' + uy_1''.$$

In order for y_2 to be a solution we need

$$u''y_1 + 2u'y_1' + uy_1'' + p[u'y_1 + uy_1'] + quy_1 = 0.$$

Rearrange terms to write this equation as

$$u''y_1 + u'[2y_1' + py_1] + u[y_1'' + py_1' + qy_1] = 0.$$

The coefficient of u is zero because y_1 is a solution. Thus we need to choose u so that

$$u''y_1 + u'[2y_1' + py_1] = 0.$$

On any interval in which $y_1(x) \neq 0$, we can write

$$u'' + \frac{2y_1' + py_1}{y_1} u' = 0.$$

To help focus on the problem of determining u, denote

$$g(x) = \frac{2y_1'(x) + p(x)y_1(x)}{y_1(x)},$$

a known function because $y_1(x)$ and $p(x)$ are known. Then

$$u'' + g(x)u' = 0.$$

Let $v = u'$ to get

$$v' + g(x)v = 0.$$

This is a linear first-order differential equation for v, with general solution

$$v(x) = Ce^{-\int g(x)\,dx}.$$

Since we need only one second solution y_2, we will take $C = 1$, so

$$v(x) = e^{-\int g(x)\,dx}.$$

Finally, since $v = u'$,

$$u(x) = \int e^{-\int g(x)\,dx}\,dx.$$

If we can perform these integrations and obtain $u(x)$, then $y_2 = uy_1$ is a second solution of $y'' + py' + qy = 0$. Further,

$$W(x) = y_1y_2' - y_1'y_2 = y_1(uy_1' + u'y_1) - y_1'uy_1 = u'y_1^2 = vy_1^2.$$

Since $v(x)$ is an exponential function, $v(x) \neq 0$. And the preceding derivation was carried out on an interval in which $y_1(x) \neq 0$. Thus $W(x) \neq 0$ and y_1 and y_2 form a fundamental set of solutions on this interval. The general solution of $y'' + py' + qy = 0$ is $c_1y_1 + c_2y_2$.

We do not recommend memorizing formulas for g, v and then u. Given one solution y_1, substitute $y_2 = uy_1$ into the differential equation and, after the cancellations that occur because y_1 is one solution, solve the resulting equation for $u(x)$.

EXAMPLE 2.4

Suppose we are given that $y_1(x) = e^{-2x}$ is one solution of $y'' + 4y' + 4y = 0$. To find a second solution, let $y_2(x) = u(x)e^{-2x}$. Then

$$y_2' = u'e^{-2x} - 2e^{-2x}u \quad \text{and} \quad y_2'' = u''e^{-2x} + 4e^{-2x}u - 4u'e^{-2x}.$$

Substitute these into the differential equation to get

$$u''e^{-2x} + 4e^{-2x}u - 4u'e^{-2x} + 4(u'e^{-2x} - 2e^{-2x}u) + 4ue^{-2x} = 0.$$

Some cancellations occur because e^{-2x} is one solution, leaving

$$u'' e^{-2x} = 0,$$

or

$$u'' = 0.$$

Two integrations yield $u(x) = cx + d$. Since we only need one second solution y_2, we only need one u, so we will choose $c = 1$ and $d = 0$. This gives $u(x) = x$ and

$$y_2(x) = xe^{-2x}.$$

Now

$$W(x) = \begin{vmatrix} e^{-2x} & xe^{-2x} \\ -2e^{-2x} & e^{-2x} - 2xe^{-2x} \end{vmatrix} = e^{-4x} \neq 0$$

for all x. Therefore, y_1 and y_2 form a fundamental set of solutions for all x, and the general solution of $y'' + 4y' + 4y = 0$ is

$$y(x) = c_1 e^{-2x} + c_2 x e^{-2x}. \quad \blacksquare$$

EXAMPLE 2.5

Suppose we want the general solution of $y'' - (3/x)y' + (4/x^2)y = 0$ for $x > 0$, and somehow we find one solution $y_1(x) = x^2$. Put $y_2(x) = x^2 u(x)$ and compute

$$y_2' = 2xu + x^2 u' \quad \text{and} \quad y_2'' = 2u + 4xu' + x^2 u''.$$

Substitute into the differential equation to get

$$2u + 4xu' + x^2 u'' - \frac{3}{x}(2xu + x^2 u') + \frac{4}{x^2}(x^2 u) = 0.$$

Then

$$x^2 u'' + xu' = 0.$$

Since the interval of interest is $x > 0$, we can write this as

$$xu'' + u' = 0.$$

With $v = u'$, this is

$$xv' + v = (xv)' = 0,$$

so $xv = c$. We will choose $c = 1$. Then

$$v = u' = \frac{1}{x}$$

so

$$u = \ln(x) + d,$$

and we choose $d = 0$ because we need only one suitable u. Then $y_2(x) = x^2 \ln(x)$ is a second solution. Further, for $x > 0$,

$$W(x) = \begin{pmatrix} x^2 & x^2 \ln(x) \\ 2x & 2x \ln(x) + x \end{pmatrix} = x^3 \neq 0.$$

Then x^2 and $x^2 \ln(x)$ form a fundamental set of solutions for $x > 0$. The general solution is for $x > 0$ is

$$y(x) = c_1 x^2 + c_2 x^2 \ln(x). \quad \blacksquare$$

SECTION 2.3   PROBLEMS

In each of Problems 1 through 10, verify that the given function is a solution of the differential equation, find a second solution by reduction of order, and finally write the general solution.

1. $y'' + 4y = 0$; $y_1(x) = \cos(2x)$

2. $y'' - 9y = 0$; $y_1(x) = e^{3x}$

3. $y'' - 10y' + 25y = 0$; $y_1(x) = e^{5x}$

4. $x^2 y'' - 7xy' + 16y = 0$; $y_1(x) = x^4$ for $x > 0$

5. $x^2 y'' - 3xy' + 4y = 0$; $y_1(x) = x^2$ for $x > 0$

6. $(2x^2 + 1)y'' - 4xy' + 4y = 0$; $y_1(x) = x$ for $x > 0$

7. $y'' - \dfrac{1}{x}y' - \dfrac{8}{x^2}y = 0$; $y_1(x) = x^4$ for $x > 0$

8. $y'' - \dfrac{2x}{1+x^2}y' + \dfrac{2}{1+x^2}y = 0$; $y_1(x) = x$

9. $y'' + \dfrac{1}{x}y' + \left(1 - \dfrac{1}{4x^2}\right)y = 0$; $y_1(x) = \dfrac{1}{\sqrt{x}}\cos(x)$ for $x > 0$

10. $(2x^2 + 3x + 1)y'' + 2xy' - 2y = 0$; $y_1(x) = x$ on any interval not containing -1 or $-\dfrac{1}{2}$

11. Verify that, for any nonzero constant a, $y_1(x) = e^{-ax}$ is a solution of $y'' + 2ay' + a^2 y = 0$. Write the general solution.

12. A second-order equation $F(x, y, y', y'') = 0$ in which y is not explicitly present can sometimes be solved by putting $u = y'$. This results in a first-order equation $G(x, u, u') = 0$. If this can be solved for $u(x)$, then $y_1(x) = \int u(x)\,dx$ is a solution of the given second-order equation. Use this method to find one solution, then find a second solution, and finally the general solution of the following.

(a) $xy'' = 2 + y'$

(b) $xy'' + 2y' = x$

(c) $1 - y' = 4y''$

(d) $y'' + (y')^2 = 0$

(e) $y'' = 1 + (y')^2$

13. A second-order equation in which x does not explicitly appear can sometimes be solved by putting $u = y'$ and thinking of y as the independent variable and u as a function of y. Write

$$y'' = \frac{d}{dx}\left[\frac{dy}{dx}\right] = \frac{du}{dx} = \frac{du}{dy}\frac{dy}{dx} = u\frac{du}{dy}$$

to convert $F(y, y', y'') = 0$ into the first-order equation $F(y, u, u(du/dy)) = 0$. Solve this equation for $u(y)$ and then set $u = y'$ to solve for y as a function of x. Use this method to find a solution (perhaps implicitly defined) of each of the following.

(a) $yy'' + 3(y')^2 = 0$

(b) $yy'' + (y+1)(y')^2 = 0$

(c) $yy'' = y^2 y' + (y')^2$

(d) $y'' = 1 + (y')^2$

(e) $y'' + (y')^2 = 0$

14. Consider $y'' + Ay' + By = 0$, in which A and B are constants and $A^2 - 4B = 0$. Show that $y_1(x) = e^{-Ax/2}$ is one solution, and use reduction of order to find the second solution $y_2(x) = xe^{-Ax/2}$.

15. Consider $y'' + (A/x)y' + (B/x^2)y = 0$ for $x > 0$, with A and B constants such that $(A - 1)^2 - 4B = 0$. Verify that $y_1(x) = x^{(1-A)/2}$ is one solution, and use reduction of order to derive the second solution $y_2(x) = x^{(1-A)/2}\ln(x)$.

2.4　　The Constant Coefficient Homogeneous Linear Equation

The linear homogeneous equation

$$y'' + Ay' + By = 0 \tag{2.4}$$

in which A and B are numbers, occurs frequently in important applications. There is a standard approach to solving this equation.

The form of equation (2.4) requires that constant multiples of derivatives of $y(x)$ must sum to zero. Since the derivative of an exponential function $e^{\lambda x}$ is a constant multiple of $e^{\lambda x}$, we will look for solutions $y(x) = e^{\lambda x}$. To see how to choose λ, substitute $e^{\lambda x}$ into equation (2.4) to get

$$\lambda^2 e^{\lambda x} + A\lambda e^{\lambda x} + Be^{\lambda x} = 0.$$

This can only be true if

$$\lambda^2 + A\lambda + B = 0.$$

This is called the *characteristic equation* of equation (2.4). Its roots are

$$\lambda = \frac{-A \pm \sqrt{A^2 - 4B}}{2},$$

leading to three cases.

2.4.1　Case 1: $A^2 - 4B > 0$

In this case the characteristic equation has two real, distinct roots,

$$a = \frac{-A + \sqrt{A^2 - 4B}}{2} \quad \text{and} \quad b = \frac{-A - \sqrt{A^2 - 4B}}{2}$$

yielding solutions $y_1(x) = e^{ax}$ and $y_2(x) = e^{bx}$ for equation (2.4). These form a fundamental set of solutions on the real line, since

$$W(x) = e^{ax}be^{bx} - e^{bx}ae^{bx} = (b - a)e^{(a+b)x}$$

and this is nonzero because $a \neq b$. The general solution in this case is

$$y(x) = c_1 e^{ax} + c_2 e^{bx}.$$

EXAMPLE 2.6

The characteristic equation of $y'' - y' - 6y = 0$ is

$$\lambda^2 - \lambda - 6 = 0,$$

with roots $a = -2$ and $b = 3$. The general solution is

$$y = c_1 e^{-2x} + c_2 e^{3x}. \quad \blacksquare$$

2.4.2   Case 2: $A^2 - 4B = 0$

Now the characteristic equation has the repeated root $\lambda = -A/2$, so $y_1(x) = e^{-Ax/2}$ is one solution. This method does not provide a second solution, but we have reduction of order for just such a circumstance. Try $y_2(x) = u(x)e^{-Ax/2}$ and substitute into the differential equation to get

$$\frac{A^2}{4}ue^{-Ax/2} - Au'e^{-Ax/2} + u''e^{-Ax/2} + A\left(-\frac{A}{2}ue^{-Ax/2} + u'e^{-Ax/2}\right) + Bue^{-Ax/2} = 0.$$

Divide by $e^{-Ax/2}$ and rearrange terms to get

$$u'' + \left(B - \frac{A^2}{4}\right)u = 0.$$

Because in the current case, $A^2 - 4B = 0$, this differential equation reduces to just $u'' = 0$, and we can choose $u(x) = x$. A second solution in this case is $y_2(x) = xe^{-Ax/2}$. Since y_1 and y_2 are linearly independent, they form a fundamental set and the general solution is

$$y(x) = c_1 e^{-Ax/2} + c_2 xe^{-Ax/2} = e^{-Ax/2}(c_1 + c_2 x).$$

EXAMPLE 2.7

The characteristic equation of $y'' - 6y' + 9y = 0$ is $\lambda^2 - 6\lambda + 9 = 0$, with repeated root $\lambda = 3$. The general solution is

$$y(x) = e^{3x}(c_1 + c_2 x). \quad \blacksquare$$

2.4.3   Case 3: $A^2 - 4B < 0$

Now the characteristic equation has complex roots

$$\frac{-A \pm \sqrt{4B - A^2}i}{2}.$$

For convenience, write

$$p = -\frac{A}{2}, \quad q = \frac{1}{2}\sqrt{4B - A^2},$$

so the roots of the characteristic equation are $p \pm iq$. This yields two solutions

$$y_1(x) = e^{(p+iq)x} \quad \text{and} \quad y_2(x) = e^{(p-iq)x}.$$

These are linearly independent because their Wronskian is

$$W(x) = \begin{vmatrix} e^{(p+iq)x} & e^{(p-iq)x} \\ (p+iq)e^{(p+iq)x} & (p-iq)e^{(p-iq)x} \end{vmatrix}$$

$$= (p-iq)e^{2px} - (p+iq)e^{2px} = -2iqe^{2px},$$

and this is nonzero in the current case in which $q \neq 0$. Therefore the general solution is

$$y(x) = c_1 e^{(p+iq)x} + c_2 e^{(p-iq)x}. \tag{2.5}$$

EXAMPLE 2.8

The characteristic equation of $y'' + 2y' + 6y = 0$ is $\lambda^2 + 2\lambda + 6 = 0$, with roots $-1 \pm \sqrt{5}i$. The general solution is

$$y(x) = c_1 e^{(-1+\sqrt{5}i)x} + c_2 e^{(-1-\sqrt{5}i)x}. \quad \blacksquare$$

2.4.4 An Alternative General Solution in the Complex Root Case

When the characteristic equation has complex roots, we can write a general solution in terms of complex exponential functions. This is sometimes inconvenient, for example, in graphing the solutions. But recall that *any* two linearly independent solutions form a fundamental set. We will therefore show how to use the general solution (2.5) to find a fundamental set of real-valued solutions. Begin by recalling the Maclaurin expansions of e^x, $\cos(x)$, and $\sin(x)$:

$$e^x = \sum_{n=0}^{\infty} \frac{1}{n!} x^n = 1 + x + \frac{1}{2!} x^2 + \frac{1}{3!} x^3 + \frac{1}{4!} x^4 + \frac{1}{5!} x^5 + \cdots,$$

$$\cos(x) = \sum_{n=0}^{\infty} \frac{(-1)^n}{(2n)!} x^{2n} = 1 - \frac{1}{2!} x^2 + \frac{1}{4!} x^4 - \frac{1}{6!} x^6 + \cdots,$$

and

$$\sin(x) = \sum_{n=0}^{\infty} \frac{(-1)^n}{(2n+1)!} x^{2n+1} = x - \frac{1}{3!} x^3 + \frac{1}{5!} x^5 - \frac{1}{7!} x^7 + \cdots,$$

with each series convergent for all real x. The eighteenth century Swiss mathematician Leonhard Euler experimented with replacing x with ix in the exponential series and noticed an interesting relationship between the series for e^x, $\cos(x)$, and $\sin(x)$. First,

$$e^{ix} = \sum_{n=0}^{\infty} \frac{1}{n!} (ix)^n$$

$$= 1 + ix + \frac{1}{2!} (ix)^2 + \frac{1}{3!} (ix)^3 + \frac{1}{4!} (ix)^4 + \frac{1}{5!} (ix)^5 + \frac{1}{6!} (ix)^6 + \cdots.$$

Now, integer powers of i repeat the values i, -1, $-i$, 1 with a period of four:

$$i^2 = -1, \quad i^3 = -i, \quad i^4 = 1, \quad i^5 = i^4 i = i, \quad i^6 = i^4 i^2 = -1, \quad i^7 = i^4 i^3 = -i,$$

and so on, continuing in cyclic fashion. Using this fact in the Maclaurin series for e^{ix}, we obtain

$$e^{ix} = 1 + ix - \frac{1}{2!} x^2 - \frac{i}{3!} x^3 + \frac{1}{4!} x^4 + \frac{i}{5!} x^5 - \frac{1}{6!} x^6 - \cdots$$

$$= \left(1 - \frac{1}{2!} x^2 + \frac{1}{4!} x^4 - \frac{1}{6!} x^6 + \cdots \right) + i \left(x - \frac{1}{3!} x^3 + \frac{1}{5!} x^5 - \cdots \right)$$

$$= \cos(x) + i\sin(x). \tag{2.6}$$

This is *Euler's formula*. In a different form, it was discovered a few years earlier by Newton's contemporary Roger Cotes (1682–1716). Cotes is not of the stature of Euler, but Newton's high opinion of him is reflected in Newton's remark, "If Cotes had lived, we would have known something."

Since $\cos(-x) = \cos(x)$ and $\sin(-x) = -\sin(x)$, replacing x by $-x$ in Euler's formula yields

$$e^{-ix} = \cos(x) - i\sin(x).$$

Now return to the problem of solving $y'' + Ay' + By = 0$ when the characteristic equation has complex roots $p \pm iq$. Since p and q are real numbers, we have

$$e^{(p+iq)x} = e^{px} e^{iqx} = e^{px}(\cos(qx) + i\sin(qx))$$

$$= e^{px}\cos(qx) + ie^{px}\sin(qx)$$

and

$$e^{(p-iq)x} = e^{px}e^{-iqx} = e^{px}(\cos(qx) - i\sin(qx))$$
$$= e^{px}\cos(qx) - ie^{px}\sin(qx).$$

The general solution (2.5) can therefore be written

$$y(x) = c_1e^{px}\cos(qx) + ic_1e^{px}\sin(qx) + c_2e^{px}\cos(qx) - ic_2e^{px}\sin(qx)$$
$$= (c_1 + c_2)e^{px}\cos(qx) + (c_1 - c_2)ie^{px}\sin(qx).$$

We obtain solutions for any numerical choices of c_1 and c_2. In particular, if we choose $c_1 = c_2 = \dfrac{1}{2}$ we obtain the solution

$$y_3(x) = e^{px}\cos(qx).$$

And if we put $c_1 = \dfrac{1}{2i}$ and $c_2 = -\dfrac{1}{2i}$ we obtain still another solution

$$y_4(x) = e^{px}\sin(qx).$$

Further, these last two solutions are linearly independent on the real line, since

$$W(x) = \begin{vmatrix} e^{px}\cos(qx) & e^{px}\sin(qx) \\ pe^{px}\cos(qx) - qe^{px}\sin(qx) & pe^{px}\sin(qx) + qe^{px}\cos(qx) \end{vmatrix}$$

$$= e^{2px}(\sin(qx)\cos(qx) + \cos^2(qx) - \sin(qx)\cos(qx) + \sin^2(qx))$$

$$= e^{2px} \neq 0 \quad \text{for all real } x.$$

We can therefore, if we prefer, form a fundamental set of solutions using y_3 and y_4, writing the general solution of $y'' + Ay' + By = 0$ in this case as

$$y(x) = e^{px}(c_1\cos(qx) + c_2\sin(qx)).$$

This is simply another way of writing the general solution of equation (2.4) in the complex root case.

EXAMPLE 2.9

Revisiting the equation $y'' - 6y' + 6y = 0$ of Example 2.8, we can also write the general solution

$$y(x) = e^{-x}\left(c_1\cos\left(\sqrt{5}x\right) + c_2\sin\left(\sqrt{5}x\right)\right). \quad \blacksquare$$

We now have the general solution of the constant coefficient linear homogeneous equation $y'' + Ay' + By = 0$ in all cases. As usual, we can solve an initial value problem by first finding the general solution of the differential equation, then solving for the constants to satisfy the initial conditions.

EXAMPLE 2.10

Solve the initial value problem

$$y'' - 4y' + 53y = 0; \qquad y(\pi) = -3, y'(\pi) = 2.$$

First solve the differential equation. The characteristic equation is

$$\lambda^2 - 4\lambda + 53 = 0,$$

with complex roots $2 \pm 7i$. The general solution is

$$y(x) = c_1 e^{2x} \cos(7x) + c_2 e^{2x} \sin(7x).$$

Now

$$y(\pi) = c_1 e^{2\pi} \cos(7\pi) + c_2 e^{2\pi} \sin(7\pi) = -c_1 e^{2\pi} = -3,$$

so

$$c_1 = 3e^{-2\pi}.$$

Thus far

$$y(x) = 3e^{-2\pi} e^{2x} \cos(7x) + c_2 e^{2x} \sin(7x).$$

Compute

$$y'(x) = 3e^{-2\pi}[2e^{2x} \cos(7x) - 7e^{2x} \sin(7x)] + 2c_2 e^{2x} \sin(7x) + 7c_2 e^{2x} \cos(7x).$$

Then

$$y'(\pi) = 3e^{-2\pi} 2e^{2\pi}(-1) + 7c_2 e^{2\pi}(-1) = 2,$$

so

$$c_2 = -\frac{8}{7} e^{-2\pi}.$$

The solution of the initial value problem is

$$y(x) = 3e^{-2\pi} e^{2x} \cos(7x) - \frac{8}{7} e^{-2\pi} e^{2x} \sin(7x)$$

$$= e^{2(x-\pi)} \left[3\cos(7x) - \frac{8}{7} \sin(7x) \right]. \ \blacksquare$$

SECTION 2.4   **PROBLEMS**

In each of Problems 1 through 12, find the general solution.

1. $y'' - y' - 6y = 0$

2. $y'' - 2y' + 10y = 0$

3. $y'' + 6y' + 9y = 0$

4. $y'' - 3y' = 0$

5. $y'' + 10y' + 26y = 0$

6. $y'' + 6y' - 40y = 0$

7. $y'' + 3y' + 18y = 0$

8. $y'' + 16y' + 64y = 0$

9. $y'' - 14y' + 49y = 0$

10. $y'' - 6y' + 7y = 0$

11. $y'' + 4y' + 9y = 0$

12. $y'' + 5y' = 0$

In each of Problems 13 through 21, solve the initial value problem.

13. $y'' + 3y' = 0;\ y(0) = 3,\ y'(0) = 6$

14. $y'' + 2y' - 3y = 0;\ y(0) = 6,\ y'(0) = -2$

15. $y'' - 2y' + y = 0;\ y(1) = y'(1) = 0$

16. $y'' - 4y' + 4y = 0;\ y(0) = 3,\ y'(0) = 5$

17. $y'' + y' - 12y = 0;\ y(2) = 2,\ y'(2) = 1$

18. $y'' - 2y' - 5y = 0;\ y(0) = 0,\ y'(0) = 3$

19. $y'' - 2y' + y = 0;\ y(1) = 12,\ y'(1) = -5$

20. $y'' - 5y' + 12y = 0;\ y(2) = 0,\ y'(2) = -4$

21. $y'' - y' + 4y = 0;\ y(-2) = 1,\ y'(-2) = 3$

22. This problem illustrates how small changes in the coefficients of a differential equation may cause dramatic changes in the solutions.

(a) Find the general solution $\varphi(x)$ of $y'' - 2ay' + a^2y = 0$, with a a nonzero constant.

(b) Find the general solution $\varphi_\epsilon(x)$ of $y'' - 2ay' + (a^2 - \epsilon^2)y = 0$, in which ϵ is a positive constant.

(c) Show that, as $\epsilon \to 0$, the differential equation in (b) approaches in a limit sense the differential equation in (a), but the solution $\varphi_\epsilon(x)$ for (b) does not in general approach the solution $\varphi(x)$ for (a).

23. (a) Find the solution ψ of the initial value problem

$$y'' - 2ay' + a^2y = 0; \qquad y(0) = c, y'(0) = d,$$

with a, c, and d constants and $a \neq 0$.

(b) Find the solution ψ_ϵ of the initial value problem

$$y'' - 2ay' + (a^2 - \epsilon^2)y = 0; \qquad y(0) = c, y'(0) = d.$$

Here ϵ is any positive number.

(c) Is it true that $\lim_{\epsilon \to 0} \psi_\epsilon(x) = \psi(x)$? How does this answer differ, if at all, from the conclusion in Problem 22(c)?

24. Suppose φ is a solution of

$$y'' + Ay' + By = 0; \qquad y(x_0) = a, y'(x_0) = b.$$

Here A, B, a, and b are constants. Suppose A and B are positive. Prove that $\lim_{x \to \infty} \varphi(x) = 0$.

2.5   Euler's Equation

In this section we will define another class of second-order differential equations for which there is an elementary technique for finding the general solution.

The second-order homogeneous equation

$$y'' + \frac{1}{x}Ay' + \frac{1}{x^2}By = 0, \tag{2.7}$$

with A and B constant, is called *Euler's equation*. It is defined on the half-lines $x > 0$ and $x < 0$. We will assume for this section that $x > 0$.

We will solve Euler's equation by transforming it to a constant coefficient linear equation, which we can solve easily. Recall that any positive number x can be written as e^t for some t (namely for $t = \ln(x)$). Make the change of variables

$$x = e^t, \quad \text{or, equivalently, } t = \ln(x)$$

and let

$$Y(t) = y(e^t).$$

That is, in the function $y(x)$, replace x by e^t, obtaining a new function of t. For example, if $y(x) = x^3$, then $Y(t) = (e^t)^3 = e^{3t}$. Now compute chain-rule derivatives. First,

$$y'(x) = \frac{dY}{dt}\frac{dt}{dx} = Y'(t)\frac{1}{x}$$

so

$$Y'(t) = xy'(x).$$

Next,

$$y''(x) = \frac{d}{dx}\, y'(x) = \frac{d}{dx}\left(\frac{1}{x}Y'(t)\right)$$

$$= -\frac{1}{x^2}Y'(t) + \frac{1}{x}\frac{d}{dx}Y'(t)$$

$$= -\frac{1}{x^2}Y'(t) + \frac{1}{x}\frac{dY'}{dt}\frac{dt}{dx}$$

$$= -\frac{1}{x^2}Y'(t) + \frac{1}{x}Y''(t)\frac{1}{x}$$

$$= \frac{1}{x^2}(Y''(t) - Y'(t)).$$

Therefore,

$$x^2 y''(x) = Y''(t) - Y'(t).$$

If we write Euler's equation as

$$x^2 y''(x) + Axy'(x) + By(x) = 0,$$

then these substitutions yield

$$Y''(t) - Y'(t) + AY'(t) + BY(t) = 0,$$

or

$$Y'' + (A - 1)Y' + BY = 0. \tag{2.8}$$

This is a constant coefficient homogeneous linear differential equation for $Y(t)$. Solve this equation, then let $t = \ln(x)$ in the solution $Y(t)$ to obtain $y(x)$ satisfying the Euler equation.

We need not repeat this derivation each time we want to solve an Euler equation, since the coefficients $A - 1$ and B for the transformed equation (2.8) are easily read from the Euler equation (2.7).

In carrying out this strategy, it is useful to recall that, for $x > 0$,

$$x^r = e^{r\ln(x)}.$$

EXAMPLE 2.11

Find the general solution of $x^2 y'' + 2xy' - 6y = 0$.

Upon letting $x = e^t$, this differential equation transforms to

$$Y'' + Y' - 6Y = 0.$$

The coefficient of Y' is $A - 1$, with $A = 2$ in Euler's equation. The general solution of this linear homogeneous differential equation is

$$Y(t) = c_1 e^{-3t} + c_2 e^{2t}$$

for all real t. Putting $t = \ln(x)$ with $x > 0$, we obtain

$$y(x) = c_1 e^{-3\ln(x)} + c_2 e^{2\ln(x)} = c_1 x^{-3} + c_2 x^2,$$

and this is the general solution of the Euler equation. ■

EXAMPLE 2.12

Consider the Euler equation $x^2 y'' - 5xy' + 9y = 0$. The transformed equation is

$$Y'' - 6Y' + 9Y = 0,$$

with general solution

$$Y(t) = c_1 e^{3t} + c_2 t e^{3t}.$$

Let $t = \ln(x)$ to obtain

$$y(x) = c_1 x^3 + c_2 x^3 \ln(x)$$

for $x > 0$. This is the general solution of the Euler equation. ∎

EXAMPLE 2.13

Solve $x^2 y'' + 3xy' + 10y = 0$
This transforms to

$$Y'' + 2Y' + 10Y = 0,$$

with general solution

$$Y(t) = c_1 e^{-t} \cos(3t) + c_2 e^{-t} \sin(3t).$$

Then

$$y(x) = c_1 x^{-1} \cos(3\ln(x)) + c_2 x^{-1} \sin(3\ln(x))$$

$$= \frac{1}{x}(c_1 \cos(3\ln(x)) + c_2 \sin(3\ln(x)))$$

for $x > 0$. ∎

As usual, we can solve an initial value problem by finding the general solution of the differential equation, then solving for the constants to satisfy the initial conditions.

EXAMPLE 2.14

Solve the initial value problem

$$x^2 y'' - 5xy' + 10y = 0; \qquad y(1) = 4, \, y'(1) = -6.$$

We will first find the general solution of the Euler equation, then determine the constants to satisfy the initial conditions. With $t = \ln(x)$, we obtain

$$Y'' - 6Y' + 10Y = 0,$$

having general solution

$$Y(t) = c_1 e^{3t} \cos(t) + c_2 e^{3t} \sin(t).$$

The general solution of the Euler equation is

$$y(x) = c_1 x^3 \cos(\ln(x)) + c_2 x^3 \sin(\ln(x)).$$

For the first initial condition, we need

$$y(1) = 4 = c_1.$$

Thus far,

$$y(x) = 4x^3 \cos(\ln(x)) + c_2 x^3 \sin(\ln(x)).$$

Then

$$y'(x) = 12x^2 \cos(\ln(x)) - 4x^2 \sin(\ln(x)) + 3c_2 x^2 \sin(\ln(x)) + c_2 x^2 \cos(\ln(x)),$$

so

$$y'(1) = 12 + c_2 = -6.$$

Then $c_2 = -18$ and the solution of the initial value problem is

$$y(x) = 4x^3 \cos(\ln(x)) - 18x^3 \sin(\ln(x)). \quad \blacksquare$$

Observe the structure of the solutions of different kinds of differential equations. Solutions of the constant coefficient linear equation $y'' + Ay' + By = 0$ must have the forms $e^{\alpha x}$, $xe^{\alpha x}$, $e^{\alpha x} \cos(\beta x)$, or $e^{\alpha x} \sin(\beta x)$, depending on the coefficients. And solutions of an Euler equation $x^2 y'' + Axy' + By = 0$ must have the forms x^r, $x^r \ln(x)$, $x^p \cos(q \ln(x))$, or $x^p \sin(q \ln(x))$. For example, x^3 could never be a solution of the linear equation and e^{-6x} could never be the solution of an Euler equation.

SECTION 2.5   PROBLEMS

In each of Problems 1 through 12, find the general solution.

1. $x^2 y'' + 2xy' - 6y = 0$

2. $x^2 y'' + 3xy' + y = 0$

3. $x^2 y'' + xy' + 4y = 0$

4. $x^2 y'' + xy' - 4y = 0$

5. $x^2 y'' + xy' - 16y = 0$

6. $x^2 y'' + 3xy' + 10y = 0$

7. $x^2 y'' + 6xy' + 6y = 0$

8. $x^2 y'' - 5xy' + 58y = 0$

9. $x^2 y'' + 25xy' + 144y = 0$

10. $x^2 y'' - 11xy' + 35y = 0$

11. $x^2 y'' - 2xy' + 12y = 0$

12. $x^2 y'' + 4y = 0$

In each of Problems 13 through 21, solve the initial value problem.

13. $x^2 y'' + 5xy' + 20y = 0$; $y(-1) = 3$, $y'(-1) = 2$ (Here the solution of Euler's equation for $x < 0$ is needed).

14. $x^2 y'' + 5xy' - 21y = 0$; $y(2) = 1$, $y'(2) = 0$

15. $x^2 y'' - xy' = 0$; $y(2) = 5$, $y'(2) = 8$

16. $x^2 y'' - 3xy' + 4y = 0$; $y(1) = 4$, $y'(1) = 5$

17. $x^2 y'' + 7xy' + 13y = 0$; $y(-1) = 1$, $y'(-1) = 3$

18. $x^2 y'' + xy' - y = 0$; $y(2) = 1$, $y'(2) = -3$

19. $x^2 y'' + 25xy' + 144y = 0$; $y(1) = -4$, $y'(1) = 0$

20. $x^2 y'' - 9xy' + 24y = 0$; $y(1) = 1$, $y'(1) = 10$

21. $x^2 y'' + xy' - 4y = 0$; $y(1) = 7$, $y'(1) = -3$

22. Here is another approach to solving an Euler equation. For $x > 0$, substitute $y = x^r$ and obtain values of r to make this a solution. Show how this leads in all cases to the same general solution as obtained by the transformation method.

2.6   The Nonhomogeneous Equation $y'' + p(x)y' + q(x)y = f(x)$

In view of Theorem 2.5, if we are able to find the general solution y_h of the linear homogeneous equation $y'' + p(x)y' + q(x)y = 0$, then the general solution of the linear nonhomogeneous equation

$$y'' + p(x)y' + q(x)y = f(x) \tag{2.9}$$

is $y = y_h + y_p$, in which y_p is *any* solution of equation (2.9).

This section is devoted to two methods for finding such a particular solution y_p.

2.6.1   The Method of Variation of Parameters

Suppose we can find a fundamental set of solutions y_1 and y_2 for the homogeneous equation. The general solution of this homogeneous equation has the form $y_h(x) = c_1 y_1(x) + c_2 y_2(x)$. The method of variation of parameters consists of attempting a particular solution of the nonhomogeneous equation by replacing the constants c_1 and c_2 with functions of x. Thus, attempt to find $u(x)$ and $v(x)$ so that

$$y_p(x) = u(x)y_1(x) + v(x)y_2(x)$$

is a solution of equation (2.9). How should we choose u and v?

First compute

$$y_p' = uy_1' + vy_2' + u'y_1 + v'y_2.$$

In order to simplify this expression, the first condition we will impose on u and v is that

$$u'y_1 + v'y_2 = 0. \tag{2.10}$$

Now

$$y_p' = uy_1' + vy_2'.$$

Next compute

$$y_p'' = u'y_1' + v'y_2' + uy_1'' + vy_2''.$$

Substitute these expressions for y_p' and y_p'' into equation (2.9):

$$u'y_1' + v'y_2' + uy_1'' + vy_2'' + p(x)(uy_1' + vy_2') + q(x)(uy_1 + vy_2) = f(x).$$

Rearrange terms in this equation to get

$$u[y_1'' + p(x)y_1' + q(x)y_1] + v[y_2'' + p(x)y_2' + q(x)y_2] + u'y_1' + v'y_2' = f(x).$$

The two terms in square brackets vanish because y_1 and y_2 are solutions of the homogeneous equation. This leaves

$$u'y_1' + v'y_2' = f(x). \tag{2.11}$$

Now solve equations (2.10) and (2.11) for u' and v' to get

$$u'(x) = -\frac{y_2(x)f(x)}{W(x)} \quad \text{and} \quad v'(x) = \frac{y_1(x)f(x)}{W(x)} \tag{2.12}$$

in which W is the Wronskian of y_1 and y_2. If we can integrate these equations to determine u and v, then we have y_p.

EXAMPLE 2.15

We will find the general solution of $y'' + y = \sec(x)$ for $-\pi/4 < x < \pi/4$.

The characteristic equation of $y'' + 4y = 0$ is $\lambda^2 + 4 = 0$, with roots $\pm 2i$. We may therefore choose $y_1(x) = \cos(2x)$ and $y_2(x) = \sin(2x)$. The Wronskian of these solutions of the homogeneous equation is

$$W(x) = \begin{vmatrix} \cos(2x) & \sin(2x) \\ -2\sin(2x) & 2\cos(2x) \end{vmatrix} = 2.$$

With $f(x) = \sec(x)$, equations (2.12) give us

$$u'(x) = -\frac{1}{2}\sin(2x)\sec(x)$$

$$= -\frac{1}{2}2\sin(x)\cos(x)\frac{1}{\cos(x)} = -\sin(x)$$

and

$$v'(x) = \frac{1}{2}\cos(2x)\sec(x) = \frac{1}{2}[2\cos^2(x) - 1]\frac{1}{\cos(x)}$$

$$= \cos(x) - \frac{1}{2}\sec(x).$$

Then

$$u(x) = \int -\sin(x)\,dx = \cos(x)$$

and

$$v(x) = \int \cos(x)\,dx - \frac{1}{2}\int \sec(x)\,dx$$

$$= \sin(x) - \frac{1}{2}\ln|\sec(x) + \tan(x)|.$$

Here we have let the constants of integration be zero because we need only one u and one v. Now we have the particular solution

$$y_p(x) = u(x)y_1(x) + v(x)y_2(x)$$

$$= \cos(x)\cos(2x) + \left(\sin(x) - \frac{1}{2}\ln|\sec(x) + \tan(x)|\right)\sin(2x).$$

The general solution of $y'' + y = \sec(x)$ is

$$y(x) = y_h(x) + y_p(x)$$

$$= c_1\cos(2x) + c_2\sin(2x)$$

$$+ \cos(x)\cos(2x) + \left(\sin(x) - \frac{1}{2}\ln|\sec(x) + \tan(x)|\right)\sin(2x). \quad\blacksquare$$

EXAMPLE 2.16

Suppose we want the general solution of

$$y'' - \frac{4}{x}y' + \frac{4}{x^2}y = x^2 + 1$$

for $x > 0$. The associated homogeneous equation is

$$y'' - \frac{4}{x}y' + \frac{4}{x^2}y = 0,$$

which we recognize as an Euler equation, with fundamental solutions $y_1(x) = x$ and $y_2(x) = x^4$ for $x > 0$.

The Wronskian of these solutions is

$$W(x) = \begin{vmatrix} x & x^4 \\ 1 & 4x^3 \end{vmatrix} = 3x^4$$

and this is nonzero for $x > 0$. From equations (2.12),

$$u'(x) = -\frac{x^4(x^2+1)}{3x^4} = -\frac{1}{3}(x^2+1)$$

and

$$v'(x) = \frac{x(x^2+1)}{3x^4} = \frac{1}{3}\left(\frac{1}{x} + \frac{1}{x^3}\right).$$

Integrate to get

$$u(x) = -\frac{1}{9}x^3 - \frac{1}{3}x$$

and

$$v(x) = \frac{1}{3}\ln(x) - \frac{1}{6x^2}.$$

A particular solution is

$$y_p(x) = \left(-\frac{1}{9}x^3 - \frac{1}{3}x\right)x + \left(\frac{1}{3}\ln(x) - \frac{1}{6x^2}\right)x^4.$$

The general solution is

$$y(x) = y_h(x) + y_p(x)$$

$$= c_1 x + c_2 x^4 - \frac{1}{9}x^4 - \frac{1}{3}x^2 + \frac{1}{3}x^4 \ln(x) - \frac{1}{6}x^2$$

$$= c_1 x + c_2 x^4 - \frac{1}{9}x^4 - \frac{1}{2}x^2 + \frac{1}{3}x^4 \ln(x).$$

for $x > 0$. ∎

2.6.2   The Method of Undetermined Coefficients

Here is a second method for finding a particular solution y_p, but it only applies if $p(x)$ and $q(x)$ are constant. Thus consider

$$y'' + Ay' + By = f(x).$$

Sometimes we can guess the general form of a solution y_p from the form of $f(x)$. For example, suppose $f(x)$ is a polynomial. Since derivatives of polynomials are polynomials, we might try a polynomial for $y_p(x)$. Substitute a polynomial with unknown coefficients into the differential equation, and then choose the coefficients to match $y'' + Ay' + By$ with $f(x)$. Or suppose $f(x)$ is an exponential function, say $f(x) = e^{-2x}$. Since derivatives of e^{-2x} are just constant multiples of e^{-2x}, we would attempt a solution of the form $y_p = Ce^{-2x}$, substitute into the differential equation, and solve for C to match the left and right sides of the differential equation.

Here are some examples of this method.

EXAMPLE 2.17

Solve $y'' - 4y = 8x^2 - 2x$.

Since $f(x) = 8x^2 - 2x$ is a polynomial of degree 2, we will attempt a solution

$$y_p(x) = ax^2 + bx + c.$$

We do not need to try a higher degree polynomial, since the degree of $y'' - 4y$ must be 2. If, for example, we included an x^3 term in y_p, then $y_p'' - 4y_p$ would have an x^3 term, and we know that it does not.

Compute

$$y_p' = 2ax + b \quad \text{and} \quad y_p'' = 2a$$

and substitute into the differential equation to get

$$2a - 4(ax^2 + bx + c) = 8x^2 - 2x.$$

Collect coefficients of like powers of x to write

$$(-4a - 8)x^2 + (-4b + 2)x + (2a - 4c) = 0.$$

For y_p to be a solution for all x, the polynomial on the left must be zero for all x. But a second degree polynomial can have only two roots, unless it is the zero polynomial. Thus all the coefficients must vanish, and we have the equations

$$-4a - 8 = 0,$$
$$-4b + 2 = 0,$$
$$2a - 4c = 0.$$

Solve these to obtain

$$a = -2, \quad b = \frac{1}{2}, \quad c = -1.$$

Thus a solution is

$$y_p(x) = -2x^2 + \frac{1}{2}x - 1,$$

as can be verified by substitution into the differential equation.

If we want the general solution of the differential equation, we need the general solution y_h of $y'' - 4y = 0$. This is

$$y_h(x) = c_1 e^{2x} + c_2 e^{-2x}.$$

The general solution of $y'' - 4y = 8x^2 - 2x$ is

$$y(x) = c_1 e^{2x} + c_2 e^{-2x} - 2x^2 + \frac{1}{2}x - 1. \quad \blacksquare$$

The method we have just illustrated is called the *method of undetermined coefficients*, because the idea is to guess a general form for y_p and then solve for the coefficients to make a solution. Here are two more examples, after which we will point out a circumstance in which we must supplement the method.

EXAMPLE 2.18

Solve $y'' + 2y' - 3y = 4e^{2x}$.

Because $f(x)$ is a constant times an exponential, and the derivative of such a function is always a constant times the same function, we attempt $y_p = ae^{2x}$. Then $y_p' = 2ae^{2x}$ and $y_p'' = 4ae^{2x}$. Substitute into the differential equation to get

$$4ae^{2x} + 4ae^{2x} - 3ae^{2x} = 4e^{2x}.$$

Then $5ae^{2x} = 4e^{2x}$, so choose $a = \dfrac{4}{5}$ to get the solution

$$y_p(x) = \frac{4}{5}e^{2x}.$$

Again, if we wish we can write the general solution

$$y(x) = c_1 e^{-3x} + c_2 e^x + \frac{4}{5}e^{2x}. \quad \blacksquare$$

EXAMPLE 2.19

Solve $y'' - 5y' + 6y = -3\sin(2x)$.

Here $f(x) = -3\sin(2x)$. Now we must be careful, because derivatives of $\sin(2x)$ can be multiples $\sin(2x)$ or $\cos(2x)$, depending on how many times we differentiate. This leads us to include both possibilities in a proposed solution:

$$y_p(x) = c\cos(2x) + d\sin(2x).$$

Compute

$$y_p' = -2c\sin(2x) + 2d\cos(2x), \quad y_p'' = -4c\cos(2x) - 4d\sin(2x).$$

Substitute into the differential equation to get

$$-4c\cos(2x) - 4d\sin(2x) - 5[-2c\sin(2x) + 2d\cos(2x)]$$
$$+6[c\cos(2x) + d\sin(2x)] = -3\sin(2x).$$

Collecting the cosine terms on one side and the sine terms on the other:

$$[2d + 10c + 3]\sin(2x) = [-2c + 10d]\cos(2x).$$

For y_p to be a solution for all real x, this equation must hold for all x. But $\sin(2x)$ and $\cos(2x)$ are linearly independent (they are solutions of $y'' + 4y = 0$, and their Wronskian is nonzero). Therefore neither can be a constant multiple of the other. The only way the last equation can hold for all x is for the coefficient to be zero on both sides:

$$2d + 10c = -3$$

and

$$10d - 2c = 0.$$

Then

$$d = -\frac{3}{52} \quad \text{and} \quad c = -\frac{15}{52}$$

and we have found a solution:

$$y_p(x) = -\frac{3}{52}\sin(2x) - \frac{15}{52}\cos(2x).$$

The general solution of this differential equation is

$$y(x) = c_1 e^{3x} + c_2 e^{2x} - \frac{3}{52}\sin(2x) - \frac{15}{52}\cos(2x). \quad \blacksquare$$

As effective as this method is, there is a difficulty that is intrinsic to the method. It can be successfully met, but one must be aware of it and know how to proceed. Consider the following example.

EXAMPLE 2.20

Solve $y'' + 2y' - 3y = 8e^x$. The coefficients on the left side are constant, and $f(x) = 8e^x$ seems simple enough, so we proceed with

$$y_p(x) = ce^x.$$

Substitute into the differential equation to get

$$ce^x + 2ce^x - 3ce^x = 8e^x,$$

or

$$0 = 8e^x.$$

Something is wrong. What happened? $\blacksquare$

The problem in this example is that e^x is a solution of $y'' + 2y' - 3y = 0$, so if we substitute ce^x into $y'' + 2y' - 3y = 8e^x$, the left side will equal zero, not $8e^x$. This difficulty will occur whenever the proposed y_p contains a term that is a solution of the homogeneous equation $y'' + Ay' + By = 0$, because then this term (which may be all of the proposed y_p) will vanish when substituted into $y'' + Ay' + By$.

There is a way out of this difficulty. If a term of the proposed y_p is a solution of $y'' + Ay' + By = 0$, multiply the proposed solution by x and try the modified function as y_p. If this also contains a term, or by itself, satisfies $y'' + Ay' + By = 0$, then multiply by x again to try x^2 times the original proposed solution. This is as far as we will have to go in the case of second-order differential equations.

Now continue Example 2.20 with this strategy.

EXAMPLE 2.21

Consider again $y'' + 2y' - 3y = 8e^x$. We saw that $y_p = ce^x$ does not work, because e^x, and hence also ce^x, satisfies $y'' + 2y' - 3y = 0$. Try $y_p = cxe^x$. Compute

$$y'_p = ce^x + cxe^x, \quad y''_p = 2ce^x + cxe^x$$

and substitute into the differential equation to get

$$2ce^x + cxe^x + 2[ce^x + cxe^x] - 3cxe^x = 8e^x.$$

Some terms cancel and we are left with

$$4ce^x = 8e^x.$$

Choose $c = 2$ to obtain the particular solution $y_p(x) = 2xe^x$. ∎

EXAMPLE 2.22

Solve $y'' - 6y' + 9y = 5e^{3x}$.

Our first impulse is to try $y_p = ce^{3x}$. But this is a solution of $y'' - 6y' + 9y = 0$. If we try $y_p = cxe^{3x}$, we also obtain an equation that cannot be solved for c. The reason is that the characteristic equation of $y'' - 6y' + 9y = 0$ is $(\lambda - 3)^2 = 0$, with repeated root 3. This means that e^{3x} and xe^{3x} are both solutions of the homogeneous equation $y'' - 6y' + 9y = 0$. Thus try $y_p(x) = cx^2e^{3x}$. Compute

$$y'_p = 2cxe^{3x} + 3cx^2e^{3x}, \quad y''_p = 2ce^{3x} + 12cxe^{3x} + 9cx^2e^{3x}.$$

Substitute into the differential equation to get

$$2ce^{3x} + 12cxe^{3x} + 9cx^2e^{3x} - 6[2cxe^{3x} + 3cx^2e^{3x}] + 9cx^2e^{3x} = 5e^{3x}.$$

After cancellations we have

$$2ce^{3x} = 5e^{3x}$$

so $c = 5/2$. We have found a particular solution $y_p(x) = 5x^2e^{3x}/2$. ∎

The last two examples suggest that in applying undetermined coefficients to $y'' + Ay' + By = f(x)$, we should first obtain the general solution of $y'' + Ay' + By = 0$. We need this anyway for a general solution of the nonhomogeneous equation, but it also tells us whether to multiply our first choice for y_p by x or x^2 before proceeding.

Here is a summary of the method of undetermined coefficients.

1. From $f(x)$, make a first conjecture for the form of y_p.
2. Solve $y'' + Ay' + By = 0$. If a solution of this equation appears in any term of the conjectured form for y_p, modify this form by multiplying it by x. If this modified function still occurs in a solution of $y'' + Ay' + By = 0$, multiply by x again (so the original y_p is multiplied by x^2 in this case).
3. Substitute the final proposed y_p into $y'' + Ay' + By = f(x)$ and solve for its coefficients.

Here is a list of functions to try in the initial stage (1) of formulating y_p. In this list $P(x)$ indicates a given polynomial of degree n, and $Q(x)$ and $R(x)$ polynomials with undetermined coefficients, of degree n.

$f(x)$	Initial Guess for y_p
$P(x)$	$Q(x)$
ce^{ax}	de^{ax}
$\alpha\cos(bx)$ or $\beta\sin(bx)$	$c\cos(bx) + d\sin(bx)$
$P(x)e^{ax}$	$Q(x)e^{ax}$
$P(x)\cos(bx)$ or $P(x)\sin(bx)$	$Q(x)\cos(bx) + R(x)\sin(bx)$
$P(x)e^{ax}\cos(bx)$ or $P(x)e^{ax}\sin(bx)$	$Q(x)e^{ax}\cos(bx) + R(x)e^{ax}\sin(bx)$

EXAMPLE 2.23

Solve $y'' + 9y = -4x\sin(3x)$.

With $f(x) = -4x\sin(3x)$, the preceding list suggests that we attempt a particular solution of the form

$$y_p(x) = (ax + b)\cos(3x) + (cx + d)\sin(3x).$$

Now solve $y'' + 9y = 0$ to obtain the fundamental set of solutions $\cos(3x)$ and $\sin(3x)$. The proposed y_p includes terms $b\cos(3x)$ and $d\sin(3x)$, which are also solutions of $y'' + 9y = 0$. Therefore, modify the proposed y_p by multiplying it by x, trying instead

$$y_p(x) = (ax^2 + bx)\cos(3x) + (cx^2 + dx)\sin(3x).$$

Compute

$$y_p' = (2ax + b)\cos(3x) - (3ax^2 + 3bx)\sin(3x)$$
$$+ (2cx + d)\sin(3x) + (3cx^2 + 3dx)\cos(3x)$$

and

$$y_p'' = 2a\cos(3x) - (6ax + 3b)\sin(3x) - (6ax + 3b)\sin(3x)$$
$$- (9ax^2 + 9bx)\cos(3x) + 2c\sin(3x) + (6cx + 3d)\cos(3x)$$
$$+ (6cx + 3d)\cos(3x) - (9cx^2 + 9dx)\sin(3x).$$

Substitute these into the differential equation to obtain

$$2a\cos(3x) - (6ax + 3b)\sin(3x) - (6ax + 3b)\sin(3x)$$
$$- (9ax^2 + 9bx)\cos(3x) + 2c\sin(3x) + (6cx + 3d)\cos(3x)$$
$$+ (6cx + 3d)\cos(3x) - (9cx^2 + 9dx)\sin(3x).$$
$$+ (9ax^2 + 9bx)\cos(3x) + (9cx^2 + 9dx)\sin(3x) = -4x\sin(3x).$$

Now collect coefficients of "like" terms ($\sin(3x)$, $x\sin(3x)$, $x^2\sin(3x)$, and so on). We get

$$(2a + 6d)\cos(3x) + (-6b + 2c)\sin(3x) + 12cx\cos(3x) + (-12a + 4)x\sin(3x) = 0,$$

with all other terms canceling. For this linear combination of $\cos(3x)$, $\sin(3x)$, $x\cos(3x)$, and $x\sin(3x)$ to be zero for all x, each coefficient must be zero. Therefore,

$$2a + 6d = 0,$$

$$-6b + 2c = 0,$$

$$12c = 0,$$

and

$$-12a + 4 = 0.$$

Then $a = \dfrac{1}{3}$, $c = 0$, $b = 0$, and $d = -\dfrac{1}{9}$. We have found the particular solution

$$y_p(x) = \frac{1}{3}x^2\cos(3x) - \frac{1}{9}x\sin(3x).$$

The general solution is

$$y(x) = c_1\cos(3x) + c_2\sin(3x) + \frac{1}{3}x^2\cos(3x) - \frac{1}{9}x\sin(3x). \quad \blacksquare$$

Sometimes a differential equation has nonconstant coefficients but transforms to a constant coefficient equation. We may then be able to use the method of undetermined coefficients on the transformed equation and then use the results to obtain solutions of the original equation.

EXAMPLE 2.24

Solve $x^2y'' - 5xy' + 8y = 2\ln(x)$.

The method of undetermined coefficients does not apply here, since the differential equation has nonconstant coefficients. However, from our experience with the Euler equation, apply the transformation $t = \ln(x)$ and let $Y(t) = y(e^t)$. Using results from Section 2.5, the differential equation transforms to

$$Y''(t) - 6Y'(t) + 8Y(t) = 2t,$$

which has constant coefficients on the left side.

The homogeneous equation $Y'' - 6Y' + 8Y = 0$ has general solution

$$Y_h(t) = c_1e^{2t} + c_2e^{4t}$$

and, by the method of undetermined coefficients, we find one solution of $Y'' - 6Y' + 8Y = 2t$ to be

$$Y_p(t) = \frac{1}{4}t + \frac{3}{16}.$$

The general solution for Y is

$$Y(t) = c_1e^{2t} + c_2e^{4t} + \frac{1}{4}t + \frac{3}{16}.$$

Since $t = \ln(x)$, the original differential equation for y has general solution

$$y(x) = c_1e^{2\ln(x)} + c_2e^{4\ln(x)} + \frac{1}{4}\ln(x) + \frac{3}{16}$$

$$= c_1x^2 + c_2x^4 + \frac{1}{4}\ln(x) + \frac{3}{16}. \quad \blacksquare$$

2.6.3   The Principle of Superposition

Consider the equation

$$y'' + p(x)y' + q(x)y = f_1(x) + f_2(x) + \cdots + f_N(x). \tag{2.13}$$

Suppose y_{pj} is a solution of

$$y'' + p(x)y' + q(x)y = f_j(x).$$

We claim that

$$y_{p1} + y_{p2} + \cdots + y_{pN}$$

is a solution of equation (2.13). This is easy to check by direct substitution into the differential equation:

$$(y_{p1} + y_{p2} + \cdots + y_{pN})'' + p(x)(y_{p1} + y_{p2} + \cdots + y_{pN})' + q(x)(y_{p1} + y_{p2} + \cdots + y_{pN})$$
$$= (y_{p1}'' + p(x)y_{p1}' + q(x)y_{p1}) + \cdots + (y_{pN}'' + p(x)y_{pN}' + q(x)y_{pN})$$
$$= f_1(x) + f_2(x) + \cdots + f_N(x).$$

This means that we can solve each equation $y'' + p(x)y' + q(x)y = f_j(x)$ individually, and the sum of these solutions is a solution of equation (2.13). This is called the *principle of superposition*, and it sometimes enables us to solve a problem by breaking it into a sum of "smaller" problems that are easier to handle individually.

EXAMPLE 2.25

Solve $y'' + 4y = x + 2e^{-2x}$.
   Consider two problems:

   Problem 1: $y'' + 4y = x$, and
   Problem 2: $y'' + 4y = 2e^{-2x}$.

   Using undetermined coefficients, we find that a solution of Problem 1 is $y_{p1}(x) = x/4$, and that a solution of Problem 2 is $y_{p2}(x) = e^{-2x}/4$. Therefore,

$$y_p(x) = \frac{1}{4}(x + e^{-2x})$$

is a solution of $y'' + 4y = x + 2e^{-2x}$. The general solution of this differential equation is

$$y(x) = c_1 \cos(2x) + c_2 \sin(2x) + \frac{1}{4}(x + e^{-2x}). \quad \blacksquare$$

2.6.4   Higher-Order Differential Equations

The methods we now have for solving $y'' + p(x)y' + q(x)y = f(x)$ under certain conditions can also be applied to higher-order differential equations, at least in theory. However, there are practical difficulties to this approach. Consider the following example.

EXAMPLE 2.26

Solve

$$\frac{d^6y}{dx^6} - 4\frac{d^4y}{dx^4} + 2\frac{dy}{dx} + 15y = 0.$$

If we take a cue from the second-order case, we attempt solutions $y = e^{\lambda x}$. Upon substituting this into the differential equation, we obtain an equation for λ:

$$\lambda^6 - 4\lambda^4 + 2\lambda + 15 = 0.$$

In the second-order case, the characteristic polynomial is always of degree 2 and easily solved. Here we encounter a sixth-degree polynomial whose roots are not obvious. They are, approximately,

$$-1.685798616 \pm 0.2107428331i,$$

$$-0.04747911354 \pm 1.279046854i,$$

and

$$1.733277730 \pm 0.4099384482i. \ \blacksquare$$

When the order of the differential equation is $n > 2$, having to find the roots of an nth degree polynomial is enough of a barrier to make this approach impractical except in special cases. A better approach is to convert this sixth-order equation to a system of first-order equations as follows. Define new variables

$$z_1 = y, \quad z_2 = y', \quad z_3 = y'', \quad z_4 = \frac{d^3y}{dx^3}, \quad z_5 = \frac{d^4y}{dx^4}, \quad z_6 = \frac{d^5y}{dx^5}.$$

Now we have a system of six first-order differential equations:

$$z_1' = z_2$$
$$z_2' = z_3$$
$$z_3' = z_4$$
$$z_4' = z_5$$
$$z_5' = z_6$$
$$z_6' = 4z_5 - 2z_2 - 15z_1.$$

The last equation in this system is exactly the original differential equation, stated in terms of the new quantities z_j.

The point to reformulating the problem in this way is that powerful matrix techniques can be invoked to find solutions. We therefore put off discussion of differential equations of order higher than 2 until we have developed the matrix machinery needed to exploit this approach.

In each of Problems 1 through 6, find the general solution using the method of variation of parameters.

1. $y'' + y = \tan(x)$

2. $y'' - 4y' + 3y = 2\cos(x + 3)$

3. $y'' + 9y = 12\sec(3x)$

4. $y'' - 2y' - 3y = 2\sin^2(x)$

5. $y'' - 3y' + 2y = \cos(e^{-x})$

6. $y'' - 5y' + 6y = 8\sin^2(4x)$

In each of Problems 7 through 16, find the general solution using the method of undetermined coefficients.

7. $y'' - y' - 2y = 2x^2 + 5$

8. $y'' - y' - 6y = 8e^{2x}$

9. $y'' - 2y' + 10y = 20x^2 + 2x - 8$

10. $y'' - 4y' + 5y = 21e^{2x}$

11. $y'' - 6y' + 8y = 3e^x$

12. $y'' + 6y' + 9y = 9\cos(3x)$

13. $y'' - 3y' + 2y = 10\sin(x)$

14. $y'' - 4y' = 8x^2 + 2e^{3x}$

15. $y'' - 4y' + 13y = 3e^{2x} - 5e^{3x}$

16. $y'' - 2y' + y = 3x + 25\sin(3x)$

In each of Problems 17 through 26, find the general solution of the differential equation, using any method.

17. $y'' - y' - 2y = e^{2x}$

18. $x^2y'' + 5xy' - 12y = \ln(x)$

19. $y'' + y' - 6y = x$

20. $y'' - y' - 12y = 2\sinh^2(x)$

21. $x^2y'' - 5xy' + 8y = 3x$

22. $x^2y'' + 3xy' + y = \dfrac{4}{x}$

23. $x^2y'' + xy' + 4y = \sin(2\ln(x))$

24. $x^2y'' + 2xy' - 6y = x^2 - 2$

25. $y'' - 4y' + 4y = e^{3x} - 1$

26. $y'' - y' - 2y = x$

In each of Problems 27 through 42, solve the initial value problem.

27. $y'' - 4y = -7e^{2x} + x$; $y(0) = 1$, $y'(0) = 3$

28. $y'' + 4y' = 8 + 34\cos(x)$; $y(0) = 3$, $y'(0) = 2$

29. $y'' + 8y' + 12y = e^{-x} + 7$; $y(0) = 1$, $y'(0) = 0$

30. $y'' - 3y' = 2e^{2x}\sin(x)$; $y(0) = 1$, $y'(0) = 2$

31. $y'' - 2y' - 8y = 10e^{-x} + 8e^{2x}$; $y(0) = 1$, $y'(0) = 4$

32. $y'' - 6y' + 9y = 4e^{3x}$; $y(0) = 1$, $y'(0) = 2$

33. $y'' - 5y' + 6y = \cos(2x)$; $y(0) = 0$, $y'(0) = 4$

34. $y'' - y' + y = 1$; $y(1) = 4$, $y'(1) = -2$

35. $y'' - 8y' + 2y = e^{-x}$; $y(-1) = 5$, $y'(-1) = 2$

36. $y'' + 6y' + 9y = -\cos(x)$; $y(0) = 1$, $y'(0) = -6$

37. $y'' - y = 5\sin^2(x)$; $y(0) = 2$, $y'(0) = -4$

38. $y'' + y = \tan(x)$; $y(0) = 4$, $y'(0) = 3$

39. $x^2y'' - 6y = 8x^2$; $y(1) = 1$, $y'(1) = 0$

40. $x^2y'' + 7xy' + 9y = 27\ln(x)$; $y(1) = 1$, $y'(1) = -4$

41. $x^2y'' - 2xy' + 2y = 10\sin(\ln(x))$;
$y(1) = 3$, $y'(1) = 0$

42. $x^2y'' - 4xy' + 6y = x^4e^x$; $y(2) = 2$, $y'(2) = 7$

2.7   Application of Second-Order Differential Equations to a Mechanical System

Envision a spring of natural (unstretched) length L and spring constant k. This constant quantifies the "stiffness" of the spring. The spring is suspended vertically. An object of mass m is attached at the lower end, stretching the spring d units past its rest length. The object comes to rest in its equilibrium position. It is then displaced vertically a distance y_0 units (up or down), and released, possibly with an initial velocity (Figure 2.4). We want to construct a mathematical model allowing us to analyze the motion of the object.

Let $y(t)$ be the displacement of the object from the equilibrium position at time t. As a convenience, take this equilibrium position to be $y = 0$. Choose down as the positive direction. Both of these choices are arbitrary.

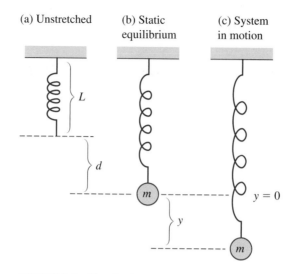

FIGURE 2.4   *Mass/spring system.*

Now consider the forces acting on the object. Gravity pulls it downward with a force of magnitude mg. By Hooke's law, the force the spring exerts on the object has magnitude ky. At the equilibrium position, the force of the spring is $-kd$, negative because it acts upward. If the object is pulled downward a distance y from this position, an additional force $-ky$ is exerted on it. Thus, the total force on the object due to the spring is

$$-kd - ky.$$

The total force due to gravity and the spring is

$$mg - kd - ky.$$

Since at the equilibrium point $(y = 0)$ this force is zero, then $mg = kd$. The net force acting on the object due to gravity and the spring is therefore just $-ky$.

Finally, there are forces tending to retard or damp out the motion. These include air resistance or viscosity of the medium if the object is suspended in some fluid such as oil. A standard assumption, arising from experiment, is that the retarding forces have magnitude proportional to the velocity y'. Thus, for some constant c called the *damping constant*, the retarding forces have magnitude cy'. The total force acting on the object due to gravity, damping and the spring itself therefore have magnitude

$$-ky - cy'.$$

Finally, there may be a driving force of magnitude $f(t)$ on the object. Now the total external force acting on the object has magnitude

$$F = -ky - cy' + f(t).$$

Assuming that the mass is constant, Newton's second law of motion enables us to write

$$my'' = -ky - cy' + f(t),$$

or

$$y'' + \frac{c}{m}y' + \frac{k}{m}y = f(t). \tag{2.14}$$

This is the *spring equation*. We will analyze the motion described by solutions of this equation, under various conditions.

2.7.1   Unforced Motion

Suppose first that $f(t) = 0$, so there is no driving force. Now the spring equation is

$$y'' + \frac{c}{m}y' + \frac{k}{m}y = 0$$

with characteristic equation

$$\lambda^2 + \frac{c}{m}\lambda + \frac{k}{m} = 0.$$

This has roots

$$\lambda = -\frac{c}{2m} \pm \frac{1}{2m}\sqrt{c^2 - 4km}.$$

As we might expect, the general solution, hence the motion of the object, will depend on its mass, the amount of damping, and the stiffness of the spring. Consider the following cases.

Case 1 $c^2 - 4km > 0$
In this event, the characteristic equation has two real, distinct roots:

$$\lambda_1 = -\frac{c}{2m} + \frac{1}{2m}\sqrt{c^2 - 4km} \quad \text{and} \quad \lambda_2 = -\frac{c}{2m} - \frac{1}{2m}\sqrt{c^2 - 4km}.$$

The general solution of equation (2.14) in this case is

$$y(t) = c_1 e^{\lambda_1 t} + c_2 e^{\lambda_2 t}.$$

Clearly $\lambda_2 < 0$. Since m and k are positive, $c^2 - 4km < c^2$, so $\sqrt{c^2 - 4km} < c$ and λ_1 is negative also. Therefore,

$$\lim_{t \to \infty} y(t) = 0,$$

regardless of initial conditions. In the case $c^2 - 4km > 0$, the motion of the object decays to zero as time increases. This case is called *overdamping*, and it occurs when the square of the damping constant exceeds four times the product of the mass and spring constant.

EXAMPLE 2.27   Overdamping

Suppose $c = 6$, $k = 5$, and $m = 1$. Now the general solution is

$$y(t) = c_1 e^{-t} + c_2 e^{-5t}.$$

Suppose, to be specific, the object was initially (at $t = 0$) drawn upward 4 units from the equilibrium position and released downward with a speed of 2 units per second. Then $y(0) = -4$ and $y'(0) = 2$, and we obtain

$$y(t) = \frac{1}{2}e^{-t}(-9 + e^{-4t}).$$

A graph of this solution is shown in Figure 2.5.

What does the solution tell us about the motion? Since $-9 + e^{-4t} < 0$ for $t > 0$, then $y(t) < 0$ and the object always remains above the equilibrium point. Its velocity $y'(t) = e^{-t}(9 - 5e^{-4t})/2$ decreases to zero as t increases, and $y(t) \to 0$ as t increases, so the object moves downward

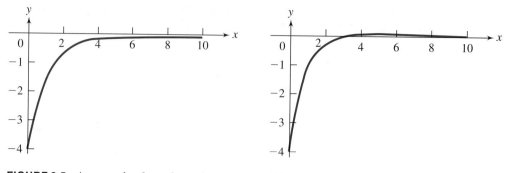

FIGURE 2.5 *An example of overdamped motion, no driving force.*

FIGURE 2.6 *An example of critical damped motion, no driving force.*

toward equilibrium with ever decreasing velocity, approaching closer to but never reaching the equilibrium point, and never coming to rest. ■

Case 2 $c^2 - 4km = 0$

Now the general solution of the spring equation (2.14) is

$$y(t) = (c_1 + c_2 t)e^{-ct/2m}.$$

This case is called *critical damping*. While $y(t) \to 0$ as $t \to \infty$, as in the overdamping case, we will see an important difference between critical and overdamping.

EXAMPLE 2.28

Let $c = 2$ and $k = m = 1$. Now $y(t) = (c_1 + c_2 t)e^{-t}$. Suppose the object is initially pulled up four units above the equilibrium position and then pushed downward with a speed of 5 units per second. Then $y(0) = -4$ and $y'(0) = 5$, so

$$y(t) = (-4 + t)e^{-t}.$$

Observe that $y(4) = 0$, so, unlike the what we saw with overdamping, the object actually reaches the equilibrium position, four seconds after it was released, and then passes through it. In fact, $y(t)$ reaches its maximum when $t = 5$ seconds, and this maximum value is $y(5) = e^{-5}$, about 0.007 unit below the equilibrium point. The velocity $y'(t) = (5 - t)e^{-t}$ is negative for $t > 5$, so the object's velocity decreases after this 5-second point. Since $y(t) \to 0$ as $t \to \infty$, the object moves with decreasing velocity back toward the equilibrium point as time increases. Figure 2.6 shows a graph of the displacement function in this case. ■

In general, when critical damping occurs, the object either passes through the equilibrium point exactly once, as just seen, or never reaches it at all, depending on the initial conditions.

Case 3 $c^2 - 4km < 0$

Now the spring constant and mass together are sufficiently large that $c^2 < 4km$, and the damping is less dominant. This case is called *underdamping*. The general solution now is

$$y(t) = e^{-ct/2m}[c_1 \cos(\beta t) + c_2 \sin(\beta t)],$$

in which

$$\beta = \frac{1}{2m}\sqrt{4km - c^2}.$$

Because c and m are positive, $y(t) \to 0$ as $t \to \infty$. However, now the motion is oscillatory because of the sine and cosine terms in the solution. The motion is not, however, periodic, because of the exponential factor, which causes the amplitude of the oscillations to decay to zero as time increases.

EXAMPLE 2.29

Suppose $c = k = 2$ and $m = 1$. Now the general solution is

$$y(t) = e^{-t}[c_1 \cos(t) + c_2 \sin(t)].$$

Suppose the object is driven downward from a point three units above equilibrium, with an initial speed of two units per second. Then $y(0) = -3$ and $y'(0) = 2$ and the solution is

$$y(t) = -e^{-t}(3\cos(t) + \sin(t)).$$

The behavior of this solution is more easily visualized if we write it in phase angle form. We want to choose C and δ so that

$$3\cos(t) + \sin(t) = C\cos(t + \delta).$$

For this, we need

$$3\cos(t) + \sin(t) = C\cos(t)\cos(\delta) - C\sin(t)\sin(\delta),$$

so

$$C\cos(\delta) = 3 \quad \text{and} \quad C\sin(\delta) = -1.$$

Then

$$\frac{C\sin(\delta)}{C\cos(\delta)} = \tan(\delta) = -\frac{1}{3},$$

so

$$\delta = \tan^{-1}\left(-\frac{1}{3}\right) = -\tan^{-1}\left(\frac{1}{3}\right).$$

To solve for C, write

$$C^2\cos^2(\delta) + C^2\sin^2(\delta) = C^2 = 3^2 + 1^2 = 10$$

so $C = \sqrt{10}$. Now we can write the solution as

$$y(t) = \sqrt{10}e^{-t}\cos(t - \tan^{-1}(1/3)).$$

The graph is therefore a cosine curve with decaying amplitude, squashed between graphs of $y = \sqrt{10}e^{-t}$ and $y = -\sqrt{10}e^{-t}$. The solution is shown in Figure 2.7, with these two exponential functions shown as reference curves. Because of the oscillatory cosine term, the object passes back and forth through the equilibrium point. In fact, it passes through equilibrium exactly when $y(t) = 0$, or

$$t = \tan^{-1}\left(\frac{1}{3}\right) + \frac{2n+1}{2}\pi$$

for $n = 0, 1, 2, 3, \cdots$. In theory, the object oscillates through the equilibrium infinitely often in this underdamping case, although the amplitudes of the oscillations decrease to zero as time increases. ∎

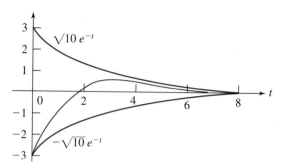

FIGURE 2.7   *An example of underdamped motion, no driving force.*

2.7.2   Forced Motion

Now suppose an external driving force of magnitude $f(t)$ acts on the object. Of course, different forces will cause different kinds of motion. As an illustration, we will analyze the motion under the influence of a periodic driving force $f(t) = A\cos(\omega t)$, with A and ω positive constants. Now the spring equation is

$$y + \frac{c}{m}y' + \frac{k}{m}y = \frac{A}{m}\cos(\omega t). \tag{2.15}$$

We know how to solve this nonhomogeneous linear equation. Begin by finding a particular solution, using the method of undetermined coefficients. Attempt a solution

$$y_p(x) = a\cos(\omega t) + b\sin(\omega t).$$

Substitution of this into equation (2.15) and rearrangement of terms yields

$$\left[-a\omega^2 + \frac{b\omega c}{m} + a\frac{k}{m} - \frac{A}{m}\right]\cos(\omega t) = \left[b\omega^2 + \frac{a\omega c}{m} - b\frac{k}{m}\right]\sin(\omega t).$$

Since $\sin(\omega t)$ and $\cos(\omega t)$ are not constant multiples of each other, the only way this can be true for all $t \geq 0$ is for the coefficient on each side of the equation to be zero. Therefore

$$-a\omega^2 + \frac{b\omega c}{m} + a\frac{k}{m} - \frac{A}{m} = 0$$

and

$$b\omega^2 + \frac{a\omega c}{m} - b\frac{k}{m} = 0.$$

Solve these for a and b, keeping in mind that A, c, k, and m are given. We get

$$a = \frac{A(k - m\omega^2)}{(k - m\omega^2)^2 + \omega^2 c^2} \quad \text{and} \quad b = \frac{A\omega c}{(k - m\omega^2)^2 + \omega^2 c^2}.$$

Let $\omega_0 = \sqrt{k/m}$. Then a particular solution of equation (2.15), for this forcing function, is given by

$$y_p(x) = \frac{mA(\omega_0^2 - \omega^2)}{m^2(\omega_0^2 - \omega^2)^2 + \omega^2 c^2}\cos(\omega t) \tag{2.16}$$

$$+ \frac{A\omega c}{m^2(\omega_0^2 - \omega^2)^2 + \omega^2 c^2}\sin(\omega t),$$

assuming that $c \neq 0$ or $\omega \neq \omega_0$.

We will now examine some specific cases to get some insight into the motion with this forcing function.

Overdamped Forced Motion   Suppose $c = 6$, $k = 5$, and $m = 1$, as we had previously in the overdamping case. Suppose also that $A = 6\sqrt{5}$ and $\omega = \sqrt{5}$. If the object is released from rest from the equilibrium position, then the displacement function satisfies the initial value problem

$$y'' + 6y' + 5y = 6\sqrt{5}\cos(\sqrt{5}t); \qquad y(0) = y'(0) = 0.$$

This problem has the unique solution

$$y(t) = \frac{\sqrt{5}}{4}(-e^{-t} + e^{-5t}) + \sin(\sqrt{5}t),$$

a graph of which is shown in Figure 2.8. As time increases, the exponential terms decrease to zero, exerting less influence on the motion, while the sine term oscillates. Thus, as t increases, the solution tends to behave more like $\sin(\sqrt{5}t)$ and the object moves up and down through the equilibrium point, with approximate period $2\pi/\sqrt{5}$. Contrast this with the overdamped motion with no forcing function, in which the object began above the equilibrium point and moved with decreasing velocity down toward it, but never reached it.

Critically Damped Forced Motion   Let $c = 2$ and $m = k = 1$. Suppose $\omega = 1$ and $A = 2$. Assume that the object is released from rest from the equilibrium position. Now the initial value problem for the position function is

$$y'' + 2y' + y = 2\cos(t); \qquad y(0) = y'(0) = 0$$

with solution

$$y(t) = -te^{-t} + \sin(t).$$

A graph of this solution is shown in Figure 2.9. The exponential term exerts a significant influence at first, but decreases to zero as time increases. The term $-te^{-t}$ decreases to zero as t increases, but not as quickly as the corresponding term $\frac{\sqrt{5}}{4}(-e^{-t} + e^{-5t})$ in the overdamping case. Nevertheless, after a while the motion settles into nearly (but not exactly, because $-te^{-t}$ is never actually zero for positive t) a sinusoidal motion back and forth through the equilibrium point. This is an example of critically damped forced motion.

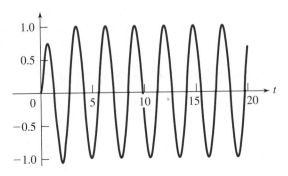

FIGURE 2.8   *An example of overdamped motion driven by $6\sqrt{5}\ \cos(\sqrt{5}t)$.*

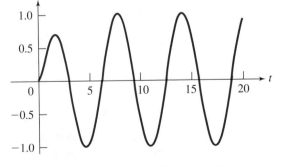

FIGURE 2.9   *An example of critical damped motion driven by $2\cos(t)$.*

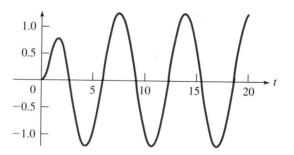

FIGURE 2.10 *An example of underdamped motion driven by $2\sqrt{2}\cos(\sqrt{2}t)$.*

Underdamped Forced Motion   Suppose now that $c = k = 2$, $m = 1$, $\omega = \sqrt{2}$, and $A = 2\sqrt{2}$. Now $c^2 - 4km < 0$, and we have underdamped motion, but this time with a forcing function. If the object is released from rest from the equilibrium position, then the initial value problem for the displacement function is

$$y'' + 2y' + 2y = 2\sqrt{2}\cos(\sqrt{2}t); \qquad y(0) = y'(0) = 0,$$

with solution

$$y(t) = -\sqrt{2}e^{-t}\sin(t) + \sin(\sqrt{2}t).$$

Unlike the other two cases, the exponential factor in this solution has a $\sin(t)$ factor. Figure 2.10 shows a graph of this function. As time increases, the term $-\sqrt{2}e^{-t}\sin(t)$ becomes less influential and the motion settles nearly into an oscillation back and forth through the equilibrium point, with period nearly $2\pi/\sqrt{2}$.

2.7.3   Resonance

In the absence of damping, an interesting phenomenon called resonance can occur. Suppose $c = 0$ but that there is still a periodic driving force $f(t) = A\cos(\omega t)$. Now the spring equation is

$$y'' + \frac{k}{m}y = \frac{A}{m}\cos(\omega t).$$

From equation (2.16) with $c = 0$, this equation has general solution

$$y(t) = c_1\cos(\omega_0 t) + c_2\sin(\omega_0 t) + \frac{A}{m(\omega_0^2 - \omega^2)}\cos(\omega t), \tag{2.17}$$

in which $\omega_0 = \sqrt{k/m}$. This number is called the *natural frequency* of the spring system, and is a function of the stiffness of the spring and mass of the object, while ω is the *input frequency* and is contained in the driving force. This general solution assumes that the natural and input frequencies are different. Of course, the closer we choose the natural and input frequencies, the larger the amplitude of the $\cos(\omega t)$ term in the solution.

Consider the case that the natural and input frequencies are the same. Now the differential equation is

$$y'' + \frac{k}{m}y = \frac{A}{m}\cos(\omega_0 t) \tag{2.18}$$

and the function given by equation (2.17) is not a solution. To solve equation (2.18), first write the general solution y_h of $y'' + (k/m)y = 0$:

$$y_h(t) = c_1\cos(\omega_0 t) + c_2\sin(\omega_0 t).$$

For a particular solution of equation (2.18), we will proceed by the method of undetermined coefficients. Since the forcing function contains a term found in y_h, we will attempt a particular solution of the form

$$y_p(t) = at \cos(\omega_0 t) + bt \sin(\omega_0 t).$$

Substitute this into equation (2.18) to obtain

$$-2a\omega_0 \sin(\omega_0 t) + 2b\omega_0 \cos(\omega_0 t) = \frac{A}{m} \cos(\omega_0 t).$$

Thus choose

$$a = 0 \quad \text{and} \quad 2b\omega_0 = \frac{A}{m},$$

leading to the particular solution

$$y_p(t) = \frac{A}{2m\omega_0} t \sin(\omega_0 t).$$

The general solution of equation (2.18) is therefore

$$y(t) = c_1 \cos(\omega_0 t) + c_2 \sin(\omega_0 t) + \frac{A}{2m\omega_0} t \sin(\omega_0 t).$$

This solution differs from that in the case $\omega \neq \omega_0$ in the factor of t in $y_p(t)$. Because of this, solutions increase in amplitude as t increases. This phenomenon is called *resonance*.

As a specific example, let $c_1 = c_2 = \omega_0 = 1$ and $A/2m = 1$ to write the solution as

$$y(t) = \cos(t) + \sin(t) + t \sin(t).$$

A graph of this function is shown in Figure 2.11, clearly revealing the increasing magnitude of the oscillations with time.

While there is always some damping in the real world, if the damping constant is close to zero compared to other factors, such as the mass, and if the natural and input frequencies are (nearly) equal, then oscillations can build up to a sufficiently large amplitude to cause resonance-like behavior and damage a system. This can occur with soldiers marching in step across a bridge. If the cadence of the march (input frequency) is near enough to the natural frequency of the material of the bridge, vibrations can build up to dangerous levels. This occurred near Manchester, England, in 1831 when a column of soldiers marching across the Broughton Bridge caused it to collapse. More recently, the Tacoma Narrows Bridge in Washington experienced increasing oscillations driven by energy from the wind, causing it to whip about in sensational

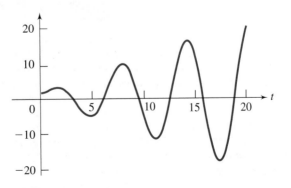

FIGURE 2.11   *Resonance.*

fashion before its collapse into the river. Videos of the wild thrashing about of the bridge are available in some libraries and engineering and science departments.

2.7.4   Beats

In the absence of damping, an oscillatory driving force can also cause a phenomenon called beats. Suppose $\omega \neq \omega_0$ and consider

$$y'' + \omega_0^2 y = \frac{A}{m}\cos(\omega_0 t).$$

The Tacoma Narrows Bridge was completed in 1940 and stood as a new standard of combined artistry and functionality. The bridge soon became known for its tendency to sway in high winds, but no one suspected what was about to occur. On November 7, 1940, energy provided by unusually strong winds, coupled with a resonating effect in the bridge's material and design, caused the oscillations in the bridge to be reinfored and build to dangerous levels. Soon, the twisting caused one side of the sidewalk to rise 28 feet above that of the other side. Concrete dropped out of the roadway, and a section of the suspension span completely rotated and fell away. Shortly thereafter, the entire center span collapsed into Puget Sound. This sensational construction failure motivated new mathematical treatments of vibration and wave phenomena in the design of bridges and other large structures. The forces that brought down this bridge are a more complicated version of the resonance phenomenon discussed in Section 2.7.3.

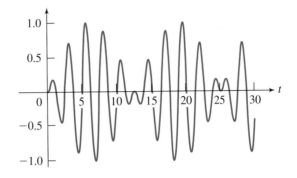

FIGURE 2.12   *Beats.*

Assuming that the object is released from rest at the equilibrium position, then $y(0) = y'(0) = 0$ and from equation (2.17) we have the solution

$$y(t) = \frac{A}{m(\omega_0^2 - \omega^2)}[\cos(\omega t) - \cos(\omega_0 t)].$$

The behavior of this solution reveals itself more clearly if we write it as

$$y(t) = \frac{2A}{m(\omega_0^2 - \omega^2)} \sin\left(\frac{1}{2}(\omega_0 + \omega)t\right) \sin\left(\frac{1}{2}(\omega_0 - \omega)t\right).$$

This formulation reveals a periodic variation of amplitude in the solution, depending on the relative sizes of $\omega_0 + \omega$ and $\omega_0 - \omega$. It is this periodic variation of amplitude that is called a *beat*. As a specific example, suppose $\omega_0 + \omega = 5$ and $\omega_0 - \omega = \frac{1}{2}$, and the constants are chosen so that $2A/[m(\omega_0^2 - \omega^2)] = 1$. In this case, the displacement function is

$$y(t) = \sin\left(\frac{5t}{2}\right) \sin\left(\frac{t}{4}\right).$$

The beats are apparent in the graph of this solution in Figure 2.12.

2.7.5   Analogy with an Electrical Circuit

If a circuit contains a resistance R, inductance L, and capacitance C, and the electromotive force is $E(t)$, then the impressed voltage is obtained as a sum of the voltage drops in the circuit:

$$E(t) = Li'(t) + Ri(t) + \frac{1}{C}q(t).$$

Here $i(t)$ is the current at time t, and $q(t)$ is the charge. Since $i = q'$, we can write the second-order linear differential equation

$$q'' + \frac{R}{L}q' + \frac{1}{LC}q = \frac{1}{L}E.$$

If R, L, and C are constant, this is a linear equation of the type we have solved for various choices of $E(t)$. It is interesting to observe that this equation is of exactly the same form as the equation for the displacement of an object attached to a spring, which is

$$y'' + \frac{c}{m}y' + \frac{k}{m}y = \frac{1}{m}f(t).$$

This means that solutions of one equation readily translate into solutions of the other and suggests the following equivalences between electrical and mechanical quantities:

displacement function $y(t) \Longleftrightarrow$ charge $q(t)$

velocity $y'(t) \Longleftrightarrow$ current $i(t)$

driving force $f(t) \Longleftrightarrow$ electromotive force $E(t)$

mass $m \Longleftrightarrow$ inductance L

damping constant $c \Longleftrightarrow$ resistance R

spring modulus $k \Longleftrightarrow$ reciprocal $1/C$ of the capacitance

EXAMPLE 2.30

Consider the circuit of Figure 2.13, driven by a potential of $E(t) = 17\sin(2t)$ volts. At time zero the current is zero and the charge on the capacitor is $1/2000$ coulomb. The charge $q(t)$ on the capacitor for $t > 0$ is obtained by solving the initial value problem

$$10q'' + 120q' + 1000q = 17\sin(2t); \quad q(0) = \frac{1}{2000}, q'(0) = 0.$$

The solution is

$$q(t) = \frac{1}{1500}e^{-6t}[7\cos(8t) - \sin(8t)] + \frac{1}{240}[-\cos(2t) + 4\sin(2t)].$$

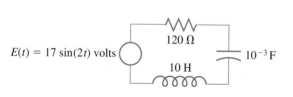

FIGURE 2.13

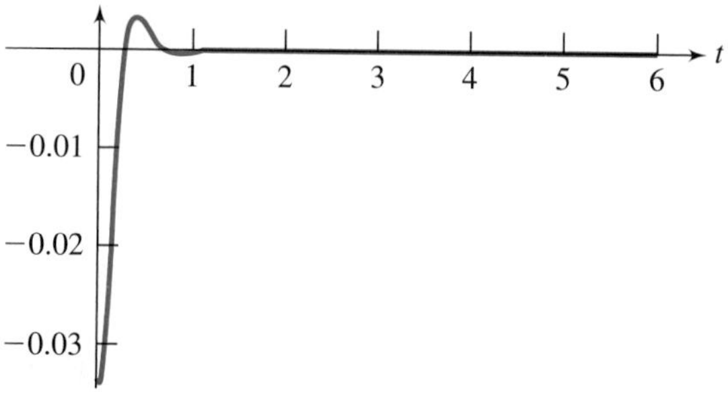

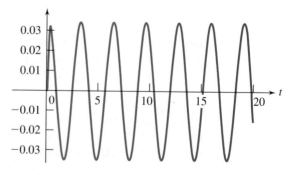

FIGURE 2.14 *Transient part of the current for the circuit of Figure 2.13.*

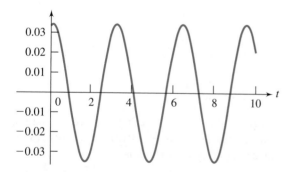

FIGURE 2.15 *Steady-state part of the current for the circuit of Figure 2.13.*

FIGURE 2.16 *Current function for the circuit of Figure 2.13.*

The current can be calculated as

$$i(t) = q'(t) = -\frac{1}{30}e^{-6t}[\cos(8t) + \sin(8t)] + \frac{1}{120}[4\cos(2t) + \sin(2t)].$$

The current is a sum of a transient part

$$-\frac{1}{30}e^{-6t}[\cos(8t) + \sin(8t)],$$

named for the fact that it decays to zero as t increases, and a steady-state part

$$\frac{1}{120}[4\cos(2t) + \sin(2t)].$$

The transient and steady-state parts are shown in Figures 2.14 and 2.15, and their sum, the current, is shown in Figure 2.16. ■

SECTION 2.7   PROBLEMS

1. The object of this problem is to gauge the relative effects of initial position and velocity on the motion in the unforced, overdamped case. Solve the initial value problems

$$y'' + 4y' + 2y = 0; \qquad y(0) = 5, y'(0) = 0$$

and

$$y'' + 4y' + 2y = 0; \qquad y(0) = 0, y'(0) = 5.$$

Graph the solutions on the same set of axes. What conclusions can be drawn from these solutions about the influence of initial position and velocity?

2. Repeat the experiment of Problem 1, except now use the critically damped unforced equation $y'' + 4y' + 4y = 0$.

3. Repeat the experiment of Problem 1 for the underdamped unforced case $y'' + 2y' + 5y = 0$.

Problems 4 through 9 explore the effects of changing the initial position or initial velocity on the motion of the bob. In each, use the same set of axes to graph the solution of the initial value problem for the given values of A and observe the effect that these changes cause in the solution.

4. $y'' + 4y' + 2y = 0; y(0) = A, y'(0) = 0;$ A has values $1, 3, 6, 10, -4$ and -7.

5. $y'' + 4y' + 2y = 0; y(0) = 0, y'(0) = A;$ A has values $1, 3, 6, 10, -4$ and -7.

6. $y'' + 4y' + 4y = 0; y(0) = A, y'(0) = 0;$ A has values $1, 3, 6, 10, -4$ and -7.

7. $y'' + 4y' + 4y = 0; y(0) = 0, y'(0) = A;$ A has values $1, 3, 6, 10, -4$ and -7.

8. $y'' + 2y' + 5y = 0; y(0) = A, y'(0) = 0;$ A has values $1, 3, 6, 10, -4$ and -7.

9. $y'' + 2y' + 5y = 0; y(0) = 0, y'(0) = A;$ A has values $1, 3, 6, 10, -4$ and -7.

10. An object having mass 1 gram is attached to the lower end of a spring having spring modulus 29 dynes per centimeter. The bob is, in turn, adhered to a dashpot that imposes a damping force of $10v$ dynes, where $v(t)$ is the velocity at time t in centimeters per second. Determine the motion of the bob if it is pulled down 3 centimeters from equilibrium and then struck upward with a blow sufficient to impart a velocity of 1 centimeter per second. Graph the solution. Solve the problem when the initial velocity is, in turn, 2, 4, 7, and 12 centimeters per second. Graph these solutions on the same set of axes to visualize the influence of the initial velocity on the motion.

11. An object having mass 1 kilogram is suspended from a spring having a spring constant of 24 newtons per meter. Attached to the object is a shock absorber, which induces a drag of $11v$ newtons (velocity is in meters per second). The system is set in motion by lowering the bob $\frac{25}{3}$ centimeters and then striking it hard enough to impart an upward velocity of 5 meters per second. Solve for and graph the displacement function. Obtain the solution for the cases that the bob is lowered, in turn, 12, 20, 30, and 45 centimeters, and graph the displacement functions for the five cases on the same set of axes to see the effect of the distance lowered.

12. When an 8-pound weight is suspended from a spring, it stretches the spring 2 inches. Determine the

equation of motion when an object with a mass of 7 kilograms is suspended from this spring, and the system is set in motion by striking the object an upward blow, imparting a velocity of 4 meters per second.

13. How many times can the bob pass through the equilibrium point in the case of overdamped motion? What condition can be placed on the initial displacement $y(0)$ to guarantee that the bob never passes through equilibrium?

14. How many times can the bob pass through the equilibrium point in the case of critical damping? What condition can be placed on $y(0)$ to ensure that the bob never passes through this position? How does the initial velocity influence whether the bob passes through the equilibrium position?

15. In underdamped motion, what effect does the damping constant c have on the frequency of the oscillations of motion?

16. Suppose $y(0) = y'(0) \neq 0$. Determine the maximum displacement of the bob in the critically damped case, and show that the time at which this maximum occurs is independent of the initial displacement.

17. Suppose the acceleration of the bob on the spring at distance d from the equilibrium position is a. Prove that the period of the motion is $2\pi\sqrt{d/a}$ in the case of undamped motion.

18. A mass m_1 is attached to a spring and allowed to vibrate with undamped motion having period p. At some later time a second mass m_2 is instantaneously fused with m_1. Prove that the new object, having mass $m_1 + m_2$, exhibits simple harmonic motion with period $p/\sqrt{1 + m_2/m_1}$.

19. Let $y(t)$ be the solution of $y'' + \omega_0^2 y = (A/m)\cos(\omega t)$, with $y(0) = y'(0) = 0$. Assuming that $\omega \neq \omega_0$, find $\lim_{\omega \to \omega_0} y(t)$. How does this limit compare with the solution of $y'' + \omega_0^2 y = (A/m)\cos(\omega_0 t)$, with $y(0) = y'(0) = 0$?

20. A 16-pound weight is suspended from a spring, stretching it $\dfrac{8}{11}$ feet. Then the weight is submerged in

a fluid that imposes a drag of $2v$ pounds. The entire system is subjected to an external force $4\cos(\omega t)$. Determine the value of ω that maximizes the amplitude of the steady-state oscillation. What is this maximum amplitude?

21. Consider overdamped forced motion governed by $y'' + 6y' + 2y = 4\cos(3t)$.

    (a) Find the solution satisfying $y(0) = 6$, $y'(0) = 0$.

    (b) Find the solution satisfying $y(0) = 0$, $y'(0) = 6$.

    (c) Graph these solutions on the same set of axes to compare the effect of initial displacement with that of initial velocity.

22. Carry out the program of Problem 21 for the critically damped forced system governed by $y'' + 4y' + 4y = 4\cos(3t)$.

23. Carry out the program of Problem 21 for the underdamped forced system governed by $y'' + y' + 3y = 4\cos(3t)$.

In each of Problems 24 through 27, use the information to find the current in the RLC circuit of Figure 2.17. Assume zero initial current and capacitor charge.

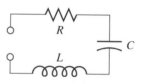

FIGURE 2.17   *RLC circuit.*

24. $R = 200\ \Omega$, $L = 0.1$ H, $C = 0.006$ F, $E(t) = te^{-t}$ volts

25. $R = 400\ \Omega$, $L = 0.12$ H, $C = 0.04$ F, $E(t) = 120\sin(20t)$ volts

26. $R = 150\ \Omega$, $L = 0.2$ H, $C = 0.05$ F, $E(t) = 1 - e^{-t}$ volts

27. $R = 450\ \Omega$, $L = 0.95$ H, $C = 0.007$ F, $E(t) = e^{-t}\sin^2(3t)$ volts

CHAPTER 3

The Laplace Transform

3.1 Definition and Basic Properties

In mathematics, a transform is usually a device that converts one type of problem into another type, presumably easier to solve. The strategy is to solve the transformed problem, then transform back the other way to obtain the solution of the original problem. In the case of the Laplace transform, initial value problems are often converted to algebra problems, a process we can diagram as follows:

initial value problem

$\Downarrow$

algebra problem

$\Downarrow$

solution of the algebra problem

$\Downarrow$

solution of the initial value problem.

DEFINITION 3.1 *Laplace Transform*

The Laplace transform $\mathcal{L}[f]$ of f is a function defined by

$$\mathcal{L}[f](s) = \int_0^\infty e^{-st} f(t)\, dt,$$

for all s such that this integral converges.

The Laplace transform converts a function f to a new function called $\mathcal{L}[f]$. Often we use t as the independent variable for f and s for the independent variable of $\mathcal{L}[f]$. Thus, $f(t)$ is the function f evaluated at t, and $\mathcal{L}[f](s)$ is the function $\mathcal{L}[f]$ evaluated at s.

It is often convenient to agree to use lowercase letters for a function put into the Laplace transform, and its upper case for the function that comes out. In this notation,

$$F = \mathcal{L}[f], \quad G = \mathcal{L}[g], \quad H = \mathcal{L}[h],$$

and so on.

EXAMPLE 3.1

Let $f(t) = e^{at}$, with a any real number. Then

$$\mathcal{L}[f](s) = F(s) = \int_0^\infty e^{-st} e^{at}\, dt = \int_0^\infty e^{(a-s)t}\, dt$$

$$= \lim_{k\to\infty} \int_0^k e^{(a-s)t}\, dt = \lim_{k\to\infty} \left[\frac{1}{a-s} e^{(a-s)t} \right]_0^k$$

$$= \lim_{k\to\infty} \left[\frac{1}{a-s} e^{(a-s)k} - \frac{1}{a-s} \right]$$

$$= -\frac{1}{a-s} = \frac{1}{s-a}$$

provided that $a - s < 0$, or $s > a$. The Laplace transform of $f(t) = e^{at}$ is $F(s) = 1/(s-a)$, defined for $s > a$. ∎

EXAMPLE 3.2

Let $g(t) = \sin(t)$. Then

$$\mathcal{L}[g](s) = G(s) = \int_0^\infty e^{-st} \sin(t)\, dt$$

$$= \lim_{k\to\infty} \int_0^k e^{-st} \sin(t)\, dt$$

$$= \lim_{k\to\infty} \left[-\frac{e^{-ks}\cos k + se^{-ks}\sin k - 1}{s^2 + 1} \right] = \frac{1}{s^2 + 1}.$$

$G(s)$ is defined for all $s > 0$. ∎

A Laplace transform is rarely computed by referring directly to the definition and integrating. Instead, we use tables of Laplace transforms of commonly used functions (such as Table 3.1) or computer software. We will also develop methods that are used to find the Laplace transform of a shifted or translated function, step functions, pulses, and various other functions that arise frequently in applications.

The Laplace transform is linear, which means that constants factor through the transform, and the transform of a sum of functions is the sum of the transform of these functions.

TABLE 3.1	**Table of Laplace Transforms of Functions**

	$f(t)$	$F(s) = \mathcal{L}[f(t)](s)$
1.	1	$\dfrac{1}{s}$
2.	t	$\dfrac{1}{s^2}$
3.	$t^n \, (n = 1, 2, 3, \cdots)$	$\dfrac{n!}{s^{n+1}}$
4.	$\dfrac{1}{\sqrt{t}}$	$\sqrt{\dfrac{\pi}{s}}$
5.	e^{at}	$\dfrac{1}{s - a}$
6.	te^{at}	$\dfrac{1}{(s - a)^2}$
7.	$t^n e^{at}$	$\dfrac{n!}{(s - a)^{n+1}}$
8.	$\dfrac{1}{a - b}(e^{at} - e^{bt})$	$\dfrac{1}{(s - a)(s - b)}$
9.	$\dfrac{1}{a - b}(ae^{at} - be^{bt})$	$\dfrac{s}{(s - a)(s - b)}$
10.	$\dfrac{(c - b)e^{at} + (a - c)e^{bt} + (b - a)e^{ct}}{(a - b)(b - c)(c - a)}$	$\dfrac{1}{(s - a)(s - b)(s - c)}$
11.	$\sin(at)$	$\dfrac{a}{s^2 + a^2}$
12.	$\cos(at)$	$\dfrac{s}{s^2 + a^2}$
13.	$1 - \cos(at)$	$\dfrac{a^2}{s(s^2 + a^2)}$
14.	$at - \sin(at)$	$\dfrac{a^3}{s^2(s^2 + a^2)}$
15.	$\sin(at) - at\cos(at)$	$\dfrac{2a^3}{(s^2 + a^2)^2}$
16.	$\sin(at) + at\cos(at)$	$\dfrac{2as^2}{(s^2 + a^2)^2}$
17.	$t\sin(at)$	$\dfrac{2as}{(s^2 + a^2)^2}$
18.	$t\cos(at)$	$\dfrac{(s^2 - a^2)}{(s^2 + a^2)^2}$
19.	$\dfrac{\cos(at) - \cos(bt)}{(b - a)(b + a)}$	$\dfrac{s}{(s^2 + a^2)(s^2 + b^2)}$
20.	$e^{at}\sin(bt)$	$\dfrac{b}{(s - a)^2 + b^2}$
21.	$e^{at}\cos(bt)$	$\dfrac{s - a}{(s - a)^2 + b^2}$
22.	$\sinh(at)$	$\dfrac{a}{s^2 - a^2}$
23.	$\cosh(at)$	$\dfrac{s}{s^2 - a^2}$
24.	$\sin(at)\cosh(at) - \cos(at)\sinh(at)$	$\dfrac{4a^3}{s^4 + 4a^4}$
25.	$\sin(at)\sinh(at)$	$\dfrac{2a^2 s}{s^4 + 4a^4}$

TABLE 3.1   *(continued)*

	$f(t)$	$F(s) = \mathcal{L}[f(t)](s)$
26.	$\sinh(at) - \sin(at)$	$\dfrac{2a^3}{s^4 - a^4}$
27.	$\cosh(at) - \cos(at)$	$\dfrac{2a^2 s}{s^4 - a^4}$
28.	$\dfrac{1}{\sqrt{\pi t}} e^{at}(1 + 2at)$	$\dfrac{s}{(s-a)^{3/2}}$
29.	$J_0(at)$	$\dfrac{1}{\sqrt{s^2 + a^2}}$
30.	$J_n(at)$	$\dfrac{1}{a^n} \dfrac{\left(\sqrt{s^2 + a^2} - s\right)^n}{\sqrt{s^2 + a^2}}$
31.	$J_0(2\sqrt{at})$	$\dfrac{1}{s} e^{-a/s}$
32.	$\dfrac{1}{t} \sin(at)$	$\tan^{-1}\left(\dfrac{a}{s}\right)$
33.	$\dfrac{2}{t}[1 - \cos(at)]$	$\ln\left(\dfrac{s^2 + a^2}{s^2}\right)$
34.	$\dfrac{2}{t}[1 - \cosh(at)]$	$\ln\left(\dfrac{s^2 - a^2}{s^2}\right)$
35.	$\dfrac{1}{\sqrt{\pi t}} - ae^{a^2 t}\operatorname{erfc}\left(\dfrac{a}{\sqrt{t}}\right)$	$\dfrac{1}{\sqrt{s} + a}$
36.	$\dfrac{1}{\sqrt{\pi t}} + ae^{a^2 t}\operatorname{erf}\left(\dfrac{a}{\sqrt{t}}\right)$	$\dfrac{\sqrt{s}}{s - a^2}$
37.	$e^{a^2 t}\operatorname{erf}(a\sqrt{t})$	$\dfrac{a}{\sqrt{s}(s - a^2)}$
38.	$e^{a^2 t}\operatorname{erfc}(a\sqrt{t})$	$\dfrac{1}{\sqrt{s}(\sqrt{s} + a)}$
39.	$\operatorname{erfc}\left(\dfrac{a}{2\sqrt{t}}\right)$	$\dfrac{1}{s} e^{-a\sqrt{s}}$
40.	$\dfrac{1}{\sqrt{\pi t}} e^{-a^2/4t}$	$\dfrac{1}{\sqrt{s}} e^{-a\sqrt{s}}$
41.	$\dfrac{1}{\sqrt{\pi(t + a)}}$	$\dfrac{1}{\sqrt{s}} e^{as}\operatorname{erfc}(\sqrt{as})$
42.	$\dfrac{1}{\pi t} \sin(2a\sqrt{t})$	$\operatorname{erf}\left(\dfrac{a}{\sqrt{s}}\right)$
43.	$f\left(\dfrac{t}{a}\right)$	$aF(as)$
44.	$e^{bt/a} f\left(\dfrac{t}{a}\right)$	$aF(as - b)$
45.	$\delta_\epsilon(t)$	$\dfrac{e^{-\epsilon s}(1 - e^{-\epsilon s})}{\epsilon s}$
46.	$\delta(t - a)$	e^{-as}
47.	$L_n(t)$	$\dfrac{1}{s}\left(\dfrac{s - 1}{s}\right)^n$
	(Laguerre polynomial)	

TABLE 3.1 *(continued)*

	$f(t)$	$F(s) = \mathcal{L}[f(t)](s)$
48.	$\dfrac{n!}{(2n)!\sqrt{\pi t}} H_{2n}(t)$ (Hermite polynomial)	$\dfrac{(1-s)^n}{s^{n+1/2}}$
49.	$\dfrac{-n!}{\sqrt{\pi}(2n+1)!} H_{2n+1}(t)$ (Hermite polynomial)	$\dfrac{(1-s)^n}{s^{n+3/2}}$
50.	triangular wave	$\dfrac{1}{as^2}\left[\dfrac{1-e^{-as}}{1+e^{-as}}\right]\left(=\dfrac{1}{as^2}\tanh\left(\dfrac{as}{2}\right)\right)$

| 51. | square wave | $\dfrac{1}{s}\tanh\left(\dfrac{as}{2}\right)$ |

| 52. | sawtooth wave | $\dfrac{1}{as^2} - \dfrac{e^{-as}}{s(1-e^{-as})}$ |

Operational Formulas

$f(t)$	$F(s)$
$af(t) + bg(t)$	$aF(s) + bG(s)$
$f'(t)$	$sF(s) - f(0+)$
$f^{(n)}(t)$	$s^n F(s) - s^{n-1} f(0) - \cdots - f^{(n-1)}(0)$
$\displaystyle\int_0^t f(\tau)\, d\tau$	$\dfrac{1}{s} F(s)$
$t f(t)$	$-F'(s)$
$t^n f(t)$	$(-1)^n F^{(n)}(s)$
$\dfrac{1}{t} f(t)$	$\displaystyle\int_s^\infty F(\sigma)\, d\sigma$
$e^{at} f(t)$	$F(s-a)$
$f(t-a) H(t-a)$	$e^{-as} F(s)$
$f(t+\tau) = f(t)$ (periodic)	$\dfrac{1}{1-e^{-\tau s}} \displaystyle\int_0^\tau e^{-st} f(t)\, dt$

THEOREM 3.1 *Linearity of the Laplace Transform*

Suppose $\mathcal{L}[f](s)$ and $\mathcal{L}[g](s)$ are defined for $s > a$, and α and β are real numbers. Then

$$\mathcal{L}[\alpha f + \beta g](s) = \alpha F(s) + \beta G(s)$$

for $s > a$.

Proof By assumption, $\int_0^\infty e^{-st} f(t) \, dt$ and $\int_0^\infty e^{-st} g(t) \, dt$ converge for $s > a$. Then

$$\mathcal{L}[\alpha f + \beta g](s) = \int_0^\infty e^{-st}(\alpha f(t) + \beta g(t)) \, dt$$

$$= \alpha \int_0^\infty e^{-st} f(t) \, dt + \beta \int_0^\infty e^{-st} g(t) \, dt = \alpha F(s) + \beta G(s)$$

for $s > a$. ∎

This conclusion extends to any finite sum:

$$\mathcal{L}[\alpha_1 f_1 + \cdots + \alpha_n f_n](s) = \alpha_1 F_1(s) + \cdots + \alpha_n F_n(s),$$

for all s such that each $F_j(s)$ is defined.

Not every function has a Laplace transform, because $\int_0^\infty e^{-st} f(t) \, dt$ may not converge for any real values of s. We will consider conditions that can be placed on f to ensure that f has a Laplace transform.

An obvious necessary condition is that $\int_0^k e^{-st} f(t) \, dt$ must be defined for every $k > 0$, because $\mathcal{L}[f](s) = \int_0^\infty e^{-st} f(t) \, dt$. For this to occur, it is enough that f be piecewise continuous on $[0, k]$ for every positive number k. We will define this concept in general terms because it occurs in other contexts as well.

DEFINITION 3.2 *Piecewise Continuity*

---

f is piecewise continuous on $[a, b]$ if there are points

$$a < t_1 < t_2 < \cdots < t_n < b$$

such that f is continuous on each open interval (a, t_1), (t_{j-1}, t_j), and (t_n, b), and all of the following one-sided limits are finite:

$$\lim_{t \to a+} f(t), \; \lim_{t \to t_j-} f(t), \; \lim_{t \to t_j+} f(t), \; \text{and} \; \lim_{t \to b-} f(t).$$

This means that f is continuous on $[a, b]$ except perhaps at finitely many points, at each of which f has finite one-sided limits from within the interval. The only discontinuities a piecewise continuous function f can experience on $[a, b]$ are finitely many jump discontinuities (gaps of finite width in the graph). Figure 3.1 shows typical jump discontinuities in a graph.

For example, let

$$f(t) = \begin{cases} t^2 & \text{for } 0 \le t \le 2 \\ 2 & \text{at } t = 2 \\ 1 & \text{for } 2 < t \le 3 \\ -1 & \text{for } 3 < t \le 4 \end{cases}.$$

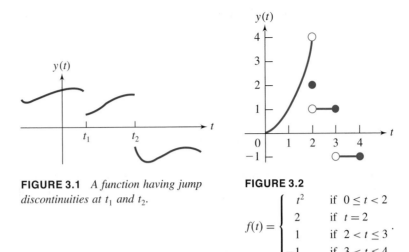

FIGURE 3.1 *A function having jump discontinuities at t_1 and t_2.*

FIGURE 3.2

$$f(t) = \begin{cases} t^2 & \text{if } 0 \le t < 2 \\ 2 & \text{if } t = 2 \\ 1 & \text{if } 2 < t \le 3 \\ -1 & \text{if } 3 < t \le 4 \end{cases}.$$

Then f is continuous $[0, 4]$ except at 2 and 3, where f has jump discontinuities. A graph of this function is shown in Figure 3.2.

If f is piecewise continuous on $[0, k]$, then so is $e^{-st}f(t)$, and $\int_0^k e^{-st}f(t)\,dt$ exists.

Existence of $\int_0^k e^{-st}f(t)\,dt$ for every positive k does not ensure existence of $\lim_{k\to\infty} \int_0^k e^{-st}f(t)\,dt$. For example, $f(t) = e^{t^2}$ is continuous on every interval $[0, k]$, but $\int_0^\infty e^{-st}e^{t^2}\,dt$ diverges for every real value of s. Thus, for convergence of $\int_0^\infty e^{-st}f(t)\,dt$, we need another condition on f. The form of this integral suggests one condition that is sufficient. If, for some numbers M and b, we have $|f(t)| \le Me^{bt}$, then

$$e^{-st}|f(t)| \le Me^{(b-s)t} \quad \text{for } s \ge b.$$

But

$$\int_0^\infty Me^{(b-s)t}\,dt$$

converges (to $M/(s-b)$) if $b - s < 0$, or $s > b$. Then, by comparison, $\int_0^\infty e^{-st}|f(t)|\,dt$ also converges if $s > b$, hence $\int_0^\infty e^{-st}f(t)\,dt$ converges if $s > b$.

This line of reasoning suggests a set of conditions which are sufficient for a function to have a Laplace transform.

THEOREM 3.2 *Existence of $\mathfrak{L}[f]$*

Suppose f is piecewise continuous on $[0, k]$ for every positive k. Suppose also that there are numbers M and b, such that $|f(t)| \le Me^{bt}$ for $t \ge 0$. Then $\int_0^\infty e^{-st}f(t)\,dt$ converges for $s > b$, hence $\mathfrak{L}[f](s)$ is defined for $s > b$. ∎

Many functions satisfy these conditions, including polynomials, $\sin(at)$, $\cos(at)$, e^{at}, and others.

The conditions of the theorem are sufficient, but not necessary for a function to have a Laplace transform. Consider, for example, $f(t) = t^{-1/2}$ for $t > 0$. This function is not piecewise continuous on any $[0, k]$ because $\lim_{t\to 0+} t^{-1/2} = \infty$. Nevertheless, $\int_0^k e^{-st} t^{-1/2} \, dt$ exists for every positive k and $s > 0$. Further,

$$\mathfrak{L}[f](s) = \int_0^\infty e^{-st} t^{-1/2} \, dt = 2 \int_0^\infty e^{-sx^2} \, dx \qquad (\text{let } x = t^{1/2})$$

$$= \frac{2}{\sqrt{s}} \int_0^\infty e^{-z^2} \, dz \qquad (\text{let } z = x\sqrt{s})$$

$$= \sqrt{\frac{\pi}{s}},$$

in which we have used the fact (found in some standard integral tables) that $\int_0^\infty e^{-z^2} \, dz = \sqrt{\pi}/2$.

Now revisit the flow chart at the start of this chapter. Taking the Laplace transform of a function is the first step in solving certain kinds of problems. The bottom of the flow chart suggests that at some point we must be able to go back the other way. After we find some function $G(s)$, we will need to produce a function g whose Laplace transform is G. This is the process of taking an inverse Laplace transform.

DEFINITION 3.3

Given a function G, a function g such that $\mathfrak{L}[g] = G$ is called an inverse Laplace transform of G.

In this event, we write

$$g = \mathfrak{L}^{-1}[G].$$

For example,

$$\mathfrak{L}^{-1}\left[\frac{1}{s-a}\right](t) = e^{at}$$

and

$$\mathfrak{L}^{-1}\left[\frac{1}{s^2+1}\right](t) = \sin(t).$$

This inverse process is ambiguous because, given G, there will be be many functions whose Laplace transform is G. For example, we know that the Laplace transform of e^{-t} is $1/(s+1)$ for $s > -1$. However, if we change $f(t)$ at just one point, letting

$$h(t) = \begin{cases} e^{-t} & \text{for } t \neq 3 \\ 0 & \text{for } t = 3, \end{cases}$$

then $\int_0^\infty e^{-st} f(t) \, dt = \int_0^\infty e^{-st} h(t) \, dt$, and h has the same Laplace transform as f. In such a case, which one do we call the inverse Laplace transform of $1/(s+1)$?

One answer is provided by Lerch's Theorem, which states that two *continuous* functions having the same Laplace transform must be equal.

THEOREM 3.3   *Lerch*

Let f and g be continuous on $[0, \infty)$ and suppose that $\mathfrak{L}[f] = \mathfrak{L}[g]$. Then $f = g$. ∎

In view of this, we will partially resolve the ambiguity in taking the inverse Laplace transform by agreeing that, given $F(s)$, we seek a continuous f whose Laplace transform is F. If there is no continuous inverse transform function, then we simply have to make some agreement as to which of several possible candidates we will call $\mathcal{L}^{-1}[F]$. In applications, context will often make this choice obvious.

Because of the linearity of the Laplace transform, its inverse is also linear.

THEOREM 3.4

If $\mathcal{L}^{-1}[F] = f$ and $\mathcal{L}^{-1}[G] = g$, and α and β are real numbers, then

$$\mathcal{L}^{-1}[\alpha F + \beta G] = \alpha f + \beta g. \quad \blacksquare$$

If Table 3.1 is used to find $\mathcal{L}[f]$, look up f in the left column and read $\mathcal{L}[f]$ from the right column. For $\mathcal{L}^{-1}[F]$, look up F in the right column and match it with f in the left.

SECTION 3.1   PROBLEMS

In each of Problems 1 through 10, use the linearity of the Laplace transform, and Table 3.1, to find the Laplace transform of the function.

1. $2\sinh(t) - 4$

2. $\cos(t) - \sin(t)$

3. $4t\sin(2t)$

4. $t^2 - 3t + 5$

5. $t - \cos(5t)$

6. $2t^2 e^{-3t} - 4t + 1$

7. $(t + 4)^2$

8. $3e^{-t} + \sin(6t)$

9. $t^3 - 3t + \cos(4t)$

10. $-3\cos(2t) + 5\sin(4t)$

In each of Problems 11 through 18, use the linearity of the inverse Laplace transform and Table 3.1 to find the (continuous) inverse Laplace transform of the function.

11. $\dfrac{-2}{s+16}$

12. $\dfrac{4s}{s^2 - 14}$

13. $\dfrac{2s - 5}{s^2 + 16}$

14. $\dfrac{3s + 17}{s^2 - 7}$

15. $\dfrac{3}{s - 7} + \dfrac{1}{s^2}$

16. $\dfrac{5}{(s+7)^2}$

17. $\dfrac{1}{s-4} - \dfrac{6}{(s-4)^2}$

18. $\dfrac{2}{s^4}\left[\dfrac{1}{s} - \dfrac{3}{s^2} + \dfrac{4}{s^6}\right]$

Suppose that $f(t)$ is defined for all $t \geq 0$. Then f is *periodic* with period T if $f(t + T) = f(t)$ for all $t \geq 0$. For example, $\sin(t)$ has period 2π. In Problems 19–22, assume that f has period T.

19. Show that

$$\mathcal{L}[f](s) = \sum_{n=0}^{\infty} \int_{nT}^{(n+1)T} e^{-st} f(t)\, dt.$$

20. Show that

$$\int_{nT}^{(n+1)T} e^{-st} f(t)\, dt = e^{-nsT} \int_0^T e^{-st} f(t)\, dt.$$

21. From Problems 19 and 20, show that

$$\mathcal{L}[f](s) = \left[\sum_{n=0}^{\infty} e^{-nsT}\right] \int_0^T e^{-st} f(t)\, dt.$$

22. Use the geometric series $\sum_{n=0}^{\infty} r^n = 1/(1 - r)$ for $|r| < 1$, together with the result of Problem 21, to show that

$$\mathcal{L}[f](s) = \dfrac{1}{1 - e^{-sT}} \int_0^T e^{-st} f(t)\, dt.$$

In each of Problems 23 through 30, a periodic function is given, sometimes by a graph. Find $\mathcal{L}[f]$, using the result of Problem 22.

23. f has period 6 and. $f(t) = \begin{cases} 5 & \text{for } 0 < t \le 3 \\ 0 & \text{for } 3 < t \le 6 \end{cases}$

24. $f(t) = |E\sin(\omega t)|$, with E and ω positive constants. (Here f has period π/ω).

25. f has the graph of Figure 3.3.

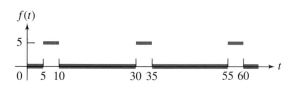

FIGURE 3.3

26. f has the graph of Figure 3.4.

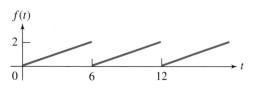

FIGURE 3.4

27. f has the graph of Figure 3.5.

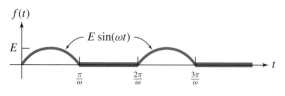

FIGURE 3.5

28. f has the graph of Figure 3.6.

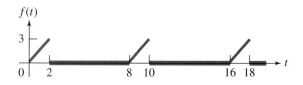

FIGURE 3.6

29. f has the graph of Figure 3.7.

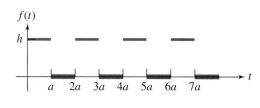

FIGURE 3.7

30. f has the graph of Figure 3.8.

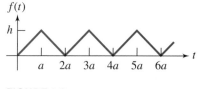

FIGURE 3.8

3.2   Solution of Initial Value Problems Using the Laplace Transform

The Laplace transform is a powerful tool for solving some kinds of initial value problems. The technique depends on the following fact about the Laplace transform of a derivative.

THEOREM 3.5   *Laplace Transform of a Derivative*

Let f be continuous on $[0, \infty)$ and suppose f' is piecewise continuous on $[0, k]$ for every positive k. Suppose also that $\lim_{k \to \infty} e^{-sk} f(k) = 0$ if $s > 0$. Then

$$\mathcal{L}[f'](s) = sF(s) - f(0). \tag{3.1}$$

That is, the Laplace transform of the derivative of f is s times the Laplace transform of f at s, minus f at zero.

Proof Begin with an integration by parts, with $u = e^{-st}$ and $dv = f'(t)\,dt$. For $k > 0$,

$$\int_0^k e^{-st} f'(t)\,dt = [e^{-st} f(t)]_0^k - \int_0^k -se^{-st} f(t)\,dt$$

$$= e^{-sk} f(k) - f(0) + s \int_0^k e^{-st} f(t)\,dt.$$

Take the limit as $k \to \infty$ and use the assumption that $e^{-sk} f(k) \to 0$ to obtain

$$\mathcal{L}[f'](s) = \lim_{k \to \infty} \left[e^{-sk} f(k) - f(0) + s \int_0^k e^{-st} f(t)\,dt \right]$$

$$= -f(0) + s \int_0^\infty e^{-st} f(t)\,dt = -f(0) + sF(s). \quad \blacksquare$$

If f has a jump discontinuity at 0 (as occurs, for example, if f is an electromotive force that is switched on at time zero), then this conclusion can be amended to read

$$\mathcal{L}[f'](s) = sF(s) - f(0+),$$

where

$$f(0+) = \lim_{t \to 0+} f(t)$$

is the right limit of $f(t)$ at 0.

For problems involving differential equations of order 2 or higher, we need a higher derivative version of the theorem. Let $f^{(j)}$ denote the jth derivative of f. As a notational convenience, we let $f^{(0)} = f$.

THEOREM 3.6 *Laplace Transform of a Higher Derivative*

Suppose $f, f', \cdots, f^{n-1}$ are continuous on $[0, \infty)$, and $f^{(n)}$ is piecewise continuous on $[0, k]$ for every positive k. Suppose also that $\lim_{k \to \infty} e^{-sk} f^{(j)}(k) = 0$ for $s > 0$ and for $j = 1, 2, \ldots, n-1$. Then

$$\mathcal{L}[f^{(n)}](s) = s^n F(s) - s^{n-1} f(0) - s^{n-2} f'(0) - \cdots - sf^{(n-2)}(0) - f^{(n-1)}(0). \quad \blacksquare \qquad (3.2)$$

The second derivative case ($n = 2$) occurs sufficiently often that we will record it separately. Under the conditions of the theorem,

$$\mathcal{L}[f''](s) = s^2 F(s) - sf(0) - f'(0). \qquad (3.3)$$

We are now ready to use the Laplace transform to solve certain initial value problems.

EXAMPLE 3.3

Solve $y' - 4y = 1$; $y(0) = 1$.

We know how to solve this problem, but we will use the Laplace transform to illustrate the technique. Write $\mathcal{L}[y](s) = Y(s)$. Take the Laplace transform of the differential equation, using the linearity of $\mathcal{L}$ and equation (3.1), with $y(t)$ in place of $f(t)$:

$$\mathcal{L}[y' - 4y](s) = \mathcal{L}[y'](s) - 4\mathcal{L}[y](s)$$

$$= (sY(s) - y(0)) - 4Y(s) = \mathcal{L}[1](s) = \frac{1}{s}.$$

Here we used the fact (from Table 3.1) that $\mathfrak{L}[1](s) = 1/s$ for $s > 0$. Since $y(0) = 1$, we now have

$$(s-4)Y(s) = y(0) + \frac{1}{s} = 1 + \frac{1}{s}.$$

At this point we have an algebra problem to solve for $Y(s)$, obtaining

$$Y(s) = \frac{1}{(s-4)} + \frac{1}{s(s-4)}$$

(note the flow chart at the beginning of this chapter). The solution of the initial value problem is

$$y = \mathfrak{L}^{-1}[Y] = \mathfrak{L}^{-1}\left[\frac{1}{s-4}\right] + \mathfrak{L}^{-1}\left[\frac{1}{s(s-4)}\right].$$

From entry 5 of Table 3.1, with $a = 4$,

$$\mathfrak{L}^{-1}\left[\frac{1}{s-4}\right] = e^{4t}.$$

And from entry 8, with $a = 0$ and $b = 4$,

$$\mathfrak{L}^{-1}\left[\frac{1}{s(s-4)}\right] = \frac{1}{-4}(e^{0t} - e^{4t}) = \frac{1}{4}(e^{4t} - 1).$$

The solution of the initial value problem is

$$y(t) = e^{4t} + \frac{1}{4}(e^{4t} - 1)$$

$$= \frac{5}{4}e^{4t} - \frac{1}{4}. \quad \blacksquare$$

One feature of this Laplace transform technique is that the initial value given in the problem is naturally incorporated into the solution process through equation (3.1). We need not find the general solution first, then solve for the constant to satisfy the initial condition.

EXAMPLE 3.4

Solve

$$y'' + 4y' + 3y = e^t; \qquad y(0) = 0, \, y'(0) = 2.$$

Apply $\mathfrak{L}$ to the differential equation to get $\mathfrak{L}[y''] + 4\mathfrak{L}[y'] + 3\mathfrak{L}[y] = \mathfrak{L}[e^t]$.
     Now

$$\mathfrak{L}[y''] = s^2Y - sy(0) - y'(0) = s^2Y - 2$$

and

$$\mathfrak{L}[y'] = sY - y(0) = sY.$$

Therefore,

$$s^2Y - 2 + 4sY + 3Y = \frac{1}{s-1}.$$

Solve for Y to obtain

$$Y(s) = \frac{2s-1}{(s-1)(s^2+4s+3)}.$$

The solution is the inverse Laplace transform of this function. Some software will produce this inverse. If we want to use Table 3.1, we must use a partial fractions decomposition to write $Y(s)$ as a sum of simpler functions. Write

$$Y(s) = \frac{2s-1}{(s-1)(s^2+4s+3)}$$

$$= \frac{2s-1}{(s-1)(s+1)(s+3)} = \frac{A}{s-1} + \frac{B}{s+1} + \frac{C}{s+3}.$$

This equation can hold only if, for all s,

$$A(s+1)(s+3) + B(s-1)(s+3) + C(s-1)(s+1) = 2s-1.$$

Now choose values of s to simplify the task of determining A, B, and C. Let $s = 1$ to get $8A = 1$, so $A = \frac{1}{8}$. Let $s = -1$ to get $-4B = -3$, so $B = \frac{3}{4}$. Choose $s = -3$ to get $8C = -7$, so $C = -\frac{7}{8}$. Then

$$Y(s) = \frac{1}{8}\frac{1}{s-1} + \frac{3}{4}\frac{1}{s+1} - \frac{7}{8}\frac{1}{s+3}.$$

Now read from Table 3.1 that

$$y(t) = \frac{1}{8}e^t + \frac{3}{4}e^{-t} - \frac{7}{8}e^{-3t}. \quad \blacksquare$$

Again, the Laplace transform has converted an initial value problem to an algebra problem, incorporating the initial conditions into the algebraic manipulations. Once we obtain $Y(s)$, the problem becomes one of inverting the transformed function to obtain $y(t)$.

Equation (3.1) has an interesting consequence that will be useful later. Under the conditions of the theorem, we know that

$$\mathcal{L}[f'] = s\mathcal{L}[f] - f(0).$$

Suppose $f(t)$ is defined by an integral, say

$$f(t) = \int_0^t g(\tau)\,d\tau.$$

Now $f(0) = 0$ and, assuming continuity of g, $f'(t) = g(t)$. Then

$$\mathcal{L}[f'] = \mathcal{L}[g] = s\mathcal{L}\left[\int_0^t g(\tau)\,d\tau\right].$$

This means that

$$\mathcal{L}\left[\int_0^t g(\tau)\,d\tau\right] = \frac{1}{s}\mathcal{L}[g], \tag{3.4}$$

enabling us to take the Laplace transform of a function defined by an integral. We will use this equation later in dealing with circuits having discontinuous electromotive forces.

Thus far we have illustrated a Laplace transform technique for solving initial value problems with constant coefficients. However, we could have solved the problems in these examples by other means. In the next three sections we will develop the machinery needed to apply the Laplace transform to problems that defy previous methods.

In each of Problems 1 through 10, use the Laplace transform to solve the initial value problem.

1. $y' + 4y = 1;\ y(0) = -3$

2. $y' - 9y = t;\ y(0) = 5$

3. $y' + 4y = \cos(t);\ y(0) = 0$

4. $y' + 2y = e^{-t};\ y(0) = 1$

5. $y' - 2y = 1 - t;\ y(0) = 4$

6. $y'' + y = 1;\ y(0) = 6,\ y'(0) = 0$

7. $y'' - 4y' + 4y = \cos(t);\ y(0) = 1,\ y'(0) = -1$

8. $y'' + 9y = t^2;\ y(0) = y'(0) = 0$

9. $y'' + 16y = 1 + t;\ y(0) = -2,\ y'(0) = 1$

10. $y'' - 5y' + 6y = e^{-t};\ y(0) = 0,\ y'(0) = 2$

11. Suppose f satisfies the hypotheses of Theorem 3.5, except for a jump discontinuity at 0. Show that $\mathcal{L}[f'](s) = sF(s) - f(0+)$, where $f(0+) = \lim_{t\to 0+} f(t)$.

12. Suppose f satisfies the hypotheses of Theorem 3.5, except for a jump discontinuity at a positive number c. Prove that

$$\mathcal{L}[f'](s) = sF(s) - f(0) - e^{-cs}[f(c+) - f(c-)],$$

where $f(c-) = \lim_{t\to c-} f(t)$.

13. Suppose g is piecewise continuous on $[0, k]$ for every $k > 0$, and that there are numbers M, b, and a such that $|g(t)| \le M e^{bt}$ for $t \ge a$. Let $\mathcal{L}[G] = g$. Show that

$$\mathcal{L}\left[\int_0^t g(w)\,dw\right](s) = \frac{1}{s}G(s) - \frac{1}{s}\int_0^a g(w)\,dw.$$

3.3   Shifting Theorems and the Heaviside Function

One point to developing the Laplace transform is to broaden the class of problems we are able to solve. Methods of Chapters 1 and 2 are primarily aimed at problems involving continuous functions. But many mathematical models deal with discontinuous processes (for example, switches thrown on and off in a circuit). For these, the Laplace transform is often effective, but we must learn more about representing discontinuous functions and applying both the transform and its inverse to them.

3.3.1   The First Shifting Theorem

We will show that the Laplace transform of $e^{at} f(t)$ is nothing more than the Laplace transform of $f(t)$, shifted a units to the right. This is achieved by replacing s by $s - a$ in $F(s)$ to obtain $F(s - a)$.

THEOREM 3.7   *First Shifting Theorem, or Shifting in the s Variable*

Let $\mathcal{L}[f](s) = F(s)$ for $s > b \ge 0$. Let a be any number. Then

$$\mathcal{L}[e^{at} f(t)](s) = F(s - a) \qquad \text{for } s > a + b$$

Proof   Compute

$$\mathcal{L}[e^{at} f(t)](s) = \int_0^\infty e^{at} e^{-st} f(s)\,ds$$

$$= \int_0^\infty e^{-(s-a)t} f(t)\,dt = F(s - a)$$

for $s - a > b$, or $s > a + b$. ∎

EXAMPLE 3.5

We know from Table 3.1 that $\mathcal{L}[\cos(bt)] = s/(s^2 + b^2)$. For the Laplace transform of $e^{at}\cos(bt)$, replace s with $s - a$ to get

$$\mathcal{L}[e^{at}\cos(bt)](s) = \frac{s - a}{(s - a)^2 + b^2}. \quad \blacksquare$$

EXAMPLE 3.6

Since $\mathcal{L}[t^3] = 6/s^4$, then

$$\mathcal{L}[t^3 e^{7t}](s) = \frac{6}{(s - 7)^4}. \quad \blacksquare$$

The first shifting theorem suggests a corresponding formula for the inverse Laplace transform: If $\mathcal{L}[f] = F$, then

$$\mathcal{L}^{-1}[F(s - a)] = e^{at} f(t).$$

Sometimes it is convenient to write this result as

$$\mathcal{L}^{-1}[F(s - a)] = e^{at}\mathcal{L}^{-1}[F(s)]. \tag{3.5}$$

EXAMPLE 3.7

Suppose we want to compute

$$\mathcal{L}^{-1}\left[\frac{4}{s^2 + 4s + 20}\right].$$

We will manipulate the quotient into a form to which we can apply the shifting theorem. Complete the square in the denominator to write

$$\frac{4}{s^2 + 4s + 20} = \frac{4}{(s + 2)^2 + 16}.$$

Think of the quotient on the right as a function of $s + 2$:

$$F(s + 2) = \frac{4}{(s + 2)^2 + 16}.$$

This means we should choose

$$F(s) = \frac{4}{s^2 + 16}.$$

Now the shifting theorem tells us that

$$\mathcal{L}[e^{-2t}\sin(4t)] = F(s - (-2)) = F(s + 2) = \frac{4}{(s + 2)^2 + 16}$$

and therefore

$$\mathcal{L}^{-1}\left[\frac{4}{(s+2)^2+16}\right] = e^{-2t}\sin(4t). \quad \blacksquare$$

EXAMPLE 3.8

Compute

$$\mathcal{L}^{-1}\left[\frac{3s-1}{s^2-6s+2}\right].$$

Again, begin with some manipulation into the form of a function of $s-a$ for some a:

$$\frac{3s-1}{s^2-6s+2} = \frac{3s-1}{(s-3)^2-7}$$

$$= \frac{3(s-3)}{(s-3)^2-7} + \frac{8}{(s-3)^2-7} = G(s-3)+K(s-3)$$

if we choose

$$G(s) = \frac{3s}{s^2-7} \quad \text{and} \quad K(s) = \frac{8}{s^2-7}.$$

Now apply equation (3.5) (in the second line) to write

$$\mathcal{L}^{-1}\left[\frac{3s-1}{s^2-6s+2}\right] = \mathcal{L}^{-1}[G(s-3)] + \mathcal{L}^{-1}[K(s-3)]$$

$$= e^{3t}\mathcal{L}^{-1}[G(s)] + e^{3t}\mathcal{L}^{-1}[K(s)]$$

$$= e^{3t}\mathcal{L}^{-1}\left[\frac{3s}{s^2-7}\right] + e^{3t}\mathcal{L}^{-1}\left[\frac{8}{s^2-7}\right]$$

$$= 3e^{3t}\mathcal{L}^{-1}\left[\frac{s}{s^2-7}\right] + 8e^{3t}\mathcal{L}^{-1}\left[\frac{1}{s^2-7}\right]$$

$$= 3e^{3t}\cosh(\sqrt{7}t) + \frac{8}{\sqrt{7}}e^{3t}\sinh(\sqrt{7}t). \quad \blacksquare$$

3.3.2   The Heaviside Function and Pulses

We will now lay the foundations for solving certain initial value problems having discontinuous forcing functions. To do this, we will use the Heaviside function.

Recall that f has a jump discontinuity at a if $\lim_{t\to a-} f(t)$ and $\lim_{t\to a-} f(t)$ both exist and are finite, but unequal. Figure 3.9 shows a typical jump discontinuity. The magnitude of the jump discontinuity is the "width of the gap" in the graph at a. This width is

$$\left|\lim_{t\to a-} f(t) - \lim_{t\to a-} f(t)\right|.$$

Functions with jump discontinuities can be treated very efficiently using the unit step function, or Heaviside function.

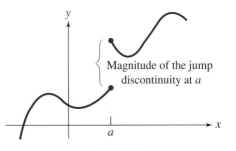

FIGURE 3.9

DEFINITION 3.4 *Heaviside Function*

The Heaviside function H is defined by

$$H(t) = \begin{cases} 0 & \text{if } t < 0 \\ 1 & \text{if } t \geq 0. \end{cases}$$

Oliver Heaviside (1850–1925) was an English electrical engineer who did much to introduce Laplace transform methods into engineering practice. A graph of H is shown in Figure 3.10. It has a jump discontinuity of magnitude 1 at 0.

The Heaviside function may be thought of as a flat switching function, "on" when $t \geq 0$, where $H(t) = 1$, and "off" when $t < 0$, where $H(t) = 0$. We will use it to achieve a variety of effects, including switching functions on and off at different times, shifting functions along the axis, and combining functions with pulses.

To begin this program, if a is any number, then $H(t - a)$ is the Heaviside function shifted a units to the right, as shown in Figure 3.11, since

$$H(t - a) = \begin{cases} 0 & \text{if } t < a \\ 1 & \text{if } t \geq a. \end{cases}$$

$H(t - a)$ models a flat signal of magnitude 1, turned off until time $t = a$ and then switched on.

We can use $H(t - a)$ to achieve the effect of turning a given function g off until time $t = a$, at which time it is switched on. In particular,

$$H(t - a)g(t) = \begin{cases} 0 & \text{if } t < a \\ g(t) & \text{if } t \geq a. \end{cases}$$

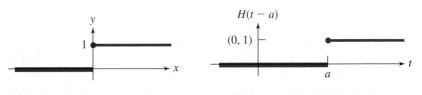

FIGURE 3.10 *The Heaviside function $H(t)$.*

FIGURE 3.11 *A shifted Heaviside function.*

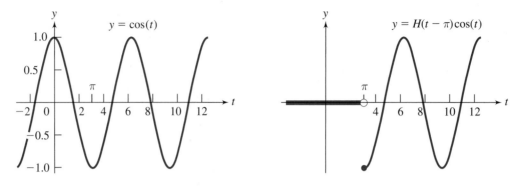

FIGURE 3.12   *Comparison of* $y = \cos(t)$ *and* $y = H(t - \pi)\cos(t)$.

is zero until time $t = a$, at which time it switches on $g(t)$. To see this in a specific case, let $g(t) = \cos(t)$ for all t. Then

$$H(t - \pi)g(t) = H(t - \pi)\cos(t) = \begin{cases} 0 & \text{if } t < \pi \\ \cos(t) & \text{if } t \geq \pi. \end{cases}$$

Graphs of $\cos(t)$ and $H(t - \pi)\cos(t)$ are shown in Figure 3.12 for comparison.

We can also use the Heaviside function to describe a pulse.

DEFINITION 3.5   *Pulse*

A pulse is a function of the form

$$k[H(t - a) - H(t - b)],$$

in which $a < b$ and k is a nonzero real number

This pulse function is graphed in Figure 3.13. It has value 0 if $t < a$ (where $H(t - a) = H(t - b) = 0$), value 1 if $a \leq t < b$ (where $H(t - a) = 1$ and $H(t - b) = 0$), and value 0 if $t \geq b$ (where $H(t - a) = H(t - b) = 1$).

Multiplying a function g by this pulse has the effect of leaving $g(t)$ switched off until time a. The function is then turned on until time b, when it is switched off again. For example, let $g(t) = e^t$. Then

$$[H(t - 1) - H(t - 2)]e^t = \begin{cases} 0 & \text{if } t < 1 \\ e^t & \text{if } 1 \leq t < 2 \\ 0 & \text{if } t \geq 2. \end{cases}$$

Figure 3.14 shows a graph of this function.

Next consider shifted functions of the form $H(t - a)g(t - a)$. If $t < a$, the $g(t - a)H(t - a) = 0$ because $H(t - a) = 0$. If $t \geq a$, then $H(t - a) = 1$ and $H(t - a)g(t - a) = g(t - a)$, which is $g(t)$ shifted a units to the right. Thus the graph of $H(t - a)g(t - a)$ is zero along the horizontal axis until $t = a$, and for $t \geq a$ is the graph of $g(t)$ for $t \geq 0$, shifted a units to the right to begin at a instead of 0.

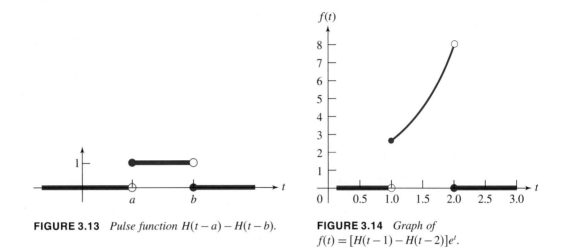

FIGURE 3.13 *Pulse function $H(t-a) - H(t-b)$.*

FIGURE 3.14 *Graph of*
$f(t) = [H(t-1) - H(t-2)]e^t$.

EXAMPLE 3.9

Consider $g(t) = t^2$ and $a = 2$. Figure 3.15 compares the graph of g with the graph of $H(t-2)$ $g(t-2)$. The graph of g is a familiar parabola. The graph of $H(t-2)g(t-2)$ is zero until time 2, then has the shape of the graph of t^2 for $t \geq 0$, but shifted 2 units to the right to start at $t = 2$. ■

It is important to understand the difference between $g(t)$, $H(t-a)g(t)$, and $H(t-a)g(t-a)$. Figure 3.16 shows graphs of these three functions for $g(t) = t^2$ and $a = 3$.

3.3.3 The Second Shifting Theorem

Sometimes $H(t-a)g(t-a)$ is referred to as a shifted function, although it is more than that because this graph is also zero for $t < a$. The second shifting theorem deals with the Laplace transform of such a function.

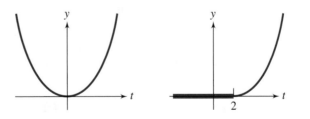

FIGURE 3.15 *Comparison of $y = t^2$ and*
$y = (t-2)^2 H(t-2)$.

FIGURE 3.16 *Comparison of $y = t^2$, $y = t^2 H(t-3)$, and $y = (t-3)^2 H(t-3)$.*

THEOREM 3.8   *Second Shifting Theorem, or Shifting In the t Variable*

Let $\mathcal{L}[f](s) = F(s)$ for $s > b$. Then

$$\mathcal{L}[H(t-a)f(t-a)](s) = e^{-as}F(s)$$

for $s > b$.

That is, we obtain the Laplace transform of $H(t-a)f(t-a)$ by multiplying the Laplace transform of $f(t)$ by e^{-as}.

Proof   Proceeding from the definition,

$$\mathcal{L}[H(t-a)f(t-a)](s) = \int_0^\infty e^{-st}H(t-a)f(t-a)\,dt$$

$$= \int_a^\infty e^{-st}f(t-a)\,dt$$

because $H(t-a) = 0$ for $t < a$, and $H(t-a) = 1$ for $t \geq a$. Now let $w = t-a$ in the last integral to obtain

$$\mathcal{L}[H(t-a)f(t-a)](s) = \int_0^\infty e^{-s(a+w)}f(w)\,dw$$

$$= e^{-as}\int_0^\infty e^{-sw}f(w)\,dw = e^{-as}F(s). \ \blacksquare$$

EXAMPLE 3.10

Suppose we want the Laplace transform of $H(t-a)$. Write this as $H(t-a)f(t-a)$, with $f(t) = 1$ for all t. Since $F(s) = 1/s$ (from Table 3.1 or by direct computation from the definition), then

$$\mathcal{L}[H(t-a)](s) = e^{-as}\mathcal{L}[1](s) = \frac{1}{s}e^{-as}. \ \blacksquare$$

EXAMPLE 3.11

Compute $\mathcal{L}[g]$, where $g(t) = 0$ for $0 \leq t < 2$ and $g(t) = t^2 + 1$ for $t \geq 2$.

Since $g(t)$ is zero until time $t = 2$, and is then $t^2 + 1$, we may write $g(t) = H(t-2)(t^2+1)$.

To apply the second shifting theorem, we must write $g(t)$ as a function, or perhaps sum of functions, of the form $f(t-2)H(t-2)$. This necessitates writing $t^2 + 1$ as a sum of functions of $t-2$. One way to do this is to expand $t^2 + 1$ in a Taylor series about 2. In this simple case we can achieve the same result by algebraic manipulation:

$$t^2 + 1 = (t-2+2)^2 + 1 = (t-2)^2 + 4(t-2) + 5.$$

Then

$$g(t) = (t^2+1)H(t-2)$$

$$= (t-2)^2H(t-2) + 4(t-2)H(t-2) + 5H(t-2).$$

Now we can apply the second shifting theorem:

$$\mathfrak{L}[g] = \mathfrak{L}[(t-2)^2 H(t-2)] + 4\mathfrak{L}[(t-2)H(t-2)] + 5\mathfrak{L}[H(t-2)]$$

$$= e^{-2s}\mathfrak{L}[t^2] + 4e^{-2s}\mathfrak{L}[t] + 5e^{-2s}\mathfrak{L}[1]$$

$$= e^{-2s}\left[\frac{2}{s^3} + \frac{4}{s^2} + \frac{5}{s}\right]. \quad \blacksquare$$

As usual, any formula for the Laplace transform of a class of functions can also be read as a formula for an inverse Laplace transform. The inverse version of the second shifting theorem is:

$$\mathfrak{L}^{-1}[e^{-as}F(s)](t) = H(t-a)f(t-a). \tag{3.6}$$

This enables us to compute the inverse Laplace transform of a known transformed function multipled by an exponential e^{-as}.

EXAMPLE 3.12

Compute

$$\mathfrak{L}^{-1}\left[\frac{se^{-3s}}{s^2+4}\right].$$

The presence of the exponential factor suggests the use of equation (3.6). Concentrate on finding

$$\mathfrak{L}^{-1}\left[\frac{s}{s^2+4}\right].$$

This inverse can be read directly from Table 3.1, and is $f(t) = \cos(2t)$. Therefore

$$\mathfrak{L}^{-1}\left[\frac{se^{-3s}}{s^2+4}\right](t) = H(t-3)\cos(2(t-3)). \quad \blacksquare$$

We are now prepared to solve certain initial value problems involving discontinuous forcing functions.

EXAMPLE 3.13

Solve the initial value problem

$$y'' + 4y = f(t); \qquad y(0) = y'(0) = 0,$$

in which

$$f(t) = \begin{cases} 0 & \text{for } t < 3 \\ t & \text{for } t \geq 3 \end{cases}$$

Because of the discontinuity in f, methods developed in Chapter 2 do not apply. First recognize that

$$f(t) = H(t-3)t.$$

Apply the Laplace transform to the differential equation to get

$$\mathcal{L}[y''] + \mathcal{L}[y] = s^2 Y(s) - sy(0) - y'(0) + 4Y(s)$$
$$= (s^2 + 4)Y(s) = \mathcal{L}[H(t-3)t],$$

in which we have inserted the initial conditions $y(0) = y'(0) = 0$.

In order to use the second shifting theorem to compute $\mathcal{L}[H(t-3)t]$, write

$$\mathcal{L}[H(t-3)t] = \mathcal{L}[H(t-3)(t-3+3)]$$
$$= \mathcal{L}[H(t-3)(t-3)] + 3\mathcal{L}[H(t-3)]$$
$$= e^{-3s}\mathcal{L}[t] + 3e^{-3s}\mathcal{L}[1] = \frac{1}{s^2}e^{-3s} + \frac{3}{s}e^{-3s}.$$

We now have

$$(s^2 + 4)Y = \frac{1}{s^2}e^{-3s} + \frac{3}{s}e^{-3s}.$$

The transform of the solution is

$$Y(s) = \frac{3s+1}{s^2(s^2+4)}e^{-3s}.$$

The solution is within reach. We must take the inverse Laplace transform of $Y(s)$. To do this, first use a partial fractions decomposition to write

$$\frac{3s+1}{s^2(s^2+4)}e^{-3s} = \frac{3}{4}\frac{1}{s}e^{-3s} - \frac{3}{4}\frac{s}{s^2+4}e^{-3s} + \frac{1}{4}\frac{1}{s^2}e^{-3s} - \frac{1}{4}\frac{1}{s^2+4}e^{-3s}.$$

Each term is an exponential times a function whose Laplace transform we know, and we can apply equation (3.6) to write

$$y(t) = \frac{3}{4}H(t-3) - \frac{3}{4}H(t-3)\cos(2(t-3))$$
$$+ \frac{1}{4}H(t-3)(t-3) - \frac{1}{4}H(t-3)\frac{1}{2}\sin(2(t-3)).$$

Because of the $H(t-3)$ factor in each term, this solution is zero until time $t = 3$, and we may write

$$y(t) = \begin{cases} 0 & \text{for } t < 3 \\ \frac{3}{4} - \frac{3}{4}\cos(2(t-3)) + \frac{1}{4}(t-3) - \frac{1}{8}\sin(2(t-3)) & \text{for } t \geq 3. \end{cases}$$

or, upon combining terms,

$$y(t) = \begin{cases} 0 & \text{for } t < 3 \\ \frac{1}{8}[2t - 6\cos(2(t-3)) - \sin(2(t-3))] & \text{for } t \geq 3. \end{cases}$$

A graph of this solution is shown in Figure 3.17. ■

In this example, it is interesting to observe that the solution is differentiable everywhere, even though the function f occurring in the differential equation had a jump discontinuity at 3. This behavior is typical of initial value problems having a discontinuous forcing function. If the differential equation has order n and φ is a solution, then φ and its first $n-1$ derivatives will be continuous, while the nth derivative will have a jump discontinuity wherever f does, and these jump discontinuities will agree in magnitude with the corresponding jump discontinuities of f.

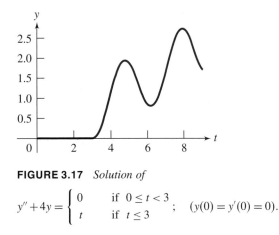

FIGURE 3.17 *Solution of*

$$y'' + 4y = \begin{cases} 0 & \text{if } 0 \le t < 3 \\ t & \text{if } t \le 3 \end{cases} ; \quad (y(0) = y'(0) = 0).$$

Often we need to write a function having several jump discontinuities in terms of Heaviside functions in order to use the shifting theorems. Here is an example.

EXAMPLE 3.14

Let

$$f(t) = \begin{cases} 0 & \text{if } t < 2 \\ t - 1 & \text{if } 2 \le t < 3 \\ -4 & \text{if } t \ge 3. \end{cases}$$

A graph of f is shown in Figure 3.18. There are jump discontinuities of magnitude 1 at $t = 2$ and magnitude 6 at $t = 3$.

Think of $f(t)$ as consisting of two nonzero parts, the part that is $t - 1$ on $[2, 3)$ and the part that is -4 on $[3, \infty)$. We want to turn on $t - 1$ at time 2 and turn it off at time 3, then turn on -4 at time 3 and leave it on.

The first effect is achieved by multiplying the pulse function $H(t - 2) - H(t - 3)$ by $t - 1$. The second is achieved by multiplying $H(t - 3)$ by 4. Therefore

$$f(t) = [H(t - 2) - H(t - 3)](t - 1) - 4H(t - 3).$$

As a check, this gives $f(t) = 0$ if $t < 2$ because all of the shifted Heaviside functions are zero for $t < 2$. For $2 \le t < 3$, $H(t - 2) = 1$ but $H(t - 3) = 0$ so $f(t) = t - 1$. And for $t \ge 3$, $H(t - 2) = H(t - 3) = 1$, so $f(t) = -4$. ∎

3.3.4   Analysis of Electrical Circuits

The Heaviside function is important in many kinds of problems, including the analysis of electrical circuits, where we anticipate turning switches on and off. Here are two examples.

EXAMPLE 3.15

Suppose the capacitor in the circuit of Figure 3.19 initially has zero charge and that there is no initial current. At time $t = 2$ seconds, the switch is thrown from position B to A, held there for 1 second, then switched back to B. We want the output voltage E_{out} on the capacitor.

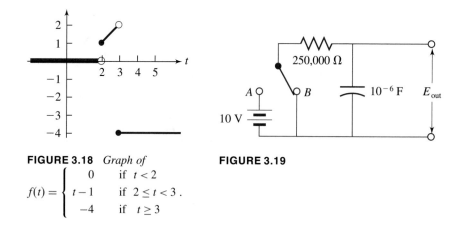

FIGURE 3.18 *Graph of*

$$f(t) = \begin{cases} 0 & \text{if } t < 2 \\ t-1 & \text{if } 2 \le t < 3 \\ -4 & \text{if } t \ge 3 \end{cases}.$$

FIGURE 3.19

From the circuit diagram, the forcing function is zero until $t = 2$, then has value 10 volts until $t = 3$, and then is zero again. Thus E is the pulse function

$$E(t) = 10[H(t-2) - H(t-3)].$$

By Kirchhoff's voltage law,

$$Ri(t) + \frac{1}{C}q(t) = E(t),$$

or

$$250{,}000q'(t) + 10^6 q(t) = E(t).$$

We want to solve for q subject to the initial condition $q(0) = 0$. Apply the Laplace transform to the differential equation, incorporating the initial condition, to write

$$250{,}000[sQ(t) - q(0)] + 10^6 Q(t) = 250{,}000sQ + 10^6 Q = \mathcal{L}[E(t)].$$

Now

$$\mathcal{L}[E(t)](s) = 10\mathcal{L}[H(t-2)](s) - 10\mathcal{L}[H(t-3)](s)$$

$$= \frac{10}{s}e^{-2s} - \frac{10}{s}e^{-3s}.$$

We now have the following equation for Q:

$$2.5(10^5)sQ(s) + 10^6 Q(s) = \frac{10}{s}e^{-2s} - \frac{10}{s}e^{-3s}$$

or

$$Q(s) = 4(10^{-5})\frac{1}{s(s+4)}e^{-2s} - 4(10)^{-5}\frac{1}{s(s+4)}e^{-3s}.$$

Use a partial fractions decomposition to write

$$Q(s) = 10^{-5}\left[\frac{1}{s}e^{-2s} - \frac{1}{s+4}e^{-2s}\right] - 10^{-5}\left[\frac{1}{s}e^{-3s} - \frac{1}{s+4}e^{-3s}\right].$$

By the second shifting theorem,

$$\mathcal{L}^{-1}\left[\frac{1}{s}e^{-2s}\right](t) = H(t-2)$$

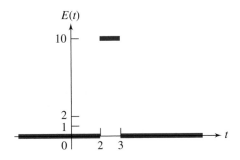

FIGURE 3.20 *Input voltage for the circuit of Figure 3.19.*

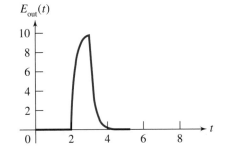

FIGURE 3.21 *Output voltage for the circuit of Figure 3.19.*

and

$$\mathcal{L}^{-1}\left[\frac{1}{s+4}e^{-2s}\right] = H(t-2)f(t-2),$$

where $f(t) = \mathcal{L}^{-1}[1/(s+4)] = e^{-4t}$. Thus

$$\mathcal{L}^{-1}\left[\frac{1}{s+4}e^{-2s}\right] = H(t-2)e^{-4(t-2)}.$$

The other two terms in $Q(s)$ are treated similarly, and we obtain

$$q(t) = 10^{-5}[H(t-2) - H(t-2)e^{-4(t-2)}] - 10^{-5}[H(t-3) - H(t-3)e^{-4(t-3)}]$$
$$= 10^{-5}H(t-2)[1 - e^{-4(t-2)}] - 10^{-5}H(t-3)[1 - e^{-4(t-3)}].$$

Finally, since the output voltage is $E_{\text{out}}(t) = 10^6 q(t)$,

$$E_{\text{out}}(t) = 10H(t-2)[1 - e^{-4(t-2)}] - 10H(t-3)[1 - e^{-4(t-3)}].$$

The input and output voltages are graphed in Figures 3.20 and 3.21. ■

EXAMPLE 3.16

The circuit of Figure 3.22 has the roles of resistor and capacitor interchanged from the circuit of the preceding example. We want to know the output voltage $i(t)R$ at any time.

The differential equation of the preceding example applies to this circuit, but now we are interested in the current. Since $i = q'$, then

$$(2.5)(10^5)i(t) + 10^6 q(t) = E(t); \qquad i(0) = q(0) = 0.$$

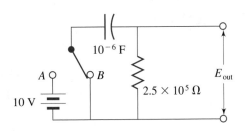

FIGURE 3.22

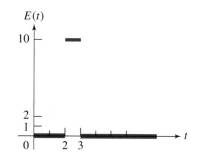

FIGURE 3.23 *Input voltage for the circuit of Figure 3.22.*

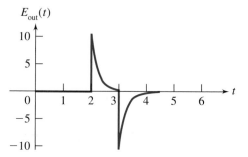

FIGURE 3.24 *Output voltage for the circuit of Figure 3.22.*

The strategy of eliminating q by differentiating and using $i = q'$ does not apply here, because $E(t)$ is not differentiable. To eliminate $q(t)$ in the present case, write

$$q(t) = \int_0^t i(\tau)\,d\tau + q(0) = \int_0^t i(\tau)\,d\tau.$$

We now have the following problem to solve for the current:

$$(2.5)(10^5)i(t) + 10^6 \int_0^t i(\tau)\,d\tau = E(t); \qquad i(0) = 0.$$

This is not a differential equation. Nevertheless, we have the means to solve it. Take the Laplace transform of the equation, using equation (3.4), to obtain

$$(2.5)(10^5)I(s) + 10^6 \frac{1}{s}I(s) = \mathfrak{L}[E](s)$$

$$= 10\frac{1}{s}e^{-2s} - 10\frac{1}{s}e^{-3s}.$$

Here $I = \mathfrak{L}[i]$. Solve for $I(s)$ to get

$$I(s) = 4(10^{-5})\frac{1}{s+4}e^{-2s} - 4(10^{-5})\frac{1}{s+4}e^{-3s}.$$

Take the inverse Laplace transform to obtain

$$i(t) = 4(10^{-5})H(t-2)e^{-4(t-2)} - 4(10^{-5})H(t-3)e^{-4(t-3)}.$$

The input and output voltages are graphed in Figures 3.23 and 3.24. ■

SECTION 3.3   PROBLEMS

In each of Problems 1 through 15, find the Laplace transform of the function.

1. $(t^3 - 3t + 2)e^{-2t}$

2. $e^{-3t}(t-2)$

3. $f(t) = \begin{cases} 1 & \text{for } 0 \le t < 7 \\ \cos(t) & \text{for } t \ge 7 \end{cases}$

4. $e^{4t}[t - \cos(t)]$

5. $f(t) = \begin{cases} t & \text{for } 0 \le t < 3 \\ 1 - 3t & \text{for } t \ge 3 \end{cases}$

6. $f(t) = \begin{cases} 2t - \sin(t) & \text{for } 0 \le t < \pi \\ 0 & \text{for } t \ge \pi \end{cases}$

7. $e^{-t}[1 - t^2 + \sin(t)]$

8. $f(t) = \begin{cases} t^2 & \text{for } 0 \le t < 2 \\ 1 - t - 3t^2 & \text{for } t \ge 2 \end{cases}$

9. $f(t) = \begin{cases} \cos(t) & \text{for } 0 \le t < 2\pi \\ 2 - \sin(t) & \text{for } t \ge 2\pi \end{cases}$

10. $f(t) = \begin{cases} -4 & \text{for } 0 \le t < 1 \\ 0 & \text{for } 1 \le t < 3 \\ e^{-t} & \text{for } t \ge 3 \end{cases}$

11. $te^{-2t}\cos(3t)$

12. $e^t[1 - \cosh(t)]$

13. $f(t) = \begin{cases} t - 2 & \text{for } 0 \le t < 16 \\ -1 & \text{for } t \ge 16 \end{cases}$

14. $f(t) = \begin{cases} 1 - \cos(2t) & \text{for } 0 \le t < 3\pi \\ 0 & \text{for } t \ge 3\pi \end{cases}$

15. $e^{-5t}(t^4 + 2t^2 + t)$

In each of Problems 16 through 25, find the inverse Laplace transform of the function.

16. $\dfrac{1}{s^2 + 4s + 12}$

17. $\dfrac{1}{s^2 - 4s + 5}$

18. $\dfrac{1}{s^3}e^{-5s}$

19. $\dfrac{se^{-2s}}{s^2 + 9}$

20. $\dfrac{3}{s+2}e^{-4s}$

21. $\dfrac{1}{s^2 + 6s + 7}$

22. $\dfrac{s-4}{s^2 - 8s + 10}$

23. $\dfrac{s+2}{s^2 + 6s + 1}$

24. $\dfrac{1}{(s-5)^3}e^{-s}$

25. $\dfrac{1}{s(s^2 + 16)}e^{-21s}$

26. Determine $\mathcal{L}[e^{-2t}\int_0^t e^{2w}\cos(3w)\,dw]$. *Hint:* Use the first shifting theorem.

In each of Problems 27 through 32, solve the initial value problem by using the Laplace transform.

27. $y'' + 4y = f(t);\ y(0) = 1,\ y'(0) = 0,$ with $f(t) = \begin{cases} 0 & \text{for } 0 \le t < 4 \\ 3 & \text{for } t \ge 4 \end{cases}$

28. $y'' - 2y' - 3y = f(t);\ y(0) = 1,\ y'(0) = 0,$ with $f(t) = \begin{cases} 0 & \text{for } 0 \le t < 4 \\ 12 & \text{for } t \ge 4 \end{cases}$

29. $y^{(3)} - 8y = g(t);\ y(0) = y'(0) = y''(0) = 0,$ with $g(t) = \begin{cases} 0 & \text{for } 0 \le t < 6 \\ 2 & \text{for } t \ge 6 \end{cases}$

30. $y'' + 5y' + 6y = f(t);\ y(0) = y'(0) = 0,$ with $f(t) = \begin{cases} -2 & \text{for } 0 \le t < 3 \\ 0 & \text{for } t \ge 3 \end{cases}$

31. $y^{(3)} - y'' + 4y' - 4y = f(t);\ y(0) = y'(0) = 0,$ $y''(0) = 1,$ with $f(t) = \begin{cases} 1 & \text{for } 0 \le t < 5 \\ 2 & \text{for } t \ge 5 \end{cases}$

32. $y'' - 4y' + 4y = f(t);\ y(0) = -2,\ y'(0) = 1,$ with $f(t) = \begin{cases} t & \text{for } 0 \le t < 3 \\ t+2 & \text{for } t \ge 3 \end{cases}$

33. Calculate and graph the output voltage in the circuit of Figure 3.19, assuming that at time zero the capacitor is charged to a potential of 5 volts and the switch is opened at 0 and closed 5 seconds later.

34. Calculate and graph the output voltage in the RL circuit of Figure 3.25 if the current is initially zero and $E(t) = \begin{cases} 0 & \text{for } 0 \le t < 5 \\ 2 & \text{for } t \ge 5. \end{cases}$

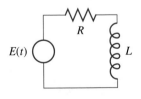

FIGURE 3.25

35. Solve for the current in the RL circuit of Problem 34 if the current is initially zero and $E(t) = \begin{cases} k & \text{for } 0 \le t < 5 \\ 0 & \text{for } t \ge 5. \end{cases}$

36. Solve for the current in the RL circuit of Problem 34 if the initial current is zero and $E(t) =$
$$\begin{cases} 0 & \text{for } 0 \leq t < 4 \\ Ae^{-t} & \text{for } t \geq 4. \end{cases}$$

37. Write the function graphed in Figure 3.26 in terms of the Heaviside function and find its Laplace transform.

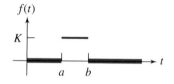

FIGURE 3.26

38. Write the function graphed in Figure 3.27 in terms of the Heaviside function and find its Laplace transform.

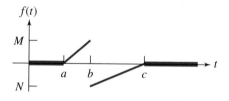

FIGURE 3.27

39. Write the function graphed in Figure 3.28 in terms of the Heaviside function and find its Laplace transform.

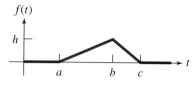

FIGURE 3.28

40. Solve for the current in the RL circuit of Figure 3.29 if the initial current is zero, $E(t)$ has period 4, and
$$E(t) = \begin{cases} 10 & \text{for } 0 \leq t < 2 \\ 0 & \text{for } 2 \leq t < 4 \end{cases}$$

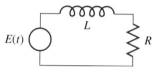

FIGURE 3.29

Hint: See Problem 22 of Section 3.1 for the Laplace transform of a periodic function. You should find that $I(s) = F(s)/(1+e^{-2s})$ for some $F(s)$. Use a geometric series to write

$$\frac{1}{1+e^{-2s}} = \sum_{n=0}^{\infty}(-1)^n e^{-2ns}$$

to write $I(s)$ as an infinite series, then take the inverse transform term by term by using a shifting theorem. Graph the current for $0 \leq t < 8$.

3.4 Convolution

In general the Laplace transform of the product of two functions is not the product of their transforms. There is, however, a special kind of product, denoted $f * g$, called the *convolution* of f with g. Convolution has the feature that the transform of $f * g$ is the product of the transforms of f and g. This fact is called the *convolution theorem*.

DEFINITION 3.6   *Convolution*

If f and g are defined on $[0, \infty)$, then the convolution $f * g$ of f with g is the function defined by

$$(f * g)(t) = \int_0^t f(t - \tau)g(\tau)\, d\tau$$

for $t \geq 0$.

THEOREM 3.9 *Convolution Theorem*

If $f * g$ is defined, then

$$\mathscr{L}[f * g] = \mathscr{L}[f]\mathscr{L}[g]$$

Proof Let $F = \mathscr{L}[f]$ and $G = \mathscr{L}[g]$. Then

$$F(s)G(s) = F(s) \int_0^\infty e^{-st} g(t)\, dt = \int_0^\infty F(s) e^{-s\tau} g(\tau)\, d\tau,$$

in which we changed the variable of integration to τ and brought $F(s)$ within the integral. Now recall that

$$e^{-s\tau} F(s) = \mathscr{L}[H(t - \tau)f(t - \tau)](s).$$

Substitute this into the integral for $F(s)G(s)$ to get

$$F(s)G(s) = \int_0^\infty \mathscr{L}[H(t - \tau)f(t - \tau)](s)g(\tau)\, d\tau. \tag{3.7}$$

But, from the definition of the Laplace transform,

$$\mathscr{L}[H(t - \tau)f(t - \tau)] = \int_0^\infty e^{-st} H(t - \tau)f(t - \tau)\, dt.$$

Substitute this into equation (3.7) to get

$$F(s)G(s) = \int_0^\infty \left[\int_0^\infty e^{-st} H(t - \tau)f(t - \tau)\, dt \right] g(\tau)\, d\tau$$

$$= \int_0^\infty \int_0^\infty e^{-st} g(\tau)H(t - \tau)f(t - \tau)\, dt\, d\tau.$$

Now recall that $H(t - \tau) = 0$ if $0 \le t < \tau$, while $H(t - \tau) = 1$ if $t \ge \tau$. Therefore,

$$F(s)G(s) = \int_0^\infty \int_\tau^\infty e^{-st} g(\tau)f(t - \tau)\, dt\, d\tau.$$

Figure 3.30 shows the $t\tau$ plane. The last integration is over the shaded region, consisting of points (t, τ) satisfying $0 \le \tau \le t < \infty$. Reverse the order of integration to write

$$F(s)G(s) = \int_0^\infty \int_0^t e^{-st} g(\tau)f(t - \tau)\, d\tau$$

$$= \int_0^\infty e^{-st} \left[\int_0^t g(\tau)f(t - \tau)\, d\tau \right] dt$$

$$= \int_0^\infty e^{-st} (f * g)(t)\, dt = \mathscr{L}[f * g](s).$$

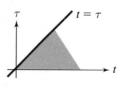

FIGURE 3.30

Therefore

$$F(s)G(s) = \mathcal{L}[f * g](s),$$

as we wanted to show. ∎

The inverse version of the convolution theorem is useful when we want to find the inverse transform of a function that is a product, and we know the inverse transform of each factor.

THEOREM 3.10

Let $\mathcal{L}^{-1}[F] = f$ and $\mathcal{L}^{-1}[G] = g$. Then

$$\mathcal{L}^{-1}[FG] = f * g. \quad ∎$$

EXAMPLE 3.17

Compute

$$\mathcal{L}^{-1}\left[\frac{1}{s(s-4)^2}\right].$$

We can do this several ways (a table, a program, a partial fractions decomposition). But we can also write

$$\mathcal{L}^{-1}\left[\frac{1}{s(s-4)^2}\right] = \mathcal{L}^{-1}\left[\frac{1}{s}\frac{1}{(s-4)^2}\right] = \mathcal{L}^{-1}[F(s)G(s)].$$

Now

$$\mathcal{L}^{-1}\left[\frac{1}{s}\right] = 1 = f(t) \quad \text{and} \quad \mathcal{L}^{-1}\left[\frac{1}{(s-4)^2}\right] = te^{4t} = g(t).$$

Therefore,

$$\mathcal{L}^{-1}\left[\frac{1}{s(s-4)^2}\right] = f(t) * g(t) = 1 * te^{4t}$$

$$= \int_0^t \tau e^{4\tau}\, d\tau = \frac{1}{4}te^{4t} - \frac{1}{16}e^{4t} + \frac{1}{16}. \quad ∎$$

The convolution operation is commutative.

THEOREM 3.11

If $f * g$ is defined, so is $g * f$, and $f * g = g * f$

Proof   Let $z = t - \tau$ in the integral defining the convolution to get

$$(f * g)(t) = \int_0^t f(t - \tau)g(\tau)\, d\tau$$

$$= \int_t^0 f(z)g(t - z)(-1)\, dz = \int_0^t f(z)g(t - z)\, dz = (g * f)(t). \quad \blacksquare$$

Commutativity can have practical importance, since the integral defining $g * f$ may be easier to evaluate than the integral defining $f * g$ in specific cases.

Convolution can sometimes enable us to write solutions of problems that are stated in very general terms.

EXAMPLE 3.18

We will solve the problem

$$y'' - 2y' - 8y = f(t); \qquad y(0) = 1, y'(0) = 0.$$

Apply the Laplace transform, inserting the initial values, to obtain

$$\mathfrak{L}[y'' - 2y' - 8y](s) = (s^2 Y(s) - s) - 2(sY(s) - 1) - 8Y(s) = \mathfrak{L}[f](s) = F(s).$$

Then

$$(s^2 - 2s - 8)Y(s) - s + 2 = F(s),$$

so

$$Y(s) = \frac{1}{s^2 - 2s - 8}F(s) + \frac{s - 2}{s^2 - 2s - 8}.$$

Use a partial fractions decomposition to write

$$Y(s) = \frac{1}{6}\frac{1}{s - 4}F(s) - \frac{1}{6}\frac{1}{s + 2}F(s) + \frac{1}{3}\frac{1}{s - 4} + \frac{2}{3}\frac{1}{s + 2}.$$

Then

$$y(t) = \frac{1}{6}e^{4t} * f(t) - \frac{1}{6}e^{-2t} * f(t) + \frac{1}{3}e^{4t} + \frac{2}{3}e^{-2t}.$$

This is the solution, for any function f having a convolution with e^{4t} and e^{-2t}. $\blacksquare$

Convolution is also used to solve certain kinds of integral equations, in which the function to be determined occurs in an integral. We saw an example of this in solving for the current in Example 3.16.

EXAMPLE 3.19

Determine f such that

$$f(t) = 2t^2 + \int_0^t f(t-\tau)e^{-\tau}\,d\tau.$$

Recognize the integral on the right as the convolution of f with e^{-t}. Thus the equation has the form

$$f(t) = 2t^2 + (f * e^{-t})(t).$$

Taking the Laplace transform of this equation yields

$$F(s) = \frac{4}{s^3} + F(s)\frac{1}{s+1}.$$

Then

$$F(s) = \frac{4}{s^3} + \frac{4}{s^4},$$

and from this we easily invert to obtain

$$f(t) = 2t^2 + \frac{2}{3}t^3. \ \blacksquare$$

SECTION 3.4   PROBLEMS

In each of Problems 1 through 8, use the convolution theorem to compute the inverse Laplace transform of the function (even if another method would work). Wherever they occur, a and b are positive constants.

1. $\dfrac{1}{(s^2+4)(s^2-4)}$

2. $\dfrac{1}{s^2+16}e^{-2s}$

3. $\dfrac{s}{(s^2+a^2)(s^2+b^2)}$

4. $\dfrac{s^2}{(s-3)(s^2+5)}$

5. $\dfrac{1}{s(s^2+a^2)^2}$

6. $\dfrac{1}{s^4(s-5)}$

7. $\dfrac{1}{s(s+2)}e^{-4s}$

8. $\dfrac{2}{s^3(s^2+5)}$

In each of Problems 9 through 16, use the convolution theorem to write a formula for the solution of the initial value problem in terms of $f(t)$.

9. $y'' - 5y' + 6y = f(t)$; $y(0) = y'(0) = 0$

10. $y'' + 10y' + 24y = f(t)$; $y(0) = 1$, $y'(0) = 0$

11. $y'' - 8y' + 12y = f(t)$; $y(0) = -3$, $y'(0) = 2$

12. $y'' - 4y' - 5y = f(t)$; $y(0) = 2$, $y'(0) = 1$

13. $y'' + 9y = f(t)$; $y(0) = -1$, $y'(0) = 1$

14. $y'' - k^2y = f(t)$; $y(0) = 2$, $y'(0) = -4$

15. $y^{(3)} - y'' - 4y' + 4y = f(t)$; $y(0) = y'(0) = 1$, $y''(0) = 0$

16. $y^{(4)} - 11y'' + 18y = f(t)$; $y(0) = y'(0) = y''(0) = y^{(3)}(0) = 0$

In each of Problems 17 through 23, solve the integral equation.

17. $f(t) = -1 + \int_0^t f(t-\alpha)e^{-3\alpha} \, d\alpha$

18. $f(t) = -t + \int_0^t f(t-\alpha)\sin(\alpha) \, d\alpha$

19. $f(t) = e^{-t} + \int_0^t f(t-\alpha) \, d\alpha$

20. $f(t) = -1 + t - 2\int_0^t f(t-\alpha)\sin(\alpha) \, d\alpha$

21. $f(t) = 3 + \int_0^t f(\alpha)\cos[2(t-\alpha)] \, d\alpha$

22. $f(t) = \cos(t) + e^{-2t}\int_0^t f(\alpha)e^{2\alpha} \, d\alpha$

23. $f(t) = e^{-3t}\left[e^t - 3\int_0^t f(\alpha)e^{3\alpha} \, d\alpha\right]$

24. Use the convolution theorem to derive the formula $\mathcal{L}[\int_0^t f(w) \, dw](s) = (1/s)F(s)$. What assumptions are needed about $f(t)$?

25. Show by example that in general $f * 1 \neq f$, where 1 denotes the function that is identically 1 for all t. *Hint*: Consider $f(t) = \cos(t)$.

26. Use the convolution theorem to determine the Laplace transform of $e^{-2t}\int_0^t e^{2w}\cos(3w) \, dw$.

27. Use the convolution theorem to show that

$$\mathcal{L}^{-1}\left[\frac{1}{s^2}F(s)\right](t) = \int_0^t \int_0^w f(\alpha) \, d\alpha \, dw.$$

3.5   Unit Impulses and the Dirac Delta Function

Sometimes we encounter the concept of an impulse, which may be intuitively understood as a force of large magnitude applied over an instant of time. We can model an impulse as follows. For any positive number ϵ, consider the pulse δ_ϵ defined by

$$\delta_\epsilon(t) = \frac{1}{\epsilon}[H(t) - H(t-\epsilon)].$$

As shown in Figure 3.31, this is a pulse of magnitude $1/\epsilon$ and duration ϵ. By letting ϵ approach zero, we obtain pulses of increasing magnitude over shorter time intervals.

Dirac's delta function is thought of as a pulse of "infinite magnitude" over an "infinitely short" duration, and is defined to be

$$\delta(t) = \lim_{\epsilon \to 0+} \delta_\epsilon(t).$$

This is not really a function in the conventional sense, but is a more general object called a distribution. Nevertheless, for historical reasons it continues to be referred to as the delta function. It is also named for the Nobel laureate physicist P.A.M. Dirac. The shifted delta function $\delta(t-a)$ is zero except for $t = a$, where it has its infinite spike.

We can define the Laplace transform of the delta function as follows. Begin with

$$\delta_\epsilon(t-a) = \frac{1}{\epsilon}[H(t-a) - H(t-a-\epsilon)].$$

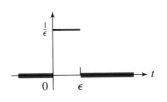

FIGURE 3.31   *Graph of*
$\delta_\epsilon(t-a)$.

Then

$$\mathcal{L}[\delta_\epsilon(t-a)] = \frac{1}{\epsilon}\left[\frac{1}{s}e^{-as} - \frac{1}{s}e^{-(a+\epsilon)s}\right] = \frac{e^{-as}(1-e^{-\epsilon s})}{\epsilon s}.$$

This suggests that we define

$$\mathcal{L}[\delta(t-a)] = \lim_{\epsilon \to 0+} \frac{e^{-as}(1-e^{-\epsilon s})}{\epsilon s} = e^{-as}.$$

In particular, upon choosing $a = 0$ we have

$$\mathcal{L}[\delta(t)] = 1.$$

Thus we think of the delta function as having constant Laplace transform equal to 1.

The following result is called the *filtering property* of the delta function. If at time a, a signal (function) is hit with an impulse, by multiplying it by $\delta(t-a)$, and the resulting signal is summed over all positive time by integrating from zero to infinity, then we obtain exactly the signal value $f(a)$.

THEOREM 3.12   Filtering Property

Let $a > 0$ and let f be integrable on $[0, \infty)$ and continuous at a. Then

$$\int_0^\infty f(t)\delta(t-a)\,dt = f(a).$$

Proof   First calculate

$$\int_0^\infty f(t)\delta_\epsilon(t-a)\,dt = \int_0^\infty \frac{1}{\epsilon}[H(t-a) - H(t-a-\epsilon)]f(t)\,dt$$

$$= \frac{1}{\epsilon}\int_a^{a+\epsilon} f(t)\,dt.$$

By the mean value theorem for integrals, there is some t_ϵ between a and $a+\epsilon$ such that

$$\int_a^{a+\epsilon} f(t)\,dt = \epsilon f(t_\epsilon).$$

Then

$$\int_0^\infty f(t)\delta_\epsilon(t-a)\,dt = f(t_\epsilon).$$

As $\epsilon \to 0+$, $a+\epsilon \to a$, so $t_\epsilon \to a$ and, by continuity, $f(t_\epsilon) \to f(a)$. Then

$$\lim_{\epsilon \to 0+}\int_0^\infty f(t)\delta_\epsilon(t-a)\,dt = \int_0^\infty f(t)\lim_{\epsilon \to 0+}\delta_\epsilon(t-a)\,dt$$

$$= \int_0^\infty f(t)\delta(t-a)\,dt = \lim_{\epsilon \to 0+} f(t_\epsilon) = f(a),$$

as we wanted to show. ■

If we apply the filtering property to $f(t) = e^{-st}$, we get

$$\int_0^\infty e^{-st}\delta(t-a)\,dt = e^{-as},$$

consistent with the definition of the Laplace transform of the delta function. Further, if we change notation in the filtering property and write it as

$$\int_0^\infty f(\tau)\delta(\tau - t)\,d\tau = f(t),$$

then we can recognize the convolution of f with δ and read the last equation as

$$f * \delta = f.$$

The delta function therefore acts as an identity for the "product" defined by the convolution of two functions.

Here is an example of a boundary value problem involving the delta function.

EXAMPLE 3.20

Solve

$$y'' + 2y' + 2y = \delta(t-3); \qquad y(0) = y'(0) = 0.$$

Apply the Laplace transform to the differential equation to get

$$s^2 Y(s) + 2sY(s) + 2Y(s) = e^{-3s},$$

hence

$$Y(s) = \frac{e^{-3s}}{s^2 + 2s + 2}.$$

To find the inverse transform of the function on the right, first write

$$Y(s) = \frac{1}{(s+1)^2 + 1}e^{-3s}.$$

Now use both shifting theorems. Because $\mathcal{L}^{-1}[1/(s^2+1)] = \sin(t)$, a shift in the s–variable gives us

$$\mathcal{L}^{-1}\left[\frac{1}{(s+1)^2 + 1}\right] = e^{-t}\sin(t).$$

Now shift in the t–variable to obtain

$$y(t) = H(t-3)e^{-(t-3)}\sin(t-3).$$

A graph of this solution is shown in Figure 3.32. The solution is differentiable for $t > 0$, except that $y'(t)$ has a jump discontinuity of magnitude 1 at $t = 3$. The magnitude of the jump is the coefficient of $\delta(t-3)$ in the differential equation. ∎

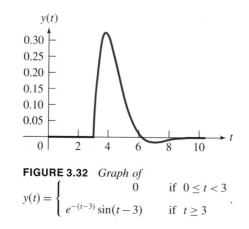

FIGURE 3.32 *Graph of*

$$y(t) = \begin{cases} 0 & \text{if } 0 \le t < 3 \\ e^{-(t-3)}\sin(t-3) & \text{if } t \ge 3 \end{cases}.$$

The delta function may be used to study the behavior of a circuit that has been subjected to transients. These are generated during switching, and the high input voltages associated with them can create excessive current in the components, damaging the circuit. Transients can also be harmful because they contain a broad spectrum of frequencies. Introducing a transient into a circuit can therefore have the effect of forcing the circuit with a range of frequencies. If one of these is near the natural frequency of the system, resonance may occur, resulting in oscillations large enough to damage the system.

For this reason, before a circuit is built, engineers sometimes use a delta function to model a transient and study its effect on the circuit.

EXAMPLE 3.21

Suppose, in the circuit of Figure 3.33, the current and charge on the capacitor are zero at time zero. We want to determine the output voltage response to a transient modeled by $\delta(t)$.

The output voltage is $q(t)/C$, so we will determine $q(t)$. By Kirchhoff's voltage law,

$$Li' + Ri + \frac{1}{C}q = i' + 10i + 100q = \delta(t).$$

Since $i = q'$,

$$q'' + 10q' + 100q = \delta(t).$$

We assume initial conditions $q(0) = q'(0) = 0$.

Apply the Laplace transform to the differential equation and use the initial conditions to obtain

$$s^2 Q(s) + 10sQ(s) + 100Q(s) = 1.$$

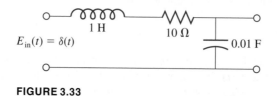

$E_{in}(t) = \delta(t)$ 1 H   10 Ω 0.01 F

FIGURE 3.33

Then

$$Q(s) = \frac{1}{s^2 + 10s + 100}.$$

In order to invert this by using a shifting theorem, complete the square to write

$$Q(s) = \frac{1}{(s+5)^2 + 75}.$$

Since

$$\mathcal{L}^{-1}\left[\frac{1}{(s^2 + 75)}\right] = \frac{1}{5\sqrt{3}} \sin(5\sqrt{3}t),$$

then

$$q(t) = \mathcal{L}^{-1}\left[\frac{1}{(s+5)^2 + 75}\right] = \frac{1}{5\sqrt{3}} e^{-5t} \sin(5\sqrt{3}t).$$

The output voltage is

$$\frac{1}{C}q(t) = 100q(t) = \frac{20}{\sqrt{3}} e^{-5t} \sin(5\sqrt{3}t).$$

A graph of this output is shown in Figure 3.34. The circuit output displays damped oscillations at its natural frequency, even though it was not explicitly forced by oscillations of this frequency. If we wish, we can obtain the current by $i(t) = q'(t)$. ∎

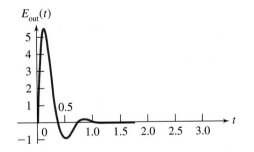

FIGURE 3.34 *Output of the circuit of Figure 3.32.*

SECTION 3.5   *PROBLEMS*

In each of Problems 1 through 5, solve the initial value problem and graph the solution.

1. $y'' + 5y' + 6y = 3\delta(t-2) - 4\delta(t-5);\ y(0) = y'(0) = 0$

2. $y'' - 4y' + 13y = 4\delta(t-3);\ y(0) = y'(0) = 0$

3. $y^{(3)} + 4y'' + 5y' + 2y = 6\delta(t);\ y(0) = y'(0) = y''(0) = 0$

4. $y'' + 16y' = 12\delta(t - 5\pi/8);\ y(0) = 3,\ y'(0) = 0.$

5. $y'' + 5y' + 6y = B\delta(t);\ y(0) = 3,\ y'(0) = 0.$ Call the solution φ. What are $\varphi(0)$ and $\varphi'(0)$? Using this information, what physical phenomenon does the Dirac delta function model?

6. Suppose f is not continuous at a, but $\lim_{t\to a+} f(t) = f(a+)$ is finite. Prove that $\int_0^\infty f(t)\delta(t-a)\,dt = f(a+)$.

7. Evaluate $\int_0^\infty (\sin(t)/t)\delta(t-\pi/6)\,dt$.

8. Evaluate $\int_0^2 t^2\delta(t-3)\,dt$.

9. Evaluate $\int_0^\infty f(t)\delta(t-2)\,dt$, where

$$f(t) = \begin{cases} t & \text{for } 0 \le t < 2 \\ t^2 & \text{for } t > 2 \\ 5 & \text{for } t = 2. \end{cases}$$

10. It is sometimes convenient to consider $\delta(t)$ as the derivative of the Heaviside function $H(t)$. Use the definitions of the derivative, the Heaviside function, and the delta function (as a limit of δ_ϵ) to give a heuristic justification for this.

11. Use the idea that $H'(t) = \delta(t)$ from Problem 10 to determine the output voltage of the circuit of Example 3.16 by differentiating the relevant equation to obtain an equation in i rather than writing the charge as an integral.

12. If $H'(t) = \delta(t)$, then $\mathcal{L}[H'(t)](s) = 1$. Show that not all of the operational rules for the Laplace transform are compatible with this expression. *Hint*: Check to see whether $[H'(t)](s) = s\mathcal{L}[H(t)](s) - H(0+)$.

13. Evaluate $\delta(t-a) * f(t)$.

14. An object of mass m is attached to the lower end of a spring of modulus k. Assume that there is no damping. Derive and solve an equation of motion for the position of the object at time $t > 0$, assuming that, at time zero, the object is pushed down from the equilibrium position with an initial velocity v_0. With what momentum does the object leave the equilibrium position?

15. Suppose an object of mass m is attached to the lower end of a spring having modulus k. Assume that there is no damping. Solve the equation of motion for the position of the object for any time $t \ge 0$ if, at time zero, the weight is struck a downward blow of magnitude mv_0. How does the position of the object in Problem 14 compare with that of the object in this problem for any positive time?

16. A 2-pound weight is attached to the lower end of a spring, stretching it $\frac{8}{3}$ inches. The weight is allowed to come to rest in the equilibrium position. At some later time, which is called time zero, the weight is struck a downward blow of magnitude $\frac{1}{4}$ pound (an impulse). Assume that there is no damping in the system. Determine the velocity with which the weight leaves the equilibrium position as well as the frequency and magnitude of the resulting oscillations.

3.6 Laplace Transform Solution of Systems

The Laplace transform can be of use in solving systems of equations involving derivatives and integrals.

EXAMPLE 3.22

Consider the system of differential equations and initial conditions for the functions x and y:

$$x'' - 2x' + 3y' + 2y = 4,$$
$$2y' - x' + 3y = 0,$$
$$x(0) = x'(0) = y(0) = 0.$$

Begin by applying the Laplace transform to the differential equations, incorporating the initial conditions. We get

$$s^2 X - 2sX + 3sY + 2Y = \frac{4}{s},$$
$$2sY - sX + 3Y = 0.$$

Solve these equations for $X(s)$ and $Y(s)$ to get

$$X(s) = \frac{4s+6}{s^2(s+2)(s-1)} \quad \text{and} \quad Y(s) = \frac{2}{s(s+2)(s-1)}.$$

A partial fractions decomposition yields

$$X(s) = -\frac{7}{2}\frac{1}{s} - 3\frac{1}{s^2} + \frac{1}{6}\frac{1}{s+2} + \frac{10}{3}\frac{1}{s-1}$$

and

$$Y(s) = -\frac{1}{s} + \frac{1}{3}\frac{1}{s+2} + \frac{2}{3}\frac{1}{s-1}.$$

Upon applying the inverse Laplace transform, we obtain the solution

$$x(t) = -\frac{7}{2} - 3t + \frac{1}{6}e^{-2t} + \frac{10}{3}e^t$$

and

$$y(t) = -1 + \frac{1}{3}e^{-2t} + \frac{2}{3}e^t. \quad \blacksquare$$

The analysis of mechanical and electrical systems having several components can lead to systems of differential equations that can be solved using the Laplace transform.

EXAMPLE 3.23

Consider the spring/mass system of Figure 3.35. Let $x_1 = x_2 = 0$ at the equilibrium position, where the weights are at rest. Choose the direction to the right as positive, and suppose the weights are at positions $x_1(t)$ and $x_2(t)$ at time t.

By two applications of Hooke's law, the restoring force on m_1 is

$$-k_1 x_1 + k_2(x_2 - x_1)$$

and that on m_2 is

$$-k_2(x_2 - x_1) - k_3 x_2.$$

By Newton's second law of motion,

$$m_1 x_1'' = -(k_1 + k_2)x_1 + k_2 x_2 + f_1(t)$$

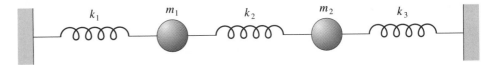

FIGURE 3.35

and

$$m_2 x_2'' = k_2 x_1 - (k_2 + k_3) x_2 + f_2(t).$$

These equations assume that damping is negligible, but allow for forcing functions acting on each mass.

As a specific example, suppose $m_1 = m_2 = 1$ and $k_1 = k_3 = 4$ while $k_2 = \frac{5}{2}$. Suppose $f_2(t) = 0$, so no external driving force acts on the second mass, while a force of magnitude $f_1(t) = 2[1 - H(t-3)]$ acts on the first. This hits the first mass with a force of constant magnitude 2 for the first 3 seconds, then turns off. Now the system of equations for the displacement functions is

$$x_1'' = -\frac{13}{2} x_1 + \frac{5}{2} x_2 + 2[1 - H(t-3)],$$

$$x_2'' = \frac{5}{2} x_1 - \frac{13}{2} x_2.$$

If the masses are initially at rest at the equilibrium position, then

$$x_1(0) = x_2(0) = x_1'(0) = x_2'(0) = 0.$$

Apply the Laplace transform to each equation of the system to get

$$s^2 X_1 = -\frac{13}{2} X_1 + \frac{5}{2} X_2 + \frac{2(1 - e^{-3s})}{s},$$

$$s^2 X_2 = \frac{5}{2} X_1 - \frac{13}{2} X_2.$$

Solve these to obtain

$$X_1(s) = \frac{2}{(s^2 + 9)(s^2 + 4)} \left(s^2 + \frac{13}{2}\right) \frac{1}{s} (1 - e^{-3s})$$

and

$$X_2(s) = \frac{5}{(s^2 + 9)(s^2 + 4)} \frac{1}{s} (1 - e^{-3s}).$$

In preparation for applying the inverse Laplace transform, use a partial fractions decomposition to write

$$X_1(s) = \frac{13}{36} \frac{1}{s} - \frac{1}{4} \frac{s}{s^2 + 4} - \frac{1}{9} \frac{s}{s^2 + 9} - \frac{13}{36} \frac{1}{s} e^{-3s} + \frac{1}{4} \frac{s}{s^2 + 4} e^{-3s} + \frac{1}{9} \frac{s}{s^2 + 9} e^{-3s}$$

and

$$X_2(s) = \frac{5}{36} \frac{1}{s} - \frac{1}{4} \frac{s}{s^2 + 4} + \frac{1}{9} \frac{s}{s^2 + 9} - \frac{5}{36} \frac{1}{s} e^{-3s} + \frac{1}{4} \frac{s}{s^2 + 4} e^{-3s} - \frac{1}{9} \frac{s}{s^2 + 9} e^{-3s}$$

Now it is routine to apply the inverse Laplace transform to obtain the solution

$$x_1(t) = \frac{13}{36} - \frac{1}{4}\cos(2t) - \frac{1}{9}\cos(3t)$$

$$+ \left[-\frac{13}{36} + \frac{1}{4}\cos(2(t-3)) - \frac{1}{9}\cos(3(t-3)) \right] H(t-3),$$

$$x_2(t) = \frac{5}{36} - \frac{1}{4}\cos(2t) + \tfrac{1}{9}\cos(3t)$$

$$+ \left[-\frac{5}{36} + \frac{1}{4}\cos(2(t-3)) - \frac{1}{9}\cos(3(t-3)) \right] H(t-3). \quad \blacksquare$$

EXAMPLE 3.24

In the circuit of Figure 3.36, suppose the switch is closed at time zero. We want to know the current in each loop. Assume that both loop currents and the charges on the capacitors are initially zero. Apply Kirchhoff's laws to each loop to get

$$40i_1 + 120(q_1 - q_2) = 10$$

$$60i_2 + 120q_2 = 120(q_1 - q_2).$$

Since $i = q'$, we can write $q(t) = \int_0^t i(\tau)\, d\tau + q(0)$. Put into the two circuit equations, we get

$$40i_1 + 120 \int_0^t [i_1(\tau) - i_2(\tau)]\, d\tau + 120[q_1(0) - q_2(0)] = 10$$

$$60i_2 + 120 \int_0^t i_2(\tau)d\tau + 120q_2(0) = 120 \int_0^t [i_1(\tau) - i_2(\tau)]\, d\tau + 120[q_1(0) - q_2(0)].$$

Put $q_1(0) = q_2(0) = 0$ in this system to get

$$40i_1 + 120 \int_0^t [i_1(\tau) - i_2(\tau)]\, d\tau = 10$$

$$60i_2 + 120 \int_0^t i_2(\tau)\, d\tau = 120 \int_0^t [i_1(\tau) - i_2(\tau)]\, d\tau.$$

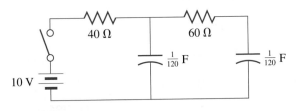

FIGURE 3.36

Apply the Laplace transform to each equation to get

$$40I_1 + \frac{120}{s}I_1 - \frac{120}{s}I_2 = \frac{10}{s}$$

$$60I_2 + \frac{120}{s}I_2 = \frac{120}{s}I_1 - \frac{120}{s}I_2.$$

After some rearrangement, we have

$$(s+3)I_1 - 3I_2 = \frac{1}{4}$$

$$2I_1 - (s+4)I_2 = 0.$$

Solve these to get

$$I_1(s) = \frac{s+4}{4(s+1)(s+6)} = \frac{3}{20}\frac{1}{s+1} + \frac{1}{10}\frac{1}{s+6}$$

and

$$I_2(s) = \frac{1}{2(s+1)(s+6)} = \frac{1}{10}\frac{1}{s+1} - \frac{1}{10}\frac{1}{s+6}.$$

Now use the inverse Laplace transform to find the solution

$$i_1(t) = \frac{3}{20}e^{-t} + \frac{1}{10}e^{-6t}, \quad i_2(t) = \frac{1}{10}e^{-t} - \frac{1}{10}e^{-6t}. \ \blacksquare$$

SECTION 3.6   PROBLEMS

In each of Problems 1 through 10, use the Laplace transform to solve the initial value problem for the system.

1. $x' - 2y' = 1, x' + y - x = 0; x(0) = y(0) = 0$

2. $2x' - 3y + y' = 0, x' + y' = t; x(0) = y(0) = 0$

3. $x' + 2y' - y = 1, 2x' + y = 0; x(0) = y(0) = 0$

4. $x' + y' - x = \cos(2t), x' + 2y' = 0; x(0) = y(0) = 0$

5. $3x' - y = 2t, x' + y' - y = 0; x(0) = y(0) = 0$

6. $x' + 4y' - y = 0, x' + 2y = e^{-t}; x(0) = y(0) = 0$

7. $x' + 2x - y' = 0, x' + y + x = t^2; x(0) = y(0) = 0$

8. $x' + 4x - y = 0, x' + y' = t; x(0) = y(0) = 0$

9. $x' + y' + x - y = 0, x' + 2y' + x = 1; x(0) = y(0) = 0$

10. $x' + 2y' - x = 0, 4x' + 3y' + y = -6; x(0) = y(0) = 0$

11. Use the Laplace transform to solve the system

$$y_1' - 2y_2' + 3y_1 = 0$$

$$y_1 - 4y_2' + 3y_3 = t,$$

$$y_1 - 2y_2' + 3y_3' = -1; y_1(0) = y_2(0) = y_3(0) = 0.$$

12. Solve for the currents in the circuit of Figure 3.37, assuming that the currents and charges are initially zero and that $E(t) = 2H(t-4) - H(t-5)$.

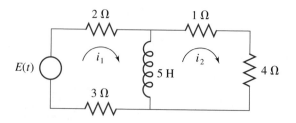

FIGURE 3.37

13. Solve for the currents in the circuit of Figure 3.37 if the currents and charges are initially zero and $E(t) = 1 - H(t-4)\sin(2(t-4))$.
14. Solve for the displacement functions of the masses in the system of Figure 3.38. Neglect damping and assume zero initial displacements and velocities, and external forces $f_1(t) = 2$ and $f_2(t) = 0$.
15. Solve for the displacement functions in the system of Figure 3.38 if $f_1(t) = 1 - H(t-2)$ and $f_2(t) = 0$. Assume zero initial displacements and velocities.

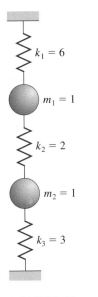

FIGURE 3.38

16. Consider the system of Figure 3.39. Let M be subjected to a periodic driving force $f(t) = A\sin(\omega t)$. The masses are initially at rest in the equilibrium position.

    (a) Derive and solve the initial value problem for the displacement functions.

    (b) Show that, if m and k_2 are chosen so that $\omega = \sqrt{k_2/m}$, then the mass m cancels the forced vibrations of M. In this case we call m a *vibration absorber*.

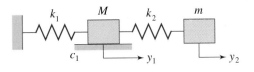

FIGURE 3.39

17. Two objects of masses m_1 and m_2 are attached to opposite ends of a spring having spring constant k (Figure 3.40). The entire apparatus is placed on a highly varnished table. Show that, if stretched and released from rest, the masses oscillate with respect to each other with period

$$2\pi\sqrt{\frac{m_1 m_2}{k(m_1 + m_2)}}.$$

FIGURE 3.40

18. Solve for the currents in the circuit of Figure 3.41 if $E(t) = 5H(t-2)$ and the initial currents are zero.

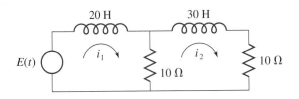

FIGURE 3.41

19. Solve for the currents in the circuit of Figure 3.41 if $E(t) = 5\delta(t-1)$.

20. Two tanks are connected by a series of pipes as shown in Figure 3.42. Tank 1 initially contains 60 gallons of brine in which 11 pounds of salt are dissolved. Tank 2 initially contains 7 pounds of salt dissolved in 18 gallons of brine. Beginning at time zero a mixture containing $\frac{1}{6}$ pound of salt for each gallon of water is pumped into tank 1 at the rate of 2 gallons per minute, while salt water solutions are interchanged between the two tanks and also flow out of tank 2 at the rates shown in the diagram. Four minutes after time zero, salt is poured into tank 2 at the rate of 11 pounds per minute for a period of 2 minutes. Determine the amount of salt in each tank for any time $t \geq 0$.

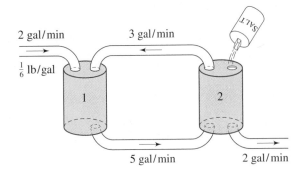

FIGURE 3.42

21. Two tanks are connected by a series of pipes as shown in Figure 3.43. Tank 1 initially contains 200 gallons of brine in which 10 pounds of salt are dissolved. Tank 2 initially contains 5 pounds of salt dissolved in 100 gallons of water. Beginning at time zero, pure water is pumped into tank 1 at the rate of 3 gallons per minute, while brine solutions are interchanged between the tanks at the rates shown in the diagram. Three minutes after time zero, 5 pounds of salt are dumped into tank 2. Determine the amount of salt in each tank for any time $t \geq 0$.

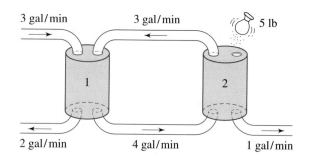

FIGURE 3.43

3.7   Differential Equations with Polynomial Coefficients

The Laplace transform can sometimes be used to solve linear differential equations having polynomials as coefficients. For this we need the fact that the Laplace transform of $tf(t)$ is the negative of the derivative of the Laplace transform of $f(t)$.

THEOREM 3.13

Let $\mathcal{L}[f](s) = F(s)$ for $s > b$ and suppose that F is differentiable. Then

$$\mathcal{L}[tf(t)](s) = -F'(s)$$

for $s > b$.

Proof   Differentiate under the integral sign to calculate

$$F'(s) = \frac{d}{ds} \int_0^\infty e^{-st} f(t)\, dt = \int_0^\infty \frac{d}{ds}(e^{-st} f(t))\, dt$$

$$= \int_0^\infty -te^{-st} f(t)\, dt = \int_0^\infty e^{-st}[-tf(t)]\, dt$$

$$= \mathcal{L}[-tf(t)](s),$$

and this is equivalent to the conclusion of the theorem. ∎

By applying this result n times, we reach the following.

COROLLARY 3.1

Let $\mathcal{L}[f](s) = F(s)$ for $s > b$ and let n be a positive integer. Suppose F is n times differentiable. Then, for $s > b$,

$$\mathcal{L}[t^n f(t)](s) = (-1)^n \frac{d^n}{ds^n} F(s). \blacksquare$$

EXAMPLE 3.25

Consider the problem

$$ty'' + (4t - 2)y' - 4y = 0; \qquad y(0) = 1.$$

If we write this differential equation in the form $y'' + p(t)y' + q(t)y = 0$, then we must choose $p(t) = (4t - 2)/t$, and this is not defined at $t = 0$, where the initial condition is given. This problem is not of the type for which we proved an existence/uniqueness theorem in Chapter 2. Further, we have only one initial condition. Nevertheless, we will look for functions satisfying the problem as stated.

Apply the Laplace transform to the differential equation to get

$$\mathcal{L}[ty''] + 4\mathcal{L}[ty''] - 2\mathcal{L}[y'] - 4\mathcal{L}[y] = 0.$$

Calculate the first three terms as follows. First,

$$\mathcal{L}[ty''] = -\frac{d}{ds}\,\mathcal{L}[y'] = -\frac{d}{ds}\,[s^2 Y - sy(0) - y'(0)]$$
$$= -2sY - s^2 Y' + 1$$

because $y(0) = 1$ and $y'(0)$, though unknown, is constant and has zero derivative. Next,

$$\mathcal{L}[ty'] = -\frac{d}{ds}\,[y']$$
$$= -\frac{d}{ds}\,[sY - y(0)] = -Y - sY'.$$

Finally,

$$\mathcal{L}[y'] = sY - y(0) = sY - 1.$$

The transform of the differential equation is therefore

$$-2sY' - s^2 Y + 1 - 4Y - 4sY' - 2sY + 2 - 4Y = 0.$$

Then

$$Y' + \frac{4s + 8}{s(s+4)}\,Y = \frac{3}{s(s+4)}.$$

This is a linear first-order differential equation, and we will find an integrating factor. First compute

$$\int \frac{4s + 8}{s(s+4)}\,ds = \ln[s^2(s+4)^2].$$

Then

$$e^{\ln[(s^2(s+4)^2)]} = s^2(s+4)^2$$

is an integrating factor. Multiply the differential equation by this factor to obtain

$$s^2(s+4)^2 Y' + (4s+8)s(s+4)Y = 3s(s+4),$$

or

$$[s^2(s+4)^2 Y]' = 3s(s+4).$$

Integrate to get

$$s^2(s+4)^2 Y = s^3 + 6s^2 + C.$$

Then

$$Y(s) = \frac{s}{(s+4)^2} + \frac{6}{(s+4)^2} + \frac{C}{s^2(s+4)^2}.$$

Upon applying the inverse Laplace transform, we obtain

$$y(t) = e^{-4t} + 2te^{-4t} + \frac{C}{32}[-1 + 2t + e^{-4t} + 2te^{-4t}].$$

This function satisfies the differential equation and the condition $y(0) = 1$ for any real number C. This problem does not have a unique solution. ∎

When we applied the Laplace transform to a constant coefficient differential equation $y'' + Ay' + By = f(t)$, we obtained an algebraic expression for Y. In this example, with polynomials occurring as coefficients, we obtained a differential equation for Y because the process of computing the transform of $t^k y(t)$ involves differentiating $Y(s)$.

In the next example, we will need the following fact.

THEOREM 3.14

Let f be piecewise continuous on $[0, k]$ for every positive number k, and suppose there are numbers M and b such that $|f(t)| \le Me^{bt}$ for $t \ge 0$. Let $\mathcal{L}[f] = F$. Then

$$\lim_{s \to \infty} F(s) = 0.$$

Proof   Write

$$|F(s)| = \left| \int_0^\infty e^{-st} f(t)\, dt \right| \le \int_0^\infty e^{-st} Me^{bt}\, dt$$

$$= \frac{M}{b-s} e^{-(s-b)t} \Big]_0^\infty = \frac{M}{s-b} \to 0$$

as $s \to \infty$. ∎

This result will enable us to solve the following initial value problem.

EXAMPLE 3.26

Suppose we want to solve

$$y'' + 2ty' - 4y = 1; \qquad y(0) = y'(0) = 0.$$

Unlike the preceding example, this problem satisfies the hypotheses of the existence/uniqueness theorem in Chapter 2.

Apply the Laplace transform to the differential equation to get

$$s^2 Y(s) - sy(0) - y'(0) + 2\mathfrak{L}[ty'](s) - 4Y(s) = \frac{1}{s}.$$

Now $y(0) = y'(0) = 0$ and

$$\mathfrak{L}[ty'](s) = -\frac{d}{ds}\left[\mathfrak{L}[y'](s)\right]$$

$$= -\frac{d}{ds}[sY(s) - y(0)] = -Y(s) - sY'(s).$$

We therefore have

$$s^2 Y(s) - 2Y(s) - 2sY'(s) - 4Y(s) = \frac{1}{s},$$

or

$$Y' + \left(\frac{3}{s} - \frac{s}{2}\right)Y = -\frac{1}{2s^2}.$$

This is a linear first-order differential equation for Y. To find an integrating factor, first compute

$$\int \left(\frac{3}{s} - \frac{s}{2}\right) ds = 3\ln(s) - \frac{1}{4}s^2.$$

The exponential of this function, or

$$s^3 e^{-s^2/4},$$

is an integrating factor. Multiply the differential equation by this function to obtain

$$(s^3 e^{-s^2/4} Y)' = -\frac{1}{2}se^{-s^2/4}.$$

Then

$$s^3 e^{-s^2/4} Y = e^{-s^2/4} + C$$

so

$$Y(s) = \frac{1}{s^3} + \frac{C}{s^3}e^{s^2/4}.$$

We do not have any further initial conditions to determine C. However, in order to have $\lim_{s\to\infty} Y(s) = 0$, we must choose $C = 0$. Then $Y(s) = 1/s^3$ so

$$y(t) = \frac{1}{2}t^2. \quad \blacksquare$$

SECTION 3.7   *PROBLEMS*

Use the Laplace transform to solve each of Problems 1 through 10.

1. $t^2 y' - 2y = 2$

2. $y'' + 4ty' - 4y = 0;\ y(0) = 0,\ y'(0) = -7$

3. $y'' - 16ty' + 32y = 14;\ y(0) = y'(0) = 0$

4. $y'' + 8ty' - 8y = 0;\ y(0) = 0,\ y'(0) = -4$

5. $ty'' + (t-1)y' + y = 0;\ y(0) = 0$

6. $y'' + 2ty' - 4y = 6;\ y(0) = 0,\ y'(0) = 0$

7. $y'' + 8ty' = 0;\ y(0) = 4,\ y'(0) = 0$

8. $y'' - 4ty' + 4y = 0;\ y(0) = 0,\ y'(0) = 10$

9. $y'' - 8ty' + 16y = 3;\ y(0) = 0,\ y'(0) = 0$

10. $(1-t)y'' + ty' - y = 0,\ y(0) = 3,\ y'(0) = -1$

CHAPTER 4

Series Solutions

Sometimes we can find an explicit, closed form solution of a differential equation or initial value problem. This occurs with

$$y' + 2y = 1; \quad y(0) = 3,$$

which has the unique solution

$$y(x) = \frac{1}{2}(1 + 5e^{-2x}).$$

This solution is explicit, giving $y(x)$ as a function of x, and is in closed form because it is a finite algebraic combination of elementary functions (which are functions such as polynomials, trigonometric functions, and exponential functions).

Sometimes standard methods do not yield a solution in closed form. For example, the problem

$$y' + e^x y = x^2; \quad y(0) = 4$$

has the unique solution

$$y(x) = e^{-e^x} \int_0^x \xi^2 e^{e^\xi} \, d\xi + 4e^{-e^x}.$$

This solution is explicit, but it is not in closed form because of the integral. It is difficult to analyze this solution, or even to evaluate it at specific points.

Sometimes a series solution is a good strategy for solving an initial value problem. Such a solution is explicit, giving $y(x)$ as an infinite series involving constants times powers of x. It may also reveal important information about the behavior of the solution—for example, whether it passes through the origin, whether it is an even or odd function, or whether the function is increasing or decreasing on a given interval. It may also be possible to make good approximations to function values from a series representation.

We will begin with power series solutions for differential equations admitting such solutions. Following this, we will develop another kind of series for problems whose solutions do not have power series expansions about a particular point.

This chapter assumes familiarity with basic facts about power series.

155

4.1   Power Series Solutions of Initial Value Problems

Consider the linear first-order initial value problem

$$y' + p(x)y = q(x); \quad y(x_0) = y_0.$$

If p and q are continuous on an open interval I about x_0, we are guaranteed by Theorem 1.3 that this problem has a unique solution defined for all x in I.

With a stronger condition on these coefficients, we can infer that the solution will have a stronger property, which we now define.

DEFINITION 4.1   *Analytic Function*

A function f is analytic at x_0 if $f(x)$ has a power series representation in some open interval about x_0:

$$f(x) = \sum_{n=0}^{\infty} a_n(x - x_0)^n$$

in some interval $(x_0 - h, x_0 + h)$

For example, $\sin(x)$ is analytic at 0, having the power series representation

$$\sin(x) = \sum_{n=0}^{\infty} \frac{(-1)^n}{(2n+1)!} x^{2n+1}.$$

This series converges for all real x.

Analyticity requires at least that f be infinitely differentiable at x_0, although this by itself is not sufficient for f to be analytic at x_0.

We claim that, when the coefficients of an initial value problem are analytic, then the solution is as well.

THEOREM 4.1

Let p and q be analytic at x_0. Then the initial value problem

$$y' + p(x)y = q(x); \quad y(x_0) = y_0$$

has a solution that is analytic at x_0. ∎

This means that an initial value problem whose coefficients are analytic at x_0 has an analytic solution at x_0. This justifies attempting to expand the solution in a power series about x_0, where the initial condition is specified. This expansion has the form

$$y(x) = \sum_{n=0}^{\infty} a_n(x - x_0)^n, \tag{4.1}$$

in which

$$a_n = \frac{1}{n!} y^{(n)}(x_0).$$

One strategy to solve the initial value problem of the theorem is to use the differential equation and the initial condition to calculate these derivatives, hence obtain coefficients in the expansion (4.1) of the solution.

EXAMPLE 4.1

Consider again the problem

$$y' + e^x y = x^2; \quad y(0) = 4.$$

The theorem guarantees an analytic solution at 0:

$$y(x) = \sum_{n=0}^{\infty} \frac{1}{n!} y^{(n)}(0) x^n$$

$$= y(0) + y'(0)x + \frac{1}{2!} y''(0) x^2 + \frac{1}{3!} y^{(3)}(0) x^3 + \cdots$$

We will know this series if we can determine the terms $y(0)$, $y'(0)$, $y''(0)$, $\cdots$.

The initial condition gives us $y(0) = 4$. Put $x = 0$ into the differential equation to get

$$y'(0) + y(0) = 0,$$

or

$$y'(0) + 4 = 0.$$

Then

$$y'(0) = -4.$$

Next determine $y''(0)$. Differentiate the differential equation to get

$$y'' + e^x y' + e^x y = 2x \tag{4.2}$$

and put $x = 0$ to get

$$y''(0) + y'(0) + y(0) = 0.$$

Then

$$y''(0) = -y'(0) - y(0) = -(-4) - 4 = 0.$$

Next we will find $y^{(3)}(x)$. Differentiate equation (4.2) to get

$$y^{(3)} + 2e^x y' + e^x y'' + e^x y = 2. \tag{4.3}$$

Then

$$y^{(3)}(0) + 2y'(0) + y''(0) + y(0) = 2,$$

or

$$y^{(3)}(0) + 2(-4) + 4 = 2.$$

Then

$$y^{(3)}(0) = 6.$$

Next differentiate equation (4.3):

$$y^{(4)} + 3e^x y' + 3e^x y'' + e^x y^{(3)} + e^x y = 0.$$

Evaluate this at 0 to get

$$y^{(4)}(0) + 3(-4) + 3(0) + 6 + 4 = 0,$$

so

$$y^{(4)}(0) = 2.$$

At this point we have the first five terms of the Maclaurin expansion of the solution:

$$y(x) = y(0) + y'(0)x + \frac{1}{2}y''(0)x^2 + \frac{1}{6}y^{(3)}(0)x^3 + \frac{1}{24}y^{(4)}(0)x^4 + \cdots$$

$$= 4 - 4x + \frac{1}{6}x^3 + \frac{1}{12}x^4 + \cdots.$$

By differentiating more times, we can write as many terms of this series as we want. ■

EXAMPLE 4.2

Consider the initial value problem

$$y' + \sin(x)y = 1 - x; \quad y(\pi) = -3.$$

Since the initial condition is given at $x = \pi$, we will seek terms in the Taylor expansion of the solution about π. This series has the form

$$y(x) = y(\pi) + y'(\pi)(x - \pi) + \frac{1}{2}y''(\pi)(x - \pi)^2$$

$$+ \frac{1}{6}y^{(3)}(\pi)(x - \pi)^3 + \frac{1}{24}y^{(4)}(\pi)(x - \pi)^4 + \cdots.$$

We know the first term, $y(\pi) = -3$. From the differential equation,

$$y'(\pi) = 1 - \pi + 3\sin(\pi) = 1 - \pi.$$

Now differentiate the differential equation:

$$y''(x) + \cos(x)y + \sin(x)y' = -1. \tag{4.4}$$

Substitute $x = \pi$ to get

$$y''(\pi) - (-3) = -1,$$

so

$$y''(\pi) = -4.$$

Next differentiate equation (4.4):

$$y^{(3)}(x) - \sin(x)y + 2\cos(x)y' + \sin(x)y'' = 0.$$

Substitute $x = \pi$ to get

$$y^{(3)}(\pi) - 2(1 - \pi) = 0,$$

so

$$y^{(3)}(\pi) = 2(1 - \pi).$$

Up to this point we have four terms of the expansion of the solution about π:

$$y(x) = -3 + (1-\pi)(x-\pi) - \frac{4}{2!}(x-\pi)^2 + \frac{2(1-\pi)}{3!}(x-\pi)^3 + \cdots$$

$$= -3 + (1-\pi)(x-\pi) - 2(x-\pi)^2 + \frac{1}{3}(1-\pi)(x-\pi)^3 + \cdots.$$

Again, with more work we can compute more terms. ∎

This method for generating a series solution of a first order linear initial value problem extends readily to second order problems, justified by the following theorem.

THEOREM 4.2

Let p, q and f be analytic at x_0. Then the initial value problem

$$y'' + p(x)y' + q(x)y = f(x); \quad y(x_0) = A, y'(x_0) = B$$

has a unique solution that is also analytic at x_0. ∎

EXAMPLE 4.3

Solve

$$y'' - xy' + e^x y = 4; \quad y(0) = 1, y'(0) = 4.$$

Methods from preceding chapters do not apply to this problem. Since $-x$, e^x, and 4 are analytic at 0, the problem has a series solution expanded about 0. The solution has the form

$$y(x) = y(0) + y'(0)x + \frac{1}{2!}y''(0)x^2 + \frac{1}{3!}y^{(3)}(0)x^3 + \cdots.$$

We already know the first two coefficients from the initial conditions. From the differential equation,

$$y''(0) = 4 - y(0) = 3.$$

Now differentiate the differential equation to get

$$y^{(3)} - y' - xy'' + e^x y + e^x y' = 0.$$

Then

$$y^{(3)}(0) = y'(0) - y(0) - y'(0) = -1.$$

Thus far we have four terms of the series solution about 0:

$$y(x) = 1 + 4x + \frac{3}{2}x^2 - \frac{1}{6}x^3 + \cdots. ∎$$

Although we have illustrated the series method for initial value problems, we can also use it to find general solutions.

EXAMPLE 4.4

We will find the general solution of

$$y'' + \cos(x)y' + 4y = 2x - 1.$$

The idea is to think of this as an initial value problem,

$$y'' + \cos(x)y' + 4y = 2x - 1; \quad y(0) = a, \, y'(0) = b,$$

with a and b arbitrary (these will be the two arbitrary constants in the general solution). Now proceed as we have been doing. We will determine terms of a solution expanded about 0. The first two coefficients are a and b. For the coefficient of x^2, we find, from the differential equation

$$y''(0) = -y'(0) - 4y(0) - 1 = -b - 4a - 1.$$

Next, differentiate the differential equation:

$$y^{(3)} - \sin(x)y' + \cos(x)y'' + 4y' = 2,$$

so

$$y^{(3)}(0) = -y''(0) - 4y'(0) + 2$$

$$= b + 4a + 1 - 4b + 2 = 4a - 3b + 3.$$

Continuing in this way, we obtain (with details omitted)

$$y(x) = a + bx + \frac{-1 - 4a - b}{2}x^2 + \frac{3 + 4a - 3b}{6}x^3$$

$$+ \frac{1 + 12a + 8b}{24}x^4 + \frac{-16 - 40a + b}{120}x^5 + \cdots . \quad \blacksquare$$

In the next section, we will revisit power series solutions, but from a different perspective.

SECTION 4.1   *PROBLEMS*

In each of Problems 1 through 10, find the first five nonzero terms of the power series solution of the initial value problem, about the point where the initial conditions are given.

1. $y'' + y' - xy = 0;$ $y(0) = -2, \, y'(0) = 0$

2. $y'' + 2xy' + (x - 1)y = 0;$ $y(0) = 1, \, y'(0) = 2$

3. $y'' - xy = 2x;$ $y(1) = 3, \, y'(1) = 0$

4. $y'' + xy' = -1 + x;$ $y(2) = 1, \, y'(2) = -4$

5. $y'' - \frac{1}{x^2}y' + \frac{1}{x}y = 0;$ $y(1) = 7, \, y'(1) = 3$

6. $y'' + x^2y = e^x;$ $y(0) = -2, \, y'(0) = 7$

7. $y'' - e^x y' + 2y = 1;$ $y(0) = -3, \, y'(0) = 1$

8. $y'' + y' - x^4y = \sin(2x);$ $y(0) = 0, \, y'(0) = -2$

9. $y'' + \frac{1}{x+2}y' - xy = 0;$ $y(0) = y'(0) = 1$

10. $y'' - y' + \frac{1}{x}y = 1;$ $y(4) = 0, \, y'(4) = 2$

In each of Problems 11 through 20, find the first five nonzero terms of the Maclaurin expansion of the general solution.

11. $y' + \sin(x)y = -x$

12. $y' - x^2y = 1$

13. $y' + xy = 1 - x + x^2$

14. $y' - y = \ln(x + 1)$

15. $y'' + xy = 0$

16. $y'' - 2y' + xy = 0$

17. $y'' - x^3 y = 1$

18. $y'' + (1-x)y' + 2xy = 0$

19. $y'' + y' - x^2 y = 0$

20. $y'' - 8xy = 1 + 2x^9$

21. Find the first five terms of the Maclaurin series solution of Airy's equation $y'' + xy = 0$, satisfying $y(0) = a, y'(0) = b$.

In each of Problems 22 through 25, the initial value problem can be solved in closed form using methods from Chapters 1 and 2. Find this solution and expand it in a Maclaurin series. Then find the Maclaurin series solution using methods of Section 4.1. The two series should agree.

22. $y'' + y = 1; y(0) = 0, y'(0) = 0$

23. $y' + y = 2; y(0) = -1$

24. $y'' + 3y' + 2y = x; y(0) = 0, y'(0) = 1$

25. $y'' - 4y' + 5y = 1; y(0) = -1, y'(0) = 4$

4.2   Power Series Solutions Using Recurrence Relations

We have just seen one way to utilize the differential equation and initial conditions to generate terms of a series solution, expanded about the point where the initial conditions are specified. Another way to generate coefficients is to develop a recurrence relation, which allows us to produce coefficients once certain preceding ones are known. We will consider three examples of this method.

EXAMPLE 4.5

Consider $y'' + x^2 y = 0$. Suppose we want a solution expanded about 0.

Instead of computing successive derivatives at 0, as we did before, now begin by substituting $y(x) = \sum_{n=0}^{\infty} a_n x^n$ into the differential equation. To do this, we need

$$y' = \sum_{n=1}^{\infty} n a^n x^{n-1} \quad \text{and} \quad y'' = \sum_{n=2}^{\infty} n(n-1) a_n x^{n-2}.$$

Notice that the series for y' begins at $n = 1$, and that for y'' at $n = 2$. Put these series into the differential equation to get

$$y'' + x^2 y = \sum_{n=2}^{\infty} n(n-1) a_n x^{n-2} + \sum_{n=0}^{\infty} a_n x^{n+2} = 0. \tag{4.5}$$

Shift indices in both summations so that the power of x occurring in each series is the same. One way to do this is to write

$$\sum_{n=2}^{\infty} n(n-1) a_n x^{n-2} = \sum_{n=0}^{\infty} (n+2)(n+1) a_{n+2} x^n$$

and

$$\sum_{n=0}^{\infty} a_n x^{n+2} = \sum_{n=2}^{\infty} a_{n-2} x^n.$$

Using these series, we can write equation (4.5) as

$$\sum_{n=0}^{\infty} (n+2)(n+1) a_{n+2} x^n + \sum_{n=2}^{\infty} a_{n-2} x^n = 0.$$

We can combine the terms for $n \geq 2$ under one summation and factor out the common x^n (this was the reason for rewriting the series). When we do this, we must list the $n = 0$ and $n = 1$ terms of the first summation separately, or else we lose terms. We get

$$2(1)a_2x^0 + 3(2)a_3x + \sum_{n=2}^{\infty}[(n+2)(n+1)a_{n+2} + a_{n-2}]x^n = 0.$$

The only way for this series to be zero for all x in some open interval about 0 is for the coefficient of each power of x to be zero. Therefore,

$$a_2 = a_3 = 0$$

and, for $n = 2, 3, \ldots,$

$$(n+2)(n+1)a_{n+2} + a_{n-2} = 0.$$

This implies that

$$a_{n+2} = -\frac{1}{(n+2)(n+1)}a_{n-2} \quad \text{for} \quad n = 2, 3, \ldots. \tag{4.6}$$

This is a recurrence relation for this differential equation. In this example, it gives a_{n+2} in terms of a_{n-2} for $n = 2, 3, \ldots$. Thus, we know a_4 in terms of a_0, a_5 in terms of a_1, a_6 in terms of a_2, and so on. The form of the recurrence relation will vary with the differential equation, but it always gives coefficients in terms of one or more previously indexed ones. Using equation (4.6), we proceed:

$$a_4 = -\frac{1}{4(3)}a_0 = -\frac{1}{12}a_0$$

(by putting $n = 2$);

$$a_5 = -\frac{1}{5(4)}a_1 = -\frac{1}{20}a_1$$

(by putting $n = 3$);

$$a_6 = -\frac{1}{6(5)}a_2 = 0 \qquad \text{(because } a_2 = 0\text{)}$$

$$a_7 = -\frac{1}{7(6)}a_3 = 0 \qquad \text{(because } a_3 = 0\text{)}$$

$$a_8 = -\frac{1}{8(7)}a_4 = \frac{1}{(56)(12)}a_0$$

$$a_9 = -\frac{1}{9(8)}a_5 = \frac{1}{(72)(20)}a_1$$

and so on. The first few terms of the series solution expanded about 0 are

$$y(x) = a_0 + a_1x + 0x^2 + 0x^3 - \frac{1}{12}a_0x^4$$

$$- \frac{1}{20}a_1x^5 + 0x^6 + 0x^7 + \frac{1}{672}x^8 + \frac{1}{1440}x^9 + \cdots$$

$$= a_0\left(1 - \frac{1}{12}x^4 + \frac{1}{672}x^6 + \cdots\right) + a_1\left(x - \frac{1}{20}x^5 + \frac{1}{1440}x^9 + \cdots\right).$$

This is actually the general solution, since a_0 and a_1 are arbitrary constants. Note that $a_0 = y(0)$ and $a_1 = y'(0)$, so a solution is completely specified by giving $y(0)$ and $y'(0)$. ∎

EXAMPLE 4.6

Consider the nonhomogeneous differential equation

$$y'' + x^2 y' + 4y = 1 - x^2.$$

Attempt a solution $y(x) = \sum_{n=0}^{\infty} a_n x^n$. Substitute this series into the differential equation to get

$$\sum_{n=2}^{\infty} n(n-1)a_n x^{n-2} + x^2 \sum_{n=1}^{\infty} n a_n x^{n-1} + 4 \sum_{n=0}^{\infty} a_n x^n = 1 - x^2.$$

Then

$$\sum_{n=2}^{\infty} n(n-1)a_n x^{n-2} + \sum_{n=1}^{\infty} n a_n x^{n+1} + \sum_{n=0}^{\infty} 4a_n x^n = 1 - x^2. \tag{4.7}$$

Shift indices in the first and second summation so that the power of x occurring in each is x^n:

$$\sum_{n=2}^{\infty} n(n-1)a_n x^{n-2} = \sum_{n=0}^{\infty} (n+2)(n+1)a_{n+2} x^n$$

and

$$\sum_{n=1}^{\infty} n a_n x^{n+1} = \sum_{n=2}^{\infty} (n-1)a_{n-1} x^n.$$

Equation (4.7) becomes

$$\sum_{n=0}^{\infty} (n+2)(n+1)a_{n+2} x^n + \sum_{n=2}^{\infty} (n-1)a_{n-1} x^n + \sum_{n=0}^{\infty} 4a_n x^n = 1 - x^2.$$

We can combine summations from $n = 2$ on, writing the $n = 0$ and $n = 1$ terms from the first and third summations separately. Then

$$2a_2 x^0 + 6a_3 x + 4a_0 x^0 + 4a_1 x + \sum_{n=2}^{\infty} [(n+2)(n+1)a_{n+2} + (n-1)a_{n-1} + 4a_n] x^n = 1 - x^2.$$

For this to hold for all x in some interval about 0, the coefficient of x^n on the left must match the coefficient of x^n on the right. By matching these coefficients, we get:

$$2a_2 + 4a_0 = 1$$

(from x^0),

$$6a_3 + 4a_1 = 0$$

(from x),

$$4(3)a_4 + a_1 + 4a_2 = -1$$

(from x^2), and, for $n \geq 3$,

$$(n+2)(n+1)a_{n+2} + (n-1)a_{n-1} + 4a_n = 0.$$

From these equations we get, in turn,

$$a_2 = \frac{1}{2} - 2a_0,$$

$$a_3 = -\frac{2}{3}a_1,$$

$$a_4 = \frac{1}{12}(-1 - a_1 - 4a_2)$$

$$= -\frac{1}{12} - \frac{1}{12}a_1 - \frac{1}{3}\left(\frac{1}{2} - 2a_0\right)$$

$$= -\frac{1}{4} + \frac{2}{3}a_0 - \frac{1}{12}a_1,$$

and, for $n = 3, 4, \ldots,$

$$a_{n+2} = -\frac{4a_n + (n-1)a_{n-1}}{(n+2)(n+1)}.$$

This is the recurrence relation for this differential equation, and it enables us to determine a_{n+2} if we know the two previous coefficients a_n and a_{n-1}. With $n = 3$ we get

$$a_5 = -\frac{4a_3 + 2a_2}{20} = -\frac{1}{20}\left(-\frac{8}{3}a_1 + 1 - 4a_0\right)$$

$$= -\frac{1}{20} + \frac{1}{5}a_0 + \frac{2}{15}a_1.$$

With $n = 4$ the recurrence relation gives us

$$a_6 = -\frac{1}{30}(4a_4 + 3a_3) = -\frac{1}{30}\left(-1 + \frac{8}{3}a_0 - \frac{1}{3}a_1 - 2a_1\right)$$

$$= \frac{1}{30} - \frac{4}{45}a_0 + \frac{7}{90}a_1.$$

Thus far we have six terms of the solution:

$$y(x) = a_0 + a_1 x + \left(\frac{1}{2} - 2a_0\right)x^2 - \frac{2}{3}a_1 x^3$$

$$+ \left(-\frac{1}{4} + \frac{2}{3}a_0 - \frac{1}{12}a_1\right)x^4 + \left(-\frac{1}{20} + \frac{1}{5}a_0 + \frac{2}{15}a_1\right)x^5$$

$$+ \left(\frac{1}{30} - \frac{4}{45}a_0 + \frac{7}{90}a_1\right)x^6 + \cdots.$$

Using the recurrence relation, we can produce as many terms of this series as we wish. A recurrence relation is particularly suited to computer generation of coefficients. Because this recurrence relation specifies each a_n (for $n \geq 3$) in terms of two preceding coefficients, it is called a *two-term recurrence relation*. It will give each a_n for $n \geq 3$ in terms of a_0 and a_1, which are arbitrary constants. Indeed, $y(0) = a_0$ and $y'(0) = a_1$, so assigning values to these constants uniquely determines the solution. ■

Sometimes we must represent one or more coefficients as power series to apply the current method. This does not alter the basic idea of collecting coefficients of like powers of x and solving for the coefficients.

EXAMPLE 4.7

Solve

$$y'' + xy' - y = e^{3x}.$$

Each coefficient is analytic at 0, so we will look for a power series solution expanded about 0. Substitute $y = \sum_{n=0}^{\infty} a_n x^n$ and also $e^{3x} = \sum_{n=0}^{\infty} (3^n/n!) x^n$ into the differential equation to get:

$$\sum_{n=2}^{\infty} n(n-1) a_n x^{n-2} + \sum_{n=1}^{\infty} n a_n x^n - \sum_{n=0}^{\infty} a_n x^n = \sum_{n=0}^{\infty} \frac{3^n}{n!} x^n.$$

Shift indices in the first summation to write this equation as

$$\sum_{n=0}^{\infty} (n+2)(n+1) a_{n+2} x^n + \sum_{n=1}^{\infty} n a_n x^n - \sum_{n=0}^{\infty} a_n x^n = \sum_{n=0}^{\infty} \frac{3^n}{n!} x^n.$$

We can collect terms from $n = 1$ on under one summation, obtaining

$$\sum_{n=1}^{\infty} [(n+2)(n+1) a_{n+2} + (n-1) a_n] x^n + 2a_2 - a_0 = 1 + \sum_{n=1}^{\infty} \frac{3^n}{n!} x^n.$$

Equate coefficients of like powers of x on both sides of the equation to obtain

$$2a_2 - a_0 = 1$$

and, for $n = 1, 2, \ldots,$

$$(n+2)(n+1) a_{n+2} + (n-1) a_n = \frac{3^n}{n!}.$$

This gives

$$a_2 = \frac{1}{2}(1 + a_0)$$

and, for $n = 1, 2, \ldots,$ we have the one-term recurrence relation (in terms of one preceding coefficient)

$$a_{n+2} = \frac{(3^n/n!) + (1-n) a_n}{(n+2)(n+1)}.$$

Using this relationship we can generate as many coefficients as we want in the solution series, in terms of the arbitrary constants a_0 and a_1. The first few terms are

$$y(x) \, a_0 + a_1 x + \frac{1 + a_0}{2} x^2 + \frac{1}{2} x^3$$

$$+ \left(\frac{1}{3} - \frac{a_0}{24} \right) x^4 + \frac{7}{40} x^5 + \frac{1}{30} \left(\frac{57}{24} + \frac{a_0}{8} \right) x^6 + \cdots. \quad \blacksquare$$

SECTION 4.2 PROBLEMS

In each of Problems 1 through 12, find the recurrence relation and use it to generate the first five terms of the Maclaurin series of the general solution.

1. $y' - xy = 1 - x$

2. $y' - x^3 y = 4$

3. $y' + (1 - x^2)y = x$

4. $y'' + 2y' + xy = 0$

5. $y'' - xy' + y = 3$

6. $y'' + xy' + xy = 0$

7. $y'' - x^2y' + 2y = x$

8. $y'' + x^2y' + 2y = 0$

9. $y'' + (1 - x)y' + 2y = 1 - x^2$

10. $y'' + y' - (1 - x + x^2)y = -5$

11. $y' + xy = \cos(x)$

12. $y'' + xy' = 1 - e^x$

4.3 Singular Points and the Method of Frobenius

In this section we will consider the second-order linear differential equation

$$P(x)y'' + Q(x)y' + R(x)y = F(x). \tag{4.8}$$

If we can divide this equation by $P(x)$ and obtain an equation of the form

$$y'' + p(x)y' + q(x)y = f(x), \tag{4.9}$$

with analytic coefficients in some open interval about x_0, then we can proceed to a power series solution of equation (4.9) by methods already developed, and thereby solve equation (4.8). In this case we call x_0 an ordinary point of the differential equation. If, however, x_0 is not an ordinary point, then this strategy fails and we must develop some new machinery.

DEFINITION 4.2 *Ordinary and Singular Points*

x_0 is an ordinary point of equation (4.8) if $P(x_0) \neq 0$ and $Q(x)/P(x)$, $R(x)/P(x)$, and $F(x)/P(x)$ are analytic at x_0.

x_0 is a singular point of equation (4.8) if x_0 is not an ordinary point.

Thus, x_0 is a singular point if $P(x_0) = 0$, or if any one of $Q(x)/P(x)$, $R(x)/P(x)$, or $F(x)/P(x)$ fails to be analytic at x_0.

EXAMPLE 4.8

The differential equation

$$x^3(x - 2)^2 y'' + 5(x + 2)(x - 2)y' + 3x^2y = 0$$

has singular points at 0 and 2, because $P(x) = x^3(x - 2)^2$ and $P(0) = P(2) = 0$. Every other real number is a regular point of this equation. ∎

In an interval about a singular point, solutions can exhibit behavior that is quite different from what we have seen in an interval about an ordinary point. In particular, the general solution of equation (4.8) may contain a logarithm term, which will tend toward ∞ in magnitude as x approaches x_0.

In order to seek some understanding of the behavior of solutions near a singular point, we will concentrate on the homogeneous equation

$$P(x)y'' + Q(x)y' + R(x)y = 0. \tag{4.10}$$

Once this case is understood, it does not add substantial further difficulty to consider the nonhomogeneous equation (4.8). Experience and research have shown that some singular points are "worse" than others, in the sense that the subtleties they bring to attempts at solution are deepened. We therefore distinguish two kinds of singular points.

DEFINITION 4.3   *Regular and Irregular Singular Points*

---

x_0 is a regular singular point of equation (4.10) if x_0 is a singular point, and the functions

$$(x - x_0)\frac{Q(x)}{P(x)} \quad \text{and} \quad (x - x_0)^2 \frac{R(x)}{P(x)}$$

are analytic at x_0.

A singular point that is not regular is said to be an irregular singular point.

EXAMPLE 4.9

We have already noted that

$$x^3(x - 2)^2 y'' + 5(x + 2)(x - 2)y' + 3x^2 y = 0$$

has singular points at 0 and 2. We will classify these singular points.

In this example, $P(x) = x^3(x - 2)^2$, $Q(x) = 5(x + 2)(x - 2)$ and $R(x) = 3x^2$. First consider $x_0 = 0$. Now

$$(x - x_0)\frac{Q(x)}{P(x)} = \frac{5x(x + 2)(x - 2)}{x^3(x - 2)^2} = \frac{5}{x^2}\frac{x + 2}{x - 2}$$

is not defined at 0, hence is not analytic there. This is enough to conclude that 0 is an irregular singular point of this differential equation.

Next let $x_0 = 2$ and consider

$$(x - 2)\frac{Q(x)}{P(x)} = 5\frac{x + 2}{x^3}$$

and

$$(x - 2)^2 \frac{R(x)}{P(x)} = \frac{3}{x}.$$

Both of these functions are analytic at 2. Therefore, 2 is a regular singular point of the differential equation. ∎

Suppose now that equation (4.10) has a regular singular point at x_0. Then there may be no solution as a power series about x_0. In this case we attempt to choose numbers c_n and a number r so that

$$y(x) = \sum_{n=0}^{\infty} c_n (x - x_0)^{n+r} \tag{4.11}$$

is a solution. This series is called a *Frobenius series*, and the strategy of attempting a solution of this form is called the *method of Frobenius*. A Frobenius series need not be a power series, since r may be negative or may be a noninteger.

A Frobenius series "begins" with $c_0 x^r$, which is constant only if $r = 0$. Thus, in computing the derivative of the Frobenius series (4.11), we get

$$y'(x) = \sum_{n=0}^{\infty} (n+r)c_n(x-x_0)^{n+r-1},$$

and this summation begins at zero again because the derivative of the $n = 0$ term need not be zero. Similarly,

$$y''(x) = \sum_{n=0}^{\infty} (n+r)(n+r-1)c_n(x-x_0)^{n+r-2}.$$

We will now illustrate the method of Frobenius.

EXAMPLE 4.10

We want to solve

$$x^2 y'' + x \left(\frac{1}{2} + 2x \right) y' + \left(x - \frac{1}{2} \right) y = 0.$$

It is routine to show that 0 is a regular singular point. Substitute a Frobenius series $y(x) = \sum_{n=0}^{\infty} c_n x^{n+r}$ into the differential equation to get

$$\sum_{n=0}^{\infty} (n+r)(n+r-1)c_n x^{n+r} + \sum_{n=0}^{\infty} \frac{1}{2}(n+r)c_n x^{n+r} + \sum_{n=0}^{\infty} 2(n+r)c_n x^{n+r+1}$$

$$+ \sum_{n=0}^{\infty} c_n x^{n+r+1} - \sum_{n=0}^{\infty} \frac{1}{2}c_n x^{n+r} = 0.$$

Shift indices in the third and fourth summations to write this equation as

$$\left[r(r-1)c_0 + \frac{1}{2}c_0 r - \frac{1}{2}c_0 \right] x^r + \sum_{n=1}^{\infty} \left[(n+r)(n+r-1)c_n + \frac{1}{2}(n+r)c_n \right.$$

$$+ 2(n+r-1)c_{n-1} + c_{n-1} - \frac{1}{2}c_n \right] x^{n+r} = 0.$$

This equation will hold if the coefficient of each x^{n+r} is zero. This gives us the equations

$$r(r-1)c_0 + \frac{1}{2}c_0 r - \frac{1}{2}c_0 = 0 \tag{4.12}$$

and

$$(n+r)(n+r-1)c_n + \frac{1}{2}(n+r)c_n + 2(n+r-1)c_{n-1} + c_{n-1} - \frac{1}{2}c_n = 0 \tag{4.13}$$

for $n = 1, 2, \ldots$. Assuming that $c_0 \neq 0$, an essential requirement in the method, equation (4.12) implies that

$$r(r-1) + \frac{1}{2}r - \frac{1}{2} = 0. \tag{4.14}$$

This is the indicial equation for this differential equation, and it determines the values of r we can use. Solve it to obtain $r_1 = 1$ and $r_2 = -\frac{1}{2}$. Equation (4.13) enables us to solve for c_n in terms of c_{n-1} to get the recurrence relation

$$c_n = -\frac{1 + 2(n + r - 1)}{(n + r)(n + r - 1) + \frac{1}{2}(n + r) - \frac{1}{2}} c_{n-1}$$

for $n = 1, 2, \ldots$.

First put $r = r_1 = 1$ into the recurrence relation to obtain

$$c_n = -\frac{1 + 2n}{n\left(n + \frac{3}{2}\right)} c_{n-1} \quad \text{for} \quad n = 1, 2, \ldots.$$

Some of these coefficients are

$$c_1 = -\frac{3}{\frac{5}{2}} c_0 = -\frac{6}{5} c_0,$$

$$c_2 = -\frac{5}{\frac{7}{2}} c_1 = -\frac{5}{7}\left(-\frac{6}{5} c_0\right) = \frac{6}{7} c_0,$$

$$c_3 = -\frac{7}{\frac{27}{2}} c_2 = -\frac{14}{27}\left(\frac{6}{7} c_0\right) = -\frac{4}{9} c_0,$$

and so on. One Frobenius solution is

$$y_1(x) = c_0\left(x - \frac{6}{5} x^2 + \frac{6}{7} x^3 - \frac{4}{9} x^4 + \cdots\right).$$

Because r_1 is a nonnegative integer, this first Frobenius solution is actually a power series about 0.

For a second Frobenius solution, substitute $r = r_2 = -\frac{1}{2}$ into the recurrence relation. To avoid confusion we will replace c_n with c_n^* in this relation. We get

$$c_n^* = -\frac{1 + 2\left(n - \frac{3}{2}\right)}{\left(n - \frac{1}{2}\right)\left(n - \frac{3}{2}\right) + \frac{1}{2}\left(n - \frac{1}{2}\right) - \frac{1}{2}} c_{n-1}^*$$

for $n = 1, 2, \ldots$. This simplifies to

$$c_n^* = -\frac{2n - 2}{n\left(n - \frac{3}{2}\right)} c_{n-1}^*.$$

It happens in this example that $c_1^* = 0$, so each $c_n^* = 0$ for $n = 1, 2, \ldots$ and the second Frobenius solution is

$$y_2(x) = \sum_{n=0}^{\infty} c_n^* x^{n-1/2} = c_0^* x^{-1/2} \quad \text{for} \quad x > 0. \; \blacksquare$$

The method of Frobenius is justified by the following theorem.

THEOREM 4.3   Method of Frobenius

———————

Suppose x_0 is a regular singular point of $P(x)y'' + Q(x)y' + R(x)y = 0$. Then there exists at least one Frobenius solution

$$y(x) = \sum_{n=0}^{\infty} c_n (x - x_0)^r$$

with $c_0 \neq 0$. Further, if the Taylor expansions of $(x - x_0)Q(x)/R(x)$ and $(x - x_0)^2 R(x)/P(x)$ about x_0 converge in an open interval $(x_0 - h, x_0 + h)$, then this Frobenius series also converges in this interval, except perhaps at x_0 itself. ■

It is significant that the theorem only guarantees the existence of one Frobenius solution. Although we obtained two such solutions in the preceding example, the next example shows that there may be only one.

EXAMPLE 4.11

Suppose we want to solve

$$x^2 y'' + 5xy' + (x + 4)y = 0.$$

Zero is a regular singular point, so attempt a Frobenius solution $y(x) = \sum_{n=0}^{\infty} c_n x^{n+r}$. Substitute into the differential equation to get

$$\sum_{n=0}^{\infty}(n+r)(n+r-1)c_n x^{n+r} + \sum_{n=0}^{\infty} 5(n+r)c_n x^{n+r} + \sum_{n=0}^{\infty} c_n x^{n+r+1} + \sum_{n=0}^{\infty} 4c_n x^{n+r} = 0.$$

Shift indices in the third summation to write this equation as

$$\sum_{n=0}^{\infty}(n+r)(n+r-1)c_n x^{n+r} + \sum_{n=0}^{\infty} 5(n+r)c_n x^{n+r} + \sum_{n=1}^{\infty} c_{n-1} x^{n+r} + \sum_{n=0}^{\infty} 4c_n x^{n+r} = 0.$$

Now combine terms to write

$$[r(r-1) + 5r + 4]c_0 x^r + \sum_{n=1}^{\infty}[(n+r)(n+r-1)c_n + 5(n+r)c_n + c_{n-1} + 4c_n]x^{n+r} = 0.$$

Setting the coefficient of x^r equal to zero (since $c_0 \neq 0$ as part of the method), we get the indicial equation

$$r(r-1) + 5r + 4 = 0$$

with the repeated root $r = -2$. The coefficient of x^{n+r} in the series, with $r = -2$ inserted, gives us the recurrence relation

$$(n-2)(n-3)c_n + 5(n-2)c_n + c_{n-1} + 4c_n = 0$$

or

$$c_n = -\frac{1}{(n-2)(n-3) + 5(n-2) + 4}c_{n-1}$$

for $n = 1, 2, \ldots$. This simplifies to

$$c_n = -\frac{1}{n^2}c_{n-1} \quad \text{for } n = 1, 2, 3, \ldots.$$

Some of the coefficients are

$$c_1 = -c_0$$

$$c_2 = -\frac{1}{4}c_1 = \frac{1}{4}c_0 = \frac{1}{(2)^2}c_0$$

$$c_3 = -\frac{1}{9}c_2 = -\frac{1}{4 \cdot 9}c_0 = -\frac{1}{(2 \cdot 3)^2}c_0$$

$$c_4 = -\frac{1}{16}c_3 = \frac{1}{4 \cdot 9 \cdot 16}c_0 = \frac{1}{(2 \cdot 3 \cdot 4)^2}c_0$$

and so on. In general,

$$c^n = (-1)^n \frac{1}{(n!)^2} c_0$$

for $n = 1, 2, 3, \ldots$. The Frobenius solution we have found is

$$y(x) = c_0[x^{-2} - x^{-1} + \frac{1}{4} - \frac{1}{36}x + \frac{1}{576}x^2 + \cdots]$$

$$= c_0 \sum_{n=0}^{\infty} (-1)^n \frac{1}{(n!)^2} x^{n-2}.$$

In this example, $xQ(x)/P(x) = x(5x/x^2) = 5$ and $x^2R(x)/P(x) = x^2(x+4)/x^2 = x+4$. These polynomials are their own Maclaurin series about 0, and these series, being finite, converge for all x. By Theorem 4.3, the Frobenius series solution converges for all x, except $x = 0$.

In this example the method of Frobenius produces only one solution. ◼

In the last example the recurrence relation produced a simple formula for c_n in terms of c_0. Depending on the coefficients in the differential equation, a formula for c_n in terms of c_0 may be quite complicated, or it may even not be possible to write a formula in terms of elementary algebraic expressions. We will give another example, having some importance for later work, in which the Frobenius method may produce only one solution.

EXAMPLE 4.12 Bessel Functions of the First Kind

The differential equation

$$x^2y'' + xy' + (x^2 - \nu^2)y = 0$$

is called Bessel's equation of order ν, for $\nu \geq 0$. Although it is a second-order differential equation, this description of it as being of order ν refers to the parameter ν appearing in it, and is traditional. Solutions of Bessel's equation are called *Bessel functions*, and we will encounter them in Chapter 16 when we treat special functions, and again in Chapter 18 when we analyze heat conduction in an infinite cylinder.

Zero is a regular singular point of Bessel's equation, so attempt a solution

$$y(x) = \sum_{n=0}^{\infty} c_n x^{n+r}.$$

Upon substituting this series into Bessel's equation, we obtain

$$[r(r-1)+r-\nu^2]c_0 x^r + [r(r+1)+(r+1)-\nu^2]c_1 x^{r+1}$$

$$+ \sum_{n=2}^{\infty} [[(n+r)(n+r-1)+(n+r)-\nu^2]c_n + c_{n-2}]x^{n+r} = 0. \qquad (4.15)$$

Set the coefficient of each power of x equal to zero. Assuming that $c_0 \neq 0$, we obtain the indicial equation

$$r^2 - \nu^2 = 0,$$

with roots $\pm \nu$. Let $r = \nu$ in the coefficient of x^{r+1} in equation (4.15) to get

$$(2\nu + 1)c_1 = 0.$$

Since $2\nu + 1 \neq 0$, we conclude that $c_1 = 0$.

From the coefficient of x^{n+r} in equation (4.15), we get

$$[(n+r)(n+r-1)+(n+r)-\nu^2]c_n + c_{n-2} = 0$$

for $n = 2, 3, \ldots$. Set $r = \nu$ in this equation and solve for c_n to get

$$c_n = -\frac{1}{n(n+2\nu)} c_{n-2}$$

for $n = 2, 3, \ldots$. Since $c_1 = 0$, this equation yields

$$c_3 = c_5 = \ldots = c_{\text{odd}} = 0.$$

For the even-indexed coefficients, write

$$c_{2n} = -\frac{1}{2n(2n+2\nu)} c_{2n-2} = -\frac{1}{2^2 n(n+\nu)} c_{2n-2}$$

$$= -\frac{1}{2^2 n(n+\nu)} \frac{-1}{2(n-1)[(2(n-1)+2\nu]} c_{2n-4}$$

$$= \frac{1}{2^4 n(n-1)(n+\nu)(n+\nu-1)} c_{2n-4}$$

$$= \ldots = \frac{(-1)^n}{2^{2n} n(n-1)\cdots(2)(1)(n+\nu)(n-1+\nu)\cdots(1+\nu)} c_0$$

$$= \frac{(-1)^n}{2^{2n} n!(1+\nu)(2+\nu)\cdots(n+\nu)} c_0.$$

One Frobenius solution of Bessel's equation of order ν is therefore

$$y_1(x) = c_0 \sum_{n=0}^{\infty} \frac{(-1)^n}{2^{2n} n!(1+\nu)(2+\nu)\cdots(n+\nu)} x^{2n+\nu}. \qquad (4.16)$$

These functions are called *Bessel functions of the first kind of order* ν. ◼

The roots of the indicial equation for Bessel's equation are $\pm \nu$. Depending on ν, we may or may not obtain two linearly independent solutions by using ν and $-\nu$ in the series solution (4.16). We will discuss this in more detail when we treat Bessel functions in Chapter 16, where we will see that, when ν is a positive integer, the functions obtained by using ν and then $-\nu$ in the recurrence relation are linearly dependent.

SECTION 4.3   *PROBLEMS*

In each of Problems 1 through 6, find all of the singular points and classify each singular point as regular or singular.

1. $x^2(x-3)^2 y'' + 4x(x^2-x-6)y' + (x^2-x-2)y = 0$

2. $(x^3-2x^2-7x-4)y'' - 2(x^2+1)y' + (5x^2-2x)y = 0$

3. $x^2(x-2)y'' + (5x-7)y' + 2(3+5x^2)y = 0$

4. $[(9-x^2)y']' + (2+x^2)y = 0$

5. $[(x-2)^{-1}y']' + x^{-5/2}y = 0$

6. $x^2 \sin^2(x-\pi)y'' + \tan(x-\pi)\tan(x)y' + (7x-2)\cos(x)y = 0$

In each of Problems 7 through 15, (a) show that zero is a regular singular point of the differential equation, (b) find and solve the indicial equation, (c) determine the recurrence relation, and (d) use the results of (b) and (c) to find the first five nonzero terms of two linearly independent Frobenius solutions.

7. $4x^2 y'' + 2xy' - xy = 0$

8. $16x^2 y'' - 4x^2 y' + 3y = 0$

9. $9x^2 y'' + 2(2x+1)y = 0$

10. $12x^2 y'' + 5xy' + (1-2x^2)y = 0$

11. $2xy'' + (2x+1)y' + 2y = 0$

12. $2x^2 y'' - xy' + (1-x^2)y = 0$

13. $2x^2 y'' + x(2x+1)y' - (2x^2+1)y = 0$

14. $3x^2 y'' + 4xy' - (3x+2)y = 0$

15. $9x^2 y'' + 9xy' + (9x^2-4)y = 0$

4.4   Second Solutions and Logarithm Factors

In the preceding section we saw that under certain conditions we can always produce a Frobenius series solution of equation (4.10), but possibly not a second, linearly independent solution. This may occur if the indicial equation has a repeated root, or even if it has distinct roots that differ by a positive integer.

In the case that the method of Frobenius only produces one solution, there is a method for finding a second, linearly independent solution. The key is to know what form to expect this solution to have, so that this template can be substituted into the differential equation to determine the coefficients. This template is provided by the following theorem. We will state the theorem with $x_0 = 0$ to simplify the notation. To apply it to a differential equation having a singular point $x_0 \neq 0$, use the change of variables $z = x - x_0$.

THEOREM 4.4   *A Second Solution in the Method of Frobenius*

Suppose 0 is a regular singular point of

$$P(x)y'' + Q(x)y' + R(x)y = 0.$$

Let r_1 and r_2 be roots of the indicial equation. If these are real, suppose $r_1 \geq r_2$. Then

1. If $r_1 - r_2$ is not an integer, there are two linearly independent Frobenius solutions

$$y_1(x) = \sum_{n=0}^{\infty} c_n x^{n+r_1} \quad \text{and} \quad y_2(x) = \sum_{n=0}^{\infty} c_n^* x^{n+r_2},$$

with $c_0 \neq 0$ and $c_0^* \neq 0$. These solutions are valid in some interval $(0, h)$ or $(-h, 0)$.

2. If $r_1 - r_2 = 0$, there is a Frobenius solution $y_1(x) = \sum_{n=0}^{\infty} c_n x^{n+r_1}$ with $c_0 \neq 0$ as well as a second solution

$$y_2(x) = y_1(x)\ln(x) + \sum_{n=1}^{\infty} c_n^* x^{n+r_1}.$$

Further, y_1 and y_2 form a fundamental set of solutions on some interval $(0, h)$.

3. If $r_1 - r_2$ is a positive integer, then there is a Frobenius series solution

$$y_1(x) = \sum_{n=0}^{\infty} c_n x^{n+r_1}.$$

In this case there is a second solution of the form

$$y_2(x) = ky_1(x)\ln(x) + \sum_{n=0}^{\infty} c_n^* x^{n+r_2}.$$

If $k = 0$ this is a second Frobenius series solution; if not the solution contains a logarithm term. In either event, y_1 and y_2 form a fundamental set on some interval $(0, h)$. ∎

We may now summarize the method of Frobenius as follows, for the equation $P(x)y'' + Q(x)y' + R(x)y = 0$. Suppose 0 is a regular singular point.

Substitute $y(x) = \sum_{n=0}^{\infty} c_n x^{n+r}$ into the differential equation. From the indicial equation, determine the values of r. If these are distinct and do not differ by an integer, we are guaranteed two linearly independent Frobenius solutions.

If the indicial equation has repeated roots, then there is just one Frobenius solution y_1. But there is a second solution

$$y_2(x) = y_1(x)\ln(x) + \sum_{n=1}^{\infty} c_n^* x^{n+r_1}.$$

The series on the right starts its summation at $n = 1$, not $n = 0$. Substitute $y_2(x)$ into the differential equation and obtain a recurrence relation for the coefficients c_n^*. Because this solution has a logarithm term, y_1 and y_2 are linearly independent.

If $r_1 - r_2$ is a positive integer, there may or may not be a second Frobenius solution. In this case there is a second solution of the form

$$y_2(x) = ky_1(x)\ln(x) + \sum_{n=0}^{\infty} c_n^* x^{n+r_2}.$$

Substitute y_2 into the differential equation and obtain an equation for k and a recurrence relation for the coefficients c_n^*. If $k = 0$, we obtain a second Frobenius solution; if not, then this second solution has a logarithm term. In either case y_1 and y_2 are linearly independent.

In the preceding section we saw in Example 4.10 a differential equation in which $r_1 - r_2$ was not an integer. There we found two linearly independent Frobenius solutions. We will illustrate cases (2) and (3) of the theorem.

EXAMPLE 4.13   Conclusion (2), Equal Roots

Consider again $x^2 y'' + 5xy' + (x + 4)y = 0$. In Example 4.11 we found one Frobenius solution

$$y_1(x) = c_0 \sum_{n=0}^{\infty} (-1)^n \frac{1}{(n!)^2} x^{n-2}.$$

The indicial equation is $(r+2)^2 = 0$ with the repeated root $r = -2$. Conclusion (2) of the theorem suggests that we attempt a second solution of the form

$$y_2(x) = y_1(x)\ln(x) + \sum_{n=1}^{\infty} c_n^* x^{n-2}.$$

Note that the series on the right begins at $n = 1$, not $n = 0$. Substitute this series into the differential equation to get, after some rearrangement of terms,

$$4y_1 + 2xy_1' + \sum_{n=1}^{\infty}(n-2)(n-3)c_n^* x^{n-2} + \sum_{n=1}^{\infty}5(n-2)c_n^* x^{n-2} + \sum_{n=1}^{\infty} c_n^* x^{n-1}$$

$$+ \sum_{n=1}^{\infty}4c_n^* x^{n-2} + \ln(x)[x^2 y_1'' + 5xy_1' + (x+4)y_1] = 0.$$

The bracketed coefficient of $\ln(x)$ is zero because y_1 is a solution of the differential equation. In the last equation, choose $c_0^* = 1$ (we need only one second solution), shift indices to write $\sum_{n=1}^{\infty} c_n^* x^{n-1} = \sum_{n=2}^{\infty} c_{n-1}^* x^{n-2}$, and substitute the series obtained for $y_1(x)$ to get

$$-2x^{-1} + c_1^* x^{-1} + \sum_{n=2}^{\infty}\left[\frac{4(-1)^n}{(n!)^2} + \frac{2(-1)^n}{(n!)^2}(n-2)\right.$$

$$\left. + (n-2)(n-3)c_n^* + 5(n-2)c_n^* + c_{n-1}^* + 4c_n^*\right] x^{n-2} = 0.$$

Set the coefficient of each power of x equal to zero. From the coefficient of x^{-1} we get

$$c_1^* = 2.$$

From the coefficient of x^{n-2} in the summation we get, after some routine algebra,

$$\frac{2(-1)^n}{(n!)^2}n + n^2 c_n^* + c_{n-1}^* = 0,$$

or

$$c_n^* = -\frac{1}{n^2}c_{n-1}^* - \frac{2(-1)^n}{n(n!)^2}$$

for $n = 2, 3, 4, \ldots$. This enables us to calculate as many coefficients as we wish. Some of the terms of the resulting solution are

$$y_2(x) = y_1(x)\ln(x) + \frac{2}{x} - \frac{3}{4} + \frac{11}{108}x - \frac{25}{3456}x^2 + \frac{137}{432{,}000}x^3 + \cdots.$$

Because of the logarithm term, it is obvious that this solution is not a constant multiple of y_1, so y_1 and y_2 form a fundamental set of solutions (on some interval $(0, h)$). The general solution is

$$y(x) = [C_1 + C_2\ln(x)]\sum_{n=0}^{\infty}\frac{(-1)^n}{(n!)^2}x^{n-2}$$

$$+ C_2\left[\frac{2}{x} - \frac{3}{4} + \frac{11}{108}x - \frac{25}{3456}x^2 + \frac{137}{432{,}000}x^3 + \cdots\right]. \quad \blacksquare$$

EXAMPLE 4.14   Conclusion (3), with $k = 0$

The equation $x^2y'' + x^2y' - 2y = 0$ has a regular singular point at 0. Substitute $y(x) = \sum_{n=0}^{\infty} c_n x^{n+r}$ and shift indices to obtain

$$[r(r-1) - 2]c_0 x^r + \sum_{n=1}^{\infty} [(n+r)(n+r-1)c_n + (n+r-1)c_{n-1} - 2c_n]x^{n+r} = 0.$$

Assume that $c_0 \neq 0$. The indicial equation is $r^2 - r - 2 = 0$, with roots $r_1 = 2$ and $r_2 = -1$. Now $r_1 - r_2 = 3$ and case (3) of the theorem applies.

For a first solution, set the coefficient of x^{n+r} equal to zero to get

$$(n+r)(n+r-1)c_n + (n+r-1)c_{n-1} - 2c_n = 0. \tag{4.17}$$

Let $r = 2$ to get

$$(n+2)(n+1)c_n + (n+1)c_{n-1} - 2c_n = 0,$$

or

$$c_n = -\frac{n+1}{n(n+3)}c_{n-1} \quad \text{for} \quad n = 1, 2, \ldots.$$

Using this recurrence relation to generate terms of the series, we obtain

$$y_1(x) = c_0 x^2 \left[1 - \frac{1}{2}x + \frac{3}{20}x^2 - \frac{1}{30}x^3 + \frac{1}{168}x^4 - \frac{1}{1120}x^5 + \frac{1}{8640}x^6 + \cdots \right].$$

Now try the second root $r = -1$ in the recurrence relation (4.17). We get

$$(n-1)(n-2)c_n^* + (n-2)c_{n-1}^* - 2c_n^* = 0$$

for $n = 1, 2, \ldots$. When $n = 3$, this gives $c_2^* = 0$, which forces $c_n^* = 0$ for $n \geq 2$. But then

$$y_2(x) = c_0^* \frac{1}{x} + c_1^*.$$

Substitute this into the differential equation to get

$$x^2(2c_0^* x^{-3}) + x^2(-c_0^* x^{-2}) - 2\left(c_1^* + c_0^* \frac{1}{x}\right) = -c_0^* - 2c_1^* = 0.$$

Then $c_1^* = -\frac{1}{2}c_0^*$ and we obtain the second solution

$$y_2(x) = c_0^* \left(\frac{1}{x} - \frac{1}{2}\right),$$

with c_0^* nonzero but otherwise arbitrary. The functions y_1 and y_2 form a fundamental set of solutions. ■

EXAMPLE 4.15   Conclusion (3), $k \neq 0$

Consider the differential equation $xy'' - y = 0$, which has a regular singular point at 0. Substitute $y(x) = \sum_{n=0}^{\infty} c_n x^{n+r}$ to obtain

$$\sum_{n=0}^{\infty} (n+r)(n+r-1)c_n x^{n+r-1} - \sum_{n=0}^{\infty} c_n x^{n+r} = 0.$$

Shift indices in the second summation to write this equation as

$$(r^2 - r)c_0 x^{r-1} + \sum_{n=1}^{\infty}[(n+r)(n+r-1)c_n - c_{n-1}]x^{n+r-1} = 0.$$

The indicial equation is $r^2 - r = 0$, with roots $r_1 = 1$, $r_2 = 0$. Here $r_1 - r_2 = 1$, a positive integer, so we are in case (3) of the theorem. The recurrence relation is

$$(n+r)(n+r-1)c_n - c_{n-1} = 0$$

for $n = 1, 2, \ldots$. Let $r = 1$ and solve for c_n:

$$c_n = \frac{1}{n(n+1)}c_{n-1} \quad \text{for} \quad n = 1, 2, 3, \ldots.$$

Some of the coefficients are

$$c_1 = \frac{1}{1(2)}c_0,$$

$$c_2 = \frac{1}{2(3)}c_1 = \frac{1}{2(2)(3)}c_0,$$

$$c_3 = \frac{1}{3(4)}c_2 = \frac{1}{2(3)(2)(3)(4)}c_0.$$

In general, we find that

$$c_n = \frac{1}{n!(n+1)!}c_0$$

for $n = 1, 2, \ldots$. This gives us a Frobenius series solution

$$y_1(x) = c_0 \sum_{n=0}^{\infty} \frac{1}{n!(n+1)!}x^{n+1}$$

$$= c_0 \left[x + \frac{1}{2}x^2 + \frac{1}{12}x^3 + \frac{1}{144}x^4 + \cdots \right].$$

In this example, if we put $r = 0$ into the recurrence relation, we get

$$n(n-1)c_n - c_{n-1} = 0$$

for $n = 1, 2, \ldots$. But if we put $n = 1$ into this equation, we get $c_0 = 0$, contrary to the assumption that $c_0 \neq 0$. Unlike the preceding example, we cannot find a second Frobenius solution by simply putting r_2 into the recurrence relation.

Try a second solution

$$y_2(x) = ky_1(x)\ln(x) + \sum_{n=0}^{\infty} c_n^* x^n$$

(here $x^{n+r_2} = x^n$ because $r_2 = 0$). Substitute this into the differential equation to get

$$x\left[ky_1'' \ln(x) + 2ky_1'\frac{1}{x} - ky_1\frac{1}{x^2} + \sum_{n=2}^{\infty} n(n-1)c_n^* x^{n-2} \right]$$

$$- ky_1 \ln(x) - \sum_{n=0}^{\infty} c_n^* x^n = 0. \tag{4.18}$$

Now

$$k \ln(x)[xy_1'' - y_1] = 0$$

because y_1 is a solution of the differential equation. For the remaining terms in equation (4.18), insert the series for $y_1(x)$ (with $c_0 = 1$ for convenience) to get

$$2k \sum_{n=0}^{\infty} \frac{1}{(n!)^2} x^n - k \sum_{n=0}^{\infty} \frac{1}{n!(n+1)!} x^n + \sum_{n=2}^{\infty} c_n^* n(n-1) x^{n-1} - \sum_{n=0}^{\infty} c_n^* x^n = 0.$$

Shift indices in the third summation to write this equation as

$$2k \sum_{n=0}^{\infty} \frac{1}{(n!)^2} x^n - k \sum_{n=0}^{\infty} \frac{1}{n!(n+1)!} x^n + \sum_{n=1}^{\infty} c_{n+1}^* (n+1) n x^n - \sum_{n=0}^{\infty} c_n^* x^n = 0.$$

Then

$$(2k - k - c_0^*)x^0 + \sum_{n=1}^{\infty} \left[\frac{2k}{(n!)^2} - \frac{k}{n!(n+1)!} + n(n+1)c_{n+1}^* - c_n^* \right] x^n = 0.$$

Then

$$k - c_0^* = 0$$

and, for $n = 1, 2, \ldots$,

$$\frac{2k}{(n!)^2} - \frac{k}{n!(n+1)!} + n(n+1)c_{n+1}^* - c_n^* = 0.$$

This gives us $k = c_0^*$ and the recurrence relation

$$c_{n+1}^* = \frac{1}{n(n+1)} \left[c_n^* - \frac{(2n+1)k}{n!(n+1)!} \right]$$

for $n = 1, 2, 3, \ldots$. Since c_0^* can be any nonzero real number, we may choose $c_0^* = 1$. Then $k = 1$. For a particular second solution, let $c_1^* = 0$, obtaining:

$$y_2(x) = y_1(x) \ln(x) + 1 - \frac{3}{4}x^2 - \frac{7}{36}x^3 - \frac{35}{1728}x^4 - \cdots. \quad \blacksquare$$

To conclude this section, we will produce a second solution for Bessel's equation, in a case where the Frobenius method yields only one solution. This will be of use later when we study Bessel functions.

EXAMPLE 4.16 Bessel Function of the Second Kind

Consider Bessel's equation of zero order ($\nu = 0$). From Example 4.12, this is

$$x^2 y'' + xy' + x^2 y = 0.$$

We know from that example that the indicial equation has only one root, $r = 0$. From equation (4.16), with $c_0 = 1$, one Frobenius solution is

$$y_1(x) = \sum_{k=0}^{\infty} (-1)^k \frac{1}{2^{2k}(k!)^2} x^{2k}.$$

Attempt a second, linearly independent solution of the form

$$y_2(x) = y_1(x) \ln(x) + \sum_{k=1}^{\infty} c_k^* x^k.$$

Substitute $y_2(x)$ into the differential equation to get

$$xy_1'' \ln(x) + 2y_1' - \frac{1}{x}y_1 + \sum_{k=2}^{\infty} k(k-1)c_k^* x^{k-1}$$

$$+ \ y_1' \ln(x) + \frac{1}{x}y_1 + \sum_{k=1}^{\infty} kc_k^* x^{k-1} + xy_1 \ln(x) + \sum_{k=1}^{\infty} c_k^* x^{k+1} = 0.$$

Terms involving $\ln(x)$ and $y_1(x)$ cancel, and we are left with

$$2y_1' + \sum_{k=2}^{\infty} k(k-1)c_k^* x^{k-1} + \sum_{k=1}^{\infty} kc_k^* x^{k-1} + \sum_{k=1}^{\infty} c_k^* x^{k+1} = 0.$$

Since $k(k-1) = k^2 - k$, part of the first summation cancels all terms except the $k=1$ term in the second summation, and we have

$$2y_1' + \sum_{k=2}^{\infty} k^2 c_k^* x^{k-1} + c_1^* + \sum_{k=1}^{\infty} c_k^* x^{k+1} = 0.$$

Substitute the series for y_1' into this equation to get

$$2\sum_{k=1}^{\infty} \frac{(-1)^k}{2^{2k-1}k!(k-1)!} x^{2k-1} + \sum_{k=2}^{\infty} k^2 c_k^* x^{k-1} + c_1^* + \sum_{k=1}^{\infty} c_k^* x^{k+1} = 0.$$

Shift indices in the last series to write this equation as

$$\sum_{k=1}^{\infty} \frac{(-1)^k}{2^{2k-2}k!(k-1)!} x^{2k-1} + c_1^* + 4c_2^* x + \sum_{k=3}^{\infty} (k^2 c_k^* + c_{k-2}^*)x^{k-1} = 0. \tag{4.19}$$

The only constant term on the left side of this equation is c_1^*, which must therefore be zero. The only even powers of x appearing in equation (4.19) are in the right-most series when k is odd. The coefficients of these powers of x must be zero, hence

$$k^2 c_k^* + c_{k-2}^* = 0 \quad \text{for} \quad k = 3, 5, 7, \ldots.$$

But then all odd-indexed coefficients are multiples of c_1^*, which is zero, so

$$c_{2k+1}^* = 0 \quad \text{for} \quad k = 0, 1, 2, \ldots.$$

To determine the even-indexed coefficients, replace k by $2j$ in the second summation of equation (4.19) and k with j in the first summation to get

$$\sum_{j=1}^{\infty} \frac{(-1)^j}{2^{2j-2}j!(j-1)!} x^{2j-1} + 4c_2^* x + \sum_{j=2}^{\infty} (4j^2 c_{2j}^* + c_{2j-2}^*)x^{2j-1} = 0.$$

Now combine terms and write this equation as

$$(4c_2^* - 1)x + \sum_{j=2}^{\infty} \left[\frac{(-1)^j}{2^{2j-2}j!(j-1)!} + 4j^2 c_{2j}^* + c_{2j-2}^* \right] x^{2j-1} = 0.$$

Equate the coefficient of each power of x to zero. We get

$$c_2^* = \frac{1}{4}$$

and the recurrence relation

$$c_{2j}^* = \frac{(-1)^{j+1}}{2^{2j}[j!]^2 j} - \frac{1}{4j^2} c_{2j-2}^* \quad \text{for} \quad j = 2, 3, 4, \ldots.$$

If we write some of these coefficients, a pattern emerges:

$$c_4^* = \frac{-1}{2^2 4^2}\left[1+\frac{1}{2}\right],$$

$$c_6^* = \frac{1}{2^2 4^2 6^2}\left[1+\frac{1}{2}+\frac{1}{3}\right],$$

and, in general,

$$c_{2j}^* = \frac{(-1)^{j+1}}{2^2 4^2 \cdots (2j)^2}\left[1+\frac{1}{2}+\cdots+\frac{1}{j}\right] = \frac{(-1)^{j+1}}{2^{2j}(j!)^2}\varnothing(j),$$

where

$$\varnothing(j) = 1+\frac{1}{2}+\cdots+\frac{1}{j} \quad \text{for} \quad j=1,2,\cdots.$$

We therefore have a second solution of Bessel's equation of order zero:

$$y_2(x) = y_1(x)\ln(x) + \sum_{k=1}^{\infty}\frac{(-1)^{k+1}}{2^{2k}(k!)^2}\varnothing(k)x^{2k}$$

for $x > 0$. This solution is linearly independent from $y_1(x)$ for $x > 0$. ∎

When a differential equation with a regular singular point has only one Frobenius series solution expanded about that point, it is tempting to try reduction of order to find a second solution. This is a workable strategy if we can write $y_1(x)$ in closed form. But if $y_1(x)$ is an infinite series, it may be better to substitute the appropriate form of the second solution from Theorem 4.4 and solve for the coefficients.

SECTION 4.4   PROBLEMS

In each of Problems 1 through 10, (a) find the indicial equation, (b) determine the appropriate form of each of two linearly independent solutions, and (c) find the first five terms of each of two linearly independent solutions. In Problems 11 through 16, find only the form that two linearly independent solutions should take.

1. $xy'' + (1-x)y' + y = 0$

2. $xy'' - 2xy' + 2y = 0$

3. $x(x-1)y'' + 3y' - 2y = 0$

4. $4x^2 y'' + 4xy' + (4x^2 - 9)y = 0$

5. $4xy'' + 2y' + y = 0$

6. $4x^2 y'' + 4xy' - y = 0$

7. $x^2 y'' - 2xy' - (x^2 - 2)y = 0$

8. $xy'' - y' + 2y = 0$

9. $x(2-x)y'' - 2(x-1)y' + 2y = 0$

10. $x^2 y'' + x(x^3 + 1)y' - y = 0$

11. $25x(1-x^2)y'' - 20(5x-2)y' + \left(25x - \frac{4}{x}\right)y = 0$

12. $6(3x-4)(5x+8)y'' + (2x-21)\left(3+\frac{16}{x}\right)y' + \left(4-\frac{27}{x^2}\right)y = 0$

13. $12x(4+3x)y'' - 2(5x+7)(7x-2)y' + 24\left(5-\frac{1}{3x}\right)y = 0$

14. $3x(2x+3)y'' + 2(6-5x)y' + 7\left(2x - \frac{8}{x}\right)y = 0$

15. $x(x+4)y'' - 3(x-2)y' + 2y = 0$

16. $(3x^3 + x^2)y'' - x(10x+1)y' + (x^2+2)y = 0$

CHAPTER 5

Numerical Approximation of Solutions

Often we are unable to produce a solution of an initial value problem in a form suitable for drawing a graph or calculating numerical values. When this happens we may turn to a scheme for approximating numerical values of the solution.

Although the idea of a numerical approximation is not new, it is the development and ready accessibility of high speed computers that have made it the success that it is today. Some problems thought to be intractable thirty years ago are now considered solved from a practical point of view. Using computers and numerical approximation techniques, we now have increasingly accurate models for weather patterns, national and international economies, global warming, ecological systems, fluid flow around airplane wings and ship hulls, and many other phenomena of interest and importance.

A good numerical approximation scheme usually includes the following features.

1. At least for first order initial value problems, the scheme usually starts at a point x_0 where the initial value is prescribed, then builds approximate values of the solution at points specified to the left or right of x_0. The accuracy of the method will depend on the distance between successive points at which the approximations are made, their increasing distance from x_0, and of course the coefficients in the differential equation. Accuracy can also be influenced by the programming and by the architecture of the computer. For some complex models, such as the Navier-Stokes equations governing fluid flow, computers have been built with architecture dedicated to efficient approximation of solutions of that particular model.

2. A good numerical scheme includes an estimate or bound on the error in the approximation. This is used to understand the accuracy in the approximation, and often to guide the user in choosing certain parameters (such as the number of points at which approximations are made, and the distance between successive points). Often a compromise must be made between increasing accuracy (say, by choosing more points) and keeping the time or cost of the computation within reason. The type of problem under consideration may dictate what might be acceptable bounds on the error. If NASA is placing a satellite in a Jupiter orbit, a one meter error might be acceptable, while an error of this magnitude would be catastrophic in performing eye surgery.

3. The method must be implemented on a computer. Only simple examples, devised for illustrative purposes, can be done by hand. Many commercially available software packages include routines for approximating and graphing solutions of differential equations. Among these are MAPLE, MATHEMATICA and MATLAB.

We will now develop some specific methods.

5.1   Euler's Method

Euler's method is a scheme for approximating the solution of

$$y' = f(x, y); \quad y(x_0) = y_0,$$

in which x_0, y_0 and the function f are given.

The method is a good introduction to numerical schemes because it is conceptually simple and geometrically appealing, although it is not the most accurate. Let $y(x)$ denote the solution (which we know exists, but do not know explicitly). The key to Euler's method is that if we know $y(x)$ at some x, then we can compute $f(x, y(x))$, and therefore know the slope $y'(x)$ of the tangent to the graph of the solution at that point. We will exploit this fact to approximate solution values at points $x_1 = x_0 + h$, $x_2 = x_0 + 2h$, ..., $x_n = x_0 + nh$.

First choose h (the *step size*) and the number n of iterations to be performed. Now form the first approximation. We know $y(x_0) = y_0$. Calculate $f(x_0, y_0)$ and draw the line having this slope through (x_0, y_0). This line is tangent to the integral curve through (x_0, y_0). Move along this tangent line to the point (x_1, y_1). Use y_1 as an approximation to $y(x_1)$. This is illustrated in Figure 5.1. We have some hope that this is a "good" approximation, for h "small", because the tangent line fits the curve closely "near" the point.

Next compute $f(x_1, y_1)$. This is the slope of the tangent to the graph of the solution of the differential equation passing through (x_1, y_1). Draw the line through (x_1, y_1) having this slope, and move along this line to (x_2, y_2). This determines y_2, which we take as an approximation to $y(x_2)$ (see Figure 5.1 again).

Continue in this way. Compute $f(x_2, y_2)$ and draw the line with this slope through (x_2, y_2). Move along this line to (x_3, y_3) and use y_3 as an approximation to $y(x_3)$.

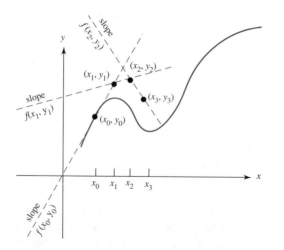

FIGURE 5.1 *Approximation points formed according to Euler's method.*

In general, once we have reached (x_k, y_k), draw the line through this point having slope $f(x_k, y_k)$ and move along this line to (x_{k+1}, y_{k+1}). Take y_{k+1} as an approximation to $y(x_{k+1})$.

This is the idea of the method. Obviously it is quite sensitive to how much $f(x, y)$ changes if x and y are varied by a small amount. The method also tends to accumulate error, since we use the approximation y_k to make the approximation y_{k+1}.

In Figure 5.2, the successively drawn line segments used to determine the approximate values move away from the actual solution curve as x increases, causing the approximations to be less accurate as more of them are made (that is, as n is chosen larger). Following segments of lines is conceptually simple and appealing, but it is not sophisticated enough to be very accurate in general.

We will now derive an analytic expression for the approximate solution value y_k at x_k. From Figure 5.1,

$$y_1 = y_0 + f(x_0, y_0)(x_1 - x_0).$$

At the next step,

$$y_2 = y_1 + f(x_1, y_1)(x_2 - x_1).$$

After we have obtained the approximate value y_k, the next step (Figure 5.3) gives

$$y_{k+1} = y_k + f(x_k, y_k)(x_{k+1} - x_k).$$

Since each $x_{k+1} - x_k = h$, we can summarize the discussion as follows.

DEFINITION 5.1 *Euler's Method*

Euler's method is to define y_{k+1} in terms of y_k by

$$y_{k+1} = y_k + f(x_k, y_k)(x_{k+1} - x_k),$$

or

$$y_{k+1} = y_k + h f(x_k, y_k),$$

for $k = 0, 1, 2, \ldots, n-1$. y_k is the Euler approximation to $y(x_k)$.

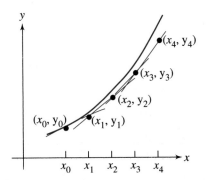

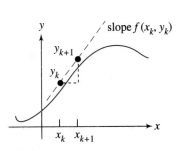

FIGURE 5.2 *Accumulating error in Euler's method.*

FIGURE 5.3

EXAMPLE 5.1

Consider

$$y' = x\sqrt{y}; \quad y(2) = 4.$$

This separable differential equation is easily solved:

$$y(x) = \left(1 + \frac{x^2}{4}\right)^2.$$

This enables us to observe how the method works by direct comparison with the exact solution.

First we must decide on h and n. Since we do not have any error estimates, we have no rationale for making a particular choice. For illustration, choose $h = 0.2$ and $n = 20$. Then $x_0 = 2$ and $x_{20} = x_0 + nh = 2 + (20)(0.2) = 6$. Now

$$y_{k+1} = y_k + 0.2 x_k \sqrt{y_k} \quad \text{for} \quad k = 0, 1, 2, \ldots, 19.$$

Table 5.1 lists the Euler approximations, and Figure 5.4 shows a graph of this approximate solution (actually, a smooth curve drawn through the approximated points), together with a graph of the actual solution, for comparison. Notice that the approximation becomes less accurate as x moves further from 2.

TABLE 5.1	Approximate Values of the Solution of $y' = x\sqrt{y}$; $y(2) = 4$; $h = 0.2$; $n = 20$		
x	$y_{app}(x)$	x	$y_{app}(x)$
2.0	4	4.2	26.62097204
2.2	4.8	4.4	30.95499533
2.4	5.763991701	4.6	35.85107012
2.6	6.916390802	4.8	41.35964033
2.8	8.28390462	5.0	47.53354060
3.0	9.895723242	5.2	54.42799784
3.2	11.783171355	5.4	62.10063249
3.4	13.98007530	5.6	70.61145958
3.6	16.52259114	5.8	80.02288959
3.8	19.44924644	6.0	90.39972950
4.0	22.80094522		

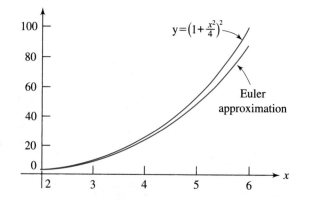

FIGURE 5.4 *Exact and Euler approximate solutions of* $y' = x\sqrt{y}$; $y(2) = 4$ *with stepsize 0.2 and twenty iterations.*

TABLE 5.2	Approximate Values of the Solution of $y' = x\sqrt{y}$; $y(2) = 4$; $h = 0.1$; $n = 40$		
x	$y_{app}(x)$	x	$y_{app}(x)$
2.0	4	4.1	25.8160330
2.1	4.4	4.2	27.89919080
2.2	4.4840499716	4.3	30.11761755
2.3	5.324524701	4.4	32.47743693
2.4	5.855248129	4.5	34.98495199
2.5	6.435991009	4.6	37.64661553
2.6	7.070222385	4.7	40.46903007
2.7	7.761559519	4.8	43.45894792
2.8	8.513768060	4.9	46.62327117
2.9	9.330762195	5.0	49.96905171
3.0	10.21660479	5.1	53.50349126
3.1	11.17550751	5.2	57.23394138
3.2	12.21183095	5.3	61.16790347
3.3	13.33008472	5.4	65.31302881
3.4	14.53492754	5.5	69.67711854
3.5	15.83116734	5.6	74.26812370
3.6	17.22376132	5.7	79.09414521
3.7	18.71781603	5.8	84.16343390
3.8	20.31858741	5.9	89.48439050
3.9	22.03148088	6.0	95.06556568
4.0	23.86205135		

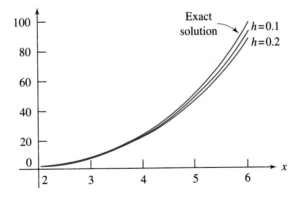

FIGURE 5.5 *Exact and Euler approximate solutions of*
$y' = x\sqrt{y}$; $y(2) = 4$, *first with $h = 0.2$ and twenty
iterations, and then $h = 0.1$ and forty iterations.*

The accuracy of this method depends on h. If we choose $h = 0.1$ and $n = 40$ (so the approximation is still for $2 \le x \le 6$), we get the approximate values of Table 5.2. A graph of this approximation is shown in Figure 5.5, showing an improved approximation by choosing h smaller. With today's computing power, we would have no difficulty using a much smaller h. ■

EXAMPLE 5.2

Consider

$$y' = \sin(xy); \quad y(2) = 1.$$

We cannot write a simple solution for this problem. Figure 5.6 shows a direction field for $y' = \sin(xy)$, and Figure 5.7 repeats this direction field, with some integral curves, including the one through $(2, 1)$. This is a graph of the solution (actually an approximation done by the software used for the direction field).

For a numerical approximation of the solution, choose $h = 0.2$ and $n = 20$ to obtain an approximate solution for $2 \le x \le 6$. The generated values are given in Table 5.3, and a smooth curve is drawn through these points in Figure 5.8. ∎

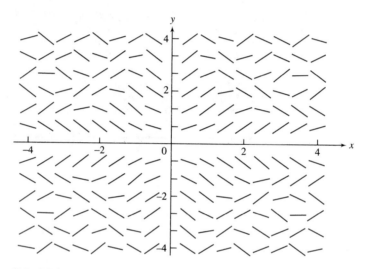

FIGURE 5.6   *A direction field for $y' = \sin(xy)$.*

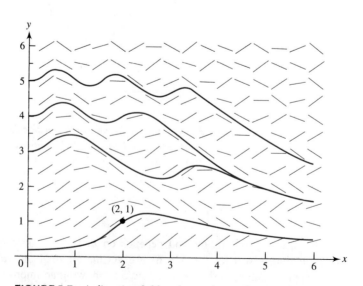

FIGURE 5.7   *A direction field and some integral curves for $y' = \sin(xy)$, including the integral curve through (2,1).*

TABLE 5.3	*Approximate Values of the Solution of* $y' = \sin(xy); y(2) = 1; h = 0.2; n = 20$		
x	$y_{app}(x)$	x	$y_{app}(x)$
2.0	1	4.2	0.7976369224
2.2	1.181859485	4.4	0.7562418383
2.4	1.284944186	4.6	0.7192812325
2.6	1.296483096	4.8	0.6860163429
2.8	1.251031045	5.0	0.6558744703
3.0	1.180333996	5.2	0.6248056314
3.2	1.102559149	5.4	0.6032491169
3.4	1.027151468	5.6	0.5801105326
2.6	0.9584362156	5.8	0.5587461082
3.8	0.8976573370	6.0	0.5389516129
4.0	0.8444064257		

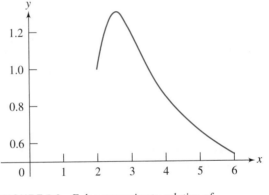

FIGURE 5.8 *Euler approximate solution of*
$y' = \sin(xy); y(2) = 1 (h = 0.2, n = 20)$.

From the examples, it appears that the error in an Euler approximation is proportional to h. It can be shown that this is indeed the case, and for this reason Euler's method is a *first order method*. If a method has error that is proportional to h^p, it is called an *order p method*.

5.1.1 A Problem in Radioactive Waste Disposal

Disposal of radioactive waste materials generated by nuclear power plants, medical research, military testing and other sources is a serious international problem. In view of the long half-lives of some of the materials involved, there is no real prospect for disposal, and the problem becomes one of safe storage. For example, Uranium-235 has a half-life of $7.13(10^8)$ years, and Thorium-232 a half-life of $1.39(10^{10})$ years. If a ton of Thorium-232 is stored, more than half of it will still be here to see our sun consume all of its fuel and die.

Storage plans have been proposed and studied on both national levels (for example, by the U.S. Atomic Energy Commission) and the international level (by the International Atomic Energy Agency of the United Nations). Countries have developed a variety of policies and plans. Argentina has embarked on a program of storing containers of radioactive materials in granite vaults. Belgium is planning to bury containers in clay deposits. Canada plans to use crystalline rocks in the Canadian shield. The Netherlands is considering salt domes. France and Japan are planning undersea depositories. And the United States has a diversified approach which have included sites at Yucca Mountain in Nevada and the Hanford Reservation in the state of Washington.

One idea which has been considered is to store the material in fifty-five gallon containers and drop them into the ocean at a point about 300 feet deep, shallow enough to prevent rupture of the drums by water pressure. It was found that drums could be manufactured that would endure indefinitely at this depth. But then another point was raised. Would the drums withstand the impact of settling on the ocean floor after being dropped from a ship?

Testing showed that the drums could indeed rupture if they impacted the bottom at a speed in excess of 40 feet per second. The question now is: will a drum achieve this velocity in a 300 foot descent through seawater?

To answer this question, we must analyze what happens when a drum is dropped into the water and allowed to settle to the bottom. Each 55-gallon drum weighs about 535 pounds after being filled with the material and some insulation. When in the water, the drum is buoyed up by a force equal to the weight of the water displaced. Fifty-five gallons is about 7.35 cubic feet, and the density of seawater is about 64 pounds per cubic foot, so each barrel will be subject to a buoyant force of about 470 pounds.

In addition to this buoyant force, the water will impose a drag on the barrel as it sinks, impeding its descent. It is well known that objects sinking in a fluid are subject to a drag force which is proportional to a power of the velocity. Engineers had to determine the constant of proportionality and the exponent for a drum in seawater. After testing, they estimated that the drag force of the water was approximately equal to $0.5v^{\sqrt{10}/3}$ pounds, in which v is the velocity in feet per second.

Let $y(t)$ be the depth of the drum in the water at time t, with downward chosen as the positive direction. Let $y = 0$ at the (calm) surface of the water. Then $v(t) = y'(t)$. The forces acting on the drum are the buoyant and drag forces (acting upward) and the force of gravity (acting downward). Since the force of gravity has magnitude mg, with m the mass of the drum, then by Newton's law,

$$m\frac{dv}{dt} = mg - 470 - 0.5v^{\sqrt{10}/3}.$$

For this problem, $mg = 535$ pounds. Use $g = 32$ ft/sec^2 to determine that $m = 16.7$ slugs. Assume that the drum is released from rest at the surface of the water. The initial value problem for the velocity of the descending drum is

$$16.7\frac{dv}{dt} = 535 - 470 - 0.5v^{\sqrt{10}/3}, \quad v(0) = 0$$

or

$$\frac{dv}{dt} = \frac{1}{16.7}\left[65 - 0.5v^{\sqrt{10}/3}\right], \quad v(0) = 0.$$

We want the velocity with which the drum hits bottom. One approach might give us a quick answer. It is not difficult to show that a drum sinking in seawater will have a terminal velocity. If the terminal velocity of the drum is less than 40 feet per second, then a drum released from rest will never reach a speed great enough to break it open upon impact with the ocean floor, regardless of the depth!

Unfortunately, a quick calculation, letting $dv/dt = 0$, shows that the terminal velocity is about 100 feet per second, not even close to 40. This estimate is therefore inconclusive in determining whether the drums have a velocity of 40 feet per second upon impact at 300 feet.

We could try solving the differential equation for $v(t)$ and integrating to get an equation for the depth at time t. Setting $y(t) = 300$ would then yield the time required for the drum to reach this depth, and we could put this time back into $v(t)$ to see if the velocity exceeds

40 feet per second at this time. The differential equation is separable. However, solving it leads to the integral

$$\int \frac{1}{v^{\sqrt{10/3}} - 130} dv,$$

which has no elementary evaluation.

Another approach would be to express the velocity as a function of the depth. A differential equation for $v(y)$ can be obtained by writing

$$\frac{dv}{dt} = \frac{dv}{dy}\frac{dy}{dt} = v\frac{dv}{dy}.$$

This gives us the initial value problem

$$\frac{dv}{dy} = \frac{65 - 0.5v^{\sqrt{10/3}}}{16.7v}; \quad v(0) = 0. \tag{5.1}$$

This equation is also separable, but we cannot perform the integrations needed to find $v(y)$ explicitly.

We have reached a position that is common in modeling a real-world phenomenon. The model (5.1) does not admit a closed form solution. At this point we will opt for a numerical approach to obtain approximate values for the velocity.

But life is not this easy! If we attempt Euler's method on the problem with equation (5.1), we cannot even get started because the initial condition is $v(0) = 0$, and v occurs in the denominator.

There is a way around this difficulty. Reverse perspective and look for depth as a function of velocity, $y(v)$. We will then calculate $y(40)$, the depth when the velocity reaches 40 feet per second. Since the velocity is an increasing function of the depth, if $y(40) > 300$ feet, we will know that the barrel could not have achieved a velocity of 40 feet per second when it reached the bottom. If $y(40) < 300$, then we will know that when the drum hits bottom it was moving at more than 40 feet per second, hence is likely to rupture.

Since $dy/dv = 1/(dv/dy)$, the initial value problem for $y(v)$ is

$$\frac{dy}{dv} = \frac{16.7v}{65 - 0.5v^{\sqrt{10/3}}}; \quad y(0) = 0.$$

Write $\sqrt{10/3} \approx 1.054$ and apply Euler's method with $h = 1$ and $n = 40$. We get $y(40) \approx 268.2$ feet. With $h = 0.5$ and $n = 80$ we get $y(40) \approx 272.3$ feet. Further reductions in step size will provide better accuracy. With $h = 0.1$ and $n = 400$ we get $y(40) \approx 275.5$ feet. Based on these numbers it would appear that the drum will exceed 40 feet per second when it has fallen 300 feet, hence has a good chance of leaking dangerous material.

A more detailed analysis, using an error bound that we have not discussed, leads to the conclusion that the drum achieves a velocity of 40 feet per second somewhere between 272 and 279 feet, giving us confidence that it has reached this velocity by the time it lands on the ocean floor. This led to the conclusion that the plan for storing radioactive waste materials in drums on the ocean floor is too dangerous to be feasible.

SECTION 5.1   PROBLEMS

In each of Problems 1 through 6, generate approximate numerical solutions using $h = 0.2$ and twenty iterations, then $h = 0.1$ and forty iterations, and finally $h = 0.05$ and eighty iterations. Graph the approximate solutions on the same set of axes. Also obtain error bounds for each case. In each of Problems 1 through 5, obtain the exact solution and graph it with the approximate solutions.

1. $y' = y\sin(x)$; $y(0) = 1$

2. $y' = x + y$; $y(1) = -3$

3. $y' = 3xy$; $y(0) = 5$

4. $y' = 2 - x$; $y(0) = 1$

5. $y' = y - \cos(x)$; $y(1) = -2$

6. $y' = x - y^2$; $y(0) = 4$

7. Approximate e as follows. Use Euler's method with $h = 0.01$ to approximate $y(1)$, where $y(x)$ is the solution of $y' = y$; $y(0) = 1$. Sketch a graph of the solution before applying Euler's method and determine whether the approximate value obtained is less than or greater than the actual value.

8. Approximate $\ln(2)$ by using Euler's method to approximate $y(2)$, where $y(x)$ is the solution of

$y' = 1/x$; $y(1) = 0$. Use $h = 0.01$. Will this approximation be less than or greater than the actual value?

9. In the analysis of the radioactive waste disposal problem, how does the constant of proportionality for the drag on the drum affect the conclusion? Carry out the numerical analysis if the drag is $0.3v^{\sqrt{10}/3}$, and again for the case that the drag is $0.8v^{\sqrt{10}/3}$.

10. Try exponents other than $\sqrt{10}/3$ for the velocity in the disposal problem to gauge the effect of this number on the conclusion. In particular, perform the analysis if the drag equals $0.5v$ (1 is slightly less than $\sqrt{10}/3$) and again for a drag effect of $0.5v^{4/3}$ (4/3 is slightly greater than $\sqrt{10}/3$).

11. Suppose the drums are dropped over a part of the ocean having a depth of 340 feet. Will the drums be likely to rupture on impact with the ocean floor?

5.2   One-Step Methods

Euler's method is a *one-step method* because the approximation at x_{k+1} depends only on the approximation at x_k, one step back. We will consider some other one-step methods for the initial value problem

$$y' = f(x, y); \quad y(x_0) = y_0.$$

As usual, let the step size be h, and denote $x_k = x_0 + kh$ for $k = 0, 1, 2, \ldots, n$.

5.2.1   The Second-Order Taylor Method

By Taylor's theorem with remainder (under certain conditions on f and h) we can write

$$y(x_{k+1}) = y(x_k) + hy'(x_k) + \frac{1}{2!}h^2 y''(x_k)$$

$$+ \cdots + \frac{1}{m!}h^m y^{(m)}(x_k) + \frac{1}{(m+1)!}h^{m+1} y^{(m+1)}(\xi_k),$$

for some ξ_k in $[x_k, x_{k+1}]$. If $y^{(m+1)}(x)$ is bounded, then the last term in this sum can be made as small as we like by choosing h small enough. We therefore form the approximation

$$y_{k+1} \approx y(x_k) + hy'(x_k) + \frac{1}{2!}h^2 y''(x_k) + \cdots + \frac{1}{m!}h^m y^{(m)}(x_k).$$

If $m = 1$, this is Euler's method, since $y'(x_k) = f(x_k, y_k)$. Now let $m = 2$. Then

$$y_{k+1} \approx y(x_k) + hy'(x_k) + \frac{1}{2!}h^2 y''(x_k). \tag{5.2}$$

We know that $y(x) = f(x, y(x))$. This suggests that in the approximation (5.2) we consider $f(x_k, y_k)$ as an approximation of $y'(x_k)$ if y_k is an approximation of $y(x_k)$. Thus consider

$$y'(x_k) \approx f(x_k, y_k).$$

This leaves the term $y''(x_k)$ in the approximation (5.2) to treat. First differentiate the expression $y'(x) = f(x, y(x))$ to get

$$y''(x) = \frac{\partial f}{\partial x}(x, y) + \frac{\partial f}{\partial y}(x, y)y'(x).$$

This suggests we consider

$$y''(x_k) \approx \frac{\partial f}{\partial x}(x_k, y_k) + \frac{\partial f}{\partial y}(x_k, y_k)f(x_k, y_k).$$

Insert these approximations of $y'(x_k)$ and $y''(x_k)$ into the approximation (5.2) to get

$$y_{k+1} \approx y_k + hf(x_k, y_k) + \frac{1}{2}h^2 \left(\frac{\partial f}{\partial x}(x_k, y_k) + \frac{\partial f}{\partial y}(x_k, y_k)f(x_k, y_k) \right).$$

This is a one-step method, because y_{k+1} is obtained from information at x_k, one step back from x_{k+1}.

DEFINITION 5.2 *Second-Order Taylor Method*

The second-order Taylor method consists of approximating $y(x_{k+1})$ by the expression

$$y_{k+1} \approx y_k + hf(x_k, y_k) + \frac{1}{2}h^2 \left(\frac{\partial f}{\partial x}(x_k, y_k) + \frac{\partial f}{\partial y}(x_k, y_k)f(x_k, y_k) \right).$$

This expression can be simplified by adopting the notation

$$f_k = f(x_k, y_k),$$

$$\frac{\partial f}{\partial x} = f_x, \quad \frac{\partial f}{\partial y} = f_y,$$

and

$$\frac{\partial f}{\partial x}(x_k, y_k) = (f_x)_k = f_{xk}, \quad \frac{\partial f}{\partial y}(x_k, y_k) = (f_y)_k = f_{yk}.$$

Now the formula is

$$y_{k+1} \approx y_k + hf_k + \frac{1}{2}h^2 \left(f_{xk} + f_k f_{yk} \right).$$

EXAMPLE 5.3

Consider

$$y' = y^2 \cos(x); \quad y(0) = 1/5.$$

With $f(x, y) = y^2 \cos(x)$, we have $f_x = -y^2 \sin(x)$ and $f_y = 2y \cos(x)$. Form

$$y_{k+1} \approx y_k + h y_k^2 \cos(x_k) + h^2 y_k^3 \cos^2(x_k) - \frac{1}{2} h^2 y_k^2 \sin(x_k).$$

With $h = 0.2$ and twenty iterations ($n = 20$) we get the approximate values given in Table 5.4, for points $x_k = 0 + 0.2k$ for $k = 0, 1, \dots, 20$.

TABLE 5.4	**Approximation Values of the Solution of $y' = y^2 \cos(x)$; $y(0) = 1/5$**		
x	$y_{app}(x)$	x	$y_{app}(x)$
0.0	0.2	2.2	0.2389919589
0.2	0.20832	2.4	0.2315347821
0.4	0.2170013470	2.6	0.2231744449
0.6	0.2256558280	2.8	0.2144516213
0.8	0.2337991830	3.0	0.2058272673
1.0	0.2408797598	3.2	0.1976613648
1.2	0.2463364693	3.4	0.1902141527
1.4	0.2496815188	3.6	0.1836603456
1.6	0.2505900093	3.8	0.1781084317
1.8	0.2489684556	4.0	0.1736197077
2.0	0.2449763987		

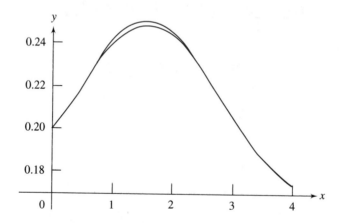

FIGURE 5.9 *Exact and second-order Taylor approximate solutions of $y' = y^2 \cos(x)$; $y(0) = \frac{1}{5}$.*

This problem can be solved exactly, and we obtain $y(x) = 1/(5 - \sin(x))$. Figure 5.9 shows a graph of this solution, together with a smooth curve drawn through the approximated function values. The student should redo the approximation, using $h = 0.1$ and $n = 40$ for comparison. ■

The Euler approximations for this example, with $h = 0.2$, are

$$y_{k+1} = y_k + (0.2)y_k^2 \cos(x_k).$$

It is instructive to compute these approximations for $n = 20$, and compare the accuracy of the Euler method with that of the second-order Taylor method for this problem.

5.2.2 The Modified Euler Method

Near the end of the nineteenth century the German mathematician Karl Runge noticed a similarity between part of the formula for the second-order Taylor method and another Taylor polynomial approximation. Write the second-order Taylor formula as

$$y_{k+1} = y_k + h\left[f_k + \frac{1}{2}h(f_x(x_k, y_k) + f_k f_y(x_k, y_k)\right]. \tag{5.3}$$

Runge observed that the term in square brackets on the right side of this equation resembles the Taylor approximation

$$f(x_k + \alpha h, y_k + \beta k) \approx f_k + \alpha h f_x(x_k, y_k) + \beta h f_y(x_k, y_k).$$

In fact, the term in square brackets in equation (5.3) is exactly the right side of the last equation if we choose $\alpha = \beta = 1/2$. This suggests the approximation

$$y_{k+1} \approx y_k + hf\left(x_k + \frac{h}{2}, y_k + \frac{hf_k}{2}\right).$$

DEFINITION 5.3   *Modified Euler Method*

The modified Euler method consists of defining the approximation y_{k+1} by

$$y_{k+1} \approx y_k + hf\left(x_k + \frac{h}{2}, y_k + \frac{hf_k}{2}\right).$$

The method is in the spirit of Euler's method, except that $f(x, y)$ is evaluated at $(x_k + h/2, y_k + hf_k/2)$ instead of at (x_k, y_k). Notice that $(x_k + h/2)$ is midway between x_k and x_{k+1}.

EXAMPLE 5.4

Consider

$$y' - \frac{1}{x}y = 2x^2; \quad y(1) = 4.$$

Write the differential equation as

$$y' = \frac{y}{x} + 2x^2 = f(x, y).$$

Using the modified Euler method with $h = 0.2$ and $n = 20$ iterations, generate the approximate solution values given in Table 5.5.

The exact solution of this initial value problem is $y(x) = x^3 + 3x$. The graph of this solution, together with a smooth curve drawn through the approximated values, are shown in Figure 5.10. The two curves coincide in the scale of the drawing. For example, $y(5) = 140$, while y_{20}, the approximated solution value at $x_{20} = 1 + 20(0.2) = 5$, is 139.7. This small a difference does not show up on the graph.

TABLE 5.5	*Approximate Values of the Solution of* $y' = (y/x) + 2x^2$; $y(1) = 4$		
x	$y_{app}(x)$	x	$y_{app}(x)$
1.0	4	3.2	42.23164616
1.2	5.320363636	3.4	49.35124526
1.4	6.927398601	3.6	57.28637379
1.6	8.869292639	3.8	66.08505841
1.8	11.19419064	4.0	75.79532194
2.0	13.95020013	4.2	86.46518560
2.2	17.18541062	4.4	98.14266841
2.4	20.94789459	4.6	110.8757877
2.6	25.25871247	4.8	124.7125592
2.8	30.24691542	5.0	139.7009975
3.0	35.87954731		

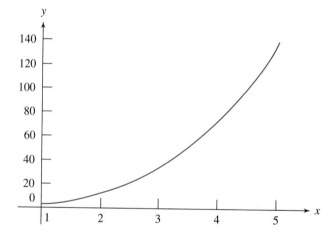

FIGURE 5.10   *Exact and modified Euler approximation of the solution of* $y' - (1/x)y = 2x^2$; $y(1) = 4$.

We leave it for the student to do this example using the other approximation schemes for comparison. For this initial value problem, the other methods with $h = 0.2$ give:

Euler: $y_{k+1} = y_k + 0.2\left(\dfrac{1}{x_k}y_k + 2x_k^2\right)$,

Modified Euler: $y_{k+1} = y_k + 0.2\left[\dfrac{y_k + 0.1\left(\frac{y_k}{x_k} + 2x_k^2\right)}{x_k + 0.1} + 2(x_k + 0.1)^2\right]$;

Second-order Taylor:

$$y_{k+1} = y_k + 0.2\left[\dfrac{y_k}{x_k} + 2x_k^2\right] + 0.02\left[-\dfrac{y_k}{x_k} + 4x_k + \left(\dfrac{y_k}{x_k} + 2x_k\right)\right].$$

5.2.3 Runge-Kutta Methods

An entire class of one-step methods is generated by replacing the right side in the modified Euler method with the general form

$$af_k + bf(x_k + \alpha h, y_k + \beta h f_k).$$

The idea is to choose the constants a, b, α and β to obtain an approximation with as favorable an error bound as possible.

The fourth order Runge-Kutta method (known as RK4) has proved both computationally efficient and accurate, and is obtained by a clever choice of these constants in approximating slopes at various points. Without derivation, we will state the method.

DEFINITION 5.4   RK4

The RK4 method of approximation is to define y_{k+1} in terms of y_k by

$$y_{k+1} = y_k + \frac{h}{6}[W_{k1} + 2W_{k2} + 2W_{k3} + W_{k4}],$$

where

$$W_{k1} = f_k, W_{k2} = f(x_k + h/2, y_k + hW_{k1}/2),$$

$$W_{k3} = f(x_k + h/2, y_k + hW_{k2}/2), W_{k4} = f(x_k + h, y_k + hW_{k3}).$$

EXAMPLE 5.5

Consider

$$y' = \frac{1}{y}\cos(x+y); \quad y(0) = 1.$$

Choose $h = 0.1$ and $n = 40$ to obtain approximate solution values at 1, 1.1 , ..., 3.9, 4. Compute

$$W_{k1} = \frac{1}{y_k}\cos(x_k + y_k),$$

$$W_{k2} = \frac{1}{y_k + 0.05W_{k1}}\cos(x_k + y_k + 0.05 + 0.05W_{k1}),$$

$$W_{k3} = \frac{1}{y_k + 0.05W_{k2}}\cos(x_k + y_k + 0.05 + 0.05W_{k2}),$$

$$W_{k4} = \frac{1}{y_k + 0.1W_{k3}}\cos(x_k + y_k + 0.1 + 0.1W_{k3}),$$

and

$$y_{k+1} = y_k + \frac{0.1}{6}(W_{k1} + 2W_{k2} + 2W_{k3} + W_{k4}).$$

For comparison, we also compute approximations using modified Euler:

$$y_{k+1} = y_k + \frac{0.1}{y_k + 0.05((1/y_k)\cos(x_k + y_k))}\cos\left(x_k + y_k + 0.05 + \frac{0.05\cos(x_k + y_k)}{y_k}\right).$$

TABLE 5.6	**Approximate Values of the Solution of** $y' = (1/y)\cos(x+y)$; $y(0) = 1$				
x	**RK4 Application**	**Modified Euler Application**	x	**RK4 Application**	**Modified Euler Application**
0.0	1	1	1.1	0.9505251773	0.9495508719
0.1	1.046496334	1.046149156	1.2	0.8982661137	0.8973115249
0.2	1.079334533	1.078757139	1.3	0.8382537806	0.837306783
0.3	1.100247716	1.099515885	1.4	0.7696832419	0.7688117656
0.4	1.110582298	1.109747010	1.5	0.6911954958	0.6904155222
0.5	1.111396688	1.110493110	1.6	0.6004493273	0.5998524927
0.6	1.103521442	1.102574266	1.7	0.4930456632	0.4928907147
0.7	1.087597013	1.086623840	1.8	0.3589118368	0.3602630404
0.8	1.064096638	1.063110255	1.9	0.156746754	0.1719452522
0.9	1.033337679	1.032347712	2.0	−1.602586399	−1.068545688
1.0	0.9954821879	0.9944964300	2.1	−1.658600340	−1.121333887
2.2	−1.711647122	−1.168193825	3.3	−2.100103902	−1.263086041
2.3	−1.76180864	−1.209281807	3.4	−2.115423092	−1.222220133
2.4	−1.809127759	−1.244631007	3.5	−2.126727488	−1.169751386
2.5	−1.853613925	−1.274170205	3.6	−2.133806037	−1.104515644
2.6	−1.895247358	−1.297734699	3.7	−2.136440412	−1.025210458
2.7	−1.933982047	−1.315071925	3.8	−2.134410465	−0.930599244
2.8	−1.969747992	−1.325843341	3.9	−2.127506124	−0.8181811612
2.9	−2.002452881	−1.329623556	4.0	−2.115514719	−0.6862852770
3.0	−2.031983404	−1.325897430			
3.1	−2.058206363	−1.314055719			
3.2	−2.080969742	−1.293389806			

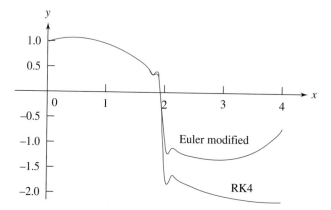

FIGURE 5.11   *Runge-Kutta and modified Euler approximations of the solution of* $y' = (1/y)\cos(x+y)$; $y(0) = 1$.

Table 5.6 shows the computed values, and Figure 5.11 shows graphs drawn through the approximated points by both methods. The two graphs are in good agreement as x nears 2, but then they diverge from each other. This divergence can be seen in the table. In general, RK4 is more accurate than modified Euler, particularly as the distance increases from the point where the initial data is specified. ■

It can be shown that the Taylor and modified Euler methods are of order h^2, while RK4 is of order h^4. Since usually $0 < h < 1$, $h^4 < h^2 < h$, so accuracy improves much faster by choosing smaller h with RK4 than with the other methods. There are higher order Runge-Kutta methods which are of order h^p for larger p. Such methods offer greater accuracy, but usually at a cost of more computing time.

All of the methods of this section are one-step methods, which have the general form $y_{k+1} = y_k + \varphi(x_k, y_k)$. In the next section, we will discuss multistep methods.

SECTION 5.2   PROBLEMS

In each of Problems 1 through 6, use the modified Euler, Taylor and RK4 methods to approximate the solution, first using $h = 0.2$ with twenty iterations, then $h = 0.1$ with forty iterations, and finally $h = 0.05$ with eighty iterations. Graph the approximate solutions for each method, and for a given h, on the same set of axes.

1. $y' = \sin(x+y); y(0) = 2$

2. $y' = y - x^2; y(1) = -4.$

   Also solve this problem exactly and include a graph of the exact solution with graphs of the approximate solutions.

3. $y' = \cos(y) + e^{-x}; y(0) = 1$

4. $y' = y^3 - 2xy; y(3) = 2$

5. $y' = -y + e^{-x}; y(0) = 4.$

   Also solve this problem exactly and include a graph of the exact solution with graphs of the approximate solutions.

6. $y' = \sec(1/y) - xy^2; y(\pi/4) = 1$

7. Do Problem 3 of Section 5.1 with RK4 instead of Euler. Which method yields the better result?

8. Do Problem 5 of Section 5.1 with RK4 instead of Euler. Which method yields the better result?

9. Derive the improved Euler method, also known as the Heun method, as follows. Begin with Euler's method and replace f_k with $(f_k + f_{k+1})/2$. Next replace y_{k+1} in f_{k+1} with $y_k + hf_k$. The result should be the approximation scheme $y_{k+1} = y_k + (h/2)(f_k + f(x_{k+1}, y_k + hf_k))$.

In each of Problems 10 through 12, use Euler, modified Euler and improved Euler to approximate the solution. Use $h = 0.2$ with $n = 20$, then $h = 0.1$ with $n = 40$ and then $h = 0.05$ with $n = 80$. Graph the approximate solutions, for each h, on the same set of axes. Whenever the solution can be found in exact form, graph this solution with the approximate solutions for comparison.

10. $y' = 1 - y; y(0) = 2$

11. $y' = -y/x + x; y(1) = 1$

12. $y' = y - e^x; y(-1) = 4$

5.3   Multistep Methods

We continue with the problem $y' = f(x, y); y(x_0) = y_0$. The solution is $y(x)$, and we presumably do not have a "good" expression for this function. We want to obtain approximate values y_k to $y(x_k)$, where $x_k = x_0 + kh$ for $k = 0, 1, \ldots, n$.

The basis for some multistep methods is the informal belief that, if $p_k(x)$ is a polynomial that approximates $f(x, y(x))$ on $[x_k, x_{k+1}]$, then $\int_{x_k}^{x_{k+1}} p_k(x)dx$ should approximate $\int_{x_k}^{x_{k+1}} f(x, y(x))dx$. Now write

$$y(x_{k+1}) - y(x_k) = \int_{x_k}^{x_{k+1}} y'(x)dx = \int_{x_k}^{x_{k+1}} f(x, y(x))dx \approx \int_{x_k}^{x_{k+1}} p_k(x)dx.$$

Therefore

$$y(x_{k+1}) \approx y(x_k) + \int_{x_k}^{x_{k+1}} p_k(x)dx. \tag{5.4}$$

So far this is deliberately vague. Nevertheless, this proposed approximation (5.4) contains the germ of an idea which we will now pursue.

First we must decide how to choose the polynomials $p_k(x)$. Suppose we have somehow arrived at satisfactory approximations $y_k, y_{k-1}, \ldots, y_{k-r}$ to the solution at $x_k, x_{k-1}, \ldots, x_{k-r}$, respectively. Then

$$f_k = f(x_k, y_k) \approx f(x_k, y(x_k)),$$

$$f_{k-1} = f(x_{k-1}, y_{k-1}) \approx f(x_{k-1}, y(x_{k-1})),$$

$$\ldots, f_{k-r} = f(x_{k-r}, y_{k-r}) \approx f(x_{k-r}, y(x_{k-r})).$$

Keep in mind here that $y(x_k)$ is the exact solution evaluated at x_k (this is unknown to us), and y_k is an approximation of this solution value, obtained by some scheme.

Now choose $p_k(x)$ to be the polynomial of degree r passing through the points

$$(x_k, f_k), (x_{k-1}, f_{k-1}), \ldots, (x_{k-r}, f_{k-r}).$$

These $r+1$ points will uniquely determine the r-degree polynomial $p_k(x)$. When this polynomial is inserted into the approximation scheme (5.4), we obtain a multistep approximation method in which the approximation y_{k+1} of $y(x_{k+1})$ is defined by

$$y_{k+1} = y_k + \int_{x_k}^{x_{k+1}} p_k(x)dx. \tag{5.5}$$

We obtain different methods for different choices of r. Consider some cases of interest.

5.3.1   Case 1 $r = 0$

Now $p_k(x)$ is a zero degree polynomial, or constant. Specifically, $p_k(x) = f_k$ for $x_k \le x \le x_{k+1}$. The approximation scheme defined by equation (5.5) becomes

$$y_{k+1} = y_k + \int_{x_k}^{x_{k+1}} f_k dx = y_k + f_k[x_{k+1} - x_k] = y_k + hf_k$$

for $k = 0, 1, 2, \ldots, n-1$. This is Euler's method, a one-step method.

5.3.2   Case 2 $r = 1$

Now $p_k(x)$ is a first degree polynomial, whose graph is the straight line through (x_k, f_k) and (x_{k-1}, f_{k-1}). Therefore

$$p_k(x) = -\frac{1}{h}(x - x_k)f_{k-1} + \frac{1}{h}(x - x_{k-1})f_k.$$

Upon inserting this into the scheme (5.5) we get

$$y_{k+1} = y_k + \int_{x_k}^{x_{k+1}} \left[-\frac{1}{h}(x - x_k)f_{k-1} + \frac{1}{h}(x - x_{k-1})f_k \right] dx.$$

A routine integration which we omit yields

$$y_{k+1} = y_k + \frac{h}{2}[3f_k - f_{k-1}]$$

for $k = 1, 2, \ldots, n - 1$. This is a two-step method because computation of y_{k+1} requires prior computation of information at the two points x_k and x_{k-1}.

For larger r, the idea is the same, but the details are move involved because $p_k(x)$ is of degree r and the integral in equation (5.5) is more involved, though still elementary. Here are the final results for two more cases.

5.3.3 Case 3 $r = 3$

$$y_{k+1} = y_k + \frac{h}{12}[23f_k - 16f_{k-1} + 5f_{k-2}]$$

for $k = 2, 3, \ldots, n - 1$. This is a three-step method, requiring information at three points to compute the approximation y_{k+1}.

5.3.4 Case 4 $r = 4$

$$y_{k+1} = y_k + \frac{h}{24}[55f_k - 59f_{k-1} + 37f_{k-2} - 9f_{k-3}] \tag{5.6}$$

for $k = 3, 4, \ldots, n - 1$. This is a four-step method.

We might expect multistep methods to improve in accuracy as the number of steps increases, since more information is packed into the computation of the approximation at the next point. This is in general true, and an r-step method using an interpolating polynomial of degree r on each subinterval has error of order $O(h^r)$. The cost in improved accuracy is that the polynomials must be computed on each interval and more data is put into computation of each successive y_{k+1}.

The schemes just given for $r = 1, 2$, and 3 are called *Adams-Bashforth multistep methods*.

One drawback to a multistep method is that some other method must be used to initiate it. For example, equation (5.6) involves f_{k-3}, and so is only valid for $k = 3, 4, \ldots, n - 1$. Some other scheme must be used to start it by feeding in y_1, y_2 and y_3 (and, of course, y_0 is given as information). Often RK4 is used as an initiator in computing these first values.

Another class of multistep methods, called *Adams-Moulton methods*, is obtained by using different data points to determine the interpolating polynomial $p_k(x)$ to use in equation (5.4). For $r = 2$, $p_k(x)$ is now chosen as the unique second degree polynomial passing through (x_{k-1}, f_{k-1}), (x_k, f_k) and (x_{k+1}, f_{k+1}). This leads to the approximating scheme

$$y_{k+1} = y_k + \frac{h}{24}[9f_{k+1} + 19f_k - 5f_{k-1} + f_{k-2}]. \tag{5.7}$$

This Adams-Moulton method is a four step method, and has error of order $O(h^4)$.

There is a significant difference between the Adams-Bashforth method (5.6) and the Adams-Moulton method (5.7). The former determines y_{k+1} in terms of three previously computed quantities, and is said to be *explicit*. The latter contains y_{k+1} on both sides of the equation (5.7), because $y_{k+1} = f(x_{k+1}, y_{k+1})$, and therefore defines y_{k+1} *implicitly* by an equation containing y_{k+1} on both sides. Equation (5.7) therefore only provides an equation containing y_{k+1}, from which y_{k+1} must then be extracted, a perhaps nontrivial task.

SECTION 5.3   PROBLEMS

In each of Problems 1 through 5, use the Taylor, modified Euler, and RK4 methods to approximate solution values. First use $h = 0.2$ with 20 iterations, then $h = 0.1$ with 40 iterations, then $h = 0.05$ with 80 iterations.

1. $y' = 4y^2 - x;\ y(3) = 0$

2. $y' = x\sin(y) - x^2;\ y(1) = -3$

3. $y' = x^2 + 4y;\ y(0) = -2$

4. $y' = 1 - \cos(x - y) + x^2;\ y(3) = 6$

5. $y' = 4x^3 - xy + \cos(y);\ y(0) = 4$

In each of Problems 6, 7 and 8, use the Adams-Bashforth-Moulton scheme, first with $h = 0.2$ and twenty iterations, then with $h = 0.1$ and forty iterations.

6. $y' = y - x^3;\ y(-2) = -4$

7. $y' = 2xy - y^3;\ y(0) = 2$

8. $y' = \ln(x) + x^2 y;\ y(2) = 1$

9. Carry out the details for deriving the two-step scheme stated for the case $r = 2$.

10. Carry out the details for deriving the three-step scheme stated for the case $r = 3$.

11. Every one-step and multistep method we have considered is a special case of the general expression

$$y_{k+1} = \sum_{j=1}^{n} \alpha_j y_{k+1-j}$$

$$+ h\varphi(x_{k+1-m}, \dots, x_k,$$

$$x_{k+1}, y_{k+1-m}, \dots, y_k, y_{k+1}).$$

By making appropriate choices of m, the $\alpha'_j s$ and φ, show how this formula gives Euler's method, the modified Euler method, the Taylor method, RK4, and the Adams-Bashforth method.

PART 2

Vectors and Linear Algebra

Some quantities are completely determined by their magnitude, or "size." This is true of temperature and mass, which are numbers referred to some scale or measurement system. Such quantities are called scalars. Length, volume, and distance are other scalars.

By contrast, a vector carries with it a sense of both magnitude and direction. The effect of a push against an object will depend not only on the magnitude or strength of the push, but also on the direction in which it is exerted.

This part is concerned with the notation and algebra of vectors and objects called matrices. This algebra will be used to solve systems of linear algebraic equations and systems of linear differential equations. It will also give us the machinery needed for the quantitative study of systems of differential equations (Part 3), in which we attempt to determine the behavior and properties of solutions when we cannot write these solutions explicitly or in closed form. In Part 4, vector algebra will be used to develop vector calculus, which extends derivatives and integrals to higher dimensions, with applications to models of physical systems, partial differential equations, and the analysis of complex-valued functions.

CHAPTER 6

Vectors and Vector Spaces

6.1   The Algebra and Geometry of Vectors

When dealing with vectors, a real number is often called a *scalar*. The temperature of an object and the grade of a motor oil are scalars.

We want to define the concept of a vector in such a way that the package contains information about both direction and magnitude. One way to do this is to define a vector (in 3-dimensional space) as an ordered triple of real numbers.

DEFINITION 6.1   *Vector*

A vector is an ordered triple (a, b, c), in which a, b, and c are real numbers.

We represent the vector (a, b, c) as an arrow from the origin $(0, 0, 0)$ to the point (a, b, c) in 3-space, as in Figure 6.1. In this way, the direction indicated by the arrow, as viewed from the origin, gives the direction of the vector. The length of the arrow is the magnitude (or norm) of the vector—a longer arrow represents a vector of greater strength. Since the distance from the origin to the point (a, b, c) is $\sqrt{a^2 + b^2 + c^2}$, we will define this number to be the magnitude of the vector (a, b, c).

DEFINITION 6.2   *Norm of a Vector*

The norm, or magnitude, of a vector (a, b, c) is the number $\|(a, b, c)\|$ defined by

$$\|(a, b, c)\| = \sqrt{a^2 + b^2 + c^2}$$

203

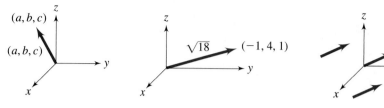

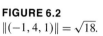

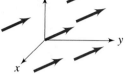

FIGURE 6.1 *The vector (a, b, c) is represented by the arrow from $(0, 0, 0)$ to the point (a, b, c).*

FIGURE 6.2 $\|(-1, 4, 1)\| = \sqrt{18}$.

FIGURE 6.3 *Parallel representations of the same vector.*

For example, the norm of $(-1, 4, 1)$ is $\|(-1, 4, 1)\| = \sqrt{1 + 16 + 1} = \sqrt{18}$. This is the length of the arrow from the origin to the point $(-1, 4, 1)$ (Figure 6.2).

The only vector that is not represented by an arrow from the origin is the zero vector $(0, 0, 0)$, which has zero magnitude and no direction. It is, however, useful to have a zero vector, because various forces in a physical process may cancel each other, resulting in a zero force or vector.

The number a is the *first component* of (a, b, c), b is the *second component*, and c the *third component*. Two vectors are *equal* if and only if each of their respective components is equal:

$$(a, b, c) = (u, v, w)$$

if and only if

$$a = u, \quad b = v, \quad c = w.$$

We will usually denote scalars (real numbers) by letters in regular type face (a, b, c, A, B, …), and vectors by letters in boldface (**a**, **b**, **c**, **A**, **B**, …). The zero vector is denoted **O**.

Although there is a difference between a vector (ordered triple) and an arrow (visual representation of a vector), we often speak of vectors and arrows interchangeably. This is useful in giving geometric interpretations to vector operations. However, any two arrows having the same length and same direction are said to represent the same vector. In Figure 6.3, all the arrows represent the same vector.

We will now develop algebraic operations with vectors and relate them to the norm.

DEFINITION 6.3   *Product of a Scalar and Vector*

The product of a real number α with a vector $\mathbf{F} = (a, b, c)$ is denoted $\alpha\mathbf{F}$, and is defined by

$$\alpha\mathbf{F} = (\alpha a, \alpha b, \alpha c).$$

Thus a vector is multiplied by a scalar by multiplying each component by the scalar. For example,

$$3(2, -5, 1) = (6, -15, 3) \quad \text{and} \quad -5(-4, 2, 10) = (20, -10, -50).$$

The following relationship between norm and the product of a scalar with a vector leads to a simple geometric interpretation of this operation.

THEOREM 6.1

Let **F** be a vector and α a scalar. Then

1. $\|\alpha\mathbf{F}\| = |\alpha|\,\|\mathbf{F}\|$.
2. $\|\mathbf{F}\| = 0$ if and only if $\mathbf{F} = \mathbf{O}$.

Proof If $\mathbf{F} = (a, b, c)$, then $\alpha\mathbf{F} = (\alpha a, \alpha b, \alpha c)$, so

$$\|\alpha\mathbf{F}\| = \sqrt{\alpha^2 a^2 + \alpha^2 b^2 + \alpha^2 c^2}$$
$$= |\alpha|\,\sqrt{a^2 + b^2 + c^2} = |\alpha|\,\|\mathbf{F}\|.$$

This proves conclusion (1). For (2), first recall that $\mathbf{O} = (0, 0, 0)$, so

$$\|\mathbf{O}\| = \sqrt{0^2 + 0^2 + 0^2} = 0.$$

Conversely, if $\|\mathbf{F}\| = 0$, then $a^2 + b^2 + c^2 = 0$, hence $a = b = c = 0$ and $\mathbf{F} = \mathbf{O}$. ∎

Consider this product of a scalar with a vector from a geometric point of view. By (1) of the theorem, the length of $\alpha\mathbf{F}$ is $|\alpha|$ times the length of **F**. Multiplying by α lengthens the arrow representing **F** if $|\alpha| > 1$, and shrinks it to a shorter arrow if $0 < |\alpha| < 1$. Of course, if $\alpha = 0$ then $\alpha\mathbf{F}$ is the zero vector, with zero length. But the algebraic sign of α has an effect as well. If α is positive, then $\alpha\mathbf{F}$ has the same direction as **F**, while if α is negative, $\alpha\mathbf{F}$ has the opposite direction.

EXAMPLE 6.1

Let $\mathbf{F} = (2, 4, 1)$, as shown in Figure 6.4. $3\mathbf{F} = (6, 12, 3)$ is along the same direction as **F**, but is represented as an arrow three times longer. But $-3\mathbf{F} = (-6, -12, -3)$, while being three times longer than **F**, is in the direction opposite that of **F** through the origin. And $\frac{1}{2}\mathbf{F} = (1, 2, 1/2)$ is in the same direction as **F**, but half as long. ∎

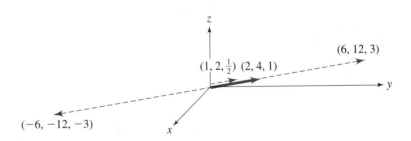

FIGURE 6.4 *Scalar multiples of a vector.*

In particular, the scalar product of -1 with $\mathbf{F} = (a, b, c)$ is the vector $(-a, -b, -c)$, having the same length as **F**, but the opposite direction. This vector is called "minus **F**," or the negative of **F**, and is denoted $-\mathbf{F}$.

Consistent with the interpretation of multiplication of a vector by a scalar, we define two vectors **F** and **G** to be *parallel* if each is a nonzero scalar multiple of the other. Of course if $\mathbf{F} = \alpha\mathbf{G}$ and $\alpha \neq 0$, then $\mathbf{G} = (1/\alpha)\mathbf{F}$. Parallel vectors may differ in length, and even be in opposite directions, but the straight lines through arrows representing these vectors are parallel lines in 3-space.

The algebraic sum of two vectors is defined as follows.

DEFINITION 6.4   *Vector Sum*

The sum of $\mathbf{F} = (a_1, b_1, c_1)$ and $\mathbf{G} = (a_2, b_2, c_2)$ is the vector

$$\mathbf{F} + \mathbf{G} = (a_1 + a_2, b_1 + b_2, c_1 + c_2).$$

That is, we add vectors by adding respective components. For example,

$$(-4, \pi, 2) + (16, 1, -5) = (12, \pi + 1, -3).$$

If $\mathbf{F} = (a_1, b_1, c_1)$ and $\mathbf{G} = (a_2, b_2, c_2)$, then the sum of $\mathbf{F}$ with $-\mathbf{G}$ is $(a_1 - a_2, b_1 - b_2, c_1 - c_2)$. It is natural to denote this vector as $\mathbf{F} - \mathbf{G}$, and refer to it as "$\mathbf{F}$ minus $\mathbf{G}$." For example, $(-4, \pi, 2)$ minus $(16, 1, -5)$ is

$$(-4, \pi, 2) - (16, 1, -5) = (-20, \pi - 1, 7).$$

We therefore subtract two vectors by subtracting their respective components.

Vector addition and multiplication of a vector by a scalar have the following computational properties.

THEOREM 6.2   *Algebra of Vectors*

Let $\mathbf{F}$, $\mathbf{G}$, and $\mathbf{H}$ be vectors and let α and β be scalars. Then

1. $\mathbf{F} + \mathbf{G} = \mathbf{G} + \mathbf{F}$.
2. $(\mathbf{F} + \mathbf{G}) + \mathbf{H} = \mathbf{F} + (\mathbf{G} + \mathbf{H})$.
3. $\mathbf{F} + \mathbf{O} = \mathbf{F}$.
4. $\alpha(\mathbf{F} + \mathbf{G}) = \alpha\mathbf{F} + \alpha\mathbf{G}$.
5. $(\alpha\beta)\mathbf{F} = \alpha(\beta\mathbf{F})$.
6. $(\alpha + \beta)\mathbf{F} = \alpha\mathbf{F} + \beta\mathbf{F}$. ∎

Conclusion (1) is the commutative law for vector addition, and (2) is the associative law. Conclusion (3) states that the zero vector behaves with vectors like the number zero does with real numbers, as far as addition is concerned. The theorem is proved by routine calculations, using the properties of real-number arithmetic. For example, to prove (4), write $\mathbf{F} = (a_1, b_1, c_1)$ and $\mathbf{G} = (a_2, b_2, c_2)$. Then

$$\begin{aligned}
\alpha(\mathbf{F} + \mathbf{G}) &= \alpha(a_1 + a_2, b_1 + b_2, c_1 + c_2) \\
&= (\alpha(a_1 + a_2), \alpha(b_1 + b_2), \alpha(c_1 + c_2)) \\
&= (\alpha a_1 + \alpha a_2, \alpha b_1 + \alpha b_2, \alpha c_1 + \alpha c_2) \\
&= (\alpha a_1, \alpha b_1, \alpha c_1) + (\alpha a_2, \alpha b_2, \alpha c_2) \\
&= \alpha(a_1, b_1, c_1) + \alpha(a_2, b_2, c_2) = \alpha\mathbf{F} + \alpha\mathbf{G}.
\end{aligned}$$

Vector addition has a simple geometric interpretation. If $\mathbf{F}$ and $\mathbf{G}$ are represented as arrows from the same point P, as in Figure 6.5, then $\mathbf{F} + \mathbf{G}$ is represented as the arrow from P to the opposite vertex of the parallelogram having $\mathbf{F}$ and $\mathbf{G}$ as two incident sides. This is called the *parallelogram law* for vector addition.

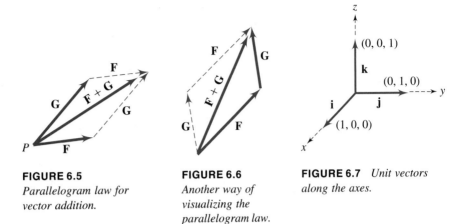

FIGURE 6.5
*Parallelogram law for
vector addition.*

FIGURE 6.6
*Another way of
visualizing the
parallelogram law.*

FIGURE 6.7 *Unit vectors
along the axes.*

The parallelogram law suggests a strategy for visualizing addition that is sometimes useful. Since two arrows having the same direction and length represent the same vector, we could apply the parallelogram law to form $\mathbf{F} + \mathbf{G}$ as in Figure 6.6, in which the arrow representing $\mathbf{G}$ is drawn from the tip of $\mathbf{F}$, rather from a common initial point with $\mathbf{F}$. We often do this in visualizing computations with vectors.

Any vector can be written as a sum of scalar multiples of "standard" vectors as follows. Define

$$\mathbf{i} = (1, 0, 0), \quad \mathbf{j} = (0, 1, 0), \quad \mathbf{k} = (0, 0, 1).$$

These are *unit vectors* (length 1) aligned along the three coordinate axes in the positive direction (Figure 6.7). In terms of these vectors,

$$\mathbf{F} = (a, b, c) = a(1, 0, 0) + b(0, 1, 0) + c(0, 0, 1) = a\mathbf{i} + b\mathbf{j} + c\mathbf{k}.$$

This is called the *standard representation* of $\mathbf{F}$. When a component of $\mathbf{F}$ is zero, we usually just omit it in the standard representation. For example,

$$(-3, 0, 1) = -3\mathbf{i} + \mathbf{k}.$$

Figure 6.8 shows two points $P_1(a_1, b_1, c_1)$ and $P_2(a_2, b_2, c_2)$. It will be useful to know the vector represented by the arrow from P_1 to P_2. Let $\mathbf{H}$ be this vector. Denote

$$\mathbf{G} = a_1\mathbf{i} + b_1\mathbf{j} + c_1\mathbf{k} \quad \text{and} \quad \mathbf{F} = a_2\mathbf{i} + b_2\mathbf{j} + c_2\mathbf{k}.$$

By the parallelogram law (Figure 6.9),

$$\mathbf{G} + \mathbf{H} = \mathbf{F}.$$

Hence

$$\mathbf{H} = \mathbf{F} - \mathbf{G} = (a_2 - a_1)\mathbf{i} + (b_2 - b_1)\mathbf{j} + (c_2 - c_1)\mathbf{k}.$$

For example, the vector represented by the arrow from $(-2, 4, 1)$ to $(14, 5, -7)$ is $16\mathbf{i} + \mathbf{j} - 8\mathbf{k}$. The vector from $(14, 5, -7)$ to $(-2, 4, 1)$ is the negative of this, or $-16\mathbf{i} - \mathbf{j} + 8\mathbf{k}$.

Vector notation and algebra are often useful in solving problems in geometry. This is not our goal here, but the reasoning involved is often useful in solving problems in the sciences and engineering. We will give three examples to demonstrate the efficiency of thinking in terms of vectors.

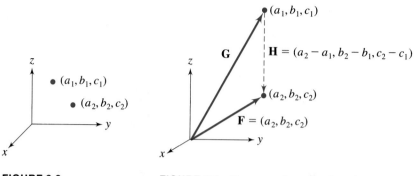

FIGURE 6.8

FIGURE 6.9   *The arrow from* (a_1, b_1, c_1) *to* (a_2, b_2, c_2) *is* $(a_2 - a_1)\mathbf{i} + (b_2 - b_1)\mathbf{j} + (c_2 - c_1)\mathbf{k}$.

EXAMPLE 6.2

Suppose we want the equation of the line L through the points $(1, -2, 4)$ and $(6, 2, -3)$.

This problem is more subtle in 3-space than in the plane because in three dimensions there is no point-slope formula. Reason as follows. Let (x, y, z) be any point on L. Then (Figure 6.10), the vector represented by the arrow from $(1, -2, 4)$ to (x, y, z) must be parallel to the vector from $(1, -2, 4)$ to $(6, 2, -3)$, because arrows representing these vectors are both along L. This means that $(x - 1)\mathbf{i} + (y + 2)\mathbf{j} + (z - 4)\mathbf{k}$ is parallel to $5\mathbf{i} + 4\mathbf{j} - 7\mathbf{k}$. Then, for some scalar t,

$$(x - 1)\mathbf{i} + (y + 2)\mathbf{j} + (z - 4)\mathbf{k} = t[5\mathbf{i} + 4\mathbf{j} - 7\mathbf{k}].$$

But then the respective components of these vectors must be equal:

$$x - 1 = 5t, \quad y + 2 = 4t, \quad z - 4 = -7t.$$

Then

$$x = 1 + 5t, \quad y = -2 + 4t, \quad z = 4 - 7t. \tag{6.1}$$

A point is on L if and only if its coordinates are $(1 + 5t, -2 + 4t, 4 - 7t)$ for some real number t (Figure 6.11). Equations (6.1) are parametric equations of the line, with t, which can be assigned any real value, as parameter. When $t = 0$, we get $(1, -2, 4)$, and when $t = 1$, we get $(6, 2, -3)$.

We can also write the equation of this line in what is called normal form. By eliminating t, this form is

$$\frac{x - 1}{5} = \frac{y + 2}{4} = \frac{z - 4}{-7}.$$

We may also envision the line as swept out by the arrow pivoted at the origin and extending to the point $(1 + 5t, -2 + 4t, 4 - 7t)$ as t varies over the real numbers. ∎

Some care must be taken in writing the normal form of a straight line. For example, the line through $(2, -1, 6)$ and $(-4, -1, 2)$ has parametric equations

$$x = 2 - 6t, \quad y = -1, \quad z = 6 - 4t.$$

If we eliminate t, we get

$$\frac{x - 2}{-6} = \frac{z - 6}{-4}, \quad y = -1.$$

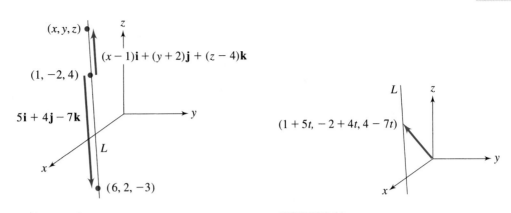

FIGURE 6.10

FIGURE 6.11

Every point on the line has second coordinate -1, and this is independent of t. This information must not be omitted from the equations of the line. If we omit $y = -1$ and write just

$$\frac{x-2}{-6} = \frac{z-6}{-4},$$

then we have the equation of a plane, not a line.

EXAMPLE 6.3

Suppose we want a vector **F** in the $x, y-$plane, making an angle of $\pi/7$ with the positive $x-$axis, and having magnitude 19.

By "find a vector" we mean determine its components. Let $\mathbf{F} = a\mathbf{i} + b\mathbf{j}$. From the right triangle in Figure 6.12,

$$\cos(\pi/7) = \frac{a}{19} \quad \text{and} \quad \sin(\pi/7) = \frac{b}{19}.$$

Then

$$\mathbf{F} = 19\cos(\pi/7)\mathbf{i} + 19\sin(\pi/7)\mathbf{j}. \quad \blacksquare$$

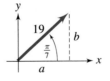

FIGURE 6.12

EXAMPLE 6.4

We will prove that the line segments formed by connecting successive midpoints of the sides of a quadrilateral form a parallelogram. Again, our overall objective is not to prove theorems of geometry, but this argument is good practice in the use of vectors.

Figure 6.13 illustrates what we want to show. Draw the quadrilateral again, with arrows (vectors) **A**, **B**, **C**, and **D** as sides. The vectors **x**, **y**, **u**, and **v** drawn with dashed lines connect

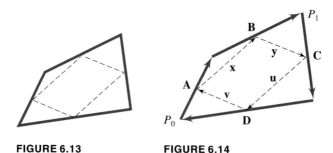

FIGURE 6.13   FIGURE 6.14

the midpoints of successive sides (Figure 6.14). We want to show that $\mathbf{x}$ and $\mathbf{u}$ are parallel and of the same length, and that $\mathbf{y}$ and $\mathbf{v}$ are also parallel and of the same length.

From the parallelogram law for vector addition and the definitions of $\mathbf{x}$ and $\mathbf{u}$,

$$\mathbf{x} = \frac{1}{2}\mathbf{A} + \frac{1}{2}\mathbf{B}$$

and

$$\mathbf{u} = \frac{1}{2}\mathbf{C} + \frac{1}{2}\mathbf{D}.$$

But also by the parallelogram law, $\mathbf{A} + \mathbf{B}$ is the arrow from P_0 to P_1, while $\mathbf{C} + \mathbf{D}$ is the arrow from P_1 to P_0. These arrows have the same length, and opposite directions. This means that

$$\mathbf{A} + \mathbf{B} = -(\mathbf{C} + \mathbf{D}).$$

But then $\mathbf{x} = -\mathbf{u}$, so these vectors are parallel and of the same length (just opposite in direction).

A similar argument shows that $\mathbf{y}$ and $\mathbf{v}$ are also parallel and of the same length, completing the proof. ∎

SECTION 6.1   PROBLEMS

In each of Problems 1 through 5, compute $\mathbf{F} + \mathbf{G}$, $\mathbf{F} - \mathbf{G}$, $\|\mathbf{F}\|$, $\|\mathbf{G}\|$, $2\mathbf{F}$, and $3\mathbf{G}$.

1. $\mathbf{F} = 2\mathbf{i} - 3\mathbf{j} + 5\mathbf{k}, \mathbf{G} = \sqrt{2}\mathbf{i} + 6\mathbf{j} - 5\mathbf{k}$

2. $\mathbf{F} = \mathbf{i} - 3\mathbf{k}, \mathbf{G} = 4\mathbf{j}$

3. $\mathbf{F} = 2\mathbf{i} - 5\mathbf{j}, \mathbf{G} = \mathbf{i} + 5\mathbf{j} - \mathbf{k}$

4. $\mathbf{F} = \sqrt{2}\mathbf{i} + \mathbf{j} - 6\mathbf{k}, \mathbf{G} = 8\mathbf{i} + 2\mathbf{k}$

5. $\mathbf{F} = \mathbf{i} + \mathbf{j} + \mathbf{k}, \mathbf{G} = 2\mathbf{i} - 2\mathbf{j} + 2\mathbf{k}$

In each of Problems 6 through 10, calculate $\mathbf{F} + \mathbf{G}$ and $\mathbf{F} - \mathbf{G}$ by representing the vectors as arrows and using the parallelogram law.

6. $\mathbf{F} = \mathbf{i}, \mathbf{G} = 6\mathbf{j}$

7. $\mathbf{F} = 2\mathbf{i} - \mathbf{j}, \mathbf{G} = \mathbf{i} - \mathbf{j}$

8. $\mathbf{F} = -3\mathbf{i} + \mathbf{j}, \mathbf{G} = 4\mathbf{j}$

9. $\mathbf{F} = \mathbf{i} - 2\mathbf{j}, \mathbf{G} = \mathbf{i} - 3\mathbf{j}$

10. $\mathbf{F} = -\mathbf{i} + 4\mathbf{j}, \mathbf{G} = -2\mathbf{i} - 2\mathbf{j}$

In each of Problems 11 through 15, determine $\alpha\mathbf{F}$ and represent $\mathbf{F}$ and $\alpha\mathbf{F}$ as arrows.

11. $\mathbf{F} = \mathbf{i} + \mathbf{j}, \alpha = -1/2$

12. $\mathbf{F} = 6\mathbf{i} - 2\mathbf{j}, \alpha = 2$

13. $\mathbf{F} = -3\mathbf{j}, \alpha = -4$

14. $\mathbf{F} = 6\mathbf{i} - 6\mathbf{j}, \alpha = 1/2$

15. $\mathbf{F} = -3\mathbf{i} + 2\mathbf{j}, \alpha = 3$

In each of Problems 16 through 21, find the parametric equations of the straight line containing the given points. Also find the normal form of this line.

16. $(1,0,4),(2,1,1)$

17. $(3, 0, 0), (-3, 1, 0)$

18. $(2, 1, 1), (2, 1, -2)$

19. $(0,1,3), (0,0,1)$

20. $(1, 0, -4), (-2, -2, 5)$

21. $(2, -3, 6), (-1, 6, 4)$

In each of Problems 22 through 26, find a vector $\mathbf{F}$ in the x, y-plane having the given length and making the angle (given in radians) with the positive x-axis. Represent the vector as an arrow in the plane.

22. $\sqrt{5}, \pi/4$

23. $6, \pi/3$

24. $5, 3\pi/5$

25. $15, 7\pi/4$

26. $25, 3\pi/2$

27. Let $P_1, P_2, \ldots, P_n$ be distinct points in 3-space, with $n \geq 3$. Let $\mathbf{F}_i$ be the vector represented by the arrow from P_i to P_{i+1} for $i = 1, 2, \ldots, n - 1$ and let $\mathbf{F}_n$ be the vector represented by the arrow from P_n to P_1. Prove that $\mathbf{F}_1 + \mathbf{F}_2 + \cdots + \mathbf{F}_n = \mathbf{O}$.

28. Let $\mathbf{F}$ be any nonzero vector. Determine a scalar t such that $\|t\mathbf{F}\| = 1$.

29. Use vectors to prove that the altitudes of any triangle intersect in a single point. (Recall that an altitude is a line from a vertex, perpendicular to the opposite side of the triangle.)

6.2   The Dot Product

Throughout this section, let $\mathbf{F} = a_1\mathbf{i} + b_1\mathbf{j} + c_1\mathbf{k}$ and $\mathbf{G} = a_2\mathbf{i} + b_2\mathbf{j} + c_2\mathbf{k}$.

DEFINITION 6.5   *Dot Product*

The dot product of $\mathbf{F}$ and $\mathbf{G}$ is the number $\mathbf{F} \cdot \mathbf{G}$ defined by

$$\mathbf{F} \cdot \mathbf{G} = a_1 a_2 + b_1 b_2 + c_1 c_2.$$

For example,

$$(\sqrt{3}\mathbf{i} + 4\mathbf{j} - \pi\mathbf{k}) \cdot (-2\mathbf{i} + 6\mathbf{j} + 3\mathbf{k}) = -2\sqrt{3} + 24 - 3\pi.$$

Sometimes the dot product is referred to as a scalar product, since the dot product of two vectors is a scalar (real number). This must not be confused with the product of a vector with a scalar. Here are some rules for operating with the dot product.

THEOREM 6.3   *Properties of the Dot Product*

Let $\mathbf{F}$, $\mathbf{G}$, and $\mathbf{H}$ be vectors, and α a, scalar. Then

1. $\mathbf{F} \cdot \mathbf{G} = \mathbf{G} \cdot \mathbf{F}$.
2. $(\mathbf{F} + \mathbf{G}) \cdot \mathbf{H} = \mathbf{F} \cdot \mathbf{H} + \mathbf{G} \cdot \mathbf{H}$.
3. $\alpha(\mathbf{F} \cdot \mathbf{G}) = (\alpha\mathbf{F}) \cdot \mathbf{G} = \mathbf{F} \cdot (\alpha\mathbf{G})$.
4. $\mathbf{F} \cdot \mathbf{F} = \|\mathbf{F}\|^2$.
5. $\mathbf{F} \cdot \mathbf{F} = 0$ if and only if $\mathbf{F} = \mathbf{O}$.

Conclusion (1) is the commutativity of the dot product (we can perform the operation in either order), and (2) is a distributive law. Conclusion (3) states that a constant factors through a dot product. Conclusion (4) is very useful in some kinds of calculations, as we will see shortly. A proof of the theorem involves routine calculations, two of which we will illustrate.

Proof   For (3), write

$$\alpha(\mathbf{F} \cdot \mathbf{G}) = \alpha(a_1 a_2 + b_1 b_2 + c_1 c_2) = (\alpha a_1)a_2 + (\alpha b_1)b_2 + (\alpha c_1)c_2$$
$$= (\alpha \mathbf{F}) \cdot \mathbf{G} = a_1(\alpha a_2) + b_1(\alpha b_2) + c_1(\alpha c_2) = \mathbf{F} \cdot (\alpha \mathbf{G}).$$

For (4), we have

$$\mathbf{F} \cdot \mathbf{F} = (a_1\mathbf{i} + b_1\mathbf{j} + c_1\mathbf{k}) \cdot (a_1\mathbf{i} + b_1\mathbf{j} + c_1\mathbf{k})$$
$$= a_1^2 + b_1^2 + c_1^2 = \|\mathbf{F}\|^2. \; \blacksquare$$

Using conclusion (4) of the theorem, we can derive a relationship we will use frequently.

LEMMA 6.1

Let $\mathbf{F}$ and $\mathbf{G}$ be vectors, and let α and β be scalars. Then

$$\|\alpha\mathbf{F} + \beta\mathbf{G}\|^2 = \alpha^2 \|\mathbf{F}\|^2 + 2\alpha\beta\mathbf{F} \cdot \mathbf{G} + \beta^2 \|\mathbf{G}\|.$$

Proof   By using Theorem 6.3, we have

$$\|\alpha\mathbf{F} + \beta\mathbf{G}\|^2 = (\alpha\mathbf{F} + \beta\mathbf{G}) \cdot (\alpha\mathbf{F} + \beta\mathbf{G})$$
$$= \alpha^2\mathbf{F} \cdot \mathbf{F} + \alpha\beta\mathbf{F} \cdot \mathbf{G} + \alpha\beta\mathbf{G} \cdot \mathbf{F} + \beta^2\mathbf{G} \cdot \mathbf{G}$$
$$= \alpha^2\mathbf{F} \cdot \mathbf{F} + 2\alpha\beta\mathbf{F} \cdot \mathbf{G} + \beta^2\mathbf{G} \cdot \mathbf{G}$$
$$= \|\mathbf{F}\|^2 + 2\alpha\beta\mathbf{F} \cdot \mathbf{G} + \|\mathbf{G}\|^2. \; \blacksquare$$

The dot product can be used to determine the angle between vectors. Represent $\mathbf{F}$ and $\mathbf{G}$ as arrows from a common point, as in Figure 6.15. Let θ be the angle between $\mathbf{F}$ and $\mathbf{G}$. The arrow from the tip of $\mathbf{F}$ to the tip of $\mathbf{G}$ represents $\mathbf{G} - \mathbf{F}$, and these three vectors form the sides of a triangle. Now recall the law of cosines, which states, for the triangle of Figure 6.16, that

$$a^2 + b^2 - 2ab\cos(\theta) = c^2. \tag{6.2}$$

Apply this to the vector triangle of Figure 6.15, with sides of length $a = \|\mathbf{G}\|$, $b = \|\mathbf{F}\|$, and $c = \|\mathbf{G} - \mathbf{F}\|$. By using Lemma 6.1 with $\alpha = -1$ and $\beta = 1$, equation (6.2) becomes

$$\|\mathbf{G}\|^2 + \|\mathbf{F}\|^2 - 2\|\mathbf{G}\| \|\mathbf{F}\| \cos(\theta) = \|\mathbf{G} - \mathbf{F}\|^2$$
$$= \|\mathbf{G}\|^2 + \|\mathbf{F}\|^2 - 2\mathbf{G} \cdot \mathbf{F}.$$

Then

$$\mathbf{F} \cdot \mathbf{G} = \|\mathbf{F}\| \|\mathbf{G}\| \cos(\theta).$$

Assuming that neither $\mathbf{F}$ nor $\mathbf{G}$ is the zero vector, then

$$\cos(\theta) = \frac{\mathbf{F} \cdot \mathbf{G}}{\|\mathbf{F}\| \|\mathbf{G}\|}. \tag{6.3}$$

This provides a simple way of computing the cosine of the angle between two arrows representing vectors. Since vectors can be drawn along straight lines, this also lets us calculate the angle between two intersecting lines.

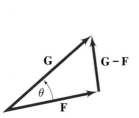

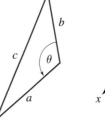

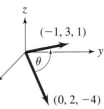

FIGURE 6.15

FIGURE 6.16
Law of cosines:
$a^2 + b^2 -$
$2ab\cos(\theta) = c^2.$

FIGURE 6.17

EXAMPLE 6.5

Let $\mathbf{F} = -\mathbf{i} + 3\mathbf{j} + \mathbf{k}$ and $\mathbf{G} = 2\mathbf{j} - 4\mathbf{k}$. The cosine of the angle between these vectors (Figure 6.17) is

$$\cos(\theta) = \frac{(-\mathbf{i}+3\mathbf{j}+\mathbf{k})\cdot(2\mathbf{j}-4\mathbf{k})}{\|-\mathbf{i}+3\mathbf{j}+\mathbf{k}\|\,\|2\mathbf{j}-4\mathbf{k}\|}$$

$$= \frac{(-1)(0)+(3)(2)+(1)(-4)}{\sqrt{1^2+3^2+1^2}\sqrt{2^2+4^2}} = \frac{2}{\sqrt{220}}.$$

Then

$$\theta = \arccos(2/\sqrt{220}),$$

which is that unique number in $[0, \pi]$ whose cosine is $2/\sqrt{220}$. θ is approximately 1.436 radians. ∎

EXAMPLE 6.6

Lines L_1 and L_2 are given, respectively, by the parametric equations

$$x = 1+6t, \quad y = 2-4t, \quad z = -1+3t$$

and

$$x = 4-3p, \quad y = 2p, \quad z = -5+4p$$

in which the parameters t and p take on all real values. We want the angle between these lines at their point of intersection, which is $(1, 2, -1)$ (on L_1 for $t = 0$ and on L_2 for $p = 1$).

Of course, two intersecting lines have two angles between them (Figure 6.18). However, the sum of these angles is π, so either angle determines the other.

The strategy for solving this problem is to find a vector along each line, then find the angle between these vectors. For a vector $\mathbf{F}$ along L_1, choose any two points on this line, say $(1, 2, -1)$ and, with $t = 1$, $(7, -2, 2)$. The vector from the first to the second point is

$$\mathbf{F} = (7-1)\mathbf{i}+(-2-2)\mathbf{j}+(2-(-1))\mathbf{k} = 6\mathbf{i} - 4\mathbf{j}+3\mathbf{k}.$$

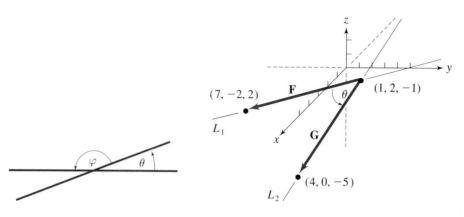

FIGURE 6.18   FIGURE 6.19

Two points on L_2 are $(1, 2, -1)$ and, with $p = 0$, $(4, 0, -5)$. The vector $\mathbf{G}$ from the first to the second of these points is

$$\mathbf{G} = (4 - 1)\mathbf{i} + (0 - 2)\mathbf{j} + (-5 - (-1))\mathbf{k} = 3\mathbf{i} - 2\mathbf{j} - 4\mathbf{k}.$$

These vectors are shown in Figure 6.19. The cosine of the angle between $\mathbf{F}$ and $\mathbf{G}$ is

$$\cos(\theta) = \frac{\mathbf{F} \cdot \mathbf{G}}{\|\mathbf{F}\| \, \|\mathbf{G}\|} = \frac{6(3) - 4(-2) + 3(-4)}{\sqrt{36 + 16 + 9}\sqrt{9 + 4 + 16}} = \frac{14}{\sqrt{1769}}.$$

One angle between the lines is $\theta = \arccos(14/\sqrt{1769})$, approximately 1.23 radians. ∎

If we had used $-\mathbf{G}$ in place of $\mathbf{G}$ in this calculation, we would have gotten $\theta = \arccos(-14/\sqrt{1769})$, or about 1.91 radians. This is the supplement of the angle found in the example.

EXAMPLE 6.7

The points $A(1, -2, 1)$, $B(0, 1, 6)$, and $C(-3, 4, -2)$ form the vertices of a triangle. Suppose we want the angle between the line $\overline{AB}$ and the line from A to the midpoint of $\overline{BC}$. This line is a median of the triangle and is shown in Figure 6.20

Visualize the sides of the triangle as vectors, as in Figure 6.21. If P is the midpoint of $\overline{BC}$, then $\mathbf{H}_1 = \mathbf{H}_2$ because both vectors have the same direction and length. From the coordinates of the vertices, calculate

$$\mathbf{F} = -\mathbf{i} + 3\mathbf{j} + 5\mathbf{k} \text{ and } \mathbf{G} = -4\mathbf{i} + 6\mathbf{j} - 3\mathbf{k}.$$

We want the angle between $\mathbf{F}$ and $\mathbf{K}$, so we need $\mathbf{K}$. By the parallelogram law,

$$\mathbf{F} + \mathbf{H}_1 = \mathbf{K} \text{ and } \mathbf{K} + \mathbf{H}_2 = \mathbf{G}.$$

Since $\mathbf{H}_1 = \mathbf{H}_2$, these equations imply that

$$\mathbf{K} = \mathbf{F} + \mathbf{H}_1 = \mathbf{F} + (\mathbf{G} - \mathbf{K}).$$

Therefore,

$$\mathbf{K} = \frac{1}{2}(\mathbf{F} + \mathbf{G}) = -\frac{5}{2}\mathbf{i} + \frac{9}{2}\mathbf{j} + \mathbf{k}.$$

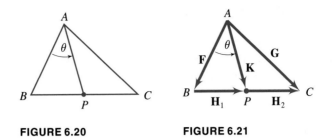

FIGURE 6.20   **FIGURE 6.21**

Now the cosine of the angle we want is

$$\cos(\theta) = \frac{\mathbf{F} \cdot \mathbf{K}}{\|\mathbf{F}\| \, \|\mathbf{K}\|} = \frac{42}{\sqrt{35}\sqrt{110}} = \frac{42}{\sqrt{3850}}.$$

θ is approximately 0.83 radians. ∎

The arrows representing two nonzero vectors $\mathbf{F}$ and $\mathbf{G}$ are perpendicular exactly when the cosine of the angle between them is zero, and by equation (6.3) this occurs when $\mathbf{F} \cdot \mathbf{G} = 0$. This suggests we use this condition to define orthogonality (perpendicularity) of vectors. If we agree to the convention that the zero vector is orthogonal to every vector, then this dot product condition allows a general definition without requiring that the vectors be nonzero.

DEFINITION 6.6   *Orthogonal Vectors*

Vectors $\mathbf{F}$ and $\mathbf{G}$ are orthogonal if and only if $\mathbf{F} \cdot \mathbf{G} = 0$.

EXAMPLE 6.8

Let $\mathbf{F} = -4\mathbf{i} + \mathbf{j} + 2\mathbf{k}$, $\mathbf{G} = 2\mathbf{i} + 4\mathbf{k}$ and $\mathbf{H} = 6\mathbf{i} - \mathbf{j} - 2\mathbf{k}$. Then $\mathbf{F} \cdot \mathbf{G} = 0$, so $\mathbf{F}$ and $\mathbf{G}$ are orthogonal. But $\mathbf{F} \cdot \mathbf{H}$ and $\mathbf{G} \cdot \mathbf{H}$ are nonzero, so $\mathbf{F}$ and $\mathbf{H}$ are not orthogonal, and $\mathbf{G}$ and $\mathbf{H}$ are not orthogonal. ∎

Sometimes orthogonality of vectors is a useful device for dealing with lines and planes in three-dimensional space.

EXAMPLE 6.9

Two lines are given parametrically by

$$L_1 : x = 2 - 4t, \quad y = 6 + t, \quad z = 3t$$

and

$$L_2 : x = -2 + p, \quad y = 7 + 2p, \quad z = 3 - 4p.$$

We want to know whether these lines are perpendicular. (It does not matter whether the lines intersect).

The idea is to form a vector along each line and test these vectors for orthogonality. For a vector along L_1, choose two points on this line, say $(2, 6, 0)$ when $t = 0$ and $(-2, 7, 3)$ when $t = 1$. Then $\mathbf{F} = -4\mathbf{i} + \mathbf{j} + 3\mathbf{k}$ is along L_1. Two points on L_2 are $(-2, 7, 3)$ when $p = 0$ and $(-1, 9, -1)$ when $p = 1$. Then $\mathbf{G} = \mathbf{i} + 2\mathbf{j} - 4\mathbf{k}$ is along L_2. Since $\mathbf{F} \cdot \mathbf{G} = -14 \neq 0$, these vectors, hence these lines, are not orthogonal. ∎

EXAMPLE 6.10

Suppose we want the equation of a plane Π containing the point $(-6, 1, 1)$ and perpendicular to the vector $\mathbf{N} = -2\mathbf{i} + 4\mathbf{j} + \mathbf{k}$.

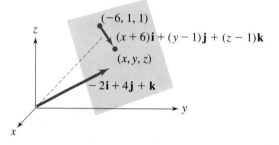

FIGURE 6.22

A strategy to find such an equation is suggested by Figure 6.22. A point (x, y, z) is on Π if and only if the vector from $(-6, 1, 1)$ to (x, y, z) is in Π and therefore is orthogonal to $\mathbf{N}$. This means that

$$((x+6)\mathbf{i} + (y-1)\mathbf{j} + (z-1)\mathbf{k}) \cdot \mathbf{N} = 0.$$

Carrying out this dot product, we get the equation

$$-2(x+6) + 4(y-1) + (z-1) = 0,$$

or

$$-2x + 4y + z = 17.$$

This is the equation of the plane. Of course the given point $(-6, 1, 1)$ satisfies this equation. ∎

We will conclude this section with the important Cauchy-Schwarz inequality, which states that the dot product of two vectors cannot be greater in absolute value than the product of the lengths of the vectors.

THEOREM 6.4 *Cauchy-Schwarz Inequality*

Let $\mathbf{F}$ and $\mathbf{G}$ be vectors. Then

$$|\mathbf{F} \cdot \mathbf{G}| \leq \|\mathbf{F}\| \, \|\mathbf{G}\| \, .$$

Proof If either vector is the zero vector, then both sides of the proposed inequality are zero. Thus suppose neither vector is the zero vector. In this event,

$$\cos(\theta) = \frac{\mathbf{F} \cdot \mathbf{G}}{\|\mathbf{F}\| \, \|\mathbf{G}\|},$$

where θ is the angle between **F** and **G**. But then

$$-1 \leq \frac{\mathbf{F} \cdot \mathbf{G}}{\|\mathbf{F}\| \|\mathbf{G}\|} \leq 1,$$

so

$$-\|\mathbf{F}\| \|\mathbf{G}\| \leq \mathbf{F} \cdot \mathbf{G} \leq \|\mathbf{F}\| \|\mathbf{G}\|,$$

which is equivalent to the Cauchy-Schwarz inequality. ∎

SECTION 6.2 *PROBLEMS*

In each of Problems 1 through 6, compute the dot product of the vectors and the cosine of the angle between them. Also determine if they are orthogonal and verify the Cauchy-Schwarz inequality for these vectors.

1. $\mathbf{i}, 2\mathbf{i} - 3\mathbf{j} + \mathbf{k}$

2. $2\mathbf{i} - 6\mathbf{j} + \mathbf{k}, \mathbf{i} - \mathbf{j}$

3. $-4\mathbf{i} - 2\mathbf{j} + 3\mathbf{k}, 6\mathbf{i} - 2\mathbf{j} - \mathbf{k}$

4. $8\mathbf{i} - 3\mathbf{j} + 2\mathbf{k}, -8\mathbf{i} - 3\mathbf{j} + \mathbf{k}$

5. $\mathbf{i} - 3\mathbf{k}, 2\mathbf{j} + 6\mathbf{k}$

6. $\mathbf{i} + \mathbf{j} + 2\mathbf{k}, \mathbf{i} - \mathbf{j} + 2\mathbf{k}$

In each of Problems 7 through 12, find the equation of the plane containing the given point and having the given vector as normal vector.

7. $(-1, 1, 2), 3\mathbf{i} - \mathbf{j} + 4\mathbf{k}$

8. $(-1, 0, 0), \mathbf{i} - 2\mathbf{j}$

9. $(2, -3, 4), 8\mathbf{i} - 6\mathbf{j} + 4\mathbf{k}$

10. $(-1, -1, -5), -3\mathbf{i} + 2\mathbf{j}$

11. $(0, -1, 4), 7\mathbf{i} + 6\mathbf{j} - 5\mathbf{k}$

12. $(-2, 1, -1), 4\mathbf{i} + 3\mathbf{j} + \mathbf{k}$

In each of Problems 13 through 16, find the cosine of the angle between $\overline{AB}$ and the line from A to the midpoint of $\overline{BC}$.

13. $A = (1, -2, 6), B = (3, 0, 1), C = (4, 2, -7)$

14. $A = (3, -2, -3), B = (-2, 0, 1), C = (1, 1, 7)$

15. $A = (1, -2, 6), B = (0, 4, -3), C = (-3, -2, 7)$

16. $A = (0, 5, -1), B = (1, -2, 5), C = (7, 0, -1)$

17. Suppose $\mathbf{F} \cdot \mathbf{X} = 0$ for every vector **X**. What can be concluded about **F**?

18. Suppose $\mathbf{F} \cdot \mathbf{i} = \mathbf{F} \cdot \mathbf{j} = \mathbf{F} \cdot \mathbf{k} = 0$. What can be concluded about **F**?

19. Suppose $\mathbf{F} \neq \mathbf{O}$. Prove that the unit vector **u** for which $|\mathbf{F} \cdot \mathbf{u}|$ is a maximum must be parallel to **F**.

20. Prove that for any vector **F**,

$$\mathbf{F} = (\mathbf{F} \cdot \mathbf{i})\mathbf{i} + (\mathbf{F} \cdot \mathbf{j})\mathbf{j} + (\mathbf{F} \cdot \mathbf{k})\mathbf{k}.$$

6.3 The Cross Product

The dot product produces a scalar from two vectors. We will now define the cross product, which produces a vector from two vectors.

For this section, let $\mathbf{F} = a_1\mathbf{i} + b_1\mathbf{j} + c_1\mathbf{k}$ and $\mathbf{G} = a_2\mathbf{i} + b_2\mathbf{j} + c_2\mathbf{k}$.

DEFINITION 6.7 *Cross Product*

The cross product of **F** with **G** is the vector $\mathbf{F} \times \mathbf{G}$ defined by

$$\mathbf{F} \times \mathbf{G} = (b_1 c_2 - b_2 c_1)\mathbf{i} + (a_2 c_1 - a_1 c_2)\mathbf{j} + (a_1 b_2 - a_2 b_1)\mathbf{k}.$$

This vector is read "**F** cross **G**." For example,

$$(\mathbf{i}+2\mathbf{j}-3\mathbf{k}) \times (-2\mathbf{i}+\mathbf{j}+4\mathbf{k}) = (8+3)\mathbf{i}+(6-4)\mathbf{j}+(1+4)\mathbf{k} = 11\mathbf{i}+2\mathbf{j}+5\mathbf{k}.$$

A cross product is often computed as a three by three "determinant," with the unit vectors in the first row, components of **F** in the second row, and components of **G** in the third. If expanded by the first row, this determinant gives **F** × **G**. For example

$$\begin{vmatrix} \mathbf{i} & \mathbf{j} & \mathbf{k} \\ 1 & 2 & -3 \\ -2 & 1 & 4 \end{vmatrix} = \begin{vmatrix} 2 & -3 \\ 1 & 4 \end{vmatrix}\mathbf{i} - \begin{vmatrix} 1 & -3 \\ -2 & 4 \end{vmatrix}\mathbf{j} + \begin{vmatrix} 1 & 2 \\ -2 & 1 \end{vmatrix}\mathbf{k}$$

$$= 11\mathbf{i}+2\mathbf{j}+5\mathbf{k} = \mathbf{F} \times \mathbf{G}.$$

The interchange of two rows in a determinant results in a change of sign. This means that interchanging **F** and **G** in the cross product results in a change of sign:

$$\mathbf{F} \times \mathbf{G} = -\mathbf{G} \times \mathbf{F}.$$

This is also apparent from the definition. Unlike addition and multiplication of real numbers and the dot product operation, the cross product is not commutative, and the order in which it is performed makes a difference. This is true of many physical processes, for example, the order in which chemicals are combined may make a significant difference.

Some of the rules we need to compute with cross products are given in the next theorem.

THEOREM 6.5   *Properties of the Cross Product*

Let **F**, **G**, and **H** be vectors and let α be a scalar.

1. $\mathbf{F} \times \mathbf{G} = -\mathbf{G} \times \mathbf{F}$.
2. $\mathbf{F} \times \mathbf{G}$ is orthogonal to both **F** and **G**.
3. $\|\mathbf{F} \times \mathbf{G}\| = \|\mathbf{F}\| \|\mathbf{G}\| \sin(\theta)$, in which θ is the angle between **F** and **G**.
4. If **F** and **G** are not zero vectors, then $\mathbf{F} \times \mathbf{G} = \mathbf{O}$ if and only **F** and **G** are parallel.
5. $\mathbf{F} \times (\mathbf{G}+\mathbf{H}) = \mathbf{F} \times \mathbf{G} + \mathbf{F} \times \mathbf{H}$.
6. $\alpha(\mathbf{F} \times \mathbf{G}) = (\alpha\mathbf{F}) \times \mathbf{G} = \mathbf{F} \times (\alpha\mathbf{G})$.

Proofs of these statements are for the most part routine calculations. We will prove (2) and (3).

Proof   For (2), compute

$$\mathbf{F} \cdot (\mathbf{F} \times \mathbf{G}) = a_1(b_1c_2 - b_2c_1) + b_1(a_2c_1 - a_1c_2) + c_1(a_1b_2 - a_2b_1) = 0.$$

Therefore **F** and **F** × **G** are orthogonal. A similar argument holds for **G**.

For (3), compute

$$\|\mathbf{F} \times \mathbf{G}\|^2 = (b_1 c_2 - b_2 c_1)^2 + (a_2 c_1 - a_1 c_2)^2 + (a_1 b_2 - a_2 b_1)^2$$

$$= (a_1^2 + b_1^2 + c_1^2)(a_2^2 + b_2^2 + c_2^2) - (a_1 a_2 + b_1 b_2 + c_1 c_2)^2$$

$$= \|\mathbf{F}\|^2 \|\mathbf{G}\|^2 - (\mathbf{F} \cdot \mathbf{G})^2$$

$$= \|\mathbf{F}\|^2 \|\mathbf{G}\|^2 - \|\mathbf{F}\|^2 \|\mathbf{G}\|^2 \cos^2(\theta)$$

$$= \|\mathbf{F}\|^2 \|\mathbf{G}\|^2 \left(1 - \cos^2(\theta)\right)$$

$$= \|\mathbf{F}\|^2 \|\mathbf{G}\|^2 \sin^2(\theta).$$

Because $0 \le \theta \le \pi$, all of the factors whose squares appear in this equation are nonnegative, and upon taking square roots we obtain conclusion (3). ■

If $\mathbf{F}$ and $\mathbf{G}$ are nonzero and not parallel, then arrows representing these vectors determine a plane in 3-dimensional space (Figure 6.23). $\mathbf{F} \times \mathbf{G}$ is orthogonal to this plane and oriented as in Figure 6.24. If a person's right hand is placed so that the fingers curl from $\mathbf{F}$ to $\mathbf{G}$, then the thumb points up along $\mathbf{F} \times \mathbf{G}$. This is referred to as the *right-hand rule*. $\mathbf{G} \times \mathbf{F} = -\mathbf{F} \times \mathbf{G}$ points in the opposite direction. As a simple example, $\mathbf{i} \times \mathbf{j} = \mathbf{k}$, and these three vectors define a standard right-handed coordinate system in 3-space.

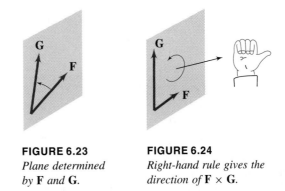

FIGURE 6.23
Plane determined by $\mathbf{F}$ and $\mathbf{G}$.

FIGURE 6.24
Right-hand rule gives the direction of $\mathbf{F} \times \mathbf{G}$.

The fact that $\mathbf{F} \times \mathbf{G}$ is orthogonal to both $\mathbf{F}$ and $\mathbf{G}$ is often useful. If they are not parallel, then vectors $\mathbf{F}$ and $\mathbf{G}$ determine a plane Π (Figure 6.23). This is consistent with the fact that three points, not on the same straight line, determine a plane. One point forms a base point for drawing the arrows representing $\mathbf{F}$ and $\mathbf{G}$, and the other two points are the terminal points of these arrows. If we know a vector orthogonal to both $\mathbf{F}$ and $\mathbf{G}$, then this vector is orthogonal to every vector in Π. Such a vector is said to be *normal* to Π. In Example 6.10 we showed how to find the equation of a plane, given a point in the plane and a normal vector. Now we can find the equation of a plane, given three points in it (not all on a line), because we can use the cross product to produce a normal vector.

EXAMPLE 6.11

Suppose we want the equation of the plane Π containing the points $(1, 2, 1)$, $(-1, 1, 3)$, and $(-2, -2, -2)$.

Begin by finding a vector normal to Π. We will do this by finding two vectors in Π and taking their cross product. The vectors from $(1, 2, 1)$ to the other two given points are in Π (Figure 6.25). These vectors are

$$\mathbf{F} = -2\mathbf{i} - \mathbf{j} + 2\mathbf{k} \text{ and } \mathbf{G} = -3\mathbf{i} - 4\mathbf{j} - 3\mathbf{k}.$$

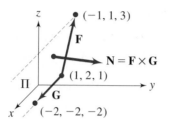

FIGURE 6.25

Form

$$\mathbf{N} = \mathbf{F} \times \mathbf{G} = \begin{vmatrix} \mathbf{i} & \mathbf{j} & \mathbf{k} \\ -2 & -1 & 2 \\ -3 & -4 & -3 \end{vmatrix} = 11\mathbf{i} - 12\mathbf{j} + 5\mathbf{k}.$$

This vector is normal to Π (orthogonal to every vector lying in Π). Now proceed as in Example 6.10. If (x, y, z) is any point in Π, then $(x-1)\mathbf{i} + (y-2)\mathbf{j} + (z-1)\mathbf{k}$ is in Π and so is orthogonal to $\mathbf{N}$. Therefore,

$$[(x-1)\mathbf{i} + (y-2)\mathbf{j} + (z-1)\mathbf{k}] \cdot \mathbf{N}$$
$$= 11(x-1) - 12(y-2) + 5(z-1) = 0.$$

This gives

$$11x - 12y + 5z = -8.$$

This is the equation of the plane in the sense that a point (x, y, z) is in the plane if and only its coordinates satisfy this equation. ■

If we had specified three points lying on a line (collinear) in this example, then we would have found that $\mathbf{F}$ and $\mathbf{G}$ are parallel, hence $\mathbf{F} \times \mathbf{G} = \mathbf{O}$. When we calculated this cross product and got a nonzero vector, we knew that the points were not collinear.

The cross product also has geometric interpretations as an area or volume.

THEOREM 6.6

Let $\mathbf{F}$ and $\mathbf{G}$ be represented by arrows lying along incident sides of a parallelogram (Figure 6.26). Then the area of this parallelogram is $\|\mathbf{F} \times \mathbf{G}\|$.

Proof The area of a parallelogram is the product of the lengths of two incident sides and the sine of the angle between them. Draw vectors $\mathbf{F}$ and $\mathbf{G}$ along two incident sides. Then

FIGURE 6.26 *Area* $= \|\mathbf{F} \times \mathbf{G}\|$.

these sides have length $\|\mathbf{F}\|$ and $\|\mathbf{G}\|$. If θ is the angle between them, then the area of the parallelogram is $\|\mathbf{F}\|\,\|\mathbf{G}\|\sin(\theta)$. But this is exactly $\|\mathbf{F}\times\mathbf{G}\|$. ∎

EXAMPLE 6.12

A parallelogram has two sides extending from $(0,1,-2)$ to $(1,2,2)$ and from $(0,1,-2)$ to $(1,4,1)$. We want to find the area of this parallelogram.

Form vectors along these sides:

$$\mathbf{F} = \mathbf{i}+\mathbf{j}+4\mathbf{k}, \quad \mathbf{G}=\mathbf{i}+3\mathbf{j}+3\mathbf{k}.$$

Calculate

$$\mathbf{F}\times\mathbf{G} = \begin{vmatrix} \mathbf{i} & \mathbf{j} & \mathbf{k} \\ 1 & 1 & 4 \\ 1 & 3 & 3 \end{vmatrix} = -9\mathbf{i}+\mathbf{j}+2\mathbf{k}$$

and the area of the parallelogram is $\|\mathbf{F}\times\mathbf{G}\| = \sqrt{86}$ square units. ∎

If a rectangular box is skewed as in Figure 6.27, the resulting solid is called a *rectangular parallelopiped*. All of its faces are parallelograms. We can find the volume of such a solid by combining dot and cross products, as follows.

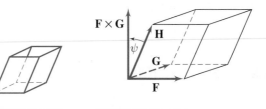

FIGURE 6.27 *Parallelopiped.*

FIGURE 6.28 *Volume* $= |\mathbf{H}\cdot(\mathbf{F}\times\mathbf{G})|.$

THEOREM 6.7

Let $\mathbf{F}$, $\mathbf{G}$ and $\mathbf{H}$ be vectors along incident sides of a rectangular parallelopiped. Then the volume of the parallelopiped is $|\mathbf{H}\cdot(\mathbf{F}\times\mathbf{G})|$.

This is the absolute value of the real number formed by taking the dot product of $\mathbf{H}$ with $\mathbf{F}\times\mathbf{G}$.

Proof Figure 6.28 shows the parallelopiped. $\mathbf{F}\times\mathbf{G}$ is normal to the plane of $\mathbf{F}$ and $\mathbf{G}$ and oriented as shown in the diagram, according to the right-hand rule. If $\mathbf{H}$ is along the third side of the parallelogram, and ψ is the angle between $\mathbf{H}$ and $\mathbf{F}\times\mathbf{G}$, then $\|\mathbf{H}\|\cos(\psi)$ is the altitude of the parallelopiped. The area of the base parallelogram is $\|\mathbf{F}\times\mathbf{G}\|$ by Theorem 6.6. Thus the volume of the parallelopiped is

$$\|\mathbf{H}\|\,\|\mathbf{F}\times\mathbf{G}\|\cos(\psi).$$

But this is $|\mathbf{H}\cdot(\mathbf{F}\times\mathbf{G})|$. ∎

EXAMPLE 6.13

One corner of a rectangular parallelopiped is at $(-1, 2, 2)$, and three incident sides extend from this point to $(0, 1, 1)$, $(-4, 6, 8)$, and $(-3, -2, 4)$. To find the volume of this solid, form the vectors

$$\mathbf{F} = (0 - (-1))\mathbf{i} + (1 - 2)\mathbf{j} + (1 - 2)\mathbf{k} = \mathbf{i} - \mathbf{j} - \mathbf{k},$$

$$\mathbf{G} = (-4 - (-1))\mathbf{i} + (6 - 2)\mathbf{j} + (8 - 2)\mathbf{k} = -3\mathbf{i} + 4\mathbf{j} + 6\mathbf{k},$$

and

$$\mathbf{H} = (-3 - (-1))\mathbf{i} + (-2 - 2)\mathbf{j} + (4 - 2)\mathbf{k} = -2\mathbf{i} - 4\mathbf{j} + 2\mathbf{k}.$$

Calculate

$$\mathbf{F} \times \mathbf{G} = \begin{vmatrix} \mathbf{i} & \mathbf{j} & \mathbf{k} \\ 1 & -1 & -1 \\ -3 & 4 & 6 \end{vmatrix} = -2\mathbf{i} - 3\mathbf{j} + \mathbf{k}.$$

Then

$$\mathbf{H} \cdot (\mathbf{F} \times \mathbf{G}) = (-2)(-2) + (-4)(-3) + (2)(1) = 18,$$

and the volume is 18 cubic units. ■

The quantity $\mathbf{H} \cdot (\mathbf{F} \times \mathbf{G})$ is called a *scalar triple product*. We will outline one of its properties in the problems.

SECTION 6.3   *PROBLEMS*

In each of Problems 1 through 6, compute $\mathbf{F} \times \mathbf{G}$ and, independently, $\mathbf{G} \times \mathbf{F}$, verifying that one is the negative of the other. Use the dot product to compute the cosine of the angle θ between $\mathbf{F}$ and $\mathbf{G}$ and use this to determine $\sin(\theta)$. Then calculate $\|\mathbf{F}\| \, \|\mathbf{G}\| \sin(\theta)$ and verify that this gives $\|\mathbf{F} \times \mathbf{G}\|$.

1. $\mathbf{F} = -3\mathbf{i} + 6\mathbf{j} + \mathbf{k}, \mathbf{G} = -\mathbf{i} - 2\mathbf{j} + \mathbf{k}$

2. $\mathbf{F} = 6\mathbf{i} - \mathbf{k}, \mathbf{G} = \mathbf{j} + 2\mathbf{k}$

3. $\mathbf{F} = 2\mathbf{i} - 3\mathbf{j} + 4\mathbf{k}, \mathbf{G} = -3\mathbf{i} + 2\mathbf{j}$

4. $\mathbf{F} = 8\mathbf{i} + 6\mathbf{j}, \mathbf{G} = 14\mathbf{j}$

5. $\mathbf{F} = 5\mathbf{i} + 3\mathbf{j} + 4\mathbf{k}, \mathbf{G} = 20\mathbf{i} + 6\mathbf{k}$

6. $\mathbf{F} = 2\mathbf{k}, \mathbf{G} = 8\mathbf{i} - \mathbf{j}$

In each of Problems 7 through 11, determine whether the points are collinear. If they are not, find an equation of the plane containing all three points.

7. $(-1, 1, 6), (2, 0, 1), (3, 0, 0)$

8. $(4, 1, 1), (-2, -2, 3), (6, 0, 1)$

9. $(1, 0, -2), (0, 0, 0), (5, 1, 1)$

10. $(0, 0, 2), (-4, 1, 0), (2, -1, 1)$

11. $(-4, 2, -6), (1, 1, 3), (-2, 4, 5)$

In each of Problems 12 through 16, find the area of the parallelogram having incident sides extending from the first point to each of the other two.

12. $(1, -3, 7), (2, 1, 1), (6, -1, 2)$

13. $(6, 1, 1), (7, -2, 4), (8, -4, 3)$

14. $(-2, 1, 6), (2, 1, -7), (4, 1, 1)$

15. $(4, 2, -3), (6, 2, -1), (2, -6, 4)$

16. $(1, 1, -8), (9, -3, 0), (-2, 5, 2)$

In each of Problems 17 through 21, find the volume of the parallepiped whose incident sides extend from the first point to each of the other three.

17. $(1, 1, 1), (-4, 2, 7), (3, 5, 7), (0, 1, 6)$

18. $(0, 1, -6), (-3, 1, 4), (1, 7, 2), (-3, 0, 4)$

19. $(1, 6, 1), (-2, 4, 2), (3, 0, 0), (2, 2, -4)$

20. $(0, 1, 7), (9, 1, 3), (-2, 4, 1), (3, 0, -3)$

21. $(1, 1, 1), (2, 2, 2), (6, 1, 3), (-2, 4, 6)$

In each of Problems 22 through 26, find a vector normal to the given plane. There are infinitely many such vectors.

22. $8x - y + z = 12$

23. $x - y + 2z = 0$

24. $x - 3y + 2z = 9$

25. $7x + y - 7z = 7$

26. $4x + 6y + 4z = -5$

27. Prove that $\mathbf{F} \times (\mathbf{G} + \mathbf{H}) = \mathbf{F} \times \mathbf{G} + \mathbf{F} \times \mathbf{H}$.

28. Prove that $(\alpha \mathbf{F}) \times \mathbf{G} = \mathbf{F} \times (\alpha \mathbf{G}) = \alpha(\mathbf{F} \times \mathbf{G})$.

29. Prove that $\mathbf{F} \times (\mathbf{G} \times \mathbf{H}) = (\mathbf{F} \cdot \mathbf{H})\mathbf{G} - (\mathbf{F} \cdot \mathbf{G})\mathbf{H}$.

30. Use vector operations to find a formula for the area of the triangle having vertices (a_i, b_i, c_i) for $i = 1, 2, 3$. What conditions must be placed on these coordinates to ensure that the points are not collinear (all on a line)?

The *scalar triple product* of $\mathbf{F}$, $\mathbf{G}$, and $\mathbf{H}$ is defined to be $[\mathbf{F}, \mathbf{G}, \mathbf{H}] = \mathbf{F} \cdot (\mathbf{G} \times \mathbf{H})$.

31. Let $\mathbf{F} = a_1\mathbf{i} + b_1\mathbf{j} + c_1\mathbf{k}$, $\mathbf{G} = a_2\mathbf{i} + b_2\mathbf{j} + c_2\mathbf{k}$, and $\mathbf{H} = a_3\mathbf{i} + b_3\mathbf{j} + c_3\mathbf{k}$. Prove that

$$[\mathbf{F}, \mathbf{G}, \mathbf{H}] = \begin{vmatrix} a_1 & b_1 & c_1 \\ a_2 & b_2 & c_2 \\ a_3 & b_3 & c_3 \end{vmatrix}.$$

6.4   The Vector Space R^n

The world of everyday experience has three space dimensions. But often we encounter settings in which more dimensions occur. If we want to specify not only the location of a particle but the time in which it occupies a particular point, we need four coordinates (x, y, z, t). And specifying the location of each particle in a system of particles may require any number of coordinates. The natural setting for such problems is R^n, the space of points having n coordinates.

DEFINITION 6.8   *n-vector*

If n is a positive integer, an n-vector is an n-tuple $(x_1, x_2, \ldots, x_n)$, with each coordinate x_j a real number. The set of all n-vectors is denoted R^n.

R^1 is the real line, consisting of all real numbers. We can think of real numbers as 1-vectors, but there is is no advantage to doing this. R^2 consists of ordered pairs (x, y) of real numbers, and each such ordered pair (or 2-vector) can be identified with a point in the plane. R^3 consists of all 3-vectors, or points in 3-space. If $n \geq 4$, we can no longer draw a set of mutually independent coordinate axes, one for each coordinate, but we can still work with vectors in R^n according to rules we will now describe.

DEFINITION 6.9   *Algebra of* R^n

---

1. Two n-vectors are added by adding their respective components:

$$(x_1, x_2, \ldots, x_n) + (y_1, y_2, \ldots, y_n) = (x_1 + y_1, x_2 + y_2, \ldots, x_n + y_n).$$

2. An n-vector is multiplied by a scalar by multiplying each component by the scalar:

$$\alpha(x_1, x_2, \ldots, x_n) = (\alpha x_1, \alpha x_2, \ldots, \alpha x_n).$$

The zero vector in R^n is the n-vector $\mathbf{O} = (0, 0, \ldots, 0)$ having each coordinate equal to zero.

The negative of $\mathbf{F} = (x_1, x_2, \ldots, x_n)$ is $-\mathbf{F} = (-x_1, -x_2, \ldots, -x_n)$. As we did with $n = 3$, we denote $\mathbf{G} + (-\mathbf{F})$ as $\mathbf{G} - \mathbf{F}$.

The algebraic rules in R^n mirror those we saw for R^3.

THEOREM 6.8

Let $\mathbf{F}$, $\mathbf{G}$, and $\mathbf{H}$ be in R^n, and let α and β be real numbers. Then

1. $\mathbf{F} + \mathbf{G} = \mathbf{G} + \mathbf{F}$.
2. $\mathbf{F} + (\mathbf{G} + \mathbf{H}) = (\mathbf{F} + \mathbf{G}) + \mathbf{H}$.
3. $\mathbf{F} + \mathbf{O} = \mathbf{F}$.
4. $(\alpha + \beta)\mathbf{F} = \alpha\mathbf{F} + \beta\mathbf{F}$.
5. $(\alpha\beta)\mathbf{F} = \alpha(\beta\mathbf{F})$.
6. $\alpha(\mathbf{F} + \mathbf{G}) = \alpha\mathbf{F} + \alpha\mathbf{G}$.
7. $\alpha\mathbf{O} = \mathbf{O}$. ∎

Because of these properties of the operations of addition of n-vectors, and multiplication of an n-vector by a scalar, we call R^n a *vector space*. In the next section we will clarify the sense in which R^n can be said to have dimension n.

The length (norm, magnitude) of $\mathbf{F} = (x_1, x_2, \ldots, x_n)$ is defined by a direct generalization from the plane and 3-space:

$$\|\mathbf{F}\| = \sqrt{x_1^2 + x_2^2 + \cdots + x_n^2}.$$

There is no analogue of the cross product for vectors in R^n when $n > 3$. However, the dot product readily extends to n-vectors.

DEFINITION 6.10   Dot Product of n-Vectors

The dot product of $(x_1, x_2, \ldots, x_n)$ and $(y_1, y_2, \ldots, y_n)$ is defined by

$$(x_1, x_2, \ldots, x_n) \cdot (y_1, y_2, \ldots, y_n) = x_1 y_1 + x_2 y_2 + \cdots + x_n y_n.$$

All of the conclusions of Theorem 6.3 remain true for n-vectors, as does Lemma 6.1. We will record these results for completeness.

THEOREM 6.9

Let $\mathbf{F}$, $\mathbf{G}$, and $\mathbf{H}$ be n-vectors, and let α and β be real numbers. Then

1. $\mathbf{F} \cdot \mathbf{G} = \mathbf{G} \cdot \mathbf{F}$.
2. $(\mathbf{F} + \mathbf{G}) \cdot \mathbf{H} = \mathbf{F} \cdot \mathbf{H} + \mathbf{G} \cdot \mathbf{H}$.
3. $\alpha(\mathbf{F} \cdot \mathbf{G}) = (\alpha\mathbf{F}) \cdot \mathbf{G} = \mathbf{F} \cdot (\alpha\mathbf{G})$.
4. $\mathbf{F} \cdot \mathbf{F} = \|\mathbf{F}\|^2$.

5. $\mathbf{F} \cdot \mathbf{F} = 0$ if and only if $\mathbf{F} = \mathbf{O}$.

6. $\|\alpha\mathbf{F} + \beta\mathbf{G}\|^2 = \alpha^2 \|\mathbf{F}\|^2 + 2\alpha\beta\mathbf{F} \cdot \mathbf{G} + \beta^2 \|\mathbf{G}\|^2$. ■

The Cauchy-Schwarz inequality holds for *n*-vectors, but the proof given previously for 3-vectors does not generalize to R^n. We will therefore give a proof that is valid for any *n*.

THEOREM 6.10 *Cauchy-Schwarz Inequality in R^n*

Let $\mathbf{F}$ and $\mathbf{G}$ be in R^n. Then

$$|\mathbf{F} \cdot \mathbf{G}| \leq \|\mathbf{F}\| \, \|\mathbf{G}\|$$

Proof The inequality reduces to $0 \leq 0$ if either vector is the zero vector. Thus suppose $\mathbf{F} \neq \mathbf{O}$ and $\mathbf{G} \neq \mathbf{O}$.

Choose $\alpha = \|\mathbf{G}\|$ and $\beta = -\|\mathbf{F}\|$ in Theorem 6.9(6). We get

$$0 \leq \|\alpha\mathbf{F} + \beta\mathbf{G}\|^2 = \|\mathbf{G}\|^2 \|\mathbf{F}\|^2 - 2 \|\mathbf{G}\| \, \|\mathbf{F}\| \mathbf{F} \cdot \mathbf{G} + \|\mathbf{F}\|^2 \|\mathbf{G}\|^2.$$

Upon dividing this inequality by $2 \|\mathbf{F}\| \, \|\mathbf{G}\|$ we obtain

$$\mathbf{F} \cdot \mathbf{G} \leq \|\mathbf{F}\| \, \|\mathbf{G}\|.$$

Now go back to Theorem 6.9(6), but this time choose $\alpha = \|\mathbf{G}\|$ and $\beta = \|\mathbf{F}\|$ to get

$$0 \leq \|\mathbf{G}\|^2 \|\mathbf{F}\|^2 + 2 \|\mathbf{G}\| \, \|\mathbf{F}\| \mathbf{F} \cdot \mathbf{G} + \|\mathbf{G}\|^2 \|\mathbf{F}\|^2$$

and upon dividing by $2 \|\mathbf{F}\| \, \|\mathbf{G}\|$ we get

$$- \|\mathbf{F}\| \, \|\mathbf{G}\| \leq \mathbf{F} \cdot \mathbf{G}.$$

We have now shown that

$$- \|\mathbf{F}\| \, \|\mathbf{G}\| \leq \mathbf{F} \cdot \mathbf{G} \leq \|\mathbf{F}\| \, \|\mathbf{G}\|,$$

and this is equivalent to the Cauchy-Schwarz inequality. ■

In view of the Cauchy-Schwarz inequality, we can define the cosine of the angle between vectors $\mathbf{F}$ and $\mathbf{G}$ in R^n by

$$\cos(\theta) = \begin{cases} 0 & \text{if } \mathbf{F} \text{ or } \mathbf{G} \text{ equals the zero vector} \\ (\mathbf{F} \cdot \mathbf{G})/(\|\mathbf{F}\| \, \|\mathbf{G}\|) & \text{if } \mathbf{F} \neq \mathbf{O} \text{ and } \mathbf{G} \neq \mathbf{O} \end{cases}.$$

This is sometimes useful in bringing some geometric intuition to R^n. For example, it is natural to define $\mathbf{F}$ and $\mathbf{G}$ to be orthogonal if the angle between them is $\pi/2$, and by this definition of $\cos(\theta)$, this is equivalent to requiring that $\mathbf{F} \cdot \mathbf{G} = 0$, consistent with orthogonality in R^2 and R^3.

We can define a *standard representation* of vectors in R^n by defining unit vectors along the *n* directions:

$$\mathbf{e}_1 = (1, 0, 0, \ldots, 0)$$

$$\mathbf{e}_2 = (0, 1, 0, \ldots, 0)$$

$$\vdots$$

$$\mathbf{e}_n = (0, 0, \ldots, 0, 1).$$

Now any *n*-vector can be written

$$(x_1, x_2, \ldots, x_n) = x_1\mathbf{e}_1 + x_2\mathbf{e}_2 + \cdots + x_n\mathbf{e}_n$$

$$= \sum_{j=1}^{n} x_j\mathbf{e}_j.$$

A set of *n*-vectors containing the zero vector, as well as sums of vectors in the set and scalar multiples of vectors in the set, is called a *subspace* of R^n.

DEFINITION 6.11   Subspace

A set S of *n*-vectors is a subspace of R^n if:

1. **O** is in S.
2. The sum of any vectors in S is in S.
3. The product of any vector in S with any real number is also in S.

Conditions (2) and (3) of the definition can be combined by requiring that $\alpha\mathbf{F} + \beta\mathbf{G}$ be in S for any vectors **F** and **G** in S, and any real numbers α and β.

EXAMPLE 6.14

Let S consist of all vectors in R^n having norm 1. In R^2 (the plane) this is the set of points on the unit circle about the origin; in R^3 this is the set of points on the unit sphere about the origin.

S is not a subspace of R^n for several reasons. First, **O** is not in S because **O** does not have norm 1. Further, a sum of vectors in S is not in S (a sum of vectors having norm 1 does not have norm 1). And, if $\alpha \neq 1$, and **F** has norm 1, then $\alpha\mathbf{F}$ does not have norm 1, so $\alpha\mathbf{F}$ is not in S. ■

In this example S failed all three criteria for being a subspace. It is enough to fail one to disqualify a set of vectors from being a subspace.

EXAMPLE 6.15

Let K consist of all scalar multiples of $(-1, 4, 2, 0)$ in R^4. We want to know if K is a subspace of R^4.

First, **O** is in K, because $\mathbf{O} = 0(-1, 4, 2, 0) = (0, 0, 0, 0)$.

Next, if **F** and **G** are in K, then $\mathbf{F} = \alpha(-1, 4, 2, 0)$ for some α and $\mathbf{G} = \beta(-1, 4, 2, 0)$ for some β, so

$$\mathbf{F} + \mathbf{G} = (\alpha + \beta)(-1, 4, 2, 0)$$

is a scalar multiple of $(-1, 4, 2, 0)$ and therefore is in K.

Finally, if $\mathbf{F} = \alpha(-1, 4, 2, 0)$ is any vector in K, and β is any scalar, then

$$\beta\mathbf{F} = (\beta\alpha)(-1, 4, 2, 0)$$

is a scalar multiple of $(-1, 4, 2, 0)$, and hence is in K. Thus K is a subspace of R^4. ■

EXAMPLE 6.16

Let S consist of just the zero vector $\mathbf{O}$ in R^n. Then S is a subspace of R^n. This is called the trivial subspace. At the other extreme, R^n is also a subspace of R^n. ∎

In R^2 and R^3 there are simple geometric characterizations of all possible subspaces.

Begin with R^2. We claim that only subspaces are the trivial subspace consisting of just the zero vector, or R^2 itself, or all vectors lying along a single line through the origin. To demonstrate this, we need the following fact.

LEMMA 6.2

Let $\mathbf{F}$ and $\mathbf{G}$ be nonzero vectors in R^2 that are not parallel. Then every vector in R^2 can be written in the form $\alpha\mathbf{F} + \beta\mathbf{G}$ for some scalars α and β.

Proof   Represent $\mathbf{F}$ and $\mathbf{G}$ as arrows from the origin (Figure 6.29). These determine nonparallel lines L_1 and L_2, respectively, through the origin, because $\mathbf{F}$ and $\mathbf{G}$ are assumed to be nonparallel. Let $\mathbf{V}$ be any 2-vector. If $\mathbf{V} = \mathbf{O}$, then $\mathbf{V} = 0\mathbf{F} + 0\mathbf{G}$. We therefore consider the case that $\mathbf{V} \neq \mathbf{O}$ and represent it as an arrow from the origin as well. We want to show that $\mathbf{V}$ must be the sum of scalar multiples of $\mathbf{F}$ and $\mathbf{G}$.

If $\mathbf{V}$ is along L_1, then $\mathbf{V} = \alpha\mathbf{F}$ for some real number α, and then $\mathbf{V} = \alpha\mathbf{F} + 0\mathbf{G}$. Similarly, if $\mathbf{V}$ is along L_2, then $\mathbf{V} = \beta\mathbf{G} = 0\mathbf{F} + \beta\mathbf{G}$.

Thus, suppose that $\mathbf{V}$ is not a scalar multiple of either $\mathbf{F}$ or $\mathbf{G}$. Then the arrow representing $\mathbf{V}$ is not along L_1 or L_2. Now carry out the construction shown in Figure 6.30. Draw lines parallel to L_1 and L_2 from the tip of $\mathbf{V}$. Arrows from the origin to where these parallels intersect L_1 and L_2 determine, respectively, vectors $\mathbf{A}$ and $\mathbf{B}$. By the parallelogram law,

$$\mathbf{V} = \mathbf{A} + \mathbf{B}.$$

But $\mathbf{A}$ is along L_1, so $\mathbf{A} = \alpha\mathbf{F}$ for some scalar α. And $\mathbf{B}$ is along L_2, and so $\mathbf{B} = \beta\mathbf{G}$ for some scalar β. Thus $\mathbf{V} = \alpha\mathbf{F} + \beta\mathbf{G}$, completing the proof. ∎

We can now completely characterize the subspaces of R^2.

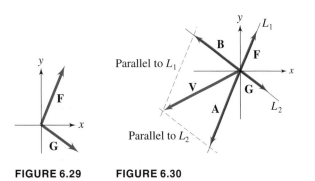

FIGURE 6.29   **FIGURE 6.30**

THEOREM 6.11   *The Subspaces of R^2*

Let S be a subspace of R^2. Then one of the following three possibilities must hold:

1. $S = R^2$, or
2. S consists of just the zero vector, or
3. S consists of all vectors parallel to some straight line through the origin.

Proof Suppose cases (1) and (2) do not hold. Because S is not the trivial subspace, S must contain at least one nonzero vector $\mathbf{F}$. We will show that every vector in S is a scalar multiple of $\mathbf{F}$.

Suppose instead that there is a nonzero vector $\mathbf{G}$ in S that is not a scalar multiple of $\mathbf{F}$. If $\mathbf{V}$ is any vector in R^2, then by Lemma 6.2, $\mathbf{V} = \alpha\mathbf{F} + \beta\mathbf{G}$ for some scalars α and β. But S is a subspace or R^2, so $\alpha\mathbf{F} + \beta\mathbf{G}$ is in S. This would imply that every vector in R^2 is in S, hence that $S = R^2$, a contradiction. Therefore there is no vector in S that is not a scalar multiple of $\mathbf{F}$.

We conclude that every vector in S is a scalar multiple of $\mathbf{F}$, and the proof is complete. ∎

By a similar argument involving more cases, we can prove that any subspace of R^3 must be either the trivial subspace, R^3 itself, all vectors parallel to some line through the origin, or all vectors parallel to some plane through the origin.

SECTION 6.4   PROBLEMS

In each of Problems 1 through 6, find the sum of the vectors and express this sum in standard form. Calculate the dot product of the vectors and the angle between them. The latter may be expressed as an inverse cosine of a number.

1. $(-1, 6, 2, 4, 0), (6, -1, 4, 1, 1)$

2. $(0, 1, 4, -3), (2, 8, 6, -4)$

3. $(1, -4, 3, 2), (16, 0, 0, 4)$

4. $(6, 1, 1, -1, 2), (4, 3, 5, 1, -2)$

5. $(0, 1, 6, -4, 1, 2, 9, -3), (6, 6, -12, 4, -3, -3, 2, 7)$

6. $(-5, 2, 2, -7, -8), (1, 1, 1, -8, 7)$

In each of Problems 7 through 13, determine whether the set of vectors is a subspace of R^n for the appropriate n.

7. S consists of all vectors (x, y, z, x, x) in R^5.

8. S consists of all vectors $(x, 2x, 3x, y)$ in R^4.

9. S consists of all vectors $(x, 0, 0, 1, 0, y)$ in R^6.

10. S consists of all vectors $(0, x, y)$ in R^3.

11. S consists of all vectors $(x, y, x + y, x - y)$ in R^4.

12. S consists of all vectors in R^7 having zero third and fifth components.

13. S consists of all vectors in R^4 whose first and second components are equal.

14. Let S consist of all vectors in R^3 on or parallel to the plane $ax + by + cz = k$, with a, b, and c real numbers, at least one of which is nonzero, and $k \neq 0$. Is S a subspace of R^3?

15. Let $\mathbf{F}$ and $\mathbf{G}$ be in R^n. Prove that
$$\|\mathbf{F} + \mathbf{G}\|^2 + \|\mathbf{F} - \mathbf{G}\|^2 = 2\left(\|\mathbf{F}\|^2 + \|\mathbf{G}\|^2\right).$$

Hint: Use the fact that the square of the norm of a vector is the dot product of the vector with itself.

16. Let $\mathbf{F}$ and $\mathbf{G}$ be orthogonal vectors in R^n. Prove that $\|\mathbf{F} + \mathbf{G}\|^2 = \|\mathbf{F}\|^2 + \|\mathbf{G}\|^2$. This is called *Pythagoras's theorem*.

17. Suppose $\mathbf{F}$ and $\mathbf{G}$ are vectors in R^n satisfying the relationship of Pythagoras's theorem (Problem 16). Does it follow that $\mathbf{F}$ and $\mathbf{G}$ are orthogonal?

6.5   Linear Independence, Spanning Sets, and Dimension in R^n

In solving systems of linear algebraic equations and systems of linear differential equations, as well as for later work in Fourier analysis, we will use terminology and ideas from linear algebra. We will define these terms in R^n, where we have some geometric intuition.

DEFINITION 6.12   *Linear Combinations in* R^n

A linear combination of k vectors $\mathbf{F}_1, \ldots, \mathbf{F}_k$ in R^n is a sum

$$\alpha_1 \mathbf{F}_1 + \cdots + \alpha_k \mathbf{F}_k$$

in which each α_j is a real number.

For example,

$$-8(-2, 4, 1, 0) + 6(1, 1, -1, 7) - \pi(8, 0, 0, 0)$$

is a linear combination of $(-2, 4, 1, 0)$, $(1, 1, -1, 7)$, and $(8, 0, 0, 0)$ in R^4. This linear combination is equal to the 4-vector

$$(22 - 8\pi, -26, -14, 42).$$

The set of all linear combinations of any given (finite) number of vectors in R^n is always a subspace of R^n.

THEOREM 6.12

Let $\mathbf{F}_1, \ldots, \mathbf{F}_k$ be in R^n, and let V consist of all vectors $\alpha_1 \mathbf{F}_1 + \cdots + \alpha_k \mathbf{F}_k$, in which each α_j can be any real number. Then V is a subspace of R^n.

Proof   First, $\mathbf{O}$ is in V (choose $\alpha_1 = \alpha_2 = \cdots = \alpha_k = 0$).

Next, suppose $\mathbf{G}$ and $\mathbf{H}$ are in V. Then

$$\mathbf{G} = \alpha_1 \mathbf{F}_1 + \cdots + \alpha_k \mathbf{F}_k \text{ and } \mathbf{H} = \beta_1 \mathbf{F}_1 + \cdots + \beta_k \mathbf{F}_k$$

for some real numbers $\alpha_1, \ldots, \alpha_k, \beta_1, \ldots, \beta_k$. Then

$$\mathbf{G} + \mathbf{H} = (\alpha_1 + \beta_1) \mathbf{F}_1 + \cdots + (\alpha_k + \beta_k) \mathbf{F}_k$$

is again a linear combination of $\mathbf{F}_1, \ldots, \mathbf{F}_k$, and so is in V.

Finally, let $\mathbf{G} = \alpha_1 \mathbf{F}_1 + \cdots + \alpha_k \mathbf{F}_k$ be in V. If c is any real number, then

$$c\mathbf{G} = (c\alpha_1) \mathbf{F}_1 + \cdots + (c\alpha_k) \mathbf{F}_k$$

is also a linear combination of $\mathbf{F}_1, \ldots, \mathbf{F}_k$, and is therefore in V. Therefore V is a subspace of R^n. ∎

Whenever we form a subspace by taking a linear combination of given vectors, we say that these vectors *span* the subspace.

DEFINITION 6.13   *Spanning Set*

Let $\mathbf{F}_1, \ldots, \mathbf{F}_k$ be vectors in a subspace S of R^n. Then $\mathbf{F}_1, \ldots, \mathbf{F}_k$ form a spanning set for S if every vector in S is a linear combination of $\mathbf{F}_1, \ldots, \mathbf{F}_k$.

In this case we say that S is spanned by $\mathbf{F}_1, \ldots, \mathbf{F}_k$, or that $\mathbf{F}_1, \ldots, \mathbf{F}_k$ span S.

For example, **i**, **j**, and **k** span R^3, because every vector in R^3 can be written $a\mathbf{i} + b\mathbf{j} + c\mathbf{k}$. The vector $\mathbf{i} + \mathbf{j}$ in R^2 spans the subspace consisting of all vectors $\alpha(\mathbf{i} + \mathbf{j})$, with α any scalar. These vectors all lie along the straight line $y = x$ through the origin in the plane.

Different sets of vectors may span the same subspace of R^n. Consider the following example.

EXAMPLE 6.17

Let V be the subspace of R^4 consisting of all vectors $(\alpha, \beta, 0, 0)$. Every vector in S can be written

$$(\alpha, \beta, 0, 0) = \alpha(1, 0, 0, 0) + \beta(0, 1, 0, 0),$$

so $(1, 0, 0, 0)$ and $(0, 1, 0, 0)$ span V. But we can also write any vector in V as

$$(\alpha, \beta, 0, 0) = \frac{\alpha}{2}(2, 0, 0, 0) + \frac{\beta}{\pi}(0, \pi, 0, 0),$$

so the vectors $(2, 0, 0, 0)$ and $(0, \pi, 0, 0)$ also span V.

Different numbers of vectors may also span the same subspace. The vectors

$$(4, 0, 0, 0), (0, 3, 0, 0), (1, 2, 0, 0)$$

also span V. To see this, write an arbitrary vector in V as

$$(\alpha, \beta, 0, 0) = \frac{\alpha - 2}{4}(4, 0, 0, 0) + \frac{\beta - 4}{3}(0, 3, 0, 0) + 2(1, 2, 0, 0). \ \blacksquare$$

The last example suggests that some spanning sets are more efficient than others. If two vectors will span a subspace V, why should we choose a spanning set with three vectors in it? Indeed, in the last example, the last vector in the spanning set $(4, 0, 0, 0), (0, 3, 0, 0), (1, 2, 0, 0)$ is a linear combination of the first two:

$$(1, 2, 0, 0) = \frac{1}{4}(4, 0, 0, 0) + \frac{2}{3}(0, 3, 0, 0).$$

Thus any linear combination of these three vectors can always be written as a linear combination of just $(4, 0, 0, 0)$ and $(0, 3, 0, 0)$. The third vector, being a linear combination of the first two, is "extraneous information."

These ideas suggest the following definition.

DEFINITION 6.14   *Linear Dependence and Independence*

Let $\mathbf{F}_1, \ldots, \mathbf{F}_k$ be vectors in R^n.

1. $\mathbf{F}_1, \ldots, \mathbf{F}_k$ are linearly dependent if and only if one of these vectors is a linear combination of the others.

2. $\mathbf{F}_1, \ldots, \mathbf{F}_k$ are linearly independent if and only if they are not linearly dependent.

Linear dependence of $\mathbf{F}_1, \ldots, \mathbf{F}_k$ means that, whatever information these vectors carry, not all of them are needed, because at least one of them can be written in terms of the others. For example, if

$$\mathbf{F}_k = \alpha_1 \mathbf{F}_1 + \cdots + \alpha_{k-1} \mathbf{F}_{k-1},$$

then knowing just $\mathbf{F}_1, \ldots, \mathbf{F}_{k-1}$ gives us $\mathbf{F}_k$ as well. In this sense, linearly dependent vectors are redundant. We can remove at least one $\mathbf{F}_j$ and the remaining $k - 1$ vectors will span the same subspace of R^n that $\mathbf{F}_1, \ldots, \mathbf{F}_k$ do.

Linear independence means that no one of the vectors $\mathbf{F}_1, \ldots, \mathbf{F}_k$ is a linear combination of the others. Whatever these vectors are telling us (for example, specifying a subspace), we need all of them or we lose information. If we omit $\mathbf{F}_k$, we cannot retrieve it from $\mathbf{F}_1, \ldots, \mathbf{F}_{k-1}$.

EXAMPLE 6.18

The vectors $(1, 1, 0)$ and $(-2, 0, 3)$ are linearly independent in R^3. To prove this, suppose instead that these vectors are linearly dependent. Then one is a linear combination of the other, say

$$(-2, 0, 3) = \alpha(1, 1, 0).$$

But then, from the first components, $\alpha = -2$, while from the second components, $\alpha = 0$, an impossibility.

These vectors span the subspace V of R^3 consisting of all vectors

$$\alpha(-2, 0, 3) + \beta(1, 1, 0).$$

Both of the vectors $(1, 1, 0)$ and $(-2, 0, 3)$ are needed to describe V. If we omit one, say $(1, 1, 0)$, then the subspace of R^3 spanned by the remaining vector, $(-2, 0, 3)$, is different from V. For example, it does not have $(1, 1, 0)$ in it. ■

The following is a useful characterization of linear dependence and independence.

THEOREM 6.13

Let $\mathbf{F}_1, \ldots, \mathbf{F}_k$ be vectors in R^n. Then

1. $\mathbf{F}_1, \ldots, \mathbf{F}_k$ are linearly dependent if and only if there are real numbers $\alpha_1, \ldots, \alpha_k$, not all zero, such that

$$\alpha_1 \mathbf{F}_1 + \alpha_2 \mathbf{F}_2 + \cdots + \alpha_k \mathbf{F}_k = \mathbf{O}.$$

2. $\mathbf{F}_1, \ldots, \mathbf{F}_k$ are linearly independent if and only if an equation

$$\alpha_1 \mathbf{F}_1 + \alpha_2 \mathbf{F}_2 + \cdots + \alpha_k \mathbf{F}_k = \mathbf{O}$$

can hold only if $\alpha_1 = \alpha_2 = \cdots = \alpha_k = 0$.

Proof   To prove (1), suppose first that $\mathbf{F}_1, \ldots, \mathbf{F}_k$ are linearly dependent. Then at least one of these vectors is a linear combination of the others. Say, to be specific, that

$$\mathbf{F}_1 = \alpha_2 \mathbf{F}_2 + \cdots + \alpha_k \mathbf{F}_k.$$

Then

$$\mathbf{F}_1 - \alpha_2 \mathbf{F}_2 + \cdots + \alpha_k \mathbf{F}_k = \mathbf{O}.$$

But this is a linear combination of $\mathbf{F}_1, \ldots, \mathbf{F}_k$ adding up to the zero vector and having a nonzero coefficient (the coefficient of $\mathbf{F}_1$ is 1).

Conversely, suppose

$$\alpha_1 \mathbf{F}_1 + \alpha_2 \mathbf{F}_2 + \cdots + \alpha_k \mathbf{F}_k = \mathbf{O}$$

with at least some $\alpha_j \neq 0$. We want to show that $\mathbf{F}_1, \ldots, \mathbf{F}_k$ are linearly dependent. By renaming the vectors if necessary, we may suppose for convenience that $\alpha_1 \neq 0$. But then

$$\mathbf{F}_1 = -\frac{\alpha_2}{\alpha_1}\mathbf{F}_2 - \cdots - \frac{\alpha_k}{\alpha_1}\mathbf{F}_k,$$

so $\mathbf{F}_1$ is a linear combination of $\mathbf{F}_2, \ldots, \mathbf{F}_k$ and hence $\mathbf{F}_1, \ldots, \mathbf{F}_k$ are linearly dependent. This completes the proof of (1).

Conclusion (2) follows from (1) and the fact that $\mathbf{F}_1, \ldots, \mathbf{F}_k$ are linearly independent exactly when these vectors are not linearly dependent. ∎

This theorem suggests a strategy for determining whether a given set of vectors is linearly dependent or independent. Given $\mathbf{F}_1, \ldots, \mathbf{F}_k$, set

$$\alpha_1\mathbf{F}_1 + \alpha_2\mathbf{F}_2 + \cdots + \alpha_k\mathbf{F}_k = \mathbf{O} \tag{6.4}$$

and attempt to solve for the coefficients $\alpha_1, \ldots, \alpha_k$. If equation (6.4) forces $\alpha_1 = \cdots = \alpha_k = 0$, then $\mathbf{F}_1, \ldots, \mathbf{F}_k$ are linearly independent. If we can find at least one nonzero α_j so that equation (6.4) is true, then $\mathbf{F}_1, \ldots, \mathbf{F}_k$ are linearly dependent.

EXAMPLE 6.19

Consider $(1, 0, 3, 1)$, $(0, 1, -6, -1)$ and $(0, 2, 1, 0)$ in R^4. We want to know whether these vectors are linearly dependent or independent. Look at a linear combination

$$c_1(1, 0, 3, 1) + c_2(0, 1, -6, -1) + c_3(0, 2, 1, 0) = (0, 0, 0, 0).$$

If this is to hold, then each component of the vector $(c_1, c_2 + 2c_3, 3c_1 - 6c_2 + c_3, c_1 - c_2)$ must be zero:

$$c_1 = 0$$

$$c_2 + 2c_3 = 0$$

$$3c_1 - 6c_2 + c_3 = 0$$

$$c_1 - c_2 = 0.$$

The first equation gives $c_1 = 0$, so the fourth equation tells us that $c_2 = 0$. But then the second equation requires that $c_3 = 0$. Therefore, the only linear combination of these three vectors that equals the zero vector is the trivial linear combination (all coefficients zero), and by (2) of Theorem 6.13, the vectors are linearly independent. ∎

In the plane R^2, two vectors are linearly dependent if and only if they are parallel. In R^3, two vectors are linearly dependent if and only if they are parallel, and three vectors are linearly dependent if and only if they are in the same plane.

Any set of vectors that includes the zero vector must be linearly dependent. Consider, for example, the vectors $\mathbf{O}, \mathbf{F}_2, \ldots, \mathbf{F}_k$. Then the linear combination

$$1\mathbf{O} + 0\mathbf{F}_2 + \cdots + 0\mathbf{F}_k = \mathbf{O}$$

is a linear combination of these vectors that add up to the zero vector, but has a nonzero coefficient (the coefficient of $\mathbf{O}$ is 1). By Theorem 6.13(1), these vectors are linearly dependent.

There is a special circumstance in which it is particularly easy to tell that a set of vectors is linearly independent. This is given in the following lemma, which we will use later.

LEMMA 6.3

Let $\mathbf{F}_1, \ldots, \mathbf{F}_k$ be vectors in R^n. Suppose each $\mathbf{F}_j$ has a nonzero element in some component where each of the other $\mathbf{F}_i's$ has a zero component. Then $\mathbf{F}_1, \ldots, \mathbf{F}_k$ are linearly independent. ∎

An example will clarify why this is true.

EXAMPLE 6.20

Consider the vectors

$$\mathbf{F}_1 = (0, 4, 0, 0, 2), \mathbf{F}_2 = (0, 0, 6, 0, -5), \mathbf{F}_3 = (0, 0, 0, -4, 12).$$

To see why these are linearly independent, suppose

$$\alpha \mathbf{F}_1 + \beta \mathbf{F}_2 + \gamma \mathbf{F}_3 = (0, 0, 0, 0, 0).$$

Then

$$(0, 4\alpha, 6\beta, -4\gamma, 2\alpha - 5\beta + 12\gamma) = (0, 0, 0, 0, 0).$$

From the second components, $4\alpha = 0$ so $\alpha = 0$. From the third components, $6\beta = 0$ so $\beta = 0$. And from the fourth components, $-4\gamma = 0$ so $\gamma = 0$. Then the vectors are linearly independent by Theorem 6.13(2). The fact that each of the vectors has a nonzero element where all the others have only zero components makes it particularly easy to conclude that $\alpha = \beta = \gamma = 0$, and that is what is needed to apply Theorem 6.13. ∎

There is another important setting in which it is easy to tell that vectors are linearly independent. Nonzero vectors $\mathbf{F}_1, \ldots, \mathbf{F}_k$ in R^n are said to be *mutually orthogonal* if each is orthogonal to each of the other vectors in the set. That is, $\mathbf{F}_i \cdot \mathbf{F}_j = 0$ if $i \neq j$. Mutually orthogonal nonzero vectors are necessarily linearly independent.

THEOREM 6.14

Let $\mathbf{F}_1, \ldots, \mathbf{F}_k$ be mutually orthogonal nonzero vectors in R^n. Then $\mathbf{F}_1, \ldots, \mathbf{F}_k$ are linearly independent.

Proof Suppose

$$\alpha_1 \mathbf{F}_1 + \alpha_2 \mathbf{F}_2 + \cdots + \alpha_k \mathbf{F}_k = \mathbf{O}.$$

For any $j = 1, \ldots, k$,

$$(\alpha_1 \mathbf{F}_1 + \alpha_2 \mathbf{F}_2 + \cdots + \alpha_k \mathbf{F}_k) \cdot \mathbf{F}_j = 0$$

$$= \alpha_1 \mathbf{F}_1 \cdot \mathbf{F}_j + \alpha_2 \mathbf{F}_2 \cdot \mathbf{F}_j + \cdots + \alpha_j \mathbf{F}_j \cdot \mathbf{F}_j + \cdots + \alpha_k \mathbf{F}_k \cdot \mathbf{F}_j$$

$$= c_j \mathbf{F}_j \cdot \mathbf{F}_j = c_j \left\| \mathbf{F}_j \right\|^2.$$

because $\mathbf{F}_i \cdot \mathbf{F}_j = 0$ if $i \neq j$. But $\mathbf{F}_j$ is not the zero vector, so $\left\| \mathbf{F}_j \right\|^2 \neq 0$, hence $c_j = 0$. Therefore, each coefficient is zero and $\mathbf{F}_1, \ldots, \mathbf{F}_k$ are linearly independent by Theorem 6.13(2). ∎

EXAMPLE 6.21

The vectors $(-4, 0, 0)$, $(0, -2, 1)$, $(0, 1, -2)$ are linearly independent in R^3, because each is orthogonal to the other two. ■

A "smallest" spanning set for a subspace of R^n is called a basis for that subspace.

DEFINITION 6.15   *Basis*

Let V be a subspace of R^n. A set of vectors $\mathbf{F}_1, \ldots, \mathbf{F}_k$ in V form a basis for V if $\mathbf{F}_1, \ldots, \mathbf{F}_k$ are linearly independent and also span V.

Thus, for $\mathbf{F}_1, \ldots, \mathbf{F}_k$ to be a basis for V, every vector in V must be a linear combination of $\mathbf{F}_1, \ldots, \mathbf{F}_k$, and if any $\mathbf{F}_j$ is omitted from the list $\mathbf{F}_1, \ldots, \mathbf{F}_k$, the remaining vectors do not span V. In particular, if $\mathbf{F}_j$ is omitted, then the subspace spanned by $\mathbf{F}_1, \ldots, \mathbf{F}_{j-1}, \mathbf{F}_{j+1}, \ldots \mathbf{F}_k$ cannot contain $\mathbf{F}_j$, because by linear independence, $\mathbf{F}_j$ is not a linear combination of $\mathbf{F}_1, \ldots, \mathbf{F}_{j-1}, \mathbf{F}_{j+1}, \ldots \mathbf{F}_k$.

EXAMPLE 6.22

$\mathbf{i}$, $\mathbf{j}$, and $\mathbf{k}$ form a basis for R^3, and $\mathbf{e}_1, \mathbf{e}_2, \ldots, \mathbf{e}_n$ form a basis for, R^n. ■

EXAMPLE 6.23

Let V be the subspace of R^n consisting of all n-vectors with zero first component. Then $\mathbf{e}_2, \ldots, \mathbf{e}_n$ form a basis for V. ■

EXAMPLE 6.24

In R^2, let V consist of all vectors parallel to the line $y = 4x$. Every vector in V is a multiple of $(1, 4)$. This vector by itself forms a basis for V. In fact, any vector $(\alpha, 4\alpha)$ with $\alpha \neq 0$ forms a basis for V. ■

EXAMPLE 6.25

In R^3, let M be the subspace of all vectors on or parallel to the plane $x + y + z = 0$. A vector (x, y, z) in R^3 is in M exactly when $z = -x - y$, so such a vector can be written

$$(x, y, z) = (x, y, -x - y) = x(1, 0, -1) + z(0, 1, -1).$$

The vectors $(1, 0, -1)$ and $(0, 1, -1)$ therefore span M. Since these two vectors are linearly independent, they form a basis for M. ■

We may think of a basis of V as a minimal linearly independent spanning set $\mathbf{F}_1, \ldots, \mathbf{F}_k$ for V. If we omit any of these vectors, the remaining vectors will not be enough to span V.

And if we use additional vectors, say the set $\mathbf{F}_1, \ldots, \mathbf{F}_k, \mathbf{H}$, then this set also spans V, but is not linearly independent (because $\mathbf{H}$ is a linear combination of $\mathbf{F}_1, \ldots, \mathbf{F}_k$).

There is nothing unique about a basis for a subspace of R^n. Any nontrivial subspace of R^n has infinitely many different bases. However, it is a theorem of linear algebra, which we will not prove, that for a given subspace V of R^n, every basis has the same *number* of vectors in it. This number is the dimension of the subspace.

DEFINITION 6.16

The dimension of a subspace of R^n is the number of vectors in any basis for the subspace.

In particular, R^n (which is a subspace of itself) has dimension n, a basis consisting of the n vectors $\mathbf{e}_1, \ldots, \mathbf{e}_n$. The subspace in Example 6.25 has dimension 2.

SECTION 6.5   PROBLEMS

In each of Problems 1 through 10, determine whether the given vectors are linearly independent or dependent in R^n for appropriate n.

1. $3\mathbf{i} + 2\mathbf{j}, \mathbf{i} - \mathbf{j}$ in R^3

2. $2\mathbf{i}, 3\mathbf{j}, 5\mathbf{i} - 12\mathbf{k}, \mathbf{i} + \mathbf{j} + \mathbf{k}$ in R^3

3. $(8, 0, 2, 0, 0, 0, 0), (0, 0, 0, 0, 1, -1, 0)$ in R^7

4. $(1, 0, 0, 0), (0, 1, 1, 0), (-4, 6, 6, 0)$ in R^4

5. $(1, 2, -3, 1), (4, 0, 0, 2), (6, 4, -6, 4)$ in R^4

6. $(0, 1, 1, 1), (-3, 2, 4, 4), (-2, 2, 34, 2), (1, 1, -6, -2)$ in R^4

7. $(1, -2), (4, 1), (6, 6)$ in R^2

8. $(-1, 1, 0, 0, 0), (0, -1, 1, 0, 0), (0, 1, 1, 1, 0)$ in R^5

9. $(-2, 0, 0, 1, 1), (1, 0, 0, 0, 0), (0, 0, 0, 0, 2),$ $(1, -1, 3, 3, 1)$ in R^4

10. $(3, 0, 0, 4), (2, 0, 0, 8)$ in R^4

11. Prove that three vectors in R^3 are linearly dependent if and only if their scalar triple product is zero. (See Problem 31 in Section 6.3).

In each of Problems 12 through 16, use the result of Problem 11 to determine whether the three vectors in R^3 are linearly dependent or independent.

12. $3\mathbf{i} + 6\mathbf{j} - \mathbf{k}, 8\mathbf{i} + 2\mathbf{j} - 4\mathbf{k}, \mathbf{i} - \mathbf{j} + \mathbf{k}$

13. $\mathbf{i} + 6\mathbf{j} - 2\mathbf{k}, -\mathbf{i} + 4\mathbf{j} - 3\mathbf{k}, \mathbf{i} + 16\mathbf{j} - 7\mathbf{k}$

14. $4\mathbf{i} - 3\mathbf{j} + \mathbf{k}, 10\mathbf{i} - 3\mathbf{j}, 2\mathbf{i} - 6\mathbf{j} + 3\mathbf{k}$

15. $8\mathbf{i} + 6\mathbf{j}, 2\mathbf{i} - 4\mathbf{j}, \mathbf{i} + \mathbf{k}$

16. $12\mathbf{i} - 3\mathbf{k}, \mathbf{i} + 2\mathbf{j} - \mathbf{k}, -3\mathbf{i} + 4\mathbf{j}$

In each of Problems 17 through 24, determine a basis for the subspace S of R^n and determine the dimension of the subspace.

17. S consists of all vectors $(x, y, -y, -x)$ in R^4.

18. S consists of all vectors $(x, y, 2x.3y)$ in R^4.

19. S consists of all vectors in the plane $2x - y + z = 0$.

20. S consists of all vectors $(x, y, -y, x - y, z)$ in R^5.

21. S consists of all vectors in R^4 with zero second component.

22. S consists of all vectors $(-x, x, y, 2y)$ in R^4.

23. S consists of all vectors parallel to the line $y = 4x$ in R^2.

24. S consists of all vectors parallel to the plane $4x + 2y - z = 0$ in R^3.

CHAPTER 7

Matrices and Systems of Linear Equations

This chapter is devoted to the notation and algebra of matrices, as well as their use in solving systems of linear algebraic equations.

To illustrate the idea of a matrix, consider a system of linear equations:

$$x_1 + 2x_2 - x_3 + 4x_4 = 0$$
$$3x_1 - 4x_2 + 2x_3 - 6x_4 = 0$$
$$x_1 - 3x_2 - 2x_3 + x_4 = 0.$$

All of the information needed to solve this system lies in its coefficients. Whether the first unknown is called x_1, or y_1, or some other name, is unimportant. It is important, however, that the coefficient of the first unknown in the second equation is 3. If we change this number we may change the solutions of the system.

We can therefore work with such a system by storing its coefficients in an array called a matrix:

$$\begin{pmatrix} 1 & 2 & -1 & 4 \\ 3 & -4 & 2 & -6 \\ 1 & -3 & -2 & 1 \end{pmatrix}.$$

This matrix displays the coefficients in the pattern in which they appear in the system of equations. The coefficients of the ith equation are in row i, and the coefficients of the jth unknown x_j are in column j. The number in row i, column j is the coefficient of x_j in equation i.

But matrices provide more than a visual aid or storage device. The algebra and calculus of matrices will form the basis for methods of solving systems of linear algebraic equations, and later for solving systems of linear differential equations and analyzing solutions of systems of nonlinear differential equations.

7.1 Matrices

DEFINITION 7.1 Matrix

An n by m matrix is an array of objects arranged in n rows and m columns.

We will denote matrices by boldface type, as was done with vectors.

When $\mathbf{A}$ is an n by m matrix, we often write that $\mathbf{A}$ is $n \times m$ (read "n by m"). The first integer is the number of rows in the matrix, and the second integer is the number of columns. The objects in the matrix may be numbers, functions, or other quantities. For example,

$$\begin{pmatrix} 2 & 1 & \pi \\ 1 & \sqrt{2} & -5 \end{pmatrix}$$

is a 2×3 matrix,

$$\begin{pmatrix} e^{2x} & e^{-4x} \\ \cos(x) & x^2 \end{pmatrix}$$

is a 2×2 matrix, and

$$\begin{pmatrix} 0 \\ -4 \\ x^3 \\ 2 \end{pmatrix}$$

is a 4×1 matrix.

A matrix having the same number of rows as columns is called a *square matrix*. The 2×2 matrix shown above is square.

The object in row i and column j of a matrix is called the i, j *element*, or i, j *entry* of the matrix. If a matrix is denoted by an upper case letter, say $\mathbf{A}$, then its i, j element is often denoted a_{ij} and we write $\mathbf{A} = [a_{ij}]$. For example, if

$$\mathbf{H} = [h_{ij}] = \begin{pmatrix} 0 & x \\ 1 - \sin(x) & 1 - 2i \\ x^2 & i \end{pmatrix}$$

then $\mathbf{H}$ is a 3×2 matrix, and $h_{11} = 0$, $h_{12} = x$, $h_{21} = 1 - \sin(x)$, $h_{22} = 1 - 2i$, $h_{31} = x^2$ and $h_{32} = i$. We will be dealing with matrices whose elements are real or complex numbers, or functions.

Sometimes it is also convenient to denote the i, j element of $\mathbf{A}$ by $(\mathbf{A})_{ij}$. In the matrix $\mathbf{H}$,

$$(\mathbf{H})_{22} = 1 - 2i \quad \text{and} \quad (\mathbf{H})_{31} = x^2.$$

DEFINITION 7.2 Equality Matrices

$\mathbf{A} = [a_{ij}]$ and $\mathbf{B} = [b_{ij}]$ are equal if and only if they have the same number of rows, the same number of columns, and for each i and j, $a_{ij} = b_{ij}$.

If two matrices either have different numbers of rows or columns, or if the objects in a particular location in the matrices are different, then the matrices are unequal.

7.1.1 Matrix Algebra

We will develop the operations of addition and multiplication of matrices and multiplication of a matrix by a number.

DEFINITION 7.3 *Matrix Addition*
_____

If $\mathbf{A} = [a_{ij}]$ and $\mathbf{B} = [b_{ij}]$ are $n \times m$ matrices, then their sum is the $n \times m$ matrix

$$\mathbf{A} + \mathbf{B} = [a_{ij} + b_{ij}].$$

We therefore add matrices by adding corresponding elements. For example,

$$\begin{pmatrix} 1 & 2 & -3 \\ 4 & 0 & 2 \end{pmatrix} + \begin{pmatrix} -1 & 6 & 3 \\ 8 & 12 & 14 \end{pmatrix} = \begin{pmatrix} 0 & 8 & 0 \\ 12 & 12 & 16 \end{pmatrix}.$$

If two matrices are of different dimensions (different numbers of rows or columns), then they cannot be added, just as we do not add 4-vectors and 7-vectors.

DEFINITION 7.4 *Product of a Matrix and a Scalar*
_____

If $\mathbf{A} = [a_{ij}]$ and α is a scalar, then $\alpha\mathbf{A}$ is the matrix defined by

$$\alpha\mathbf{A} = [\alpha a_{ij}].$$

This means that we multiply a matrix by α by multiplying each element of the matrix by α. For example,

$$3 \begin{pmatrix} 2 & 0 \\ 0 & 0 \\ 1 & 4 \\ 2 & 6 \end{pmatrix} = \begin{pmatrix} 6 & 0 \\ 0 & 0 \\ 3 & 12 \\ 6 & 18 \end{pmatrix}$$

and

$$x \begin{pmatrix} 1 & x \\ -x & \cos(x) \end{pmatrix} = \begin{pmatrix} x & x^2 \\ -x^2 & x\cos(x) \end{pmatrix}.$$

Some, but not all, pairs of matrices can be multiplied.

DEFINITION 7.5 *Multiplication of Matrices*
_____

Let $\mathbf{A} = [a_{ij}]$ be an $n \times r$ matrix, and $\mathbf{B} = [b_{ij}]$ an $r \times m$ matrix. Then the matrix product $\mathbf{AB}$ is the $n \times m$ matrix whose i, j element is

$$a_{i1}b_{1j} + a_{i2}b_{2j} + \cdots + a_{ir}b_{rj}.$$

That is,

$$\mathbf{AB} = \left[\sum_{k=1}^{r} a_{ik}b_{kj} \right].$$

If we think of each row of **A** as an r-vector, and each column of **B** as an r-vector, then the i, j element of **AB** is the dot product of row i of **A** with column j of **B** :

$$i, j \text{ element of } \mathbf{AB} = (\text{row } i \text{ of } \mathbf{A}) \cdot (\text{column } j \text{ of } \mathbf{B}).$$

This is why the number of columns of **A** must equal the number of rows of **B** for **AB** to be defined. These rows of **A** and columns of **B** must be vectors of the same length in order to take this dot product. Thus not every pair of matrices can be multiplied. Further, even when **AB** is defined, **BA** need not be.

We will give one rationale for defining matrix multiplication in this way shortly. First we will look at some examples of matrix products and then develop the rules of matrix algebra.

EXAMPLE 7.1

Let

$$\mathbf{A} = \begin{pmatrix} 1 & 3 \\ 2 & 5 \end{pmatrix} \quad \text{and} \quad \mathbf{B} = \begin{pmatrix} 1 & 1 & 3 \\ 2 & 1 & 4 \end{pmatrix}.$$

Then **A** is 2×2 and **B** is 2×3, so **AB** is defined (number of columns of **A** equals the number of rows of **B**). Further, **AB** is 2×3 (number of rows of **A**, number of columns of **B**).

Now compute

$$\mathbf{AB} = \begin{pmatrix} 1 & 3 \\ 2 & 5 \end{pmatrix} \begin{pmatrix} 1 & 1 & 3 \\ 2 & 1 & 4 \end{pmatrix}$$

$$= \begin{pmatrix} (1,3) \cdot (1,2) & (1,3) \cdot (1,1) & (1,3) \cdot (3,4) \\ (2,5) \cdot (1,2) & (2,5) \cdot (1,1) & (2,5) \cdot 3,4) \end{pmatrix}$$

$$= \begin{pmatrix} 7 & 4 & 15 \\ 12 & 7 & 26 \end{pmatrix}.$$

In this example, **BA** is not defined, because the number of columns of **B**, which is 3, does not equal the number of rows of **A**, which is 2. ∎

EXAMPLE 7.2

Let

$$\mathbf{A} = \begin{pmatrix} 1 & 1 & 2 & 1 \\ 4 & 1 & 6 & 2 \end{pmatrix} \quad \text{and} \quad \mathbf{B} = \begin{pmatrix} -1 & 8 \\ 2 & 1 \\ 1 & 1 \\ 12 & 6 \end{pmatrix}.$$

Since **A** is 2×4 and **B** is 4×2, **AB** is defined and is a 2×2 matrix:

$$\mathbf{AB} = \begin{pmatrix} (1,1,2,1) \cdot (-1,2,1,12) & (1,1,2,1) \cdot (8,1,1,6) \\ (4,1,6,2) \cdot (-1,2,1,12) & (4,1,6,2) \cdot (8,1,1,6) \end{pmatrix}$$

$$= \begin{pmatrix} 15 & 17 \\ 28 & 51 \end{pmatrix}.$$

In this example **BA** is also defined, and is 4×4:

$$BA = \begin{pmatrix} -1 & 8 \\ 2 & 1 \\ 1 & 1 \\ 12 & 6 \end{pmatrix} \begin{pmatrix} 1 & 1 & 2 & 1 \\ 4 & 1 & 6 & 2 \end{pmatrix}$$

$$= \begin{pmatrix} 31 & 7 & 46 & 15 \\ 6 & 3 & 10 & 4 \\ 5 & 2 & 8 & 3 \\ 36 & 18 & 60 & 24 \end{pmatrix}. \ \blacksquare$$

As the last example shows, even when both **AB** and **BA** are defined, these may be matrices of different dimensions. Matrix multiplication is noncommutative, and it is the exception rather than the rule to have **AB** equal **BA**.

If **A** is a square matrix, then **AA** is defined and is also square. Denote **AA** as $\mathbf{A}^2$. Similarly, $\mathbf{A}(\mathbf{A}^2) = \mathbf{A}^3$ and, for any positive integer k, $\mathbf{A}^k = \mathbf{AA} \cdots \mathbf{A}$, a product with k factors.

Some of the rules for manipulating matrices are like those for real numbers.

THEOREM 7.1

Let **A**, **B**, and **C** be matrices. Then, whenever the indicated operations are defined, we have:

1. $\mathbf{A} + \mathbf{B} = \mathbf{B} + \mathbf{A}$.
2. $\mathbf{A}(\mathbf{B} + \mathbf{C}) = \mathbf{AB} + \mathbf{AC}$.
3. $(\mathbf{A} + \mathbf{B})\mathbf{C} = \mathbf{AC} + \mathbf{BC}$.
4. $\mathbf{A}(\mathbf{BC}) = (\mathbf{AB})\mathbf{C}$.

For (1), both matrices must have the same dimensions, say $n \times m$. For (2), **B** and **C** must have the same dimensions, and the number of columns in **A** must equal the number of rows in **B** and in **C**. For (4), **A** must be $n \times r$, **B** must be $r \times k$ and **C** must be $k \times m$. Then $\mathbf{A}(\mathbf{BC})$ and $(\mathbf{AB})\mathbf{C}$ are $n \times m$.

Proof   The theorem is proved by direct appeal to the definitions. We will provide the details for (1) and (2). To prove (1), let $\mathbf{A} = [a_{ij}]$ and $\mathbf{B} = [b_{ij}]$. Then

$$\mathbf{A} + \mathbf{B} = [a_{ij} + b_{ij}] = [b_{ij} + a_{ij}] = \mathbf{B} + \mathbf{A},$$

because each a_{ij} and b_{ij} is a number or function and the addition of these objects is commutative.

For (2), let $\mathbf{A} = [a_{ij}]$, $\mathbf{B} = [b_{ij}]$ and $\mathbf{C} = [c_{ij}]$. Suppose **A** is $n \times k$ and **B** and **C** are $k \times m$. Then $\mathbf{B} + \mathbf{C}$ is $k \times m$, so $\mathbf{A}(\mathbf{B} + \mathbf{C})$ is defined and is $n \times m$. And **AB** and **BC** are both defined and $n \times m$. There remains to show that the i, j element of $\mathbf{AB} + \mathbf{AC}$ is the same as the i, j element of $\mathbf{A}(\mathbf{B} + \mathbf{C})$.

Row i of **A**, and columns j of **B** and **C**, are k-vectors, and from properties of the dot product,

$$i, j \text{ element of } \mathbf{A}(\mathbf{B} + \mathbf{C}) = (\text{row } i \text{ of } \mathbf{A}) \cdot (\text{column } j \text{ of } \mathbf{B} + \mathbf{C})$$

$$= (\text{row } i \text{ of } \mathbf{A}) \cdot (\text{column } j \text{ of } \mathbf{B}) + (\text{row } i \text{ of } \mathbf{A}) \cdot (\text{column } j \text{ of } \mathbf{C})$$

$$= (i, j \text{ element of } \mathbf{AB}) + (i, j \text{ element of } \mathbf{AC})$$

$$= i, j \text{ element of } \mathbf{AB} + \mathbf{AC}. \ \blacksquare$$

We have already noted that matrix multiplication does not behave in some ways like multiplication of numbers. Here is a summary of three significant differences.

Difference 1 For matrices, even when **AB** and **BA** are both defined, possibly $\mathbf{AB} \neq \mathbf{BA}$.

EXAMPLE 7.3

$$\begin{pmatrix} 1 & 0 \\ -2 & 4 \end{pmatrix} \begin{pmatrix} -2 & 6 \\ 1 & 3 \end{pmatrix} = \begin{pmatrix} -2 & 6 \\ 8 & 0 \end{pmatrix}$$

but

$$\begin{pmatrix} -2 & 6 \\ 1 & 3 \end{pmatrix} \begin{pmatrix} 1 & 0 \\ -2 & 4 \end{pmatrix} = \begin{pmatrix} -14 & 24 \\ -5 & 12 \end{pmatrix}. \blacksquare$$

Difference 2 There is no cancellation in products. If $\mathbf{AB} = \mathbf{AC}$, we cannot infer that $\mathbf{B} = \mathbf{C}$.

EXAMPLE 7.4

$$\begin{pmatrix} 1 & 1 \\ 3 & 3 \end{pmatrix} \begin{pmatrix} 4 & 2 \\ 3 & 16 \end{pmatrix} = \begin{pmatrix} 1 & 1 \\ 3 & 3 \end{pmatrix} \begin{pmatrix} 2 & 7 \\ 5 & 11 \end{pmatrix}$$

$$= \begin{pmatrix} 7 & 18 \\ 21 & 54 \end{pmatrix}.$$

But

$$\begin{pmatrix} 4 & 2 \\ 3 & 16 \end{pmatrix} \neq \begin{pmatrix} 2 & 7 \\ 5 & 11 \end{pmatrix}. \blacksquare$$

Difference 3 The product of two nonzero matrices may be zero.

EXAMPLE 7.5

$$\begin{pmatrix} 1 & 2 \\ 0 & 0 \end{pmatrix} \begin{pmatrix} 6 & 4 \\ -3 & -2 \end{pmatrix} = \begin{pmatrix} 0 & 0 \\ 0 & 0 \end{pmatrix}. \blacksquare$$

7.1.2 Matrix Notation for Systems of Linear Equations

Matrix notation is very efficient for writing systems of linear algebraic equations. Consider, for example, the system

$$2x_1 - x_2 + 3x_3 + x_4 = 1$$
$$x_1 + 3x_2 - 2x_4 = 0$$
$$-4x_1 - x_2 + 2x_3 - 9x_4 = -3.$$

The matrix of coefficients of this system is the 3×4 matrix

$$\mathbf{A} = \begin{pmatrix} 2 & -1 & 3 & 1 \\ 1 & 3 & 0 & -2 \\ -4 & -1 & 2 & -9 \end{pmatrix}.$$

Row i contains the coefficients of the ith equation, and column j contains the coefficients of x_j. Define

$$\mathbf{X} = \begin{pmatrix} x_1 \\ x_2 \\ x_3 \\ x_4 \end{pmatrix} \quad \text{and} \quad \mathbf{B} = \begin{pmatrix} 1 \\ 0 \\ -3 \end{pmatrix}.$$

Then

$$\mathbf{AX} = \begin{pmatrix} 2 & -1 & 3 & 1 \\ 1 & 3 & 0 & -2 \\ -4 & -1 & 2 & -9 \end{pmatrix} \begin{pmatrix} x_1 \\ x_2 \\ x_3 \\ x_4 \end{pmatrix}$$

$$= \begin{pmatrix} 2x_1 - x_2 + 3x_3 + x_4 \\ x_1 + 3x_2 - 2x_4 \\ -4x_1 - x_2 + 2x_3 - 9x_4 \end{pmatrix} = \begin{pmatrix} 1 \\ 0 \\ -3 \end{pmatrix}.$$

We can therefore write the system of equations in matrix form as

$$\mathbf{AX} = \mathbf{B}.$$

This is more than just notation. Soon this matrix formulation will enable us to use matrix operations to solve the system.

A similar approach can be taken toward systems of linear differential equations. Consider the system

$$x_1' + tx_2' - x_3' = 2t - 1$$

$$t^2 x_1' - \cos(t)x_2' - x_3' = e^t.$$

Let

$$\mathbf{A} = \begin{pmatrix} 1 & t & -1 \\ t^2 & -\cos(t) & -1 \end{pmatrix}, \quad \mathbf{X} = \begin{pmatrix} x_1 \\ x_2 \\ x_3 \end{pmatrix}, \quad \text{and} \quad \mathbf{F} = \begin{pmatrix} 2t - 1 \\ e^t \end{pmatrix}.$$

Then the system can be written

$$\mathbf{AX}' = \mathbf{F},$$

in which $\mathbf{X}'$ is formed by differentiating each matrix element of $\mathbf{X}$. As with systems of linear algebraic equations, this formulation will enable us to bring matrix methods to bear on solving the system of differential equations.

In both of these formulations, the definition of matrix product played a key role. Matrix multiplication may seem unmotivated at first, but it is just right for converting a system of linear algebraic or differential equations to a matrix equation.

7.1.3 Some Special Matrices

Some matrices occur often enough to warrant special names and notation.

DEFINITION 7.6   *Zero Matrix*

$\mathbf{O}_{n,m}$ denotes the $n \times m$ zero matrix, having each element equal to zero.

For example,

$$\mathbf{O}_{2,3} = \begin{pmatrix} 0 & 0 & 0 \\ 0 & 0 & 0 \end{pmatrix}.$$

If $\mathbf{A}$ is $n \times m$, then

$$\mathbf{A} + \mathbf{O}_{n,m} = \mathbf{O}_{n,m} + \mathbf{A} = \mathbf{A}.$$

The negative of $\mathbf{A}$ is the matrix obtained by replacing each element of $\mathbf{A}$ with its negative. This matrix is denoted $-\mathbf{A}$. If $\mathbf{A} = [a_{ij}]$, then $-\mathbf{A} = [-a_{ij}]$. If $\mathbf{A}$ is $n \times m$, then

$$\mathbf{A} + (-\mathbf{A}) = \mathbf{O}_{n,m}.$$

Usually we write $\mathbf{A} + (-\mathbf{B})$ as $\mathbf{A} - \mathbf{B}$.

DEFINITION 7.7 *Identity Matrix*

The $n \times n$ identity matrix is the matrix $\mathbf{I}_n$ having each i, j element equal to zero if $i \neq j$, and each $i, i-$ element equal to 1.

For example,

$$\mathbf{I}_2 = \begin{pmatrix} 1 & 0 \\ 0 & 1 \end{pmatrix} \quad \text{and} \quad \mathbf{I}_3 = \begin{pmatrix} 1 & 0 & 0 \\ 0 & 1 & 0 \\ 0 & 0 & 1 \end{pmatrix}.$$

THEOREM 7.2

If $\mathbf{A}$ is $n \times m$, then

$$\mathbf{A}\mathbf{I}_m = \mathbf{I}_n\mathbf{A} = \mathbf{A}. \ \blacksquare$$

We leave a proof of this to the student.

EXAMPLE 7.6

Let

$$\mathbf{A} = \begin{pmatrix} 1 & 0 \\ 2 & 1 \\ -1 & 8 \end{pmatrix}.$$

Then

$$\mathbf{I}_3\mathbf{A} = \begin{pmatrix} 1 & 0 & 0 \\ 0 & 1 & 0 \\ 0 & 0 & 1 \end{pmatrix} \begin{pmatrix} 1 & 0 \\ 2 & 1 \\ -1 & 8 \end{pmatrix} = \begin{pmatrix} 1 & 0 \\ 2 & 1 \\ -1 & 8 \end{pmatrix} = \mathbf{A}$$

and

$$\mathbf{A}\mathbf{I}_2 = \begin{pmatrix} 1 & 0 \\ 2 & 1 \\ -1 & 8 \end{pmatrix} \begin{pmatrix} 1 & 0 \\ 0 & 1 \end{pmatrix} = \begin{pmatrix} 1 & 0 \\ 2 & 1 \\ -1 & 8 \end{pmatrix} = \mathbf{A}. \ \blacksquare$$

DEFINITION 7.8 Transpose

If $\mathbf{A} = [a_{ij}]$ is an $n \times m$ matrix, then the transpose of $\mathbf{A}$ is the $m \times n$ matrix $\mathbf{A}^t = [a_{ji}]$.

The transpose of $\mathbf{A}$ is formed by making row k of $\mathbf{A}$, column k of $\mathbf{A}^t$.

EXAMPLE 7.7

Let

$$\mathbf{A} = \begin{pmatrix} -1 & 6 & 3 & 3 \\ 0 & \pi & 12 & -5 \end{pmatrix}.$$

This is a 2×4 matrix. The transpose is the 4×2 matrix

$$\mathbf{A}^t = \begin{pmatrix} -1 & 0 \\ 6 & \pi \\ 3 & 12 \\ 3 & -5 \end{pmatrix}. \quad \blacksquare$$

THEOREM 7.3

1. $(\mathbf{I}_n)^t = \mathbf{I}_n$.
2. For any matrix $\mathbf{A}$, $(\mathbf{A}^t)^t = \mathbf{A}$.
3. If $\mathbf{AB}$ is defined, then $(\mathbf{AB})^t = \mathbf{B}^t \mathbf{A}^t$.

Conclusion (1) should not be surprising, since row i of $\mathbf{I}_n$ is the same as column i, so interchanging rows and columns has no effect.

Similarly, (2) is intutively clear. If we interchange rows and columns of $\mathbf{A}$ to form $\mathbf{A}^t$, and then interchange the rows and columns of $\mathbf{A}^t$, we should put everything back where it was, resulting in $\mathbf{A}$ again.

We will prove conclusion (3).

Proof Let $\mathbf{A} = [a_{ij}]$ be $n \times k$ and let $\mathbf{B} = [b_{ij}]$ be $k \times m$. Then $\mathbf{AB}$ is defined and is $n \times m$. Since $\mathbf{B}^t$ is $m \times k$ and $\mathbf{A}^t$ is $k \times n$, then $\mathbf{B}^t \mathbf{A}^t$ is defined and is $m \times n$. Thus $(\mathbf{AB})^t$ and $\mathbf{B}^t \mathbf{A}^t$ have the same dimensions. Now we must show that the i, j element of $(\mathbf{AB})^t$ equals the i, j element of $\mathbf{B}^t \mathbf{A}^t$. Falling back on the definition of matrix product, we have

$$i, j \text{ element of } \mathbf{B}^t \mathbf{A}^t = \sum_{s=1}^{k} (\mathbf{B}^t)_{is} (\mathbf{A}^t)_{sj} = \sum_{s=1}^{k} b_{si} a_{js}$$

$$= \sum_{s=1}^{k} a_{js} b_{si} = j, i \text{ element of } \mathbf{AB} = i, j \text{ element of } (\mathbf{AB})^t.$$

This completes the proof of (3). $\blacksquare$

In some calculations it is convenient to write the dot product of two n-vectors as a matrix product, using the transpose. Write the n-vector $(x_1, x_2, \ldots, x_n)$ as a $1 \times n$ column matrix:

$$\mathbf{X} = \begin{pmatrix} x_1 \\ x_2 \\ \vdots \\ x_n \end{pmatrix}.$$

Then

$$\mathbf{X}^t = \begin{pmatrix} x_1 & x_2 & \cdots & x_n \end{pmatrix},$$

an $n \times 1$ matrix. Let $(y_1, y_2, \cdots, y_n)$ also be an n-vector, which we write as an $1 \times n$ column matrix:

$$\mathbf{Y} = \begin{pmatrix} y_1 \\ y_2 \\ \vdots \\ y_n \end{pmatrix}.$$

Then $\mathbf{X}^t\mathbf{Y}$ is the 1×1 matrix

$$\mathbf{X}^t\mathbf{Y} = \begin{pmatrix} x_1 & x_2 & \cdots & x_n \end{pmatrix} \begin{pmatrix} y_1 \\ y_2 \\ \vdots \\ y_n \end{pmatrix}$$

$$= (x_1 y_1 + x_2 y_2 + \cdots + x_n y_n) = \mathbf{X} \cdot \mathbf{Y}.$$

Here we have written the resulting 1×1 matrix as just its single element, without the matrix brackets. This is common practice for 1×1 matrices. We now have the dot product of two n-vectors, written as $1 \times n$ column vectors, as the matrix product

$$\mathbf{X}^t\mathbf{Y}.$$

This will prove particularly useful when we treat eigenvalues of matrices.

7.1.4   Another Rationale for the Definition of Matrix Multiplication

We have seen that matrix multiplication allows us to write linear systems of algebraic and differential equations in compact matrix form as $\mathbf{AX} = \mathbf{B}$ or $\mathbf{AX}' = \mathbf{F}$.

Matrix products are also tailored to other purposes, such as changes of variables in linear equations. To illustrate, consider a 2×2 linear system

$$a_{11}x_1 + a_{12}x_2 = c_1$$
$$a_{21}x_1 + a_{22}x_2 = c_2. \tag{7.1}$$

Change variables by putting

$$x_1 = h_{11}y_1 + h_{12}y_2$$
$$x_2 = h_{21}y_1 + h_{22}y_2. \tag{7.2}$$

Then

$$a_{11}(h_{11}y_1 + h_{12}y_2) + a_{12}(h_{21}y_1 + h_{22}y_2) = c_1$$

and

$$a_{21}(h_{11}y_1 + h_{12}y_2) + a_{22}(h_{21}y_1 + h_{22}y_2) = c_2.$$

After rearranging terms, the transformed system is

$$(a_{11}h_{11} + a_{12}h_{21})y_1 + (a_{11}h_{12} + a_{12}h_{22})y_2 = c_1$$
$$(a_{21}h_{11} + a_{22}h_{21})y_1 + (a_{21}h_{12} + a_{22}h_{22})y_2 = c_2. \tag{7.3}$$

Now carrry out the same transformation using matrices. Write the original system (7.1) as $\mathbf{AX} = \mathbf{C}$, where

$$\mathbf{A} = \begin{pmatrix} a_{11} & a_{12} \\ a_{21} & a_{22} \end{pmatrix}, \quad \mathbf{X} = \begin{pmatrix} x_1 \\ x_2 \end{pmatrix} \quad \text{and} \quad \mathbf{C} = \begin{pmatrix} c_1 \\ c_2 \end{pmatrix}$$

and the equations of the transformation (7.2) as $\mathbf{X} = \mathbf{HY}$, where

$$\mathbf{H} = \begin{pmatrix} h_{11} & h_{12} \\ h_{21} & h_{22} \end{pmatrix} \quad \text{and} \quad \mathbf{Y} = \begin{pmatrix} y_1 \\ y_2 \end{pmatrix}.$$

Then

$$\mathbf{AX} = \mathbf{A}(\mathbf{HY}) = (\mathbf{AH})\mathbf{Y} = \mathbf{C}.$$

Now observe that

$$\mathbf{AH} = \begin{pmatrix} a_{11} & a_{12} \\ a_{21} & a_{22} \end{pmatrix} \begin{pmatrix} h_{11} & h_{12} \\ h_{21} & h_{22} \end{pmatrix}$$

$$= \begin{pmatrix} a_{11}h_{11} + a_{12}h_{21} & a_{11}h_{12} + a_{12}h_{22} \\ a_{21}h_{11} + a_{22}h_{21} & a_{21}h_{12} + a_{22}h_{22} \end{pmatrix},$$

exactly as we found in the system (7.3) by term by term substitution. The definition of matrix product is just what is needed to carry out a linear change of variables. This idea also applies to linear transformations in systems of differential equations.

7.1.5 Random Walks in Crystals

We will conclude this section with another application of matrix multiplication, this time to the problem of enumerating the paths atoms can take through a crystal lattice.

Crystals have sites arranged in a lattice pattern. An atom may jump from a site it occupies to any adjacent, vacant site. If more than one adjacent site is vacant, the atom "selects" its target site at random. The path such an atom makes through the crystal is called a *random walk*.

We can represent the lattice of locations and adjacencies by drawing a point for each location, with a line between two points only if an atom can move directly from one to the other in the crystal. Such a diagram is called a *graph*. Figure 7.1 shows a typical graph. In this graph an atom could move from point v_1 to v_2 or v_3, to which it is connected by lines, but not directly to v_6 because there is no line between v_1 and v_6.

Two points are called *adjacent* in G if there is a line between them in the graph. A point is not considered adjacent to itself—there are no lines starting and ending at the same point.

A *walk* of length n in such a graph is a sequence $t_1, \ldots, t_{n+1}$ of points (not necessarily different) with each t_j adjacent to t_{j+1} in the graph. Such a walk represents a possible path an atom might take through various sites in the crystal. Points may repeat in a walk because an atom may return to the same site any number of times. A $v_i - v_j$ walk is a walk that begins at v_i and ends at v_j.

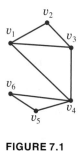

FIGURE 7.1
A typical
graph.

Physicists and materials engineers who study crystals are interested in the following question: given a crystal with n sites labeled $v_1, \ldots, v_n$, how many different walks of length k are there between any two sites (or from a site back to itself)?

Matrices enter into the solution of this problem as follows. Define the *adjacency matrix* $\mathbf{A}$ of the graph to be the $n \times n$ matrix having each i, i element zero, and for $i \neq j$, the i, j-element equal to 1 if there is a line in the graph between v_i and v_j, and 0 if there is no such line. For example, the graph of Figure 7.1 has adjacency matrix

$$\mathbf{A} = \begin{pmatrix} 0 & 1 & 1 & 1 & 0 & 0 \\ 1 & 0 & 1 & 0 & 0 & 0 \\ 1 & 1 & 0 & 1 & 0 & 0 \\ 1 & 0 & 1 & 0 & 1 & 1 \\ 0 & 0 & 0 & 1 & 0 & 1 \\ 0 & 0 & 0 & 1 & 1 & 0 \end{pmatrix}.$$

The $1, 2$ element of $\mathbf{A}$ is 1 because there is a line between v_1 and v_2, while the $1, 5$ element is zero because there is no line between v_1 and v_5.

The following remarkable theorem uses the adjacency matrix to solve the walk-enumeration problem.

THEOREM 7.4

Let $\mathbf{A} = [a_{ij}]$ be the adjacency matrix of a graph G having points $v_1, \ldots, v_n$. Let k be any positive integer. Then the number of distinct $v_i - v_j$ walks of length k in G is equal to the i, j element of $\mathbf{A}^k$.

We can therefore calculate the number of random walks of length k between any two points (or from any point back to itself) by reading the elements of the kth power of the adjacency matrix.

Proof   Proceed by mathematical induction on k. First consider the case $k = 1$. If $i \neq j$, there is a $v_i - v_j$ walk of length 1 in G exactly when there is a line between v_i and v_j, and in this case $a_{ij} = 1$. There is no $v_i - v_j$ walk of length 1 if v_i and v_j have no line between them, and in this case $a_{ij} = 0$. If $i = j$, there is no $v_i - v_i$ walk of length 1, and $a_{ii} = 0$. Thus, in the case $k = 1$, the i, j element of $\mathbf{A}$ gives the number of walks of length 1 from v_i to v_j, and the conclusion of the theorem is true.

Now assume that the conclusion of the theorem is true for walks of length k. We will prove that the conclusion holds for walks of length $k + 1$. Thus, we are assuming that the i, j

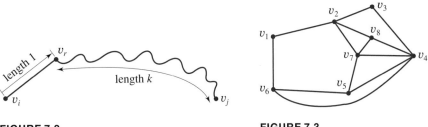

FIGURE 7.2   **FIGURE 7.3**

element of $\mathbf{A}^k$ is the number of distinct $v_i - v_j$ walks of length k in G, and we want to prove that the i, j element of $\mathbf{A}^{k+1}$ is the number of distinct $v_i - v_j$ walks of length $k + 1$.

Consider how a $v_i - v_j$ walk of length $k + 1$ is formed. First there must be a $v_i - v_r$ walk of length 1 from v_i to some point v_r adjacent to v_i, followed by a $v_r - v_j$ walk of length k (Figure 7.2). Therefore

number of distinct $v_i - v_j$ walks of length $k + 1 =$ sum of the number of

distinct $v_r - v_j$ walks of length k,

with the sum taken over all points v_r adjacent to v_i. Now $a_{ir} = 1$ if v_r is adjacent to v_i, and $a_{ir} = 0$ otherwise. Further, by the inductive hypothesis, the number of distinct $v_r - v_j$ walks of length k is the r, j element of $\mathbf{A}^k$. Denote $\mathbf{A}^k = \mathbf{B} = [b_{ij}]$. Then, for $r = 1, \ldots n$,

$$a_{ir}b_{rj} = 0 \text{ if } v_r \text{ is not adjacent to } v_i$$

and

$$a_{ir}b_{rj} = \text{the number of distinct } v_i - v_j \text{ walks of length } k + 1$$

passing through v_r, if v_r is adjacent to v_i.

Therefore the number of $v_i - v_j$ walks of length $k + 1$ in G is

$$a_{i1}b_{1j} + a_{i2}b_{2j} + \cdots + a_{in}b_{nj}$$

because this counts the number of walks of length k from v_r to v_j for each point v_r adjacent to v_i. But this sum is exactly the i, j element of $\mathbf{AB}$, which is $\mathbf{A}^{k+1}$. This completes the proof by induction. ∎

For example, the adjacency matrix of the graph of Figure 7.3 is

$$\mathbf{A} = \begin{pmatrix} 0 & 1 & 0 & 0 & 0 & 1 & 0 & 0 \\ 1 & 0 & 1 & 0 & 0 & 0 & 1 & 1 \\ 0 & 1 & 0 & 1 & 0 & 0 & 0 & 0 \\ 0 & 0 & 1 & 0 & 1 & 1 & 1 & 1 \\ 0 & 0 & 0 & 1 & 0 & 1 & 1 & 0 \\ 1 & 0 & 0 & 1 & 1 & 0 & 0 & 0 \\ 0 & 1 & 0 & 1 & 1 & 0 & 0 & 1 \\ 0 & 1 & 0 & 1 & 0 & 0 & 1 & 0 \end{pmatrix}.$$

Suppose we want the number of $v_4 - v_7$ walks of length 3 in G. Calculate

$$\mathbf{A}^3 = \begin{pmatrix} 0 & 5 & 1 & 4 & 2 & 4 & 3 & 2 \\ 6 & 2 & 7 & 4 & 5 & 4 & 9 & 8 \\ 1 & 7 & 0 & 8 & 3 & 2 & 3 & 2 \\ 4 & 4 & 8 & 6 & 8 & 8 & 11 & 10 \\ 2 & 5 & 3 & 8 & 4 & 6 & 8 & 4 \\ 4 & 4 & 2 & 8 & 6 & 2 & 4 & 4 \\ 3 & 9 & 3 & 11 & 8 & 4 & 6 & 7 \\ 2 & 8 & 2 & 10 & 4 & 4 & 7 & 4 \end{pmatrix}.$$

We read from the 4, 7 element of $\mathbf{A}^3$ that there are 11 walks of length 3 from v_4 to v_7. For this relatively simple graph, we can actually list all these walks:

$$v_4 v_7 v_4 v_7; \; v_4 v_3 v_4 v_7; \; v_4 v_8 v_4 v_7; \; v_4 v_5 v_4 v_7; \; v_4 v_6 v_4 v_7;$$

$$v_4 v_7 v_8 v_7; \; v_4 v_7 v_5 v_7; \; v_4 v_7 v_2 v_7; \; v_4 v_3 v_2 v_7; \; v_4 v_8 v_2 v_7; \; v_4 v_6 v_5 v_7.$$

Obviously it would not be practical to determine the number of $v_i - v_j$ walks of length k by explicitly listing them if k or n is large. Software routines for matrix calculations make this theorem a practical solution to the random walk counting problem.

SECTION 7.1   PROBLEMS

In each of Problems 1 through 6, carry out the requested computation with the given matrices $\mathbf{A}$ and $\mathbf{B}$.

1. $\mathbf{A} = \begin{pmatrix} 1 & -1 & 3 \\ 2 & -4 & 6 \\ -1 & 1 & 2 \end{pmatrix}, \mathbf{B} = \begin{pmatrix} -4 & 0 & 0 \\ -2 & -1 & 6 \\ 8 & 15 & 4 \end{pmatrix}$;

     $2\mathbf{A} - 3\mathbf{B}$

2. $\mathbf{A} = \begin{pmatrix} -2 & 2 \\ 0 & 1 \\ 14 & 2 \\ 6 & 8 \end{pmatrix}, \mathbf{B} = \begin{pmatrix} 3 & 4 \\ 2 & 1 \\ 14 & 16 \\ 1 & 25 \end{pmatrix}$; $-5\mathbf{A} + 3\mathbf{B}$

3. $\mathbf{A} = \begin{pmatrix} x & 1-x \\ 2 & e^x \end{pmatrix}, \mathbf{B} = \begin{pmatrix} 1 & -6 \\ x & \cos(x) \end{pmatrix}$; $\mathbf{A}^2 + 2\mathbf{AB}$

4. $\mathbf{A} = (14), \mathbf{B} = (-12); -3\mathbf{A} - 5\mathbf{B}$

5. $\mathbf{A} = \begin{pmatrix} 1 & -2 & 1 & 7 & -9 \\ 8 & 2 & -5 & 0 & 0 \end{pmatrix}$,

     $\mathbf{B} = \begin{pmatrix} -5 & 1 & 8 & 21 & 7 \\ 12 & -6 & -2 & -1 & 9 \end{pmatrix}$; $4\mathbf{A} + 8\mathbf{B}$

6. $\mathbf{A} = \begin{pmatrix} -2 & 3 \\ 1 & 1 \end{pmatrix}, \mathbf{B} = \begin{pmatrix} 0 & 8 \\ -5 & 1 \end{pmatrix}$; $\mathbf{A}^3 - \mathbf{B}^2$

In each of Problems 7 through 16, determine which of $\mathbf{AB}$ and $\mathbf{BA}$ are defined. Carry out the products that are defined.

7. $\mathbf{A} = \begin{pmatrix} -4 & 6 & 2 \\ -2 & -2 & 3 \\ 1 & 1 & 8 \end{pmatrix}, \mathbf{B} = \begin{pmatrix} -2 & 4 & 6 & 12 & 5 \\ -3 & -3 & 1 & 1 & 4 \\ 0 & 0 & 1 & 6 & -9 \end{pmatrix}$

8. $\mathbf{A} = \begin{pmatrix} -2 & -4 \\ 3 & -1 \end{pmatrix}, \mathbf{B} = \begin{pmatrix} 6 & 8 \\ 1 & -4 \end{pmatrix}$

9. $\mathbf{A} = \begin{pmatrix} -1 & 6 & 2 & 14 & -22 \end{pmatrix}, \mathbf{B} = \begin{pmatrix} -3 \\ 2 \\ 6 \\ 0 \\ -4 \end{pmatrix}$

10. $\mathbf{A} = \begin{pmatrix} -3 & 1 \\ 6 & 2 \\ 18 & -22 \\ 1 & 6 \end{pmatrix}, \mathbf{B} = \begin{pmatrix} -16 & 0 & 0 & 28 \\ 0 & 1 & 1 & 26 \end{pmatrix}$

11. $\mathbf{A} = \begin{pmatrix} -21 & 4 & 8 & -3 \\ 12 & 1 & 0 & 14 \\ 1 & 16 & 0 & -8 \\ 13 & 4 & 8 & 0 \end{pmatrix}, \mathbf{B} = \begin{pmatrix} -9 & 16 & 3 & 2 \\ 5 & 9 & 14 & 0 \end{pmatrix}$

12. $\mathbf{A} = \begin{pmatrix} -2 & 4 \\ 3 & 9 \end{pmatrix}, \mathbf{B} = \begin{pmatrix} 1 & -3 & 7 & 2 \\ -5 & 6 & 1 & 0 \end{pmatrix}$

13. $\mathbf{A} = \begin{pmatrix} -4 & -2 & 0 \\ 0 & 5 & 3 \\ -3 & 1 & 1 \end{pmatrix}, \mathbf{B} = \begin{pmatrix} 1 & -3 & 4 \end{pmatrix}$

14. $\mathbf{A} = \begin{pmatrix} 3 \\ 0 \\ -1 \\ 4 \end{pmatrix}$, $\mathbf{B} = \begin{pmatrix} 3 & -2 & 7 \end{pmatrix}$

15. $\mathbf{A} = \begin{pmatrix} 7 & -8 \\ 1 & 6 \end{pmatrix}$, $\mathbf{B} = \begin{pmatrix} 1 & -4 & 3 \\ -4 & 7 & 0 \end{pmatrix}$

16. $\mathbf{A} = \begin{pmatrix} -3 & 2 \\ 0 & -2 \\ 1 & 8 \\ 3 & -3 \end{pmatrix}$, $\mathbf{B} = \begin{pmatrix} -5 & 5 & 7 & 2 \end{pmatrix}$

In each of Problems 17 through 21, determine if $\mathbf{AB}$ is defined and if $\mathbf{BA}$ is defined. For those products that are defined, give the dimensions of the product matrix.

17. $\mathbf{A}$ is 14×21, $\mathbf{B}$ is 21×14.

18. $\mathbf{A}$ is 18×4, $\mathbf{B}$ is 18×4.

19. $\mathbf{A}$ is 6×2, $\mathbf{B}$ is 4×6.

20. $\mathbf{A}$ is 1×3, $\mathbf{B}$ is 3×3.

21. $\mathbf{A}$ is 7×6, $\mathbf{B}$ is 7×7.

22. Find nonzero 2×2 matrices $\mathbf{A}$, $\mathbf{B}$, and $\mathbf{C}$ such that $\mathbf{BA} = \mathbf{CA}$ but $\mathbf{B} \neq \mathbf{C}$.

23. Let G be the graph of Figure 7.4. Determine the number of $v_1 - v_4$ walks of length 3, the number of $v_2 - v_3$ walks of length 3, and the number of $v_2 - v_4$ walks of length 4 in G.

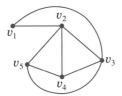

FIGURE 7.4

24. Let G be the graph of Figure 7.5. Determine the number of $v_1 - v_4$ walks of length 4 in G. Determine the number of $v_2 - v_3$ walks of length 2.

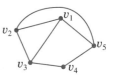

FIGURE 7.5

25. Let G be the graph of Figure 7.6. Determine the number of $v_4 - v_5$ walks of length 2, the number of $v_2 - v_3$ walks of length 3, and the number of $v_1 - v_2$ and $v_4 - v_5$ walks of length 4 in G.

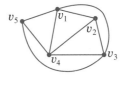

FIGURE 7.6

26. Let $\mathbf{A}$ be the adjacency matrix of a graph G.

(a) Prove that the $i, j-$ element of $\mathbf{A}^2$ equals the number of points of G that are neighbors of v_i in G. This number is called the *degree* of v_i.

(b) Prove that the $i, j-$ element of $\mathbf{A}^3$ equals twice the number of triangles in G containing v_i as a vertex. A triangle in G consists of three points, each a neighbor of the other two.

7.2   Elementary Row Operations and Elementary Matrices

When we solve a system of linear algebraic equations by elimination of unknowns, we routinely perform three kinds of operations: interchange of equations, multiplication of an equation by a nonzero constant, and addition of a constant multiple of one equation to another equation.

When we write a homogeneous system in matrix form $\mathbf{AX} = \mathbf{O}$, row k of $\mathbf{A}$ lists the coefficients in equation k of the system. The three operations on equations correspond, respectively, to the interchange of two rows of $\mathbf{A}$, multiplication of a row $\mathbf{A}$ by a constant, and addition of a scalar multiple of one row of $\mathbf{A}$ to another row of $\mathbf{A}$. We will focus on these row operations in anticipation of using them to solve the system.

DEFINITION 7.9

Let $\mathbf{A}$ be an $n \times m$ matrix. The three elementary row operations that can be performed on $\mathbf{A}$ are:

1. Type I operation: interchange two rows of $\mathbf{A}$.
2. Type II operation: Multiply a row of $\mathbf{A}$ by a nonzero constant.
3. Type III operation: Add a scalar multiple of one row to another row.

The rows of $\mathbf{A}$ are m-vectors. In a Type II operation, multiply a row by a nonzero constant by multiplying this row vector by the number. That is, multiply each element of the row by that number. Similarly, in a Type III operation, we add a scalar multiple of one row vector to another row vector.

EXAMPLE 7.8

Let

$$\mathbf{A} = \begin{pmatrix} -2 & 1 & 6 \\ 1 & 1 & 2 \\ 0 & 1 & 3 \\ 2 & -3 & 4 \end{pmatrix}.$$

Type I operation: if we interchange rows 2 and 4 of $\mathbf{A}$, we obtain the new matrix

$$\begin{pmatrix} -2 & 1 & 6 \\ 2 & -3 & 4 \\ 0 & 1 & 3 \\ 1 & 1 & 2 \end{pmatrix}.$$

Type II operation: multiply row 2 of $\mathbf{A}$ by 7 to get

$$\begin{pmatrix} -2 & 1 & 6 \\ 7 & 7 & 14 \\ 0 & 1 & 3 \\ 2 & -3 & 4 \end{pmatrix}.$$

Type III operation: add 2 times row 1 to row 3 of $\mathbf{A}$, obtaining

$$\begin{pmatrix} -2 & 1 & 6 \\ 1 & 1 & 2 \\ -4 & 3 & 15 \\ 2 & -3 & 4 \end{pmatrix}. \ \blacksquare$$

Elementary row operations can be performed on any matrix. When performed on an identity matrix, we obtain special matrices that will be particularly useful. We therefore give matrices formed in this way a name.

DEFINITION 7.10   Elementary Matrix

An elementary matrix is a matrix formed by performing an elementary row operation on $\mathbf{I}_n$.

For example,

$$\begin{pmatrix} 0 & 1 & 0 \\ 1 & 0 & 0 \\ 0 & 0 & 1 \end{pmatrix}$$

is an elementary matrix, obtained from $\mathbf{I}_3$ by interchanging rows 1 and 2. And

$$\begin{pmatrix} 1 & 0 & 0 \\ 0 & 1 & 0 \\ -4 & 0 & 1 \end{pmatrix}$$

is the elementary matrix formed by adding -4 times row 1 of $\mathbf{I}_3$ to row 3.

The following theorem is the reason why elementary matrices are interesting. It says that each elementary row operation on $\mathbf{A}$ can be performed by multiplying $\mathbf{A}$ on the left by an elementary matrix.

THEOREM 7.5

Let $\mathbf{A}$ be an $n \times m$ matrix. Let $\mathbf{B}$ be formed from $\mathbf{A}$ by an elementary row operation. Let $\mathbf{E}$ be the elementary matrix formed by performing this elementary row operation on $\mathbf{I}_n$. Then

$$\mathbf{B} = \mathbf{EA}. \ \blacksquare$$

We leave a proof to the exercises. It is instructive to see the theorem in practice.

EXAMPLE 7.9

Let

$$\mathbf{A} = \begin{pmatrix} 1 & -5 \\ 9 & 4 \\ -3 & 2 \end{pmatrix}.$$

Suppose we form $\mathbf{B}$ from $\mathbf{A}$ by interchanging rows 2 and 3 of $\mathbf{A}$. We can do this directly. But we can also form an elementary matrix by performing this operation on $\mathbf{I}_3$ to form

$$\mathbf{E} = \begin{pmatrix} 1 & 0 & 0 \\ 0 & 0 & 1 \\ 0 & 1 & 0 \end{pmatrix}.$$

Then

$$\mathbf{EA} = \begin{pmatrix} 1 & 0 & 0 \\ 0 & 0 & 1 \\ 0 & 1 & 0 \end{pmatrix} \begin{pmatrix} 1 & -5 \\ 9 & 4 \\ -3 & 2 \end{pmatrix} = \begin{pmatrix} 1 & -5 \\ -3 & 2 \\ 9 & 4 \end{pmatrix} = \mathbf{B}. \ \blacksquare$$

EXAMPLE 7.10

Let

$$A = \begin{pmatrix} 0 & -7 & 3 & 6 \\ 5 & 1 & -11 & 3 \end{pmatrix}.$$

Form C from A by multiplying row 2 by -8. Again, we can do this directly. However, if we form E from by performing this operation on I_2, then

$$E = \begin{pmatrix} 1 & 0 \\ 0 & -8 \end{pmatrix}$$

and

$$EA = \begin{pmatrix} 1 & 0 \\ 0 & -8 \end{pmatrix} \begin{pmatrix} 0 & -7 & 3 & 6 \\ 5 & 1 & -11 & 3 \end{pmatrix}$$

$$= \begin{pmatrix} 0 & -7 & 3 & 6 \\ -40 & -8 & 88 & -24 \end{pmatrix} = C. \ \blacksquare$$

EXAMPLE 7.11

Let

$$A = \begin{pmatrix} -6 & 14 & 2 \\ 4 & 4 & -9 \\ -3 & 2 & 13 \end{pmatrix}.$$

Form D from A by adding 6 times row 1 to row 2. If we perform this operation on I_3 to form

$$E = \begin{pmatrix} 1 & 0 & 0 \\ 6 & 1 & 0 \\ 0 & 0 & 1 \end{pmatrix},$$

then

$$EA = \begin{pmatrix} 1 & 0 & 0 \\ 6 & 1 & 0 \\ 0 & 0 & 1 \end{pmatrix} \begin{pmatrix} -6 & 14 & 2 \\ 4 & 4 & -9 \\ -3 & 2 & 13 \end{pmatrix}$$

$$= \begin{pmatrix} -6 & 14 & 2 \\ -32 & 88 & 3 \\ -3 & 2 & 13 \end{pmatrix} = B. \ \blacksquare$$

Later we will want to perform not just one elementary row operation, but a sequence of such operations. Suppose we perform operation $\mathcal{O}_1$ on A to form A_1, then operation $\mathcal{O}_2$ on A_1 to form A_2, and so on until finally we perform $\mathcal{O}_r$ on A_{r-1} to get A_r. This process can be diagrammed:

$$A \underset{\mathcal{O}_1}{\rightarrow} A_1 \underset{\mathcal{O}_2}{\rightarrow} A_2 \underset{\mathcal{O}_3}{\rightarrow} \cdots \underset{\mathcal{O}_{r-1}}{\rightarrow} A_{r-1} \underset{\mathcal{O}_r}{\rightarrow} A_r.$$

Let $\mathbf{E}_j$ be the elementary matrix obtained by performing operation $\mathcal{O}_j$ on $\mathbf{I}_n$. Then

$$\mathbf{A}_1 = \mathbf{E}_1\mathbf{A},$$

$$\mathbf{A}_2 = \mathbf{E}_2\mathbf{A}_1 = (\mathbf{E}_2\mathbf{E}_1)\mathbf{A},$$

$$\mathbf{A}_3 = \mathbf{E}_3\mathbf{A}_2 = (\mathbf{E}_3\mathbf{E}_2\mathbf{E}_1)\mathbf{A},$$

$$\vdots$$

$$\mathbf{A}_r = \mathbf{E}_r\mathbf{A}_{r-1} = (\mathbf{E}_r\mathbf{E}_{r-1}\cdots\mathbf{E}_3\mathbf{E}_2\mathbf{E}_1)\mathbf{A}.$$

This forms a matrix $\Omega = \mathbf{E}_r\mathbf{E}_{r-1}\cdots\mathbf{E}_2\mathbf{E}_1$ such that

$$\mathbf{A}_r = \Omega\mathbf{A}.$$

The significance of this equation is that we have produced a matrix Ω such that multiplying $\mathbf{A}$ on the left by Ω performs a given sequence of elementary row operations. Ω is formed as a product $\mathbf{E}_r\mathbf{E}_{r-1}\ldots\mathbf{E}_2\mathbf{E}_1$ of elementary matrices, *in the correct order*, with each elementary matrix performing one of the prescribed elementary row operations in the sequence ($\mathbf{E}_1$ performs the first operation, $\mathbf{E}_2$ the second, and so on until $\mathbf{E}_r$ performs the last). We will record this result as a theorem.

THEOREM 7.6

Let $\mathbf{A}$ be an $n \times m$ matrix. If $\mathbf{B}$ is produced from $\mathbf{A}$ by any finite sequence of elementary row operations, then there is an $n \times n$ matrix Ω such that

$$\mathbf{B} = \Omega\mathbf{A}. \ \blacksquare$$

The proof of the theorem is contained in the line of reasoning outlined just prior to its statement.

EXAMPLE 7.12

Let

$$\mathbf{A} = \begin{pmatrix} 2 & 1 & 0 \\ 0 & 1 & 2 \\ -1 & 3 & 2 \end{pmatrix}.$$

We will form a new matrix $\mathbf{B}$ from $\mathbf{A}$ by performing, in order, the following operations:
$\mathcal{O}_1$: interchange rows 1 and 2 of $\mathbf{A}$ to form $\mathbf{A}_1$.
$\mathcal{O}_2$: multiply row 3 of $\mathbf{A}_1$ by 2 to form $\mathbf{A}_2$.
$\mathcal{O}_3$: add two times row 1 to row 3 of $\mathbf{A}_2$ to get $\mathbf{A}_3 = \mathbf{B}$.
If we perform this sequence in order, starting with A, we get

$$\mathbf{A} \underset{\mathcal{O}_1}{\rightarrow} \mathbf{A}_1 = \begin{pmatrix} 0 & 1 & 2 \\ 2 & 1 & 0 \\ -1 & 3 & 2 \end{pmatrix} \underset{\mathcal{O}_2}{\rightarrow} \mathbf{A}_2 = \begin{pmatrix} 0 & 1 & 2 \\ 2 & 1 & 0 \\ -2 & 6 & 4 \end{pmatrix}$$

$$\underset{\mathcal{O}_3}{\rightarrow} \mathbf{A}_3 = \begin{pmatrix} 0 & 1 & 2 \\ 2 & 1 & 0 \\ -2 & 8 & 8 \end{pmatrix} = \mathbf{B}.$$

To produce Ω such that $\mathbf{B} = \Omega\mathbf{A}$, perform this sequence of operations in turn, beginning with $\mathbf{I}_3$:

$$\mathbf{I}_3 \xrightarrow[\mathcal{O}_1]{} \begin{pmatrix} 0 & 1 & 0 \\ 1 & 0 & 0 \\ 0 & 0 & 1 \end{pmatrix} \xrightarrow[\mathcal{O}_2]{} \begin{pmatrix} 0 & 1 & 0 \\ 1 & 0 & 0 \\ 0 & 0 & 2 \end{pmatrix}$$

$$\xrightarrow[\mathcal{O}_3]{} \begin{pmatrix} 0 & 1 & 0 \\ 1 & 0 & 0 \\ 0 & 2 & 2 \end{pmatrix} = \Omega.$$

Now check that

$$\Omega\mathbf{A} = \begin{pmatrix} 0 & 1 & 0 \\ 1 & 0 & 0 \\ 0 & 2 & 2 \end{pmatrix} \begin{pmatrix} 2 & 1 & 0 \\ 0 & 1 & 2 \\ -1 & 3 & 2 \end{pmatrix}$$

$$= \begin{pmatrix} 0 & 1 & 2 \\ 2 & 1 & 0 \\ -2 & 8 & 8 \end{pmatrix} = \mathbf{B}.$$

It is also easy to check that $\Omega = \mathbf{E}_3\mathbf{E}_2\mathbf{E}_1$, where $\mathbf{E}_j$ is the elementary matrix obtained by performing operation $\mathcal{O}_j$ on $\mathbf{I}_3$. ∎

EXAMPLE 7.13

Let

$$\mathbf{A} = \begin{pmatrix} 6 & -1 & 1 & 4 \\ 9 & 3 & 7 & -7 \\ 0 & 2 & 1 & 5 \end{pmatrix}.$$

We want to perform, in succession and in the given order, the following operations:

$\mathcal{O}_1$: add (-3)(row 2) to row 3,
$\mathcal{O}_2$: add 2(row 1) to row 2,
$\mathcal{O}_3$: interchange rows 1 and 3,
$\mathcal{O}_4$: multiply row 2 by -4.

Suppose the end result of these operations is the matrix $\mathbf{B}$. We will produce a 3×3 matrix Ω such that $\mathbf{B} = \Omega\mathbf{A}$. Perform the sequence of operations, starting with $\mathbf{I}_3$:

$$\mathbf{I}_3 \xrightarrow[\mathcal{O}_1]{} \begin{pmatrix} 1 & 0 & 0 \\ 0 & 1 & 0 \\ 0 & -3 & 1 \end{pmatrix} \xrightarrow[\mathcal{O}_2]{} \begin{pmatrix} 1 & 0 & 0 \\ 2 & 1 & 0 \\ 0 & -3 & 1 \end{pmatrix}$$

$$\xrightarrow[\mathcal{O}_3]{} \begin{pmatrix} 0 & -3 & 1 \\ 2 & 1 & 0 \\ 1 & 0 & 0 \end{pmatrix} \xrightarrow[\mathcal{O}_4]{} \begin{pmatrix} 0 & -3 & 1 \\ -8 & -4 & 0 \\ 1 & 0 & 0 \end{pmatrix} = \Omega.$$

Then

$$\Omega\mathbf{A} = \begin{pmatrix} 0 & -3 & 1 \\ -8 & -4 & 0 \\ 1 & 0 & 0 \end{pmatrix} \begin{pmatrix} 6 & -1 & 1 & 4 \\ 9 & 3 & 7 & -7 \\ 0 & 2 & 1 & 5 \end{pmatrix}$$

$$= \begin{pmatrix} -27 & -7 & -20 & 26 \\ -84 & -4 & -36 & -4 \\ 6 & -1 & 1 & 4 \end{pmatrix} = \mathbf{B}.$$

It is straightforward to check that $\Omega = \mathbf{E}_4\mathbf{E}_3\mathbf{E}_2\mathbf{E}_1$, where $\mathbf{E}_j$ is the elementary matrix obtained from $\mathbf{I}_3$ by applying operation $\mathcal{O}_j$. If the operations $\mathcal{O}_j$ are performed in succession, starting with $\mathbf{A}$, then $\mathbf{B}$ results. ∎

DEFINITION 7.11   Row Equivalence

Two matrices are row equivalent if and only if one can be obtained from the other by a sequence of elementary row operaitons.

In each of the last two examples, $\mathbf{B}$ is row equivalent to $\mathbf{A}$. The relationship of row equivalence has the following properties:

THEOREM 7.7

1. Every matrix is row equivalent to itself. (This is the reflexive property).
2. If $\mathbf{A}$ is row equivalent to $\mathbf{B}$, then $\mathbf{B}$ is row equivalent to $\mathbf{A}$. (This is the symmetry property).
3. If $\mathbf{A}$ is row equivalent to $\mathbf{B}$, and $\mathbf{B}$ to $\mathbf{C}$, then $\mathbf{A}$ is row equivalent to $\mathbf{C}$. (This is transitivity). ∎

It is sometimes of interest to undo the effect of an elementary row operation. This can always be done by the same kind of elementary row operation. Consider each kind of operation in turn.

If we interchange rows i and j of $\mathbf{A}$ to form $\mathbf{B}$, then interchanging rows i and j of $\mathbf{B}$ yields $\mathbf{A}$ again. Thus a Type I operation can reverse a Type I operation.

If we form $\mathbf{C}$ from $\mathbf{A}$ by multiplying row i by nonzero α, then multiplying row i of $\mathbf{C}$ by $1/\alpha$ brings us back to $\mathbf{A}$. A Type II operation can reverse a Type II operation.

Finally, suppose we form $\mathbf{D}$ from $\mathbf{A}$ by adding α (row i) to row j. Then

$$\mathbf{A} = \begin{pmatrix} a_{11} & a_{12} & \cdots & a_{1m} \\ \cdots & \cdots & \cdots & \cdots \\ a_{i1} & a_{i2} & \cdots & a_{im} \\ \cdots & \cdots & \cdots & \cdots \\ a_{j1} & a_{j2} & \cdots & a_{jm} \\ \cdots & \cdots & \cdots & \cdots \\ a_{n1} & a_{n2} & \cdots & a_{nm} \end{pmatrix}$$

and

$$\mathbf{D} = \begin{pmatrix} a_{11} & a_{12} & \cdots & a_{1m} \\ \cdots & \cdots & \cdots & \cdots \\ a_{i1} & a_{i2} & \cdots & a_{im} \\ \cdots & \cdots & \cdots & \cdots \\ \alpha a_{i1} + a_{j1} & \alpha a_{i2} + a_{j2} & \cdots & \alpha a_{im} + a_{jm} \\ \cdots & \cdots & \cdots & \cdots \\ a_{n1} & a_{n2} & \cdots & a_{nm} \end{pmatrix}.$$

Now we can get from $\mathbf{D}$ back to $\mathbf{A}$ by adding $-\alpha$(row i) to row j of $\mathbf{D}$. Thus a Type III operation can be used to reverse a Type III operation.

This ability to reverse the effects of elementary row operations will be useful later, and we will record it as a theorem.

THEOREM 7.8

Let E_1 be an elementary matrix that performs an elementary row operation on a matrix A. Then there is an elementary matrix E_2 such that $E_2(E_1A) = A$. ■

In fact, $E_2E_1 = I_n$.

SECTION 7.2   *PROBLEMS*

In each of Problems 1 through 8, perform the row operation, or sequence of row operations, directly on A, and then find a matrix Ω such that the final result is ΩA.

1. $A = \begin{pmatrix} -2 & 1 & 4 & 2 \\ 0 & 1 & 16 & 3 \\ 1 & -2 & 4 & 8 \end{pmatrix}$; multiply row 2 by $\sqrt{3}$.

2. $A = \begin{pmatrix} 3 & -6 \\ 1 & 1 \\ 8 & -2 \\ 0 & 5 \end{pmatrix}$; add 6 times row 2 to row 3.

3. $A = \begin{pmatrix} -2 & 14 & 6 \\ 8 & 1 & -3 \\ 2 & 9 & 5 \end{pmatrix}$; add $\sqrt{13}$ times row 3 to row 1, then interchange rows 2 and 1, then multiply row 1 by 5.

4. $A = \begin{pmatrix} -4 & 6 & -3 \\ 12 & 4 & -4 \\ 1 & 3 & 0 \end{pmatrix}$; interchange rows 2 and 3, then add negative row 1 to row 2.

5. $A = \begin{pmatrix} -3 & 15 \\ 2 & 8 \end{pmatrix}$; add $\sqrt{3}$ times row 2 to row 1, then multiply row 2 by 15, then interchange rows 1 and 2.

6. $A = \begin{pmatrix} 3 & -4 & 5 & 9 \\ 2 & 1 & 3 & -6 \\ 1 & 13 & 2 & 6 \end{pmatrix}$; add row 1 to row 3, then

add $\sqrt{3}$ times row 1 to row 2, then multiply row 3 by row 4, then add row 2 to row 3.

7. $A = \begin{pmatrix} -1 & 0 & 3 & 0 \\ 1 & 3 & 2 & 9 \\ -9 & 7 & -5 & 7 \end{pmatrix}$; multiply row 3 by 4, then add 14 times row 1 to row 2, then interchange rows 3 and 2.

8. $A = \begin{pmatrix} 0 & -9 & 14 \\ 1 & 5 & 2 \\ 9 & 15 & 0 \end{pmatrix}$; interchange rows 2 and 3, then add 3 times row 2 to row 3, then interchange rows 1 and 3, then multiply row 3 by 4.

In Problems 9, 10, and 11, A is an $n \times m$ matrix.

9. Let B be formed from A by interchanging rows s and t. Let E be formed from I_n by interchanging rows s and t. Prove that $B = EA$.

10. Let B be formed from A by multiplying row s by α, and let E be formed from I_n by multiplying row s by α. Prove that $B = EA$.

11. Let B be formed from A by adding α times row s to row t. Let E be formed from I_n by adding α times row s to row t. Prove that $B = EA$.

7.3   The Row Echelon Form of a Matrix

Sometimes a matrix has a special form that makes it convenient to work with in solving certain problems. For solving systems of linear algebraic equations, we want the *reduced row echelon form*, or *reduced form*, of a matrix.

Let A be an $n \times m$ matrix. A *zero row* of A is a row having each element equal to zero. If at least one element of a row is nonzero, that row is a *nonzero row*. The *leading entry* of a nonzero row is its first nonzero element, reading from left to right. For example, if

$$A = \begin{pmatrix} 0 & 2 & 7 \\ 1 & -2 & 0 \\ 0 & 0 & 0 \\ 0 & 0 & 9 \end{pmatrix},$$

then row three is a zero row and rows one, two, and four are nonzero rows. The leading entry of row 1 is 2, the leading entry of row 2 is 1, and the leading entry of row 4 is 9. We do not speak of a leading entry of a zero row.

We can now define a reduced row echelon matrix.

DEFINITION 7.12 *Reduced Row Echelon Matrix*

A matrix is in reduced row echelon form if it satisfies the following conditions:

1. The leading entry of any nonzero row is 1.
2. If any row has its leading entry in column j, then all other elements of column j are zero.
3. If row i is a nonzero row and row k is a zero row, then $i < k$.
4. If the leading entry of row r_1 is in column c_1, and the leading entry of row r_2 is in column c_2, and if $r_1 < r_2$, then $c_1 < c_2$.

A matrix in reduced row echelon form is said to be in reduced form, or to be a reduced matrix.

A reduced matrix has a very special structure. By condition (1), if we move from left to right along a nonzero row, the first nonzero number we see is 1. Condition (2) means that, if we stand at the leading entry 1 of any row, and look straight up or down, we see only zeros in the rest of this column. A reduced matrix need not have any zero rows. But if there is a zero row, it must be below any nonzero row. That is, all the zero rows are at the bottom of the matrix. Condition (4) means that the leading entries move downward to the right as we look at the matrix.

EXAMPLE 7.14

The following four matrices are all reduced:

$$\begin{pmatrix} 1 & -4 & 1 & 0 \\ 0 & 0 & 0 & 1 \end{pmatrix}, \begin{pmatrix} 0 & 1 & 3 & 0 \\ 0 & 0 & 0 & 1 \\ 0 & 0 & 0 & 0 \end{pmatrix},$$

$$\begin{pmatrix} 0 & 1 & 2 & 0 & 0 \\ 0 & 0 & 0 & 1 & 0 \\ 0 & 0 & 0 & 0 & 0 \\ 0 & 0 & 0 & 0 & 0 \end{pmatrix}, \quad \text{and} \quad \begin{pmatrix} 1 & 0 & 0 & 3 & 1 \\ 0 & 1 & 0 & -2 & 4 \\ 0 & 0 & 1 & 0 & 1 \\ 0 & 0 & 0 & 0 & 0 \end{pmatrix}. \ \blacksquare$$

EXAMPLE 7.15

To see one context in which reduced matrices are interesting, consider the last matrix of the preceding example and suppose it is the matrix of coefficients of a system of homogeneous linear equations. This system is $\mathbf{AX} = \mathbf{O}$, and the equations are:

$$x_1 + 3x_4 + x_5 = 0$$
$$x_2 - 2x_4 + 4x_5 = 0$$
$$x_3 + x_5 = 0.$$

The fourth row represents the equation $0x_1 + 0x_2 + 0x_3 + 0x_4 = 0$, which we do not write out (it is satisfied by any numbers x_1 through x_4, and so provides no information). Because the matrix of coefficients is in reduced form, this system is particularly easy to solve. From the third equation,

$$x_3 = -x_5.$$

From the second equation,

$$x_2 = 2x_4 - 4x_5.$$

And from the first equation,

$$x_1 = -3x_4 - x_5.$$

We can therefore choose $x_4 = \alpha$, any number, and $x_5 = \beta$, any number, and obtain a solution by choosing the other unknowns as

$$x_1 = -3\alpha - \beta, \quad x_2 = 2\beta - 4\beta, \quad x_3 = -\beta.$$

The form of the reduced matrix is selected just so that as a matrix of coefficients of a system of linear equations, the solution of these equations can be read by inspection. ■

EXAMPLE 7.16

The matrix

$$A = \begin{pmatrix} 0 & 1 & 5 & 0 & 0 \\ 0 & 0 & 1 & 0 & 0 \\ 0 & 0 & 0 & 1 & 0 \\ 0 & 0 & 0 & 0 & 1 \end{pmatrix}$$

is not reduced. The leading entry of row 2 is 1, as it must be, but there is a nonzero element in the column containing this leading entry. However, **A** is row equivalent to a reduced matrix. If we add -5 (row 2) to row 1, we obtain

$$B = \begin{pmatrix} 0 & 1 & 0 & 0 & 0 \\ 0 & 0 & 1 & 0 & 0 \\ 0 & 0 & 0 & 1 & 0 \\ 0 & 0 & 0 & 0 & 1 \end{pmatrix},$$

and this is a reduced matrix. ■

EXAMPLE 7.17

The matrix

$$C = \begin{pmatrix} 2 & 0 & 0 \\ 0 & 1 & 0 \\ 1 & 0 & 1 \end{pmatrix}$$

is not reduced. The leading entry of the first row is not 1, and the first column, containing this leading entry of row 1, has another nonzero element. In addition, the leading entry of row 3 is to the left of the leading entry of row 2, and this violates condition (4). However, **C** is row equivalent to a reduced matrix. First form **D** by multiplying row 1 by $\frac{1}{2}$:

$$\mathbf{D} = \begin{pmatrix} 1 & 0 & 0 \\ 0 & 1 & 0 \\ 1 & 0 & 1 \end{pmatrix}.$$

Now form **F** from **D** by adding $-$ (row 1) to row 3:

$$\mathbf{F} = \begin{pmatrix} 1 & 0 & 0 \\ 0 & 1 & 0 \\ 0 & 0 & 1 \end{pmatrix}.$$

Then **F** is a reduced matrix that is row equivalent to **C**, since it was formed by a sequence of elementary row operations, starting with **C**. ▨

In the last two examples we had matrices that were not in reduced form, but could in both cases proceed to a reduced matrix by elementary row operations. We claim that this is always possible (although in general more operations may be needed than in these two examples).

--- **THEOREM 7.9** ---

Every matrix is row equivalent to a reduced matrix.

Proof The proof consists of exhibiting a sequence of elementary row operations that will produce a reduced matrix. Let **A** be any matrix.

If **A** is a zero matrix, we are done. Thus suppose that **A** has at least one nonzero row.

Reading from left to right across the matrix, find the first column having a nonzero element. Suppose this is in column c_1. Reading from top to bottom in this column, suppose α is the top nonzero element. Say α is in row r_1. Multiply this row by $1/\alpha$ to obtain a matrix **B** in which column c_1 has its top nonzero element equal to 1, and this is in row r_1. If any row below r_1 in **B** has a nonzero element β in column c_1, add $-\beta$ times row r_1 to this row. In this way we obtain a matrix **C** that is row equivalent to **A**, having 1 in the r_1, c_1 position, and all other elements of column c_1 equal to zero.

Now interchange, if necessary, rows 1 and r_1 of **C** to obtain a matrix **D** having leading entry 1 in row 1 and column c_1, and all other elements of this column equal to zero. Further, by choice of c_1, any column of **D** to the left of column c_1 has all zero elements (if there is such a column). **D** is row equivalent to **A**.

If **D** is reduced, we are done. If not, repeat this procedure, but now look for the first column, say column c_2, to the right of column c_1 having a nonzero element below row 1. Let γ be the top nonzero element of this column lying below row 1. Say this element occurs in row r_2. Multiply row r_2 by $1/\gamma$ to obtain a new matrix **E** having 1 in the r_2, c_2 position. If this column has a nonzero element δ above or below row r_2, add $-\delta$ (row r_2) to this row. In this way we obtain a matrix **F** that is row equivalent to **A** and has leading entry 1 in row r_2 and all other elements of column c_2 equal to zero. Finally, form **G** from **F** by interchanging rows r_2 and 2, if necessary.

If **G** is reduced we are done. If not, locate the first column to the right of column c_2 having a nonzero element and repeat the procedure done to form the first two rows of **G**.

Since **A** has only finitely many columns, eventually this process terminates in a reduced matrix **R**. Since **R** was obtained from **A** by elementary row operations, **R** is row equivalent to **A** and the proof is complete. ▨

The process of obtaining a reduced matrix row equivalent to a given matrix **A** is referred to as *reducing* **A**. It is possible to reduce a matrix in many different ways (that is, by different sequences of elementary row operations). We claim that this does not matter and that for a given **A** any reduction process will result in the same reduced matrix.

THEOREM 7.10

Let **A** be a matrix. Then there is exactly one reduced matrix $\mathbf{A}_R$ that is row equivalent to **A**. ∎

We leave a proof of this result to the student. In view of this theorem, we can speak of *the* reduced form of a given matrix **A**. We will denote this matrix $\mathbf{A}_R$.

EXAMPLE 7.18

Let

$$\mathbf{A} = \begin{pmatrix} -2 & 1 & 3 \\ 0 & 1 & 1 \\ 2 & 0 & 1 \end{pmatrix}.$$

We want to find $\mathbf{A}_R$. Column 1 has a nonzero element in row 1. Begin with:

$$\mathbf{A} = \begin{pmatrix} -2 & 1 & 3 \\ 0 & 1 & 1 \\ 2 & 0 & 1 \end{pmatrix}.$$

Begin with the operations:

$$\text{multiply row 1 by } -\frac{1}{2} \rightarrow \begin{pmatrix} 1 & -\frac{1}{2} & -\frac{3}{2} \\ 0 & 1 & 1 \\ 2 & 0 & 1 \end{pmatrix}$$

$$\rightarrow \text{add } (-2)(\text{row 1}) \text{ to row 3} \rightarrow \begin{pmatrix} 1 & -\frac{1}{2} & -\frac{3}{2} \\ 0 & 1 & 1 \\ 0 & 1 & 4 \end{pmatrix}.$$

In the last matrix, column 2 has a nonzero element below row 1, the highest being 1 in the 2, 2 position. Since we want a 1 here, we do not have to multiply this row by anything. However, we want zeros above and below this 1, in the 1, 2 and 3, 2 positions. Thus add 1/2 times row 2 to row 1, and $-$ row 2 to row 3 in the last matrix to obtain

$$\begin{pmatrix} 1 & 0 & -1 \\ 0 & 1 & 1 \\ 0 & 0 & 3 \end{pmatrix}.$$

In this matrix column 3 has a nonzero element below row 2, in the 3, 3 location. Multiply row 3 by 1/3 to obtain

$$\begin{pmatrix} 1 & 0 & -1 \\ 0 & 1 & 1 \\ 0 & 0 & 1 \end{pmatrix}.$$

Finally, we want zeros above the 3, 3 position in column 3. Add row 3 to row 1 and $-$ row 3 to row 2 to get

$$A_R = \begin{pmatrix} 1 & 0 & 0 \\ 0 & 1 & 0 \\ 0 & 0 & 1 \end{pmatrix}.$$

This is $\mathbf{A}_R$ because it is a reduced matrix and it is row equivalent to **A**. ∎

To illustrate the last theorem, we will use a different sequence of elementary row operations to reduce **A**, arriving at the same final result. Proceed:

$$\mathbf{A} \to (\text{add row 3 to row 1}) \to \begin{pmatrix} 0 & 1 & 4 \\ 0 & 1 & 1 \\ 2 & 0 & 1 \end{pmatrix}$$

$$\text{add } (-1)(\text{row 2}) \text{ to row 1} \to \begin{pmatrix} 0 & 0 & 3 \\ 0 & 1 & 1 \\ 2 & 0 & 1 \end{pmatrix}$$

$$\frac{1}{3}(\text{row 1}) \to \begin{pmatrix} 0 & 0 & 1 \\ 0 & 1 & 1 \\ 2 & 0 & 1 \end{pmatrix}$$

$$\text{add } (-1)(\text{row 1}) \text{ to rows 2 and 3} \to \begin{pmatrix} 0 & 0 & 1 \\ 0 & 1 & 0 \\ 2 & 0 & 0 \end{pmatrix}$$

$$\text{interchange rows 1 and 3} \to \begin{pmatrix} 2 & 0 & 0 \\ 0 & 1 & 0 \\ 0 & 0 & 1 \end{pmatrix}$$

$$\frac{1}{2}(\text{row 1}) \to \begin{pmatrix} 1 & 0 & 0 \\ 0 & 1 & 0 \\ 0 & 0 & 1 \end{pmatrix} = \mathbf{A}_R.$$

EXAMPLE 7.19

Let

$$\mathbf{B} = \begin{pmatrix} 0 & 0 & 0 & 0 & 0 \\ 0 & 0 & 2 & 0 & 0 \\ 0 & 1 & 0 & 1 & 1 \\ 0 & 4 & 3 & 4 & 0 \end{pmatrix}.$$

Reduce **B** as follows:

$$\text{add } -4(\text{row 3}) \text{ to row 4} \to \begin{pmatrix} 0 & 0 & 0 & 0 & 0 \\ 0 & 0 & 2 & 0 & 0 \\ 0 & 1 & 0 & 1 & 1 \\ 0 & 0 & 3 & 0 & -4 \end{pmatrix}$$

$$\text{interchange rows 3 and 1} \to \begin{pmatrix} 0 & 1 & 0 & 1 & 1 \\ 0 & 0 & 2 & 0 & 0 \\ 0 & 0 & 0 & 0 & 0 \\ 0 & 0 & 3 & 0 & -4 \end{pmatrix}$$

$$\frac{1}{2}(\text{row 2}) \to \begin{pmatrix} 0 & 1 & 0 & 1 & 1 \\ 0 & 0 & 1 & 0 & 0 \\ 0 & 0 & 0 & 0 & 0 \\ 0 & 0 & 3 & 0 & -4 \end{pmatrix}$$

$$\text{add }(-3)(\text{row 2}) \text{ to row } 4 \rightarrow \begin{pmatrix} 0 & 1 & 0 & 1 & 1 \\ 0 & 0 & 1 & 0 & 0 \\ 0 & 0 & 0 & 0 & 0 \\ 0 & 0 & 0 & 0 & -4 \end{pmatrix}$$

$$-\frac{1}{4}(\text{row 4}) \rightarrow \begin{pmatrix} 0 & 1 & 0 & 1 & 1 \\ 0 & 0 & 1 & 0 & 0 \\ 0 & 0 & 0 & 0 & 0 \\ 0 & 0 & 0 & 0 & 1 \end{pmatrix}$$

$$\text{add }(-1)(\text{row 4}) \text{ to row } 1 \rightarrow \begin{pmatrix} 0 & 1 & 0 & 1 & 0 \\ 0 & 0 & 1 & 0 & 0 \\ 0 & 0 & 0 & 0 & 0 \\ 0 & 0 & 0 & 0 & 1 \end{pmatrix}$$

$$\text{interchange row 3 and } 4 \rightarrow \begin{pmatrix} 0 & 1 & 0 & 1 & 0 \\ 0 & 0 & 1 & 0 & 0 \\ 0 & 0 & 0 & 0 & 1 \\ 0 & 0 & 0 & 0 & 0 \end{pmatrix}.$$

This is a reduced matrix, hence it is the reduced matrix $\mathbf{B}_R$ of $\mathbf{B}$. ∎

In view of Theorem 7.6 of the preceding section, we immediately have the following.

THEOREM 7.11

Let $\mathbf{A}$ be an $n \times m$ matrix. Then there is an $n \times n$ matrix Ω such that $\Omega\mathbf{A} = \mathbf{A}_R$. ∎

There is a convenient notational device that enables us to find both Ω and $\mathbf{A}_R$ together. We know what Ω is. If $\mathbf{A}$ is $n = n \times m$, then Ω is an $n \times n$ matrix formed by starting with $\mathbf{I}_n$ and carrying out, in order, the same sequence of elementary row operations used to reduce $\mathbf{A}$. A simple way to form Ω while reducing $\mathbf{A}$ is to form an $n \times (n+m)$ matrix $[\mathbf{I}_n \vdots \mathbf{A}]$ by placing $\mathbf{I}_n$ alongside $\mathbf{A}$ on its left. The first n columns of this matrix $[\mathbf{I}_n \vdots \mathbf{A}]$ are just $\mathbf{I}_n$, and the last m columns are $\mathbf{A}$. Now reduce $\mathbf{A}$ by elementary row operations, performing the same operations on the first n columns $(\mathbf{I}_n)$ as well. When $\mathbf{A}$ is reduced, the resulting $n \times (n+m)$ matrix will have the form $[\Omega \vdots \mathbf{A}_R]$, and we read Ω as the first n columns.

EXAMPLE 7.20

Let

$$\mathbf{A} = \begin{pmatrix} -3 & 1 & 0 \\ 4 & -2 & 1 \end{pmatrix}.$$

We want to find a 2×2 matrix Ω such that $\Omega\mathbf{A} = \mathbf{A}_R$. Since $\mathbf{A}$ is 2×3, form the matrix

$$[\mathbf{I}_2 \vdots \mathbf{A}] = \begin{pmatrix} 1 & 0 & \vdots & -3 & 1 & 0 \\ 0 & 1 & \vdots & 4 & -2 & 1 \end{pmatrix}.$$

Now reduce the last three columns, performing the same operations on the first two. The column of dashes is just a bookkeeping device to separate $\mathbf{A}$ from $\mathbf{I}_2$. Proceed

$$[\mathbf{I}_2 \vdots \mathbf{A}] \rightarrow -\frac{1}{3}(\text{row } 1) \rightarrow \begin{pmatrix} -\frac{1}{3} & 0 & \vdots & 1 & -\frac{1}{3} & 0 \\ 0 & 1 & \vdots & 4 & -2 & 1 \end{pmatrix}$$

$$\rightarrow \frac{1}{4}(\text{row } 2) \rightarrow \begin{pmatrix} -\frac{1}{3} & 0 & \vdots & 1 & -\frac{1}{3} & 0 \\ 0 & \frac{1}{4} & \vdots & 1 & -\frac{1}{2} & \frac{1}{4} \end{pmatrix}$$

$$\rightarrow (\text{row } 2 - \text{row } 1) \rightarrow \begin{pmatrix} -\frac{1}{3} & 0 & \vdots & 1 & -\frac{1}{3} & 0 \\ \frac{1}{3} & \frac{1}{4} & \vdots & 0 & -\frac{1}{6} & \frac{1}{4} \end{pmatrix}$$

$$\rightarrow (-6)(\text{row } 2) \rightarrow \begin{pmatrix} -\frac{1}{3} & 0 & \vdots & 1 & -\frac{1}{3} & 0 \\ -2 & -\frac{3}{2} & \vdots & 0 & 1 & -\frac{3}{2} \end{pmatrix}$$

$$\rightarrow \frac{1}{3}(\text{row } 2) + (\text{row } 1) \rightarrow \begin{pmatrix} -1 & -\frac{1}{2} & \vdots & 1 & 0 & -\frac{1}{2} \\ -2 & -\frac{3}{2} & \vdots & 0 & 1 & -\frac{3}{2} \end{pmatrix}.$$

The last three columns are in reduced form, so they form $\mathbf{A}_R$. The first two columns form Ω:

$$\Omega = \begin{pmatrix} -1 & -\frac{1}{2} \\ -2 & -\frac{3}{2} \end{pmatrix}.$$

As a check on this, form the product

$$\Omega\mathbf{A} = \begin{pmatrix} -1 & -\frac{1}{2} \\ -2 & -\frac{3}{2} \end{pmatrix} \begin{pmatrix} -3 & 1 & 0 \\ 4 & -2 & 1 \end{pmatrix} = \begin{pmatrix} 1 & 0 & -\frac{1}{2} \\ 0 & 1 & -\frac{3}{2} \end{pmatrix} = \mathbf{A}_R. \ \blacksquare$$

SECTION 7.3 PROBLEMS

In each of the following, find the reduced form of $\mathbf{A}$ and produce a matrix Ω such that $\Omega\mathbf{A} = \mathbf{A}_R$.

1. $\mathbf{A} = \begin{pmatrix} 1 & -1 & 3 \\ 0 & 1 & 2 \\ 0 & 0 & 0 \end{pmatrix}$

2. $\mathbf{A} = \begin{pmatrix} 3 & 1 & 1 & 4 \\ 0 & 1 & 0 & 0 \end{pmatrix}$

3. $\mathbf{A} = \begin{pmatrix} -1 & 4 & 1 & 1 \\ 0 & 0 & 0 & 0 \\ 0 & 0 & 0 & 0 \\ 0 & 0 & 0 & 1 \end{pmatrix}$

4. $\mathbf{A} = \begin{pmatrix} 1 & 0 & 1 & 1 & -1 \\ 0 & 1 & 0 & 0 & 2 \end{pmatrix}$

5. $\mathbf{A} = \begin{pmatrix} 6 & 1 \\ 0 & 0 \\ 1 & 3 \\ 0 & 1 \end{pmatrix}$

6. $\mathbf{A} = \begin{pmatrix} 2 & 2 \\ 1 & 1 \end{pmatrix}$

7. $\mathbf{A} = \begin{pmatrix} -1 & 4 & 6 \\ 2 & 3 & -5 \\ 7 & 1 & 1 \end{pmatrix}$

8. $\mathbf{A} = \begin{pmatrix} -3 & 4 & 4 \\ 0 & 0 & 0 \end{pmatrix}$

9. $A = \begin{pmatrix} -1 & 2 & 3 & 1 \\ 1 & 0 & 0 & 0 \end{pmatrix}$

11. $A = \begin{pmatrix} 4 & 1 & -7 \\ 2 & 2 & 0 \\ 0 & 1 & 0 \end{pmatrix}$

10. $A = \begin{pmatrix} 8 & 2 & 1 & 0 \\ 0 & 1 & 1 & 3 \\ 4 & 0 & 0 & -3 \end{pmatrix}$

12. $A = \begin{pmatrix} 6 \\ -3 \\ 1 \\ 1 \end{pmatrix}$

7.4 The Row and Column Spaces of a Matrix and Rank of a Matrix

In this section we will develop three numbers associated with matrices that play a significant role in the solution of systems of linear equations.

Suppose A is an $n \times m$ matrix with real number elements. Each row of A has m elements and can be thought of as a vector in R^m. There are n such vectors. The set of all linear combinations of these row vectors is a subspace of R^m called the *row space* of A. This space is spanned by the row vectors. If these row vectors are linearly independent, they form a basis for this row space and this space has dimension n. If they are not linearly independent, then some subset of them forms a basis for the row space, and this space has dimension $< n$.

If we look down instead of across, we can think of each column of A as a vector in R^n. We often write these vectors as columns simply to keep in mind their origin, although they can be written in standard vector notation. The set of all linear combinations of these columns forms a subspace of R^n. This is the *column space* of A. If these columns are linearly independent, they form a basis for this column space, which then has dimension m; otherwise, this dimension is less than m.

EXAMPLE 7.21

Let

$$B = \begin{pmatrix} -2 & 6 & 1 \\ 2 & 2 & -4 \\ 10 & -8 & 12 \\ 3 & 1 & -2 \\ 5 & -5 & 7 \end{pmatrix}.$$

The row space is the subspace of R^3 spanned by the row vectors of B. This row space consists of all vectors

$$\alpha(-2, 6, 1) + \beta(2, 2, -4) + \gamma(10, -8, 12) + \delta(3, 1, -2) + \epsilon(5, -5, 7).$$

The first three row vectors are linearly independent. The last two are linear combinations of the first three. Specifically,

$$(3, 1, -2) = \frac{4}{101}(-2, 6, 1) + \frac{181}{202}(2, 2, -4) + \frac{13}{101}(10, -8, 12)$$

and

$$(5, -5, 7) = -\frac{7}{101}(-2, 6, 1) - \frac{39}{202}(2, 2, -4) + \frac{53}{101}(10, -8, 12).$$

The first three row vectors form a basis for the row space, which therefore has dimension 3. The row space of B is all of R^3.

The column space of **B** is the subspace of R^5 consisting of all vectors

$$\alpha \begin{pmatrix} -2 \\ 2 \\ 10 \\ 3 \\ 5 \end{pmatrix} + \beta \begin{pmatrix} 6 \\ 2 \\ -8 \\ 1 \\ -5 \end{pmatrix} + \gamma \begin{pmatrix} 1 \\ -4 \\ 12 \\ -2 \\ 7 \end{pmatrix}.$$

These three column vectors are linearly independent in R^5. Neither is a linear combination of the other two, or, equivalently, the only way this linear combination can be the zero vector is for $\alpha = \beta = \gamma = 0$. Therefore the column space of **B** has dimension 3 and is a subspace of the dimension 5 space R^5. ■

In this example the row space of matrix had the same dimension as the column space, even though the row vectors were in R^m and the column vectors in R^n, with $n \neq m$. This is not a coincidence.

THEOREM 7.12

For any matrix **A** having real numbers as elements, the row and column spaces have the same dimension.

Proof   Suppose **A** is $n \times m$:

$$A = \begin{pmatrix} a_{11} & a_{12} & \cdots & a_{1r} & a_{1,r+1} & \cdots & a_{1m} \\ a_{21} & a_{22} & \cdots & a_{2r} & a_{2,r+1} & \cdots & a_{2m} \\ \vdots & \vdots & \vdots & \vdots & \vdots & \vdots & \vdots \\ a_{r1} & a_{r2} & \cdots & a_{rr} & a_{r,r+1} & \cdots & a_{rm} \\ a_{r+1,1} & a_{r+1,2} & \cdots & a_{r+1,r} & a_{r+1,r+1} & \cdots & a_{r+1,m} \\ \vdots & \vdots & \vdots & \vdots & \vdots & \vdots & \vdots \\ a_{n1} & a_{n2} & \cdots & a_{nr} & a_{n,r+1} & \cdots & a_{nm} \end{pmatrix}.$$

Denote the row vectors $\mathbf{R}_1, \ldots, \mathbf{R}_n$, so

$$\mathbf{R}_i = (a_{i1}, a_{i2}, \cdots, a_{im}) \text{ in } R^m.$$

Now suppose that the dimension of the row space of **A** is r. Then exactly r of these row vectors are linearly independent. As a notational convenience, suppose the first r rows $\mathbf{R}_1, \ldots, \mathbf{R}_r$ are linearly independent. Then each of $\mathbf{R}_{r+1}, \ldots, \mathbf{R}_n$ is a linear combination of these r vectors. Write

$$\mathbf{R}_{r+1} = \beta_{r+1,1}\mathbf{R}_1 + \cdots + \beta_{r+1,r}\mathbf{R}_r,$$

$$\mathbf{R}_{r+2} = \beta_{r+2,1}\mathbf{R}_1 + \cdots + \beta_{r+2,r}\mathbf{R}_r,$$

$$\vdots$$

$$\mathbf{R}_n = \beta_{n,1}\mathbf{R}_1 + \cdots + \beta_{n,r}\mathbf{R}_r.$$

Now observe that column j of $\mathbf{A}$ can be written

$$
\begin{pmatrix} a_{1j} \\ a_{2j} \\ \vdots \\ a_{rj} \\ a_{r+1,j} \\ \vdots \\ a_{nj} \end{pmatrix} = a_{1j} \begin{pmatrix} 1 \\ 0 \\ \vdots \\ 0 \\ \beta_{r+1,1} \\ \vdots \\ \beta_{n1} \end{pmatrix} + a_{2j} \begin{pmatrix} 0 \\ 1 \\ \vdots \\ 0 \\ \beta_{r+1,2} \\ \vdots \\ \beta_{n,2} \end{pmatrix} + \cdots + a_{rj} \begin{pmatrix} 0 \\ 0 \\ \vdots \\ 1 \\ \beta_{r+1,r} \\ \vdots \\ \beta_{n,r} \end{pmatrix}.
$$

This means that each column vector of $\mathbf{A}$ is a linear combination of the r n-vectors on the right side of this equation. These r vectors therefore span the column space of $\mathbf{A}$. If these vectors are linearly independent, then the dimension of the column space is r. If not, then remove from this list of vectors any that are linear combinations of the others and thus determine a basis for the column space having fewer than r vectors. In any event,

Dimension of the column space of $\mathbf{A} \leq$ dimension of the row space of $\mathbf{A}$.

By essentially repeating this argument, with row and column vectors interchanged, we obtain

Dimension of the row space of $\mathbf{A} \leq$ dimension of the column space of $\mathbf{A}$,

and these two inequalities together prove the theorem. ∎

It is interesting to ask what effect elementary row operations have on the row space of a matrix. The answer is—none! We will need this fact shortly.

THEOREM 7.13

Let $\mathbf{A}$ be an $n \times m$ matrix, and let $\mathbf{B}$ be formed from $\mathbf{A}$ by an elementary row operation. Then the row space of $\mathbf{A}$ and the row space of $\mathbf{B}$ are the same.

Proof If $\mathbf{B}$ is obtained by a Type I operation, we simply interchange two rows. Then $\mathbf{A}$ and $\mathbf{B}$ still have the same row vectors, just listed in a different order, so these row vectors span the same row space.

Suppose $\mathbf{B}$ is obtained by a Type II operation, multiplying row i by a nonzero constant c. Linear combinations of the rows of $\mathbf{A}$ have the form

$$
\alpha_1 \mathbf{R}_1 + \cdots + \alpha_i \mathbf{R}_i + \cdots + \alpha_n \mathbf{R}_n
$$

while linear combinations of the rows of $\mathbf{B}$ are

$$
\alpha_1 \mathbf{R}_1 + \cdots + c\alpha_i \mathbf{R}_i + \cdots + \alpha_n \mathbf{R}_n
$$

Since α_i can be any number, so can $c\alpha_i$, so these linear combinations yield the same vectors when the coefficients are chosen arbitrarily. Thus the row space of $\mathbf{A}$ and $\mathbf{B}$ are again the same.

Finally, suppose $\mathbf{B}$ is obtained from $\mathbf{A}$ by adding c (row i) to row j. The column vectors of $\mathbf{B}$ are now

$$
\mathbf{R}_1, \ldots \mathbf{R}_{j-1}, c\mathbf{R}_i + \mathbf{R}_j, \mathbf{R}_{j+1}, \ldots, \mathbf{R}_n.
$$

But we can write an arbitrary linear combination of these rows of $\mathbf{B}$ as

$$\alpha_1 \mathbf{R}_1 + \cdots + \alpha_{j-1} \mathbf{R}_{j-1} + \alpha_j \left(c \mathbf{R}_i + \mathbf{R}_j \right) + \alpha_{j+1} \mathbf{R}_{j+1} + \cdots + \alpha_n \mathbf{R}_n,$$

and this is

$$\alpha_1 \mathbf{R}_1 + \cdots + (\alpha_i + c\alpha_j) \mathbf{R}_i + \cdots + \alpha_j \mathbf{R}_j + \cdots + \alpha_n \mathbf{R}_n,$$

which is again just a linear combination of the row vectors of $\mathbf{A}$. Thus again the row spaces of $\mathbf{A}$ and $\mathbf{B}$ are the same, and the theorem is proved. ∎

COROLLARY 7.1
_____

For any matrix $\mathbf{A}$, the row spaces of $\mathbf{A}$ and $\mathbf{A}_R$ are the same. ∎

This follows immediately from Theorem 6.13. Each time we perform an elementary row operation on a matrix, we leave the row space unchanged. Since we obtain $\mathbf{A}_R$ from $\mathbf{A}$ by elementary row operations, then $\mathbf{A}$ and $\mathbf{A}_R$ must have the same row spaces.

The dimensions of the row and column spaces will be important when we consider solutions of systems of linear equations. There is another number that will play a significant role in this, the rank of a matrix.

DEFINITION 7.13   Rank
_____

The rank of a matrix $\mathbf{A}$ is the number of nonzero rows in $\mathbf{A}_R$.

We denote the rank of $\mathbf{A}$ as $rank(\mathbf{A})$. If $\mathbf{B}$ is a reduced matrix, then $\mathbf{B} = \mathbf{B}_R$, so the rank of $\mathbf{B}$ is just the number of nonzero rows of $\mathbf{B}$ itself. Further, for any matrix $\mathbf{A}$

$$rank(\mathbf{A}) = \text{number of nonzero rows of } \mathbf{A}_R = rank(\mathbf{A}_R).$$

We claim that the rank of a matrix is equal to the dimension of its row space (or column space). First we will show this for reduced matrices.

LEMMA 7.1
_____

Let $\mathbf{B}$ be a reduced matrix. Then the rank of $\mathbf{B}$ equals the dimension of the row space of $\mathbf{B}$.

Proof   Let $\mathbf{R}_1, \ldots, \mathbf{R}_r$ be the nonzero row vectors of $\mathbf{B}$. The row space consists of all linear combinations

$$c_1 \mathbf{R}_1 + \cdots + c_r \mathbf{R}_r.$$

If nonzero row j has its leading entry in column k, then the kth component of $\mathbf{R}_j$ is 1. Because $\mathbf{B}$ is reduced, all the other elements of column k are zero, hence each other $\mathbf{R}_i$ has k^{th} component zero. By Lemma 5.3, $\mathbf{R}_1, \ldots, \mathbf{R}_r$ are linearly independent. Therefore these vectors form a basis for the row space of $\mathbf{B}$, and the dimension of this space is r. But

$$r = \text{number of nonzero rows of } \mathbf{B} = \text{number of nonzero rows of } \mathbf{B}_R = rank(\mathbf{B}). \ ∎$$

EXAMPLE 7.22

Let

$$
\mathbf{B} = \begin{pmatrix} 0 & 1 & 0 & 0 & 3 & 0 & 6 \\ 0 & 0 & 1 & 0 & -2 & 1 & 5 \\ 0 & 0 & 0 & 1 & 2 & 0 & -4 \\ 0 & 0 & 0 & 0 & 0 & 0 & 0 \end{pmatrix}.
$$

Then $\mathbf{B}$ is in reduced form, so $\mathbf{B} = \mathbf{B}_R$. The rank of $\mathbf{B}$ is its number of nonzero rows, which is 3. Further, the nonzero row vectors are

$$(0, 1, 0, 0, 3, 0, 6), (0, 0, 1, 0, -2, 1, 5), (0, 0, 0, 1, 2, 0, -4)$$

and these are linearly independent. Indeed, if a linear combination of these vectors yielded the zero vector, we would have

$$\alpha(0, 1, 0, 0, 3, 0, 6) + \beta(0, 0, 1, 0, -2, 1, 5) + \gamma(0, 0, 0, 1, 2, 0, -4)$$
$$= (0, 0, 0, 0, 0, 0, 0).$$

But then

$$(0, \alpha, \beta, \gamma, 3\alpha - 2\beta + 2\gamma, \beta, 6\alpha + 5\beta - 4\gamma) = (0, 0, 0, 0, 0, 0, 0),$$

and from the second, third, and fourth components we read that $\alpha = \beta = \gamma = 0$. By Theorem 6.13(2), these three row vectors are linearly independent and form a basis for the row space, which therefore has dimension 3. ∎

Using this as a stepping stone, we can prove the result for arbitrary matrices.

THEOREM 7.14

For any matrix $\mathbf{A}$, the rank of $\mathbf{A}$ equals the dimension of the row space of $\mathbf{A}$.

Proof   From the lemma, we know that

$$rank(\mathbf{A}) = rank(\mathbf{A}_R) = \text{dimension of the row space of } \mathbf{A}_R$$
$$= \text{dimension of the row space of } \mathbf{A},$$

since $\mathbf{A}$ and $\mathbf{A}_R$ have the same row space. ∎

Of course, we can also assert that

$$rank(\mathbf{A}) = \text{dimension of the column space of } \mathbf{A}.$$

If $\mathbf{A}$ is $n \times m$, then so is $\mathbf{A}_R$. Now $\mathbf{A}_R$ cannot have more than n nonzero rows (because it has only n rows). This means that

$$rank(\mathbf{A}) \leq \text{ number of rows of } \mathbf{A}.$$

There is a special circumstance in which the rank of a square matrix actually equals its number of rows.

THEOREM 7.15

Let $\mathbf{A}$ be an $n \times n$ matrix. Then $rank(\mathbf{A}) = n$ if and only if $\mathbf{A}_R = \mathbf{I}_n$.

Proof If $\mathbf{A}_R = \mathbf{I}_n$, then the number of nonzero rows in $\mathbf{A}_R$ is n, since $\mathbf{I}_n$ has no zero rows. Hence in this case $rank(\mathbf{A}) = n$.

Conversely, suppose that $rank(\mathbf{A}) = n$. Then $\mathbf{A}_R$ has n nonzero rows, hence no zero rows. By definition of a reduced matrix, each row of $\mathbf{A}_R$ has leading entry 1. Since each row, being a nonzero row, has a leading entry, then the i, i elements of $\mathbf{A}_R$ are all equal to 1. But it is also required that, if column j contains a leading entry, then all other elements of that column are zero. Thus $\mathbf{A}_R$ must have each i, j element equal to zero if $i \neq j$, so $\mathbf{A}_R = \mathbf{I}_n$. ∎

EXAMPLE 7.23

Let

$$\mathbf{A} = \begin{pmatrix} 1 & -1 & 4 & 2 \\ 0 & 1 & 3 & 2 \\ 3 & -2 & 15 & 8 \end{pmatrix}.$$

We find that

$$\mathbf{A}_R = \begin{pmatrix} 1 & 0 & 7 & 0 \\ 0 & 1 & 3 & 2 \\ 0 & 0 & 0 & 0 \end{pmatrix}.$$

Therefore $rank(\mathbf{A}) = 2$. This is also the dimension of the row space of $\mathbf{A}$ and of the column space of $\mathbf{A}$. ∎

In the next section we will use the reduced form of a matrix to solve homogeneous systems of linear algebraic equations.

SECTION 7.4 **PROBLEMS**

In each of Problems 1 through 14, (a) find the reduced form of the matrix, and from this the rank, (b) find a basis for the row space of the matrix, and the dimension of this space, and (c) find a basis for the column space and the dimension of this space.

1. $\begin{pmatrix} -4 & 1 & 3 \\ 2 & 2 & 0 \end{pmatrix}$

2. $\begin{pmatrix} 1 & -1 & 4 \\ 0 & 1 & 3 \\ 2 & -1 & 11 \end{pmatrix}$

3. $\begin{pmatrix} -3 & 1 \\ 2 & 2 \\ 4 & -3 \end{pmatrix}$

4. $\begin{pmatrix} 6 & 0 & 0 & 1 & 1 \\ 12 & 0 & 0 & 2 & 2 \\ 1 & -1 & 0 & 0 & 0 \end{pmatrix}$

5. $\begin{pmatrix} 8 & -4 & 3 & 2 \\ 1 & -1 & 1 & 0 \end{pmatrix}$

6. $\begin{pmatrix} 1 & 3 & 0 \\ 0 & 0 & 1 \end{pmatrix}$

7. $\begin{pmatrix} 2 & 2 & 1 \\ 1 & -1 & 3 \\ 0 & 0 & 1 \\ 4 & 0 & 7 \end{pmatrix}$

8. $\begin{pmatrix} 0 & -1 & 0 \\ 0 & 0 & -1 \\ 0 & 0 & 2 \end{pmatrix}$

9. $\begin{pmatrix} 0 & 4 & 3 \\ 6 & 1 & 0 \\ 2 & 2 & 2 \end{pmatrix}$

10. $\begin{pmatrix} 1 & 0 & 0 \\ 2 & 0 & 0 \\ 1 & 0 & -1 \\ 3 & 0 & 0 \end{pmatrix}$

11. $\begin{pmatrix} -3 & 2 & 2 \\ 1 & 0 & 5 \\ 0 & 0 & 2 \end{pmatrix}$

12. $\begin{pmatrix} -4 & -2 & 1 & 6 \\ 0 & 4 & -4 & 2 \\ 1 & 0 & 0 & 0 \end{pmatrix}$

13. $\begin{pmatrix} -2 & 5 & 7 \\ 0 & 1 & -3 \\ -4 & 11 & 11 \end{pmatrix}$

14. $\begin{pmatrix} -3 & 2 & 1 & 1 & 0 \\ 6 & -4 & -2 & -2 & 0 \end{pmatrix}$

15. Show that for any matrix $\mathbf{A}$, $rank(\mathbf{A}) = rank(\mathbf{A}^t)$.

7.5   Solution of Homogeneous Systems of Linear Equations

We will apply the matrix machinery we have developed to the solution of systems of n linear homogeneous equations in m unknowns:

$$a_{11}x_1 + a_{12}x_2 + \cdots + a_{1m}x_m = 0$$
$$a_2 x_1 + a_{22}x_2 + \cdots + a_{2m}x_m = 0$$
$$\vdots$$
$$a_{n1}x_1 + a_{n2}x_2 + \cdots + a_{nm}x_m = 0.$$

This term *homogeneous* applies here because the right side of each equation is zero.

As a prelude to a matrix approach to solving this system, consider the simple system

$$x_1 - 3x_2 + 2x_3 = 0$$
$$-2x_1 + x_2 - 3x_3 = 0.$$

We can solve this easily by "eliminating unknowns." Add 2(equation 1) to equation 2 to get

$$-5x_2 + x_3 = 0,$$

hence

$$x_2 = \frac{1}{5}x_3.$$

Now put this into the first equation of the system to get

$$x_1 - \frac{3}{5}x_3 + 2x_3 = 0,$$

or

$$x_1 + \frac{7}{5}x_3 = 0.$$

Then

$$x_1 = -\frac{7}{5}x_3.$$

We now have the solution:

$$x_1 = -\frac{7}{5}\alpha, \; x_2 = \frac{1}{5}\alpha, \; x_3 = \alpha,$$

in which α can be any number. For this system, two of the unknowns can be written as constant multiples of the third, which can be assigned any value. The system therefore has infinitely many solutions.

For this simple system we do not need matrices. However, it is instructive to see how matrices could be used here. First, write this system in matrix form as $\mathbf{AX} = \mathbf{O}$, where

$$\mathbf{A} = \begin{pmatrix} 1 & -3 & 2 \\ -2 & 1 & -3 \end{pmatrix} \quad \text{and} \quad \mathbf{X} = \begin{pmatrix} x_1 \\ x_2 \\ x_3 \end{pmatrix}.$$

Now reduce $\mathbf{A}$. We find that

$$\mathbf{A}_R = \begin{pmatrix} 1 & 0 & \frac{7}{5} \\ 0 & 1 & -\frac{1}{5} \end{pmatrix}.$$

The system $\mathbf{A}_R\mathbf{X} = \mathbf{0}$ is just

$$x_1 + \frac{7}{5}x_3 = 0$$

$$x_2 - \frac{1}{5}x_3 = 0.$$

This reduced system has the advantage of simplicity—we can solve it on sight, obtaining the same solutions that we got for the original system.

This is not a coincidence. $\mathbf{A}_R$ is formed from $\mathbf{A}$ by elementary row operations. Since each row of $\mathbf{A}$ contains the coefficients of an equation of the system, these row operations correspond in the system to interchanging equations, multiplying an equation by a nonzero constant, and adding a constant multiple of one equation to another equation of the system. This is why these elementary row operations were selected. But these operations always result in new systems having the same solutions as the original system (a proof of this will be given shortly). The reduced system $\mathbf{A}_R\mathbf{X} = \mathbf{O}$ therefore has the same solutions as $\mathbf{AX} = \mathbf{O}$. But $\mathbf{A}_R$ is defined in just such a way that we can just read the solutions, giving some unknowns in terms of others, as we saw in this simple case.

We will look at two more examples and then say more about the method in general.

EXAMPLE 7.24

Solve the system

$$x_1 - 3x_2 + x_3 - 7x_4 + 4x_5 = 0$$

$$x_1 + 2x_2 - 3x_3 = 0$$

$$x_2 - 4x_3 + x_5 = 0.$$

This is the system $\mathbf{AX} = \mathbf{O}$, with

$$\mathbf{A} = \begin{pmatrix} 1 & -3 & 1 & -7 & 4 \\ 1 & 2 & -3 & 0 & 0 \\ 0 & 1 & -4 & 0 & 1 \end{pmatrix}.$$

We find that

$$\mathbf{A}_R = \begin{pmatrix} 1 & 0 & 0 & -\frac{35}{16} & \frac{13}{16} \\ 0 & 1 & 0 & \frac{28}{16} & -\frac{20}{16} \\ 0 & 0 & 1 & \frac{7}{16} & -\frac{9}{16} \end{pmatrix}.$$

The systems $\mathbf{AX} = \mathbf{O}$ and $\mathbf{A}_R\mathbf{X} = \mathbf{O}$ have the same solutions. But the equations of the reduced system $\mathbf{A}_R\mathbf{X} = \mathbf{O}$ are

$$x_1 - \frac{35}{16}x_4 + \frac{13}{16}x_5 = 0$$

$$x_2 + \frac{28}{16}x_4 - \frac{20}{16}x_5 = 0$$

$$x_3 + \frac{7}{16}x_4 - \frac{9}{16}x_5 = 0.$$

From these we immediately read the solution. We can let $x_4 = \alpha$ and $x_5 = \beta$ (any numbers), and then

$$x_1 = \frac{35}{16}\alpha - \frac{13}{16}\beta, \ x_2 = -\frac{28}{16}\alpha + \frac{20}{16}\beta, \ x_3 = -\frac{7}{16}\alpha + \frac{9}{16}\beta. \ \blacksquare$$

Not only did we essentially have the solution once we obtained $\mathbf{A}_R$, but we also knew the number of arbitrary constants that appear in the solution. In the last example this number was 2. This was the number of columns, minus the number of rows having leading entries (or $m - rank(\mathbf{A})$).

It is convenient to write solutions of $\mathbf{AX} = \mathbf{O}$ as column vectors. In the last example, we could write

$$\mathbf{X} = \begin{pmatrix} \frac{35}{16}\alpha - \frac{13}{16}\beta \\ -\frac{28}{16}\alpha + \frac{20}{16}\beta \\ -\frac{7}{16}\alpha + \frac{9}{16}\beta \\ \alpha \\ \beta \end{pmatrix}.$$

This formulation also makes it easy to display other information about solutions. In this example, we can also write

$$\mathbf{X} = \gamma \begin{pmatrix} 35 \\ -28 \\ -7 \\ 16 \\ 0 \end{pmatrix} + \delta \begin{pmatrix} -13 \\ 20 \\ 9 \\ 0 \\ 16 \end{pmatrix}.$$

in which $\gamma = \alpha/16$ can be any number (since α can be any number), and $\delta = \beta/16$ is also any number. This displays the solution as a linear combination of two linearly independent vectors. We will say more about the significance of this in the next section.

EXAMPLE 7.25

Solve the system

$$-x_2 + 2x_3 + 4x_4 = 0$$

$$-x_3 + 3x_4 = 0$$

$$2x_1 + x_2 + 3x_3 + 7x_4 = 0$$

$$6x_1 + 2x_2 + 10x_3 + 28x_4 = 0.$$

Let

$$\mathbf{A} = \begin{pmatrix} 0 & -1 & 2 & 4 \\ 0 & 0 & -1 & 3 \\ 2 & 1 & 3 & 7 \\ 6 & 2 & 10 & 28 \end{pmatrix}.$$

We find that

$$\mathbf{A}_R = \begin{pmatrix} 1 & 0 & 0 & 13 \\ 0 & 1 & 0 & -10 \\ 0 & 0 & 1 & -3 \\ 0 & 0 & 0 & 0 \end{pmatrix}.$$

From the first three rows of $\mathbf{A}_R$, read that

$$x_1 + 13x_4 = 0$$

$$x_2 - 10x_4 = 0$$

$$x_3 - 3x_4 = 0.$$

Thus the solution is given by

$$x_1 = -13\alpha, \, x_2 = 10\alpha, \, x_3 = 3\alpha, \, x_4 = \alpha,$$

in which α can be any number. We can write the solution as

$$\mathbf{X} = \alpha \begin{pmatrix} -13 \\ 10 \\ 3 \\ 1 \end{pmatrix}$$

with α any number. In this example every solution is a constant multiple of one 4− vector. Note also that $m - rank(\mathbf{A}) = 4 - 3 = 1$. ■

We will now firm up some of the ideas we have discussed informally, and then look at additional examples.

First, everything we have done in this section has been based on the assertion that $\mathbf{AX} = \mathbf{0}$ and $\mathbf{A}_R\mathbf{X} = \mathbf{O}$ have the same solutions. We will prove this.

THEOREM 7.16

Let $\mathbf{A}$ be an $n \times m$ matrix. Then the linear homogeneous systems $\mathbf{AX} = \mathbf{O}$ and $\mathbf{A}_R\mathbf{X} = \mathbf{O}$ have the same solutions.

Proof   We know that there is an $n \times n$ matrix Ω such that $\Omega\mathbf{A} = \mathbf{A}_R$. Further, Ω can be written as a product of elementary matrices $\mathbf{E}_1 \cdots \mathbf{E}_r$.

Suppose first that $\mathbf{X} = \mathbf{C}$ is a solution of $\mathbf{AX} = \mathbf{O}$. Then $\mathbf{AC} = \mathbf{O}$, so

$$\Omega(\mathbf{AC}) = (\Omega\mathbf{A})\mathbf{C} = \mathbf{A}_R\mathbf{C} = \Omega\mathbf{O} = \mathbf{O}.$$

Then $\mathbf{C}$ is also a solution of $\mathbf{A}_R\mathbf{X} = \mathbf{O}$.

Conversely, suppose $\mathbf{K}$ is a solution of $\mathbf{A}_R\mathbf{X} = \mathbf{O}$. Then $\mathbf{A}_R\mathbf{K} = \mathbf{O}$. We want to show that $\mathbf{AK} = \mathbf{O}$ also. Because $\mathbf{A}_R\mathbf{K} = \mathbf{O}$, we have $(\Omega\mathbf{A})\mathbf{K} = \mathbf{O}$, or

$$(\mathbf{E}_r \cdots \mathbf{E}_1\mathbf{A})\mathbf{K} = \mathbf{O}.$$

By Theorem 7.8, for each $\mathbf{E}_j$, there is elementary matrix $\mathbf{E}_j^*$ that reverses the effect of $\mathbf{E}_j$. Then, from the last equation we have

$$\mathbf{E}_1^*\mathbf{E}_2^*\cdots\mathbf{E}_{r-1}^*\mathbf{E}_r^*(\mathbf{E}_r\mathbf{E}_{r-1}\cdots\mathbf{E}_2\mathbf{E}_1\mathbf{A})\mathbf{K} = \mathbf{O}.$$

But $\mathbf{E}_r^*\mathbf{E}_r = \mathbf{I}_n$, because $\mathbf{E}_r^*$ reverses the effect of $\mathbf{E}_r$. Similarly, $\mathbf{E}_{r-1}^*\mathbf{E}_{r-1} = \mathbf{I}_n$, until finally the last equation becomes

$$\mathbf{E}_1^*(\mathbf{E}_1\mathbf{A})\mathbf{K} = \mathbf{A}\mathbf{K} = \mathbf{O}.$$

Thus $\mathbf{K}$ is a solution of $\mathbf{A}\mathbf{X} = \mathbf{O}$ and the proof is complete. ∎

The method for solving $\mathbf{A}\mathbf{X} = \mathbf{O}$, which we illustrated above, is called the of the *Gauss-Jordan method*, or *complete pivoting*. Here is an outline of the method. Keep in mind that, in a system $\mathbf{A}\mathbf{X} = \mathbf{O}$, row k gives the coefficients of equation k, and column j contains the coefficients of x_j as we look down the set of equations.

Gauss-Jordan Method for Solving $\mathbf{A}\mathbf{X} = \mathbf{O}$

1. Find $\mathbf{A}_R$.
2. Look down the columns of $\mathbf{A}_R$. If column j contains the leading entry of some row (so all other elements of this column are zero), then x_j is said to be *dependent*. Determine all the dependent unknowns. The remaining unknowns (if any) are said to be *independent*.
3. Each nonzero row of $\mathbf{A}_R$ represents an equation in the reduced system, having one dependent unknown (in the column having the leading entry 1) and all other unknowns in this equation (if any) independent. This enables us to write this dependent unknown in terms of the independent ones.
4. After step (3) is carried out for each nonzero row, we have each dependent unknown in terms of the independent ones. The independent unknowns can then be assigned any values, and these determine the dependent unknowns, solving the system. We can write the resulting solution as a linear combination of column solutions, one for each independent unknown. The resulting expression, containing an arbitrary constant for each independent unknown, is called the *general solution* of the system.

EXAMPLE 7.26

Solve the system

$$-x_1 + x_3 + x_4 + 2x_5 = 0$$
$$x_2 + 3x_3 + 4x_5 = 0$$
$$x_1 + 2x_2 + x_3 + x_4 + x_5 = 0$$
$$-3x_1 + x_2 + 4x_5 = 0.$$

The matrix of coefficients is

$$\mathbf{A} = \begin{pmatrix} -1 & 0 & 1 & 1 & 2 \\ 0 & 1 & 3 & 0 & 4 \\ 1 & 2 & 1 & 1 & 1 \\ -3 & 1 & 0 & 0 & 4 \end{pmatrix}.$$

We find that

$$\mathbf{A}_R = \begin{pmatrix} 1 & 0 & 0 & 0 & -\frac{9}{8} \\ 0 & 1 & 0 & 0 & \frac{5}{8} \\ 0 & 0 & 1 & 0 & \frac{9}{8} \\ 0 & 0 & 0 & 1 & -\frac{1}{4} \end{pmatrix}.$$

Because columns 1 through 4 of $\mathbf{A}_R$ contain of leading entries of rows, x_1, x_2, x_3 and x_4 are dependent, while the remaining unknown, x_5 is independent. The equations of the reduced system (which has the same solutions as the original system) are:

$$x_1 - \frac{9}{8}x_5 = 0$$

$$x_2 + \frac{5}{8}x_5 = 0$$

$$x_3 + \frac{9}{8}x_5 = 0$$

$$x_4 - \frac{1}{4}x_5 = 0.$$

We wrote these out for illustration, but in fact the solution can be read immediately from $\mathbf{A}_R$. We can choose $x_5 = \alpha$, any number, and then

$$x_1 = \frac{9}{8}\alpha,\, x_2 = -\frac{5}{8}\alpha,\, x_3 = -\frac{9}{8}\alpha,\, x_4 = \frac{1}{4}\alpha.$$

The dependent unknowns are given by $\mathbf{A}_R$ in terms of the independent unknowns (only one in this case).

We can write this solution more neatly as

$$\mathbf{X} = \gamma \begin{pmatrix} 9 \\ -5 \\ -9 \\ 2 \\ 8 \end{pmatrix}$$

in which $\gamma = \alpha/8$ can be any number. This is the general solution of $\mathbf{AX} = \mathbf{O}$. In this example, $m - rank(\mathbf{A}) = 5 - 4 = 1$. ∎

EXAMPLE 7.27

Consider the system

$$3x_1 - 11x_2 + 5x_3 = 0$$

$$4x_1 + x_2 - 10x_3 = 0$$

$$4x_1 + 9x_2 - 6x_3 = 0.$$

The matrix of coefficients is

$$\mathbf{A} = \begin{pmatrix} 3 & -11 & 5 \\ 4 & 1 & -10 \\ 4 & 9 & -6 \end{pmatrix}.$$

The reduced matrix is

$$\mathbf{A}_R = \begin{pmatrix} 1 & 0 & 0 \\ 0 & 1 & 0 \\ 0 & 0 & 1 \end{pmatrix} = \mathbf{I}_3.$$

The reduced system is just

$$x_1 = 0, \, x_2 = 0, \, x_3 = 0.$$

This system has only the trivial solution, with each $x_j = 0$. Notice that in this example there are no independent unknowns. If there were, we could assign them any values and have infinitely many solutions. ∎

EXAMPLE 7.28

Consider the system

$$2x_1 - 4x_2 + x_3 + x_4 + 6x_5 + 12x_6 - 5x_7 = 0$$
$$-4x_1 + x_2 + 6x_3 + 3x_4 + 10x_5 - 9x_6 + 8x_7 = 0$$
$$7x_1 + 2x_2 + 4x_3 - 8x_4 + 6x_5 - 5x_6 + 15x_7 = 0$$
$$2x_1 + x_2 + 6x_3 + 3x_4 - 4x_5 - 2x_6 - 21x_7 = 0.$$

The coefficient matrix is

$$\mathbf{A} = \begin{pmatrix} 2 & -4 & 1 & 1 & 6 & 12 & -5 \\ -4 & 1 & 6 & 3 & 10 & -9 & 8 \\ 7 & 2 & 4 & -8 & 6 & -5 & 15 \\ 2 & 1 & 6 & 3 & -4 & -2 & -21 \end{pmatrix}.$$

We find that

$$\mathbf{A}_R = \begin{pmatrix} 1 & 0 & 0 & 0 & \frac{-7}{3} & \frac{7}{6} & \frac{-29}{6} \\ 0 & 1 & 0 & 0 & \frac{-233}{82} & \frac{-395}{164} & \frac{-375}{164} \\ 0 & 0 & 1 & 0 & \frac{1379}{738} & \frac{-995}{1476} & \frac{2161}{1476} \\ 0 & 0 & 0 & 1 & \frac{-1895}{738} & \frac{1043}{1476} & \frac{-8773}{1476} \end{pmatrix}.$$

From this matrix we see that x_1, x_2, x_3, x_4 are dependent, and x_5, x_6, x_7 are independent. We read immediately from $\mathbf{A}_R$ that

$$x_1 = \frac{7}{3}x_5 - \frac{7}{6}x_6 + \frac{29}{6}x_7$$

$$x_2 = \frac{233}{82}x_5 + \frac{395}{164}x_6 + \frac{375}{164}x_7$$

$$x_3 = -\frac{1379}{738}x_5 + \frac{995}{1476}x_6 - \frac{2161}{1476}x_7$$

$$x_4 = \frac{1895}{738}x_5 - \frac{1043}{1476}x_6 + \frac{8773}{1476}x_7,$$

while x_5, x_6 and x_7 can (independent of each other) be assigned any numerical values. To make the solution look neater, write $x_5 = 1476\alpha$, $x_6 = 1476\beta$ and $x_7 = 1476\gamma$, where α, β and γ are any numbers. Now the solution can be written

$$x_1 = 3444\alpha - 1722\beta + 7134\gamma, \ x_2 = 4194\alpha + 3555\beta + 3375\gamma$$

$$x_3 = -2758\alpha + 995\beta - 2161\gamma, \ x_4 = 3790\alpha - 1043\beta + 8773\gamma$$

$$x_5 = 1476\alpha, \ x_6 = 1476\beta, \ x_7 = 1476\gamma,$$

with α, β and γ any numbers. In column notation,

$$\mathbf{X} = \alpha \begin{pmatrix} 3444 \\ 4194 \\ -2758 \\ 3790 \\ 1476 \\ 0 \\ 0 \end{pmatrix} + \beta \begin{pmatrix} -1722 \\ 3555 \\ 995 \\ -1043 \\ 0 \\ 1476 \\ 0 \end{pmatrix} + \gamma \begin{pmatrix} 7134 \\ 3375 \\ -2161 \\ 8773 \\ 0 \\ 0 \\ 1476 \end{pmatrix}.$$

This is the general solution, being a linear combination of three linearly independent 7− vectors. In this example, $m - rank(\mathbf{A}) = 7 - 4 = 3$. ■

In each of these examples, after we found the general solution, we noted that the number $m - rank(\mathbf{A})$, the number of columns minus the rank of $\mathbf{A}$, coincided with the number of linearly independent column solutions in the general solution (the number of arbitrary unknowns in the general solution). We will see shortly that this is always true.

In the next section we will put the Gauss-Jordan method into a vector space context. This will result in an understanding of the algebraic structure of the solutions of a system $\mathbf{AX} = \mathbf{O}$, as well as practical criteria for determining when such a system has a nonzero solution.

SECTION 7.5   PROBLEMS

In each of Problems 1 through 12, find the general solution of the system and write it as a column matrix or sum of column matrices.

1. $x_1 + 2x_2 - x_3 + x_4 = 0$
$x_2 - x_3 + x_4 = 0$

2. $-3x_1 + x_2 - x_3 + x_4 + x_5 = 0$
$x_2 + x_3 + 4x_5 = 0$
$-3x_3 + 2x_4 + x_5 = 0$

3. $-2x_1 + x_2 + 2x_3 = 0$
$x_1 - x_2 = 0$
$x_1 + x_2 = 0$

4. $4x_1 + x_2 - 3x_3 + x_4 = 0$
$2x_1 - x_3 = 0$

5. $x_1 - x_2 + 3x_3 - x_4 + 4x_5 = 0$
$2x_1 - 2x_2 + x_3 + x_4 = 0$
$x_1 - 2x_3 + x_5 = 0$
$x_3 + x_4 - x_5 = 0$

6. $6x_1 - x_2 + x_3 = 0$
$x_1 - x_4 + 2x_5 = 0$
$x_1 - 2x_5 = 0$

7. $-10x_1 - x_2 + 4x_3 - x_4 + x_5 - x_6 = 0$
$x_2 - x_3 + 3x_4 = 0$
$2x_1 - x_2 + x_5 = 0$
$x_2 - x_4 + x_6 = 0$

8. $8x_1 - 2x_3 + x_6 = 0$
$2x_1 - x_2 + 3x_4 - x_6 = 0$
$x_2 + x_3 - 2x_5 - x_6 = 0$
$x_4 - 3x_5 + 2x_6 = 0$

9. $x_2 - 3x_4 + x_5 = 0$
$2x_1 - x_2 + x_4 = 0$
$2x_1 - 3x_2 + 4x_5 = 0$

11. $x_1 - 2x_2 + x_5 - x_6 + x_7 = 0$
$x_3 - x_4 + x_5 - 2x_6 + 3x_7 = 0$
$x_1 - x_5 + 2x_6 = 0$
$2x_1 - 3x_4 + x_5 = 0$

10. $4x_1 - 3x_2 + x_4 + x_5 - 3x_6 = 0$
$2x_2 + 4x_4 - x_5 - 6x_6 = 0$
$3x_1 - 2x_2 + 4x_5 - x_6 = 0$
$2x_1 + x_2 - 3x_3 + 4x_4 = 0$

12. $2x_1 - 4x_5 + x_7 + x_8 = 0$
$2x_2 - x_6 + x_7 - x_8 = 0$
$x_3 - 4x_4 + x_8 = 0$
$x_2 - x_3 + x_4 = 0$
$x_2 - x_5 + x_6 - x_7 = 0$

7.6   The Solution Space of $AX = O$

Suppose $\mathbf{A}$ is an $n \times m$ matrix. We have been writing solutions of $\mathbf{AX} = \mathbf{O}$ as column $m-$vectors. Now observe that the set of all solutions has the algebraic structure of a subspace of R^m.

THEOREM 7.17

Let $\mathbf{A}$ be an $n \times m$ matrix. Then the set of solutions of the system $\mathbf{AX} = \mathbf{O}$ is a subspace of R^m.

Proof   Let S be the set of all solutions of $\mathbf{AX} = \mathbf{O}$. Then S is a set of vectors in R^m.
Since $\mathbf{AO} = \mathbf{O}$, $\mathbf{O}$ is in S. Now suppose $\mathbf{X}_1$ and $\mathbf{X}_2$ are solutions, and α and β are real numbers. Then

$$\mathbf{A}(\alpha\mathbf{X}_1 + \beta\mathbf{X}_2) = \alpha\mathbf{AX}_1 + \beta\mathbf{AX}_2 = \alpha\mathbf{O} + \beta\mathbf{O} = \mathbf{O},$$

so $\alpha\mathbf{X}_1 + \beta\mathbf{X}_2$ is also a solution, hence is in S. Therefore S is a subspace of R^m. ∎

We would like to know a basis for this solution space, because then every solution is a linear combination of the basis vectors. This is similar to finding a fundamental set of solutions for a linear homogeneous differential equation, because then every solution is a linear combination of these fundamental solutions.

In examples in the preceding section, we were always able to write the general solution as a linear combination of $m - rank(\mathbf{A})$ linearly independent solution (vectors). This suggests that this number is the dimension of the solution space.

To see why this is true in general, notice that we obtain a dependent x_j corresponding to each row having a leading entry. Since only nonzero rows have leading entries, the number of dependent unknowns is the number of nonzero rows of $\mathbf{A}_R$. But then the number of independent unknowns is the total number of unknowns, m, minus the number of dependent unknowns (the number of nonzero rows of $\mathbf{A}_R$). Since the number of nonzero rows of $\mathbf{A}_R$ is the rank of $\mathbf{A}$, then the general solution can always be written as a linear combination of $m - rank(A)$ independent solutions.

Further, as a practical matter, solving the system $\mathbf{AX} = \mathbf{O}$ by solving the system $\mathbf{A}_R\mathbf{X} = \mathbf{O}$ automatically displays the general solution as a linear combination of this number of basis vectors for the solution space.

We will summarize this discussion as a theorem.

THEOREM 7.18

Let $\mathbf{A}$ be $n \times m$. Then the solution space of the system $\mathbf{AX} = \mathbf{O}$ has dimension

$$m - rank(\mathbf{A})$$

or, equivalently

$$m - (\text{number of nonzero rows in } \mathbf{A}_R). \blacksquare$$

EXAMPLE 7.29

Consider the system

$$-4x_1 + x_2 + 3x_3 - 10x_4 + x_5 = 0$$
$$2x_1 + 8x_2 - x_3 - x_4 + 3x_5 = 0$$
$$-6x_1 + x_2 + x_3 - 5x_4 - 2x_5 = 0.$$

The matrix of coefficients is

$$\mathbf{A} = \begin{pmatrix} -4 & 1 & 3 & -10 & 1 \\ 2 & 8 & -1 & -1 & 3 \\ -6 & 1 & 1 & -5 & -2 \end{pmatrix},$$

and we find that

$$\mathbf{A}_R = \begin{pmatrix} 1 & 0 & 0 & \frac{33}{118} & \frac{65}{118} \\ 0 & 1 & 0 & \frac{-32}{59} & \frac{21}{59} \\ 0 & 0 & 1 & \frac{-164}{59} & \frac{56}{59} \end{pmatrix}.$$

Now $\mathbf{A}$ has $m = 5$ columns, and $\mathbf{A}_R$ has 3 nonzero rows, so $rank(\mathbf{A}) = 3$ and the solution space of $\mathbf{AX} = \mathbf{O}$ has dimension

$$m - rank(\mathbf{A}) = 5 - 3 = 2.$$

From the reduced system we read the solutions

$$x_1 = -\frac{33}{118}\alpha - \frac{65}{118}\beta, \, x_2 = \frac{32}{59}\alpha - \frac{21}{59}\beta,$$

$$x_3 = \frac{164}{59}\alpha - \frac{56}{59}\beta, \, x_4 = \alpha, \, x_5 = \beta,$$

in which α and β are any numbers. It is neater to replace α with 118γ and β with 118δ (which still can be any numbers) and write the general solution as

$$\mathbf{X} = \begin{pmatrix} -33\gamma - 65\delta \\ 64\gamma - 42\delta \\ 328\gamma - 112\delta \\ 118\gamma \\ 118\delta \end{pmatrix} = \gamma \begin{pmatrix} -33 \\ 64 \\ 328 \\ 118 \\ 0 \end{pmatrix} + \delta \begin{pmatrix} -65 \\ -42 \\ -112 \\ 0 \\ 118 \end{pmatrix}.$$

This displays the general solution (arbitrary element of the solution space) as a linear combination of two linearly independent vectors which form a basis for the dimension two solution space. $\blacksquare$

We know that a system $\mathbf{AX} = \mathbf{O}$ always has at least the zero (trivial) solution. This may be the only solution it has. Rank provides a useful criterion for determining when a system $\mathbf{AX} = \mathbf{O}$ has a nontrivial solution.

THEOREM 7.19

Let $\mathbf{A}$ be $n \times m$. Then the system $\mathbf{AX} = \mathbf{O}$ has a nontrivial solution if and only if

$$m > rank(\mathbf{A}). \quad \blacksquare$$

This means that the system of homogeneous equations has a nontrivial solution exactly when the number of unknowns exceeds the rank of the coefficient matrix (the number of nonzero rows in the reduced matrix).

Proof   We have seen that the dimension of the solution space is $m - rank(\mathbf{A})$. There is a nontrivial solution if and only if this solution space has something in it besides the zero solution, and this occurs exactly when the dimension of this solution space is positive. But $m - rank(\mathbf{A}) > 0$ is equivalent to $m > rank(\mathbf{A})$. $\blacksquare$

This theorem has important consequences. First, suppose the number of unknowns exceeds the number of equations. Then $n < m$. But $rank(\mathbf{A}) \leq n$ is always true, so in this case

$$m - rank(\mathbf{A}) \geq m - n > 0$$

and by Theorem 7.19, the system has nontrivial solutions.

COROLLARY 7.2

A homogeneous system $\mathbf{AX} = \mathbf{O}$ with more unknowns than equations always has a nontrivial solution. $\blacksquare$

For another consequence of Theorem 7.19, suppose that $\mathbf{A}$ is square, so $n = m$. Now the dimension of the solution space of $\mathbf{AX} = \mathbf{O}$ is $n - rank(\mathbf{A})$. If this number is positive, the system has nontrivial solutions. If $n - rank(\mathbf{A})$ is not positive, then it must be zero, because $rank(\mathbf{A}) \leq n$ is always true. But $n - rank(\mathbf{A}) = 0$ corresponds to a solution space with only the zero solution. And it also corresponds, by Theorem 7.15, to $\mathbf{A}$ having the identity matrix as its reduced matrix. This means that a square system $\mathbf{AX} = \mathbf{O}$, having as the same number of unknowns as equations, has only the trivial solution exactly when the reduced form of $\mathbf{A}$ is the identity matrix.

COROLLARY 7.3

Let $\mathbf{A}$ be an $n \times n$ matrix of real numbers. Then the system $\mathbf{AX} = \mathbf{O}$ has only the trivial solution exactly when $\mathbf{A}_R = \mathbf{I}_n$. $\blacksquare$

EXAMPLE 7.30

Consider the system

$$-4x_1 + x_2 - 7x_3 = 0$$
$$2x_1 + 9x_2 - 13x_3 = 0$$
$$x_1 + x_2 + 10x_3 = 0.$$

The matrix of coefficients is 3×3:

$$\mathbf{A} = \begin{pmatrix} -4 & 1 & -7 \\ 2 & 9 & -13 \\ 1 & 1 & 10 \end{pmatrix}.$$

We find that

$$\mathbf{A}_R = \begin{pmatrix} 1 & 0 & 0 \\ 0 & 1 & 0 \\ 0 & 0 & 1 \end{pmatrix} = I_3.$$

This means that the system $\mathbf{AX} = \mathbf{O}$ has only the solution $x_1 = x_2 = x_3 = 0$. This makes sense in view of the fact that the system $\mathbf{AX} = \mathbf{O}$ has the same solutions as the reduced system $\mathbf{A}_R \mathbf{X} = \mathbf{O}$, and when $\mathbf{A}_R = \mathbf{I}_3$ this reduced system is just $\mathbf{X} = \mathbf{O}$. ■

SECTION 7.6   PROBLEMS

1.–12. For $n = 1, \cdots, 12$, use the solution of Problem n, Section 7.5, to determine the dimension of the solution space of the system of homogeneous equations.

13. Can a system $\mathbf{AX} = \mathbf{O}$, in which there are at least as many equations as unknowns, have a nontrivial solution?

14. Prove Corollary 7.2.

15. Prove Corollary 7.3.

7.7   Nonhomogeneous Systems of Linear Equations

We will now consider nonhomogeneous linear systems of equations:

$$a_{11}x_1 + a_{12}x_2 + \cdots + a_{1m}x_m = b_1$$
$$a_2x_1 + a_{22}x_2 + \cdots + a_{2m}x_m = b_2$$
$$\vdots$$
$$a_{n1}x_1 + a_{n2}x_2 + \cdots + a_{nm}x_m = b_n.$$

We can write this system in matrix form as $\mathbf{AX} = \mathbf{B}$, in which $\mathbf{A} = [a_{ij}]$ is the $n \times m$ matrix of coefficients,

$$\mathbf{X} = \begin{pmatrix} x_1 \\ x_2 \\ \vdots \\ x_m \end{pmatrix} \quad \text{and} \quad \mathbf{B} = \begin{pmatrix} b_1 \\ b_2 \\ \vdots \\ b_n \end{pmatrix}.$$

This system has n equations in m unknowns. Of course, if each $b_j = 0$ then this is a homogeneous system $\mathbf{AX} = \mathbf{O}$.

A homogeneous system always has at least one a solution, the zero solution. A nonhomogeneous system need not have any solution at all.

EXAMPLE 7.31

Consider the system

$$2x_1 - 3x_2 = 6$$
$$4x_1 - 6x_2 = 18.$$

If there were a solution $x_1 = \alpha$, $x_2 = \beta$, then from the first equation we would have $2\alpha - 3\beta = 6$. But then the second equation would give us $4\alpha - 6\beta = 18 = 2(2\alpha - 3\beta) = 12$, a contradiction. ∎

We therefore have an existence question to worry about with the nonhomogeneous system. Before treating this issue, we will ask: what must solutions of $\mathbf{AX} = \mathbf{B}$ look like?

7.7.1   The Structure of Solutions of $\mathbf{AX} = \mathbf{B}$

We can take a cue from linear second order differential equations. There we saw that the every solution of $y'' + py' + qy = f(x)$ is a sum of a solution the homogeneous equation $y'' + py' + qy = 0$, and a particular solution of $y'' + py' + qy = f(x)$. We will show that the same idea holds true for linear algebraic systems of equations as well.

THEOREM 7.20

Let $\mathbf{U}_p$ be any solution of $\mathbf{AX} = \mathbf{B}$. Then every solution of $\mathbf{AX} = \mathbf{B}$ is of the form $\mathbf{U}_p + \mathbf{H}$, in which $\mathbf{H}$ is a solution of $\mathbf{AX} = \mathbf{O}$.

Proof   Let $\mathbf{W}$ be any solution of $\mathbf{AX} = \mathbf{B}$. Since $\mathbf{U}_p$ is also a solution of this system, then

$$\mathbf{A}(\mathbf{W} - \mathbf{U}_p) = \mathbf{AW} - \mathbf{AU}_p = \mathbf{B} - \mathbf{B} = \mathbf{O}.$$

Then $\mathbf{W} - \mathbf{U}_p$ is a solution of $\mathbf{AX} = \mathbf{O}$. Letting $\mathbf{H} = \mathbf{W} - \mathbf{U}_p$, then $\mathbf{W} = \mathbf{U}_p + \mathbf{H}$.
Conversely, if $\mathbf{W} = \mathbf{U}_p + \mathbf{H}$, where $\mathbf{H}$ is a solution of $\mathbf{AX} = \mathbf{O}$, then

$$\mathbf{AW} = \mathbf{A}(\mathbf{U}_p + \mathbf{H}) = \mathbf{AU}_p + \mathbf{AH} = \mathbf{B} + \mathbf{O} = \mathbf{B},$$

so $\mathbf{W}$ is a solution of $\mathbf{AX} = \mathbf{B}$. ∎

This means that, if $\mathbf{U}_p$ is any solution of $\mathbf{AX} = \mathbf{B}$, and $\mathbf{H}$ is the general solution of $\mathbf{AX} = \mathbf{O}$, then the expression $\mathbf{U}_p + \mathbf{H}$ contains all possible solutions of $\mathbf{AX} = \mathbf{B}$. For this reason we call such $\mathbf{U}_p + \mathbf{H}$ the *general solution* of $\mathbf{AX} = \mathbf{B}$, for any particular solution $\mathbf{U}_p$ of $\mathbf{AX} = \mathbf{B}$.

EXAMPLE 7.32

Consider the system

$$-x_1 + x_2 + 3x_3 = -2$$
$$x_2 + 2x_3 = 4.$$

Here

$$\mathbf{A} = \begin{pmatrix} -1 & 1 & 3 \\ 0 & 1 & 2 \end{pmatrix} \quad \text{and} \quad \mathbf{B} = \begin{pmatrix} -2 \\ 4 \end{pmatrix}.$$

We find from methods of the preceding sections that the general solution of $\mathbf{AX} = \mathbf{O}$ is

$$\alpha \begin{pmatrix} 1 \\ -2 \\ 1 \end{pmatrix}.$$

By a method we will describe shortly,

$$\mathbf{U}_p = \begin{pmatrix} 6 \\ 4 \\ 0 \end{pmatrix}$$

is a particular solution of $\mathbf{AX} = \mathbf{B}$. Therefore every solution of $\mathbf{AX} = \mathbf{B}$ is contained in the expression

$$\alpha \begin{pmatrix} 1 \\ -2 \\ 1 \end{pmatrix} + \begin{pmatrix} 6 \\ 4 \\ 0 \end{pmatrix},$$

in which α is any number. This is the general solution of the system $\mathbf{AX} = \mathbf{B}$. ∎

7.7.2 Existence and Uniqueness of Solutions of AX = B

Now we know what to look for in solving $\mathbf{AX} = \mathbf{B}$. In this section we will develop criteria to determine when a solution $\mathbf{U}_p$ exists, as well as a method that automatically produces the general solution in the form $\mathbf{X} = \mathbf{H} + \mathbf{U}_p$, where $\mathbf{H}$ is the general solution of $\mathbf{AX} = \mathbf{O}$.

DEFINITION 7.14   *Consistent System of Equations*

A nonhomogeneous system $\mathbf{AX} = \mathbf{B}$ is said to be consistent if there exists a solution. If there is no solution, the system is inconsistent.

The difference between a system $\mathbf{AX} = \mathbf{O}$ and $\mathbf{AX} = \mathbf{B}$ is $\mathbf{B}$. For the homogeneous system, it is enough to specify the coefficient matrix $\mathbf{A}$ when working with the system. But for $\mathbf{AX} = \mathbf{B}$, we must incorporate $\mathbf{B}$ into our computations. For this reason, we introduce the *augmented matrix* $[\mathbf{A}\vdots\mathbf{B}]$. If $\mathbf{A}$ is $n \times m$, $[\mathbf{A}\vdots\mathbf{B}]$ is the $n \times (m+1)$ matrix formed by adjoining $\mathbf{B}$ to $\mathbf{A}$ as a new last column. For example, if

$$\mathbf{A} = \begin{pmatrix} -3 & 2 & 6 & 1 \\ 0 & 3 & 3 & -5 \\ 2 & 4 & 4 & -6 \end{pmatrix} \quad \text{and} \quad \mathbf{B} = \begin{pmatrix} 5 \\ 2 \\ -8 \end{pmatrix}$$

then

$$\left[\mathbf{A}\vdots\mathbf{B} \right] = \begin{pmatrix} -3 & 2 & 6 & 1 & \vdots & 5 \\ 0 & 3 & 3 & -5 & \vdots & 2 \\ 2 & 4 & 4 & -6 & \vdots & -8 \end{pmatrix}.$$

The column of dots does not count in the dimension of the matrix, and is simply a visual device to clarify that we are dealing with an augmented matrix giving both $\mathbf{A}$ and $\mathbf{B}$ for a system $\mathbf{AX} = \mathbf{B}$. If we just attached $\mathbf{B}$ as a last column without such an indicator, we might we dealing with a homogeneous system having 3 equations in 5 unknowns.

Continuing with these matrices for the moment, reduce **A** to find $\mathbf{A}_R$:

$$\mathbf{A}_R = \begin{pmatrix} 1 & 0 & 0 & \frac{1}{3} \\ 0 & 1 & 0 & -3 \\ 0 & 0 & 1 & \frac{4}{3} \end{pmatrix}.$$

Next, reduce $[\mathbf{A}\!\vdots\!\mathbf{B}]$ (ignore the dotted column in the row operations) to get

$$[\mathbf{A}\!\vdots\!\mathbf{B}]_R = \begin{pmatrix} 1 & 0 & 0 & \frac{1}{3} & \vdots & -\frac{16}{3} \\ 0 & 1 & 0 & -3 & \vdots & \frac{15}{4} \\ 0 & 0 & 1 & \frac{4}{3} & \vdots & -\frac{37}{12} \end{pmatrix}.$$

Notice that

$$[\mathbf{A}\!\vdots\!\mathbf{B}]_R = [\mathbf{A}_R\!\vdots\!\mathbf{C}].$$

If we reduce the augmented matrix $[\mathbf{A}\!\vdots\!\mathbf{B}]$, we obtain in the first m columns the reduced form of **A**, together with some new last column. The reason for this can be seen by reviewing how we reduce a matrix. Perform elementary row operations, beginning with the left-most column containing a leading entry, and work from left to right through the columns of the matrix. In finding the reduced form of the augmented matrix $[\mathbf{A}\!\vdots\!\mathbf{B}]$, we deal with columns $1, \cdots m$, which constitute **A**. The row operations used to reduce $[\mathbf{A}\!\vdots\!\mathbf{B}]$ will, of course, operate on the elements of the last column as well, eventually resulting in what is called **C** in the last equation. We will state this result as a theorem.

THEOREM 7.21

Let **A** be $n \times m$ and let **B** be $m \times 1$. Then for some $m \times 1$ matrix **C**,

$$[\mathbf{A}\!\vdots\!\mathbf{B}]_R = [\mathbf{A}_R\!\vdots\!\mathbf{C}]. \quad \blacksquare$$

The reason this result is important is that the original system $\mathbf{AX} = \mathbf{B}$ and the reduced system $\mathbf{A}_R\mathbf{X} = \mathbf{C}$ have the same solutions (as in the homogeneous case, because the elementary row operations do not change the solutions of the system). But because of the special form of $\mathbf{A}_R$, the system $\mathbf{A}_R\mathbf{X} = \mathbf{C}$ is either easy to solve by inspection, or to see that there is no solution.

EXAMPLE 7.33

Consider the system

$$\begin{pmatrix} -3 & 2 & 2 \\ 1 & 4 & -6 \\ 0 & -2 & 2 \end{pmatrix} \mathbf{X} = \begin{pmatrix} 8 \\ 1 \\ -2 \end{pmatrix}.$$

We will reduce the augmented matrix

$$[\mathbf{A}\!:\!\mathbf{B}] = \begin{pmatrix} -3 & 2 & 2 & \vdots & 8 \\ 1 & 4 & -6 & \vdots & 1 \\ 0 & -2 & 2 & \vdots & -2 \end{pmatrix}.$$

One way to proceed is

$$[\mathbf{A}\!:\!\mathbf{B}] \rightarrow \text{interchange rows 1 and 2} \rightarrow \begin{pmatrix} 1 & 4 & -6 & \vdots & 1 \\ -3 & 2 & 2 & \vdots & 8 \\ 0 & -2 & 2 & \vdots & -2 \end{pmatrix}$$

$$\rightarrow \text{add } 3(\text{row 1}) \text{ to row } 2 \rightarrow \begin{pmatrix} 1 & 4 & -6 & \vdots & 1 \\ 0 & 14 & -16 & \vdots & 11 \\ 0 & -2 & 2 & \vdots & -2 \end{pmatrix}$$

$$\rightarrow \frac{1}{14}(\text{row 2}) \rightarrow \begin{pmatrix} 1 & 4 & -6 & \vdots & 1 \\ 0 & 1 & -\frac{8}{7} & \vdots & \frac{11}{14} \\ 0 & -2 & 2 & \vdots & -2 \end{pmatrix}$$

$$\rightarrow -4(\text{row 2}) \text{ to row 1, } 2(\text{row 2}) \text{ to row 3} \rightarrow \begin{pmatrix} 1 & 0 & -\frac{10}{7} & \vdots & -\frac{15}{7} \\ 0 & 1 & -\frac{8}{7} & \vdots & \frac{11}{14} \\ 0 & 0 & -\frac{2}{7} & \vdots & -\frac{3}{7} \end{pmatrix}$$

$$\rightarrow -\frac{7}{2}(\text{row 3}) \rightarrow \begin{pmatrix} 1 & 0 & -\frac{10}{7} & \vdots & -\frac{15}{7} \\ 0 & 1 & -\frac{8}{7} & \vdots & \frac{11}{14} \\ 0 & 0 & 1 & \vdots & \frac{3}{2} \end{pmatrix}$$

$$\rightarrow \frac{10}{7}(\text{row 3}) \text{ to row 1, } \frac{8}{7}(\text{row 3}) \text{ to row 2} \rightarrow \begin{pmatrix} 1 & 0 & 0 & \vdots & 0 \\ 0 & 1 & 0 & \vdots & \frac{5}{2} \\ 0 & 0 & 1 & \vdots & \frac{3}{2} \end{pmatrix}.$$

As can be seen in this process, we actually arrived at $\mathbf{A}_R$ in the first three rows and columns, and whatever ends up in the last column is what we call $\mathbf{C}$:

$$[\mathbf{A}\!:\!\mathbf{B}]_R = [A_R\!:\!\mathbf{C}].$$

Notice that the reduced augmented matrix is $[\mathbf{I}_3\!:\!\mathbf{C}]$ and represents the reduced system $\mathbf{I}_3\mathbf{X} = \mathbf{C}$. This is the system

$$\begin{pmatrix} 1 & 0 & 0 \\ 0 & 1 & 0 \\ 0 & 0 & 1 \end{pmatrix} \mathbf{X} = \begin{pmatrix} 0 \\ \frac{5}{2} \\ \frac{3}{2} \end{pmatrix},$$

which we solve by inspection to get $x_1 = 0$, $x_2 = 5/2$, $x_3 = 3/2$. Thus reducing $[\mathbf{A}\!:\!\mathbf{B}]$ immediately yields the solution

$$\mathbf{U}_p = \begin{pmatrix} 0 \\ \frac{5}{2} \\ \frac{3}{2} \end{pmatrix}$$

of the original system $\mathbf{AX} = \mathbf{B}$. Because $\mathbf{A}_R = \mathbf{I}_3$, Corollary 7.3 tells us that the homogeneous system $\mathbf{AX} = \mathbf{O}$ has only the trivial solution, and therefore $\mathbf{H} = \mathbf{O}$ in Theorem 7.20 and $\mathbf{U}_p$ is the unique solution of $\mathbf{AX} = \mathbf{B}$. ∎

EXAMPLE 7.34

The system

$$2x_1 - 3x_2 = 6$$
$$4x_1 - 6x_2 = 18$$

is inconsistent, as we saw in Example 7.31. We will put the fact that this system has no solution into the context of the current discussion. Write the augmented matrix

$$[\mathbf{A}\!:\!\mathbf{B}] = \begin{pmatrix} 2 & -3 & \vdots & 6 \\ 4 & -6 & \vdots & 18 \end{pmatrix}.$$

Reduce this matrix. We find that

$$[\mathbf{A}\!:\!\mathbf{B}]_R = \begin{pmatrix} 1 & -\frac{3}{2} & \vdots & 0 \\ 0 & 0 & \vdots & 1 \end{pmatrix}.$$

From this we immediately read the reduced system $\mathbf{A}_R \mathbf{X} = \mathbf{C}$:

$$\mathbf{A}_R \mathbf{X} = \begin{pmatrix} 1 & -\frac{3}{2} \\ 0 & 0 \end{pmatrix} \mathbf{X} = \begin{pmatrix} 0 \\ 1 \end{pmatrix}.$$

This system has the same solutions as the original system. But the second equation of the reduced system is

$$0x_1 + 0x_2 = 1,$$

which has no solution. Therefore $\mathbf{AX} = \mathbf{B}$ has no solution either. ∎

In this example, the reduced system has an impossible equation because $\mathbf{A}_R$ has a zero second row, while the second row of $[\mathbf{A}\!:\!\mathbf{B}]_R$ has a nonzero element in the augmented column. Whenever this happens, we obtain an equation having all zero coefficients of the unknowns, but equal to a nonzero number. In such a case the reduced system $\mathbf{A}_R\mathbf{X} = \mathbf{C}$, hence the original system $\mathbf{AX} = \mathbf{B}$, can have no solution. The key to recognizing when this will occur is that it happens when the rank of $\mathbf{A}_R$ (its number of nonzero rows) is less than the rank of $[\mathbf{A}\!:\!\mathbf{B}]$.

THEOREM 7.22

The nonhomogeneous system $\mathbf{AX} = \mathbf{B}$ has a solution if and only if $\mathbf{A}$ and $[\mathbf{A} \vdots \mathbf{B}]$ have the same rank.

Proof   Let $\mathbf{A}$ be $n \times m$. Suppose first that $rank(\mathbf{A}) = rank([\mathbf{A} \vdots \mathbf{B}]) = r$. By Theorems 7.12 and 7.14, the column space of $[\mathbf{A} \vdots \mathbf{B}]$ has dimension r. Certainly r cannot exceed the number of columns of $\mathbf{A}$, so $\mathbf{B}$, which is column $m + 1$ of $[\mathbf{A} \vdots \mathbf{B}]$, must be a linear combination of the first m columns of $[\mathbf{A} \vdots \mathbf{B}]$, which form $\mathbf{A}$. This means that, for some numbers $\alpha_1, \ldots, \alpha_m$,

$$
\mathbf{B} = \alpha_1 \begin{pmatrix} a_{11} \\ a_{21} \\ \vdots \\ a_{n1} \end{pmatrix} + \alpha_2 \begin{pmatrix} a_{12} \\ a_{22} \\ \vdots \\ a_{n2} \end{pmatrix} + \cdots + \alpha_m \begin{pmatrix} a_{1m} \\ a_{2m} \\ \vdots \\ a_{nm} \end{pmatrix}
$$

$$
= \begin{pmatrix} \alpha_1 a_{11} + \alpha_2 a_{12} + \cdots + \alpha_m a_{1m} \\ \alpha_1 a_{21} + \alpha_2 a_{22} + \cdots + \alpha_m a_{2m} \\ \vdots \\ \alpha_1 a_{n1} + \alpha_2 a_{n2} + \cdots + \alpha_m a_{nm} \end{pmatrix} = \mathbf{A} \begin{pmatrix} \alpha_1 \\ \alpha_2 \\ \vdots \\ \alpha_m \end{pmatrix}.
$$

But then $\begin{pmatrix} \alpha_1 \\ \alpha_2 \\ \vdots \\ \alpha_m \end{pmatrix}$ is a solution of $\mathbf{AX} = \mathbf{B}$.

Conversely, suppose $\mathbf{AX} = \mathbf{B}$ has a solution $\begin{pmatrix} \alpha_1 \\ \alpha_2 \\ \vdots \\ \alpha_m \end{pmatrix}$. Then

$$
\mathbf{B} = \mathbf{A} \begin{pmatrix} \alpha_1 \\ \alpha_2 \\ \vdots \\ \alpha_m \end{pmatrix} = \begin{pmatrix} \alpha_1 a_{11} + \alpha_2 a_{12} + \cdots + \alpha_m a_{1m} \\ \alpha_1 a_{21} + \alpha_2 a_{22} + \cdots + \alpha_m a_{2m} \\ \vdots \\ \alpha_1 a_{n1} + \alpha_2 a_{n2} + \cdots + \alpha_m a_{nm} \end{pmatrix}
$$

$$
= \alpha_1 \begin{pmatrix} a_{11} \\ a_{21} \\ \vdots \\ a_{n1} \end{pmatrix} + \alpha_2 \begin{pmatrix} a_{12} \\ a_{22} \\ \vdots \\ a_{n2} \end{pmatrix} + \cdots + \alpha_m \begin{pmatrix} a_{1m} \\ a_{2m} \\ \vdots \\ a_{nm} \end{pmatrix}.
$$

Then $\mathbf{B}$ is a linear combination of the columns of $\mathbf{A}$, thought of as vectors in R^n. But then the column space of $\mathbf{A}$ is the same as the column space of $[\mathbf{A} \vdots \mathbf{B}]$. Then

$$
\begin{aligned}
rank(\mathbf{A}) = {}& \text{dimension of the column space of } \mathbf{A} \\
= {}& \text{dimension of the column space of } [\mathbf{A} \vdots \mathbf{B}] = rank[\mathbf{A} \vdots \mathbf{B}],
\end{aligned}
$$

and the proof is complete. ∎

EXAMPLE 7.35

Solve the system

$$x_1 - x_2 + 2x_3 = 3$$
$$-4x_1 + x_2 + 7x_3 = -5$$
$$-2x_1 - x_2 + 11x_3 = 14.$$

The augmented matrix is

$$[\mathbf{A} \vdots \mathbf{B}] = \begin{pmatrix} 1 & -1 & 2 & \vdots & 3 \\ -4 & 1 & 7 & \vdots & -5 \\ -2 & -1 & 11 & \cdots & 14 \end{pmatrix}.$$

When we reduce this matrix we obtain

$$[\mathbf{A} \vdots \mathbf{B}]_R = [\mathbf{A}_R \vdots \mathbf{C}] = \begin{pmatrix} 1 & 0 & -3 & \vdots & 0 \\ 0 & 1 & -5 & \vdots & 0 \\ 0 & 0 & 0 & \vdots & 1 \end{pmatrix}.$$

The first three columns of this reduced matrix make up $\mathbf{A}_R$. But

$$rank(\mathbf{A}) = 2 \text{ and } rank([\mathbf{A} \vdots \mathbf{B}]_R) = 3,$$

so this system has no solution. The last equation of the reduced system is

$$0x_1 + 0x_2 + 0x_3 = 1,$$

which can have no solution. ∎

EXAMPLE 7.36

Solve

$$x_1 - x_3 + 2x_4 + x_5 + 6x_6 = -3$$
$$x_2 + x_3 + 3x_4 + 2x_5 + 4x_6 = 1$$
$$x_1 - 4x_2 + 3x_3 + x_4 + 2x_6 = 0.$$

The augmented matrix is

$$[\mathbf{A} \vdots \mathbf{B}] = \begin{pmatrix} 1 & 0 & -1 & 2 & 1 & 6 & \vdots & -3 \\ 0 & 1 & 1 & 3 & 2 & 4 & \vdots & 1 \\ 1 & -4 & 3 & 1 & 0 & 2 & \vdots & 0 \end{pmatrix}.$$

Reduce this to get

$$[\mathbf{A} \vdots \mathbf{B}]_R = \begin{pmatrix} 1 & 0 & 0 & \frac{27}{8} & \frac{15}{8} & \frac{60}{8} & \vdots & -\frac{17}{8} \\ 0 & 1 & 0 & \frac{13}{8} & \frac{9}{8} & \frac{20}{8} & \vdots & \frac{1}{8} \\ 0 & 0 & 1 & \frac{11}{8} & \frac{7}{8} & \frac{12}{8} & \vdots & \frac{7}{8} \end{pmatrix}.$$

The first six columns of this matrix form $\mathbf{A}_R$ and we read that $\text{rank}(\mathbf{A}) = 3 = \text{rank}([\mathbf{A} \vdots \mathbf{B}]_R)$. From $[\mathbf{A} \vdots \mathbf{B}]_R$, identify x_1, x_2, x_3 as dependent and x_4, x_5, x_6 as independent. The number of independent unknowns is $m - \text{rank}(\mathbf{A}) = 6 - 3 = 3$, and this is the dimension of the solution space of $\mathbf{AX} = \mathbf{O}$. From the reduced augmented matrix, the first equation of the reduced system is

$$x_1 + \frac{27}{8}x_4 + \frac{15}{8}x_5 + \frac{60}{8}x_6 = -\frac{17}{8},$$

so

$$x_1 = -\frac{27}{8}x_4 - \frac{15}{8}x_5 - \frac{60}{8}x_6 - \frac{17}{8}.$$

We will not write out all of the equations of the reduced system. The point is that we can read directly from $[\mathbf{A} \vdots \mathbf{B}]_R$ that

$$x_2 = -\frac{13}{8}x_4 - \frac{9}{8}x_5 - \frac{20}{8}x_6 + \frac{1}{8}$$

and

$$x_3 = -\frac{11}{8}x_4 - \frac{7}{8}x_5 - \frac{12}{8}x_6 + \frac{7}{8},$$

while x_4, x_5, x_6 can be assigned any numerical values. We can write this solution as

$$\mathbf{X} = \begin{pmatrix} -\frac{27}{8}x_4 - \frac{15}{8}x_5 - \frac{60}{8}x_6 - \frac{17}{8} \\ -\frac{13}{8}x_4 - \frac{9}{8}x_5 - \frac{20}{8}x_6 + \frac{1}{8} \\ -\frac{11}{8}x_4 - \frac{7}{8}x_5 - \frac{12}{8}x_6 + \frac{7}{8} \\ x_4 \\ x_5 \\ x_6 \end{pmatrix}.$$

If we let $x_4 = 8\alpha$, $x_5 = 8\beta$, and $x_6 = 8\gamma$, with α, β and γ any numbers, then the general solution is

$$\mathbf{X} = \alpha \begin{pmatrix} -27 \\ -13 \\ -11 \\ 8 \\ 0 \\ 0 \end{pmatrix} + \beta \begin{pmatrix} -15 \\ -9 \\ -7 \\ 0 \\ 8 \\ 0 \end{pmatrix} + \gamma \begin{pmatrix} -60 \\ -20 \\ -12 \\ 0 \\ 0 \\ 8 \end{pmatrix} + \begin{pmatrix} -\frac{17}{8} \\ \frac{1}{8} \\ \frac{7}{8} \\ 0 \\ 0 \\ 0 \end{pmatrix}.$$

This is in the form $\mathbf{H} + \mathbf{U}_p$, with $\mathbf{H}$ the general solution of $\mathbf{AX} = \mathbf{O}$ and $\mathbf{U}_p$ a particular solution of $\mathbf{AX} = \mathbf{B}$. ∎

Since the general solution is of the form $\mathbf{X} = \mathbf{H} + \mathbf{U}_p$, with $\mathbf{H}$ the general solution of $\mathbf{AX} = \mathbf{O}$, the only way $\mathbf{AX} = \mathbf{B}$ can have a unique solution is if $\mathbf{H} = \mathbf{O}$, that is, the homogeneous system must have only the trivial solution. But, for a system with the same number of unknowns as equations, this can occur only if $\mathbf{A}_R$ is the identity matrix.

THEOREM 7.23

Let $\mathbf{A}$ be $n \times n$. Then the nonhomogeneous system $\mathbf{AX} = \mathbf{B}$ has a unique solution if and only if $\mathbf{A}_R = \mathbf{I}_n$. ∎

This, in turn, occurs exactly when $rank(\mathbf{A}) = n$.

EXAMPLE 7.37

Consider the system

$$\begin{pmatrix} 2 & 1 & -11 \\ -5 & 1 & 9 \\ 1 & 1 & 14 \end{pmatrix} X = \begin{pmatrix} -6 \\ 12 \\ -5 \end{pmatrix}.$$

The augmented matrix is

$$[\mathbf{A} \vdots \mathbf{B}] = \begin{pmatrix} 2 & 1 & -11 & \vdots & -6 \\ -5 & 1 & 9 & \vdots & 12 \\ 1 & 1 & 14 & \vdots & -5 \end{pmatrix}$$

and we find that

$$[\mathbf{A} \vdots \mathbf{B}]_R = \begin{pmatrix} 1 & 0 & 0 & \vdots & -\frac{86}{31} \\ 0 & 1 & 0 & \vdots & -\frac{191}{155} \\ 0 & 0 & 1 & \vdots & -\frac{11}{155} \end{pmatrix}.$$

The first three columns tell us that $\mathbf{A}_R = \mathbf{I}_3$. The homogeneous system $\mathbf{AX} = \mathbf{O}$ has only the trivial solution. Then $\mathbf{AX} = \mathbf{B}$ has a unique solution, which we read from $[\mathbf{A} \vdots \mathbf{B}]_R$:

$$\mathbf{X} = \begin{pmatrix} \frac{-86}{31} \\ \frac{-191}{155} \\ \frac{-11}{155} \end{pmatrix}.$$

Note that $rank(\mathbf{A}) = 3$ and the dimension of the solution space $\mathbf{AX} = \mathbf{O}$ is $n - rank(\mathbf{A}) = 3 - 3 = 0$, consistent with this solution space having no elements except the zero vector. ∎

SECTION 7.7   PROBLEMS

In each of Problems 1 through 14, find the general solution of the system or show that the system has no solution.

1. $3x_1 - 2x_2 + x_3 = 6$
$x_1 + 10x_2 - x_3 = 2$
$-3x_1 - 2x_2 + x_3 = 0$

2. $4x_1 - 2x_2 + 3x_3 + 10x_4 = 1$
$x_1 - 3x_4 = 8$
$2x_1 - 3x_2 + x_4 = 16$

3. $2x_1 - 3x_2 + x_4 - x_6 = 0$
$3x_1 - 2x_3 + x_5 = 1$
$x_2 - x_4 + 6x_6 = 3$

4. $2x_1 - 3x_2 = 1$
$-x_1 + 3x_2 = 0$
$x_1 - 4x_2 = 3$

5. $3x_2 - 4x_4 = 10$
$x_1 - 3x_2 + 4x_5 - x_6 = 8$
$x_2 + x_3 - 6x_4 + x_6 = -9$
$x_1 - x_2 + x_6 = 0$

6. $2x_1 - 3x_2 + x_4 = 1$
$3x_2 + x_3 - x_4 = 0$
$2x_1 - 3x_2 + 10x_3 = 0$

7. $8x_2 - 4x_3 + 10x_6 = 1$
$\qquad x_3 + x_5 - x_6 = 2$
$\qquad x_4 - 3x_5 + 2x_6 = 0$

8. $\qquad 2x_1 - 3x_3 = 1$
$\qquad x_1 - x_2 + x_3 = 1$
$\qquad 2x_1 - 4x_2 + x_3 = 2$

9. $\qquad 14x_3 - 3x_5 + x_7 = 2$
$\qquad x_1 + x_2 + x_3 - x_4 + x_6 = -4$

10. $3x_1 - 2x_2 = -1$
$\qquad 4x_1 + 3x_2 = 4$

11. $\qquad 7x_1 - 3x_2 + 4x_3 = -7$
$\qquad 2x_1 + x_2 - x_3 + 4x_4 = 6$
$\qquad x_2 - 3x_4 = -5$

12. $\qquad -4x_1 + 5x_2 - 6x_3 = 2$
$\qquad 2x_1 - 6x_2 + x_3 = -5$
$\qquad -6x_1 + 16x_2 - 11x_3 = 1$

13. $\qquad 4x_1 - x_2 + 4x_3 = 1$
$\qquad x_1 + x_2 - 5x_3 = 0$
$\qquad -2x_1 + x_2 + 7x_3 = 4$

14. $\qquad -6x_1 + 2x_2 - x_3 + x_4 = 0$
$\qquad x_1 + 4x_2 - x_4 = -5$
$\qquad x_1 + x_2 + x_3 - 7x_4 = 0$

15. Let $\mathbf{A}$ be an $n \times m$ matrix with rank r. Prove that the reduced system $\mathbf{A}_R\mathbf{X} = \mathbf{B}$ has a solution if and only if $b_{r+1} = \cdots = b_n = 0$.

7.8 Matrix Inverses

DEFINITION 7.15 *Matrix Inverse*

Let $\mathbf{A}$ be an $n \times n$ matrix. Then $\mathbf{B}$ is an inverse of $\mathbf{A}$ if

$$\mathbf{AB} = \mathbf{BA} = \mathbf{I}_n.$$

In this definition $\mathbf{B}$ must also be $n \times n$ because both $\mathbf{AB}$ and $\mathbf{BA}$ must be defined. Further, if $\mathbf{B}$ is an inverse of $\mathbf{A}$, then $\mathbf{A}$ is also an inverse of $\mathbf{B}$.

It is easy to find nonzero square matrices that have no inverse. For example, let

$$\mathbf{A} = \begin{pmatrix} 1 & 0 \\ 2 & 0 \end{pmatrix}.$$

If $\mathbf{B}$ is an inverse of $\mathbf{A}$, say $\mathbf{B} = \begin{pmatrix} a & b \\ c & d \end{pmatrix}$, then we must have

$$\mathbf{AB} = \begin{pmatrix} 1 & 0 \\ 2 & 0 \end{pmatrix}\begin{pmatrix} a & b \\ c & d \end{pmatrix} = \begin{pmatrix} a & b \\ 2a & 2b \end{pmatrix} = \begin{pmatrix} 1 & 0 \\ 0 & 1 \end{pmatrix}.$$

But then

$$a = 1, b = 0, 2a = 0 \quad \text{and} \quad b = 1$$

which are impossible conditions. On the other hand, some matrices do have inverses. For example,

$$\begin{pmatrix} 2 & 1 \\ 1 & 4 \end{pmatrix}\begin{pmatrix} \frac{4}{7} & -\frac{1}{7} \\ -\frac{1}{7} & \frac{2}{7} \end{pmatrix} = \begin{pmatrix} \frac{4}{7} & -\frac{1}{7} \\ -\frac{1}{7} & \frac{2}{7} \end{pmatrix}\begin{pmatrix} 2 & 1 \\ 1 & 4 \end{pmatrix} = \begin{pmatrix} 1 & 0 \\ 0 & 1 \end{pmatrix}.$$

DEFINITION 7.16   Nonsingular and Singular Matrices
_____

A square matrix is said to be nonsingular if it has an inverse. If it has no inverse, the matrix is called singular.

If a matrix has an inverse, then it can have only one.

THEOREM 7.24   *Uniqueness of Inverses*

Let $\mathbf{B}$ and $\mathbf{C}$ be inverses of $\mathbf{A}$. Then $\mathbf{B} = \mathbf{C}$.

Proof   Write

$$\mathbf{B} = \mathbf{BI}_n = \mathbf{B(AC)} = \mathbf{(BA)C} = \mathbf{I}_n\mathbf{C} = \mathbf{C}. \quad \blacksquare$$

In view of this we will denote the inverse of $\mathbf{A}$ as $\mathbf{A}^{-1}$. Here are properties of inverse matrices. In proving parts of the theorem, we repeatedly employ the strategy that, if $\mathbf{AB} = \mathbf{BA} = \mathbf{I}_n$, then $\mathbf{B}$ must be the inverse of $\mathbf{A}$.

THEOREM 7.25

1. $\mathbf{I}_n$ is nonsingular and $\mathbf{I}_n^{-1} = \mathbf{I}_n$.
2. If $\mathbf{A}$ and $\mathbf{B}$ are nonsingular $n \times n$ matrices, then $\mathbf{AB}$ is nonsingular and

$$(\mathbf{AB})^{-1} = \mathbf{B}^{-1}\mathbf{A}^{-1}.$$

3. If $\mathbf{A}$ is nonsingular, so is $\mathbf{A}^{-1}$, and

$$(\mathbf{A}^{-1})^{-1} = \mathbf{A}.$$

4. If $\mathbf{A}$ is nonsingular, so is $\mathbf{A}^t$, and

$$(\mathbf{A}^t)^{-1} = (\mathbf{A}^{-1})^t.$$

5. If $\mathbf{A}$ and $\mathbf{B}$ are $n \times n$ and either is singular, then $\mathbf{AB}$ and $\mathbf{BA}$ are both singular.

Proof   For (2), compute

$$(\mathbf{AB})(\mathbf{B}^{-1}\mathbf{A}^{-1}) = \mathbf{A}(\mathbf{BB}^{-1})\mathbf{A}^{-1} = \mathbf{AA}^{-1} = \mathbf{I}_n.$$

Similarly, $(\mathbf{B}^{-1}\mathbf{A}^{-1})(\mathbf{AB}) = \mathbf{I}_n$. Therefore $(\mathbf{AB})^{-1} = \mathbf{B}^{-1}\mathbf{A}^{-1}$.

For (4), use Theorem 7.3(3) to write

$$(\mathbf{A}^t)(\mathbf{A}^{-1})^t = (\mathbf{A}^{-1}\mathbf{A})^t = (\mathbf{I}_n)^t = \mathbf{I}_n.$$

Similarly,

$$(\mathbf{A}^{-1})^t(\mathbf{A}^t) = (\mathbf{AA}^{-1})^t = \mathbf{I}_n.$$

Therefore $(\mathbf{A}^t)^{-1} = (\mathbf{A}^{-1})^t$. $\blacksquare$

We will be able to give a very short proof of (5) when we have developed determinants. We saw before that not every matrix has an inverse. How can we tell whether a matrix is singular or nonsingular? The following theorem gives a reasonable test.

THEOREM 7.26

An $n \times n$ matrix $\mathbf{A}$ is nonsingular if and only if $\mathbf{A}_R = \mathbf{I}_n$.

Alternatively, an $n \times n$ matrix is nonsingular if and only if its rank is n. The proof consists of understanding a relationship between a matrix having an inverse, and its reduced form being the identity matrix. The key lies in noticing that we can form the columns of a matrix product $\mathbf{AB}$ by multiplying, in turn, $\mathbf{A}$ by each column of $\mathbf{B}$:

$$\text{column } j \text{ of } \mathbf{AB} = \mathbf{A}(\text{column } j \text{ of } \mathbf{B}) = \mathbf{A} \begin{pmatrix} b_{1j} \\ b_{2j} \\ \vdots \\ b_{nj} \end{pmatrix}.$$

Proof We will build an inverse for $\mathbf{A}$ a column at a time. To have $\mathbf{AB} = \mathbf{I}_n$, we must be able to choose the columns of $\mathbf{B}$ so that

$$\text{column } j \text{ of } \mathbf{AB} = \mathbf{A} \begin{pmatrix} b_{1j} \\ b_{2j} \\ \vdots \\ b_{nj} \end{pmatrix} = \text{column } j \text{ of } \mathbf{I}_n = \begin{pmatrix} 0 \\ 0 \\ \vdots \\ 1 \\ \vdots \\ 0 \end{pmatrix}, \tag{7.4}$$

with a 1 in the jth place and zeros elsewhere.

Suppose now that $\mathbf{A}_R = \mathbf{I}_n$. Then, by Theorem 7.23, the system (7.4) has a unique solution for each $j = 1, \cdots, n$. These solutions form the columns of a matrix $\mathbf{B}$ such that $\mathbf{AB} = \mathbf{I}_n$, and then $\mathbf{B} = \mathbf{A}^{-1}$. (Actually we must show that $\mathbf{AB} = \mathbf{I}_n$ also, but we leave this as an exercise).

Conversely, suppose $\mathbf{A}$ is nonsingular. Then system (7.4) has a unique solution for $j = 1, \dots, n$, because these solutions are the columns of $\mathbf{A}^{-1}$. Then, by Theorem 7.23, $\mathbf{A}_R = \mathbf{I}_n$. ∎

7.8.1 A Method for Finding $\mathbf{A}^{-1}$

We know some computational rules for working with matrix inverses, as well as a criterion for a matrix to have an inverse. Now we want an efficient way of computing $\mathbf{A}^{-1}$ from $\mathbf{A}$.

Theorem 7.26 suggests a strategy. We know that, in any event, there is an $n \times n$ matrix Ω such that $\Omega \mathbf{A} = \mathbf{A}_R$. Ω is a product of elementary matrices representing the elementary row operations used to reduce $\mathbf{A}$. Previously we found Ω by adjoining $\mathbf{I}_n$ to the left of $\mathbf{A}$ to form an $n \times 2n$ matrix $[\mathbf{I}_n \vdots \mathbf{A}]$. Reduce $\mathbf{A}$, performing the elementary row operations on all of $[\mathbf{I}_n \vdots \mathbf{A}]$ to eventually arrive at $[\Omega \vdots \mathbf{I}_n]$. This produces Ω such that

$$\Omega \mathbf{A} = \mathbf{A}_R.$$

If $\mathbf{A}_R = \mathbf{I}_n$ then $\Omega = \mathbf{A}^{-1}$. If $\mathbf{A}_R \neq \mathbf{I}_n$, then $\mathbf{A}$ has no inverse.

EXAMPLE 7.38

Let

$$\mathbf{A} = \begin{pmatrix} 5 & -1 \\ 6 & 8 \end{pmatrix}.$$

We want to know if $\mathbf{A}$ is nonsingular and, if it is, produce its inverse.

Form

$$[\mathbf{I}_2 \vdots \mathbf{A}] = \begin{pmatrix} 1 & 0 & \vdots & 5 & -1 \\ 0 & 1 & \vdots & 6 & 8 \end{pmatrix}.$$

Reduce **A** (the last two columns), carrying out the same operations on the first two columns:

$$[\mathbf{I}_2 \vdots \mathbf{A}] \rightarrow \frac{1}{5}(\text{row } 1) \rightarrow \begin{pmatrix} \frac{1}{5} & 0 & \vdots & 1 & -\frac{1}{5} \\ 0 & 1 & \vdots & 6 & 8 \end{pmatrix}$$

$$\rightarrow -6(\text{row } 1)+(\text{row } 2) \rightarrow \begin{pmatrix} \frac{1}{5} & 0 & \vdots & 1 & -\frac{1}{5} \\ -\frac{6}{5} & 1 & \vdots & 0 & \frac{46}{5} \end{pmatrix}$$

$$\rightarrow \frac{5}{46}(\text{row } 2) \rightarrow \begin{pmatrix} \frac{1}{5} & 0 & \vdots & 1 & -\frac{1}{5} \\ -\frac{6}{46} & \frac{5}{46} & \vdots & 0 & 1 \end{pmatrix}$$

$$\rightarrow \frac{1}{5}(\text{row } 2)+(\text{row } 1) \rightarrow \begin{pmatrix} \frac{8}{46} & \frac{1}{46} & \vdots & 1 & 0 \\ -\frac{6}{46} & \frac{5}{46} & \vdots & 0 & 1 \end{pmatrix}.$$

In the last two columns we read $\mathbf{A}_R = \mathbf{I}_2$. This means that **A** is nonsingular. From the first two columns,

$$\mathbf{A}^{-1} = \frac{1}{46} \begin{pmatrix} 8 & 1 \\ -6 & 5 \end{pmatrix}. \quad \blacksquare$$

EXAMPLE 7.39

Let

$$\mathbf{A} = \begin{pmatrix} -3 & 21 \\ 4 & -28 \end{pmatrix}.$$

Perform a reduction:

$$[\mathbf{I}_2 \vdots \mathbf{A}] = \begin{pmatrix} 1 & 0 & \vdots & -3 & 21 \\ 0 & 1 & \vdots & 4 & -28 \end{pmatrix}$$

$$\rightarrow -\frac{1}{3}(\text{row } 1) \rightarrow \begin{pmatrix} -\frac{1}{3} & 0 & \vdots & 1 & -7 \\ 0 & 1 & \vdots & 4 & -28 \end{pmatrix}$$

$$-4(\text{row } 1)+(\text{row } 2) \rightarrow \begin{pmatrix} -\frac{1}{3} & 0 & \vdots & 1 & -7 \\ \frac{4}{3} & 1 & \vdots & 0 & 0 \end{pmatrix}.$$

We read $\mathbf{A}_R$ from the last two columns, which form a 2×2 reduced matrix. Since this is not $\mathbf{I}_2$, **A** is singular and has no inverse. $\blacksquare$

Here is how inverses relate to the solution of systems of linear equations in which the number of unknowns equals the number of equations.

THEOREM 7.27

Let **A** be an $n \times n$ matrix.

1. A homogeneous system $\mathbf{AX} = \mathbf{O}$ has a nontrivial solution if and only if **A** is singular.
2. A nonhomogeneous system $\mathbf{AX} = \mathbf{B}$ has a solution if and only if **A** is nonsingular. In this case the unique solution is $\mathbf{X} = \mathbf{A}^{-1}\mathbf{B}$. ■

For a homogeneous system $\mathbf{AX} = \mathbf{O}$, if **A** were nonsingular then we could multiply the equation on the left by $\mathbf{A}^{-1}$ to get

$$\mathbf{X} = \mathbf{A}^{-1}\mathbf{O} = \mathbf{O}.$$

Thus in the nonsingular case, a homogeneous system can have only a trivial solution. In the singular case, we know that $rank(A) < n$, so the solution space has positive dimension $n - rank(\mathbf{A})$ and therefore has nontrivial solutions in it.

In the nonsingular case, we can multiply a nonhomogeneous equation $\mathbf{AX} = \mathbf{B}$ on the left by $\mathbf{A}^{-1}$ to get the unique solution

$$\mathbf{X} = \mathbf{A}^{-1}\mathbf{B}.$$

However, if **A** is singular, then $rank(\mathbf{A}) < n$, and then Theorem 7.22 tells us that the system $\mathbf{AX} = \mathbf{B}$ can have no solution.

EXAMPLE 7.40

Consider the nonhomogeneous system

$$2x_1 - x_2 + 3x_3 = 4$$
$$x_1 + 9x_2 - 2x_3 = -8$$
$$4x_1 - 8x_2 + 11x_3 = 15.$$

The matrix of coefficients is

$$\mathbf{A} = \begin{pmatrix} 2 & -1 & 3 \\ 1 & 9 & -2 \\ 4 & -8 & 11 \end{pmatrix}$$

and we find that

$$\mathbf{A}^{-1} = \frac{1}{53}\begin{pmatrix} 83 & -13 & -25 \\ -19 & 10 & 7 \\ -44 & 12 & 19 \end{pmatrix}.$$

The unique solution of this system is

$$\mathbf{X} = \mathbf{A}^{-1}\mathbf{B} = \frac{1}{53}\begin{pmatrix} 83 & -13 & -25 \\ -19 & 10 & 7 \\ -44 & 12 & 19 \end{pmatrix}\begin{pmatrix} 4 \\ -8 \\ 15 \end{pmatrix}$$

$$= \begin{pmatrix} \frac{61}{53} \\ -\frac{51}{53} \\ \frac{13}{53} \end{pmatrix}. ■$$

In each of Problems 1 through 10, find the inverse of the matrix or show that the matrix is singular.

1. $\begin{pmatrix} -1 & 2 \\ 2 & 1 \end{pmatrix}$

2. $\begin{pmatrix} 12 & 3 \\ 4 & 1 \end{pmatrix}$

3. $\begin{pmatrix} -5 & 2 \\ 1 & 2 \end{pmatrix}$

4. $\begin{pmatrix} -1 & 0 \\ 4 & 4 \end{pmatrix}$

5. $\begin{pmatrix} 6 & 2 \\ 3 & 3 \end{pmatrix}$

6. $\begin{pmatrix} 1 & 1 & -3 \\ 2 & 16 & 1 \\ 0 & 0 & 4 \end{pmatrix}$

7. $\begin{pmatrix} -3 & 4 & 1 \\ 1 & 2 & 0 \\ 1 & 1 & 3 \end{pmatrix}$

8. $\begin{pmatrix} -2 & 1 & -5 \\ 1 & 1 & 4 \\ 0 & 3 & 3 \end{pmatrix}$

9. $\begin{pmatrix} -2 & 1 & 1 \\ 0 & 1 & 1 \\ -3 & 0 & 6 \end{pmatrix}$

10. $\begin{pmatrix} 12 & 1 & 14 \\ -3 & 2 & 0 \\ 0 & 9 & 14 \end{pmatrix}$

In each of Problems 11 through 15, find the unique solution of the system, using Theorem 7.27(2).

11. $x_1 - x_2 + 3x_3 - x_4 = 1$
    $x_2 - 3x_3 + 5x_4 = 2$
    $x_1 - x_3 + x_4 = 0$
    $x_1 + 2x_3 - x_4 = -5$

12. $8x_1 - x_2 - x_3 = 4$
    $x_1 + 2x_2 - 3x_3 = 0$
    $2x_1 - x_2 + 4x_3 = 5$

13. $2x_1 - 6x_2 + 3x_3 = -4$
    $-x_1 + x_2 + x_3 = 5$
    $2x_1 + 6x_2 - 5x_3 = 8$

14. $12x_1 + x_2 - 3x_3 = 4$
    $x_1 - x_2 + 3x_3 = -5$
    $-2x_1 + x_2 + x_3 = 0$

15. $4x_1 + 6x_2 - 3x_3 = 0$
    $2x_1 + 3x_2 - 4x_3 = 0$
    $x_1 - x_2 + 3x_3 = -7$

16. Let $\mathbf{A}$ be nonsingular. Prove that, for any positive integer k, $\mathbf{A}^k$ is nonsingular, and $(\mathbf{A}^k)^{-1} = (\mathbf{A}^{-1})^k$.

17. Let $\mathbf{A}$, $\mathbf{B}$ and $\mathbf{C}$ be $n \times n$ real matrices. Suppose $\mathbf{BA} = \mathbf{AC} = \mathbf{I}_n$. Prove that $\mathbf{B} = \mathbf{C}$.

CHAPTER 8

Determinants

If A is a square matrix, the determinant of A is a sum of products of elements of A, formed according to a procedure we will now describe. First we need some information about permutations.

8.1   Permutations

If n is a positive integer, a *permutation* of order n is an arrangement of the integers $1, \ldots, n$ in any order. For example, suppose p is a permutation that reorders the integers $1, \ldots, 6$ as

$$3, 1, 4, 5, 2, 6.$$

Then

$$p(1) = 3, \quad p(2) = 1, \quad p(3) = 4, \quad p(4) = 5, \quad p(5) = 2, \quad p(6) = 6,$$

with $p(j)$ the number the permutation has put in place j.

For small n it is possible to list all permutations on $1, \ldots, n$. Here is a short list:

For $n = 2$ there are two permutations on the integers $1, 2$, one leaving them in place and the second interchanging them:

$$1, 2$$

$$2, 1.$$

For $n = 3$ there are six permutations on $1, 2, 3$, and they are

$$1, 2, 3$$
$$1, 3, 2$$
$$2, 1, 3$$
$$2, 3, 1$$
$$3, 1, 2$$
$$3, 2, 1.$$

For $n = 4$ there are twenty four permutations on $1, 2, 3, 4$:

$$1, 2, 3, 4; 1, 2, 4, 3; 1, 3, 2, 4; 1, 3, 4, 2; 1, 4, 2, 3; 1, 4, 3, 2;$$
$$2, 1, 3, 4; 2, 1, 4, 3; 2, 3, 1, 4; 2, 3, 4, 1; 2, 4, 1, 3; 2, 4, 3, 1;$$
$$3, 1, 2, 4; 3, 1, 4, 2; 3, 2, 1, 4; 3, 2, 4, 1; 3, 4, 1, 2; 3, 4, 2, 1;$$
$$4, 1, 2, 3; 4, 1, 3, 2; 4, 2, 1, 3; 4, 2, 3, 1; 4, 3, 1, 2; 4, 3, 2, 1.$$

An examination of this list of permutations suggests a systematic approach by which they were all listed, and such an approach will work in theory for higher n. However, we can also observe that the number of permutations on $1, \ldots, n$ increases rapidly with n.

There are $n! = 1 \cdot 2 \cdot \cdots \cdot n$ permutations on $1, \ldots, n$. This fact is not difficult to derive. Imagine a row of n boxes, and start putting the integers from 1 to n into the boxes, one to each box. There are n choices for a number to put into the first box, $n - 1$ choices for the second, $n - 2$ for the third, and so on until there is only one left to put in the last box. There is a total of $n(n-1)(n-2) \cdots 1 = n!$ ways to do this, hence $n!$ permutations on n objects.

A permutation is characterized as even or odd, according to a rule we will now illustrate. Consider the permutation

$$2, 5, 1, 4, 3.$$

on the integers $1, \ldots, 5$. For each number k in the list, count the number of integers to its right that are smaller than k. In this way form a list

k	number of integers smaller than k to the right of k
2	1
5	3
1	0
4	1
3	0

Sum the integers in the right column to get 5, which is odd. We therefore call this permutation odd. As an example of an even permutation, consider

$$2, 1, 5, 4, 3.$$

Now the list is

k	number of integers smaller than k to the right of k
2	1
1	0
5	2
4	1
3	0

and the integers in the right column sum to 4, an even number. This permutation is even.

If p is a permutation, let

$$sgn(p) = \begin{cases} 0 & \text{if } p \text{ is even} \\ 1 & \text{if } p \text{ is odd} \end{cases}.$$

SECTION 8.1   PROBLEMS

1. The six permutations of $1, 2, 3$ are given in the discussion. Which of these permutations are even and which are odd?

2. The 24 permutations of $1, 2, 3, 4$ are given in the discussion. Which of these are even and which are odd?

3. Show that half of the permutations on $1, 2, \ldots, n$ are even, and the other half are odd.

8.2   Definition of the Determinant

Let $\mathbf{A} = [a_{ij}]$ be an $n \times n$ matrix, with numbers or functions as elements.

DEFINITION 8.1

The determinant of $\mathbf{A}$, denoted $\det(\mathbf{A})$, is the sum of all products

$$(-1)^{sgn(p)} a_{1p(1)} a_{2p(2)} \cdots a_{np(n)},$$

taken over all permutations p on $1, \ldots, n$. This sum is denoted

$$\sum_{p} (-1)^{sgn(p)} a_{1p(1)} a_{2p(2)} \cdots a_{np(n)}. \tag{8.1}$$

Each term in the defining sum (8.1) contains exactly one element from each row and from each column, chosen according to the indices $j, p(j)$ determined by the permutation. Each product in the sum is multiplied by 1 if the permutation is even, and by -1 if p is odd.

Since there are $n!$ permutations on $1, \ldots, n$, this sum involves $n!$ terms and is therefore quite daunting for, say $n \geq 4$. We will examine the small cases $n = 2$ and $n = 3$ and then look for ways of evaluating $\det(\mathbf{A})$ for larger n.

In the case $n = 2$,

$$\mathbf{A} = \begin{pmatrix} a_{11} & a_{12} \\ a_{21} & a_{22} \end{pmatrix}.$$

We have seen that there are 2 permutations on $1, 2$, namely

$$p : 1, 2$$

which is an even permutation, and

$$q : 2, 1$$

which is odd. Then

$$\det(\mathbf{A}) = (-1)^{sgn(p)} a_{1p(1)} a_{2p(2)} + (-1)^{sgn(q)} a_{1q(1)} a_{2q(2)}$$
$$= (-1)^0 a_{11} a_{22} + (-1)^1 a_{12} a_{21}$$
$$= a_{11} a_{22} - a_{12} a_{21}.$$

This rule for evaluating $\det(\mathbf{A})$ holds for any 2×2 matrix.

In the case $n = 3$,

$$\mathbf{A} = \begin{pmatrix} a_{11} & a_{12} & a_{13} \\ a_{21} & a_{22} & a_{23} \\ a_{31} & a_{32} & a_{33} \end{pmatrix}.$$

The permutations of $1, 2, 3$ are

$$p_1 : 1, 2, 3$$
$$p_2 : 1, 3, 2$$
$$p_3 : 2, 1, 3$$
$$p_4 : 2, 3, 1$$
$$p_5 : 3, 1, 2$$
$$p_6 : 3, 2, 1.$$

It is routine to check that p_1, p_5 and p_6 are even, and p_2, p_3 and p_4 are odd. Then

$$\det(\mathbf{A}) = (-1)^{sgn(p_1)} a_{1p_1(1)} a_{2p_1(2)} a_{3p_1(3)} + (-1)^{sgn(p_2)} a_{1p_2(1)} a_{2p_2(2)} a_{3p_2(3)}$$
$$+ (-1)^{sgn(p_3)} a_{1p_3(1)} a_{2p_3(2)} a_{3p_3(3)} + (-1)^{sgn(p_4)} a_{1p_4(1)} a_{2p_4(2)} a_{3p_4(3)}$$
$$+ (-1)^{sgn(p_5)} a_{1p_5(1)} a_{2p_5(2)} a_{3p_5(3)} + (-1)^{sgn(p_6)} a_{1p_6(1)} a_{2p_6(2)} a_{3p_6(3)}$$
$$= a_{11} a_{22} a_{33} - a_{11} a_{23} a_{32} - a_{12} a_{21} a_{33} + a_{12} a_{23} a_{31} + a_{13} a_{21} a_{32} - a_{13} a_{22} a_{31}.$$

If $\mathbf{A}$ is 4×4, then evaluation of $\det(\mathbf{A})$ by direct recourse to the definition will involve 24 terms, as well as explicitly listing all 24 permutations on $1, 2, 3, 4$. This is not practical. We will therefore develop some properties of determinants which will make their evaluation more efficient.

SECTION 8.2 **PROBLEMS**

In Problems 1 through 4, use the formula for $\det(\mathbf{A})$ in the 3×3 case to evaluate the determinant of the given matrix.

1. $\mathbf{A} = \begin{pmatrix} 1 & 6 & 0 \\ 1 & 2 & -1 \\ 0 & 1 & 1 \end{pmatrix}$

2. $\mathbf{A} = \begin{pmatrix} -1 & 3 & 1 \\ 2 & 2 & 0 \\ 1 & 1 & 4 \end{pmatrix}$

3. $\mathbf{A} = \begin{pmatrix} 6 & -3 & 5 \\ 2 & 1 & 4 \\ 0 & 1 & -4 \end{pmatrix}$

4. $\mathbf{A} = \begin{pmatrix} -4 & 0 & 1 \\ 0 & 1 & 1 \\ 0 & 0 & 0 \end{pmatrix}$

5. The permutations on $1, 2, 3, 4$ were listed in Section 8.1. Use this list to write a formula for $\det(\mathbf{A})$ when $\mathbf{A}$ is 4×4.

8.3 Properties of Determinants

We will develop some of the properties of determinants that are used in evaluating them and deriving some of their properties. There are effective computer routines for evaluating quite large determinants, but these are also based on the properties we will display.

First, it is standard to use vertical lines to denote determinants, so we will often write

$$\det(\mathbf{A}) = |\mathbf{A}| \, .$$

This should not be confused with absolute value. If $\mathbf{A}$ has numerical elements, then $|\mathbf{A}|$ is a number and can be positive, negative or zero.

Throughout the rest of this chapter let $\mathbf{A}$ and $\mathbf{B}$ be $n \times n$ matrices.

Our first result says that a matrix having a zero row has a zero determinant.

THEOREM 8.1

If $\mathbf{A}$ has a zero row, then $|\mathbf{A}| = 0$. ∎

This is easy to see from the defining sum (8.1). Suppose, for some i , each $a_{ij} = 0$. Each term of the sum (8.1) contains a factor $a_{ip_j(i)}$ from row i, hence each term in the sum is zero.

Next, we claim that multiplying a row of a matrix by a scalar α has the effect of multiplying the determinant of the matrix by α.

THEOREM 8.2

Let $\mathbf{B}$ be formed from $\mathbf{A}$ by multiplying row k by a scalar α. Then

$$|\mathbf{B}| = \alpha \, |\mathbf{A}| \, . \quad \blacksquare$$

The effect of multiplying row k of $\mathbf{A}$ by α is to replace each a_{kj} by αa_{kj}. Then $b_{ij} = a_{ij}$ for $i \neq k$, and $b_{kj} = \alpha a_{kj}$, so

$$|\mathbf{A}| = \sum_p (-1)^{sgn(p)} a_{1p(1)} a_{2p(2)} \cdots a_{kp(k)} \cdots a_{np(n)}$$

and

$$|\mathbf{B}| = \sum_{p} (-1)^{sgn(p)} b_{1p(1)} b_{2p(2)} \cdots b_{kp(k)} \cdots b_{np(n)}$$

$$= \sum_{p} (-1)^{sgn(p)} a_{1p(1)} a_{2p(2)} \cdots (\alpha a_{kp(k)}) \cdots a_{np(n)}$$

$$= \alpha \sum_{p} (-1)^{sgn(p)} a_{1p(1)} a_{2p(2)} \cdots a_{kp(k)} \cdots a_{np(n)} = \alpha |\mathbf{A}|.$$

The next result states that the interchange of two rows in a matrix causes a sign change in the determinant.

THEOREM 8.3

Let **B** be formed from **A** by interchanging two rows. Then

$$|\mathbf{A}| = - |\mathbf{B}|. \quad \blacksquare$$

A proof of this involves a close examination of the effect of a row interchange on the terms of the sum (8.1), and we will not go through these details. The result is easy to see in the case of 2×2 determinants. Let

$$\mathbf{A} = \begin{pmatrix} a_{11} & a_{12} \\ a_{21} & a_{22} \end{pmatrix} \quad \text{and} \quad \mathbf{B} = \begin{pmatrix} a_{21} & a_{22} \\ a_{11} & a_{12} \end{pmatrix}.$$

Then

$$|\mathbf{A}| = a_{11} a_{22} - a_{12} a_{21}$$

and

$$|\mathbf{B}| = a_{21} a_{12} - a_{22} a_{11} = - |\mathbf{A}|.$$

This result has two important consequences. The first is that the determinant of a matrix with two identical rows must be zero.

COROLLARY 8.1

If two rows of **A** are the same, then $|\mathbf{A}| = 0. \quad \blacksquare$

The reason for this is that, if we form **B** from **A** by interchanging the identical rows, then $\mathbf{B} = \mathbf{A}$, so $|\mathbf{B}| = |\mathbf{A}|$. But by Theorem 8.3, $|\mathbf{B}| = - |\mathbf{A}|$, so $|\mathbf{A}| = 0$.

COROLLARY 8.2

If for some scalar α, row k of **A** is α times row i, then $|\mathbf{A}| = 0$.

To see this, consider two cases. First, if $\alpha = 0$, then row k of **A** is a zero row, so $|\mathbf{A}| = 0$. If $\alpha \neq 0$, then we can multiply row k of **A** by $1/\alpha$ to obtain a matrix **B** having rows i and k the same. Then $|\mathbf{B}| = 0$. But $|\mathbf{B}| = (1/\alpha) |\mathbf{A}|$ by Theorem 8.2, so $|\mathbf{A}| = 0$.

Next, we claim that the determinant of a product is the product of the determinants.

THEOREM 8.4

Let **A** and **B** be $n \times n$ matrices. Then, $|\mathbf{AB}| = |\mathbf{A}|\,|\mathbf{B}|$. ■

Obviously this extends to a product involving any finite number of $n \times n$ matrices. The theorem enables us to evaluate the determinant of such a product without carrying out the matrix multiplications of all the factors. We will illustrate the theorem when we have efficient ways of evaluating determinants.

The following theorem gives the determinant of a matrix that is written as a sum of matrices in a special way.

THEOREM 8.5

Suppose each element of row k of **A** is written as a sum $\alpha_{kj} + \beta_{kj}$. Form two matrices from **A**. The first, $\mathbf{A}_1$, is identical to **A** except the elements of row k are α_{kj}. The second, $\mathbf{A}_2$, is identical to **A** except the elements of row k are β_{kj}. Then

$$|\mathbf{A}| = |\mathbf{A}_1| + |\mathbf{A}_2| .$$ ■

If we display the elements of these matrices, the conclusion states that

$$
\begin{vmatrix}
a_{11} & \cdots & a_{1j} & \cdots & a_{1n} \\
\vdots & \vdots & \vdots & \vdots & \vdots \\
\alpha_{k1}+\beta_{k1} & \cdots & \alpha_{kj}+\beta_{kj} & \cdots & \alpha_{kn}+\beta_{kn} \\
\vdots & \vdots & \vdots & \vdots & \vdots \\
a_{n1} & \cdots & a_{nj} & \cdots & a_{nn}
\end{vmatrix}
=
\begin{vmatrix}
a_{11} & \cdots & a_{1j} & \cdots & a_{1n} \\
\vdots & \vdots & \vdots & \vdots & \vdots \\
\alpha_{k1} & \cdots & \alpha_{kj} & \cdots & \alpha_{kn} \\
\vdots & \vdots & \vdots & \vdots & \vdots \\
a_{n1} & \cdots & a_{nj} & \cdots & a_{nn}
\end{vmatrix}
$$

$$
+
\begin{vmatrix}
a_{11} & \cdots & a_{1j} & \cdots & a_{1n} \\
\vdots & \vdots & \vdots & \vdots & \vdots \\
\beta_{k1} & \cdots & \beta_{kj} & \cdots & \beta_{kn} \\
\vdots & \vdots & \vdots & \vdots & \vdots \\
a_{n1} & \cdots & a_{nj} & \cdots & a_{nn}
\end{vmatrix} .
$$

This result can be seen by examining the terms of (8.1) for each of these determinants:

$$|\mathbf{A}| = \sum_p (-1)^{sgn(p)} a_{1p(1)} a_{2p(2)} \cdots (\alpha_{kp(k)} + \beta_{kp(k)}) \cdots a_{np(n)}$$

$$= \sum_p (-1)^{sgn(p)} a_{1p(1)} a_{2p(2)} \cdots \alpha_{kp(k)} \cdots a_{np(n)}$$

$$+ \sum_p (-1)^{sgn(p)} a_{1p(1)} a_{2p(2)} \cdots + \beta_{kp(k)} \cdots a_{np(n)} = |\mathbf{A}_1| + |\mathbf{A}_2| .$$

As a corollary to this, adding a scalar multiple of one row to another of a matrix does not change the value of the determinant.

COROLLARY 8.3

Let **B** be formed from **A** by adding γ times row i to row k. Then $|\mathbf{B}| = |\mathbf{A}|$. ∎

This result follows immediately from the preceding theorem by noting that row k of **B** is $\gamma a_{ij} + a_{kj}$. Then

$$
|\mathbf{B}| = \begin{vmatrix}
a_{11} & \cdots & a_{1j} & \cdots & a_{1n} \\
\vdots & \vdots & \vdots & \vdots & \vdots \\
a_{i1} & \cdots & a_{ij} & \cdots & a_{in} \\
\vdots & \vdots & \vdots & \vdots & \vdots \\
\gamma a_{i1} + a_{k1} & \cdots & \gamma a_{ij} + a_{kj} & \cdots & \gamma a_{in} + a_{kn} \\
\vdots & \vdots & \vdots & \vdots & \vdots \\
a_{n1} & \cdots & a_{nj} & \cdots & a_{nn}
\end{vmatrix}
$$

$$
= \gamma \begin{vmatrix}
a_{11} & \cdots & a_{1j} & \cdots & a_{1n} \\
\vdots & \vdots & \vdots & \vdots & \vdots \\
a_{i1} & \cdots & a_{ij} & \cdots & a_{in} \\
\vdots & \vdots & \vdots & \vdots & \vdots \\
a_{i1} & \cdots & a_{ij} & \cdots & a_{in} \\
\vdots & \vdots & \vdots & \vdots & \vdots \\
a_{n1} & \cdots & a_{nj} & \cdots & a_{nn}
\end{vmatrix} + \begin{vmatrix}
a_{11} & \cdots & a_{1j} & \cdots & a_{1n} \\
\vdots & \vdots & \vdots & \vdots & \vdots \\
a_{i1} & \cdots & a_{ij} & \cdots & a_{in} \\
\vdots & \vdots & \vdots & \vdots & \vdots \\
a_{k1} & \cdots & a_{kj} & \cdots & a_{kn} \\
\vdots & \vdots & \vdots & \vdots & \vdots \\
a_{n1} & \cdots & a_{nj} & \cdots & a_{nn}
\end{vmatrix} = |\mathbf{A}|.
$$

In the last line, the first term is γ times a determinant with rows i and k identical, hence is zero. The second term is just $|\mathbf{A}|$.

We now know the effect of elementary row operations on a determinant. In summary:

Type I operation—interchange of two rows. This changes the sign of the determinant.

Type II operation—multiplication of a row by a scalar α. This multiplies the determinant by α.

Type III operation—addition of a scalar multiple of one row to another row. This does not change the determinant.

Recall that the transpose $\mathbf{A}^t$ of a matrix **A** is obtained by writing the rows of **A** as the columns of $\mathbf{A}^t$. We claim that a matrix and its transpose have the same determinant.

THEOREM 8.6

$|\mathbf{A}| = |\mathbf{A}^t|$. ∎

For example, consider the 2×2 case:

$$
\mathbf{A} = \begin{pmatrix} a_{11} & a_{12} \\ a_{21} & a_{22} \end{pmatrix}, \quad \mathbf{A}^t = \begin{pmatrix} a_{11} & a_{21} \\ a_{12} & a_{22} \end{pmatrix}.
$$

Then

$$
|\mathbf{A}| = a_{11}a_{22} - a_{12}a_{21} \quad \text{and} \quad |\mathbf{A}^t| = a_{11}a_{22} - a_{21}a_{12} = |\mathbf{A}|.
$$

A proof of this theorem consists of comparing terms of the determinants. If $\mathbf{A} = [a_{ij}]$ then $\mathbf{A}^t = [a_{ji}]$. Now, from the defining sum (8.1),

$$|\mathbf{A}| = \sum_p (-1)^{sgn(p)} a_{1p(1)} a_{2p(2)} \cdots a_{np(n)}$$

and

$$|\mathbf{A}^t| = \sum_p (-1)^{sgn(p)} (\mathbf{A}^t)_{ip(1)} (\mathbf{A}^t)_{2p(2)} \cdots (\mathbf{A}^t)_{np(n)}$$

$$= \sum_q (-1)^{sgn(q)} a_{q(1)1} a_{q(2)2} \cdots a_{q(n)n}.$$

One can show that each term $(-1)^{sgn(p)} a_{1p(1)} a_{2p(2)} \cdots a_{np(n)}$ in the sum for $|\mathbf{A}|$ is equal to a corresponding term $(-1)^{sgn(q)} a_{q(1)1} a_{q(2)2} \cdots a_{q(n)n}$ in the sum for $|\mathbf{A}^t|$. The key is to realize that, because q is a permutation of $1, \ldots, n$, we can rearrange the terms in the latter product to write them in increasing order of the first (row) index. This induces a permutation on the second (column) index, and we can match this term up with a corresponding term in the sum for $|\mathbf{A}|$. We will not elaborate the details of this argument.

One consequence of this result is that we can perform not only elementary row operations on a matrix, but also the corresponding elementary column operations, and we know the effect of each operation on the determinant. In particular, from the column perspective:

If two columns of $\mathbf{A}$ are identical, or if one column is a zero column, then $|\mathbf{A}| = 0$.

Interchange of two columns of $\mathbf{A}$ changes the sign of the determinant.

Multiplication of a column by a scalar α multiplies the determinant by α.

And addition of a scalar multiple of one column to another column does not change the determinant.

These operations on rows and columns of a matrix, and their effect on the determinant of the newly formed matrix, form the basis for strategies to evaluate determinants.

SECTION 8.3   PROBLEMS

1. Let $\mathbf{A} = [a_{ij}]$ be an $n \times n$ matrix and let α be any scalar. Let $\mathbf{B} = [\alpha a_{ij}]$. Thus $\mathbf{B}$ is formed by multiplying each element of $\mathbf{A}$ by α. Prove that $|\mathbf{B}| = \alpha^n |\mathbf{A}|$.

2. Let $\mathbf{A} = [a_{ij}]$ be an $n \times n$ matrix. Let α be a nonzero number. Form a new matrix $\mathbf{B} = [\alpha^{i-j} a_{ij}]$. How are $|\mathbf{A}|$ and

$|\mathbf{B}|$ related? *Hint*: It is useful to examine the 2×2 and 3×3 cases to get some idea of what $\mathbf{B}$ looks like.

3. An $n \times n$ matrix is skew-symmetric if $\mathbf{A} = -\mathbf{A}^t$. Prove that the determinant of a skew-symmetric matrix of odd order is zero.

8.4   Evaluation of Determinants by Elementary Row and Column Operations

The use of elementary row and column operations to evaluate a determinant is predicated upon the following observation. If a row or column of an $n \times n$ matrix $\mathbf{A}$ has all zero elements except possibly for a_{ij} in row i and column j, then the determinant of $\mathbf{A}$ is $(-1)^{i+j} a_{ij}$ times the determinant of the $(n-1) \times (n-1)$ matrix obtained by deleting row i and column j from $\mathbf{A}$.

This reduces the problem of evaluating an $n \times n$ determinant to one of evaluating a smaller determinant, having one less row and one less calumn.

Here is a statement of this result, with (1) the row version and (2) the column version.

THEOREM 8.7

1. Row Version

$$
\begin{vmatrix}
a_{11} & \cdots & a_{1,j-1} & a_{1j} & a_{1,j+1} & \cdots & a_{1n} \\
\vdots & \vdots & \vdots & \vdots & \vdots & \vdots & \vdots \\
a_{i-1,1} & \cdots & a_{i-1,j-1} & a_{i-1,j} & a_{i-1,j+1} & \cdots & a_{i-1,n} \\
0 & \cdots & 0 & a_{ij} & 0 & \cdots & 0 \\
a_{i+1,1} & \cdots & a_{i+1,j-1} & a_{i+1,j} & a_{i+1,j+1} & \cdots & a_{i+1,n} \\
\vdots & \vdots & \vdots & \vdots & \vdots & \vdots & \vdots \\
a_{n1} & \cdots & a_{n,j-1} & a_{nj} & a_{n,j+1} & \cdots & a_{nn}
\end{vmatrix}
$$

$$
=(-1)^{i+j}a_{ij}
\begin{vmatrix}
a_{11} & \cdots & a_{1,j-1} & a_{1,j+1} & \cdots & a_{1n} \\
\vdots & \vdots & \vdots & \vdots & \vdots & \vdots \\
a_{i-1,1} & \cdots & a_{i-1,j-1} & a_{i-1,j+1} & \cdots & a_{i-1,n} \\
a_{i+1,1} & \cdots & a_{i+1,j-1} & a_{i+1,j+1} & \cdots & a_{i+1,n} \\
\vdots & \vdots & \vdots & \vdots & \vdots & \vdots \\
a_{n1} & \cdots & a_{n,j-1} & a_{n,j+1} & \cdots & a_{nn}
\end{vmatrix}.
$$

2. Column Version

$$
\begin{vmatrix}
a_{11} & \cdots & a_{1,j-1} & 0 & a_{1,j+1} & \cdots & a_{1n} \\
\vdots & \vdots & \vdots & \vdots & \vdots & \vdots & \vdots \\
a_{i-1,1} & \cdots & a_{i-1,j-1} & 0 & a_{i-1,j+1} & \cdots & a_{i-1,n} \\
a_{i1} & \cdots & a_{i,j-1} & a_{ij} & a_{i,j+1} & \cdots & a_{i,n} \\
a_{i+1,1} & \cdots & a_{i+1,j-1} & 0 & a_{i+1,j+1} & \cdots & a_{i+1,n} \\
\vdots & \vdots & \vdots & \vdots & \vdots & \vdots & \vdots \\
a_{n1} & \cdots & a_{n,j-1} & 0 & a_{n,j+1} & \cdots & a_{nn}
\end{vmatrix}
$$

$$
=(-1)^{i+j}a_{ij}
\begin{vmatrix}
a_{11} & \cdots & a_{1,j-1} & a_{1,j+1} & \cdots & a_{1n} \\
\vdots & \vdots & \vdots & \vdots & \vdots & \vdots \\
a_{i-1,1} & \cdots & a_{i-1,j-1} & a_{i-1,j+1} & \cdots & a_{i-1,n} \\
a_{i+1,1} & \cdots & a_{i+1,j-1} & a_{i+1,j+1} & \cdots & a_{i+1,n} \\
\vdots & \vdots & \vdots & \vdots & \vdots & \vdots \\
a_{n1} & \cdots & a_{n,j-1} & a_{n,j+1} & \cdots & a_{nn}
\end{vmatrix}.
$$

This result suggests one strategy for evaluating a determinant. Given an $n \times n$ matrix $\mathbf{A}$, use the row and/or column operations to obtain a new matrix $\mathbf{B}$ having at most one nonzero element in some row or column. Then $|\mathbf{A}|$ is a scalar multiple of $|\mathbf{B}|$, and $|\mathbf{B}|$ is a scalar multiple of the $(n-1) \times (n-1)$ determinant formed by deleting from $\mathbf{B}$ the row and column containing this nonzero element. We can then repeat this strategy on this $(n-1) \times (n-1)$ matrix, eventually reducing the problem to one of evaluating a "small" determinant.

Here is an illustration of this process.

EXAMPLE 8.1

Let

$$
\mathbf{A} = \begin{pmatrix}
-6 & 0 & 1 & 3 & 2 \\
-1 & 5 & 0 & 1 & 7 \\
8 & 3 & 2 & 1 & 7 \\
0 & 1 & 5 & -3 & 2 \\
1 & 15 & -3 & 9 & 4
\end{pmatrix}.
$$

We want to evaluate $|\mathbf{A}|$. There are many ways to proceed with the strategy we are illustrating. To begin, we can exploit the fact that $a_{13} = 1$ and use elementary row operations to get zeros in the rest of column 3. Of course $a_{23} = 0$ to begin with, so we need only worry about column 3 entries in rows 3, 4, 5. Add (-2)(row 1) to row 3, -5(row 1) to row 4 and 3(row 1) to row 5 to get

$$
\mathbf{B} = \begin{pmatrix}
-6 & 0 & 1 & 3 & 2 \\
-1 & 5 & 0 & 1 & 7 \\
20 & 3 & 0 & -5 & 3 \\
30 & 1 & 0 & -18 & -8 \\
-17 & 15 & 0 & 18 & 10
\end{pmatrix}.
$$

Because we have used Type III row operations,

$$|\mathbf{A}| = |\mathbf{B}|.$$

Further, by Theorem 8.7,

$$|\mathbf{B}| = (-1)^{1+3} b_{13} |\mathbf{C}| = (1) |\mathbf{C}| = |\mathbf{C}|,$$

where $\mathbf{C}$ is the 4×4 matrix obtained by deleting row 1 and column 3 of $\mathbf{B}$:

$$
\mathbf{C} = \begin{pmatrix}
-1 & 5 & 1 & 7 \\
20 & 3 & -5 & 3 \\
30 & 1 & -18 & -8 \\
-17 & 15 & 18 & 10
\end{pmatrix}.
$$

This is a 4×4 matrix, "smaller" than $\mathbf{A}$. We will now apply the strategy to $|\mathbf{C}|$. We can, for example, exploit the -1 entry in the 1, 1 position of $\mathbf{C}$, this time using column operations to get zeros in row 1, columns 2, 3, 4 of the new matrix. Specifically, add 5(column 1) to column 2, add column 1 to column 3, and add 7(column 1) to column 4 of $\mathbf{C}$ to get

$$
\mathbf{D} = \begin{pmatrix}
-1 & 0 & 0 & 0 \\
20 & 103 & 15 & 143 \\
30 & 151 & 12 & 202 \\
-17 & -70 & 1 & -109
\end{pmatrix}.
$$

Again, because we used Type III operations (this time on columns) of $\mathbf{C}$, then

$$|\mathbf{C}| = |\mathbf{D}|.$$

But by the theorem, because we are using the element $d_{11} = -1$ as the single nonzero element of row 1, we have

$$|\mathbf{D}| = (-1)^{1+1} d_{11} |\mathbf{E}| = -|\mathbf{E}|,$$

in which $\mathbf{E}$ is the 3×3 matrix obtained by deleting row 1 and column 1 from $\mathbf{D}$:

$$E = \begin{pmatrix} 103 & 15 & 143 \\ 151 & 12 & 202 \\ -70 & 1 & -109 \end{pmatrix}.$$

To evaluate $|\mathbf{E}|$, we can exploit the entry $3, 2$ entry $e_{31} = 1$. Add -15(row 3) to row 1 and -12(row 3) to row 2 to get

$$\mathbf{F} = \begin{pmatrix} 1153 & 0 & 1778 \\ 991 & 0 & 1510 \\ -70 & 1 & -109 \end{pmatrix}.$$

Then

$$|\mathbf{E}| = |\mathbf{F}|.$$

By the theorem, using the only nonzero element $f_{32} = 1$ of column 2 of $\mathbf{F}$, we have

$$|\mathbf{F}| = (-1)^{3+2}(1)\,|\mathbf{G}| = -\,|\mathbf{G}|$$

in which $\mathbf{G}$ is the 2×2 matrix obtained by deleting row 3 and column 2 of $\mathbf{F}$:

$$\mathbf{G} = \begin{pmatrix} 1153 & 1778 \\ 991 & 1510 \end{pmatrix}.$$

At the 2×2 state, we evaluate the determinant directly:

$$|\mathbf{G}| = (1153)(1510) - (1778)(991) = -20,968.$$

Working back, we now have

$$|\mathbf{A}| = |\mathbf{B}| = |\mathbf{C}| = |\mathbf{D}| = -\,|\mathbf{E}| = -\,|\mathbf{F}| = |\mathbf{G}| = -20,968. \quad \blacksquare$$

The method is actually quicker to apply than might appear from this example, because we included comments as we proceeded with the calculations.

SECTION 8.4   *PROBLEMS*

In each of Problems 1 through 10, use the strategy of this section to evaluate the determinant of the matrix.

1. $\begin{pmatrix} -2 & 4 & 1 \\ 1 & 6 & 3 \\ 7 & 0 & 4 \end{pmatrix}$

2. $\begin{pmatrix} 2 & -3 & 7 \\ 14 & 1 & 1 \\ -13 & -1 & 5 \end{pmatrix}$

3. $\begin{pmatrix} -4 & 5 & 6 \\ -2 & 3 & 5 \\ 2 & -2 & 6 \end{pmatrix}$

4. $\begin{pmatrix} 2 & -5 & 8 \\ 4 & 3 & 8 \\ 13 & 0 & -4 \end{pmatrix}$

5. $\begin{pmatrix} 17 & -2 & 5 \\ 1 & 12 & 0 \\ 14 & 7 & -7 \end{pmatrix}$,

6. $\begin{pmatrix} -3 & 3 & 9 & 6 \\ 1 & -2 & 15 & 6 \\ 7 & 1 & 1 & 5 \\ 2 & 1 & -1 & 3 \end{pmatrix}$

7. $\begin{pmatrix} 0 & 1 & 1 & -4 \\ 6 & -3 & 2 & 2 \\ 1 & -5 & 1 & -2 \\ 4 & 8 & 2 & 2 \end{pmatrix}$

9. $\begin{pmatrix} 10 & 1 & -6 & 2 \\ 0 & 3 & 3 & 9 \\ 0 & 1 & 1 & 7 \\ -2 & 6 & 8 & 8 \end{pmatrix}$

8. $\begin{pmatrix} 2 & 7 & -1 & 0 \\ 3 & 1 & 1 & 8 \\ -2 & 0 & 3 & 1 \\ 4 & 8 & -1 & 0 \end{pmatrix}$

10. $\begin{pmatrix} -7 & 16 & 2 & 4 \\ 1 & 0 & 0 & 5 \\ 0 & 3 & -4 & 4 \\ 6 & 1 & 1 & -5 \end{pmatrix}$

8.5   Cofactor Expansions

Theorem 8.5 suggests the following. If we select any row i of a square matrix **A**, we can write

$$
\begin{vmatrix} a_{11} & a_{12} & \cdots & \cdots & a_{1n} \\ \vdots & \vdots & \vdots & \vdots & \vdots \\ a_{i1} & a_{i2} & \cdots & \cdots & a_{in} \\ \vdots & \vdots & \vdots & \vdots & \vdots \\ a_{n1} & a_{n2} & \cdots & \cdots & a_{nn} \end{vmatrix} = \begin{vmatrix} a_{11} & a_{12} & \cdots & \cdots & a_{1n} \\ \vdots & \vdots & \vdots & \vdots & \vdots \\ a_{i1} & 0 & \cdots & \cdots & 0 \\ \vdots & \vdots & \vdots & \vdots & \vdots \\ a_{n1} & a_{n2} & \cdots & \cdots & a_{nn} \end{vmatrix}
$$

$$
+ \begin{vmatrix} a_{11} & a_{12} & \cdots & \cdots & a_{1n} \\ \vdots & \vdots & \vdots & \vdots & \vdots \\ 0 & a_{i2} & \cdots & \cdots & 0 \\ \vdots & \vdots & \vdots & \vdots & \vdots \\ a_{n1} & a_{n2} & \cdots & \cdots & a_{nn} \end{vmatrix} + \cdots + \begin{vmatrix} a_{11} & a_{12} & \cdots & \cdots & a_{1n} \\ \vdots & \vdots & \vdots & \vdots & \vdots \\ 0 & 0 & \cdots & \cdots & a_{in} \\ \vdots & \vdots & \vdots & \vdots & \vdots \\ a_{n1} & a_{n2} & \cdots & \cdots & a_{nn} \end{vmatrix}. \qquad (8.2)
$$

Each of the determinants on the right of equation (8.2) has a row in which every element but possibly one is zero, so Theorem 8.7 applies to each of these determinants. The first determinant on the right is $(-1)^{i+1}a_{i1}$ times the determinant of the matrix obtained by deleting row i and column 1 from **A**. The second determinant on the right is $(-1)^{i+2}a_{i2}$ times the determinant of the matrix obtained by deleting row i and column 2 from **A**. And so on, until the last matrix on the right is $(-1)^{i+n}a_{in}$ times the determinant of the matrix obtained by deleting row i and column n from **A**. We can put all of this more succinctly by introducing the following standard terminology.

DEFINITION 8.2   *Minor*

If **A** is an $n \times n$ matrix, the minor of a_{ij} is denoted M_{ij}, and is the determinant of the $(n-1) \times (n-1)$ matrix obtained by deleting row i and column j of **A**.

   Cofactor   The number $(-1)^{i+j}M_{ij}$ is called the cofactor of a_{ij}.

We can now state the following formula for a determinant.

THEOREM 8.8   *Cofactor Expansion by a Row*

If **A** is $n \times n$, then for any integer i with $i \leq i \leq n$,

$$|\mathbf{A}| = \sum_{j=1}^{n} (-1)^{i+j} a_{ij} M_{ij}. \quad \blacksquare \qquad (8.3)$$

This is just equation (8.2) in the notation of cofactors. The sum (8.3) is called the *cofactor expansion* of $|\mathbf{A}|$ by row i because it is the sum, across this row, of each matrix element times its cofactor. This yields $|\mathbf{A}|$ no matter which row is used. Of course, if some $a_{ik} = 0$ then we need not calculate that term in equation (8.3), so it is to our advantage to expand by a row having as many zero elements as possible. The strategy of the preceding subsection was to create such a row using row and column operations, resulting in what was a cofactor expansion, by a row having only one (possibly) nonzero element.

EXAMPLE 8.2

Let

$$\mathbf{A} = \begin{pmatrix} -6 & 3 & 7 \\ 12 & -5 & -9 \\ 2 & 4 & -6 \end{pmatrix}.$$

If we expand by row 1, we get

$$|\mathbf{A}| = \sum_{j=1}^{3} (-1)^{1+j} M_{1j}$$

$$= (-1)^{1+1}(-6) \begin{vmatrix} -5 & -9 \\ 4 & -6 \end{vmatrix} + (-1)^{1+2}(3) \begin{vmatrix} 12 & -9 \\ 2 & -6 \end{vmatrix}$$

$$+ (-1)^{1+3}(7) \begin{vmatrix} 12 & -5 \\ 2 & 4 \end{vmatrix}$$

$$= (-6)(30 + 36) - 3(-72 + 18) + 7(-48 + 10) = 172.$$

Just for illustration, expand by row 3:

$$|\mathbf{A}| = \sum_{j=1}^{3} (-1)^{3+j} a_{3j} M_{3j} = (-1)^{3+1} 2 \begin{vmatrix} 3 & 7 \\ -5 & -9 \end{vmatrix}$$

$$+ (-1)^{3+2}(4) \begin{vmatrix} -6 & 7 \\ 12 & -9 \end{vmatrix} + (-1)^{3+3}(-6) \begin{vmatrix} -6 & 3 \\ 12 & -5 \end{vmatrix}$$

$$= 2(-27 + 35) - 4(54 - 84) - 6(30 - 36) = 172. \quad \blacksquare$$

Because, for purposes of evaluating determinants, row and column operations can both be used, we can also develop a cofactor expansion of $|\mathbf{A}|$ by column j. In this expansion, we move down a column of a matrix and sum each term of the column times its cofactor.

THEOREM 8.9 *Cofactor Expansion by a Column*

Let **A** be an $n \times n$ matrix. Then for any j with $1 \leq j \leq n$,

$$|\mathbf{A}| = \sum_{i=1}^{n}(-1)^{i+j}a_{ij}M_{ij}. \quad \blacksquare \tag{8.4}$$

This differs from the expansion (8.3) in that the latter expands across a row, while the sum (8.4) expands down a column. All of these expansions, by any row or column of **A**, yield $|\mathbf{A}|$.

EXAMPLE 8.3

Consider again

$$\mathbf{A} = \begin{pmatrix} -6 & 3 & 7 \\ 12 & -5 & -9 \\ 2 & 4 & -6 \end{pmatrix}.$$

Expanding by column 1 gives us

$$|\mathbf{A}| = \sum_{i=1}^{3}(-1)^{i+1}a_{i1}M_{i1} = (-1)^{1+1}(-6)\begin{vmatrix} -5 & -9 \\ 4 & -6 \end{vmatrix}$$

$$+ (-1)^{2+1}(12)\begin{vmatrix} 3 & 7 \\ 4 & -6 \end{vmatrix} + (-1)^{3+1}(2)\begin{vmatrix} 3 & 7 \\ -5 & -9 \end{vmatrix}$$

$$= (-6)(30+36) - 12(-18-28) + 2(-27+35) = 172.$$

If we expand by column 2 we get

$$|\mathbf{A}| = \sum_{i=1}^{3}(-1)^{i+2}a_{i2}M_{i2} = (-1)^{1+2}(3)\begin{vmatrix} 12 & -9 \\ 2 & -6 \end{vmatrix}$$

$$+ (-1)^{2+2}(-5)\begin{vmatrix} -6 & 7 \\ 2 & -6 \end{vmatrix} + (-1)^{3+2}(4)\begin{vmatrix} -6 & 7 \\ 12 & -9 \end{vmatrix}$$

$$= (-3)(-72+18) - 5(36-14) - 4(54-84) = 172. \quad \blacksquare$$

SECTION 8.5   **PROBLEMS**

In Problems 1–10, use cofactor expansions, combined with elementary row and column operations when this is useful, to evaluate the determinant of the matrix.

1. $\begin{pmatrix} -4 & 2 & -8 \\ 1 & 1 & 0 \\ 1 & -3 & 0 \end{pmatrix}$

2. $\begin{pmatrix} 1 & 1 & 6 \\ 2 & -2 & 1 \\ 3 & -1 & 4 \end{pmatrix}$

3. $\begin{pmatrix} 7 & -3 & 1 \\ 1 & -2 & 4 \\ -3 & 1 & 0 \end{pmatrix}$

4. $\begin{pmatrix} 5 & -4 & 3 \\ -1 & 1 & 6 \\ -2 & -2 & 4 \end{pmatrix}$

5. $\begin{pmatrix} -5 & 0 & 1 & 6 \\ 2 & -1 & 3 & 7 \\ 4 & 4 & -5 & -8 \\ 1 & -1 & 6 & 2 \end{pmatrix}$

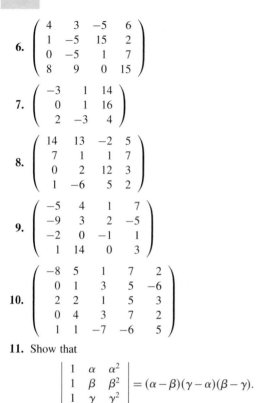

6. $\begin{pmatrix} 4 & 3 & -5 & 6 \\ 1 & -5 & 15 & 2 \\ 0 & -5 & 1 & 7 \\ 8 & 9 & 0 & 15 \end{pmatrix}$

7. $\begin{pmatrix} -3 & 1 & 14 \\ 0 & 1 & 16 \\ 2 & -3 & 4 \end{pmatrix}$

8. $\begin{pmatrix} 14 & 13 & -2 & 5 \\ 7 & 1 & 1 & 7 \\ 0 & 2 & 12 & 3 \\ 1 & -6 & 5 & 2 \end{pmatrix}$

9. $\begin{pmatrix} -5 & 4 & 1 & 7 \\ -9 & 3 & 2 & -5 \\ -2 & 0 & -1 & 1 \\ 1 & 14 & 0 & 3 \end{pmatrix}$

10. $\begin{pmatrix} -8 & 5 & 1 & 7 & 2 \\ 0 & 1 & 3 & 5 & -6 \\ 2 & 2 & 1 & 5 & 3 \\ 0 & 4 & 3 & 7 & 2 \\ 1 & 1 & -7 & -6 & 5 \end{pmatrix}$

11. Show that

$$\begin{vmatrix} 1 & \alpha & \alpha^2 \\ 1 & \beta & \beta^2 \\ 1 & \gamma & \gamma^2 \end{vmatrix} = (\alpha - \beta)(\gamma - \alpha)(\beta - \gamma).$$

This is *Vandermonde's determinant*. This and the next problem are best done with a little thought in using facts about determinants, rather than a brute-force approach.

12. Show that

$$\begin{vmatrix} \alpha & \beta & \gamma & \delta \\ \beta & \gamma & \delta & \alpha \\ \gamma & \delta & \alpha & \beta \\ \delta & \alpha & \beta & \gamma \end{vmatrix} = (\alpha + \beta + \gamma + \delta)(\beta - \alpha + \delta - \gamma)$$

$$\times \begin{vmatrix} 0 & 1 & -1 & 1 \\ 1 & \gamma & \delta & \alpha \\ 1 & \delta & \alpha & \beta \\ 1 & \alpha & \beta & \gamma \end{vmatrix}.$$

13. Let $\mathbf{A}$ be a square matrix such that $\mathbf{A}^{-1} = \mathbf{A}^t$. Prove that $|\mathbf{A}| = \pm 1$.

14. Prove that three points (x_1, y_1), (x_2, y_2) and (x_3, y_3) are collinear (on the same straight line) if and only if

$$\begin{vmatrix} 1 & x_1 & y_1 \\ 1 & x_2 & y_2 \\ 1 & x_3 & y_3 \end{vmatrix} = 0.$$

Hint: This determinant is zero exactly when one row or column is a linear combination of the other two.

8.6   Determinants of Triangular Matrices

The main diagonal of a square matrix $\mathbf{A}$ consists of the elements $a_{11}, a_{22}, \ldots, a_{nn}$. We call $\mathbf{A}$ *upper triangular* if all the elements below the main diagonal are zero. That is, $a_{ij} = 0$ if $i > j$. Such a matrix has the appearance

$$\mathbf{A} = \begin{pmatrix} a_{11} & a_{12} & a_{13} & \cdots & a_{1,n-1} & a_{1n} \\ 0 & a_{22} & a_{23} & \cdots & a_{2,n-1} & a_{2n} \\ 0 & 0 & a_{33} & \cdots & a_{3,n-1} & a_{3n} \\ \vdots & \vdots & \vdots & \vdots & \vdots & \vdots \\ 0 & 0 & 0 & \cdots & a_{n-1,n-1} & a_{n-1,n} \\ 0 & 0 & 0 & 0 & 0 & a_{nn} \end{pmatrix}.$$

If we expand $|\mathbf{A}|$ by cofactors down the first column, we have

$$|\mathbf{A}| = a_{11} \begin{vmatrix} a_{22} & a_{23} & \cdots & a_{2,n-1} & a_{2n} \\ 0 & a_{33} & \cdots & a_{3,n-1} & a_{3n} \\ \vdots & \vdots & \vdots & \vdots & \vdots \\ 0 & 0 & \cdots & a_{n-1,n-1} & a_{n-1,n} \\ 0 & 0 & \cdots & 0 & a_{nn} \end{vmatrix},$$

and the determinant on the right is again upper triangular, so expand by its first column to get

$$|\mathbf{A}| = a_{11}a_{22}\begin{vmatrix} a_{33} & a_{34} & \cdots & a_{3n} \\ 0 & a_{44} & \cdots & a_{3n} \\ \vdots & \vdots & \cdots & \vdots \\ 0 & 0 & \cdots & a_{nn} \end{vmatrix}$$

with another upper triangular determinant on the right. Continuing in this way, we obtain

$$|\mathbf{A}| = a_{11}a_{22}\cdots a_{nn}.$$

The determinant of an upper triangular matrix is the product of its main diagonal elements.

The same conclusion holds for lower triangular matrices (all elements above the main diagonal are zero). Now we can expand the determinant along the top row, each time obtaining just one minor that is again lower triangular.

EXAMPLE 8.4

$$\begin{vmatrix} 15 & -7 & 4 & 7 & 3 \\ 0 & 12 & -6 & 3 & 9 \\ 0 & 0 & \sqrt{2} & 15 & -4 \\ 0 & 0 & 0 & \pi & 22 \\ 0 & 0 & 0 & 0 & e \end{vmatrix} = (15)(12)\sqrt{2}\pi e = 180\sqrt{2}\pi e. \quad\blacksquare$$

SECTION 8.6   PROBLEMS

Evaluate the following determinants.

1.
$$\begin{vmatrix} -4 & 0 & 0 & 0 & 0 & 0 \\ 12 & 7 & 0 & 0 & 0 & 0 \\ 3 & -4 & 2 & 0 & 0 & 0 \\ 0 & 1 & 1 & -2 & 0 & 0 \\ 1 & -4 & 16 & 1 & 5 & 0 \\ 10 & -4 & 16 & 1 & 17 & 4 \end{vmatrix}$$

2.
$$\begin{vmatrix} 6 & 1 & -1 & 2 & 2 & 1 \\ 0 & -4 & 2 & 2 & -3 & 1 \\ 0 & 0 & -5 & 10 & 1 & -7 \\ 0 & 0 & 0 & 14 & 0 & 0 \\ 0 & 0 & 0 & 0 & 13 & -4 \\ 0 & 0 & 0 & 0 & 0 & 3 \end{vmatrix}$$

3.
$$\begin{vmatrix} 3 & 0 & 0 & 0 & 0 \\ 2 & -6 & 0 & 0 & 0 \\ 17 & 14 & 2 & 0 & 0 \\ 22 & -2 & 15 & 8 & 0 \\ 43 & 12 & 1 & -1 & 5 \end{vmatrix}$$

8.7   A Determinant Formula for a Matrix Inverse

Determinants can be used to tell whether a matrix is singular or nonsingular. In the latter case, there is a way of writing the inverse of a matrix by using determinants.

First, here is a simple test for nonsingularity. We will use the fact that we reduce a matrix by using elementary row operations, whose effects on determinants are known (Type I operations change the sign, Type II operations multiply the determinant by a nonzero constant, and Type III operations do not change the determinant at all). This means that, for any square matrix $\mathbf{A}$, $|\mathbf{A}| = \alpha |\mathbf{A}_R|$ for some nonzero constant α.

THEOREM 8.10

Let $\mathbf{A}$ be an $n \times n$ matrix. Then $\mathbf{A}$ is nonsingular if and only if $|\mathbf{A}| \neq 0$. ∎

Proof Suppose first that $|\mathbf{A}| \neq 0$. Since $|\mathbf{A}| = \alpha |\mathbf{A}_R|$ for some nonzero constant α, $\mathbf{A}_R$ can have no zero row, so $\mathbf{A}_R = \mathbf{I}_n$. Then $rank(\mathbf{A}) = n$, so $\mathbf{A}$ is nonsingular by Theorems 7.26 and 7.15.

Conversely, suppose $\mathbf{A}$ is nonsingular. Then $\mathbf{A}_R = \mathbf{I}_n$. Then $|\mathbf{A}| = \alpha |\mathbf{A}_R| \neq 0$. ∎

Using this result, we can give a short proof of Theorem 7.25(5). Suppose $\mathbf{A}$ and $\mathbf{B}$ are $n \times n$ matrices, and $\mathbf{AB}$ is singular. Then

$$|\mathbf{AB}| = |\mathbf{A}| \, |\mathbf{B}| = 0,$$

so $|\mathbf{A}| = 0$ or $|\mathbf{B}| = 0$, hence either $\mathbf{A}$ or $\mathbf{B}$ (or possibly both) must be singular.

We will now write a formula for the inverse of a square matrix, in terms of cofactors of the matrix.

THEOREM 8.11

Let $\mathbf{A}$ be an $n \times n$ nonsingular matrix. Define an $n \times n$ matrix $\mathbf{B}$ by putting

$$b_{ij} = \frac{1}{|\mathbf{A}|} (-1)^{i+j} M_{ji}.$$

Then, $\mathbf{B} = \mathbf{A}^{-1}$.

That is, the i, j element of $\mathbf{A}^{-1}$ is the cofactor of a_{ji} (not a_{ij}), divided by the determinant of $\mathbf{A}$.

Proof By the way $\mathbf{B}$ is defined, the i, j element of $\mathbf{AB}$ is

$$(\mathbf{AB})_{ij} = \sum_{k=1}^{n} a_{ik} b_{kj} = \frac{1}{|\mathbf{A}|} \sum_{k=1}^{n} (-1)^{j+k} a_{ik} M_{jk}.$$

Now examine the sum on the right. If $i = j$, we get

$$(\mathbf{AB})_{ii} = \frac{1}{|\mathbf{A}|} \sum_{k=1}^{n} (-1)^{i+k} a_{ik} M_{ik}$$

and the summation is exactly the cofactor expansion of $|\mathbf{A}|$ by row i. Therefore

$$(\mathbf{AB})_{ii} = \frac{|\mathbf{A}|}{|\mathbf{A}|} = 1.$$

If $i \neq j$, then the summation in the expression for $(\mathbf{AB})_{ij}$ is the cofactor expansion, by row j, of the determinant of the matrix formed from $\mathbf{A}$ by replacing row j by row i. But this matrix then has two identical rows, hence has determinant zero. Then $(\mathbf{AB})_{ij} = 0$ if $i \neq j$, and we conclude that $\mathbf{AB} = \mathbf{I}_n$. A similar argument shows that $\mathbf{BA} = \mathbf{I}_n$, hence $\mathbf{B} = \mathbf{A}^{-1}$. ∎

This method of computing a matrix inverse is not as efficient in general as the reduction method discussed previously. Nevertheless, it works well for small matrices, and in some discussions it is useful to have a formula for the elements of a matrix inverse.

EXAMPLE 8.5

Let

$$\mathbf{A} = \begin{pmatrix} -2 & 4 & 1 \\ 6 & 3 & -3 \\ 2 & 9 & -5 \end{pmatrix}.$$

Then

$$\begin{vmatrix} -2 & 4 & 1 \\ 6 & 3 & -3 \\ 2 & 9 & -5 \end{vmatrix} = 120$$

so **A** is nonsingular. Compute the nine elements of the inverse matrix **B**:

$$b_{11} = \frac{1}{120}M_{11} = \frac{1}{120}\begin{vmatrix} 3 & -3 \\ 9 & -5 \end{vmatrix} = \frac{12}{120} = \frac{1}{10},$$

$$b_{12} = \frac{1}{120}(-1)M_{21} = -\frac{1}{120}\begin{vmatrix} 4 & 1 \\ 9 & -5 \end{vmatrix} = \frac{29}{120},$$

$$b_{13} = \frac{1}{120}M_{31} = \frac{1}{120}\begin{vmatrix} 4 & 1 \\ 3 & -3 \end{vmatrix} = -\frac{1}{8},$$

$$b_{21} = -\frac{1}{120}M_{12} = -\frac{1}{120}\begin{vmatrix} 6 & -3 \\ 2 & -5 \end{vmatrix} = \frac{1}{5},$$

$$b_{22} = \frac{1}{120}\begin{vmatrix} -2 & 1 \\ 2 & -5 \end{vmatrix} = \frac{1}{15},$$

$$b_{23} = -\frac{1}{120}M_{32} = -\frac{1}{120}\begin{vmatrix} -2 & 1 \\ 6 & -3 \end{vmatrix} = 0,$$

$$b_{31} = \frac{1}{120}M_{13} = \frac{1}{120}\begin{vmatrix} 6 & 3 \\ 2 & 9 \end{vmatrix} = \frac{2}{5},$$

$$b_{32} = -\frac{1}{120}M_{23} = -\frac{1}{120}\begin{vmatrix} -2 & 4 \\ 2 & 9 \end{vmatrix} = \frac{13}{60},$$

$$b_{33} = \frac{1}{120}\begin{vmatrix} -2 & 4 \\ 6 & 3 \end{vmatrix} = -\frac{1}{4}.$$

Then

$$\mathbf{B} = \mathbf{A}^{-1} = \begin{pmatrix} \frac{1}{10} & \frac{29}{120} & \frac{-1}{8} \\ \frac{1}{5} & \frac{1}{15} & 0 \\ \frac{2}{5} & \frac{13}{60} & \frac{-1}{4} \end{pmatrix}. \blacksquare$$

SECTION 8.7 PROBLEMS

In each of Problems 1 through 10, use Theorem 8.10 to determine whether the matrix is nonsingular. If it is, use Theorem 8.11 to find its inverse.

1. $\begin{pmatrix} 2 & -1 \\ 1 & 6 \end{pmatrix}$

2. $\begin{pmatrix} 3 & 0 \\ 1 & 4 \end{pmatrix}$

3. $\begin{pmatrix} -1 & 1 \\ 1 & 4 \end{pmatrix}$

4. $\begin{pmatrix} 2 & 5 \\ -7 & -3 \end{pmatrix}$

5. $\begin{pmatrix} 6 & -1 & 3 \\ 0 & 1 & -4 \\ 2 & 2 & -3 \end{pmatrix}$

6. $\begin{pmatrix} -14 & 1 & -3 \\ 2 & -1 & 3 \\ 1 & 1 & 7 \end{pmatrix}$

7. $\begin{pmatrix} 0 & -4 & 3 \\ 2 & -1 & 6 \\ 1 & -1 & 7 \end{pmatrix}$

8. $\begin{pmatrix} 11 & 0 & -5 \\ 0 & 1 & 0 \\ 4 & -7 & 9 \end{pmatrix}$

9. $\begin{pmatrix} 3 & 1 & -2 & 1 \\ 4 & 6 & -3 & 9 \\ -2 & 1 & 7 & 4 \\ 13 & 0 & 1 & 5 \end{pmatrix}$

10. $\begin{pmatrix} 7 & -3 & -4 & 1 \\ 8 & 2 & 0 & 0 \\ 1 & 5 & -1 & 7 \\ 3 & -2 & -5 & 9 \end{pmatrix}$

8.8 Cramer's Rule

Cramer's rule is a determinant formula for solving a system of equations $\mathbf{AX} = \mathbf{B}$ when $\mathbf{A}$ is $n \times n$ and nonsingular. In this case, the system has the unique solution $\mathbf{X} = \mathbf{A}^{-1}\mathbf{B}$. We can, therefore, find $\mathbf{X}$ by computing $\mathbf{A}^{-1}$ and then $\mathbf{A}^{-1}\mathbf{B}$. Here is another way to find $\mathbf{X}$.

THEOREM 8.12 *Cramer's Rule*

Let $\mathbf{A}$ be a nonsingular $n \times n$ matrix of numbers. Then the unique solution of $\mathbf{AX} = \mathbf{B}$ is

$\begin{pmatrix} x_1 \\ x_2 \\ \vdots \\ x_n \end{pmatrix}$, where

$$x_k = \frac{1}{|\mathbf{A}|} |\mathbf{A}(k; \mathbf{B})|$$

and $\mathbf{A}(k; \mathbf{B})$ is the matrix obtained from $\mathbf{A}$ by replacing column k of $\mathbf{A}$ by $\mathbf{B}$. ■

Here is a heuristic argument to suggest why this works. Let

$$\mathbf{B} = \begin{pmatrix} b_1 \\ b_2 \\ \vdots \\ b_n \end{pmatrix}.$$

Multiply column k of $\mathbf{A}$ by x_k. The determinant of the resulting matrix is $x_k\,|\mathbf{A}|$, so

$$x_k\,|\mathbf{A}| = \begin{vmatrix} a_{11} & a_{12} & \cdots & a_{1k}x_k & \cdots & a_{1n} \\ a_{21} & a_{22} & \cdots & a_{2k}x_k & \cdots & a_{2n} \\ \vdots & \vdots & \vdots & \vdots & \vdots & \vdots \\ a_{n1} & a_{n2} & \cdots & a_{nk}x_k & \cdots & a_{nn} \end{vmatrix}.$$

For each $j \neq k$, add x_j times column j to column k. This Type III operation does not change the value of the determinant, and we get

$$x_k\,|\mathbf{A}| = \begin{vmatrix} a_{11} & a_{12} & \cdots & a_{11}x_1+a_{12}x_2+\cdots+a_{1n}x_n & \cdots & a_{1n} \\ a_{21} & a_{22} & \cdots & a_{21}x_1+a_{22}x_2+\cdots+a_{2n}a_n & \cdots & a_{2n} \\ \vdots & \vdots & \vdots & \vdots & \vdots & \vdots \\ a_{n1} & a_{n2} & \cdots & a_{n1}x_1+a_{n2}x_2+\cdots+a_{nn}x_n & \cdots & a_{nn} \end{vmatrix}$$

$$= \begin{vmatrix} a_{11} & a_{12} & \cdots & b_1 & \cdots & a_{1n} \\ a_{21} & a_{22} & \cdots & b_2 & \cdots & a_{2n} \\ \vdots & \vdots & \vdots & \vdots & \vdots & \vdots \\ a_{n1} & a_{n2} & \cdots & b_n & \cdots & a_{nn} \end{vmatrix} = |\mathbf{A}(k;\mathbf{B})|.$$

Solving for x_k yields the conclusion of Cramer's Rule.

EXAMPLE 8.6

Solve the system

$$x_1 - 3x_2 - 4x_3 = 1$$
$$-x_1 + x_2 - 3x_3 = 14$$
$$x_2 - 3x_3 = 5.$$

The matrix of coefficients is

$$\mathbf{A} = \begin{pmatrix} 1 & -3 & -4 \\ -1 & 1 & -3 \\ 0 & 1 & -3 \end{pmatrix}.$$

We find that $|\mathbf{A}| = 13$. By Cramer's rule,

$$x_1 = \frac{1}{13}\begin{vmatrix} 1 & -3 & -4 \\ 14 & 1 & -3 \\ 5 & 1 & -3 \end{vmatrix} = -\frac{117}{13} = -9,$$

$$x_2 = \frac{1}{13}\begin{vmatrix} 1 & 1 & -4 \\ -1 & 14 & -3 \\ 0 & 5 & -3 \end{vmatrix} = -\frac{10}{13},$$

$$x_3 = \frac{1}{13}\begin{vmatrix} 1 & -3 & 1 \\ -1 & 1 & 14 \\ 0 & 1 & 5 \end{vmatrix} = -\frac{25}{13}. \quad\blacksquare$$

Cramer's rule is not as efficient as the Gauss-Jordan reduction. Gauss-Jordan also applies to homogeneous systems, and to systems with different numbers of equations than unknowns. However, Cramer's rule does provide a formula for the solution, and this is useful in some contexts.

In each of Problems 1 through 10, either find the solution by Cramer's rule or show that the rule does not apply.

1.
$$15x_1 - 4x_2 = 5$$
$$8x_1 + x_2 = -4$$

2.
$$x_1 + 4x_2 = 3$$
$$x_1 + x_2 = 0$$

3.
$$8x_1 - 4x_2 + 3x_3 = 0$$
$$x_1 + 5x_2 - x_3 = -5$$
$$-2x_1 + 6x_2 + x_3 = -4$$

4.
$$5x_1 - 6x_2 + x_3 = 4$$
$$-x_1 + 3x_2 - 4x_3 = 5$$
$$2x_1 + 3x_2 + x_3 = -8$$

5.
$$x_1 + x_2 - 3x_3 = 0$$
$$x_2 - 4x_3 = 0$$
$$x_1 - x_2 - x_3 = 5$$

6.
$$6x_1 + 4x_2 - x_3 + 3x_4 - x_5 = 7$$
$$x_1 - 4x_2 + x_5 = -5$$
$$x_1 - 3x_2 + x_3 - 4x_5 = 0$$
$$-2x_1 + x_3 - 2x_5 = 4$$
$$x_3 - x_4 - x_5 = 8$$

7.
$$2x_1 - 4x_2 + x_3 - x_4 = 6$$
$$x_2 - 3x_3 = 10$$
$$x_1 - 4x_3 = 0$$
$$x_2 - x_3 + 2x_4 = 4$$

8.
$$2x_1 - 3x_2 + x_4 = 2$$
$$x_2 - x_3 + x_4 = 2$$
$$x_3 - 2x_4 = 5$$
$$x_1 - 3x_2 + 4x_3 = 0$$

9.
$$14x_1 - 3x_3 = 5$$
$$2x_1 - 4x_3 + x_4 = 2$$
$$x_1 - x_2 + x_3 - 3x_4 = 1$$
$$x_3 - 4x_4 = -5$$

10.
$$x_2 - 4x_4 = 18$$
$$x_1 - x_2 + 3x_3 = -1$$
$$x_1 + x_2 - 3x_3 + x_4 = 5$$
$$x_2 + 3x_4 = 0$$

8.9 The Matrix Tree Theorem

In 1847, G.R. Kirchhoff published a classic paper in which he derived many of the electrical circuit laws that bear his name. One of these is the *matrix tree theorem*, which we will discuss now.

Figure 8.1 shows a typical electrical circuit. The underlying geometry of the circuit is shown in Figure 8.2. This diagram of points and connecting lines is called a *graph*, and was seen in the context of the movement of atoms in crystals in Section 7.1.5. A *labeled graph* has symbols attached to the points.

Some of Kirchhoff's results depend on geometric properties of the circuit's underlying graph. One such property is the arrangement of the closed loops. Another is the number of spanning trees in the labeled graph. A *spanning tree* is a collection of lines in the graph forming no closed loops, but containing a path between any two points of the graph. Figure 8.3 shows a labeled graph and two spanning trees in this graph.

Kirchhoff derived a relationship between deteminants and the number of labeled trees in a graph.

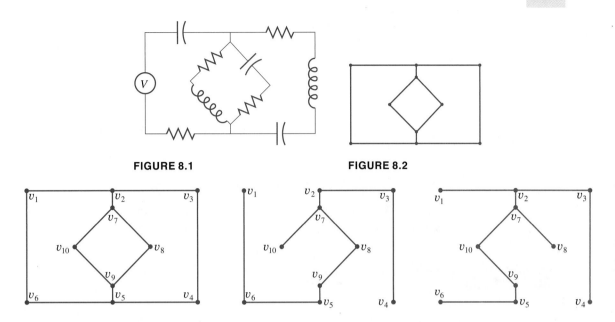

FIGURE 8.1   **FIGURE 8.2**

FIGURE 8.3 *A labeled graph and two of its spanning trees.*

THEOREM 8.13 *Matrix Tree Theorem*

Let G be a graph with vertices labeled $v_1, \ldots, v_n$. Form an $n \times n$ matrix $\mathbf{T} = [t_{ij}]$ as follows. If $i = j$, then t_{ii} is the number of lines to v_i in the graph. If $i \neq j$, then $t_{ij} = 0$ if there is no line between v_i and v_j in G, and $t_{ij} = -1$ if there is such a line. Then, all cofactors of $\mathbf{T}$ are equal, and their common value is the number of spanning trees in G. ■

EXAMPLE 8.7

For the labeled graph of Figure 8.4, $\mathbf{T}$ is the 7×7 matrix

$$
T = \begin{pmatrix}
3 & -1 & 0 & 0 & 0 & -1 & -1 \\
-1 & 3 & -1 & -1 & 0 & 0 & 0 \\
0 & -1 & 3 & -1 & 0 & -1 & 0 \\
0 & -1 & -1 & 4 & -1 & 0 & -1 \\
0 & 0 & 0 & -1 & 3 & -1 & -1 \\
-1 & 0 & -1 & 0 & -1 & 4 & -1 \\
-1 & 0 & 0 & -1 & -1 & -1 & 4
\end{pmatrix}.
$$

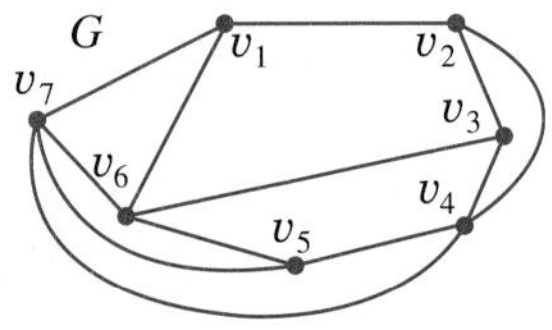

FIGURE 8.4 *Graph G.*

Evaluate any cofactor of **T**. For example, covering up row 1 and column 1, we have

$$(-1)^{1+1} M_{11} = \begin{vmatrix} 3 & -1 & -1 & 0 & 0 & 0 \\ -1 & 3 & -1 & 0 & -1 & 0 \\ -1 & -1 & 4 & -1 & 0 & -1 \\ 0 & 0 & -1 & 3 & -1 & -1 \\ 0 & -1 & 0 & -1 & 4 & -1 \\ 0 & 0 & -1 & -1 & -1 & 4 \end{vmatrix}$$

$$= 386.$$

Evaluation of any cofactor of **T** yields the same result. ∎

Even with this small graph, it would clearly be impractical to enumerate the spanning trees by attempting to list them all.

SECTION 8.9 PROBLEMS

1. Find the number of spanning trees in the graph of Figure 8.5.

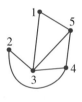

FIGURE 8.5

2. Find the number of spanning trees in the graph of Figure 8.6.

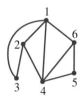

FIGURE 8.6

3. Find the number of spanning trees in the graph of Figure 8.7.

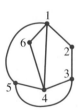

FIGURE 8.7

4. Find the number of spanning trees in the graph of Figure 8.8.

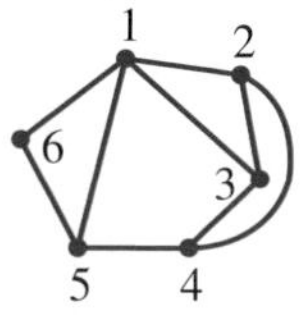

FIGURE 8.8

5. Find the number of spanning trees in the graph of Figure 8.9.

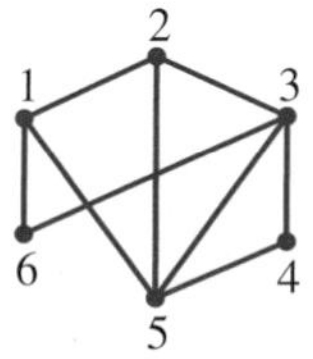

FIGURE 8.9

6. A complete graph on n points consists of n points with a line between each pair of points. This graph is often denoted K_n. With the points labeled $1, 2, \ldots, n$, show that the number of spanning trees in K_n is n^{n-2} for $n = 3, 4, \ldots$.

CHAPTER 9

Eigenvalues, Diagonalization, and Special Matrices

Suppose $\mathbf{A}$ is an $n \times n$ matrix of real numbers. If we write an n-vector $\mathbf{E}$ as a column

$$\mathbf{E} = \begin{pmatrix} \alpha_1 \\ \alpha_2 \\ \vdots \\ \alpha_n \end{pmatrix},$$

then $\mathbf{AE}$ is an $n \times 1$ matrix which we may also think of as an n-vector. We may therefore consider $\mathbf{A}$ as an operator that moves vectors about in R^n. Because $\mathbf{A}(a\mathbf{E}_1 + b\mathbf{E}_2) = a\mathbf{AE}_1 + b\mathbf{AE}_2$, $\mathbf{A}$ is called a *linear operator*.

Vectors have directions associated with them. Depending on $\mathbf{A}$, the direction of $\mathbf{AE}$ will generally be different from that of $\mathbf{E}$. It may happen, however, that for some vector $\mathbf{E}$, $\mathbf{AE}$ and $\mathbf{E}$ are parallel. In this event there is a number λ such that $\mathbf{AE} = \lambda\mathbf{E}$. Then λ is called an *eigenvalue* of $\mathbf{A}$, with $\mathbf{E}$ an associated *eigenvector*.

The idea of an operator moving a vector to a parallel position is simple and geometrically appealing. It also has powerful ramifications in a variety of contexts. Eigenvalues contain important information about the solutions of systems of differential equations, and in models of physical phenomena may they have physical significance as well (such as the modes of vibration of a mechanical system, or the energy states of an atom).

9.1   Eigenvalues and Eigenvectors

Let $\mathbf{A}$ be an $n \times n$ matrix of real or complex numbers.

DEFINITION 9.1   *Eigenvalues and Eigenvectors*

A real or complex number λ is an eigenvalue of $\mathbf{A}$ if there is a nonzero $n \times 1$ matrix (vector) $\mathbf{E}$ such that

$$\mathbf{AE} = \lambda\mathbf{E}.$$

Any nonzero vector $\mathbf{E}$ satisfying this relationship is called an eigenvector associated with the eigenvalue λ.

Eigenvalues are also known as *characteristic values* of a matrix, and eigenvectors can be called *characteristic vectors*.

We will typically write eigenvectors as column matrices and think of them as vectors in R^n. If an eigenvector has complex components, we may think of it as a vector in C^n, which consists of n-tuples of complex numbers. Since an eigenvector must be nonzero vector, at least one component is nonzero.

If α is a nonzero scalar and $\mathbf{AE} = \lambda\mathbf{E}$, then

$$\mathbf{A}(\alpha\mathbf{E}) = \alpha(\mathbf{AE}) = \alpha(\lambda\mathbf{E}) = \lambda(\alpha\mathbf{E}).$$

This means that nonzero scalar multiples of eigenvectors are again eigenvectors.

EXAMPLE 9.1

Since

$$\begin{pmatrix} 1 & 0 \\ 0 & 0 \end{pmatrix}\begin{pmatrix} 0 \\ 4 \end{pmatrix} = \begin{pmatrix} 0 \\ 0 \end{pmatrix} = 0\begin{pmatrix} 0 \\ 4 \end{pmatrix},$$

0 is an eigenvalue of this matrix, with $\begin{pmatrix} 0 \\ 4 \end{pmatrix}$ an associated eigenvector. Although the zero vector cannot be an eigenvector, the number zero can be an eigenvalue of a matrix. For any scalar $\alpha \neq 0$, $\begin{pmatrix} 0 \\ 4\alpha \end{pmatrix}$ is also an eigenvector associated with the eigenvalue 0. ∎

EXAMPLE 9.2

Let

$$\mathbf{A} = \begin{pmatrix} 1 & -1 & 0 \\ 0 & 1 & 1 \\ 0 & 0 & -1 \end{pmatrix}.$$

Then 1 is an eigenvalue with associated eigenvector $\begin{pmatrix} 6 \\ 0 \\ 0 \end{pmatrix}$, because

$$\mathbf{A}\begin{pmatrix} 6 \\ 0 \\ 0 \end{pmatrix} = \begin{pmatrix} 6 \\ 0 \\ 0 \end{pmatrix} = 1\begin{pmatrix} 6 \\ 0 \\ 0 \end{pmatrix}.$$

Because any nonzero multiple of an eigenvector is an eigenvector, then $\begin{pmatrix} \alpha \\ 0 \\ 0 \end{pmatrix}$ is also an eigenvector associated with eigenvalue 1, for any nonzero number α.

Another eigenvalue of $\mathbf{A}$ is -1, with associated eigenvector $\begin{pmatrix} 1 \\ 2 \\ -4 \end{pmatrix}$, because

$$\begin{pmatrix} 1 & -1 & 0 \\ 0 & 1 & 1 \\ 0 & 0 & -1 \end{pmatrix}\begin{pmatrix} 1 \\ 2 \\ -4 \end{pmatrix}$$

$$= \begin{pmatrix} -1 \\ -2 \\ 4 \end{pmatrix} = -1\begin{pmatrix} 1 \\ 2 \\ -4 \end{pmatrix}.$$

Again, any vector $\begin{pmatrix} \alpha \\ 2\alpha \\ -4\alpha \end{pmatrix}$, with $\alpha \neq 0$, is an eigenvector associated with -1. ∎

We would like a way of finding all of the eigenvalues of a matrix $\mathbf{A}$. The machinery to do this is at our disposal, and we reason as follows. For λ to be an eigenvalue of $\mathbf{A}$, there must be an associated eigenvector $\mathbf{E}$, and $\mathbf{AE} = \lambda\mathbf{E}$. Then $\lambda\mathbf{E} - \mathbf{AE} = \mathbf{O}$, or

$$\lambda\mathbf{I}_n\mathbf{E} - \mathbf{AE} = \mathbf{O}.$$

The identity matrix was inserted so we could write the last equation as

$$(\lambda\mathbf{I}_n - \mathbf{A})\mathbf{E} = \mathbf{O}.$$

This makes $\mathbf{E}$ a nontrivial solution of the $n \times n$ system of linear equations

$$(\lambda\mathbf{I}_n - \mathbf{A})\mathbf{X} = \mathbf{O}.$$

But this system can have a nontrivial solution if and only if the coefficient matrix has determinant zero, that is, $|\lambda\mathbf{I}_n - \mathbf{A}| = 0$. Thus λ is an eigenvalue of $\mathbf{A}$ exactly when $|\lambda\mathbf{I}_n - \mathbf{A}| = 0$. This is the equation

$$\begin{vmatrix} \lambda - a_{11} & -a_{12} & \cdots & -a_{1n} \\ -a_{21} & \lambda - a_{22} & \cdots & -a_{2n} \\ \vdots & \vdots & \vdots & \vdots \\ -a_{n1} & -a_{n2} & \cdots & \lambda - a_{nn} \end{vmatrix} = 0.$$

When the determinant on the left is expanded, it is a polynomial of degree n in λ, called the *characteristic polynomial of* $\mathbf{A}$. The roots of this polynomial are the eigenvalues of $\mathbf{A}$. Corresponding to any root λ, any nontrivial solution $\mathbf{E}$ of $(\lambda\mathbf{I}_n - \mathbf{A})\mathbf{X} = \mathbf{O}$ is an eigenvector associated with λ.

We will summarize these conclusions.

THEOREM 9.1

Let $\mathbf{A}$ be an $n \times n$ matrix of real or complex numbers. Then

1. λ is an eigenvalue of $\mathbf{A}$ if and only if $|\lambda \mathbf{I}_n - \mathbf{A}| = 0$.
2. If λ is an eigenvalue of $\mathbf{A}$, then any nontrivial solution of $(\lambda \mathbf{I}_n - \mathbf{A})\mathbf{X} = \mathbf{O}$ is an associated eigenvector. ∎

DEFINITION 9.2 *Characteristic Polynomial*

The polynomial $|\lambda \mathbf{I}_n - \mathbf{A}|$ is the characteristic polynomial of $\mathbf{A}$, and is denoted $p_{\mathbf{A}}(\lambda)$.

If $\mathbf{A}$ is $n \times n$, then $p_{\mathbf{A}}(\lambda)$ is an nth degree polynomial with real or complex coefficients determined by the elements of $\mathbf{A}$. This polynomial therefore has n roots, though some may be repeated. An $n \times n$ matrix $\mathbf{A}$ always has n eigenvalues $\lambda_1, \ldots, \lambda_n$, in which each eigenvalue is listed according to its multiplicity as a root of the characteristic polynomial. For example, if

$$p_{\mathbf{A}}(\lambda) = (\lambda - 1)(\lambda - 3)^2(\lambda - i)^4$$

we list 7 eigenvalues: $1, 3, 3, i, i, i, i$. The eigenvalue 3 has multiplicity 2 and i has multiplicity 4.

EXAMPLE 9.3

Let

$$\mathbf{A} = \begin{pmatrix} 1 & -1 & 0 \\ 0 & 1 & 1 \\ 0 & 0 & -1 \end{pmatrix}$$

as in Example 9.2. The characteristic polynomial is

$$p_{\mathbf{A}}(\lambda) = \begin{vmatrix} \lambda - 1 & 1 & 0 \\ 0 & \lambda - 1 & -1 \\ 0 & 0 & \lambda + 1 \end{vmatrix}$$

$$= (\lambda - 1)^2(\lambda + 1).$$

The eigenvalues of $\mathbf{A}$ are $1, 1, -1$.

To find eigenvectors associated with eigenvalue 1, solve

$$(1\mathbf{I}_3 - \mathbf{A})\mathbf{X} = \begin{pmatrix} 0 & 1 & 0 \\ 0 & 0 & -1 \\ 0 & 0 & 2 \end{pmatrix} \mathbf{X} = \mathbf{O}.$$

This has general solution

$$\begin{pmatrix} \alpha \\ 0 \\ 0 \end{pmatrix}$$

and these are the eigenvectors associated with eigenvalue 1, with $\alpha \neq 0$.

For eigenvectors associated with -1, solve

$$(-1\mathbf{I}_3 - \mathbf{A})\mathbf{X} = \begin{pmatrix} -2 & 1 & 0 \\ 0 & -2 & -1 \\ 0 & 0 & 0 \end{pmatrix} \mathbf{X} = \mathbf{O}.$$

The general solution is

$$\begin{pmatrix} \beta \\ 2\beta \\ -4\beta \end{pmatrix}$$

and these are the eigenvectors associated with eigenvalue -1, as long as $\beta \neq 0$. ∎

EXAMPLE 9.4

Let

$$\mathbf{A} = \begin{pmatrix} 1 & -2 \\ 2 & 0 \end{pmatrix}.$$

The characteristic polynomial is

$$p_\mathbf{A}(x) = \left| \lambda \begin{pmatrix} 1 & 0 \\ 0 & 1 \end{pmatrix} - \begin{pmatrix} 1 & -2 \\ 2 & 0 \end{pmatrix} \right|$$

$$= \left| \begin{matrix} \lambda - 1 & 2 \\ -2 & \lambda \end{matrix} \right| = \lambda(\lambda - 1) + 4 = \lambda^2 - \lambda + 4.$$

This has roots $(1 + \sqrt{15}i)/2$ and $(1 - \sqrt{15}i)/2$, and these are the eigenvalues of $\mathbf{A}$. Even though $\mathbf{A}$ has real elements, the eigenvalues may be complex.

To find eigenvectors associated with $(1 + \sqrt{15}i)/2$, solve the system $(\lambda \mathbf{I}_2 - \mathbf{A})\mathbf{X} = \mathbf{O}$, which for this λ is

$$\left[\frac{1 + \sqrt{15}i}{2} \begin{pmatrix} 1 & 0 \\ 0 & 1 \end{pmatrix} - \begin{pmatrix} 1 & -2 \\ 2 & 0 \end{pmatrix} \right] \mathbf{X} = \mathbf{O}.$$

This is the system

$$\begin{pmatrix} \frac{1+\sqrt{15}i}{2} - 1 & 2 \\ -2 & \frac{1+\sqrt{15}i}{2} \end{pmatrix} \begin{pmatrix} x_1 \\ x_2 \end{pmatrix} = \begin{pmatrix} 0 \\ 0 \end{pmatrix}$$

or

$$\frac{-1 + \sqrt{15}i}{2} x_1 + 2x_2 = 0$$

$$-2x_1 + \frac{1 + \sqrt{15}i}{2} x_2 = 0.$$

We find the general solution of this system to be

$$\alpha \begin{pmatrix} 1 \\ \frac{1 - \sqrt{15}i}{4} \end{pmatrix},$$

and this is an eigenvector associated with the eigenvalue $\frac{1+\sqrt{15}i}{2}$ for any nonzero scalar α.

Corresponding to the eigenvalue $\frac{1-\sqrt{15}i}{2}$ solve the system

$$\begin{pmatrix} \frac{1-\sqrt{15}i}{2} - 1 & 2 \\ -2 & \frac{1-\sqrt{15}i}{2} \end{pmatrix} \mathbf{X} = \mathbf{O},$$

obtaining the general solution

$$\beta \begin{pmatrix} 1 \\ \frac{1+\sqrt{15}i}{4} \end{pmatrix}.$$

This is an eigenvector corresponding to the eigenvalue $\frac{1-\sqrt{15}i}{2}$ for any $\beta \neq 0$. ∎

Finding the eigenvalues of a matrix is equivalent to finding the roots of an nth degree polynomial, and if $n \geq 3$ this may be difficult. There are efficient computer routines which are usually based on the idea of putting the matrix through a sequence of transformations, the effect of which on the eigenvalues is known. This strategy was used previously to evaluate determinants. There are also approximation techniques, but these are sensitive to error. A number that is very close to an eigenvalue may not behave like an eigenvalue.

We will conclude this section with a theorem due to Gerschgorin. If real eigenvalues are plotted on the real line, and complex eigenvalues as points in the plane, Gerschgorin's theorem enables us to delineate regions of the plane containing the eigenvalues.

9.1.1 Gerschgorin's Theorem

THEOREM 9.2 *Gerschgorin*

Let $\mathbf{A}$ be an $n \times n$ matrix of real or complex numbers. For $k = 1, \ldots, n$, let

$$r_k = \sum_{j=1, j \neq k}^{n} |a_{kj}|.$$

Let C_k be the circle of radius r_k centered at (α_k, β_k), where $a_{kk} = \alpha_k + i\beta_k$. Then each eigenvalue of $\mathbf{A}$, when plotted as a point in the complex plane, lies on or within one of the circles $C_1, \ldots, C_n$. ∎

The circles C_k are called *Gerschgorin circles*. For the radius of C_k, read across row k and add the magnitudes of the row elements, omitting the diagonal element a_{kk}. The center of C_k is a_{kk}, plotted as a point in the complex plane. If the Gerschgorin circles are drawn and the disks they bound are shaded, then we have a picture of a region containing all of the eigenvalues of $\mathbf{A}$.

EXAMPLE 9.5

Let

$$\mathbf{A} = \begin{pmatrix} 12i & 1 & 9 & -4 \\ 1 & -6 & 2+i & -1 \\ 4 & 1 & -1 & 4i \\ 1-3i & -9 & 1 & 4-7i \end{pmatrix}.$$

$\mathbf{A}$ has characteristic polynomial

$$p_\mathbf{A}(\lambda) = \lambda^4 + (3-5i)\lambda^3 + (18-4i)\lambda^2 + (290+90i)\lambda + 1374 - 1120i.$$

It is not clear what the roots of this polynomial are. Form the Gerschgorin circles. Their radii are:

$$r_1 = 1 + 9 + 4 = 14,$$

$$r_2 = 1 + \sqrt{5} + 1 = 2 + \sqrt{5},$$

$$r_3 = 4 + 1 + 4 = 9$$

and

$$r_4 = \sqrt{10} + 9 + 1 = 10 + \sqrt{10}.$$

C_1 has radius 14 and center $(0, 12)$, C_2 has radius $2 + \sqrt{5}$ and center $(-6, 0)$, C_3 has radius 9 and center $(-1, 0)$ and C_4 has radius $10 + \sqrt{10}$ and center $(4, -7)$. Figure 9.1 shows the Gerschgorin circles containing the eigenvalues of **A**. ■

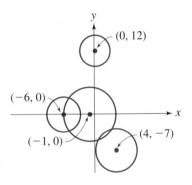

FIGURE 9.1 *Gerschgorin circles.*

Gerschgorin's theorem is not intended as an approximation scheme, since the Gerschgorin circles may have large radii. For some problems, however, just knowing some information about possible locations of eigenvalues can be important. For example, in studies of the stability of fluid flow, it is important to know whether there are eigenvalues in the right half-plane.

SECTION 9.1   PROBLEMS

In each of Problems 1 through 16, (a) find the eigenvalues of the matrix, (b) corresponding to each eigenvalue, find an eigenvector, and (c) sketch the Gerschgorin circles and (approximately) locate the eigenvalues as points in the plane.

1. $\begin{pmatrix} 1 & 3 \\ 2 & 1 \end{pmatrix}$

2. $\begin{pmatrix} -2 & 0 \\ 1 & 4 \end{pmatrix}$

3. $\begin{pmatrix} -5 & 0 \\ 1 & 2 \end{pmatrix}$

4. $\begin{pmatrix} 6 & -2 \\ -3 & 4 \end{pmatrix}$

5. $\begin{pmatrix} 1 & -6 \\ 2 & 2 \end{pmatrix}$

6. $\begin{pmatrix} 0 & 1 \\ 0 & 0 \end{pmatrix}$

7. $\begin{pmatrix} 2 & 0 & 0 \\ 1 & 0 & 2 \\ 0 & 0 & 3 \end{pmatrix}$

8. $\begin{pmatrix} -2 & 1 & 0 \\ 1 & 3 & 0 \\ 0 & 0 & -1 \end{pmatrix}$

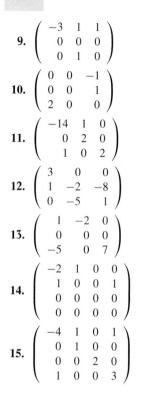

9. $\begin{pmatrix} -3 & 1 & 1 \\ 0 & 0 & 0 \\ 0 & 1 & 0 \end{pmatrix}$

10. $\begin{pmatrix} 0 & 0 & -1 \\ 0 & 0 & 1 \\ 2 & 0 & 0 \end{pmatrix}$

11. $\begin{pmatrix} -14 & 1 & 0 \\ 0 & 2 & 0 \\ 1 & 0 & 2 \end{pmatrix}$

12. $\begin{pmatrix} 3 & 0 & 0 \\ 1 & -2 & -8 \\ 0 & -5 & 1 \end{pmatrix}$

13. $\begin{pmatrix} 1 & -2 & 0 \\ 0 & 0 & 0 \\ -5 & 0 & 7 \end{pmatrix}$

14. $\begin{pmatrix} -2 & 1 & 0 & 0 \\ 1 & 0 & 0 & 1 \\ 0 & 0 & 0 & 0 \\ 0 & 0 & 0 & 0 \end{pmatrix}$

15. $\begin{pmatrix} -4 & 1 & 0 & 1 \\ 0 & 1 & 0 & 0 \\ 0 & 0 & 2 & 0 \\ 1 & 0 & 0 & 3 \end{pmatrix}$

16. $\begin{pmatrix} 5 & 1 & 0 & 9 \\ 0 & 1 & 0 & 9 \\ 0 & 0 & 0 & 9 \\ 0 & 0 & 0 & 0 \end{pmatrix}$

17. Show that the eigenvalues of $\begin{pmatrix} \alpha & \beta \\ \beta & \gamma \end{pmatrix}$, in which α, β and γ are real numbers, are real.

18. Show that the eigenvalues of $\begin{pmatrix} \alpha & \beta & \gamma \\ \beta & \delta & \epsilon \\ \gamma & \epsilon & \zeta \end{pmatrix}$ are real, if all of the matrix elements are real.

19. Let λ be an eigenvalue of $\mathbf{A}$ with eigenvector $\mathbf{E}$. Show that, for any positive integer k, λ^k is an eigenvalue of $\mathbf{A}^k$, with eigenvector $\mathbf{E}$.

20. Let λ be an eigenvalue of $\mathbf{A}$ with eigenvector $\mathbf{E}$, and μ an eigenvalue of $\mathbf{A}$ with eigenvector $\mathbf{L}$. Suppose $\lambda \neq \mu$. Show that $\mathbf{E}$ and $\mathbf{L}$ are linearly independent as vectors in R^n.

21. Let $\mathbf{A}$ be an $n \times n$ matrix. Prove that the constant term of $p_{\mathbf{A}}(x)$ is $(-1)^n |\mathbf{A}|$. Use this to show that any singular matrix must have zero as one of its eigenvalues.

9.2   Diagonalization of Matrices

We have referred to the elements a_{ii} of a square matrix as its *main diagonal elements*. All other elements are called *off-diagonal elements*.

DEFINITION 9.3   *Diagonal Matrix*

A square matrix having all off-diagonal elements equal to zero is called a diagonal matrix.

We often write a diagonal matrix having main diagonal elements $d_1, \ldots, d_n$ as

$$\begin{pmatrix} d_1 & & & O \\ & d_2 & & \\ & & \ddots & \\ O & & & d_n \end{pmatrix},$$

with O in the upper right and lower left corners to indicate that all off-diagonal elements are zero.

Here are some properties of diagonal matrices that make them pleasant to work with.

THEOREM 9.3

Let

$$\mathbf{D} = \begin{pmatrix} d_1 & & & O \\ & d_2 & & \\ & & \ddots & \\ O & & & d_n \end{pmatrix} \quad \text{and} \quad \mathbf{W} = \begin{pmatrix} w_1 & & & O \\ & w_2 & & \\ & & \ddots & \\ O & & & w_n \end{pmatrix}.$$

Then

1.

$$\mathbf{DW} = \mathbf{WD} = \begin{pmatrix} d_1 w_1 & & & O \\ & d_2 w_2 & & \\ & & \ddots & \\ O & & & d_n w_n \end{pmatrix}.$$

2. $|\mathbf{D}| = d_1 d_2 \cdots d_n$.

3. $\mathbf{D}$ is nonsingular if and only if each main diagonal element is nonzero.

4. If each $d_j \neq 0$, then

$$\mathbf{D}^{-1} = \begin{pmatrix} 1/d_1 & & & O \\ & 1/d_2 & & \\ & & \ddots & \\ O & & & 1/d_n \end{pmatrix}.$$

5. The eigenvalues of $\mathbf{D}$ are its main diagonal elements.

6. An eigenvector associated with d_j is

$$\begin{pmatrix} 0 \\ \vdots \\ 0 \\ 1 \\ 0 \\ \vdots \\ 0 \end{pmatrix},$$

with 1 in row j and all other elements zero. ∎

We leave a proof of these conclusions to the student. Notice that (2) follows from the fact that a diagonal matrix is upper (and lower) triangular.

"Most" square matrices are not diagonal matrices. However, some matrices are related to diagonal matrices in a way that enables us to utilize the nice features of diagonal matrices.

DEFINITION 9.4 *Diagonalizable Matrix*

An $n \times n$ matrix $\mathbf{A}$ is diagonalizable if there exists an $n \times n$ matrix $\mathbf{P}$ such that $\mathbf{P}^{-1}\mathbf{AP}$ is a diagonal matrix.

When such $\mathbf{P}$ exists, we say that $\mathbf{P}$ diagonalizes $\mathbf{A}$.

The following theorem not only tells us when a matrix is diagonalizable, but also how to find a matrix **P** that diagonalizes it.

THEOREM 9.4 *Diagonalizability*

Let **A** be an $n \times n$ matrix. Then **A** is diagonalizable if it has n linearly independent eigenvectors. Further, if **P** is the $n \times n$ matrix having these eigenvectors as columns, then $\mathbf{P}^{-1}\mathbf{A}\mathbf{P}$ is the diagonal matrix having the corresponding eigenvalues down its main diagonal. ■

Here is what this means. Suppose $\lambda_1, \ldots, \lambda_n$ are the eigenvalues of **A** (some possibly repeated), and $\mathbf{V}_1, \ldots, \mathbf{V}_n$ are corresponding eigenvectors. If these eigenvectors are linearly independent, we can form a nonsingular matrix **P** using $\mathbf{V}_j$ as column j. It is the linear independence of the eigenvectors that makes **P** nonsingular. We claim that $\mathbf{P}^{-1}\mathbf{A}\mathbf{P}$ is the diagonal matrix having the eigenvalues of **A** down its main diagonal, in the order corresponding to the order the eigenvectors were listed as columns of **P**.

EXAMPLE 9.6

Let

$$\mathbf{A} = \begin{pmatrix} -1 & 4 \\ 0 & 3 \end{pmatrix}.$$

A has eigenvalues $-1, 3$ and corresponding eigenvectors $\begin{pmatrix} 1 \\ 0 \end{pmatrix}$ and $\begin{pmatrix} 1 \\ 1 \end{pmatrix}$ respectively. Form

$$\mathbf{P} = \begin{pmatrix} 1 & 1 \\ 0 & 1 \end{pmatrix}.$$

Because the eigenvectors are linearly independent, this matrix is nonsingular (note that $|\mathbf{P}| \neq 0$). We find that

$$\mathbf{P}^{-1} = \begin{pmatrix} 1 & -1 \\ 0 & 1 \end{pmatrix}.$$

Now compute

$$\mathbf{P}^{-1}\mathbf{A}\mathbf{P} = \begin{pmatrix} 1 & -1 \\ 0 & 1 \end{pmatrix} \begin{pmatrix} -1 & 4 \\ 0 & 3 \end{pmatrix} \begin{pmatrix} 1 & 1 \\ 0 & 1 \end{pmatrix}$$

$$= \begin{pmatrix} -1 & 0 \\ 0 & 3 \end{pmatrix},$$

which has the eigenvalues down the main diagonal, corresponding to the order in which the eigenvectors were written as columns of **P**.

If we use the other order in writing the eigenvectors as columns, and define

$$\mathbf{Q} = \begin{pmatrix} 1 & 1 \\ 1 & 0 \end{pmatrix},$$

then we get

$$\mathbf{Q}^{-1}\mathbf{A}\mathbf{Q} = \begin{pmatrix} 3 & 0 \\ 0 & -1 \end{pmatrix}. \quad ■$$

Any linearly independent eigenvectors can be used in this diagonalization process. For example, if we use $\begin{pmatrix} 6 \\ 0 \end{pmatrix}$ and $\begin{pmatrix} -4 \\ -4 \end{pmatrix}$, which are simply nonzero scalar multiples of the previously used eigenvectors, then we can define

$$\mathbf{S} = \begin{pmatrix} 6 & -4 \\ 0 & -4 \end{pmatrix}$$

and now

$$\mathbf{S}^{-1}\mathbf{AS} = \begin{pmatrix} -1 & 0 \\ 0 & 3 \end{pmatrix}.$$

EXAMPLE 9.7

Here is an example with more complicated arithmetic, but the idea remains the same. Let

$$\mathbf{A} = \begin{pmatrix} -1 & 1 & 3 \\ 2 & 1 & 4 \\ 1 & 0 & -2 \end{pmatrix}.$$

The eigenvalues are $-1, -\frac{1}{2} + \frac{1}{2}\sqrt{29}, -\frac{1}{2} - \frac{1}{2}\sqrt{29}$, with corresponding eigenvectors, respectively,

$$\begin{pmatrix} 1 \\ -3 \\ 1 \end{pmatrix}, \begin{pmatrix} 3 + \sqrt{29} \\ 10 + 2\sqrt{29} \\ 2 \end{pmatrix}, \begin{pmatrix} 3 - \sqrt{29} \\ 10 - 2\sqrt{29} \\ 2 \end{pmatrix}.$$

These are linearly independent. Form the matrix

$$\mathbf{P} = \begin{pmatrix} 1 & 3 + \sqrt{29} & 3 - \sqrt{29} \\ -3 & 10 + 2\sqrt{29} & 10 - 2\sqrt{29} \\ 1 & 2 & 2 \end{pmatrix}.$$

We find that

$$\mathbf{P}^{-1} = \frac{\sqrt{29}}{812} \begin{pmatrix} \frac{232}{\sqrt{29}} & -\frac{116}{\sqrt{29}} & \frac{232}{\sqrt{29}} \\ -16 - 2\sqrt{29} & -1 + \sqrt{29} & -19 + 5\sqrt{29} \\ -16 - 2\sqrt{29} & 1 + \sqrt{29} & 19 + 5\sqrt{29} \end{pmatrix}.$$

Then

$$\mathbf{P}^{-1}\mathbf{AP} = \begin{pmatrix} -1 & 0 & 0 \\ 0 & \frac{-1+\sqrt{29}}{2} & 0 \\ 0 & 0 & \frac{-1-\sqrt{29}}{2} \end{pmatrix}. \ \blacksquare$$

In this example, although we found $\mathbf{P}^{-1}$ explicitly, we did not actually need it to diagonalize $\mathbf{A}$. Theorem 9.4 assures us that $\mathbf{P}^{-1}\mathbf{AP}$ is a diagonal matrix with the eigenvalues of $\mathbf{A}$ down its main diagonal. All we really needed was to know that $\mathbf{A}$ had three linearly independent eigenvectors. This is a useful fact to keep in mind, particularly if $\mathbf{P}$ and $\mathbf{P}^{-1}$ are cumbersome to compute.

EXAMPLE 9.8

Let

$$\mathbf{A} = \begin{pmatrix} -1 & -4 \\ 3 & -2 \end{pmatrix}.$$

The eigenvalues are $(-3 + \sqrt{47}i)/2$ and $(-3 - \sqrt{47}i)/2$. Corresponding eigenvectors are, respectively,

$$\begin{pmatrix} 8 \\ 1 - \sqrt{47}i \end{pmatrix}, \begin{pmatrix} 8 \\ 1 + \sqrt{47}i \end{pmatrix}.$$

Since these eigenvalues are linearly independent, there is a nonsingular 2×2 matrix $\mathbf{P}$ that diagonalizes $\mathbf{A}$:

$$\mathbf{P}^{-1}\mathbf{A}\mathbf{P} = \begin{pmatrix} \frac{-3+\sqrt{47}i}{2} & 0 \\ 0 & \frac{-3-\sqrt{47}i}{2} \end{pmatrix}.$$

Of course, if we need $\mathbf{P}$ for some other calculation, as will occur later, we can write it down:

$$\mathbf{P} = \begin{pmatrix} 8 & 8 \\ 1 - \sqrt{47}i & 1 + \sqrt{47}i \end{pmatrix}.$$

And, if we wish, we can compute

$$\mathbf{P}^{-1} = \frac{\sqrt{47}i}{752} \begin{pmatrix} -1 - i\sqrt{47} & 8 \\ 1 - i\sqrt{47} & -8 \end{pmatrix}.$$

However, even without explicitly writing $\mathbf{P}^{-1}$, we know what $\mathbf{P}^{-1}\mathbf{A}\mathbf{P}$ is. ∎

EXAMPLE 9.9

It is not necessary that $\mathbf{A}$ have n distinct eigenvalues in order to have n linearly independent eigenvectors. For example, let

$$\mathbf{A} = \begin{pmatrix} 5 & -4 & 4 \\ 12 & -11 & 12 \\ 4 & -4 & 5 \end{pmatrix}.$$

The eigenvalues are $1, 1, -3$, with 1 having multiplicity 2. Associated with -3 we find an eigenvector

$$\begin{pmatrix} 1 \\ 3 \\ 1 \end{pmatrix}.$$

To find eigenvectors associated with 1 we must solve the system

$$(\mathbf{I}_3 - \mathbf{A})\mathbf{X} = \begin{pmatrix} -4 & 4 & -4 \\ -12 & 12 & -12 \\ -4 & 4 & -4 \end{pmatrix} \begin{pmatrix} x_1 \\ x_2 \\ x_3 \end{pmatrix} = \begin{pmatrix} 0 \\ 0 \\ 0 \end{pmatrix}.$$

This system has general solution

$$\alpha \begin{pmatrix} 1 \\ 0 \\ -1 \end{pmatrix} + \beta \begin{pmatrix} 0 \\ 1 \\ 1 \end{pmatrix}.$$

We can therefore find two linearly independent eigenvectors associated with eigenvalue 1, for example,

$$\begin{pmatrix} 1 \\ 0 \\ -1 \end{pmatrix} \quad \text{and} \quad \begin{pmatrix} 0 \\ 1 \\ 1 \end{pmatrix}.$$

We can now form the nonsingular matrix

$$\mathbf{P} = \begin{pmatrix} 1 & 1 & 0 \\ 3 & 0 & 1 \\ 1 & -1 & 1 \end{pmatrix}$$

that diagonalizes **A**:

$$\mathbf{P}^{-1}\mathbf{AP} = \begin{pmatrix} -3 & 0 & 0 \\ 0 & 1 & 0 \\ 0 & 0 & 1 \end{pmatrix}. \ \blacksquare$$

Here is a proof of Theorem 9.4, explaining why a matrix **P** formed from linearly independent eigenvectors must diagonalize **A**. The proof makes use of an observation we have made before. When multiplying two $n \times n$ matrices **A** and **B**,

$$\text{column } j \text{ of } \mathbf{AB} = \mathbf{A}(\text{column } j \text{ of } \mathbf{B}).$$

Proof Let the eigenvalues of **A** be $\lambda_1, \ldots, \lambda_n$ and corresponding eigenvectors $\mathbf{V}_1, \ldots, \mathbf{V}_n$. These form the columns of **P**.

Since these eigenvectors are assumed to be linearly independent, the dimension of the column space of **P** is n. Therefore $rank(\mathbf{P}) = n$ and **P** is nonsingular by Theorems 7.15 and 7.26. Now compute $\mathbf{P}^{-1}\mathbf{AP}$ as follows. First,

$$\text{column } j \text{ of } \mathbf{AP} = \mathbf{A}(\text{column } j \text{ of } \mathbf{P}) = \mathbf{AV}_j = \lambda_j \mathbf{V}_j.$$

Thus the columns of **AP** are $\lambda_1 \mathbf{V}_1, \ldots, \lambda_n \mathbf{V}_n$ and **AP** has the form

$$\mathbf{AP} = \begin{pmatrix} | & | & \cdots & | \\ \lambda_1 V_1 & \lambda_2 V_2 & \cdots & \lambda_n V_n \\ | & | & \cdots & | \end{pmatrix}.$$

Then

$$\text{column } j \text{ of } \mathbf{P}^{-1}\mathbf{AP} = \mathbf{P}^{-1}(\text{column } j \text{ of } \mathbf{AP})$$

$$= \mathbf{P}^{-1}[\lambda_j \mathbf{V}_j] = \lambda_j \mathbf{P}^{-1}\mathbf{V}_j.$$

But $\mathbf{V}_j$ is column j of **P**, so

$$\mathbf{P}^{-1}\mathbf{V}_j = \text{column } j \text{ of } \mathbf{P}^{-1}\mathbf{P} = \begin{pmatrix} 0 \\ 0 \\ \vdots \\ 1 \\ \vdots \\ 0 \end{pmatrix}$$

in which the column matrix on the right has all zero elements except 1 in row j. Combining the last two equations, we have

$$\text{column } j \text{ of } \mathbf{P}^{-1}\mathbf{AP} = \lambda_j \mathbf{P}^{-1}\mathbf{V}_j = \lambda_j \begin{pmatrix} 0 \\ 0 \\ \vdots \\ 1 \\ \vdots \\ 0 \end{pmatrix} = \begin{pmatrix} 0 \\ 0 \\ \vdots \\ \lambda_j \\ \vdots \\ 0 \end{pmatrix}.$$

We now know the columns of $\mathbf{P}^{-1}\mathbf{AP}$, and putting them together gives us

$$\mathbf{P}^{-1}\mathbf{AP} = \begin{pmatrix} \lambda_1 & 0 & 0 & \cdots & 0 \\ 0 & \lambda_2 & 0 & \cdots & 0 \\ 0 & 0 & \lambda_3 & \cdots & 0 \\ \vdots & \vdots & \vdots & \vdots & \vdots \\ 0 & 0 & 0 & \cdots & \lambda_n \end{pmatrix}. \quad \blacksquare$$

We can strengthen the conclusions of Theorem 9.4. So far, if $\mathbf{A}$ has n linearly independent eigenvectors, then we can diagonalize $\mathbf{A}$. We will now show that this is the only time $\mathbf{A}$ can be diagonalized. Further, if, for any $\mathbf{Q}$, $\mathbf{Q}^{-1}\mathbf{AQ}$ is a diagonal matrix, then $\mathbf{Q}$ must have linearly independent eigenvectors of $\mathbf{A}$ as its columns.

THEOREM 9.5

Let $\mathbf{A}$ be an $n \times n$ diagonalizable matrix. Then $\mathbf{A}$ has n linearly independent eigenvectors. Further, if $\mathbf{Q}^{-1}\mathbf{AQ}$ is a diagonal matrix, then the diagonal elements of $\mathbf{Q}^{-1}\mathbf{AQ}$ are the eigenvalues of $\mathbf{A}$, and the columns of $\mathbf{Q}$ are corresponding eigenvectors.

Proof Suppose that

$$\mathbf{Q}^{-1}\mathbf{AQ} = \begin{pmatrix} d_1 & & & O \\ & d_2 & & \\ & & \ddots & \\ O & & & d_n \end{pmatrix} = \mathbf{D}.$$

Denote column j of $\mathbf{Q}$ as $\mathbf{V}_j$. Then $\mathbf{V}_1, \ldots, \mathbf{V}_n$ are linearly independent, because $\mathbf{Q}$ is nonsingular. We will show that d_j is an eigenvalue of $\mathbf{A}$, with corresponding eigenvector $\mathbf{V}_j$.

Write $\mathbf{AQ} = \mathbf{QD}$ and compute both sides of this product separately. First, since the columns of $\mathbf{Q}$ are $\mathbf{V}_1, \ldots, \mathbf{V}_n$,

$$\mathbf{QD} = \begin{pmatrix} | & | & \cdots & | \\ \mathbf{V}_1 & \mathbf{V}_2 & \cdots & \mathbf{V}_n \\ | & | & \cdots & | \end{pmatrix} \mathbf{D}$$

$$= \begin{pmatrix} | & | & \cdots & | \\ d_1\mathbf{V}_1 & d_2\mathbf{V}_2 & \cdots & d_n\mathbf{V}_n \\ | & | & \cdots & | \end{pmatrix},$$

a matrix having $d_j \mathbf{V}_j$ as column j. Now compute

$$\mathbf{AQ} = \mathbf{A} \begin{pmatrix} | & | & \cdots & | \\ \mathbf{V}_1 & \mathbf{V}_2 & \cdots & \mathbf{V}_n \\ | & | & \cdots & | \end{pmatrix}$$

$$= \begin{pmatrix} | & | & \cdots & | \\ \mathbf{AV}_1 & \mathbf{AV}_2 & \cdots & \mathbf{AV}_n \\ | & | & \cdots & | \end{pmatrix},$$

a matrix having $\mathbf{AV}_j$ as column j. Since $\mathbf{AQ} = \mathbf{QD}$, then column j of $\mathbf{AQ}$ equals column j of $\mathbf{QD}$, so

$$\mathbf{AV}_j = d_j \mathbf{V}_j$$

which proves that d_j is an eigenvalue of A with associated eigenvector $\mathbf{V}_j$. ∎

As a consequence of this theorem, we see that not every matrix is diagonalizable.

EXAMPLE 9.10

Let

$$\mathbf{B} = \begin{pmatrix} 1 & -1 \\ 0 & 1 \end{pmatrix}.$$

$\mathbf{B}$ has eigenvalues 1, 1, and every eigenvector has the form $\alpha \begin{pmatrix} 1 \\ 0 \end{pmatrix}$. There are not two linearly independent eigenvectors, so $\mathbf{B}$ is not diagonalizable.

We could also proceed here by contradiction. If $\mathbf{B}$ were diagonalizable, then for some $\mathbf{P}$,

$$\mathbf{P}^{-1}\mathbf{AP} = \begin{pmatrix} 1 & 0 \\ 0 & 1 \end{pmatrix}.$$

From Theorem 9.5, the columns of $\mathbf{P}$ must be eigenvectors, so $\mathbf{P}$ must have the form

$$\mathbf{P} = \begin{pmatrix} \alpha & \beta \\ 0 & 0 \end{pmatrix}.$$

But this matrix is singular (it has zero determinant, and its columns are multiples of each other, hence linearly dependent). Thus no matrix can diagonalize $\mathbf{B}$. ∎

The key to diagonalization of an $n \times n$ matrix $\mathbf{A}$ is therefore the existence of n linearly independent eigenvectors. We saw (Example 9.9) that this does not require that the eigenvalues be distinct. However, if $\mathbf{A}$ does have n distinct eigenvalues, we claim that it must have n linearly independent eigenvectors, hence must be diagonalizable.

THEOREM 9.6

Let the $n \times n$ matrix $\mathbf{A}$ have n distinct eigenvalues. Then corresponding eigenvectors are linearly independent.

Proof   We will show by induction that any k distinct eigenvalues have associated with them k linearly independent eigenvectors. For $k = 1$, an eigenvector associated with a single eigenvalue is linearly independent, being a nonzero vector. Now suppose that any $k - 1$ distinct eigenvalues have associated with them $k - 1$ linearly independent eigenvectors. Suppose we have distinct eigenvalues $\lambda_1, \ldots, \lambda_k$. Let $\mathbf{V}_1, \ldots, \mathbf{V}_k$ be associated eigenvectors. We want to show that $\mathbf{V}_1, \ldots, \mathbf{V}_k$ are linearly independent.

If these eigenvectors were linearly dependent, there would be numbers $c_1, \ldots, c_k$ not all zero such that

$$c_1 \mathbf{V}_1 + \cdots + c_k \mathbf{V}_k = \mathbf{O}.$$

By relabeling if necessary, we may suppose for convenience that $c_1 \neq 0$. Now

$$(\lambda_1 \mathbf{I}_n - \mathbf{A})(c_1 \mathbf{V}_1 + \cdots + c_k \mathbf{V}_k) = \mathbf{O}$$

$$= c_1(\lambda_1 \mathbf{I}_n - \mathbf{A})\mathbf{V}_1 + c_2(\lambda_1 \mathbf{I}_n - \mathbf{A})\mathbf{V}_2 + \cdots + c_k(\lambda_1 \mathbf{I}_n - \mathbf{A})\mathbf{V}_k$$

$$= c_1(\lambda_1 \mathbf{V}_1 - \mathbf{A}\mathbf{V}_1) + c_2(\lambda_1 \mathbf{V}_2 - \mathbf{A}\mathbf{V}_2) + \cdots + c_k(\lambda_1 \mathbf{V}_k - \mathbf{A}\mathbf{V}_k)$$

$$= c_1(\lambda_1 \mathbf{V}_1 - \lambda_1 \mathbf{V}_1) + c_2(\lambda_1 \mathbf{V}_2 - \lambda_2 \mathbf{V}_2) + \cdots + c_k(\lambda_1 \mathbf{V}_k - \lambda_k \mathbf{V}_k)$$

$$= c_2(\lambda_1 - \lambda_2)\mathbf{V}_2 + \cdots + c_k(\lambda_1 - \lambda_k)\mathbf{V}_k.$$

But $\mathbf{V}_2, \ldots, \mathbf{V}_k$ are linearly independent by the inductive hypothesis, so each of these coefficients must be zero. Since $\lambda_1 - \lambda_j \neq 0$ for $j = 2, \ldots k$ by the assumption that the eigenvalues are distinct, then

$$c_2 = \cdots = c_k = 0.$$

But then $c_1 \mathbf{V}_1 = \mathbf{O}$. Since $\mathbf{V}_1$ is an eigenvector and cannot be $\mathbf{O}$, then $c_1 = 0$ also, a contradiction. Therefore $\mathbf{V}_1, \ldots, \mathbf{V}_k$ are linearly independent.

COROLLARY 9.1

If an $n \times n$ matrix $\mathbf{A}$ has n distinct eigenvalues, then $\mathbf{A}$ is diagonalizable. ∎

EXAMPLE 9.11

Let

$$\mathbf{A} = \begin{pmatrix} -2 & 0 & 0 & 5 \\ 1 & 3 & 0 & 0 \\ 0 & 4 & 4 & 0 \\ 2 & 0 & 0 & -3 \end{pmatrix}.$$

The eigenvalues of $\mathbf{A}$ are $3, 4, -\frac{5}{2} + \frac{1}{2}\sqrt{41}, -\frac{5}{2} - \frac{1}{2}\sqrt{41}$. Because these are distinct, $\mathbf{A}$ is diagonalizable. For some $\mathbf{P}$,

$$\mathbf{P}^{-1}\mathbf{A}\mathbf{P} = \begin{pmatrix} 3 & 0 & 0 & 0 \\ 0 & 4 & 0 & 0 \\ 0 & 0 & -\frac{5}{2} + \frac{1}{2}\sqrt{41} & 0 \\ 0 & 0 & 0 & -\frac{5}{2} - \frac{1}{2}\sqrt{41} \end{pmatrix}.$$

We do not need to actually produce $\mathbf{P}$ explicitly to conclude this. ∎

In each of Problems 1 through 10, produce a matrix that diagonalizes the given matrix, or show that this matrix is not diagonalizable.

1. $\begin{pmatrix} 0 & -1 \\ 4 & 3 \end{pmatrix}$

2. $\begin{pmatrix} 5 & 3 \\ 1 & 3 \end{pmatrix}$

3. $\begin{pmatrix} 1 & 0 \\ -4 & 1 \end{pmatrix}$

4. $\begin{pmatrix} -5 & 3 \\ 0 & 9 \end{pmatrix}$

5. $\begin{pmatrix} 5 & 0 & 0 \\ 1 & 0 & 3 \\ 0 & 0 & -2 \end{pmatrix}$

6. $\begin{pmatrix} 0 & 0 & 0 \\ 1 & 0 & 2 \\ 0 & 1 & 3 \end{pmatrix}$

7. $\begin{pmatrix} -2 & 0 & 1 \\ 1 & 1 & 0 \\ 0 & 0 & -2 \end{pmatrix}$

8. $\begin{pmatrix} 2 & 0 & 0 \\ 0 & 2 & 1 \\ 0 & -1 & 2 \end{pmatrix}$

9. $\begin{pmatrix} 1 & 0 & 0 & 0 \\ 0 & 4 & 1 & 0 \\ 0 & 0 & -3 & 1 \\ 0 & 0 & 1 & -2 \end{pmatrix}$

10. $\begin{pmatrix} -2 & 0 & 0 & 0 \\ -4 & -2 & 0 & 0 \\ 0 & 0 & -2 & 0 \\ 0 & 0 & 0 & -2 \end{pmatrix}$

11. Suppose $\mathbf{A}^2$ is diagonalizable. Prove that $\mathbf{A}$ is diagonalizable.

12. Let $\mathbf{A}$ have eigenvalues $\lambda_1, \ldots, \lambda_n$ and suppose $\mathbf{P}$ diagonalizes $\mathbf{A}$. Prove that, for any positive integer k,

$$\mathbf{A}^k = \mathbf{P} \begin{pmatrix} \lambda_1^k & & & O \\ & \lambda_2^k & & \\ & & \ddots & \\ O & & & \lambda_n^k \end{pmatrix} \mathbf{P}^{-1}.$$

In each of Problems 13 through 16, compute the indicated power of the matrix, using the idea of Problem 12.

13. $\mathbf{A} = \begin{pmatrix} -1 & 0 \\ 1 & -5 \end{pmatrix} ; \mathbf{A}^{18}$

14. $\mathbf{A} = \begin{pmatrix} -3 & -3 \\ -2 & 4 \end{pmatrix} ; \mathbf{A}^{16}$

15. $\mathbf{A} = \begin{pmatrix} 0 & -2 \\ 1 & 0 \end{pmatrix} ; \mathbf{A}^{43}$

16. $\mathbf{A} = \begin{pmatrix} -2 & 3 \\ 3 & -4 \end{pmatrix} ; \mathbf{A}^{31}$

9.3   Orthogonal and Symmetric Matrices

Recall that the transpose of a matrix is obtained by interchanging the rows with the columns. For example, if

$$\mathbf{A} = \begin{pmatrix} -6 & 3 \\ 1 & -7 \end{pmatrix}$$

then

$$\mathbf{A}^t = \begin{pmatrix} -6 & 1 \\ 3 & -7 \end{pmatrix}.$$

Usually $\mathbf{A}^t$ is simply another matrix. However, in the special circumstance that the transpose of a matrix is its inverse, we call $\mathbf{A}$ an *orthogonal matrix*.

DEFINITION 9.5   *Orthogonal Matrix*

A square matrix $\mathbf{A}$ is orthogonal if and only if $\mathbf{A}\mathbf{A}^t = \mathbf{A}^t\mathbf{A} = \mathbf{I}_n$.

An orthogonal matrix is therefore nonsingular, and we find its inverse simply by taking its transpose.

EXAMPLE 9.12

Let

$$\mathbf{A} = \begin{pmatrix} 0 & \frac{1}{\sqrt{5}} & \frac{2}{\sqrt{5}} \\ 1 & 0 & 0 \\ 0 & \frac{2}{\sqrt{5}} & -\frac{1}{\sqrt{5}} \end{pmatrix}.$$

Then

$$\mathbf{A}\mathbf{A}^t = \begin{pmatrix} 0 & \frac{1}{\sqrt{5}} & \frac{2}{\sqrt{5}} \\ 1 & 0 & 0 \\ 0 & \frac{2}{\sqrt{5}} & -\frac{1}{\sqrt{5}} \end{pmatrix} \begin{pmatrix} 0 & 1 & 0 \\ \frac{1}{\sqrt{5}} & 0 & \frac{2}{\sqrt{5}} \\ \frac{2}{\sqrt{5}} & 0 & -\frac{1}{\sqrt{5}} \end{pmatrix} = \mathbf{I}_3$$

and a similar calculation gives $\mathbf{A}^t\mathbf{A} = \mathbf{I}_3$. Therefore this matrix is orthogonal, and

$$\mathbf{A}^{-1} = \mathbf{A}^t = \begin{pmatrix} 0 & 1 & 0 \\ \frac{1}{\sqrt{5}} & 0 & \frac{2}{\sqrt{5}} \\ \frac{2}{\sqrt{5}} & 0 & -\frac{1}{\sqrt{5}} \end{pmatrix}. \ \blacksquare$$

Because the transpose of the transpose of a matrix is the original matrix, a matrix is orthogonal exactly when its transpose is orthogonal.

THEOREM 9.7

$\mathbf{A}$ is an orthogonal matrix if and only if $\mathbf{A}^t$ is an orthogonal matrix. $\blacksquare$

Orthogonal matrices have several interesting properties. We will show first that the determinant of an orthogonal matrix must be 1 or -1.

THEOREM 9.8

If A is an orthogonal matrix, then $|\mathbf{A}| = \pm 1$.

Proof   Since $\mathbf{A}\mathbf{A}^t = \mathbf{I}_n$, then $|\mathbf{A}\mathbf{A}^t| = 1 = |\mathbf{A}|\,|\mathbf{A}^t| = |\mathbf{A}|^2$. $\blacksquare$

The next property of orthogonal matrices is actually the rationale for the name orthogonal. A set of vectors in R^n is said to be *orthogonal* if any two distinct vectors in the set are orthogonal (that is, their dot product is zero). The set is *orthonormal* if, in addition, each vector has length 1. We claim that the rows of an orthogonal matrix form an orthonormal set of vectors, as do the columns.

This can be seen in the matrix of the last example. The row vectors are

$$\left(0 \quad \tfrac{1}{\sqrt{5}} \quad \tfrac{2}{\sqrt{5}} \right), \left(1 \quad 0 \quad 0 \right), \left(0 \quad \tfrac{2}{\sqrt{5}} \quad -\tfrac{1}{\sqrt{5}} \right).$$

These each have length 1, and each is orthogonal to each of the other two. Similarly, the columns of that matrix are

$$\begin{pmatrix} 0 \\ 1 \\ 0 \end{pmatrix}, \begin{pmatrix} \tfrac{1}{\sqrt{5}} \\ 0 \\ \tfrac{2}{\sqrt{5}} \end{pmatrix}, \begin{pmatrix} \tfrac{2}{\sqrt{5}} \\ 0 \\ -\tfrac{1}{\sqrt{5}} \end{pmatrix}.$$

Each is orthogonal to the other two, and each has length 1.

Not only do the row (column) vectors of an orthogonal matrix form an orthonormal set of vectors in R^n, but this property completely characterizes orthogonal matrices.

THEOREM 9.9

Let $\mathbf{A}$ be a real $n \times n$ matrix. Then

1. $\mathbf{A}$ is orthogonal if and only if the row vectors form an orthonormal set of vectors in R^n.

2. $\mathbf{A}$ is orthogonal if and only if the column vectors form an orthonormal set of vectors in R^n. ∎

Proof Recall that the i, j element of $\mathbf{AB}$ is the dot product of row i of $\mathbf{A}$ with column j of $\mathbf{B}$. Further, the columns of $\mathbf{A}^t$ are the rows of $\mathbf{A}$. Therefore,

$$i, j \text{ element of } \mathbf{AA}^t = (\text{row } i \text{ of } \mathbf{A}) \cdot (\text{column } j \text{ of } \mathbf{A}^t)$$

$$= (\text{row } i \text{ of } \mathbf{A}) \cdot (\text{row } j \text{ of } \mathbf{A}).$$

Now suppose that $\mathbf{A}$ is an orthogonal matrix. Then $\mathbf{AA}^t = \mathbf{I}_n$, so the i, j element of $\mathbf{AA}^t$ is zero if $i \neq j$. Therefore the dot product of two distinct rows of $\mathbf{A}$ is zero, and the rows form an orthogonal set of vectors. Further, the dot product of row i with itself is the i, i element of $\mathbf{AA}^t$, and this is 1, so the rows form an orthonormal set of vectors.

Conversely, suppose the rows of $\mathbf{A}$ form an orthonormal set of vectors. Then the dot product row i with row j is zero if $i \neq j$, so the i, j element of $\mathbf{AA}^t$ is zero if $i \neq j$. Further, the i, i element of $\mathbf{AA}^t$ is the dot product of row i with itself, and this is 1. Therefore $\mathbf{AA}^t = \mathbf{I}_n$. Similarly, $\mathbf{A}^t\mathbf{A}$ is $\mathbf{I}_n$, so $\mathbf{A}$ is an orthogonal matrix. This proves (1). A proof of (2) is similar. ∎

We now have a great deal of information about orthogonal matrices. We will use this to completely determine all 2×2 orthogonal matrices. Let

$$\mathbf{Q} = \begin{pmatrix} a & b \\ c & d \end{pmatrix}.$$

What do we have to say about a, b, c and d to make this an orthogonal matrix? First, the two row vectors must be orthogonal (zero dot product), and must have length 1, so

$$ac + bd = 0 \tag{9.1}$$

$$a^2 + b^2 = 1 \tag{9.2}$$

$$c^2 + d^2 = 1. \tag{9.3}$$

The two column vectors must also be orthogonal, so in addition,

$$ab + cd = 0. \tag{9.4}$$

Finally, $|\mathbf{Q}| = \pm 1$, so

$$ad - bc = \pm 1.$$

This leads to two cases.
    Case 1—$ad - bc = 1$.
    Multiply equation (9.1) by d to get

$$acd + bd^2 = 0.$$

Substitute $ad = 1 + bc$ into this equation to get

$$c(1 + bc) + bd^2 = 0$$

or

$$c + b(c^2 + d^2) = 0.$$

But $c^2 + d^2 = 1$ from equation (9.3), so $c + b = 0$, hence

$$c = -b.$$

Put this into equation (9.4) to get

$$ab - bd = 0.$$

Then $b = 0$ or $a = d$, leading to two subcases.
    Case 1-(a)—$b = 0$. Then $c = -b = 0$ also, so

$$\mathbf{Q} = \begin{pmatrix} a & 0 \\ 0 & d \end{pmatrix}.$$

But each row vector has length 1, so $a^2 = d^2 = 1$. Further, $|\mathbf{Q}| = ad = 1$ in the present case, so $a = d = 1$ or $a = d = -1$. In these cases,

$$\mathbf{Q} = \mathbf{I}_2 \quad \text{or} \quad \mathbf{Q} = -\mathbf{I}_2.$$

    Case 1-(b)—$b \neq 0$. Then $a = d$, so

$$\mathbf{Q} = \begin{pmatrix} a & b \\ -b & a \end{pmatrix}.$$

Since $a^2 + b^2 = 1$, there is some θ in $[0, 2\pi)$ such that $a = \cos(\theta)$ and $b = \sin(\theta)$. Then

$$\mathbf{Q} = \begin{pmatrix} \cos(\theta) & \sin(\theta) \\ -\sin(\theta) & \cos(\theta) \end{pmatrix}.$$

This includes the two results of case 1(a) by choosing $\theta = 0$ or $\theta = \pi$.
    Case 2—$ad - bc = -1$.
    By an analysis similar to that just done, we find now that, for some θ,

$$\mathbf{Q} = \begin{pmatrix} \cos(\theta) & \sin(\theta) \\ \sin(\theta) & -\cos(\theta) \end{pmatrix}.$$

    These two cases give all the 2×2 orthogonal matrices. For example, with $\theta = \pi/4$ we get the orthogonal matrices

$$\begin{pmatrix} \frac{1}{\sqrt{2}} & \frac{1}{\sqrt{2}} \\ -\frac{1}{\sqrt{2}} & \frac{1}{\sqrt{2}} \end{pmatrix} \quad \text{and} \quad \begin{pmatrix} \frac{1}{\sqrt{2}} & \frac{1}{\sqrt{2}} \\ \frac{1}{\sqrt{2}} & -\frac{1}{\sqrt{2}} \end{pmatrix}$$

and with $\theta = \pi/6$ we get

$$\begin{pmatrix} \frac{\sqrt{3}}{2} & \frac{1}{2} \\ -\frac{1}{2} & \frac{\sqrt{3}}{2} \end{pmatrix} \quad \text{and} \quad \begin{pmatrix} \frac{\sqrt{3}}{2} & \frac{1}{2} \\ \frac{1}{2} & -\frac{\sqrt{3}}{2} \end{pmatrix}.$$

We can recognize the orthogonal matrices

$$\begin{pmatrix} \cos(\theta) & \sin(\theta) \\ -\sin(\theta) & \cos(\theta) \end{pmatrix}$$

as rotations in the plane. If the positive x, y system is rotated counterclockwise θ radians to form a new x', y' system, the coordinates in the two systems are related by

$$\begin{pmatrix} x' \\ y' \end{pmatrix} = \begin{pmatrix} \cos(\theta) & \sin(\theta) \\ -\sin(\theta) & \cos(\theta) \end{pmatrix} \begin{pmatrix} x \\ y \end{pmatrix}.$$

We will now consider another kind of matrix that is related to the class of orthogonal matrices.

DEFINITION 9.6   *Symmetric Matrix*

A square matrix is symmetric if $\mathbf{A} = \mathbf{A}^t$.

This means that each $a_{ij} = a_{ji}$, or that the matrix elements are the same if reflected across the main diagonal. For example,

$$\begin{pmatrix} -7 & -2 & 1 & 14 \\ -2 & 2 & -9 & 47 \\ 1 & -9 & 6 & \pi \\ 14 & 47 & \pi & 22 \end{pmatrix}$$

is symmetric.

A symmetric matrix need not have real numbers as elements. However, when it does, it has the remarkable property of having only real eigenvalues.

THEOREM 9.10

The eigenvalues of a real, symmetric matrix are real numbers. ■

Before showing why this is true, we will review some facts about complex numbers. A complex number $z = a + ib$ has magnitude $|z| = \sqrt{a^2 + b^2}$. The conjugate of z is defined to be $\bar{z} = a - ib$. When z is represented as the point (a, b) in the plane, $\bar{z}$ is the point $(a, -b)$, which is the reflection of (a, b) across the x-axis. A number is real exactly when it equals its own conjugate. Further,

$$z\bar{z} = a^2 + b^2 = |z|^2$$

and

$$\overline{(\bar{z})} = z.$$

We take the conjugate $\overline{\mathbf{A}}$ of a matrix $\mathbf{A}$ by taking the conjugate of each of its elements. The product of a conjugate is the conjugate of a product:

$$\overline{(\mathbf{AB})} = (\overline{\mathbf{A}})(\overline{\mathbf{B}}).$$

Further, the operation of taking the conjugate commutes with the operation of taking a transpose:

$$\overline{\mathbf{C}}^t = \overline{(\mathbf{C}^t)}.$$

For example, if

$$\mathbf{C} = \begin{pmatrix} i & 1-2i \\ 3 & 0 \\ -2+i & 4 \end{pmatrix}$$

then

$$\overline{\mathbf{C}} = \begin{pmatrix} -i & 1+2i \\ 3 & 0 \\ -2-i & 4 \end{pmatrix}$$

and

$$\overline{\mathbf{C}}^t = \begin{pmatrix} -i & 3 & -2-i \\ 1+2i & 0 & 4 \end{pmatrix} = \overline{(\mathbf{C}^t)}.$$

We will now prove that the eigenvalues of a real symmetric matrix must be real.

Proof   Let $\mathbf{A}$ be an $n \times n$ matrix of real numbers. Let λ be an eigenvalue, and let

$$\mathbf{E} = \begin{pmatrix} e_1 \\ e_2 \\ \vdots \\ e_n \end{pmatrix}$$

be an associated eigenvector. Then $\mathbf{AE} = \lambda\mathbf{E}$. Multiply this equation on the left by the $1 \times n$ matrix

$$\overline{\mathbf{E}}^t = \begin{pmatrix} \overline{e_1} & \overline{e_2} & \cdots & \overline{e_n} \end{pmatrix}$$

to get

$$\overline{\mathbf{E}}^t \mathbf{AE} = \overline{\mathbf{E}}^t \lambda\mathbf{E} = \lambda\overline{\mathbf{E}}^t \mathbf{E}$$

$$= \lambda \begin{pmatrix} \overline{e_1} & \overline{e_2} & \cdots & \overline{e_n} \end{pmatrix} \begin{pmatrix} e_1 \\ e_2 \\ \vdots \\ e_n \end{pmatrix}$$

$$= \lambda [\overline{e_1}e_1 + \overline{e_2}e_2 + \cdots + \overline{e_n}e_n]$$

$$= \lambda \left(|e_1|^2 + |e_2|^2 + \cdots + |e_n|^2 \right), \tag{9.5}$$

which is a real number. Here we are using the standard convention that a 1×1 matrix is identified with its single element.

Now compute

$$\overline{\overline{\mathbf{E}}^t \mathbf{AE}} = \overline{(\overline{\mathbf{E}})}^t \overline{\mathbf{A}}\,\overline{\mathbf{E}} = \mathbf{E}^t \mathbf{A}\overline{\mathbf{E}}, \tag{9.6}$$

in which we have used the fact that $\mathbf{A}$ has real elements to write $\overline{\mathbf{A}} = \mathbf{A}$.

Now $\mathbf{E}^t\mathbf{A}\overline{\mathbf{E}}$ is a 1×1 matrix, and so is the same as its transpose. Recalling that the transpose of a product is the product of the transposes in the reverse order, take the transpose of the last equation (9.6) to get

$$\mathbf{E}^t\mathbf{A}\overline{\mathbf{E}} = \left(\mathbf{E}^t\mathbf{A}\overline{\mathbf{E}}\right)^t = \overline{\mathbf{E}}^t\mathbf{A}(\mathbf{E}^t)^t = \overline{\mathbf{E}}^t\mathbf{A}\mathbf{E}. \tag{9.7}$$

From equations (9.6) and (9.7) we have

$$\overline{\mathbf{E}^t\mathbf{A}\mathbf{E}} = \overline{\mathbf{E}}^t\mathbf{A}\mathbf{E}.$$

Therefore the 1×1 matrix $\overline{\mathbf{E}}^t\mathbf{A}\mathbf{E}$, being equal to its conjugate, is a real number. Now return to equation (9.5). We have just shown that the left side of this equation is real. Therefore the right side must be real. But $\left(|e_1|^2 + |e_2|^2 + \cdots + |e_n|^2\right)$ is certainly real. Therefore λ is real, and the theorem is proved. ∎

One ramification of this theorem is that a real, symmetric matrix also has real eigenvectors. We claim that, more than this, eigenvectors from distinct eigenvalues are orthogonal.

THEOREM 9.11

Let $\mathbf{A}$ be a real symmetric matrix. Then eigenvectors associated with distinct eigenvalues are orthogonal.

Proof Let λ and μ be distinct eigenvalues with, respectively, eigenvectors

$$\mathbf{E} = \begin{pmatrix} e_1 \\ e_2 \\ \vdots \\ e_n \end{pmatrix} \quad \text{and} \quad \mathbf{G} = \begin{pmatrix} g_1 \\ g_2 \\ \vdots \\ g_n \end{pmatrix}.$$

Identifying, as usual, a real number with the 1×1 matrix having this number as its only element, the dot product of these two n-vectors can be written as a matrix product

$$e_1g_1 + \cdots + e_ng_n = \mathbf{E}^t\mathbf{G}.$$

Since $\mathbf{AE} = \lambda\mathbf{E}$ and $\mathbf{AG} = \mu\mathbf{G}$, we have

$$\lambda\mathbf{E}^t\mathbf{G} = (\lambda\mathbf{E})^t\mathbf{G} = (\mathbf{AE})^t\mathbf{G} = (\mathbf{E}^t\mathbf{A}^t)\mathbf{G}$$
$$= (\mathbf{E}^t\mathbf{A})\mathbf{G} = \mathbf{E}^t(\mathbf{AG}) = \mathbf{E}^t(\mu\mathbf{G}) = \mu\mathbf{E}^t\mathbf{G}.$$

Then

$$(\lambda - \mu)\mathbf{E}^t\mathbf{G} = \mathbf{0}.$$

But $\lambda \neq \mu$, so $\mathbf{E}^t\mathbf{G} = 0$ and the dot product of these two eigenvectors is zero. These eigenvectors are therefore orthogonal. ∎

EXAMPLE 9.13

Let

$$\mathbf{A} = \begin{pmatrix} 3 & 0 & -2 \\ 0 & 2 & 0 \\ -2 & 0 & 0 \end{pmatrix},$$

a 3×3 real symmetric matrix. The eigenvalues are $2, -1, 4$, with associated eigenvectors

$$\begin{pmatrix} 0 \\ 1 \\ 0 \end{pmatrix}, \begin{pmatrix} 1 \\ 0 \\ 2 \end{pmatrix}, \begin{pmatrix} 2 \\ 0 \\ -1 \end{pmatrix}.$$

These form an orthogonal set of vectors. ■

In this example, the eigenvectors, while orthogonal to each other, are not all of length 1. However, a scalar multiple of an eigenvector is an eigenvector, so we can also write the following eigenvectors of **A**:

$$\begin{pmatrix} 0 \\ 1 \\ 0 \end{pmatrix}, \begin{pmatrix} \frac{1}{\sqrt{5}} \\ 0 \\ \frac{2}{\sqrt{5}} \end{pmatrix}, \begin{pmatrix} \frac{2}{\sqrt{5}} \\ 0 \\ -\frac{1}{\sqrt{5}} \end{pmatrix}.$$

These are still mutually orthogonal (multiplying by a positive scalar does not change orientation), but are now orthonormal. They can therefore be used as columns of an orthogonal matrix

$$\mathbf{Q} = \begin{pmatrix} 0 & \frac{1}{\sqrt{5}} & \frac{2}{\sqrt{5}} \\ 1 & 0 & 0 \\ 0 & \frac{2}{\sqrt{5}} & -\frac{1}{\sqrt{5}} \end{pmatrix}.$$

These column vectors, being orthogonal to each other, are linearly independent by Theorem 6.14. But whenever we form a matrix from linearly independent eigenvectors of **A**, this matrix diagonalizes **A**. Further, since **Q** is an orthogonal matrix, $\mathbf{Q}^{-1} = \mathbf{Q}^t$. Therefore, as we can easily verify in this example,

$$\mathbf{Q}^{-1}\mathbf{A}\mathbf{Q} = \begin{pmatrix} 2 & 0 & 0 \\ 0 & -1 & 0 \\ 0 & 0 & 4 \end{pmatrix}.$$

The idea we have just illustrated forms the basis for the following result.

THEOREM 9.12

Let **A** be a real, symmetric matrix. Then there is a real, orthogonal matrix that diagonalizes **A**. ■

EXAMPLE 9.14

Let

$$\mathbf{A} = \begin{pmatrix} 2 & 1 & 0 \\ 1 & -2 & 4 \\ 0 & 4 & 2 \end{pmatrix}.$$

The eigenvalues are $\sqrt{21}, -\sqrt{21}$ and 2, with associated eigenvectors, respectively

$$\begin{pmatrix} 1 \\ \sqrt{21} - 2 \\ 4 \end{pmatrix}, \begin{pmatrix} 1 \\ -\sqrt{21} - 2 \\ 4 \end{pmatrix}, \begin{pmatrix} -4 \\ 0 \\ 1 \end{pmatrix}.$$

These eigenvectors are mutually orthogonal, but not orthonormal. Divide each eigenvector by its length to get the three new eigenvectors:

$$\frac{1}{\alpha}\begin{pmatrix} \frac{1}{\sqrt{21}} - 2 \\ 4 \end{pmatrix}, \frac{1}{\alpha}\begin{pmatrix} -\frac{1}{\sqrt{21}} - 2 \\ 4 \end{pmatrix}, \frac{1}{\beta}\begin{pmatrix} -4 \\ 0 \\ 1 \end{pmatrix}$$

where

$$\alpha = \sqrt{42 - 4\sqrt{21}} \quad \text{and} \quad \beta = \sqrt{17}.$$

The orthogonal matrix $\mathbf{Q}$ having these normalized eigenvectors as columns diagonalizes $\mathbf{A}$. ∎

SECTION 9.3　PROBLEMS

In each of Problems 1 through 12, find the eigenvalues of the matrix and, for each eigenvalue, a corresponding eigenvector. Check that eigenvectors associated with distinct eigenvalues are orthogonal. Find an orthogonal matrix that diagonalizes the matrix.

1. $\begin{pmatrix} 4 & -2 \\ -2 & 1 \end{pmatrix}$

2. $\begin{pmatrix} -3 & 5 \\ 5 & 4 \end{pmatrix}$

3. $\begin{pmatrix} 6 & 1 \\ 1 & 4 \end{pmatrix}$

4. $\begin{pmatrix} -13 & 1 \\ 1 & 4 \end{pmatrix}$

5. $\begin{pmatrix} 0 & 1 & 0 \\ 1 & -2 & 0 \\ 0 & 0 & 3 \end{pmatrix}$

6. $\begin{pmatrix} 0 & 1 & 1 \\ 1 & 2 & 0 \\ 1 & 0 & 2 \end{pmatrix}$

7. $\begin{pmatrix} 5 & 0 & 2 \\ 0 & 0 & 0 \\ 2 & 0 & 0 \end{pmatrix}$

8. $\begin{pmatrix} 2 & -4 & 0 \\ -4 & 0 & 0 \\ 0 & 0 & 0 \end{pmatrix}$

9. $\begin{pmatrix} 0 & 0 & 0 \\ 0 & 1 & -2 \\ 0 & -2 & 0 \end{pmatrix}$

10. $\begin{pmatrix} 1 & 3 & 0 \\ 3 & 0 & 1 \\ 0 & 1 & 1 \end{pmatrix}$

11. $\begin{pmatrix} 0 & 0 & 0 & 0 \\ 0 & 1 & -2 & 0 \\ 0 & -2 & 1 & 0 \\ 0 & 0 & 0 & 0 \end{pmatrix}$

12. $\begin{pmatrix} 5 & 0 & 0 & 0 \\ 0 & 0 & -1 & 0 \\ 0 & -1 & 0 & 0 \\ 0 & 0 & 0 & 0 \end{pmatrix}$

9.4　Quadratic Forms

DEFINITION 9.7

A (complex) *quadratic form* is an expression

$$\sum_{j=1}^{n}\sum_{k=1}^{n} a_{jk}\overline{z}_j z_k, \tag{9.8}$$

in which each a_{jk} and z_j are complex numbers.

For $n = 2$ this quadratic form is

$$a_{11}\overline{z}_1 z_1 + a_{12}\overline{z}_1 z_2 + a_{21} z_1 \overline{z}_2 + a_{22} z_2 \overline{z}_2.$$

The terms involving $z_j z_k$ with $j \neq k$, are the *mixed product terms*.

The quadratic form is real if each a_{jk} and z_j is real. In this case we usually write z_j as x_j. Since $\overline{x}_j = x_j$ when x_j is real, the form (9.8) in this case is

$$\sum_{j=1}^{n} \sum_{k=1}^{n} a_{jk} x_j x_k.$$

For $n = 2$, this is

$$a_{11} x_1^2 + (a_{12} + a_{21}) x_1 x_2 + a_{22} x_2^2.$$

The terms involving x_1^2 and x_2^2 are the squared terms in this real quadratic form, and x_{12} is the mixed product term.

It is often convenient to write a quadratic form (9.8) in matrix form. If $\mathbf{A} = [a_{ij}]$ and

$$\mathbf{Z} = \begin{pmatrix} z_1 \\ z_2 \\ \vdots \\ z_n \end{pmatrix}$$

then

$$\overline{\mathbf{Z}}^t \mathbf{A} \mathbf{Z} = \begin{pmatrix} \overline{z}_1 & \overline{z}_2 & \cdots & \overline{z}_n \end{pmatrix} \begin{pmatrix} a_{11} & a_{12} & \cdots & a_{1n} \\ a_{21} & a_{22} & \cdots & a_{2n} \\ \vdots & \vdots & \vdots & \vdots \\ a_{n1} & a_{n2} & \cdots & a_{nn} \end{pmatrix} \begin{pmatrix} z_1 \\ z_2 \\ \vdots \\ z_n \end{pmatrix}$$

$$= \begin{pmatrix} a_{11}\overline{z}_1 + \cdots + a_{1n}\overline{z}_n & \cdots & a_{n1}\overline{z}_1 + \cdots + a_{nn}\overline{z}_n \end{pmatrix} \begin{pmatrix} z_1 \\ z_2 \\ \vdots \\ z_n \end{pmatrix}$$

$$= a_{11}\overline{z}_1 z_1 + \cdots + a_{1n}\overline{z}_n z_1 + \cdots + a_{n1}\overline{z}_1 z_n + \cdots + a_{nn}\overline{z}_n z_n$$

$$= \sum_{j=1}^{n} \sum_{k=1}^{n} a_{jk} \overline{z}_j z_k.$$

Similarly, any real quadratic form can be written in matrix form as $\mathbf{X}^t \mathbf{A} \mathbf{X}$.

Given a quadratic form, we may choose different matrices $\mathbf{A}$ such that the form is $\mathbf{Z}^t \mathbf{A} \mathbf{Z}$.

EXAMPLE 9.15

Let

$$\mathbf{A} = \begin{pmatrix} 1 & 4 \\ 3 & 2 \end{pmatrix}.$$

Then

$$(\ x_1 \quad x_2 \ ) \begin{pmatrix} 1 & 4 \\ 3 & 2 \end{pmatrix} \begin{pmatrix} x_1 \\ x_2 \end{pmatrix} = (\ x_1 + 3x_2 \quad 4x_1 + 2x_2 \ ) \begin{pmatrix} x_1 \\ x_2 \end{pmatrix}$$

$$= x_1^2 + 3x_1 x_2 + 4x_1 x_2 + 2x_2^2$$

$$= x_1^2 + 7x_1 x_2 + 2x_2^2.$$

But we can also write this quadratic form as

$$x_1^2 + \frac{7}{2}x_1 x_2 + \frac{7}{2}x_2 x_1 + 2x_2^2 = (\ x_1 \quad x_2 \ ) \begin{pmatrix} 1 & \frac{7}{2} \\ \frac{7}{2} & 2 \end{pmatrix} \begin{pmatrix} x_1 \\ x_2 \end{pmatrix}.$$

The advantage of the latter formulation is that the quadratic form is $\mathbf{X}^t \mathbf{AX}$ with $\mathbf{A}$ a symmetric matrix. ∎

There is an expression involving a quadratic form that gives the eigenvalues of a matrix in terms of an associated eigenvector. We will have use for this shortly.

LEMMA 9.1

Let $\mathbf{A}$ be an $n \times n$ matrix of real or complex numbers. Let λ be an eigenvalue with eigenvector $\mathbf{Z}$. Then

$$\lambda = \frac{\overline{\mathbf{Z}}^t \mathbf{AZ}}{\overline{\mathbf{Z}}^t \mathbf{Z}}. \quad \blacksquare$$

Proof Since $\mathbf{AZ} = \lambda \mathbf{Z}$, then $\overline{\mathbf{Z}}^t \mathbf{AZ} = \lambda \overline{\mathbf{Z}}^t \mathbf{Z}$. ∎

Using a calculation done in equation (9.5), we can write

$$\lambda = \frac{1}{\sum_{j=1}^{n} |z_j|^2} \sum_{j=1}^{n} \sum_{k=1}^{n} a_{jk} \overline{z}_j z_k.$$

Quadratic forms arise in a variety of contexts. In mechanics, the kinetic energy of a particle is a real quadratic form, and in analytic geometry a conic is the locus of points in the plane for which a quadratic form in the coordinates is equal to some constant. For example,

$$x_1^2 + \frac{1}{4}x_2^2 = 9$$

is the equation of an ellipse in the x_1, x_2 plane.

In some problems involving quadratic forms, calculations are simplified if we transform from the $x_1, x_2, \ldots, x_n$ coordinate system to a $y_1, y_2, \ldots, y_n$ system in which there are no mixed product terms. That is, we want to choose $y_1, \ldots, y_n$ so that

$$\sum_{j=1}^{n} \sum_{k=1}^{n} a_{ij} x_j x_k = \sum_{j=1}^{n} \beta_j y_j^2. \tag{9.9}$$

The $y_1, \ldots, y_n$ coordinates are called *principal axes* for the quadratic form.

This kind of transformation is commonly done in analytic geometry, where a rotation of axes is used to eliminate mixed product terms in the equation of a conic. For example, the change of variables

$$x_1 = \frac{1}{\sqrt{2}}y_1 + \frac{1}{\sqrt{2}}y_2$$

$$x_2 = \frac{1}{\sqrt{2}}y_1 - \frac{1}{\sqrt{2}}y_2$$

transforms the quadratic form

$$x_1^2 - 2x_1x_2 + x_2^2$$

to

$$2y_2^2,$$

with no mixed product term. Using this transformed form, we could analyze the graph of

$$x_1^2 - 2x_1x_2 + x_2^2 = 4$$

in the x_1, x_2- system, in terms of the graph of

$$y_2^2 = 2$$

in the y_1, y_2- system. In the y_1, y_2- plane it is clear that the graph consists of two horizontal straight lines $y_2 = \pm\sqrt{2}$.

We will now show that a transformation that eliminates the mixed product terms of a real quadratic form always exists.

THEOREM 9.13 *Principal Axis Theorem*

Let $\mathbf{A}$ be a real symmetric matrix with eigenvalues $\lambda_1, \ldots, \lambda_n$. Let $\mathbf{Q}$ be an orthogonal matrix that diagonalizes $\mathbf{A}$. Then the change of variables $\mathbf{X} = \mathbf{QY}$ transforms $\sum_{j=1}^{n}\sum_{k=1}^{n} a_{jk}x_jx_k$ to

$$\sum_{j=1}^{n} \lambda_j y_j^2.$$

Proof The proof is a straightforward calculation:

$$\sum_{j=1}^{n}\sum_{k=1}^{n} a_{ij}x_jx_k = \mathbf{X}^t\mathbf{AX}$$

$$= (\mathbf{QY})^t\mathbf{A}(\mathbf{QY}) = (\mathbf{Y}^t\mathbf{Q}^t)\mathbf{A}(\mathbf{QY})$$

$$= \mathbf{Y}^t(\mathbf{Q}^t\mathbf{AQ})\mathbf{Y}$$

$$= \begin{pmatrix} y_1 & \cdots & y_n \end{pmatrix} \begin{pmatrix} \lambda_1 & & & O \\ & \lambda_2 & & \\ & & \ddots & \\ O & & & \lambda_n \end{pmatrix} \begin{pmatrix} y_1 \\ \vdots \\ y_n \end{pmatrix}$$

$$= \lambda_1 y_1^2 + \cdots + \lambda_n y_n^2. \blacksquare$$

The expression $\lambda_1 y_1^2 + \cdots + \lambda_n y_n^2$ is called the *standard form* of the quadratic form $\mathbf{X}^t\mathbf{AX}$.

EXAMPLE 9.16

Consider again $x_1^2 - 2x_1x_2 + x_2^2$. This is $\mathbf{X}^t\mathbf{A}\mathbf{X}$ with

$$\mathbf{A} = \begin{pmatrix} 1 & -1 \\ -1 & 1 \end{pmatrix}.$$

The eigenvalues of $\mathbf{A}$ are 0 and 2, with corresponding eigenvectors

$$\begin{pmatrix} 1 \\ 1 \end{pmatrix} \quad \text{and} \quad \begin{pmatrix} 1 \\ -1 \end{pmatrix}.$$

Dividing each eigenvector by its length, we obtain the eigenvectors

$$\begin{pmatrix} \frac{1}{\sqrt{2}} \\ \frac{1}{\sqrt{2}} \end{pmatrix} \quad \text{and} \quad \begin{pmatrix} \frac{1}{\sqrt{2}} \\ -\frac{1}{\sqrt{2}} \end{pmatrix}.$$

These form the columns of an orthogonal matrix $\mathbf{Q}$ that diagonalizes $\mathbf{A}$:

$$\mathbf{Q} = \begin{pmatrix} \frac{1}{\sqrt{2}} & \frac{1}{\sqrt{2}} \\ \frac{1}{\sqrt{2}} & -\frac{1}{\sqrt{2}} \end{pmatrix}.$$

The transformation defined by $\mathbf{X} = \mathbf{Q}\mathbf{Y}$ is

$$\begin{pmatrix} x_1 \\ x_2 \end{pmatrix} = \begin{pmatrix} \frac{1}{\sqrt{2}} & \frac{1}{\sqrt{2}} \\ \frac{1}{\sqrt{2}} & -\frac{1}{\sqrt{2}} \end{pmatrix} \begin{pmatrix} y_1 \\ y_2 \end{pmatrix},$$

which gives exactly the transformation used above to reduce the quadratic form $x_1^2 - 2x_1x_2 + x_2^2$ to the standard form $2y_2^2$. ■

EXAMPLE 9.17

Analyze the conic $4x_1^2 - 3x_1x_2 + 2x_2^2 = 8$. First write the quadratic form as $\mathbf{X}^t\mathbf{A}\mathbf{X} = 8$, where

$$\mathbf{A} = \begin{pmatrix} 4 & -\frac{3}{2} \\ -\frac{3}{2} & 2 \end{pmatrix}.$$

The eigenvalues of $\mathbf{A}$ are $(6 \pm \sqrt{13})/2$. By the principal axis theorem there is an orthogonal matrix $\mathbf{Q}$ that transforms the equation of the conic to standard form:

$$\frac{6 + \sqrt{13}}{2} y_1^2 + \frac{6 - \sqrt{13}}{2} y_2^2 = 8.$$

This is an ellipse in the y_1, y_2– plane. Figure 9.2 shows a graph of this ellipse. ■

FIGURE 9.2

In each of Problems 1 through 6, find a matrix **A** such that the quadratic form is $\mathbf{X}^t\mathbf{A}\mathbf{X}$.

1. $x_1^2 + 2x_1x_2 + 6x_2^2$

2. $3x_1^2 + 3x_2^2 - 4x_1x_2 - 3x_1x_3 + 2x_2x_3 + x_3^2$

3. $x_1^2 - 4x_1x_2 + x_2^2$

4. $2x_1^2 - x_2^2 + 2x_1x_2$

5. $-x_1^2 + x_4^2 - 2x_1x_4 + 3x_2x_4 - x_1x_3 + 4x_2x_3$

6. $x_1^2 - x_2^2 - x_1x_3 + 4x_2x_3$

In Problems 7 through 13, find the standard form of the quadratic form.

7. $-5x_1^2 + 4x_1x_2 + 3x_2^2$

8. $4x_1^2 - 12x_1x_2 + x_2^2$

9. $-3x_1^2 + 4x_1x_2 + 7x_2^2$

10. $4x_1^2 - 4x_1x_2 + x_2^2$

11. $-6x_1x_2 + 4x_2^2$

12. $5x_1^2 + 4x_1x_2 + 2x_2^2$

13. $-2x_1x_2 + 2x_3^2$

In each of Problems 14 through 18, use the principal axis theorem to analyze the conic.

14. $x_1^2 - 2x_1x_2 + 4x_2^2 = 6$

15. $3x_1^2 + 5x_1x_2 - 3x_2^2 = 5$

16. $-2x_1^2 + 3x_2^2 + x_1x_2 = 5$

17. $4x_1^2 - 4x_2^2 + 6x_1x_2 = 8$

18. $6x_1^2 + 2x_1x_2 + 5x_2^2 = 14$

In each of Problems 19 through 22, write the quadratic form defined by the matrix.

19. $\begin{pmatrix} -2 & 1 \\ 1 & 6 \end{pmatrix}$

20. $\begin{pmatrix} 14 & -3 & 0 \\ -3 & 2 & 1 \\ 0 & 1 & 7 \end{pmatrix}$

21. $\begin{pmatrix} 6 & 1 & -7 \\ 1 & 2 & 0 \\ -7 & 0 & 1 \end{pmatrix}$

22. $\begin{pmatrix} 7 & 1 & -2 \\ 1 & 0 & -1 \\ -2 & -1 & 3 \end{pmatrix}$

23. Give an example of a real, 3×3 matrix that cannot be the coefficient matrix of a real quadratic form.

9.5   Unitary, Hermitian, and Skew Hermitian Matrices

If **U** is a nonsingular complex matrix, then $\mathbf{U}^{-1}$ exists and is generally also a complex matrix. We claim that the operations of taking the complex conjugate and of taking a matrix inverse can be performed in either order.

LEMMA 9.2

$\overline{\mathbf{U}}^{-1} = \overline{\mathbf{U}^{-1}}$.

Proof   We know that the conjugate of a product is the product of the conjugates, so

$$\mathbf{I}_n = \overline{\mathbf{I}_n} = \overline{\mathbf{U}\mathbf{U}^{-1}} = \overline{\mathbf{U}}\,\overline{\mathbf{U}^{-1}}.$$

This implies that $\overline{\mathbf{U}^{-1}}$ is the inverse of $\overline{\mathbf{U}}$. ■

Now define a matrix to be *unitary* if the inverse of its conjugate (or conjugate of its inverse) is equal to its transpose.

DEFINITION 9.8   Unitary Matrix

An $n \times n$ complex matrix **U** is unitary if and only if $\overline{\mathbf{U}}^{-1} = \mathbf{U}^t$.

This condition is equivalent to saying that

$$\overline{\mathbf{U}}\mathbf{U}^t = \mathbf{I}_n.$$

EXAMPLE 9.18

Let

$$\mathbf{U} = \begin{pmatrix} i/\sqrt{2} & 1/\sqrt{2} \\ -i/\sqrt{2} & 1/\sqrt{2} \end{pmatrix}.$$

Then **U** is unitary because

$$\overline{\mathbf{U}}\mathbf{U}^t = \begin{pmatrix} -i/\sqrt{2} & 1/\sqrt{2} \\ i/\sqrt{2} & 1/\sqrt{2} \end{pmatrix} \begin{pmatrix} i/\sqrt{2} & -i/\sqrt{2} \\ 1/\sqrt{2} & 1/\sqrt{2} \end{pmatrix}$$

$$= \begin{pmatrix} 1 & 0 \\ 0 & 1 \end{pmatrix}. \blacksquare$$

If **U** is a real matrix, then the unitary condition $\overline{\mathbf{U}}\mathbf{U}^t = \mathbf{I}_n$ becomes $\mathbf{U}\mathbf{U}^t = \mathbf{I}_n$, which makes **U** an orthogonal matrix. Unitary matrices are the complex analogues of orthogonal matrices. Since the rows (or columns) of an orthogonal matrix form an orthonormal set of vectors, we will develop the complex analogue of the concept of orthonormality.

Recall that, for two vectors $(x_1, \ldots, x_n)$ and $(y_1, \ldots y_n)$ in R^n, we can define the column matrices

$$\mathbf{X} = \begin{pmatrix} x_1 \\ x_2 \\ \vdots \\ x_n \end{pmatrix} \quad \text{and} \quad \mathbf{Y} = \begin{pmatrix} y_1 \\ y_2 \\ \vdots \\ y_n \end{pmatrix}$$

and obtain the dot product $\mathbf{X} \cdot \mathbf{Y}$ as $\mathbf{X}^t\mathbf{Y}$. In particular, this gives the square of the length of **X** as

$$\mathbf{X}^t\mathbf{X} = x_1^2 + x_2^2 + \cdots + x_n^2.$$

To generalize this to the complex case, suppose we have complex n-vectors $(z_1, z_2, \ldots, z_n)$ and $(w_1, w_2, \ldots, w_n)$. Form the column matrices

$$\mathbf{Z} = \begin{pmatrix} z_1 \\ z_2 \\ \vdots \\ z_n \end{pmatrix} \quad \text{and} \quad \mathbf{W} = \begin{pmatrix} w_1 \\ w_2 \\ \vdots \\ w_n \end{pmatrix}.$$

It is tempting to define the dot product of these complex vectors as $\mathbf{Z}^t\mathbf{W}$. The problem with this is that then we get

$$\mathbf{Z}^t\mathbf{Z} = z_1^2 + z_2^2 + \cdots + z_n^2$$

and this will in general be complex. We want to interpret the dot product of a vector with itself as the square of its length, and this should be a nonnegative real number. We get around this by defining the dot product of complex **Z** and **W** to be

$$\mathbf{Z} \cdot \mathbf{W} = \overline{\mathbf{Z}}^t\mathbf{W} = \overline{z_1}w_1 + \overline{z_2}w_2 + \cdots + \overline{z_n}w_n.$$

In this way the dot product of $\mathbf{Z}$ with itself is

$$\overline{\mathbf{Z}}^t\mathbf{Z} = \overline{z_1}z_1 + \overline{z_2}z_2 + \cdots + \overline{z_n}z_n$$

$$= |z_1|^2 + |z_2|^2 + \cdots + |z_n|^2,$$

a nonnegative real number

With this as background, we will define the complex analogue of an orthonormal set of vectors.

DEFINITION 9.9   Unitary System of Vectors

Complex n-vectors $\mathbf{F}_1, \ldots, \mathbf{F}_r$ form a unitary system if $\mathbf{F}_j \cdot \mathbf{F}_k = 0$ for $j \neq k$, and each $\mathbf{F}_j \cdot \mathbf{F}_j = 1$.

If each $\mathbf{F}_j$ has all real components, then this corresponds exactly to an orthonormal set of vectors in R^n. We can now state the analogue of Theorem 9.9 for unitary matrices.

THEOREM 9.14

Let $\mathbf{U}$ be an $n \times n$ complex matrix. Then $\mathbf{U}$ is unitary if and only if its row vectors form a unitary system. ∎

The proof is like that of Theorem 8.9, and is left to the student. It is not difficult to show that $\mathbf{U}$ is also unitary if and only if its column vectors form a unitary system.

EXAMPLE 9.19

Consider again

$$\mathbf{U} = \begin{pmatrix} i/\sqrt{2} & 1/\sqrt{2} \\ -i/\sqrt{2} & 1/\sqrt{2} \end{pmatrix}.$$

The row vectors, written as 2×1 matrices, are

$$\mathbf{F}_1 = \begin{pmatrix} i/\sqrt{2} \\ 1/\sqrt{2} \end{pmatrix} \quad \text{and} \quad \mathbf{F}_2 = \begin{pmatrix} -i/\sqrt{2} \\ 1/\sqrt{2} \end{pmatrix}.$$

Then

$$\mathbf{F}_1 \cdot \mathbf{F}_2 = \begin{pmatrix} i/\sqrt{2} & 1/\sqrt{2} \end{pmatrix} \begin{pmatrix} -i/\sqrt{2} \\ 1/\sqrt{2} \end{pmatrix} = 0,$$

$$\mathbf{F}_1 \cdot \mathbf{F}_1 = \begin{pmatrix} i/\sqrt{2} & 1/\sqrt{2} \end{pmatrix} \begin{pmatrix} i/\sqrt{2} \\ 1/\sqrt{2} \end{pmatrix} = 1$$

and

$$\mathbf{F}_2 \cdot \mathbf{F}_2 = \begin{pmatrix} -i/\sqrt{2} & 1/\sqrt{2} \end{pmatrix} \begin{pmatrix} -i/\sqrt{2} \\ 1/\sqrt{2} \end{pmatrix} = 1. \ \blacksquare$$

We will show that the eigenvalues of a unitary matrix must lie on the unit circle in the complex plane.

THEOREM 9.15

Let λ be an eigenvalue of the unitary matrix $\mathbf{U}$. Then $|\lambda| = 1$.

Proof Let $\mathbf{E}$ be an eigenvector associated with λ. Then $\mathbf{UE} = \lambda\mathbf{E}$, so $\overline{\mathbf{UE}} = \overline{\lambda}\overline{\mathbf{E}}$. Then

$$\left(\overline{\mathbf{UE}}\right)^t = \overline{\lambda}\,\overline{\mathbf{E}}^t,$$

so

$$\overline{\mathbf{E}}^t\overline{\mathbf{U}}^t = \overline{\lambda}\,\overline{\mathbf{E}}^t.$$

But $\mathbf{U}$ is unitary, so $\overline{\mathbf{U}}^t = \mathbf{U}^{-1}$, and

$$\overline{\mathbf{E}}^t\mathbf{U}^{-1} = \overline{\lambda}\,\overline{\mathbf{E}}^t.$$

Multiply both sides of this equation on the right by $\mathbf{UE}$ to get

$$\overline{\mathbf{E}}^t\mathbf{E} = \overline{\lambda}\,\overline{\mathbf{E}}^t\mathbf{UE} = \overline{\lambda}\,\overline{\mathbf{E}}^t\lambda\mathbf{E} = \overline{\lambda}\lambda\overline{\mathbf{E}}^t\mathbf{E}.$$

Now $\overline{\mathbf{E}}^t\mathbf{E}$ is the dot product of the eigenvector with itself, and so is a positive number. Dividing the last equation by $\overline{\mathbf{E}}^t\mathbf{E}$ gives $\overline{\lambda}\lambda = 1$. But then $|\lambda|^2 = 1$, so $|\lambda| = 1$. ∎

We have defined a matrix to be unitary if its transpose is the conjugate of its inverse. A matrix is *hermitian* if its transpose is equal to its conjugate. If the transpose equals the negative of its conjugate, the matrix is called *skew-hermitian*.

DEFINITION 9.10

---

1. *Hermitian Matrix*
   An $n \times n$ complex matrix $\mathbf{H}$ is hermitian if and only if $\overline{\mathbf{H}} = \mathbf{H}^t$.

2. *Skew-Hermitian*
   Matrix An $n \times n$ complex matrix $\mathbf{S}$ is skew-hermitian if and only if $\overline{\mathbf{S}} = -\mathbf{S}^t$.

In the case that $\mathbf{H}$ has real elements, hermitian is the same as symmetric, because in this case $\overline{\mathbf{H}} = \mathbf{H}$.

EXAMPLE 9.20

Let

$$\mathbf{H} = \begin{pmatrix} 15 & 8i & 6-2i \\ -8i & 0 & -4+i \\ 6+2i & -4-i & -3 \end{pmatrix}.$$

Then

$$\overline{\mathbf{H}} = \begin{pmatrix} 15 & -8i & 6+2i \\ 8i & 0 & -4-i \\ 6-2i & -4+i & -3 \end{pmatrix} = \mathbf{H}^t,$$

so **H** is hermitian.

If

$$\mathbf{S} = \begin{pmatrix} 0 & 8i & 2i \\ 8i & 0 & 4i \\ 2i & 4i & 0 \end{pmatrix}$$

then **S** is skew-hermitian because

$$\overline{\mathbf{S}} = \begin{pmatrix} 0 & -8i & -2i \\ -8i & 0 & -4i \\ -2i & -4i & 0 \end{pmatrix} = -\mathbf{S}^t. \quad \blacksquare$$

The following theorem says something about quadratic forms with hermitian or skew-hermitian matrices.

THEOREM 9.16

Let

$$\mathbf{Z} = \begin{pmatrix} z_1 \\ z_2 \\ \vdots \\ z_n \end{pmatrix}$$

be a complex matrix. Then

1. If **H** is hermitian, then $\overline{\mathbf{Z}}^t\mathbf{HZ}$ is real.
2. If **S** is skew-hermitian, then $\overline{\mathbf{Z}}^t\mathbf{SZ}$ is zero or pure-imaginary.

Proof   For (1), suppose **H** is hermitian. Then $\overline{\mathbf{H}}^t = \mathbf{H}$, so

$$\overline{\overline{\mathbf{Z}}^t\mathbf{HZ}} = \overline{\overline{\mathbf{Z}}}^t\overline{\mathbf{HZ}} = \mathbf{Z}^t\overline{\mathbf{HZ}}.$$

But $\overline{\mathbf{Z}}^t\mathbf{HZ}$ is a 1×1 matrix and so equals its own transpose. Continuing from the last equation, we have

$$\mathbf{Z}^t\overline{\mathbf{HZ}} = \left(\mathbf{Z}^t\overline{\mathbf{HZ}}\right)^t = \overline{\mathbf{Z}}^t\overline{\mathbf{H}}^t(\mathbf{Z}^t)^t = \overline{\mathbf{Z}}^t\mathbf{HZ}.$$

Therefore

$$\overline{\overline{\mathbf{Z}}^t\mathbf{HZ}} = \overline{\mathbf{Z}}^t\mathbf{HZ}.$$

Since $\overline{\mathbf{Z}}^t\mathbf{HZ}$ equals its own conjugate, then $\overline{\mathbf{Z}}^t\mathbf{HZ}$ is real.

To prove (2) suppose $\mathbf{S}$ is skew-hermitian. Then $\overline{\mathbf{S}}^t = -\mathbf{S}$. By an argument like that done in the proof of (1), we get

$$\overline{\overline{\mathbf{Z}}^t \mathbf{S} \mathbf{Z}} = -\overline{\mathbf{Z}}^t \mathbf{S} \mathbf{Z}.$$

Now write $\overline{\mathbf{Z}}^t \mathbf{S} \mathbf{Z} = \alpha + i\beta$. The last equation becomes

$$\alpha - i\beta = -\alpha - i\beta.$$

Then $\alpha = -\alpha$, so $\alpha = 0$ and $\overline{\mathbf{Z}}^t \mathbf{S} \mathbf{Z}$ is pure imaginary. ∎

Using these results on quadratic forms, we can say something about the eigenvalues of hermitian and skew-hermitian matrices.

THEOREM 9.17

1. The eigenvalues of a hermitian matrix are real.

2. The eigenvalues of a skew-hermitian matrix are zero or pure imaginary. ∎

Proof For (1), let λ be an eigenvalue of the hermitian matrix $\mathbf{H}$, with associated eigenvector $\mathbf{E}$. By Lemma 8.1,

$$\lambda = \frac{\overline{\mathbf{E}}^t \mathbf{H} \mathbf{E}}{\overline{\mathbf{E}}^t \mathbf{E}}.$$

But by (1) of the preceding theorem, the numerator of this quotient is real. The denominator is the square of the length of $\mathbf{E}$, and so is also real. Therefore λ is real.

For (2), let λ be an eigenvalue of the skew-hermitian matrix $\mathbf{S}$, with associated eigenvector $\mathbf{E}$. Again by Lemma 8.1,

$$\lambda = \frac{\overline{\mathbf{E}}^t \mathbf{S} \mathbf{E}}{\overline{\mathbf{E}}^t \mathbf{E}}.$$

By (2) of the preceding theorem, the numerator of this quotient is either zero or pure imaginary. Since the denominator is a positive real number, then λ is either zero or pure imaginary. ∎

Figure 9.3 shows a graphical representation of the conclusions of Theorems 9.15 and 9.17. When plotted as points in the complex plane, eigenvalues of a unitary matrix lie on the unit circle about the origin, eigenvalues of a hermitian matrix lie on the horizontal (real) axis, and eigenvalues of a skew-hermitian matrix lie on the vertical (imaginary) axis.

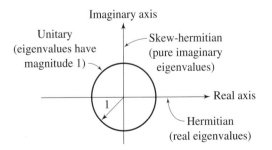

FIGURE 9.3 *Eigenvalue locations.*

SECTION 9.5   PROBLEMS

In each of Problems 1 through 9, determine whether the matrix is unitary, hermitian, skew-hermitian, or none of these. Find the eigenvalues of each matrix and an associated eigenvector for each eigenvalue. Determine which matrices are diagonalizable. If a matrix is diagonalizable, produce a matrix that diagonalizes it.

1. $\begin{pmatrix} 0 & 2i \\ 2i & 4 \end{pmatrix}$

2. $\begin{pmatrix} 3 & 4i \\ 4i & -5 \end{pmatrix}$

3. $\begin{pmatrix} 0 & 1 & 0 \\ -1 & 0 & 1-i \\ 0 & -1-i & 0 \end{pmatrix}$

4. $\begin{pmatrix} 1/\sqrt{2} & i/\sqrt{2} & 0 \\ -1/\sqrt{2} & i/\sqrt{2} & 0 \\ 0 & 0 & 1 \end{pmatrix}$

5. $\begin{pmatrix} 3 & 2 & 0 \\ 2 & 0 & i \\ 0 & -i & 0 \end{pmatrix}$

6. $\begin{pmatrix} -1 & 0 & 3-i \\ 0 & 1 & 0 \\ 3+i & 0 & 0 \end{pmatrix}$

7. $\begin{pmatrix} i & 1 & 0 \\ -1 & 0 & 2i \\ 0 & 2i & 0 \end{pmatrix}$

8. $\begin{pmatrix} 3i & 0 & 0 \\ -1 & 0 & i \\ 0 & -i & 0 \end{pmatrix}$

9. $\begin{pmatrix} 8 & -1 & i \\ -1 & 0 & 0 \\ -i & 0 & 0 \end{pmatrix}$

10. Let **A** be unitary, hermitian or skew-hermitian. Prove that $\overline{\mathbf{A}\mathbf{A}^t} = \overline{\mathbf{A}}\mathbf{A}$.

11. Prove that the main diagonal elements of a skew-hermitian matrix must be zero or pure imaginary.

12. Prove that the main diagonal elements of a hermitian matrix must be real.

13. Prove that the product of two unitary matrices is unitary.

$$\frac{d}{dt}e^{At} = \frac{d}{dt}\left[I_n + At + \frac{1}{2!}A^2t^2 + \frac{1}{3!}A^3t^3 + \cdots\right] = A + A^2t + \frac{1}{2!}A^3t^2 + \cdots$$

PART 3

$$\frac{d}{dt}e^{At} = \frac{d}{dt}\left[I_n + At + \frac{1}{2!}A^2t^2 + \frac{1}{3!}A\right.$$
$$= A\left[I_n + At + \frac{1}{2!}A^2t^2 + \cdots\right]$$
$$= Ae^{At}.$$

CHAPTER 10
Systems of Linear Differential Equations

CHAPTER 11
Qualitative Methods and Systems of Nonlinear Differential Equations

Systems of Differential Equations and Qualitative Methods

We will now use matrices to study systems of differential equations. These arise, for example, in modeling mechanical and electrical systems having more than one component.

We will separate our study of systems of differential equations into two chapters. The first, Chapter 10, is devoted to systems of linear differential equations. For these, powerful matrix methods can be brought to bear to write solutions. For systems of nonlinear differential equations, for which we usually cannot write explicit solutions, we must develop a different set of tools designed to determine qualitative properties of solutions. This is done in Chapter 11.

CHAPTER 10

Systems of Linear Differential Equations

Before beginning to study linear systems, recall from Section 2.6.4 that a linear differential equation of order n always gives rise to a system of n first-order linear differential equations, in such a way that the solution of the system gives the solution of the original n^{th} order equation. Systems can be treated using matrix techniques, which are now at our disposal. For this reason we did not spend time on differential equations of order higher than 2 in Part 1. We will assume familiarity with vectors in R^n, matrix algebra, determinants, and eigenvalues and eigenvectors. These can be reviewed as needed from Part 2.

We begin by laying the foundations for the use of matrices to solve linear systems of differential equations.

10.1   Theory of Systems of Linear First-Order Differential Equations

In this chapter we will consider systems of n first-order linear differential equations in n unknown functions:

$$x'_1(t) = a_{11}(t)x_1(t) + a_{12}(t)x_2(t) + \cdots + a_{1n}(t)x_n(t) + g_1(t)$$
$$x'_2(t) = a_{21}(t)x_1(t) + a_{22}(t)x_2(t) + \cdots + a_{2n}(t)x_n(t) + g_2(t)$$
$$\vdots$$
$$x'_n(t) = a_{n1}(t)x_1(t) + a_{n2}(t)x_2(t) + \cdots + a_{nn}(t)x_n(t) + g_n(t)$$

361

Let

$$\mathbf{A}(t) = \begin{pmatrix} a_{11}(t) & a_{12}(t) & \cdots & a_{1n}(t) \\ a_{21}(t) & a_{22}(t) & \cdots & a_{2n}(t) \\ \vdots & \vdots & \cdots & \vdots \\ a_{n1}(t) & a_{n2}(t) & \cdots & a_{nn}(t) \end{pmatrix},$$

$$\mathbf{X}(t) = \begin{pmatrix} x_1(t) \\ x_2(t) \\ \vdots \\ x_n(t) \end{pmatrix} \quad \text{and} \quad \mathbf{G}(t) = \begin{pmatrix} g_1(t) \\ g_2(t) \\ \vdots \\ g_n(t) \end{pmatrix}.$$

Differentiate a matrix by differentiating each element, so

$$\mathbf{X}'(t) = \begin{pmatrix} x_1'(t) \\ x_2'(t) \\ \vdots \\ x_n'(t) \end{pmatrix}.$$

Matrix differentiation follows the "normal" rules we learn in calculus. For example,

$$(\mathbf{X}(t)\mathbf{Y}(t))' = \mathbf{X}'(t)\mathbf{Y}(t) + \mathbf{X}(t)\mathbf{Y}'(t),$$

in which the order of the factors must be maintained.

Now the system of differential equations is

$$\mathbf{X}'(t) = \mathbf{A}(t)\mathbf{X}(t) + \mathbf{G}(t) \tag{10.1}$$

or

$$\mathbf{X}' = \mathbf{A}\mathbf{X} + \mathbf{G}.$$

This system is *nonhomogeneous* if $\mathbf{G}(t) \neq \mathbf{O}$ for at least some t, in which $\mathbf{O}$ denotes the $n \times 1$ zero matrix

$$\begin{pmatrix} 0 \\ 0 \\ \vdots \\ 0 \end{pmatrix}.$$

If $\mathbf{G}(t) = \mathbf{O}$ for all the relevant values of t, then the system is *homogeneous*, and we write just

$$\mathbf{X}' = \mathbf{A}\mathbf{X}.$$

A *solution* of $\mathbf{X}' = \mathbf{A}\mathbf{X} + \mathbf{G}$ is any $n \times 1$ matrix of functions that satisfies this matrix equation.

EXAMPLE 10.1

The 2×2 system

$$x_1' = 3x_1 + 3x_2 + 8$$

$$x_2' = x_1 + 5x_2 + 4e^{3t}$$

can be written

$$\begin{pmatrix} x_1 \\ x_2 \end{pmatrix}' = \begin{pmatrix} 3 & 3 \\ 1 & 5 \end{pmatrix} \begin{pmatrix} x_1 \\ x_2 \end{pmatrix} + \begin{pmatrix} 8 \\ 4e^{3t} \end{pmatrix}.$$

One solution is

$$\mathbf{X}(t) = \begin{pmatrix} 3e^{2t} + e^{6t} - 4e^{3t} - \frac{10}{3} \\ -e^{2t} + e^{6t} + \frac{2}{3} \end{pmatrix},$$

as can be verified by substitution into the system. In terms of individual components, this solution is

$$x_1(t) = 3e^{2t} + e^{6t} - 4e^{3t} - \frac{10}{3}$$

$$x_2(t) = -e^{2t} + e^{6t} + \frac{2}{3}. \blacksquare$$

On February 20, 1962, John Glenn became the first American to orbit the Earth. His flight lasted nearly five hours and included three complete circuits of the globe. This and subsequent Mercury orbitings paved the way for the space shuttle program, which now includes shuttles launched from the NASA Kennedy Space Center to carry out experiments under zero gravity, as well as delivery of personnel and equipment to the developing international space station. Ultimate goals of space shuttle missions include studying how humans function in a zero-gravity environment over extended periods of time, scientific observations of phenomena in space and on our own planet, and the commercial development of space. Computation of orbits and forces involved in shuttle missions involves the solution of large systems of differential equations.

Initial conditions for the system (10.1) have the form

$$\mathbf{X}(t_0) = \begin{pmatrix} x_1(t_0) \\ x_2(t_0) \\ \vdots \\ x_n(t_0) \end{pmatrix} = \mathbf{X}^0,$$

in which $\mathbf{X}^0$ is a given $n \times 1$ matrix of constants. The initial value problem we will consider for systems is the problem:

$$\mathbf{X}' = \mathbf{AX} + \mathbf{G}; \quad \mathbf{X}(t_0) = \mathbf{X}^0. \tag{10.2}$$

This is analogous to the initial value problem

$$x' = ax + g; \quad x(t_0) = x_0$$

for single first-order equations. Theorem 1.3 gave criteria for existence and uniqueness of solutions of this initial value problem. The analogous result for the initial value problem (10.2) is given by the following.

THEOREM 10.1 *Existence and Uniqueness*

Let I be an open interval containing t_0. Suppose each $a_{ij}(t)$ and $g_j(t)$ are continuous on I. Let $\mathbf{X}^0$ be a given $n \times 1$ matrix of real numbers. Then the initial value problem

$$\mathbf{X}' = \mathbf{AX} + \mathbf{G}; \quad \mathbf{X}(t_0) = \mathbf{X}^0$$

has a unique solution defined for all t in I. ∎

EXAMPLE 10.2

Consider the initial value problem

$$x_1' = x_1 + tx_2 + \cos(t)$$
$$x_2' = t^3 x_1 - e^t x_2 + 1 - t$$
$$x_1(0) = 2, x_2(0) = -5.$$

This is the system

$$\mathbf{X}' = \begin{pmatrix} 1 & t \\ t^3 & -e^t \end{pmatrix} \mathbf{X} + \begin{pmatrix} \cos(t) \\ 1 - t \end{pmatrix},$$

with

$$\mathbf{X}^0 = \begin{pmatrix} 2 \\ -5 \end{pmatrix}.$$

This initial value problem has a unique solution defined for all real t, because each $a_{ij}(t)$ and $g_j(t)$ are continuous for all real t. ∎

We will now determine what we must look for to find all solutions of $\mathbf{X}' = \mathbf{AX} + \mathbf{G}$. This will involve a program that closely parallels that for the single first-order equation $x' = ax + g$, beginning with the homogeneous case.

10.1.1   Theory of the Homogeneous System $X' = AX$

We begin with the homogeneous system $\mathbf{X}' = \mathbf{AX}$. Because solutions of $\mathbf{X}' = \mathbf{AX}$ are $n \times 1$ matrices of real functions, these solutions have an algebraic structure, and we can form linear combinations (finite sums of scalar multiples of solutions). In the homogeneous case, any linear combination of solutions is again a solution.

THEOREM 10.2

Let $\boldsymbol{\Phi}_1, \ldots, \boldsymbol{\Phi}_k$ be solutions of $\mathbf{X}' = \mathbf{AX}$, all defined on some open interval I. Let $c_1, \ldots, c_k$ be any real numbers. Then the linear combination $c_1 \boldsymbol{\Phi}_1 + \cdots + c_k \boldsymbol{\Phi}_k$ is also a solution of $\mathbf{X}' = \mathbf{AX}$, defined on I.

Proof   Compute

$$(c_1 \boldsymbol{\Phi}_1 + \cdots + c_k \boldsymbol{\Phi}_k)' = c_1 \boldsymbol{\Phi}_1' + \cdots + c_k \boldsymbol{\Phi}_k' = c_1 \mathbf{A} \boldsymbol{\Phi}_1 + \cdots + c_k \mathbf{A} \boldsymbol{\Phi}_k$$
$$= \mathbf{A}(c_1 \boldsymbol{\Phi}_1 + \cdots + c_k \boldsymbol{\Phi}_k). \quad \blacksquare$$

Because of this, the set of all solutions of $\mathbf{X}' = \mathbf{AX}$ has the structure of a vector space, called the *solution space* of this system. It is not necessary to have a background in vector spaces to follow the discussion of solutions of $\mathbf{X}' = \mathbf{AX}$ that we are about to develop. However, for those who do have this background we will make occasional reference to show how ideas fit into this algebraic framework.

In a linear combination $c_1 \boldsymbol{\Phi}_1 + \cdots + c_k \boldsymbol{\Phi}_k$ of solutions, any $\boldsymbol{\Phi}_j$ that is already a linear combination of the other solutions is unnecessary. For example, suppose $\boldsymbol{\Phi}_1 = a_2 \boldsymbol{\Phi}_2 + \cdots + a_k \boldsymbol{\Phi}_k$. Then

$$c_1 \boldsymbol{\Phi}_1 + \cdots + c_k \boldsymbol{\Phi}_k = c_1(a_2 \boldsymbol{\Phi}_2 + \cdots + a_k \boldsymbol{\Phi}_k) + c_2 \boldsymbol{\Phi}_2 + \cdots + c_k \boldsymbol{\Phi}_k$$
$$= (c_1 a_2 + c_2) \boldsymbol{\Phi}_2 + \cdots + (c_1 a_k + c_k) \boldsymbol{\Phi}_k.$$

In this case any linear combination of $\boldsymbol{\Phi}_1, \boldsymbol{\Phi}_2, \ldots, \boldsymbol{\Phi}_k$ is actually a linear combination of just $\boldsymbol{\Phi}_2, \ldots, \boldsymbol{\Phi}_k$, and $\boldsymbol{\Phi}_1$ is not needed. $\boldsymbol{\Phi}_1$ is redundant in the sense that, if we have $\boldsymbol{\Phi}_2, \ldots, \boldsymbol{\Phi}_k$, then we have $\boldsymbol{\Phi}_1$ also. We describe this situation by saying that the functions $\boldsymbol{\Phi}_1, \boldsymbol{\Phi}_2, \ldots, \boldsymbol{\Phi}_k$ are linearly dependent. If no one of the functions is a linear combination of the others, then these functions are called linearly independent.

DEFINITION 10.1

Linear Dependence
Solutions $\boldsymbol{\Phi}_1, \boldsymbol{\Phi}_2, \ldots, \boldsymbol{\Phi}_k$, of $\mathbf{X}' = \mathbf{AX}$, defined on an interval I, are linearly dependent on I if one solution is a linear combination of the others on this interval.

Linear Independence
Solutions $\boldsymbol{\Phi}_1, \boldsymbol{\Phi}_2, \ldots, \boldsymbol{\Phi}_k$, of $\mathbf{X}' = \mathbf{AX}$, defined on an interval I, are linearly independent on I if no solution in this list is a linear combination of the others on this interval.

Thus a set of solutions is linearly independent if it is not linearly dependent.

Linear dependence of functions is a stronger condition than linear dependence of vectors. For vectors in R^n, $\mathbf{V}_1$ is a linear combination of $\mathbf{V}_2$ and $\mathbf{V}_3$ if $\mathbf{V}_1 = a\mathbf{V}_2 + b\mathbf{V}_3$ for some real numbers a and b. In this case $\mathbf{V}_1, \mathbf{V}_2, \mathbf{V}_3$ are linearly dependent. But for solutions $\mathbf{\Phi}_1, \mathbf{\Phi}_2, \mathbf{\Phi}_3$ of $\mathbf{X}' = \mathbf{A}\mathbf{X}$, $\mathbf{\Phi}_1$ is a linear combination of $\mathbf{\Phi}_2$ and $\mathbf{\Phi}_3$ if there are numbers a and b such that $\mathbf{\Phi}_1(t) = a\mathbf{\Phi}_2(t) + b\mathbf{\Phi}_2(t)$ for all t in the relevant interval, perhaps the entire real line. It is not enough to have this condition hold for just some values of t.

EXAMPLE 10.3

Consider the system

$$\mathbf{X}' = \begin{pmatrix} 1 & -4 \\ 1 & 5 \end{pmatrix} \mathbf{X}.$$

It is routine to check that

$$\mathbf{\Phi}_1(t) = \begin{pmatrix} -2e^{3t} \\ e^{3t} \end{pmatrix} \quad \text{and} \quad \mathbf{\Phi}_2(t) = \begin{pmatrix} (1-2t)e^{3t} \\ te^{3t} \end{pmatrix}$$

are solutions, defined for all real values of t. These solutions are linearly independent on the entire real line, since neither is a constant multiple of the other (for all real t).

The function

$$\mathbf{\Phi}_3(t) = \begin{pmatrix} (11-6t)e^{3t} \\ (-4+3t)e^{3t} \end{pmatrix}$$

is also a solution. However, $\mathbf{\Phi}_1, \mathbf{\Phi}_2, \mathbf{\Phi}_3$ are linearly dependent, because, for all real t,

$$\mathbf{\Phi}_3(t) = -4\mathbf{\Phi}_1(t) + 3\mathbf{\Phi}_2(t).$$

This means that $\mathbf{\Phi}_3$ is a linear combination of $\mathbf{\Phi}_1$ and $\mathbf{\Phi}_2$, and the list of solutions $\mathbf{\Phi}_1, \mathbf{\Phi}_2, \mathbf{\Phi}_3$, although longer, carries no more information about the solution of $\mathbf{X}' = \mathbf{A}\mathbf{X}$ than the list of solutions $\mathbf{\Phi}_1, \mathbf{\Phi}_2$. ■

If $\mathbf{\Phi}$ is a solution of $\mathbf{X}' = \mathbf{A}\mathbf{X}$, then $\mathbf{\Phi}$ is an $n \times 1$ column matrix of functions:

$$\mathbf{\Phi}(t) = \begin{pmatrix} f_1(t) \\ f_2(t) \\ \vdots \\ f_n(t) \end{pmatrix}.$$

For any choice of t, say $t = t_0$, this is an $n \times 1$ matrix of real numbers which can be thought of as a vector in R^n. This point of view, and some facts about determinants, provides us with a test for linear independence of solutions of $\mathbf{X}' = \mathbf{A}\mathbf{X}$.

The following theorem reduces the question of linear independence of n solutions of $\mathbf{X}' = \mathbf{A}\mathbf{X}$, to a question of whether an $n \times n$ determinant of real numbers is nonzero.

THEOREM 10.3 *Test for Linear Independence of Solutions*

Suppose that

$$\mathbf{\Phi}_1(t) = \begin{pmatrix} \varphi_{11}(t) \\ \varphi_{21}(t) \\ \vdots \\ \varphi_{n1}(t) \end{pmatrix}, \mathbf{\Phi}_2(t) = \begin{pmatrix} \varphi_{12}(t) \\ \varphi_{22}(t) \\ \vdots \\ \varphi_{n2}(t) \end{pmatrix}, \ldots, \mathbf{\Phi}_n(t) = \begin{pmatrix} \varphi_{1n}(t) \\ \varphi_{2n}(t) \\ \vdots \\ \varphi_{nn}(t) \end{pmatrix}$$

are solutions of $\mathbf{X}' = \mathbf{A}\mathbf{X}$ on an open interval I. Let t_0 be any number in I. Then

1. $\mathbf{\Phi}_1, \mathbf{\Phi}_2, \ldots, \mathbf{\Phi}_n$ are linearly independent on I if and only if $\mathbf{\Phi}_1(t_0), \ldots, \mathbf{\Phi}_n(t_0)$ are linearly independent, when considered as vectors in R^n.

2. $\mathbf{\Phi}_1, \mathbf{\Phi}_2, \ldots, \mathbf{\Phi}_n$ are linearly independent on I if and only if

$$
\begin{vmatrix}
\varphi_{11}(t_0) & \varphi_{12}(t_0) & \cdots & \varphi_{1n}(t_0) \\
\varphi_{21}(t_0) & \varphi_{22}(t_0) & \cdots & \varphi_{2n}(t_0) \\
\vdots & \vdots & \cdots & \vdots \\
\varphi_{n1}(t_0) & \varphi_{n2}(t_0) & \cdots & \varphi_{nn}(t_0)
\end{vmatrix} \neq 0. \; \blacksquare
$$

Conclusion (2) is an effective test for linear independence of n solutions of $\mathbf{X}' = \mathbf{A}\mathbf{X}$ on an open interval. Evaluate each solution at some point of the interval. Each $\mathbf{\Phi}_j(t_0)$ is an $n \times 1$ (constant) column matrix. Evaluate the determinant of the $n \times n$ matrix having these columns. If this determinant is nonzero, then the solutions are linearly independent; if it is zero, they are linearly dependent.

Another way of looking at (2) of this theorem is that it reduces a question of linear independence of n solutions of $\mathbf{X}' = \mathbf{A}\mathbf{X}$, to a question of linear independence of n vectors in R^n. This is because the determinant in (2) is nonzero exactly when its row (or column) vectors are linearly independent.

EXAMPLE 10.4

From the preceding example,

$$
\mathbf{\Phi}_1(t) = \begin{pmatrix} -2e^{3t} \\ e^{3t} \end{pmatrix} \quad \text{and} \quad \mathbf{\Phi}_2(t) = \begin{pmatrix} (1-2t)e^{3t} \\ te^{3t} \end{pmatrix}
$$

are solutions of

$$
\mathbf{X}' = \begin{pmatrix} 1 & -4 \\ 1 & 5 \end{pmatrix} \mathbf{X}
$$

on the entire real line, which is an open interval. Evaluate these solutions at some convenient point, say $t = 0$:

$$
\mathbf{\Phi}_1(0) = \begin{pmatrix} -2 \\ 1 \end{pmatrix} \quad \text{and} \quad \mathbf{\Phi}_2(0) = \begin{pmatrix} 1 \\ 0 \end{pmatrix}.
$$

Use these as columns of a 2×2 matrix and evaluate its determinant:

$$
\begin{vmatrix} -2 & 1 \\ 1 & 0 \end{vmatrix} = -1 \neq 0.
$$

Therefore $\mathbf{\Phi}_1$ and $\mathbf{\Phi}_2$ are linearly independent solutions. $\blacksquare$

A proof of Theorem 10.3 makes use of the uniqueness of solutions of the initial value problem (Theorem 10.1).

Proof For (1), let t_0 be any point in I. Suppose first that $\mathbf{\Phi}_1, \ldots, \mathbf{\Phi}_n$ are linearly dependent on I. Then one of the solutions is a linear combination of the others. By reordering if necessary, say $\mathbf{\Phi}_1$ is a linear combination of $\mathbf{\Phi}_2, \ldots, \mathbf{\Phi}_n$. Then there are numbers $c_2, \ldots, c_n$ so that

$$
\mathbf{\Phi}_1(t) = c_2 \mathbf{\Phi}_2(t) + \cdots + c_n \mathbf{\Phi}_n(t)
$$

for all t in I. In particular,

$$\boldsymbol{\Phi}_1(t_0) = c_2\boldsymbol{\Phi}_2(t_0) + \cdots + c_n\boldsymbol{\Phi}_n(t_0).$$

This implies that the vectors $\boldsymbol{\Phi}_1(t_0), \ldots, \boldsymbol{\Phi}_n(t_0)$ are linearly dependent vectors in R^n.

Conversely, suppose that $\boldsymbol{\Phi}_1(t_0), \ldots, \boldsymbol{\Phi}_n(t_0)$ are linearly dependent in R^n. Then one of these vectors is a linear combination of the others. Again, as a convenience, suppose $\boldsymbol{\Phi}_1(t_0)$ is a linear combination of $\boldsymbol{\Phi}_2(t_0), \ldots, \boldsymbol{\Phi}_n(t_0)$. Then there are numbers $c_2, \ldots, c_n$ such that

$$\boldsymbol{\Phi}_1(t_0) = c_2\boldsymbol{\Phi}_2(t_0) + \cdots + c_n\boldsymbol{\Phi}_n(t_0).$$

Define

$$\boldsymbol{\Phi}(t) = \boldsymbol{\Phi}_1(t) - c_2\boldsymbol{\Phi}_2(t) - \cdots - c_n\boldsymbol{\Phi}_n(t)$$

for all t in I. Then $\boldsymbol{\Phi}$ is a linear combination of solutions of $\mathbf{X}' = \mathbf{A}\mathbf{X}$, hence is a solution. Further

$$\boldsymbol{\Phi}(t_0) = \begin{pmatrix} 0 \\ 0 \\ \vdots \\ 0 \end{pmatrix}.$$

Therefore, on I, $\boldsymbol{\Phi}$ is a solution of the initial value problem

$$\mathbf{X}' = \mathbf{A}\mathbf{X}; \quad \mathbf{X}(t_0) = \mathbf{O}.$$

But the zero function

$$\boldsymbol{\Psi}(t) = \begin{pmatrix} 0 \\ 0 \\ \vdots \\ 0 \end{pmatrix}$$

is also a solution of this initial value problem. Since this initial value problem has a unique solution, then for all t in I,

$$\boldsymbol{\Phi}(t) = \boldsymbol{\Psi}(t) = \begin{pmatrix} 0 \\ 0 \\ \vdots \\ 0 \end{pmatrix}.$$

Therefore

$$\boldsymbol{\Phi}(t) = \boldsymbol{\Phi}_1(t) - c_2\boldsymbol{\Phi}_2(t) - \cdots - c_n\boldsymbol{\Phi}_n(t) = \begin{pmatrix} 0 \\ 0 \\ \vdots \\ 0 \end{pmatrix}$$

for all t in I, which means that

$$\boldsymbol{\Phi}_1(t) = c_2\boldsymbol{\Phi}_2(t) + \cdots + c_n\boldsymbol{\Phi}_n(t)$$

for all t in I. Therefore $\boldsymbol{\Phi}_1$ is a linear combination of $\boldsymbol{\Phi}_2, \ldots, \boldsymbol{\Phi}_n$, hence $\boldsymbol{\Phi}_1, \boldsymbol{\Phi}_2, \ldots, \boldsymbol{\Phi}_n$ are linearly dependent on I.

Conclusion (2) follows from (1) and the fact that n vectors in R^n are linearly independent if and only if the determinant of the $n \times n$ matrix having these vectors as columns is nonzero. ∎

Thus far we know how to test n solutions of $\mathbf{X}' = \mathbf{A}\mathbf{X}$ for linear independence, if $\mathbf{A}$ is $n \times n$. We will now show that n linearly independent solutions are enough to determine all solutions of $\mathbf{X}' = \mathbf{A}\mathbf{X}$ on an open interval I. We saw a result like this previously when it was found that two linear independent solutions of $y'' + p(x)y' + q(x)y = 0$ determine all solutions of this equation.

THEOREM 10.4

Let $\mathbf{A} = [a_{ij}(t)]$ be an $n \times n$ matrix of functions that are continuous on an open interval I. Then

1. The system $\mathbf{X}' = \mathbf{A}\mathbf{X}$ has n linearly independent solutions defined on I.
2. Given any n linearly independent solutions $\mathbf{\Phi}_1, \ldots, \mathbf{\Phi}_n$ defined on I, every solution on I is a linear combination of $\mathbf{\Phi}_1, \ldots, \mathbf{\Phi}_n$. ∎

By (2), every solution of $\mathbf{X}' = \mathbf{A}\mathbf{X}$, defined on I, must be of the form $c_1\mathbf{\Phi}_1 + c_2\mathbf{\Phi}_2 + \cdots + c_n\mathbf{\Phi}_n$. For this reason, this linear combination, with $\mathbf{\Phi}_1, \ldots, \mathbf{\Phi}_n$ any n linearly independent solutions, is called the *general solution* of $\mathbf{X}' = \mathbf{A}\mathbf{X}$ on I.

Proof To prove that there are n linearly independent solutions, define the $n \times 1$ constant matrices

$$
\mathbf{E}^{(1)} = \begin{pmatrix} 1 \\ 0 \\ 0 \\ \vdots \\ 0 \end{pmatrix}, \mathbf{E}^{(2)} = \begin{pmatrix} 0 \\ 1 \\ 0 \\ \vdots \\ 0 \end{pmatrix}, \ldots, \mathbf{E}^{(n)} = \begin{pmatrix} 0 \\ 0 \\ 0 \\ \vdots \\ 1 \end{pmatrix}.
$$

Pick any t_0 in I. We know from Theorem 10.1 that the initial value problem

$$
\mathbf{X}' = \mathbf{A}\mathbf{X}; \quad \mathbf{X}(t_0) = \mathbf{E}^{(j)}
$$

has a unique solution $\mathbf{\Phi}_j$ defined on I, for $j = 1, 2, \ldots n$. These solutions are linearly independent by Theorem 10.3, because the way the initial conditions were chosen, the $n \times n$ matrix whose columns are these solutions evaluated at t_0 is $\mathbf{I}_n$, with determinant 1. This proves (1).

To prove (2), suppose now that $\mathbf{\Psi}_1, \ldots, \mathbf{\Psi}_n$ are any n linearly independent solutions of $\mathbf{X}' = \mathbf{A}\mathbf{X}$, defined on I. Let $\mathbf{\Lambda}$ be any solution. We want to prove that $\mathbf{\Lambda}$ is a linear combination of $\mathbf{\Psi}_1, \ldots, \mathbf{\Psi}_n$.

Pick any t_0 in I. We will first show that there are numbers $c_1, \ldots, c_n$ such that

$$
\mathbf{\Lambda}(t_0) = c_1\mathbf{\Psi}_1(t_0) + \cdots + c_n\mathbf{\Psi}_n(t_0).
$$

Now $\mathbf{\Lambda}(t_0)$, and each $\mathbf{\Psi}_j(t_0)$, is an $n \times 1$ column matrix of constants. Form the $n \times n$ matrix $\mathbf{S}$ using $\mathbf{\Psi}_1(t_0), \ldots, \mathbf{\Psi}_n(t_0)$ as its columns, and consider the system of n linear algebraic equations in n unknowns

$$
\mathbf{S}\begin{pmatrix} c_1 \\ c_2 \\ \vdots \\ c_n \end{pmatrix} = \mathbf{\Lambda}(t_0). \tag{10.3}
$$

The columns of $\mathbf{S}$ are linearly independent vectors in R^n, because $\boldsymbol{\Psi}_1, \ldots, \boldsymbol{\Psi}_n$ are linearly independent. Therefore $\mathbf{S}$ is nonsingular, and the system (10.3) has a unique solution. This solution gives constants $c_1, \ldots, c_n$ such that

$$\boldsymbol{\Lambda}(t_0) = c_1 \boldsymbol{\Psi}_1(t_0) + \cdots + c_n \boldsymbol{\Psi}_n(t_0).$$

We now claim that

$$\boldsymbol{\Lambda}(t) = c_1 \boldsymbol{\Psi}_1(t) + \cdots + c_n \boldsymbol{\Psi}_n(t)$$

for all t in I. But observe that $\boldsymbol{\Lambda}$ and $c_1 \boldsymbol{\Psi}_1 + \cdots + c_n \boldsymbol{\Psi}_n$ are both solutions of the initial value problem

$$\mathbf{X}' = \mathbf{A}\mathbf{X}; \quad \mathbf{X}(t_0) = \boldsymbol{\Lambda}(t_0).$$

Since this problem has a unique solution, then $\boldsymbol{\Lambda}(t) = c_1 \boldsymbol{\Psi}_1(t) + \cdots + c_n \boldsymbol{\Psi}_n(t)$ for all t in I, and the proof is complete. ■

In the language of linear algebra, the solution space of $\mathbf{X}' = \mathbf{A}\mathbf{X}$ has dimension n, the order of the coefficient matrix $\mathbf{A}$. Any n linearly independent solutions form a basis for this vector space.

EXAMPLE 10.5

Previously we saw that

$$\boldsymbol{\Phi}_1(t) = \begin{pmatrix} -2e^{3t} \\ e^{3t} \end{pmatrix} \quad \text{and} \quad \boldsymbol{\Phi}_2(t) = \begin{pmatrix} (1-2t)e^{3t} \\ te^{3t} \end{pmatrix}$$

are linearly independent solutions of

$$\mathbf{X}' = \begin{pmatrix} 1 & -4 \\ 1 & 5 \end{pmatrix} \mathbf{X}.$$

Because $\mathbf{A}$ is 2×2 and we have 2 linearly independent solutions, the general solution of this system is

$$\boldsymbol{\Phi}(t) = c_1 \begin{pmatrix} -2e^{3t} \\ e^{3t} \end{pmatrix} + c_2 \begin{pmatrix} (1-2t)e^{3t} \\ te^{3t} \end{pmatrix}.$$

The expression on the right contains every solution of this system. In terms of components,

$$x_1(t) = -2c_1 e^{3t} + c_2(1-2t)e^{3t},$$
$$x_2(t) = c_1 e^{3t} + c_2 te^{3t}. \quad ■$$

We will now make a useful observation. In the last example, form a 2×2 matrix $\boldsymbol{\Omega}(t)$ having $\boldsymbol{\Phi}_1(t)$ and $\boldsymbol{\Phi}_2(t)$ as columns:

$$\boldsymbol{\Omega}(t) = \begin{pmatrix} -2e^{3t} & (1-2t)e^{3t} \\ e^{3t} & te^{3t} \end{pmatrix}.$$

Now observe that, if $\mathbf{C} = \begin{pmatrix} c_1 \\ c_2 \end{pmatrix}$, then

$$
\begin{aligned}
\mathbf{\Omega}(t)\mathbf{C} &= \begin{pmatrix} -2e^{3t} & (1-2t)e^{3t} \\ e^{3t} & te^{3t} \end{pmatrix} \begin{pmatrix} c_1 \\ c_2 \end{pmatrix} \\
&= \begin{pmatrix} c_1\left[-2e^{3t}\right] + c_2[(1-2t)e^{3t}] \\ c_1[e^{3t}] + c_2[te^{3t}] \end{pmatrix} \\
&= c_1 \begin{pmatrix} -2e^{3t} \\ e^{3t} \end{pmatrix} + c_2 \begin{pmatrix} (1-2t)e^{3t} \\ te^{3t} \end{pmatrix} \\
&= c_1 \mathbf{\Phi}_1(t) + c_2 \mathbf{\Phi}_2(t).
\end{aligned}
$$

The point is that we can write the general solution $c_1\mathbf{\Phi}_1 + c_2\mathbf{\Phi}_2$ compactly as $\mathbf{\Omega}(t)\mathbf{C}$, with $\mathbf{\Omega}(t)$ a square matrix having the independent solutions as columns, and $\mathbf{C}$ a column matrix of arbitrary constants. We call a matrix $\mathbf{\Omega}$ formed in this way a *fundamental matrix* for the system $\mathbf{X}' = \mathbf{AX}$. In terms of this fundamental matrix, the general solution is $\mathbf{X}(t) = \mathbf{\Omega}(t)\mathbf{C}$.

We can see that $\mathbf{\Omega}(t)\mathbf{C}$ also satisfies the matrix differential equation $\mathbf{X}' = \mathbf{AX}$. Recall that we differentiate a matrix by differentiating each element of the matrix. Then, because $\mathbf{C}$ is a constant matrix,

$$
(\mathbf{\Omega}(t)\mathbf{C})' = \mathbf{\Omega}(t)'\mathbf{C} = \begin{pmatrix} -6e^{3t} & e^{3t} - 6te^{3t} \\ 3e^{3t} & e^{3t} + 3te^{3t} \end{pmatrix} \mathbf{C}.
$$

Now compute

$$
\begin{aligned}
\mathbf{A}(\mathbf{\Omega}(t)\mathbf{C}) &= (\mathbf{A}\mathbf{\Omega}(t))\mathbf{C} \\
&= \begin{pmatrix} 1 & -4 \\ 1 & 5 \end{pmatrix} \begin{pmatrix} -2e^{3t} & (1-2t)e^{3t} \\ e^{3t} & te^{3t} \end{pmatrix} \mathbf{C} \\
&= \begin{pmatrix} -2e^{3t} - 4e^{3t} & (1-2t)e^{3t} - 4te^{3t} \\ -2e^{3t} + 5e^{3t} & (1-2t)e^{3t} + 5te^{3t} \end{pmatrix} \mathbf{C} \\
&= \begin{pmatrix} -6e^{3t} & (1-6t)e^{3t} \\ 3e^{3t} & e^{3t} + 3te^{3t} \end{pmatrix}.
\end{aligned}
$$

Therefore

$$
(\mathbf{\Omega}(t)\mathbf{C})' = \mathbf{A}(\mathbf{\Omega}(t)\mathbf{C}),
$$

as occurs if $\mathbf{\Omega}(t)\mathbf{C}$ is a solution of $\mathbf{X}' = \mathbf{AX}$.

DEFINITION 10.2

$\mathbf{\Omega}$ is a fundamental matrix for the $n \times n$ system $\mathbf{X}' = \mathbf{AX}$ if the columns of $\mathbf{\Omega}$ are linearly independent solutions of this system.

Writing the general solution of $\mathbf{X}' = \mathbf{AX}$ as $\mathbf{X}(t) = \mathbf{\Omega}\mathbf{C}$ is particularly convenient for solving initial value problems.

EXAMPLE 10.6

Solve the initial value problem

$$\mathbf{X}' = \begin{pmatrix} 1 & -4 \\ 1 & 5 \end{pmatrix}; \quad \mathbf{X}(0) = \begin{pmatrix} -2 \\ 3 \end{pmatrix}.$$

We know from Example 10.5 that the general solution if $\mathbf{X}(t) = \mathbf{\Omega}(t)\mathbf{C}$, where

$$\mathbf{\Omega}(t) = \begin{pmatrix} -2e^{3t} & (1-2t)e^{3t} \\ e^{3t} & te^{3t} \end{pmatrix}.$$

We need to choose $\mathbf{C}$ so that

$$\mathbf{X}(0) = \mathbf{\Omega}(0)\mathbf{C} = \begin{pmatrix} -2 \\ 3 \end{pmatrix}.$$

Putting $t = 0$ into $\mathbf{\Omega}$, we must solve the algebraic system

$$\begin{pmatrix} -2 & 1 \\ 1 & 0 \end{pmatrix} \mathbf{C} = \begin{pmatrix} -2 \\ 3 \end{pmatrix}.$$

The solution is

$$\mathbf{C} = \begin{pmatrix} -2 & 1 \\ 1 & 0 \end{pmatrix}^{-1} \begin{pmatrix} -2 \\ 3 \end{pmatrix}$$

$$= \begin{pmatrix} 0 & 1 \\ 1 & 2 \end{pmatrix} \begin{pmatrix} -2 \\ 3 \end{pmatrix} = \begin{pmatrix} 3 \\ 4 \end{pmatrix}.$$

The unique solution of the initial value problem is therefore

$$\mathbf{\Phi}(t) = \mathbf{\Omega}(t) \begin{pmatrix} 3 \\ 4 \end{pmatrix}$$

$$= \begin{pmatrix} -2e^{-3t} - 8te^{3t} \\ 3e^{3t} + 4te^{3t} \end{pmatrix}. \blacksquare$$

In this example $\mathbf{\Omega}(0)^{-1}$ could be found by linear algebra methods (Sections 7.8.1 and 8.7) or by using a software package.

10.1.2 General Solution of the Nonhomogeneous System $\mathbf{X}' = \mathbf{AX} + \mathbf{G}$

Solutions of the nonhomogeneous system $\mathbf{X}' = \mathbf{AX} + \mathbf{G}$ do not have the algebraic structure of a vector space, because linear combinations of solutions are not solutions. However, we will show that the general solution of this system (an expression containing all possible solutions) is the sum of the general solution of the homogeneous system $\mathbf{X}' = \mathbf{AX}$, and any particular solution of the nonhomogeneous system. This is completely analogous to Theorem 2.5 for the second order equation $y'' + p(x)y' + q(x)y = f(x)$.

THEOREM 10.5

Let $\mathbf{\Omega}$ be a fundamental matrix for $\mathbf{X}' = \mathbf{AX}$, and let $\mathbf{\Psi}_p$ be any solution of $\mathbf{X}' = \mathbf{AX} + \mathbf{G}$.

Then the general solution of $\mathbf{X}' = \mathbf{AX} + \mathbf{G}$ is $\mathbf{X} = \mathbf{\Omega}\mathbf{C} + \mathbf{\Psi}_p$, in which $\mathbf{C}$ is an $n \times 1$ matrix of arbitrary constants.

Proof First, $\mathbf{\Omega C} + \mathbf{\Psi}_p$ is a solution of the nonhomogeneous system, because

$$(\mathbf{\Omega C} + \mathbf{\Psi}_p)' = (\mathbf{\Omega C})' + \mathbf{\Psi}_p'$$

$$= \mathbf{A}(\mathbf{\Omega C}) + \mathbf{A}\mathbf{\Psi}_p + \mathbf{G} = \mathbf{A}(\mathbf{\Omega C} + \mathbf{\Psi}_p) + \mathbf{G}.$$

Now let $\mathbf{\Phi}$ be any solution of $\mathbf{X}' = \mathbf{AX} + \mathbf{G}$. We claim that $\mathbf{\Phi} - \mathbf{\Psi}_p$ is a solution of $\mathbf{X}' = \mathbf{AX}$. To see this, calculate

$$(\mathbf{\Phi} - \mathbf{\Psi}_p)' = \mathbf{\Phi}' - \mathbf{\Psi}_p'$$

$$= \mathbf{A}\mathbf{\Phi} + \mathbf{G} - (\mathbf{A}\mathbf{\Psi}_p + \mathbf{G}) = \mathbf{A}(\mathbf{\Phi} - \mathbf{\Psi}_p).$$

Since $\mathbf{\Omega C}$ is the general solution of $\mathbf{X}' = \mathbf{AX}$, there is a constant $n \times 1$ matrix $\mathbf{K}$ such that $\mathbf{\Phi} - \mathbf{\Psi}_p = \mathbf{\Omega K}$. Then $\mathbf{\Phi} = \mathbf{\Omega K} + \mathbf{\Psi}_p$, completing the proof.

We now know what to look for in solving a system of n linear, first-order differential equations in n unknown functions. For the homogeneous system, $\mathbf{X}' = \mathbf{AX}$, we look for n linearly independent solutions to form a fundamental matrix $\mathbf{\Omega}(t)$. For the nonhomogeneous system $\mathbf{X}' = \mathbf{AX} + \mathbf{G}$, we first find the general solution $\mathbf{\Omega C}$ of $\mathbf{X}' = \mathbf{AX}$, and any particular solution $\mathbf{\Psi}_p$ of $\mathbf{X}' = \mathbf{AX} + \mathbf{G}$. The general solution of $\mathbf{X}' = \mathbf{AX} + \mathbf{G}$ is then $\mathbf{\Omega C} + \mathbf{\Psi}_p$.

This is an overall strategy. Now we need ways of implementing it and actually producing fundamental matrices and particular solutions for given systems.

SECTION 10.1 PROBLEMS

In each of Problems 1 through 5, (a) verify that the given functions satisfy the system, (b) form a fundamental matrix $\mathbf{\Omega}(t)$ for the system, (c) write the general solution in the form $\mathbf{\Omega}(t)\mathbf{C}$, carry out this product, and verify that the rows of $\mathbf{\Omega}(t)\mathbf{C}$ are the components of the given solution, and (d) find the unique solution satisfying the initial conditions.

1. $\quad x_1' = 5x_1 + 3x_2, x_2' = x_1 + 3x_2$

$\quad x_1(t) = -c_1 e^{2t} + 3c_2 e^{6t}, x_2(t) = c_1 e^{2t} + c_2 e^{6t}$

$\quad x_1(0) = 0, x_2(0) = 4$

2. $\quad x_1' = 2x_1 + x_2, x_2' = -3x_1 + 6x_2$

$\quad x_1(t) = c_1 e^{4t} \cos(t) + c_2 e^{4t} \sin(t),$

$\quad x_2(t) = 2c_1 e^{4t}[\cos(t) - \sin(t)] + 2c_2 e^{4t}[\cos(t) + \sin(t)]$

$\quad x_1(0) = -2, x_2(0) = 1$

3. $\quad x_1'(t) = 3x_1 + 8x_2, x_2'(t) = x_1 - x_2$

$\quad x_1(t) = 4c_1 e^{(1+2\sqrt{3})t} + 4c_2 e^{(1-2\sqrt{3})t},$

$\quad x_2(t) = (-1+\sqrt{3})c_1 e^{(1+2\sqrt{3})t} + (-1-\sqrt{3})c_2 e^{(1-2\sqrt{3})t}$

$\quad x_1(0) = 2, x_2(0) = 2$

4. $\quad x_1' = x_1 - x_2, x_2' = 4x_1 + 2x_2$

$$x_1(t) = 2e^{3t/2}\left[c_1 \cos\left(\frac{\sqrt{15}t}{2}\right) + c_2 \sin\left(\frac{\sqrt{15}t}{2}\right)\right],$$

$$x_2(t) = c_1 e^{3t/2}\left[-\cos\left(\frac{\sqrt{15}t}{2}\right) + \sqrt{15}\sin\left(\frac{\sqrt{15}t}{2}\right)\right]$$

$$-c_2 e^{3t/2}\left[\sin\left(\frac{\sqrt{15}t}{2}\right) + \sqrt{15}\cos\left(\frac{\sqrt{15}t}{2}\right)\right],$$

$\quad x_1(0) = -2, x_2(0) = 7$

5. $\quad x_1' = 5x_1 - 4x_2 + 4x_3, x_2' = 12x_1 - 11x_2 + 12x_3,$

$\quad x_3' = 4x_1 - 4x_2 + 5x_3,$

$\quad x_1(t) = c_1 e^t + c_3 e^{-3t}, x_2(t) = c_2 e^{2t} + c_3 e^{-3t},$

$\quad x_3(t) = (c_2 - c_1)e^t + c_3 e^{-3t},$

$\quad x_1(0) = 1, x_2(0) = -3, x_3(0) = 5$

10.2 Solution of $X' = AX$ when A is Constant

Consider the system $\mathbf{X}' = \mathbf{AX}$, with $\mathbf{A}$ an $n \times n$ matrix of real numbers. In the case $y' = ay$, with a constant, we get exponential solutions $y = ce^{ax}$. This suggests we try a similar solution for the system.

Try $\mathbf{X} = \boldsymbol{\xi}e^{\lambda t}$, with $\boldsymbol{\xi}$ an $n \times 1$ matrix of constants to be determined, and λ a number to be determined. Substitute this proposed solution into the differential equation to get

$$\boldsymbol{\xi}\lambda e^{\lambda t} = \mathbf{A}(\boldsymbol{\xi}e^{\lambda t}).$$

This requires that

$$\mathbf{A}\boldsymbol{\xi} = \lambda\boldsymbol{\xi}.$$

We should therefore choose λ as an eigenvalue of $\mathbf{A}$, and $\boldsymbol{\xi}$ as an associated eigenvector. We will summarize this discussion.

THEOREM 10.6

Let $\mathbf{A}$ be an $n \times n$ matrix of real numbers. Then $\boldsymbol{\xi}e^{\lambda t}$ is a nontrivial solution of $\mathbf{X}' = \mathbf{AX}$ if and only if λ is an eigenvalue of $\mathbf{A}$, with associated eigenvector $\boldsymbol{\xi}$. ∎

We need n linearly independent solutions to form a fundamental matrix. We will have these if we can find n linearly independent eigenvectors, whether or not some eigenvalues may be repeated.

THEOREM 10.7

Let $\mathbf{A}$ be an $n \times n$ matrix of real numbers. Suppose $\mathbf{A}$ has eigenvalues $\lambda_1, \ldots, \lambda_n$, and suppose there are associated eigenvectors $\boldsymbol{\xi}_1, \ldots, \boldsymbol{\xi}_n$ that are linearly independent. Then $\boldsymbol{\xi}_1 e^{\lambda_1 t}, \ldots, \boldsymbol{\xi}_n e^{\lambda_n t}$ are linearly independent solutions of $\mathbf{X}' = \mathbf{AX}$, on the entire real line.

Proof We know that each $\boldsymbol{\xi}_j e^{\lambda_j t}$ is a nontrivial solution. The question is whether these solutions are linearly independent. Form the $n \times n$ matrix having these solutions, evaluated at $t = 0$, as its columns. This matrix has n linearly independent columns $\boldsymbol{\xi}_1, \ldots, \boldsymbol{\xi}_n$, and therefore has a nonzero determinant. By Theorem 10.3(2), $\boldsymbol{\xi}_1 e^{\lambda_1 t}, \ldots, \boldsymbol{\xi}_n e^{\lambda_n t}$ are linearly independent on the real line. ∎

EXAMPLE 10.7

Consider the system

$$\mathbf{X}' = \begin{pmatrix} 4 & 2 \\ 3 & 3 \end{pmatrix}\mathbf{X}.$$

$\mathbf{A}$ has eigenvalues 1 and 6, with corresponding eigenvectors $\begin{pmatrix} 1 \\ -\frac{3}{2} \end{pmatrix}$ and $\begin{pmatrix} 1 \\ 1 \end{pmatrix}$. These eigenvectors are linearly independent (originating from distinct eigenvalues), so we have two linearly independent solutions,

$$\begin{pmatrix} 1 \\ -\frac{3}{2} \end{pmatrix}e^t \quad \text{and} \quad \begin{pmatrix} 1 \\ 1 \end{pmatrix}e^{6t}.$$

We can write the general solution as

$$\mathbf{X}(t) = c_1 \begin{pmatrix} 1 \\ -\frac{3}{2} \end{pmatrix} e^t + c_2 \begin{pmatrix} 1 \\ 1 \end{pmatrix} e^{6t}.$$

Equivalently, we can write the fundamental matrix

$$\mathbf{\Omega}(t) = \begin{pmatrix} e^t & e^{6t} \\ -\frac{3}{2}e^t & e^{6t} \end{pmatrix}.$$

In terms of $\mathbf{\Omega}$, the general solution is $\mathbf{X}(t) = \mathbf{\Omega}(t)\mathbf{C}$.

In terms of components,

$$x_1(t) = c_1 e^t + c_2 e^{6t}$$

$$x_2(t) = -\frac{3}{2}c_1 e^t + c_2 e^{6t}. \quad \blacksquare$$

EXAMPLE 10.8

Solve the system

$$\mathbf{X}' = \begin{pmatrix} 5 & -4 & 4 \\ 12 & -11 & 12 \\ 4 & -4 & 5 \end{pmatrix} \mathbf{X}.$$

The eigenvalues of $\mathbf{A}$ are $-3, 1, 1$. Even though one eigenvalue is repeated, $\mathbf{A}$ has three linearly independent eigenvectors. They are:

$$\begin{pmatrix} 1 \\ 3 \\ 1 \end{pmatrix} \text{ associated with eigenvalue } -3$$

and

$$\begin{pmatrix} 1 \\ 1 \\ 0 \end{pmatrix} \quad \text{and} \quad \begin{pmatrix} -1 \\ 0 \\ 1 \end{pmatrix} \text{ associated with 1.}$$

This gives us three linearly independent solutions

$$\begin{pmatrix} 1 \\ 3 \\ 1 \end{pmatrix} e^{-3t}, \begin{pmatrix} 1 \\ 1 \\ 0 \end{pmatrix} e^t, \begin{pmatrix} -1 \\ 0 \\ 1 \end{pmatrix} e^t.$$

A fundamental matrix is

$$\mathbf{\Omega}(t) = \begin{pmatrix} e^{-3t} & e^t & -e^t \\ 3e^{-3t} & e^t & 0 \\ e^{-3t} & 0 & e^t \end{pmatrix}.$$

The general solution is $\mathbf{X}(t) = \mathbf{\Omega}(t)\mathbf{C}$. $\blacksquare$

EXAMPLE 10.9 A Mixing Problem

Two tanks are connected by a series of pipes, as shown in Figure 10.1. Tank 1 initially contains 20 liters of water in which 150 grams of chlorine are dissolved. Tank 2 initially contains 50 grams of chlorine dissolved in 10 liters of water.

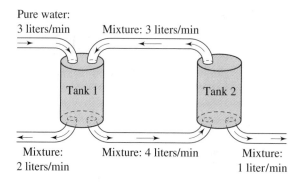

Pure water:
3 liters/min
Mixture: 3 liters/min

Tank 1

Tank 2

Mixture:
2 liters/min

Mixture: 4 liters/min

Mixture:
1 liter/min

FIGURE 10.1

Beginning at time $t = 0$, pure water is pumped into tank 1 at a rate of 3 liters per minute, while chlorine/water solutions are interchanged between the tanks and also flow out of both tanks at the rates shown. The problem is to determine the amount of chlorine in each tank at any time $t > 0$.

At the given rates of input and discharge of solutions, the amount of solution in each tank will remain constant. Therefore, the ratio of chlorine to chlorine/water solution in each tank should, in the long run, approach that of the input, which is pure water. We will use this observation as a check of the analysis we are about to do.

Let $x_j(t)$ be the number of grams of chlorine in tank j at time t. Reading from Figure 10.1,

$$\text{rate of change of } x_j(t) = x_j'(t) = \text{ rate in minus rate out}$$

$$= 3\left(\frac{\text{liter}}{\text{min}}\right) \cdot 0\left(\frac{\text{gram}}{\text{liter}}\right) + 3\left(\frac{\text{liter}}{\text{min}}\right) \cdot \frac{x_2}{10}\left(\frac{\text{gram}}{\text{liter}}\right)$$

$$- 2\left(\frac{\text{liter}}{\text{min}}\right) \cdot \frac{x_1}{20}\left(\frac{\text{gram}}{\text{liter}}\right) - 4\left(\frac{\text{liter}}{\text{min}}\right) \cdot \frac{x_1}{20}\left(\frac{\text{gram}}{\text{liter}}\right)$$

$$= -\frac{6}{20}x_1 + \frac{3}{10}x_2.$$

Similarly, with the dimensions excluded,

$$x_2'(t) = 4\frac{x_1}{20} - 3\frac{x_2}{10} - \frac{x_2}{10} = \frac{4}{20}x_1 - \frac{4}{10}x_2.$$

The system is $\mathbf{X}' = \mathbf{AX}$, with

$$\mathbf{A} = \begin{pmatrix} -\frac{3}{10} & \frac{3}{10} \\ \frac{1}{5} & -\frac{2}{5} \end{pmatrix}.$$

The initial conditions are

$$x_1(0) = 150, \, x_2(0) = 50,$$

or

$$\mathbf{X}(0) = \begin{pmatrix} 150 \\ 50 \end{pmatrix}.$$

The eigenvalues of $\mathbf{A}$ are $-\frac{1}{10}$ and $-\frac{3}{5}$, and corresponding eigenvectors are, respectively,

$$\begin{pmatrix} \frac{3}{2} \\ 1 \end{pmatrix} \quad \text{and} \quad \begin{pmatrix} -1 \\ 1 \end{pmatrix}.$$

These are linearly independent and we can write the fundamental matrix

$$\mathbf{\Omega}(t) = \begin{pmatrix} \frac{3}{2}e^{-t/10} & -e^{-3t/5} \\ e^{-t/10} & e^{-3t/5} \end{pmatrix}.$$

The general solution is $\mathbf{X}(t) = \mathbf{\Omega}(t)\mathbf{C}$. To solve the initial value problem, we must find $\mathbf{C}$ so that

$$\mathbf{X}(0) = \begin{pmatrix} 150 \\ 50 \end{pmatrix} = \mathbf{\Omega}(0)\mathbf{C} = \begin{pmatrix} \frac{3}{2} & -1 \\ 1 & 1 \end{pmatrix}\mathbf{C}.$$

Then

$$\mathbf{C} = \begin{pmatrix} \frac{3}{2} & -1 \\ 1 & 1 \end{pmatrix}^{-1} \begin{pmatrix} 150 \\ 50 \end{pmatrix}$$

$$= \begin{pmatrix} \frac{2}{5} & \frac{2}{5} \\ -\frac{2}{5} & \frac{3}{5} \end{pmatrix} \begin{pmatrix} 150 \\ 50 \end{pmatrix} = \begin{pmatrix} 80 \\ -30 \end{pmatrix}.$$

The solution of the initial value problem is

$$\mathbf{X}(t) = \begin{pmatrix} \frac{3}{2}e^{-t/10} & -e^{-3t/5} \\ e^{-t/10} & e^{-3t/5} \end{pmatrix} \begin{pmatrix} 80 \\ -30 \end{pmatrix}$$

$$= \begin{pmatrix} 120e^{-t/10} + 30e^{-3t/5} \\ 80e^{-t/10} - 30e^{-3t/5} \end{pmatrix}.$$

Notice that $x_1(t) \to 0$ and $x_2(t) \to 0$ as $t \to \infty$, as we expected. ∎

10.2.1 Solution of X' = AX when A has Complex Eigenvalues

Consider a system $\mathbf{X}' = \mathbf{A}\mathbf{X}$. If $\mathbf{A}$ is a real matrix, the characteristic polynomial of $\mathbf{A}$ has real coefficients. It may, however, have some complex roots. Suppose $\lambda = \alpha + i\beta$ is a complex eigenvalue, with eigenvector $\boldsymbol{\xi}$. Then $\mathbf{A}\boldsymbol{\xi} = \lambda\boldsymbol{\xi}$, so

$$\overline{\mathbf{A}\boldsymbol{\xi}} = \overline{\lambda\boldsymbol{\xi}}.$$

But $\overline{\mathbf{A}} = \mathbf{A}$ if $\mathbf{A}$ has real elements, so

$$\mathbf{A}\overline{\boldsymbol{\xi}} = \overline{\lambda}\overline{\boldsymbol{\xi}}.$$

This means that $\overline{\lambda} = \alpha - i\beta$ is also an eigenvalue, with eigenvector $\overline{\boldsymbol{\xi}}$. This means that $\boldsymbol{\xi}e^{\lambda t}$ and $\overline{\boldsymbol{\xi}}e^{\overline{\lambda}t}$ can be used as two of the n linearly independent solutions needed to form a fundamental matrix.

This resulting fundamental matrix will contain some complex entries. There is nothing wrong with this. However, sometimes it is convenient to have a fundamental matrix with only real entries. We will show how to replace these two columns, involving complex numbers, with two other linearly independent solutions involving only real quantities. This can be done for any pair of columns arising from a pair of complex conjugate eigenvalues.

THEOREM 10.8

Let $\mathbf{A}$ be an $n \times n$ real matrix. Let $\alpha + i\beta$ be a complex eigenvalue with corresponding eigenvector $\mathbf{U} + i\mathbf{V}$, in which $\mathbf{U}$ and $\mathbf{V}$ are real $n \times 1$ matrices. Then

$$e^{\alpha t}[\mathbf{U}\cos(\beta t) - \mathbf{V}\sin(\beta t)]$$

and

$$e^{\alpha t}[\mathbf{U}\sin(\beta t) + \mathbf{V}\cos(\beta t)]$$

are real linearly independent solutions of $\mathbf{X}' = \mathbf{A}\mathbf{X}$. ∎

EXAMPLE 10.10

Solve the system $\mathbf{X}' = \mathbf{A}\mathbf{X}$, with

$$\mathbf{A} = \begin{pmatrix} 2 & 0 & 1 \\ 0 & -2 & -2 \\ 0 & 2 & 0 \end{pmatrix}.$$

The eigenvalues are $2, -1 + \sqrt{3}i, -1 - \sqrt{3}i$. Corresponding eigenvectors are, respectively,

$$\begin{pmatrix} 1 \\ 0 \\ 0 \end{pmatrix}, \begin{pmatrix} 1 \\ -2\sqrt{3}i \\ -3 + \sqrt{3}i \end{pmatrix}, \begin{pmatrix} 1 \\ 2\sqrt{3}i \\ -3 - \sqrt{3}i \end{pmatrix}.$$

One solution is

$$\begin{pmatrix} 1 \\ 0 \\ 0 \end{pmatrix} e^{2t}$$

and two other solutions are

$$\begin{pmatrix} 1 \\ -2\sqrt{3}i \\ -3 + \sqrt{3}i \end{pmatrix} e^{(-1+\sqrt{3}i)t} \quad \text{and} \quad \begin{pmatrix} 1 \\ 2\sqrt{3}i \\ -3 - \sqrt{3}i \end{pmatrix} e^{(-1-\sqrt{3}i)t}.$$

These three solutions are linearly independent and can be used as columns of a fundamental matrix

$$\mathbf{\Omega}_1(t) = \begin{pmatrix} e^{2t} & e^{(-1+\sqrt{3}i)t} & e^{(-1-\sqrt{3}i)t} \\ 0 & -2\sqrt{3}ie^{(-1+\sqrt{3}i)t} & 2\sqrt{3}ie^{(-1-\sqrt{3}i)t} \\ 0 & (-3+\sqrt{3}i)e^{(-1+\sqrt{3}i)t} & (-3-\sqrt{3}i)e^{(-1-\sqrt{3}i)t} \end{pmatrix}.$$

However, we can also produce a real fundamental matrix as follows. First write

$$\begin{pmatrix} 1 \\ -2\sqrt{3}i \\ -3 + \sqrt{3}i \end{pmatrix} = \begin{pmatrix} 1 \\ 0 \\ -3 \end{pmatrix} + i \begin{pmatrix} 0 \\ -2\sqrt{3} \\ \sqrt{3} \end{pmatrix} = \mathbf{U} + i\mathbf{V}$$

with

$$\mathbf{U} = \begin{pmatrix} 1 \\ 0 \\ -3 \end{pmatrix} \quad \text{and} \quad \mathbf{V} = \begin{pmatrix} 0 \\ -2\sqrt{3} \\ \sqrt{3} \end{pmatrix}.$$

Then

$$\begin{pmatrix} 1 \\ -2\sqrt{3}i \\ -3+\sqrt{3}i \end{pmatrix} e^{(-1+\sqrt{3}i)t} = (\mathbf{U}+i\mathbf{V})\left[e^{-t}\cos(\sqrt{3}t) + ie^{-t}\sin(\sqrt{3}t)\right]$$

$$= \mathbf{U}e^{-t}\cos(\sqrt{3}t) - \mathbf{V}e^{-t}\sin(\sqrt{3}t) + i\Big[\mathbf{V}e^{-t}\cos(\sqrt{3}t)$$

$$+ \mathbf{U}e^{-t}\sin(\sqrt{3}t)\Big], \tag{10.4}$$

And

$$\begin{pmatrix} 1 \\ 2\sqrt{3}i \\ -3-\sqrt{3}i \end{pmatrix} e^{(-1-\sqrt{3}i)t} = (\mathbf{U}-i\mathbf{V})\left[e^{-t}\cos(\sqrt{3}t) - ie^{-t}\sin(\sqrt{3}t)\right]$$

$$= \mathbf{U}e^{-t}\cos(\sqrt{3}t) - \mathbf{V}e^{-t}\sin(\sqrt{3}t) - i\Big[\mathbf{V}e^{-t}\cos(\sqrt{3}t)$$

$$+ \mathbf{U}e^{-t}\sin(\sqrt{3}t)\Big]. \tag{10.5}$$

The functions (10.4) and (10.5) are solutions, so any linear combination of these is also a solution. Taking their sum and dividing by 2 yields the solution

$$\mathbf{\Phi}_1(t) = \mathbf{U}e^{-t}\cos(\sqrt{3}t) - \mathbf{V}e^{-t}\sin(\sqrt{3}t).$$

And taking their difference and dividing by $2i$ yields the solution

$$\mathbf{\Phi}_2(t) = \mathbf{V}e^{-t}\cos(\sqrt{3}t) + \mathbf{U}e^{-t}\sin(\sqrt{3}t).$$

Using these, together with the solution found from the eigenvalue 2, we can form the fundamental matrix

$$\mathbf{\Omega}_2(t) = \begin{pmatrix} e^{2t} & e^{-t}\cos(\sqrt{3}t) & e^{-t}\sin(\sqrt{3}t) \\ 0 & 2\sqrt{3}e^{-t}\sin(\sqrt{3}t) & -2\sqrt{3}e^{-t}\cos(\sqrt{3}t) \\ 0 & e^{-t}[-3\cos(\sqrt{3}t)-\sqrt{3}\sin(\sqrt{3}t)] & e^{-t}[\sqrt{3}\cos(\sqrt{3}t)-3\sin(\sqrt{3}t)] \end{pmatrix}.$$

Either fundamental matrix can be used to write the general solution, $\mathbf{X}(t) = \mathbf{\Omega}_1(t)\mathbf{C}$ or $\mathbf{X}(t) = \mathbf{\Omega}_2(t)\mathbf{K}$. However, the latter involves only real numbers and real-valued functions. ▪

A proof of the theorem follows the reasoning of the example, and is left to the student.

10.2.2 Solution of X′ = AX when A does not have *n* Linearly Independent Eigenvectors

We know how to produce a fundamental matrix for $\mathbf{X}' = \mathbf{AX}$ when $\mathbf{A}$ has n linearly independent eigenvectors. This certainly occurs if $\mathbf{A}$ has n distinct eigenvalues, and may even occur when $\mathbf{A}$ has repeated eigenvalues. However, we may encounter a matrix $\mathbf{A}$ having repeated eigenvalues, for which there are not n linearly independent eigenvectors. In this case we cannot yet write a fundamental matrix. This section is devoted to a procedure to follow in this case to find a fundamental matrix.

We will begin with two examples and then make some general remarks.

EXAMPLE 10.11

We will solve the system $\mathbf{X'} = \mathbf{AX}$, with

$$\mathbf{A} = \begin{pmatrix} 1 & 3 \\ -3 & 7 \end{pmatrix}.$$

$\mathbf{A}$ has one eigenvalue 4 of multiplicity 2. Eigenvectors all have the form $\alpha \begin{pmatrix} 1 \\ 1 \end{pmatrix}$, with $\alpha \neq 0$.
$\mathbf{A}$ does not have two linearly independent eigenvectors.

We can immediately write one solution

$$\mathbf{\Phi}_1(t) = \begin{pmatrix} 1 \\ 1 \end{pmatrix} e^{4t}.$$

We need another solution. Write $\mathbf{E}_1 = \begin{pmatrix} 1 \\ 1 \end{pmatrix}$ and attempt a second solution

$$\mathbf{\Phi}_2(t) = \mathbf{E}_1 t e^{4t} + \mathbf{E}_2 e^{4t},$$

in which $\mathbf{E}_2$ is a 2×1 constant matrix to be determined. For this to be a solution, we need to have $\mathbf{\Phi}_2'(t) = \mathbf{A}\mathbf{\Phi}_2(t)$:

$$\mathbf{E}_1 [e^{4t} + 4 t e^{4t}] + 4\mathbf{E}_2 e^{4t} = \mathbf{A}\mathbf{E}_1 t e^{4t} + \mathbf{A}\mathbf{E}_2 e^{4t}.$$

Divide this equation by e^{4t} to get

$$\mathbf{E}_1 + 4\mathbf{E}_1 t + 4\mathbf{E}_2 = \mathbf{A}\mathbf{E}_1 t + \mathbf{A}\mathbf{E}_2.$$

But $\mathbf{A}\mathbf{E}_1 = 4\mathbf{E}_1$, so the terms having t as a factor cancel and we are left with

$$\mathbf{A}\mathbf{E}_2 - 4\mathbf{E}_2 = \mathbf{E}_1.$$

Write this equation as

$$(\mathbf{A} - 4\mathbf{I}_2)\mathbf{E}_2 = \mathbf{E}_1.$$

If $\mathbf{E}_2 = \begin{pmatrix} a \\ b \end{pmatrix}$, this is the linear system of two equations in two unknowns:

$$(\mathbf{A} - 4\mathbf{I}_2) \begin{pmatrix} a \\ b \end{pmatrix} = \begin{pmatrix} 1 \\ 1 \end{pmatrix},$$

or

$$\begin{pmatrix} -3 & 3 \\ -3 & 3 \end{pmatrix} \begin{pmatrix} a \\ b \end{pmatrix} = \begin{pmatrix} 1 \\ 1 \end{pmatrix}.$$

This system has general solution $\mathbf{E}_2 = \begin{pmatrix} s \\ \frac{1+3s}{3} \end{pmatrix}$, in which s can be any nonzero number. Let $s = 1$ to get $\mathbf{E}_2 = \begin{pmatrix} 1 \\ \frac{4}{3} \end{pmatrix}$ and hence the second solution

$$\mathbf{\Phi}_2(t) = \mathbf{E}_1 t e^{4t} + \mathbf{E}_2 e^{4t} = \begin{pmatrix} 1 \\ 1 \end{pmatrix} t e^{4t} + \begin{pmatrix} 1 \\ \frac{4}{3} \end{pmatrix} e^{4t}$$

$$= \begin{pmatrix} 1+t \\ \frac{4}{3}+t \end{pmatrix} e^{4t}.$$

If we use $\mathbf{\Phi}_1(0)$ and $\mathbf{\Phi}_2(0)$ as columns to form the matrix

$$\begin{pmatrix} 1 & 1 \\ 1 & \frac{4}{3} \end{pmatrix},$$

then this matrix has determinant $1/3$, hence $\mathbf{\Phi}_1$ and $\mathbf{\Phi}_2$ are linearly independent by Theorem 10.3(2). Therefore $\mathbf{\Phi}_1(t)$ and $\mathbf{\Phi}_2(t)$ are linearly independent and can be used as columns of a fundamental matrix

$$\mathbf{\Omega}(t) = \begin{pmatrix} e^{4t} & (1+t)e^{4t} \\ e^{4t} & (\frac{4}{3}+t)e^{4t} \end{pmatrix}.$$

The general solution of $\mathbf{X}' = \mathbf{AX}$ is $\mathbf{X}(t) = \mathbf{\Omega}(t)\mathbf{C}$. ∎

The procedure followed in this example is similar in spirit to solving the differential equation $y'' - 5y' + 6y = e^{3x}$ by undetermined coefficients. We are tempted to try $y_p(x) = ae^{3x}$, but this will not work because e^{3x} is a solution of $y'' - 5y' + 6y = 0$. We therefore try $y_p(x) = axe^{3x}$, multiplying the first attempt ae^{3x} by x. The analogous step for the system was to try the second solution $\mathbf{\Phi}_2(t) = \mathbf{E}_1 te^{4t} + \mathbf{E}_2 e^{4t}$.

We will continue to explore the case of repeated eigenvalues with another example.

EXAMPLE 10.12

Consider the system $\mathbf{X}' = \mathbf{AX}$, in which

$$\mathbf{A} = \begin{pmatrix} -2 & -1 & -5 \\ 25 & -7 & 0 \\ 0 & 1 & 3 \end{pmatrix}.$$

$\mathbf{A}$ has eigenvalue -2 with multiplicity 3, and corresponding eigenvectors are all nonzero scalar multiples of $\begin{pmatrix} -1 \\ -5 \\ 1 \end{pmatrix}$. This gives us one solution of $\mathbf{X}' = \mathbf{AX}$. Denoting $\begin{pmatrix} -1 \\ -5 \\ 1 \end{pmatrix} = \mathbf{E}_1$, we have one solution

$$\mathbf{\Phi}_1(t) = \begin{pmatrix} -1 \\ -5 \\ 1 \end{pmatrix} e^{-2t} = \mathbf{E}_1 e^{-2t}.$$

We need three linearly independent solutions. We will try a second solution of the form

$$\mathbf{\Phi}_2(t) = \mathbf{E}_1 te^{-2t} + \mathbf{E}_2 e^{-2t},$$

in which $\mathbf{E}_2$ is a 3×1 matrix to be determined. Substitute this proposed solution into $\mathbf{X}' = \mathbf{AX}$ to get

$$\mathbf{E}_1[e^{-2t} - 2te^{-2t}] + \mathbf{E}_2[-2e^{-2t}] = \mathbf{A}\mathbf{E}_1 te^{-2t} + \mathbf{A}\mathbf{E}_2 e^{-2t}.$$

Upon dividing by the common factor of e^{-2t}, and recalling that $\mathbf{A}\mathbf{E}_1 = -2\mathbf{E}_1$, this equation becomes

$$\mathbf{E}_1 - 2t\mathbf{E}_1 - 2\mathbf{E}_2 = -2t\mathbf{E}_1 + \mathbf{A}\mathbf{E}_2.$$

or

$$\mathbf{A}\mathbf{E}_2 + 2\mathbf{E}_2 = \mathbf{E}_1.$$

We can write this equation as

$$(\mathbf{A} + 2\mathbf{I}_3)\mathbf{E}_2 = \mathbf{E}_1,$$

or

$$\begin{pmatrix} 0 & -1 & -5 \\ 25 & -5 & 0 \\ 0 & 1 & 5 \end{pmatrix} \mathbf{E}_2 = \begin{pmatrix} -1 \\ -5 \\ 1 \end{pmatrix}.$$

With $\mathbf{E}_2 = \begin{pmatrix} \alpha \\ \beta \\ \gamma \end{pmatrix}$, this is the nonhomogeneous system

$$\begin{pmatrix} 0 & -1 & -5 \\ 25 & -5 & 0 \\ 0 & 1 & 5 \end{pmatrix} \begin{pmatrix} \alpha \\ \beta \\ \gamma \end{pmatrix} = \begin{pmatrix} -1 \\ -5 \\ 1 \end{pmatrix},$$

with general solution $\begin{pmatrix} -s \\ 1-5s \\ s \end{pmatrix}$, in which s can be any number. For a specific solution, choose $s = 1$ and let

$$\mathbf{E}_2 = \begin{pmatrix} -1 \\ -4 \\ 1 \end{pmatrix}.$$

This gives us the second solution

$$\boldsymbol{\Phi}_2(t) = \mathbf{E}_1 t e^{-2t} + \mathbf{E}_2 e^{-2t}$$

$$= \begin{pmatrix} -1 \\ -5 \\ 1 \end{pmatrix} t e^{-2t} + \begin{pmatrix} -1 \\ -4 \\ 1 \end{pmatrix} e^{-2t}$$

$$= \begin{pmatrix} -1-t \\ -4-5t \\ 1+t \end{pmatrix} e^{-2t}.$$

We need one more solution. Try for a solution of the form

$$\boldsymbol{\Phi}_3(t) = \frac{1}{2}\mathbf{E}_1 t^2 e^{-2t} + \mathbf{E}_2 t e^{-2t} + \mathbf{E}_3 e^{-2t}.$$

We want to solve for $\mathbf{E}_3$. Substitute this proposed solution into $\mathbf{X}' = \mathbf{A}\mathbf{X}$ to get

$$\mathbf{E}_1[te^{-2t} - t^2 e^{-2t}] + \mathbf{E}_2[e^{-2t} - 2te^{-2t}] + \mathbf{E}_3[-2e^{-2t}] = \frac{1}{2}\mathbf{A}\mathbf{E}_1 t^2 e^{-2t} + \mathbf{A}\mathbf{E}_2 t e^{-2t} + \mathbf{A}\mathbf{E}_3 e^{-2t}.$$

Divide this equation by e^{-2t} and use the fact that $\mathbf{A}\mathbf{E}_1 = -2\mathbf{E}_1$ and $\mathbf{A}\mathbf{E}_2 = \begin{pmatrix} 1 \\ 3 \\ -1 \end{pmatrix}$ to get

$$\mathbf{E}_1 t - \mathbf{E}_1 t^2 + \mathbf{E}_2 - 2\mathbf{E}_2 t - 2\mathbf{E}_3 = -\mathbf{E}_1 t^2 + \begin{pmatrix} 1 \\ 3 \\ -1 \end{pmatrix} t + \mathbf{A}\mathbf{E}_3. \qquad (10.6)$$

Now

$$
\mathbf{E}_1 t - 2\mathbf{E}_2 t = \left[\begin{pmatrix} -1 \\ -5 \\ 1 \end{pmatrix} - 2 \begin{pmatrix} -1 \\ -4 \\ 1 \end{pmatrix} \right] t = \begin{pmatrix} 1 \\ 3 \\ -1 \end{pmatrix} t,
$$

so equation (10.6) has three terms cancel, and it reduces to

$$
\mathbf{E}_2 - 2\mathbf{E}_3 = \mathbf{A}\mathbf{E}_3.
$$

Write this equation as

$$
(\mathbf{A} + 2\mathbf{I}_3)\mathbf{E}_3 = \mathbf{E}_2
$$

or

$$
\begin{pmatrix} 0 & -1 & -5 \\ 25 & -5 & 0 \\ 0 & 1 & 5 \end{pmatrix} \mathbf{E}_3 = \begin{pmatrix} -1 \\ -4 \\ 1 \end{pmatrix},
$$

with general solution

$$
\begin{pmatrix} \frac{1-25s}{25} \\ 1 - 5s \\ s \end{pmatrix}
$$

in which s can be any number. Choosing $s = 1$, we can let

$$
\mathbf{E}_3 = \begin{pmatrix} -\frac{24}{25} \\ -4 \\ 1 \end{pmatrix}.
$$

A third solution is

$$
\mathbf{\Phi}_3(t) = \frac{1}{2} \begin{pmatrix} -1 \\ -5 \\ 1 \end{pmatrix} t^2 e^{-2t} + \begin{pmatrix} -1 \\ -4 \\ 1 \end{pmatrix} t e^{-2t} + \begin{pmatrix} -\frac{24}{25} \\ -4 \\ 1 \end{pmatrix} e^{-2t}
$$

$$
= \begin{pmatrix} -\frac{24}{25} - t - \frac{1}{2}t^2 \\ -4 - 4t - \frac{5}{2}t^2 \\ 1 + t + \frac{1}{2}t^2 \end{pmatrix} e^{-2t}.
$$

To show that $\mathbf{\Phi}_1$, $\mathbf{\Phi}_2$ and $\mathbf{\Phi}_3$ are linearly independent, Theorem 10.3(2) is convenient. Form the 3×3 matrix having these solutions, evaluated at $t = 0$, as columns:

$$
\begin{pmatrix} -1 & -1 & -\frac{24}{25} \\ -5 & -4 & -4 \\ 1 & 1 & 1 \end{pmatrix}.
$$

The determinant of this matrix is $-\frac{1}{25}$, so this matrix is nonsingular and the solutions are linearly independent. We can use these solutions as columns of a fundamental matrix

$$
\mathbf{\Omega}(t) = \begin{pmatrix} -e^{-2t} & (-1-t)e^{-2t} & \left(-\frac{24}{25} - t - \frac{1}{2}t^2\right)e^{-2t} \\ -5e^{-2t} & (-4-5t)e^{-2t} & \left(-4 - 4t - \frac{5}{2}t^2\right)e^{-2t} \\ e^{-2t} & (1+t)e^{-2t} & \left(1 + t + \frac{1}{2}t^2\right)e^{-2t} \end{pmatrix}.
$$

The general solution of $\mathbf{X}' = \mathbf{A}\mathbf{X}$ is $\mathbf{X}(t) = \mathbf{\Omega}(t)\mathbf{C}$. ∎

These examples suggest a procedure which we will now outline in general. Begin with a system $\mathbf{X}' = \mathbf{A}\mathbf{X}$, with $\mathbf{A}$ an $n \times n$ matrix of real numbers. We want the general solution, so we need n linearly independent solutions.

Case 1—A has n linearly independent eigenvectors.

Use these eigenvectors to write n linearly independent solutions and use these as columns of a fundamental matrix. (This case may occur even if $\mathbf{A}$ does not have n distinct eigenvalues).

Case 2—A does not have n linearly independent eigenvectors.

Let the eigenvalues of $\mathbf{A}$ be $\lambda_1, \ldots, \lambda_n$ At least one eigenvalue must be repeated, because if $\mathbf{A}$ has n distinct eigenvectors, the corresponding eigenvectors must be linearly independent, putting us back in case 1. Suppose $\lambda_1, \ldots, \lambda_r$ are the distinct eigenvalues, while $\lambda_{r+1}, \ldots, \lambda_n$ repeat some of these first r eigenvalues. If $\mathbf{V}_j$ is an eigenvector corresponding to λ_j for $j = 1, \ldots r$, we can immediately write r linearly independent solutions

$$\mathbf{\Psi}_1(t) = \mathbf{V}_1 e^{\lambda_1 t}, \ldots, \mathbf{\Psi}_r(t) = \mathbf{V}_r e^{\lambda_r t}.$$

Now work with the repeated eigenvalues. Suppose μ is a repeated eigenvalue, say $\mu = \lambda_1$ with multiplicity k. We already have one solution corresponding to μ, namely $\mathbf{\Psi}_1$. To be consistent in notation with the examples just done, denote $\mathbf{V}_1 = \mathbf{E}_1$ and $\mathbf{\Psi}_1 = \mathbf{\Phi}_1$. Then

$$\mathbf{\Phi}_1(t) = \mathbf{V}_1 e^{\lambda_1 t} = \mathbf{E}_1 e^{\mu t}$$

is one solution corresponding to μ. For a second solution corresponding to μ, let

$$\mathbf{\Phi}_2(t) = \mathbf{E}_1 t e^{\mu t} + \mathbf{E}_2 e^{\mu t}.$$

Substitute this proposed solution into $\mathbf{X}' = \mathbf{A}\mathbf{X}$ and solve for $\mathbf{E}_2$. If $k = 2$, this yields a second solution corresponding to μ and we move on to another multiple eigenvalue. If $k \geq 3$, we do not yet have all the solutions corresponding to μ, so we attempt

$$\mathbf{\Phi}_3(t) = \frac{1}{2}\mathbf{E}_1 t^2 e^{\mu t} + \mathbf{E}_2 t e^{\mu t} + \mathbf{E}_3 e^{\mu t}.$$

Substitute $\mathbf{\Phi}_3(t)$ into the differential equation and solve for $\mathbf{E}_3$ to get a third solution corresponding to μ. If $\mu \geq 4$, continue with

$$\mathbf{\Phi}_4(t) = \frac{1}{3!}\mathbf{E}_1 t^3 e^{\mu t} + \frac{1}{2!}\mathbf{E}_2(t) t^2 e^{\mu t} + \mathbf{E}_3 t e^{\mu t} + \mathbf{E}_4 e^{\mu t},$$

substitute into the differential equation and solve for $\mathbf{E}_4$, and so on. Eventually, we reach

$$\mathbf{\Phi}_k(t) = \frac{1}{(k-1)!}\mathbf{E}_1 t^{k-1} e^{\mu t} + \frac{1}{(k-2)!}\mathbf{E}_2 t^{k-2} e^{\mu t} + \cdots + \mathbf{E}_{k-1} t e^{\mu t} + \mathbf{E}_k e^{\mu t};$$

substitute into the differential equation and solve for $\mathbf{E}_k$.

This procedure gives, for an eigenvalue μ of multiplicity k, k linearly independent solutions of $\mathbf{X}' = \mathbf{A}\mathbf{X}$. Repeat the procedure for each eigenvalue until n linearly independent solutions have been found.

10.2.3   Solution of X' = AX by Diagonalizing A

We now take a different tack and attempt to exploit diagonalization.

Consider the system

$$\mathbf{X}' = \begin{pmatrix} -2 & 0 & 0 \\ 0 & 4 & 0 \\ 0 & 0 & -6 \end{pmatrix} \mathbf{X}.$$

The constant coefficient matrix $\mathbf{A}$ is a diagonal matrix, and this system really consists of three independent differential equations, each involving just one of the variables:

$$x_1' = -2x_1,$$
$$x_2' = 4x_2,$$
$$x_3' = -6x_3,$$

Such a system is said to be *uncoupled*. Each equation is easily solved independent of the others, obtaining

$$x_1 = c_1 e^{-2t}, x_2 = c_2 e^{4t}, x_3 = c_3 e^{-6t}.$$

The system is uncoupled because the coefficient matrix $\mathbf{A}$ is diagonal. Because of this, we can immediately write the eigenvalues $-2, 4, -6$ of $\mathbf{A}$, and find the corresponding eigenvectors

$$\begin{pmatrix} 1 \\ 0 \\ 0 \end{pmatrix}, \begin{pmatrix} 0 \\ 1 \\ 0 \end{pmatrix}, \begin{pmatrix} 0 \\ 0 \\ 1 \end{pmatrix}$$

Therefore $\mathbf{X}' = \mathbf{AX}$ has fundamental matrix

$$\mathbf{\Omega}(t) = \begin{pmatrix} e^{-2t} & 0 & 0 \\ 0 & e^{4t} & 0 \\ 0 & 0 & e^{-6t} \end{pmatrix}$$

and the general solution is $\mathbf{X}(t) = \mathbf{\Omega}(t)\mathbf{C}$. However we wish to approach this system, the point is that it is easy to solve because $\mathbf{A}$ is a diagonal matrix.

Now in general $\mathbf{A}$ need not be diagonal. However, $\mathbf{A}$ may be diagonalizable (Section 9.2). This will occur exactly when $\mathbf{A}$ has n linearly independent eigenvectors. In this event, we can form a matrix $\mathbf{P}$, whose columns are eigenvectors of $\mathbf{A}$, such that

$$\mathbf{P}^{-1}\mathbf{AP} = \mathbf{D} = \begin{pmatrix} \lambda_1 & 0 & \cdots & 0 \\ 0 & \lambda_2 & \cdots & 0 \\ \vdots & \vdots & \cdots & \vdots \\ 0 & 0 & \cdots & \lambda_n \end{pmatrix}.$$

$\mathbf{D}$ is the diagonal matrix having the eigenvalues $\lambda_1, \ldots, \lambda_n$ down its main diagonal. This will hold even if some of the eigenvalues have multiplicities greater than 1, provided that $\mathbf{A}$ has n linearly independent eigenvectors.

Now make the change of variables $\mathbf{X} = \mathbf{PZ}$ in the differential equation $\mathbf{X}' = \mathbf{AX}$. First compute

$$\mathbf{X}' = (\mathbf{PZ})' = \mathbf{PZ}' = \mathbf{AX} = \mathbf{APZ}.,$$

so

$$\mathbf{Z}' = \mathbf{P}^{-1}\mathbf{APZ} = \mathbf{DZ}.$$

The uncoupled system $\mathbf{Z}' = \mathbf{DZ}$ can be solved by inspection. A fundamental matrix for $\mathbf{Z}' = \mathbf{DZ}$ is

$$\mathbf{\Omega_D}(t) = \begin{pmatrix} e^{\lambda_1 t} & 0 & \cdots & \cdots & 0 \\ 0 & e^{\lambda_2 t} & \cdots & \cdots & 0 \\ \vdots & \vdots & \vdots & \cdots & \vdots \\ 0 & 0 & \cdots & e^{\lambda_{n-1} t} & 0 \\ 0 & 0 & \cdots & 0 & e^{\lambda_n t} \end{pmatrix}$$

and the general solution of $\mathbf{Z}' = \mathbf{DZ}$ is

$$\mathbf{Z}(t) = \mathbf{\Omega_D}(t)\mathbf{C}.$$

Then

$$\mathbf{X}(t) = \mathbf{PZ}(t) = \mathbf{P\Omega_D}(t)\mathbf{C}$$

is the general solution of the original system $\mathbf{X}' = \mathbf{AX}$. That is, $\mathbf{\Omega}(t) = \mathbf{P\Omega_D}(t)$ is a fundamental matrix for $\mathbf{X}' = \mathbf{AX}$.

In this process we need $\mathbf{P}$, whose columns are eigenvectors of $\mathbf{A}$, but we never actually need to calculate $\mathbf{P}^{-1}$.

EXAMPLE 10.13

Solve

$$\mathbf{X}' = \begin{pmatrix} 3 & 3 \\ 1 & 5 \end{pmatrix}\mathbf{X}.$$

The eigenvalues and associated eigenvectors of $\mathbf{A}$ are

$$2, \begin{pmatrix} -3 \\ 1 \end{pmatrix} \quad \text{and} \quad 6, \begin{pmatrix} 1 \\ 1 \end{pmatrix}.$$

Because $\mathbf{A}$ has distinct eigenvalues, $\mathbf{A}$ is diagonalizable. Make the change of variables $\mathbf{X} = \mathbf{PZ}$, where

$$\mathbf{P} = \begin{pmatrix} -3 & 1 \\ 1 & 1 \end{pmatrix}.$$

This transforms $\mathbf{X}' = \mathbf{AX}$ to $\mathbf{Z}' = \mathbf{DZ}$, where

$$\mathbf{D} = \begin{pmatrix} 2 & 0 \\ 0 & 6 \end{pmatrix}.$$

This uncoupled system has fundamental matrix

$$\mathbf{\Omega_D}(t) = \begin{pmatrix} e^{2t} & 0 \\ 0 & e^{6t} \end{pmatrix}.$$

Then $\mathbf{X}' = \mathbf{AX}$ has fundamental matrix

$$\mathbf{\Omega}(t) = \mathbf{P\Omega_D}(t) = \begin{pmatrix} -3 & 1 \\ 1 & 1 \end{pmatrix}\begin{pmatrix} e^{2t} & 0 \\ 0 & e^{6t} \end{pmatrix}$$

$$= \begin{pmatrix} -3e^{2t} & e^{6t} \\ e^{2t} & e^{6t} \end{pmatrix}.$$

The general solution of $\mathbf{X}' = \mathbf{AX}$ is $\mathbf{X}(t) = \mathbf{\Omega}(t)\mathbf{C}$. ∎

10.2.4 Exponential Matrix Solutions of $\mathbf{X}' = \mathbf{AX}$

A first-order differential equation $y' = ay$ has general solution $y(x) = ce^{ax}$. At the risk of stretching the analogy too far, we might conjecture whether there might be a solution $e^{\mathbf{A}t}\mathbf{C}$ for a matrix differential equation $\mathbf{X}' = \mathbf{AX}$. We will now show how to define the exponential matrix $e^{\mathbf{A}t}$ to make sense out of this conjecture. For this section, let $\mathbf{A}$ be an $n \times n$ matrix of real numbers.

The Taylor expansion of the real exponential function,

$$e^t = 1 + t + \frac{1}{2!}t^2 + \frac{1}{3!}t^3 + \cdots.$$

suggests the following.

DEFINITION 10.3 **Exponential Matrix**

The exponential matrix e^{At} is the $n \times n$ matrix defined by

$$e^{At} = I_n + At + \frac{1}{2!}A^2t^2 + \frac{1}{3!}A^3t^3 + \cdots.$$

It can be shown that this series converges for all real t, in the sense that the infinite series of elements in the i, j place converges.

Care must be taken in computing with exponential matrices, because matrix multiplication is not commutative. The analogue of the relationship $e^{at}e^{bt} = e^{(a+b)t}$ is given by the following.

THEOREM 10.9

Let **B** be an $n \times n$ real matrix. Suppose $AB = BA$. Then

$$e^{(A+B)t} = e^{At}e^{Bt}. \quad \blacksquare$$

Because **A** is a constant matrix,

$$\frac{d}{dt}e^{At} = \frac{d}{dt}\left[I_n + At + \frac{1}{2!}A^2t^2 + \frac{1}{3!}A^3t^3 + \frac{1}{4!}A^4t^4 + \cdots \right]$$

$$= A + A^2t + \frac{1}{2!}A^3t^2 + \frac{1}{3!}A^4t^3 + \cdots$$

$$= A\left[I_n + At + \frac{1}{2!}A^2t^2 + \frac{1}{3!}A^3t^3 + \frac{1}{4!}A^4t^4 + \cdots \right]$$

$$= Ae^{At}.$$

The derivative of e^{At}, obtained by differentiating each element, is the product Ae^{At} of two $n \times n$ matrices, and has the same form as the derivative of the scalar exponential function e^{at}. One ramification of this derivative formula is that, for any $n \times 1$ constant matrix **K**, $e^{At}K$ is a solution of $X' = AX$.

LEMMA 10.1

For any real $n \times 1$ constant matrix **K**, $e^{At}K$ is a solution of $X' = AX$.

Proof Compute

$$\Phi'(t) = (e^{At}K)' = Ae^{At}K = A\Phi(t). \quad \blacksquare$$

Even more, e^{At} is a fundamental matrix for $X' = AX$.

THEOREM 10.10

$e^{\mathbf{A}t}$ is a fundamental matrix for $\mathbf{X}' = \mathbf{A}\mathbf{X}$.

Proof   Let $\mathbf{E}_j$ be the $n \times 1$ matrix with 1 in the $j, 1$ place and all other entries zero:

$$\mathbf{E}_j = \begin{pmatrix} 0 \\ 0 \\ \vdots \\ 1 \\ \vdots \\ 0 \\ 0 \end{pmatrix}.$$

Then $e^{\mathbf{A}t}\mathbf{E}_j$ is the jth column of $e^{\mathbf{A}t}$. This column is a solution of $\mathbf{X}' = \mathbf{A}\mathbf{X}$ by the lemma. Further, the columns of $e^{\mathbf{A}t}$ are linearly independent by Theorem 10.3(2), because if we put $t = 0$, we get $e^{\mathbf{A}t} = \mathbf{I}_n$, which has a nonzero determinant. Thus $\boldsymbol{\Omega}$ is a fundamental matrix for $\mathbf{X}' = \mathbf{A}\mathbf{X}$. ∎

In theory, then, we can find the general solution $e^{\mathbf{A}t}\mathbf{C}$ of $\mathbf{X}' = \mathbf{A}\mathbf{X}$, if we can compute $e^{\mathbf{A}t}$. This, however, can be a daunting task. As an example, for an apparently simple matrix such as

$$\mathbf{A} = \begin{pmatrix} 1 & 2 \\ -2 & 4 \end{pmatrix},$$

we find using a software package that $e^{\mathbf{A}t} =$

$$\begin{pmatrix} e^{5t/2}\cos(\sqrt{7}t/2) + \sqrt{7}e^{5t/2}\sin(\sqrt{7}t/2) & \frac{4}{\sqrt{7}}e^{5t/2}\sin(\sqrt{7}t/2) \\ -\frac{4}{\sqrt{7}}e^{5t/2}\sin(\sqrt{7}t/2) & e^{5t/2}\cos(\sqrt{7}t/2) - \sqrt{7}e^{5t/2}\sin(\sqrt{7}t/2) \end{pmatrix}.$$

This is a fundamental matrix for $\mathbf{X}' = \mathbf{A}\mathbf{X}$. It would be at least as easy, for this $\mathbf{A}$, to find the eigenvalues of $\mathbf{A}$, which are $\frac{5}{2} \pm \frac{1}{2}i\sqrt{7}$, then find corresponding eigenvectors, $\begin{pmatrix} 4 \\ 3 \pm i\sqrt{7} \end{pmatrix}$, and use these to obtain a fundamental matrix.

We will now pursue an interesting line of thought. We claim that, even though $e^{\mathbf{A}t}$ may be tedious or even impractical to compute for a given $\mathbf{A}$, it is often possible to compute the product $e^{\mathbf{A}t}\mathbf{K}$, for carefully chosen $\mathbf{K}$, as a finite sum, and hence generate solutions to $\mathbf{X}' = \mathbf{A}\mathbf{X}$. To do this we need the following.

LEMMA 10.2

Let $\mathbf{A}$ be an $n \times n$ real matrix and $\mathbf{K}$ an $n \times 1$ real matrix. Let μ be any number. Then

1. $e^{\mu\mathbf{I}_n t}\mathbf{K} = e^{\mu t}\mathbf{K}$.
2. $e^{\mathbf{A}t}\mathbf{K} = e^{\mu t}e^{(\mathbf{A}-\mu\mathbf{I}_n)t}\mathbf{K}$.

Proof   For (1), since $(\mathbf{I}_n)^m = \mathbf{I}_n$ for any positive integer m, we have

$$e^{\mu\mathbf{I}_n t}\mathbf{K} = \left[\mathbf{I}_n + \mu\mathbf{I}_n t + \frac{1}{2!}(\mu\mathbf{I}_n)^2 t^2 + \frac{1}{3!}(\mu\mathbf{I}_n)^3 t^3 + \cdots \right]\mathbf{K}$$

$$= \left[1 + \mu t + \frac{1}{2!}\mu^2 t^2 + \frac{1}{3!}\mu^3 t^3 + \cdots \right]\mathbf{I}_n\mathbf{K} = e^{\mu t}\mathbf{K}.$$

For (2), first observe that $\mu \mathbf{I}_n$ and $\mathbf{A} - \mu \mathbf{I}_n$ commute, since

$$\mu \mathbf{I}_n (\mathbf{A} - \mu \mathbf{I}_n) = \mu (\mathbf{I}_n \mathbf{A} - \mu (\mathbf{I}_n)^2)$$
$$= \mu (\mathbf{A} - \mu \mathbf{I}_n) = (\mathbf{A} - \mu \mathbf{I}_n)(\mu \mathbf{I}_n).$$

Then, using Theorem 10.9,

$$e^{\mathbf{A}t} \mathbf{K} = e^{\mathbf{A}t + \mu \mathbf{I}_n t - \mu \mathbf{I}_n t} \mathbf{K} = e^{(\mathbf{A} - \mu \mathbf{I}_n)t} e^{\mu \mathbf{I}_n t} \mathbf{K}$$
$$= e^{(\mathbf{A} - \mu \mathbf{I}_n)t} e^{\mu t} \mathbf{K} = e^{\mu t} e^{(\mathbf{A} - \mu \mathbf{I}_n)t} \mathbf{K}. \quad \blacksquare$$

Now suppose we want to solve $\mathbf{X}' = \mathbf{A} \mathbf{X}$. Let $\lambda_1, \ldots, \lambda_r$ be the distinct eigenvalues of $\mathbf{A}$, and let λ_j have multiplicity m_j. Then

$$m_1 + \cdots + m_r = n.$$

For each λ_j, find as many linearly independent eigenvectors as possible. For λ_j, this can be any number from 1 to m_j inclusive. If this yields n linearly independent eigenvectors, then we can write the general solution as a sum of eigenvectors $\boldsymbol{\xi}_j$ times exponential functions $e^{\lambda_j t}$, and we do not need $e^{\mathbf{A}t}$.

Thus suppose some λ_j has multiplicity $m_j \geq 2$, but there are fewer than m_j linearly independent eigenvectors. Find an $n \times 1$ constant matrix $\mathbf{K}_1$ that is linearly independent from the eigenvectors found for λ_j and such that

$$(\mathbf{A} - \lambda_j \mathbf{I}_n) \mathbf{K}_1 \neq \mathbf{O}, \quad \text{but} \quad (\mathbf{A} - \lambda_j \mathbf{I}_n)^2 \mathbf{K}_1 = \mathbf{O}.$$

Then $e^{\mathbf{A}t} \mathbf{K}_1$ is a solution of $\mathbf{X}' = \mathbf{A} \mathbf{X}$. Further, because of the way $\mathbf{K}_1$ was chosen

$$e^{\mathbf{A}t} \mathbf{K}_1 = e^{\lambda_j t} e^{(\mathbf{A} - \lambda_j \mathbf{I}_n)t} \mathbf{K}_1 = e^{\lambda_j t} \left[\mathbf{K}_1 + (\mathbf{A} - \lambda_j \mathbf{I}_n) \mathbf{K}_1 t \right],$$

with all other terms of the series for $e^{(\mathbf{A} - \lambda_j \mathbf{I}_n)t} \mathbf{K}_1$ vanishing because $(\mathbf{A} - \lambda_j \mathbf{I}_n)^2 \mathbf{K}_1 = \mathbf{O}$ forces $(\mathbf{A} - \lambda_j \mathbf{I}_n)^m \mathbf{K}_1 = \mathbf{O}$ for $m \geq 2$. We can therefore compute $e^{\lambda_j t} \mathbf{K}_1$ as a sum of just two terms.

If we now have m_j solutions corresponding to λ_j, then leave this eigenvalue and move on to any others that do not yet have as many linearly independent solutions as their multiplicity. If we do not yet have m_j solutions corresponding to λ_j, then find a constant $n \times 1$ matrix $\mathbf{K}_2$ such that

$$(\mathbf{A} - \lambda_j \mathbf{I}_n) \mathbf{K}_2 \neq \mathbf{O} \quad \text{and} \quad (\mathbf{A} - \lambda_j \mathbf{I}_n)^2 \mathbf{K}_2 \neq \mathbf{O}$$

but

$$(\mathbf{A} - \lambda_j \mathbf{I}_n)^3 \mathbf{K}_2 = \mathbf{O}.$$

Then $e^{\mathbf{A}t} \mathbf{K}_2$ is a solution of $\mathbf{X}' = \mathbf{A} \mathbf{X}$, and we can compute this solution as a sum of just three terms:

$$e^{\mathbf{A}t} \mathbf{K}_2 = e^{\lambda_j t} e^{(\mathbf{A} - \lambda_j \mathbf{I}_n)t} \mathbf{K}_2 = e^{\lambda_j t} \left[\mathbf{K}_2 + (\mathbf{A} - \lambda_j \mathbf{I}_n) \mathbf{K}_2 t + \frac{1}{2!} (\mathbf{A} - \lambda_j \mathbf{I}_n)^2 t^2 \right].$$

The other terms in the infinite series for $e^{\mathbf{A}t} \mathbf{K}_2$ vanish because

$$(\mathbf{A} - \lambda_j \mathbf{I}_n)^3 \mathbf{K}_2 = (\mathbf{A} - \lambda_j \mathbf{I}_n)^4 \mathbf{K}_2 = \cdots = \mathbf{O}.$$

If this gives us m_j solutions associated with λ_j, move on to another eigenvalue for which we do not yet have as many solutions as the multiplicity of the eigenvalue. If not, produce an $n \times 1$ constant matrix $\mathbf{K}_3$ such that

$$(\mathbf{A} - \lambda_j \mathbf{I}_n) \mathbf{K}_3 \neq \mathbf{O}, \ (\mathbf{A} - \lambda_j \mathbf{I}_n)^2 \mathbf{K}_3 \neq \mathbf{O} \quad \text{and} \quad (\mathbf{A} - \lambda_j \mathbf{I}_n)^3 \mathbf{K}_3 \neq \mathbf{O}$$

but

$$(\mathbf{A} - \lambda_j \mathbf{I}_n)^4 \mathbf{K}_3 = \mathbf{0}.$$

Then $e^{\mathbf{A}t} \mathbf{K}_3$ can be computed as a sum of four terms.

Keep repeating this process. For λ_j it must terminate after at most $m_j - 1$ steps, because we began with at least one eigenvector associated with λ_j and then produced more solutions to obtain a total of m_j linearly independent solutions associated with λ_j. Once these are obtained, we move on to another eigenvalue for which we have fewer solutions than its multiplicity, and repeat this process for that eigenvalue, and so on. Eventually we generate a total of n linearly independent solutions, thus obtaining the general solution of $\mathbf{X}' = \mathbf{A}\mathbf{X}$.

EXAMPLE 10.14

Consider $\mathbf{X}' = \mathbf{A}\mathbf{X}$, where

$$\mathbf{A} = \begin{pmatrix} 2 & 1 & 0 & 3 \\ 0 & 2 & 1 & 1 \\ 0 & 0 & 2 & 4 \\ 0 & 0 & 0 & 4 \end{pmatrix}.$$

The eigenvalues are $4, 2, 2, 2$. Associated with 4 we find the eigenvector $\begin{pmatrix} 9 \\ 6 \\ 8 \\ 4 \end{pmatrix}$, so one solution of $\mathbf{X}' = \mathbf{A}\mathbf{X}$ is

$$\mathbf{\Phi}_1(t) = \begin{pmatrix} 9 \\ 6 \\ 8 \\ 4 \end{pmatrix} e^{4t}.$$

Associated with 2 we find that every eigenvector has the form

$$\begin{pmatrix} \alpha \\ 0 \\ 0 \\ 0 \end{pmatrix}.$$

A second solution is

$$\mathbf{\Phi}_2(t) = \begin{pmatrix} 1 \\ 0 \\ 0 \\ 0 \end{pmatrix} e^{2t}.$$

Now find a 4×1 constant matrix $\mathbf{K}_1$ such that $(\mathbf{A} - 2\mathbf{I}_4)\mathbf{K}_1 \neq \mathbf{O}$, but $(\mathbf{A} - 2\mathbf{I}_4)^2 \mathbf{K}_1 = \mathbf{O}$. First compute

$$(\mathbf{A} - 2\mathbf{I}_4)^2 = \begin{pmatrix} 0 & 1 & 0 & 3 \\ 0 & 0 & 1 & 1 \\ 0 & 0 & 0 & 4 \\ 0 & 0 & 0 & 2 \end{pmatrix}^2$$

$$= \begin{pmatrix} 0 & 0 & 1 & 7 \\ 0 & 0 & 0 & 6 \\ 0 & 0 & 0 & 8 \\ 0 & 0 & 0 & 4 \end{pmatrix}.$$

Solve $(\mathbf{A} - 2\mathbf{I}_4)^2 \mathbf{K}_1 = \mathbf{O}$ to find solutions of the form

$$\begin{pmatrix} \alpha \\ \beta \\ 0 \\ 0 \end{pmatrix}.$$

We will choose the solution

$$\mathbf{K}_1 = \begin{pmatrix} 0 \\ 1 \\ 0 \\ 0 \end{pmatrix}$$

to avoid duplicating the eigenvector already found associated with 2. Then

$$(\mathbf{A} - 2\mathbf{I}_4)\mathbf{K}_1 = \begin{pmatrix} 0 & 1 & 0 & 3 \\ 0 & 0 & 1 & 1 \\ 0 & 0 & 0 & 4 \\ 0 & 0 & 0 & 2 \end{pmatrix} \begin{pmatrix} 0 \\ 1 \\ 0 \\ 0 \end{pmatrix} = \begin{pmatrix} 1 \\ 0 \\ 0 \\ 0 \end{pmatrix} \neq \mathbf{O},$$

as required. Thus form the third solution

$$\boldsymbol{\Phi}_3(t) = e^{\mathbf{A}t}\mathbf{K}_1 = e^{2t}\left[\mathbf{K}_1 + (\mathbf{A} - 2\mathbf{I}_4)\mathbf{K}_1 t\right]$$

$$= e^{2t}\left[\begin{pmatrix} 0 \\ 1 \\ 0 \\ 0 \end{pmatrix} + \begin{pmatrix} 0 & 1 & 0 & 3 \\ 0 & 0 & 1 & 1 \\ 0 & 0 & 0 & 4 \\ 0 & 0 & 0 & 2 \end{pmatrix} \begin{pmatrix} 0 \\ 1 \\ 0 \\ 0 \end{pmatrix} t\right]$$

$$= e^{2t}\left[\begin{pmatrix} 0 \\ 1 \\ 0 \\ 0 \end{pmatrix} + \begin{pmatrix} 1 \\ 0 \\ 0 \\ 0 \end{pmatrix} t\right] = \begin{pmatrix} t \\ 1 \\ 0 \\ 0 \end{pmatrix} e^{2t}.$$

The three solutions found up to this point are linearly independent. Now we need a fourth solution. It must come from the eigenvalue 2, because 4 has multiplicity 1 and we have one solution corresponding to this eigenvalue. Look for $\mathbf{K}_2$ such that

$$(\mathbf{A} - 2\mathbf{I}_4)\mathbf{K}_2 \neq \mathbf{O} \quad \text{and} \quad (\mathbf{A} - 2\mathbf{I}_4)^2\mathbf{K}_2 \neq \mathbf{O}$$

but

$$(\mathbf{A} - 2\mathbf{I}_4)^3\mathbf{K}_2 = \mathbf{O}.$$

First compute

$$(\mathbf{A} - 2\mathbf{I}_4)^3 = \begin{pmatrix} 0 & 0 & 0 & 18 \\ 0 & 0 & 0 & 12 \\ 0 & 0 & 0 & 16 \\ 0 & 0 & 0 & 8 \end{pmatrix}.$$

Solutions of $(\mathbf{A} - 2\mathbf{I}_4)^3\mathbf{K}_2 = \mathbf{O}$ are of the form

$$\begin{pmatrix} \alpha \\ \beta \\ \gamma \\ 0 \end{pmatrix}.$$

We will choose

$$\mathbf{K}_2 = \begin{pmatrix} 1 \\ 1 \\ 1 \\ 0 \end{pmatrix}$$

to avoid duplicating previous choices. Of course other choices are possible. It is routine to verify that $(\mathbf{A} - 2\mathbf{I}_4)\mathbf{K}_2 \neq \mathbf{O}$ and $(\mathbf{A} - 2\mathbf{I}_4)^2\mathbf{K}_2 \neq \mathbf{O}$. Thus form the fourth solution

$$\boldsymbol{\Phi}_4(t) = e^{\mathbf{A}t}\mathbf{K}_2 = e^{2t}\left[\mathbf{K}_2 + (\mathbf{A} - 2\mathbf{I}_n)\mathbf{K}_2 t + \frac{1}{2!}(\mathbf{A} - 2\mathbf{I}_n)^2 t^2\right]$$

$$= e^{2t}\left[\begin{pmatrix} 1 \\ 1 \\ 1 \\ 0 \end{pmatrix} + \begin{pmatrix} 0 & 1 & 0 & 3 \\ 0 & 0 & 1 & 1 \\ 0 & 0 & 0 & 4 \\ 0 & 0 & 0 & 2 \end{pmatrix}\begin{pmatrix} 1 \\ 1 \\ 1 \\ 0 \end{pmatrix} t + \frac{1}{2}\begin{pmatrix} 0 & 0 & 1 & 7 \\ 0 & 0 & 0 & 6 \\ 0 & 0 & 0 & 8 \\ 0 & 0 & 0 & 4 \end{pmatrix}\begin{pmatrix} 1 \\ 1 \\ 1 \\ 0 \end{pmatrix} t^2\right]$$

$$= \begin{pmatrix} 1 + t + \frac{1}{2}t^2 \\ 1 + t \\ 1 \\ 0 \end{pmatrix} e^{2t}.$$

We now have four linearly independent solutions, hence the general solution. We can also write the fundamental matrix

$$\boldsymbol{\Omega}(t) = \begin{pmatrix} 9e^{4t} & e^{2t} & te^{2t} & (1 + t + \frac{1}{2}t^2)e^{2t} \\ 6e^{4t} & 0 & e^{2t} & (1 + t)e^{2t} \\ 8e^{4t} & 0 & 0 & e^{2t} \\ 4e^{4t} & 0 & 0 & 0 \end{pmatrix}. \quad \blacksquare$$

SECTION 10.2   PROBLEMS

In each of Problems 1 through 5, find a fundamental matrix for the system and use it to write the general solution. These coefficients matrices for these systems have real, distinct eigenvalues.

1. $x_1' = 3x_1, x_2' = 5x_1 - 4x_2$

2. $x_1' = 4x_1 + 2x_2, x_2' = 3x_1 + 3x_2$

3. $x_1' = x_1 + x_2, x_2' = x_1 + x_2$

4. $x_1' = 2x_1 + x_2 - 2x_3, x_2' = 3x_1 - 2x_2, x_3' = 3x_1 - x_2 - 3x_3$

5. $x_1' = x_1 + 2x_2 + x_3, x_2' = 6x_1 - x_2, x_3' = -x_1 - 2x_2 - x_3$

In each of Problems 6 through 11, find a fundamental matrix for the system and use it to solve the initial value problem. The matrices of these systems have real, distinct eigenvalues.

6. $x_1' = 3x_1 - 4x_2, x_2' = 2x_1 - 3x_2; x_1(0) = 7, x_2(0) = 5$

7. $x_1' = x_1 - 2x_2, x_2' = -6x_1; x_1(0) = 1, x_2(0) = -19$

8. $x_1' = 2x_1 - 10x_2, x_2' = -x_1 - x_2; x_1(0) = -3, x_2(0) = 6$

9. $x_1' = 3x_1 - x_2 + x_3, x_2' = x_1 + x_2 - x_3, x_3' = x_1 - x_2 + x_3;$
$\qquad x_1(0) = 1, x_2(0) = 5, x_3(0) = 1$

10. $x_1' = 2x_1 + x_2 - 2x_3, x_2' = 3x_1 - 2x_2, x_3' = 3x_1 + x_2 - 3x_3;$
$\qquad x_1(0) = 1, x_2(0) = 7, x_3(0) = 3$

11. $x_1' = 2x_1 + 3x_2 + 3x_3, x_2' = -x_2 - 3x_3, x_3' = 2x_3;$
$\qquad x_1(0) = 9, x_2(0) = -1, x_3(0) = -3$

12. Show that the change of variables $z = \ln(t)$ for $t > 0$ transforms the system

$$tx_1' = ax_1 + bx_2,\ tx_2' = cx_1 + dx_2$$

into a linear system $\mathbf{X}' = \mathbf{AX}$, assuming that a, b, c and d are real constants.

13. Use the idea of Problem 12 to solve the system

$$tx_1' = 6x_1 + 2x_2,\ tx_2' = 4x_1 + 4x_2.$$

14. Solve the system

$$tx_1' = -x_1 - 3x_2,\ tx_2' = x_1 - 5x_2.$$

In each of Problems 15 through 19, find a real-valued fundamental matrix for the system $\mathbf{X}' = \mathbf{AX}$, with $\mathbf{A}$ the given matrix.

15. $\begin{pmatrix} 2 & -4 \\ 1 & 2 \end{pmatrix}$

16. $\begin{pmatrix} 0 & 5 \\ -1 & -2 \end{pmatrix}$

17. $\begin{pmatrix} 3 & -5 \\ 1 & -1 \end{pmatrix}$

18. $\begin{pmatrix} 1 & -1 & 1 \\ 1 & -1 & 0 \\ 1 & 0 & -1 \end{pmatrix}$

19. $\begin{pmatrix} -2 & 1 & 0 \\ -5 & 0 & 0 \\ 0 & 3 & -2 \end{pmatrix}$

In each of Problems 20 through 23, find a real-valued fundamental matrix for the system $\mathbf{X}' = \mathbf{AX}$, with $\mathbf{A}$ the given matrix. Use this to solve the initial value problem, with $\mathbf{X}(0)$ the given $n \times 1$ matrix.

20. $\begin{pmatrix} 3 & 2 \\ -5 & 1 \end{pmatrix};\begin{pmatrix} 2 \\ 8 \end{pmatrix}$

21. $\begin{pmatrix} 3 & -2 \\ 5 & -3 \end{pmatrix};\begin{pmatrix} 1 \\ 10 \end{pmatrix}$

22. $\begin{pmatrix} 2 & -5 \\ 1 & -2 \end{pmatrix};\begin{pmatrix} 5 \\ 0 \end{pmatrix}$

23. $\begin{pmatrix} 3 & -3 & 1 \\ 2 & -1 & 0 \\ 1 & -1 & 1 \end{pmatrix};\begin{pmatrix} 7 \\ 4 \\ 3 \end{pmatrix}$

24. Can a matrix with at least one complex, non-real element have only real eigenvalues? If not, give a proof. It it can, give an example.

In each of Problems 25 through 30, find a fundamental matrix for the system $\mathbf{X}' = \mathbf{AX}$, using the method of Section 10.2.2, with $\mathbf{A}$ the given matrix.

25. $\begin{pmatrix} 3 & 2 \\ 0 & 3 \end{pmatrix}$

26. $\begin{pmatrix} 2 & 0 \\ 5 & 2 \end{pmatrix}$

27. $\begin{pmatrix} 2 & 5 & 6 \\ 0 & 8 & 9 \\ 0 & -1 & 2 \end{pmatrix}$

28. $\begin{pmatrix} 1 & 5 & 0 \\ 0 & 1 & 0 \\ 4 & 8 & 1 \end{pmatrix}$

29. $\begin{pmatrix} 1 & 5 & -2 & 6 \\ 0 & 3 & 0 & 4 \\ 0 & 3 & 0 & 4 \\ 0 & 0 & 0 & 1 \end{pmatrix}$

30. $\begin{pmatrix} 0 & 1 & 0 & 0 \\ 0 & 0 & 1 & 0 \\ 0 & 0 & 0 & 1 \\ -1 & -2 & 0 & 0 \end{pmatrix}$

In each of Problems 31 through 35, find the general solution of the system $\mathbf{X}' = \mathbf{AX}$, with $\mathbf{A}$ the given matrix, and use this general solution to solve the initial value problem, for the given $n \times 1$ matrix $\mathbf{X}(0)$. Use the method of Section 10.2.2 for these problems.

31. $\begin{pmatrix} 7 & -1 \\ 1 & 5 \end{pmatrix};\begin{pmatrix} 5 \\ 3 \end{pmatrix}$

32. $\begin{pmatrix} 2 & 0 \\ 5 & 2 \end{pmatrix};\begin{pmatrix} 4 \\ 3 \end{pmatrix}$

33. $\begin{pmatrix} -4 & 1 & 1 \\ 0 & 2 & -5 \\ 0 & 0 & -4 \end{pmatrix};\begin{pmatrix} 0 \\ 4 \\ 12 \end{pmatrix}$

34. $\begin{pmatrix} -5 & 2 & 1 \\ 0 & -5 & 3 \\ 0 & 0 & -5 \end{pmatrix};\begin{pmatrix} 2 \\ -3 \\ 4 \end{pmatrix}$

35. $\begin{pmatrix} 1 & -2 & 0 & 0 \\ 1 & -1 & 0 & 0 \\ 0 & 0 & 5 & -3 \\ 0 & 0 & 3 & -1 \end{pmatrix};\begin{pmatrix} 2 \\ -2 \\ 1 \\ 4 \end{pmatrix}$

In each of Problems 36 through 40, find the general solution of the system by diagonalizing the coefficient matrix.

36. $x_1' = -2x_1 + x_2,\ x_2' = -4x_1 + 3x_2$

37. $x_1' = 3x_1 + 3x_2,\ x_1' = x_1 + 5x_2$

38. $x_1' = x_1 + x_2,\ x_2' = x_1 + x_2$

39. $x_1' = 6x_1 + 5x_2,\ x_2' = x_1 + 2x_2$

40. $x_1' = 3x_1 - 2x_2,\ x_2' = 9x_1 - 3x_2$

In each of Problems 41-45, solve the system $\mathbf{X}' = \mathbf{AX}$, with $\mathbf{A}$ the matrix of the indicated problem, by finding $e^{\mathbf{A}t}$.

41. $\mathbf{A}$ as in Problem 25.

42. $\mathbf{A}$ as in Problem 26.

43. $\mathbf{A}$ as in Problem 27.

44. $\mathbf{A}$ as in Problem 28.

45. $\mathbf{A}$ as in Problem 29.

In each of Problems 46-50, solve the initial value problem of the referred problem, using the exponential matrix.

46. Problem 31.

47. Problem 32.

48. Problem 33.

49. Problem 34.

50. Problem 35.

10.3 Solution of $X' = AX + G$

We now turn to the nonhomogeneous system $\mathbf{X}'(t) = \mathbf{A}(t)\mathbf{X}(t) + \mathbf{G}(t)$, assuming that the elements of the $n \times n$ matrix $\mathbf{A}(t)$, and the $n \times 1$ matrix $\mathbf{G}(t)$, are continuous on some interval I, which may be the entire real line.

Recall that the general solution of $\mathbf{X}' = \mathbf{AX} + \mathbf{G}$ has the form $\mathbf{X}(t) = \mathbf{\Omega}(t)\mathbf{C} + \mathbf{\Psi}_p(t)$, where $\mathbf{\Omega}(t)$ is an $n \times n$ fundamental matrix for the homogeneous system $\mathbf{X}' = \mathbf{AX}$, $\mathbf{C}$ is an $n \times 1$ matrix of arbitrary constants, and $\mathbf{\Psi}_p$ is a particular solution of $\mathbf{X}' = \mathbf{AX} + \mathbf{G}$. At least when $\mathbf{A}$ is a real, constant matrix, we have a strategy for finding $\mathbf{\Omega}$. We will concentrate in this section on strategies for finding a particular solution $\mathbf{\Psi}_p$.

10.3.1 Variation of Parameters

Recall the variation of parameters method for second-order differential equations. If $y_1(x)$ and $y_2(x)$ form a fundamental set of solutions for

$$y''(x) + p(x)y'(x) + q(x)y(x) = 0,$$

then the general solution of this homogeneous equation is

$$y_h(x) = c_1 y_1(x) + c_2 y_2(x).$$

To find a particular solution $y_p(x)$ of the nonhomogeneous equation

$$y''(x) + p(x)y'(x) + q(x)y(x) = f(x)$$

replace the constants in y_h by functions and attempt to choose $u(x)$ and $v(x)$ so that

$$y_p(x) = u(x)y_1(x) + v(x)y_2(x)$$

is a solution.

The variation of parameters method for the matrix equation $\mathbf{X}' = \mathbf{AX} + \mathbf{G}$ follows the same idea. Suppose we can find a fundamental matrix for the homogeneous system $\mathbf{X}' = \mathbf{AX}$. The general solution of this homogeneous system is then $\mathbf{X}_h(t) = \mathbf{\Omega}(t)\mathbf{C}$, in which $\mathbf{C}$ is an $n \times 1$ matrix of arbitrary constants. Look for a particular solution of $\mathbf{X}' = \mathbf{AX} + \mathbf{G}$ of the form

$$\mathbf{\Psi}_p(t) = \mathbf{\Omega}(t)\mathbf{U}(t),$$

in which $\mathbf{U}(t)$ is an $n \times 1$ matrix of functions of t which is to be determined.

Substitute this proposed solution into the differential equation to get

$$(\mathbf{\Omega U})' = \mathbf{A}(\mathbf{\Omega U}) + \mathbf{G},$$

or

$$\mathbf{\Omega}'\mathbf{U} + \mathbf{\Omega U}' = (\mathbf{A\Omega})\mathbf{U} + \mathbf{G}.$$

Now $\boldsymbol{\Omega}$ is a fundamental matrix for $\mathbf{X}' = \mathbf{AX}$, so $\boldsymbol{\Omega}' = \mathbf{A}\boldsymbol{\Omega}$. Therefore $\boldsymbol{\Omega}'\mathbf{U} = (\mathbf{A}\boldsymbol{\Omega})\mathbf{U}$ and the last equation reduces to

$$\boldsymbol{\Omega}\mathbf{U}' = \mathbf{G}.$$

Since $\boldsymbol{\Omega}$ is a fundamental matrix, the columns of $\boldsymbol{\Omega}$ are linearly independent. This means that $\boldsymbol{\Omega}$ is nonsingular, so the last equation can be solved for $\mathbf{U}'$ to get

$$\mathbf{U}' = \boldsymbol{\Omega}^{-1}\mathbf{G}.$$

As in the case of second order differential equations, we now have the derivative of the function we want. Then

$$\mathbf{U}(t) = \int \boldsymbol{\Omega}^{-1}(t)\mathbf{G}(t)\,dt,$$

in which we integrate a matrix by integrating each element of the matrix.

Once we find a suitable $\mathbf{U}(t)$, we have a particular solution $\boldsymbol{\Psi}_p(t) = \boldsymbol{\Omega}(t)\mathbf{U}(t)$ of $\mathbf{X}' = \mathbf{AX} + \mathbf{G}$. The general solution of this nonhomogeneous equation is then

$$\mathbf{X}(t) = \boldsymbol{\Omega}(t)\mathbf{C} + \boldsymbol{\Omega}(t)\mathbf{U}(t),$$

in which $\mathbf{C}$ is an $n \times 1$ matrix of constants.

EXAMPLE 10.15

Solve the system

$$\mathbf{X}' = \begin{pmatrix} 1 & -10 \\ -1 & 4 \end{pmatrix}\mathbf{X} + \begin{pmatrix} e^t \\ \sin(t) \end{pmatrix}.$$

First we need a fundamental matrix for $\mathbf{X}' = \mathbf{AX}$. The eigenvalues of $\mathbf{A}$ are -1 and 6, with associated eigenvectors, respectively, $\begin{pmatrix} 5 \\ 1 \end{pmatrix}$ and $\begin{pmatrix} -2 \\ 1 \end{pmatrix}$. Therefore a fundamental matrix for $\mathbf{X}' = \mathbf{AX}$ is

$$\boldsymbol{\Omega}(t) = \begin{pmatrix} 5e^{-t} & -2e^{6t} \\ e^{-t} & e^{6t} \end{pmatrix}.$$

We find (details provided at the end of the example) that

$$\boldsymbol{\Omega}^{-1}(t) = \frac{1}{7}\begin{pmatrix} e^t & 2e^t \\ -e^{-6t} & 5e^{-6t} \end{pmatrix}.$$

Compute

$$\mathbf{U}'(t) = \boldsymbol{\Omega}^{-1}(t)\mathbf{G}(t) = \frac{1}{7}\begin{pmatrix} e^t & 2e^t \\ -e^{-6t} & 5e^{-6t} \end{pmatrix}\begin{pmatrix} e^t \\ \sin(t) \end{pmatrix}$$

$$= \frac{1}{7}\begin{pmatrix} e^{2t} + 2e^t \sin(t) \\ -e^{-5t} + 5e^{-6t}\sin(t) \end{pmatrix}.$$

Then

$$\mathbf{U}(t) = \int \boldsymbol{\Omega}^{-1}(t)\mathbf{G}(t)\,dt = \frac{1}{7}\begin{pmatrix} \int e^{2t}\,dt + 2\int e^t \sin(t)\,dt \\ -\int e^{-5t}\,dt + 5\int e^{-6t}\sin(t)\,dt \end{pmatrix}$$

$$= \begin{pmatrix} \frac{1}{14}e^{2t} + \frac{1}{7}e^t[\sin(t) - \cos(t)] \\ \frac{1}{35}e^{-5t} + \frac{5}{259}e^{-6t}[-6\sin(t) - \cos(t)] \end{pmatrix}.$$

The general solution of $\mathbf{X}' = \mathbf{AX} + \mathbf{G}$ is

$$\mathbf{X}(t) = \mathbf{\Omega}(t)\mathbf{C} + \mathbf{\Omega}(t)\mathbf{U}(t) = \begin{pmatrix} 5e^{-t} & -2e^{6t} \\ e^{-t} & e^{6t} \end{pmatrix} \mathbf{C}$$

$$+ \begin{pmatrix} 5e^{-t} & -2e^{6t} \\ e^{-t} & e^{6t} \end{pmatrix} \begin{pmatrix} \frac{1}{14}e^{2t} + \frac{1}{7}e^{t}[\sin(t) - \cos(t)] \\ \frac{1}{35}e^{-5t} + \frac{5}{259}e^{-6t}[-6\sin(t) - \cos(t)] \end{pmatrix}$$

$$= \begin{pmatrix} 5e^{-t} & -2e^{6t} \\ e^{-t} & e^{6t} \end{pmatrix} \mathbf{C} + \begin{pmatrix} \frac{3}{10}e^{t} + \frac{35}{37}\sin(t) - \frac{25}{37}\cos(t) \\ \frac{1}{10}e^{t} + \frac{1}{37}\sin(t) - \frac{6}{37}\cos(t) \end{pmatrix}.$$

If we want to write the solution in terms of the component functions, let $\mathbf{C} = \begin{pmatrix} c_1 \\ c_2 \end{pmatrix}$ to obtain

$$x_1(t) = 5c_1 e^{-t} - 2c_2 e^{6t} + \frac{3}{10}e^{t} + \frac{35}{37}\sin(t) - \frac{25}{37}\cos(t),$$

$$x_2(t) = c_1 e^{-t} + c_2 e^{6t} + \frac{1}{10}e^{t} + \frac{1}{37}\sin(t) - \frac{6}{37}\cos(t). \quad \blacksquare$$

Although the coefficient matrix $\mathbf{A}$ in this example was constant, this is not a requirement of the variation of parameters method.

In the example we needed $\mathbf{\Omega}^{-1}(t)$. Standard software packages will produce this inverse. We could also proceed as follows, reducing $\mathbf{\Omega}(t)$ and recording the row operations beginning with the identity matrix, as discussed in Section 7.8.1:

$$\begin{pmatrix} 1 & 0 & \vdots & 5e^{-t} & -2e^{6t} \\ 0 & 1 & \vdots & e^{-t} & e^{6t} \end{pmatrix}$$

add $-\frac{1}{5}$(row 1) to row 2

$$\begin{pmatrix} 1 & 0 & \vdots & 5e^{-t} & -2e^{6t} \\ -\frac{1}{5} & 1 & \vdots & 0 & \frac{7}{5}e^{6t} \end{pmatrix}$$

multiply row 1 by $\frac{1}{5}e^{t}$

$$\begin{pmatrix} \frac{1}{5}e^{t} & 0 & \vdots & 1 & -\frac{2}{5}e^{7t} \\ -\frac{1}{5} & 1 & \vdots & 0 & \frac{7}{5}e^{6t} \end{pmatrix}$$

multiply row 2 by $\frac{5}{7}e^{-6t}$

$$\begin{pmatrix} \frac{1}{5}e^{t} & 0 & \vdots & 1 & -\frac{2}{5}e^{7t} \\ -\frac{1}{7}e^{-6t} & \frac{5}{7}e^{-6t} & \vdots & 0 & 1 \end{pmatrix}$$

add $\frac{2}{5}e^{7t}$(row 2) to row 1

$$\begin{pmatrix} \frac{1}{7}e^{t} & \frac{2}{7}e^{t} & \vdots & 1 & 0 \\ -\frac{1}{7}e^{-6t} & \frac{5}{7}e^{-6t} & \vdots & 0 & 1 \end{pmatrix}.$$

Since the last two columns for $\mathbf{I}_2$, the first two columns are $\mathbf{\Omega}^{-1}(t)$.

Variation of Parameters and the Laplace Transform There is a connection between the variation of parameters method and the Laplace transform. Suppose we want a particular solution $\mathbf{\Psi}_p$ of $\mathbf{X}' = \mathbf{A}\mathbf{X} + \mathbf{G}$, in which $\mathbf{A}$ is an $n \times n$ real matrix. The variation of parameters method is to find a particular solution $\mathbf{\Psi}_p(t) = \mathbf{\Omega}(t)\mathbf{U}(t)$, where $\mathbf{\Omega}(t)$ is a fundamental matrix for $\mathbf{X}' = \mathbf{A}\mathbf{X}$. Explicitly,

$$\mathbf{U}(t) = \int \mathbf{\Omega}^{-1}(t)\mathbf{G}(t)dt.$$

We can choose a particular $\mathbf{U}(t)$ by carrying out this integration from 0 to t:

$$\mathbf{U}(t) = \int_0^t \mathbf{\Omega}^{-1}(s)\mathbf{G}(s)ds.$$

Then

$$\mathbf{\Psi}_p(t) = \mathbf{\Omega}(t)\int_0^t \mathbf{\Omega}^{-1}(s)\mathbf{G}(s)ds = \int_0^t \mathbf{\Omega}(t)\mathbf{\Omega}^{-1}(s)\mathbf{G}(s)ds.$$

In this equation $\mathbf{\Omega}$ can be any fundamental matrix for $\mathbf{X}' = \mathbf{A}\mathbf{X}$. In particular, suppose we choose $\mathbf{\Omega}(t) = e^{\mathbf{A}t}$. This is sometimes called the *transition matrix* for $\mathbf{X}' = \mathbf{A}\mathbf{X}$, since it is a fundamental matrix such that $\mathbf{\Omega}(0) = \mathbf{I}_n$. Now $\mathbf{\Omega}^{-1}(s) = e^{-\mathbf{A}s}$, so

$$\mathbf{\Omega}(t)\mathbf{\Omega}^{-1}(s) = e^{\mathbf{A}t}e^{-\mathbf{A}s} = e^{\mathbf{A}(t-s)} = \mathbf{\Omega}(t-s)$$

and

$$\mathbf{\Psi}_p(t) = \int_0^t \mathbf{\Omega}(t-s)\mathbf{G}(s)ds.$$

This equation has the same form as the Laplace transform convolution of $\mathbf{\Omega}$ and $\mathbf{G}$, except that in the current setting these are matrix functions. Now define the Laplace transform of a matrix to be the matrix obtained by taking the Laplace transform of each of its elements. This extended Laplace transform has many of the same computational properties as the Laplace transform for scalar functions. In particular, we can define the convolution integral

$$\mathbf{\Omega}(t) * \mathbf{G}(t) = \int_0^t \mathbf{\Omega}(t-s)\mathbf{G}(s)ds.$$

In terms of this convolution,

$$\mathbf{\Psi}_p(t) = \mathbf{\Omega}(t) * \mathbf{G}(t).$$

This is a general formula for a particular solution of $\mathbf{X}' = \mathbf{A}\mathbf{X} + \mathbf{G}$ when $\mathbf{\Omega}(t) = e^{\mathbf{A}t}$.

EXAMPLE 10.16

Consider the system

$$\mathbf{X}' = \begin{pmatrix} 1 & -4 \\ 1 & 5 \end{pmatrix}\mathbf{X} + \begin{pmatrix} e^{2t} \\ t \end{pmatrix}.$$

We find that

$$e^{\mathbf{A}t} = \begin{pmatrix} (1-2t)e^{3t} & -4te^{3t} \\ te^{3t} & (1+2t)e^{3t} \end{pmatrix} = \mathbf{\Omega}(t).$$

A particular solution of $\mathbf{X}' = \mathbf{AX} + \mathbf{G}$ is given by

$$\mathbf{\Psi}_p(t) = \int_0^t \mathbf{\Omega}(t-s)\mathbf{G}(s)\,ds$$

$$= \int_0^t \begin{pmatrix} (1-2(t-s))e^{3(t-s)} & -4(t-s)e^{3(t-s)} \\ (t-s)e^{3(t-s)} & (1+2(t-s)))e^{3(t-s)} \end{pmatrix} \begin{pmatrix} e^{2s} \\ s \end{pmatrix} dt$$

$$= \int_0^t \begin{pmatrix} (1-2t+2s)\,e^{3t}e^{-s} - 4\,(t-s)\,e^{3t}se^{-3s} \\ (t-s)\,e^{3t}e^{-s} + (1+2t-2s)\,e^{3t}se^{-3s} \end{pmatrix} ds$$

$$= \begin{pmatrix} \int_0^t [(1-2t+2s)\,e^{3t}e^{-s} - 4\,(t-s)\,e^{3t}se^{-3s}]\,ds \\ \int_0^t [(t-s)\,e^{3t}e^{-s} + (1+2t-2s)\,e^{3t}se^{-3s}]\,ds \end{pmatrix}$$

$$= \begin{pmatrix} -3e^{2t} + \frac{89}{27}e^{3t} - \frac{22}{9}e^{3t}t - \frac{4}{9}t - \frac{8}{27} \\ e^{2t} + \frac{11}{9}e^{3t}t - \frac{28}{27}e^{3t} - \frac{1}{9}t + \frac{1}{27} \end{pmatrix}.$$

The general solution of $\mathbf{X}' = \mathbf{AX} + \mathbf{G}$ is

$$\mathbf{X}(t) = \begin{pmatrix} (1-2t)e^{3t} & -4te^{3t} \\ te^{3t} & (1+2t)e^{3t} \end{pmatrix} \mathbf{C}$$

$$+ \begin{pmatrix} -3e^{2t} + \frac{89}{27}e^{3t} - \frac{22}{9}e^{3t}t - \frac{4}{9}t - \frac{8}{27} \\ e^{2t} + \frac{11}{9}e^{3t}t - \frac{28}{27}e^{3t} - \frac{1}{9}t + \frac{1}{27} \end{pmatrix}. \blacksquare$$

10.3.2   Solution of $\mathbf{X}' = \mathbf{AX} + \mathbf{G}$ by Diagonalizing A

Consider the case that $\mathbf{A}$ is a constant, diagonalizable matrix. Then $\mathbf{A}$ has n linearly independent eigenvectors. These form columns of a nonsingular matrix $\mathbf{P}$ such that

$$\mathbf{P}^{-1}\mathbf{AP} = \mathbf{D} = \begin{pmatrix} \lambda_1 & 0 & \cdots & 0 \\ 0 & \lambda_2 & \cdots & 0 \\ \vdots & \vdots & \cdots & \vdots \\ 0 & 0 & \cdots & \lambda_n \end{pmatrix},$$

with eigenvalues down the main diagonal in the order corresponding to the eigenvector columns of $\mathbf{P}$. As we did in the homogeneous case $\mathbf{X}' = \mathbf{AX}$, make the change of variables $\mathbf{X} = \mathbf{PZ}$. Then the system $\mathbf{X}' = \mathbf{AX} + \mathbf{G}$ becomes

$$\mathbf{X}' = \mathbf{PZ}' = \mathbf{A}(\mathbf{PZ}) + \mathbf{G},$$

or

$$\mathbf{PZ}' = (\mathbf{AP})\mathbf{Z} + \mathbf{G}.$$

Multiply this equation on the left by $\mathbf{P}^{-1}$ to get

$$\mathbf{Z}' = (\mathbf{P}^{-1}\mathbf{AP})\mathbf{Z} + \mathbf{P}^{-1}\mathbf{G} = \mathbf{DZ} + \mathbf{P}^{-1}\mathbf{G}.$$

This is an uncoupled system of the form

$$z_1' = \lambda_1 z_1 + f_1(t)$$
$$z_2' = \lambda_2 z_2 + f_2(t)$$
$$\vdots$$
$$z_n' = \lambda_n z_n + f_n(t),$$

where

$$\mathbf{P}^{-1}\mathbf{G}(t) = \begin{pmatrix} f_1(t) \\ f_2(t) \\ \vdots \\ f_n(t) \end{pmatrix}.$$

Solve these n first-order differential equations independently, form $\mathbf{Z}(t) = \begin{pmatrix} z_1(t) \\ z_2(t) \\ \vdots \\ z_n(t) \end{pmatrix}$, and then

the solution of $\mathbf{X}' = \mathbf{AX} + \mathbf{G}$ is $\mathbf{X}(t) = \mathbf{PZ}(t)$.

Unlike diagonalization in solving the homogeneous system $\mathbf{X}' = \mathbf{AX}$, in this nonhomogeneous case we must explicitly calculate $\mathbf{P}^{-1}$ in order to determine $\mathbf{P}^{-1}\mathbf{G}(t)$, the nonhomogeneous term in the transformed system.

EXAMPLE 10.17

Consider

$$\mathbf{X}' = \begin{pmatrix} 3 & 3 \\ 1 & 5 \end{pmatrix} \mathbf{X} + \begin{pmatrix} 8 \\ 4e^{3t} \end{pmatrix}.$$

The eigenvalues of $\mathbf{A}$ are 2 and 6, with eigenvectors, respectively, $\begin{pmatrix} -3 \\ 1 \end{pmatrix}$ and $\begin{pmatrix} 1 \\ 1 \end{pmatrix}$.

Let

$$\mathbf{P} = \begin{pmatrix} -3 & 1 \\ 1 & 1 \end{pmatrix}.$$

Then

$$\mathbf{P}^{-1}\mathbf{AP} = \begin{pmatrix} 2 & 0 \\ 0 & 6 \end{pmatrix}.$$

Compute

$$\mathbf{P}^{-1} = \begin{pmatrix} -\frac{1}{4} & \frac{1}{4} \\ \frac{1}{4} & \frac{3}{4} \end{pmatrix}.$$

The transformation $\mathbf{X} = \mathbf{PZ}$ transforms the original system into

$$\mathbf{Z}' = \begin{pmatrix} 2 & 0 \\ 0 & 6 \end{pmatrix} \mathbf{Z} + \mathbf{P}^{-1} \begin{pmatrix} 8 \\ 4e^{3t} \end{pmatrix}$$

$$= \begin{pmatrix} 2 & 0 \\ 0 & 6 \end{pmatrix} \mathbf{Z} + \begin{pmatrix} -\frac{1}{4} & \frac{1}{4} \\ \frac{1}{4} & \frac{3}{4} \end{pmatrix} \begin{pmatrix} 8 \\ 4e^{3t} \end{pmatrix},$$

or

$$\mathbf{Z}' = \begin{pmatrix} 2 & 0 \\ 0 & 6 \end{pmatrix} \mathbf{Z} + \begin{pmatrix} -2 + e^{3t} \\ 2 + 3e^{3t} \end{pmatrix}.$$

This is the uncoupled system

$$z_1' = 2z_1 - 2 + e^{3t}$$

$$z_2' = 6z_2 + 2 + 3e^{3t}.$$

Solve these linear first-order differential equations independently:

$$z_1(t) = c_1 e^{2t} + e^{3t} + 1,$$

$$z_2(t) = c_2 e^{6t} - e^{3t} - \frac{1}{3}.$$

Then

$$\mathbf{Z}(t) = \begin{pmatrix} c_1 e^{2t} + e^{3t} + 1 \\ c_2 e^{6t} - e^{3t} - \frac{1}{3} \end{pmatrix}.$$

Then

$$\mathbf{X}(t) = \mathbf{PZ}(t) = \begin{pmatrix} -3 & 1 \\ 1 & 1 \end{pmatrix} \begin{pmatrix} c_1 e^{2t} + e^{3t} + 1 \\ c_2 e^{6t} - e^{3t} - \frac{1}{3} \end{pmatrix}$$

$$= \begin{pmatrix} -3c_1 e^{2t} + c_2 e^{6t} - 4e^{3t} - \frac{10}{3} \\ c_1 e^{2t} + c_2 e^{6t} + \frac{2}{3} \end{pmatrix}$$

$$= \begin{pmatrix} -3e^{2t} & e^{6t} \\ e^{2t} & e^{6t} \end{pmatrix} \mathbf{C} + \begin{pmatrix} -4e^{3t} - \frac{10}{3} \\ \frac{2}{3} \end{pmatrix}. \tag{10.7}$$

This is the general solution of $\mathbf{X}' = \mathbf{AX} + \mathbf{G}$. It is the general solution of $\mathbf{X}' = \mathbf{AX}$, plus a particular solution of $\mathbf{X}' = \mathbf{AX} + \mathbf{G}$. Indeed,

$$\begin{pmatrix} -3e^{2t} & e^{6t} \\ e^{2t} & e^{6t} \end{pmatrix}$$

is a fundamental matrix for the homogeneous system $\mathbf{X}' = \mathbf{AX}$. ∎

To illustrate the solution of an initial value problem, suppose we want the solution of

$$\mathbf{X}' = \begin{pmatrix} 3 & 3 \\ 1 & 5 \end{pmatrix} \mathbf{X} + \begin{pmatrix} 8 \\ 4e^{3t} \end{pmatrix}; \mathbf{X}(0) = \begin{pmatrix} 2 \\ -7 \end{pmatrix}.$$

Since we have the general solution (10.7) of this system, all we need to do is determine C so that this initial condition is satisfied. We need

$$\mathbf{X}(0) = \begin{pmatrix} -3 & 1 \\ 1 & 1 \end{pmatrix} \mathbf{C} + \begin{pmatrix} -4 - \frac{10}{3} \\ \frac{2}{3} \end{pmatrix}$$

$$= \begin{pmatrix} -3 & 1 \\ 1 & 1 \end{pmatrix} \mathbf{C} + \begin{pmatrix} -\frac{22}{3} \\ \frac{2}{3} \end{pmatrix} = \begin{pmatrix} 2 \\ -7 \end{pmatrix}.$$

This is the equation

$$\mathbf{PC} = \begin{pmatrix} 2 + \frac{22}{3} \\ -7 - \frac{2}{3} \end{pmatrix} = \begin{pmatrix} \frac{28}{3} \\ -\frac{23}{3} \end{pmatrix}.$$

We already have $\mathbf{P}^{-1}$, so

$$\mathbf{C} = \mathbf{P}^{-1} \begin{pmatrix} \frac{28}{3} \\ -\frac{23}{3} \end{pmatrix} = \begin{pmatrix} -\frac{1}{4} & \frac{1}{4} \\ \frac{1}{4} & \frac{3}{4} \end{pmatrix} \begin{pmatrix} \frac{28}{3} \\ -\frac{23}{3} \end{pmatrix}$$

$$= \begin{pmatrix} -\frac{17}{4} \\ -\frac{41}{12} \end{pmatrix}.$$

The initial value problem has the unique solution

$$\mathbf{X}' = \begin{pmatrix} -3e^{2t} & e^{6t} \\ e^{2t} & e^{6t} \end{pmatrix} \begin{pmatrix} -\frac{17}{4} \\ -\frac{41}{12} \end{pmatrix} + \begin{pmatrix} -4e^{3t} - \frac{10}{3} \\ \frac{2}{3} \end{pmatrix}$$

$$= \begin{pmatrix} \frac{51}{4}e^{2t} - \frac{41}{12}e^{6t} - 4e^{3t} - \frac{10}{3} \\ -\frac{17}{4}e^{2t} - \frac{41}{12}e^{6t} + \frac{2}{3} \end{pmatrix}.$$

SECTION 10.3   PROBLEMS

In each of Problems 1 through 5, use variation of parameters to find the general solution of $\mathbf{X}' = \mathbf{A}\mathbf{X} + \mathbf{G}$, with $\mathbf{A}$ and $\mathbf{G}$ as given.

1. $\begin{pmatrix} 5 & 2 \\ -2 & 1 \end{pmatrix}, \begin{pmatrix} -3e^t \\ e^{3t} \end{pmatrix}$

2. $\begin{pmatrix} 2 & -4 \\ 1 & -2 \end{pmatrix}, \begin{pmatrix} 1 \\ 3t \end{pmatrix}$

3. $\begin{pmatrix} 7 & -1 \\ 1 & 5 \end{pmatrix}, \begin{pmatrix} 2e^{6t} \\ 6te^{6t} \end{pmatrix}$

4. $\begin{pmatrix} 2 & 0 & 0 \\ 0 & 6 & -4 \\ 0 & 4 & -2 \end{pmatrix}; \begin{pmatrix} e^{2t}\cos(3t) \\ -2 \\ -2 \end{pmatrix}$

5. $\begin{pmatrix} 1 & 0 & 0 & 0 \\ 4 & 3 & 0 & 0 \\ 0 & 0 & 3 & 0 \\ -1 & 2 & 9 & 1 \end{pmatrix}, \begin{pmatrix} 0 \\ -2e^t \\ 0 \\ e^t \end{pmatrix}$

In each of Problems 6 through 9, use variation of parameters to solve the initial value problem $\mathbf{X}' = \mathbf{A}\mathbf{X} + \mathbf{G}$; $\mathbf{X}(0) = \mathbf{X}^0$, with $\mathbf{A}$, $\mathbf{G}$ and $\mathbf{X}^0$ as given (in that order).

6. $\begin{pmatrix} 2 & 0 \\ 5 & 2 \end{pmatrix}, \begin{pmatrix} 2 \\ 10t \end{pmatrix}; \begin{pmatrix} 0 \\ 3 \end{pmatrix}$

7. $\begin{pmatrix} 5 & -4 \\ 4 & -3 \end{pmatrix}, \begin{pmatrix} 2e^t \\ 2e^t \end{pmatrix}; \begin{pmatrix} -1 \\ 3 \end{pmatrix}$

8. $\begin{pmatrix} 2 & -3 & 1 \\ 0 & 2 & 4 \\ 0 & 0 & 1 \end{pmatrix}, \begin{pmatrix} 10e^{2t} \\ 6e^{2t} \\ -e^{2t} \end{pmatrix}; \begin{pmatrix} 5 \\ 11 \\ -2 \end{pmatrix}$

9. $\begin{pmatrix} 1 & -3 & 0 \\ 3 & -5 & 0 \\ 4 & 7 & -2 \end{pmatrix}, \begin{pmatrix} te^{-2t} \\ te^{-2t} \\ t^2e^{-2t} \end{pmatrix}; \begin{pmatrix} 6 \\ 2 \\ 3 \end{pmatrix}$

10. Recall that a transition matrix for $\mathbf{X}' = \mathbf{A}\mathbf{X}$ is a fundamental matrix $\mathbf{\Phi}(t)$ such that $\mathbf{\Phi}(0) = \mathbf{I}_n$.

(a) Prove that, for a transition matrix $\mathbf{\Omega}(t)$, $\mathbf{\Omega}^{-1}(t) = \mathbf{\Omega}(-t)$ and $\mathbf{\Omega}(t+s) = \mathbf{\Omega}(t)\mathbf{\Omega}(s)$ for real s and t.

(b) Suppose $\mathbf{\Omega}(t)$ is any fundamental matrix for $\mathbf{X}' = \mathbf{A}\mathbf{X}$. Prove that $\mathbf{\Phi}(t) = \mathbf{\Omega}(t)\mathbf{\Omega}^{-1}(0)$ is a transition matrix. That is, $\mathbf{\Phi}(t)$ is a fundamental matrix and $\mathbf{\Phi}(0) = \mathbf{I}_n$.

In each of Problems 11, 12 and 13, verify that the given matrix is a fundamental matrix for the system and use it to find a transition matrix.

11. $x_1' = 4x_1 + 2x_2, x_2' = 3x_1 + 3x_2;$ $\begin{pmatrix} 2e^t & e^{6t} \\ -3e^t & e^{6t} \end{pmatrix}$

12. $x_1' = -10x_2, x_2 = \frac{5}{2}x_1 - 10x_2;$ $\begin{pmatrix} 2e^{-5t} & (1+5t)e^{-5t} \\ e^{-5t} & \frac{5}{2}te^{-5t} \end{pmatrix}$

13. $x_1' = 5x_1 - 4x_2 + 4x_3, x_2' = 12x_1 - 11x_2 + 12x_3,$

$$x_3' = 4x_1 - 4x_2 + 5x_3; \begin{pmatrix} e^{-3t} & e^t & 0 \\ 3e^{-3t} & 0 & e^t \\ e^{-3t} & -e^t & e^t \end{pmatrix}$$

In each of Problems 14 through 18, find the general solution of the system by diagonalization. The general solutions of the associated homogeneous systems $\mathbf{X}' = \mathbf{A}\mathbf{X}$ were requested in Problems 36 through 40 of Section 10.2.

14. $x_1' = -2x_1 + x_2, \, x_2' = -4x_1 + 3x_2 + 10\cos(t)$

15. $x_1' = 3x_1 + 3x_2 + 8, \, x_2' = x_1 + 5x_2 + 4e^{3t}$

16. $x_1' = x_1 + x_2 + 6e^{3t}, \, x_2' = x_1 + x_2 + 4$

17. $x_1' = 6x_1 + 5x_2 - 4\cos(3t), \, x_2' = x_1 + 2x_2 + 8$

18. $x_1' = 3x_1 - 2x_2 + 3e^{2t}, \, x_2' = 9x_1 - 3x_2 + e^{2t}$

In each of Problems 19 through 23, solve the initial value problem by diagonalization.

19. $x_1' = x_1 + x_2 + 6e^{2t}, \, x_2' = x_1 + x_2 + 2e^{2t}$;
$\qquad x_1(0) = 6, \, x_2(0) = 0$

20. $x_1' = x_1 - 2x_2 + 2t, \, x_2' = -x_1 + 2x_2 + 5$;
$\qquad x_1(0) = 13, \, x_2(0) = 12$

21. $x_1' = 2x_1 - 5x_2 + 5\sin(t), \, x_2' = x_1 - 2x_2$;
$\qquad x_1(0) = 10, \, x_2(0) = 5$

22. $x_1' = 5x_1 - 4x_2 + 4x_3 - 3e^{-3t}, \, x_2' = 12x_1 - 11x_2 + 12x_3 + t, \, x_3' = 4x_1 - 4x_2 + 5x_3$;
$\qquad x_1(0) = 1, \, x_2(0) = -1, \, x_3(0) = 2$

23. $x_1' = 3x_1 - x_2 - x_3, \, x_2' = x_1 + x_2 - x_3 + t, \, x_3' = x_1 - x_2 + x_3 + 2e^t$;
$\qquad x_1(0) = 1, \, x_2(0) = 2, \, x_3(0) = -2$

CHAPTER 11

Qualitative Methods and Systems of Nonlinear Differential Equations

---

11.1   Nonlinear Systems and Existence of Solutions

The preceding chapter was devoted to matrix methods for solving systems of differential equations. Matrices are suited to linear problems. In algebra, the equations we solve by matrix methods are linear, and in differential equations the systems we solve by matrices are also linear.

However, many interesting problems in mathematics, the sciences, engineering, economics, business and other areas involve systems of nonlinear differential equations, or nonlinear systems. We will consider such systems having the special form:

$$
\begin{aligned}
x_1'(t) &= F_1(t, x_1, x_2, \ldots, x_n), \\
x_2'(t) &= F_2(t, x_1, x_2, \ldots, x_n), \\
&\vdots \\
x_n'(t) &= F_n(t, x_1, x_2, \ldots, x_n).
\end{aligned}
\tag{11.1}
$$

This assumes that each equation of the system can be written with a first derivative isolated on one side, and a function of t and the unknown functions $x_1(t), \ldots, x_n(t)$ on the other.

Initial conditions for this system have the form

$$
x_1(t_0) = x_1^0, x_2(t_0) = x_2^0, \ldots, x_n(t_0) = x_n^0,
\tag{11.2}
$$

in which t_0 is a given number and $x_1^0, \ldots, x_n^0$ are given numbers. An initial value problem consists of finding a solution of the system (11.1) satisfying the initial conditions (11.2).

We will state an existence/uniqueness result for this initial value problem. In the statement, an open rectangular parallelepiped in $(n+1)-$ dimensional $t, x_1, \ldots, x_n-$ space consists of all points $(t, x_1, \ldots, x_n)$ in R^{n+1} whose coordinates satisfy inequalities

$$
\alpha < t < \beta, \alpha_1 < x_1 < \beta_1, \ldots, \alpha_n < x_n < \beta_n.
$$

If $n = 1$ this is an open rectangle in the t, x plane, and in three space these points form an open three-dimensional box in 3-space. "Open" means that only points in the interior of parallelopiped, and no points on the bounding faces, are included.

THEOREM 11.1 *Existence/Uniqueness for Nonlinear Systems*

Let $F_1, \ldots, F_n$ and their first partial derivatives be continuous at all points of an open rectangular parallelepiped K in R^{n+1}. Let $(t_0, x_1^0, \ldots, x_n^0)$ be a point of K. Then there exists a positive number h such that the initial value problem consisting of the system (11.1) and the initial conditions (11.2) has a unique solution

$$x_1 = \varphi_1(t), x_2 = \varphi_2(t), \ldots, x_n = \varphi_n(t)$$

defined for $t_0 - h < t < t_0 + h$. ∎

Many systems we encounter are nonlinear and cannot be solved in terms of elementary functions. This is why we need an existence theorem, and why we will shortly develop qualitative methods to determine properties of solutions without having them explicitly in hand.

As we develop ideas and methods for analyzing nonlinear systems, it will be helpful to have some examples to fall back on and against which to measure new ideas. Here are two examples that are important and that come with some physical intuition about how solutions should behave.

EXAMPLE 11.1   The Simple Damped Pendulum

We will derive a system of differential equations describing the motion of a simple pendulum, as shown in Figure 11.1. Although we have some intuition about how a pendulum bob should move, nevertheless the system of differential equations describing this motion is nonlinear and cannot be solved in closed form.

Suppose the pendulum bob has mass m, and is at the end of a rod of length L. The rod is assumed to be so light that its weight does not figure into the motion of the bob. It serves only to constrain the bob to remain at fixed distance L from the point of suspension. The position of the bob at any time is described by its displacement angle $\theta(t)$ from the vertical. At some time we call $t = 0$ the bob is displaced by an angle θ_0 and released from rest.

To describe the motion of the bob, we must analyze the forces acting on it. Gravity acts downward with a force of magnitude mg. The damping force (air resistance, friction of the bar at its pivot point) is assumed to have magnitude $c\theta'(t)$ for some positive constant c. By Newton's laws of motion, the rate of change of angular momentum about any point, with respect to time,

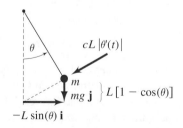

FIGURE 11.1   *Simple, damped pendulum.*

equals the moment of the resultant force about that point. The angular momentum is $mL^2\theta'(t)$. From the diagram, the horizontal distance between the bob and the vertical center position at time t is $L\sin(\theta(t))$. Then,

$$mL^2\theta''(t) = -cL\theta'(t) - mgL\sin(\theta(t)).$$

The negative signs on the right take into account the fact that, if the bob is displaced to the right, these forces tend to make the bob rotate clockwise, which is the negative orientation.

It is customary to write this differential equation as

$$\theta'' + \gamma\theta' + \omega^2\sin(\theta) = 0, \tag{11.3}$$

with $\gamma = c/mL$ and $\omega^2 = g/L$.

Convert this second order equation to a system as follows. Let

$$x = \theta, y = \theta'.$$

Then the pendulum equation (11.3) becomes

$$x' = y,$$

$$y' + \gamma y + \omega^2\sin(x) = 0,$$

or

$$x' = y$$

$$y' = -\omega^2\sin(x) - \gamma y.$$

This is a nonlinear system because of the $\sin(x)$ term. We cannot write a solution of this system in closed form. However, we will soon have methods to analyze the behavior of solutions and hence the motion itself.

In matrix form, the pendulum system is

$$\mathbf{X}' = \begin{pmatrix} 0 & 1 \\ 0 & -\gamma \end{pmatrix}\mathbf{X} + \begin{pmatrix} 0 \\ -\omega^2\sin(x) \end{pmatrix},$$

in which $\mathbf{X} = \begin{pmatrix} x \\ y \end{pmatrix}$. ∎

EXAMPLE 11.2 Nonlinear Spring

Consider an object of mass m attached to a spring. If the object is displaced and released, its motion is governed by Hooke's law, which states that the force exerted on the mass by the spring is $F(r) = -kr$, with k a positive constant and r the distance displaced from the equilibrium position (position at which the object is at rest). Figure 2.4 shows a typical such mass/spring system, with r used here for the displacement instead of y used in Chapter 2.

This is a linear model, since F is a linear function (a constant times r to the first power). The spring model becomes nonlinear if $F(r)$ is nonlinear. Simple nonlinear models are achieved by adding terms to $-kr$. What kind of terms should we add? Intuition tells us that the spring should not care whether we displace an object left or right before releasing it. Since displacements in opposite directions carry opposite signs, this means that we want $F(-r) = -F(r)$, so F should be an odd function. This suggests adding multiples of odd powers of r. The simplest such model is

$$F(r) = -kr + \alpha r^3.$$

If we also allow a damping force which in magnitude is proportional to the velocity, then by Newton's law this spring motion is governed by the second order differential equation

$$mr'' = -kr + \alpha r^3 - cr'.$$

To convert this to a system, let $x = r$ and $y = r'$. The system is

$$x' = y,$$

$$y' = -\frac{k}{m}x + \frac{\alpha}{m}x^3 - \frac{c}{m}y.$$

In matrix form, this system is

$$\mathbf{X}' = \begin{pmatrix} 0 & 1 \\ -k/m & -c/m \end{pmatrix} \mathbf{X} + \begin{pmatrix} 0 \\ \alpha x^3/m \end{pmatrix}. \quad \blacksquare$$

SECTION 11.1   PROBLEMS

1. Apply the existence/uniqueness theorem to the system for the simple damped pendulum, with initial conditions $x(0) = a$, $y(0) = b$. What are the physical interpretations of the initial conditions? Are there any restrictions on the numbers a and b in applying the theorem to assert the existence of a unique solution in some interval $(-h, h)$?

2. Apply the existence/uniqueness theorem to the system for the nonlinear spring system, with initial conditions

$x(0) = a$, $y(0) = b$. What are the physical interpretations of the initial conditions? Are there any restrictions on the numbers a and b in applying the theorem to assert the existence of a unique solution in some interval $(-h, h)$?

3. Suppose the driving force for the nonlinear spring has additional terms, say $F(r) = -kr + \alpha r^3 + \beta r^5$. Does this problem still have a unique solution in some interval $(-h, h)$?

11.2   The Phase Plane, Phase Portraits and Direction Fields

Throughout this chapter we will consider systems of two first-order differential equations in two unknowns. In this case it is convenient to denote the variables as x and y rather than x_1 and x_2. Thus consider the system

$$x'(t) = f(x(t), y(t)),$$
$$y'(t) = g(x(t), y(t)), \tag{11.4}$$

in which f and g are continuous, with continuous first partial derivatives, in some part of the plane. We often write this system as

$$\mathbf{X}' = \mathbf{F}(x(t), y(t)),$$

where

$$\mathbf{X} = \begin{pmatrix} x \\ y \end{pmatrix} \quad \text{and} \quad \mathbf{F}(x, y) = \begin{pmatrix} f(x, y) \\ g(x, y) \end{pmatrix}.$$

The system (11.4) is a special case of the system (11.1). We assume in (11.4) that neither f nor g has an explicit dependence on t. Rather, f and g depend only on x and y, and t appears only through dependencies of these two variables on t. We refer to such a system as *autonomous*.

Working in the plane will allow us the considerable advantage of geometric intuition. If $x = \varphi(t)$, $y = \psi(t)$ is a solution of (11.4), the point $(\varphi(t), \psi(t))$ traces out a curve in the plane as t varies. Such a curve is called a *trajectory*, or *orbit*, of the system. A copy of the plane containing drawings of trajectories is called a *phase portrait* for the system (11.4). In this context, the x, y plane is called the *phase plane*.

We may consider trajectories as oriented, with $(\varphi(t), \psi(t))$ moving along the trajectory in a certain direction as t increases. If we think of t as time, then $(\varphi(t), \psi(t))$ traces out the path of motion of a particle, moving under the influence of the system (11.4), as time increases. In the case of orbits that are closed curves, we take counterclockwise orientation as the positive orientation, unless specific exception is made.

In some phase portraits, short arrows are also drawn. The arrow at any point is along the tangent to the trajectory through that point, and in the direction of motion along this trajectory. This type of drawing combines the phase portrait with a direction field, and gives an overall sense of the flow of the trajectories, as well as graphs of some specific trajectories.

One way to construct trajectories is to write

$$\frac{dy}{dx} = \frac{dy/dt}{dx/dt} = \frac{g(x, y)}{f(x, y)}.$$

Because the system is autonomous, this is a differential equation in x and y and we can attempt to solve it and graph solutions. If the system is nonautonomous, then f/g may depend explicitly on t then we cannot use this strategy to generate trajectories.

EXAMPLE 11.3

Consider the autonomous system

$$x' = y = f(x, y)$$

$$y' = x^2 y^2 = g(x, y).$$

Then

$$\frac{dy}{dx} = \frac{x^2 y^2}{y} = x^2 y,$$

a separable differential equation we write as

$$\frac{1}{y} dy = x^2 dx.$$

Integrate to get

$$\ln |y| = \frac{1}{3} x^3 + C,$$

or

$$y = A e^{x^3/3}.$$

Graphs of these curves for various values of A form trajectories of this system, some of which are shown in Figure 11.2. ∎

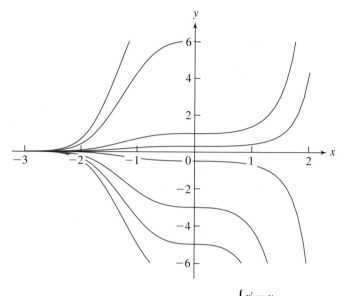

FIGURE 11.2 *Some trajectories of the system* $\begin{cases} x' = y \\ y' = x^2 y^2 \end{cases}$.

EXAMPLE 11.4

For the autonomous system

$$x' = -2y - x\sin(xy),$$
$$y' = 2x + y\sin(xy) \tag{11.5}$$

we have

$$\frac{dy}{dx} = -\frac{2x + y\sin(xy)}{2y + x\sin(xy)}.$$

This is not separable, but we can write

$$(2x + y\sin(xy))dx + (2y + x\sin(xy))dy = 0,$$

which is exact. We find the potential function $H(x, y) = x^2 + y^2 - \cos(xy)$, and the general solution of this differential equation is defined implicitly by

$$H(x, y) = x^2 + y^2 - \cos(xy) = C,$$

in which C is an arbitrary constant. Figure 11.3 shows a phase portrait for this system (11.5), consisting of graphs of these curves for various choices of C. ■

Usually we will not be so fortunate as to be able to solve $dy/dx = g(x, y)/f(x, y)$ in closed form. In such a case we may still be able to use a software package to generate a phase portrait. Figure 11.4 is a phase portrait of the system

$$x' = x\cos(y)$$
$$y' = x^2 - y^3 + \sin(x - y)$$

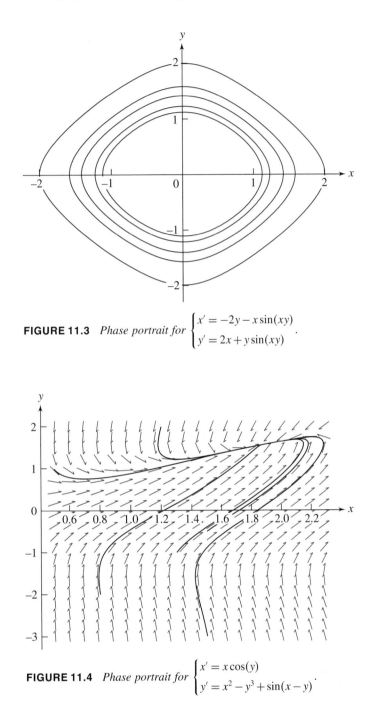

FIGURE 11.3 *Phase portrait for* $\begin{cases} x' = -2y - x\sin(xy) \\ y' = 2x + y\sin(xy) \end{cases}$.

FIGURE 11.4 *Phase portrait for* $\begin{cases} x' = x\cos(y) \\ y' = x^2 - y^3 + \sin(x - y) \end{cases}$.

generated in this way. Figure 11.5 (p. 410) is a phase portrait for a damped pendulum with $\omega^2 = 10$ and $\gamma = 0.3$, and Figure 11.6 (p. 410) is a phase portrait for a nonlinear spring system with $\alpha = 0.2$, $k/m = 4$ and $c/m = 2$. We will consider phase portraits for the damped pendulum and nonlinear spring system in more detail when we treat almost linear systems.

If $x = \varphi(t)$, $y = \psi(t)$ is a solution of (11.4), and c is a constant, we call the pair $\varphi(t + c)$, $\psi(t + c)$ a *translation* of φ and ψ. We will use the following fact.

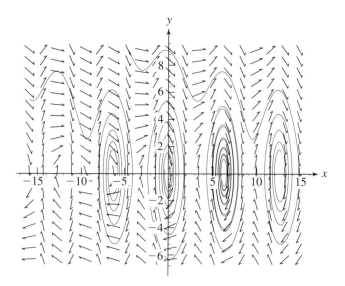

FIGURE 11.5   *Phase portrait for a damped pendulum.*

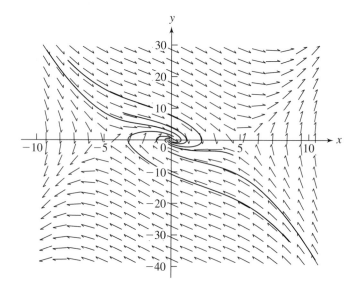

FIGURE 11.6   *Phase portrait for a nonlinear spring.*

LEMMA 11.1

A translation of a solution of the system (11.4) is also a solution of this system.

Proof   Suppose $x = \varphi(t)$, $y = \psi(t)$ is a solution. This means that

$$x'(t) = \varphi'(t) = f(\varphi(t), \psi(t)) \text{ and } y'(t) = \psi'(t) = g(\varphi(t), \psi(t)).$$

Let

$$\widetilde{x}(t) = \varphi(t + c) \text{ and } \widetilde{y}(t) = \psi(t + c)$$

for some constant c. By the chain rule,

$$\frac{d\tilde{x}}{dt} = \frac{d\varphi(t+c)}{d(t+c)} \frac{d(t+c)}{dt} = \varphi'(t+c)$$

$$= f(\varphi(t+c), \psi(t+c)) = f(\tilde{x}(t), \tilde{y}(t))$$

and, similarly,

$$\frac{d\tilde{y}}{dt} = \psi'(t+c) = g(\varphi(t+c), \psi(t+c)) = g(\tilde{x}(t), \tilde{y}(t)).$$

Therefore $x = \tilde{x}(t)$, $y = \tilde{y}(t)$ is also a solution. ∎

We may think of a translation as a reparamatrization of the trajectory, which of course does not alter the fact that it is a trajectory. If we think of the point $(\varphi(t), \psi(t))$ as moving along the orbit, a translation simply means rescheduling the point to change the times at which it passes through given points of the orbit.

We will need the following facts about trajectories.

THEOREM 11.2

Let F and G be continuous, with continuous first partial derivatives, in the (x, y) plane. Then,

1. If (a, b) is a point in the plane, there is a trajectory through (a, b)
2. Two trajectories passing through the same point must be translations of each other.

Proof Conclusion (1) follows immediately from Theorem 11.1, since the initial value problem

$$x' = f(x, y), y' = g(x, y); \quad x(0) = a, y(0) = b$$

has a solution, and the graph of this solution is a trajectory through (a, b).

For (2), suppose $x = \varphi_1(t)$, $y = \psi_1(t)$ and $x = \varphi_2(t)$, $y = \psi_2(t)$ are trajectories of the system (11.4). Suppose both trajectories pass through (a, b). Then for some t_0,

$$\varphi_1(t_0) = a \text{ and } \psi_1(t_0) = b$$

and for some t_1,

$$\varphi_2(t_1) = a \text{ and } \psi_2(t_1) = b.$$

Let $c = t_0 - t_1$ and define $\tilde{x}(t) = \varphi_1(t+c)$ and $\tilde{y}(t) = \psi_1(t+c)$. Then $x = \tilde{x}(t)$, $y = \tilde{y}(t)$ is a trajectory, by Lemma 11.1. Further,

$$\tilde{x}(t_1) = \varphi_1(t_0) = a \text{ and } \tilde{y}(t_1) = \psi(t_0) = b.$$

Therefore $x = \tilde{x}(t)$, $y = \tilde{y}(t)$ is the unique solution of the initial value problem

$$x' = f(x, y), y' = g(x, y); \quad x(t_1) = a, y(t_1) = b.$$

But $x = \varphi_2(t)$, $y = \psi_2(t)$ is also the solution of this problem. Therefore, for all t,

$$\varphi_2(t) = \tilde{x}(t) = \varphi_1(t+c) \text{ and } \psi_2(t) = \tilde{y}(t) = \psi_1(t+c).$$

This proves that the two trajectories $x = \varphi_1(t)$, $y = \psi_1(t)$ and $x = \varphi_2(t)$, $y = \psi_2(t)$ are translations of each other. ∎

If we think of translations of trajectories as the same trajectory (just a change in the parameter), then conclusion (2) states that distinct trajectories cannot cross each other. This would violate uniqueness of the solution of the system that passes through the point of intersection. Conclusion (2) of Theorem 11.2 does not hold for systems that are not autonomous.

EXAMPLE 11.5

Consider the system

$$x'(t) = \frac{1}{t}x = f(t, x, y)$$

$$y'(t) = -\frac{1}{t}y + x = g(t, x, y).$$

This is nonautonomous, since f and g have explicit t-dependencies. We can solve this system. The first equation is separable. Write

$$\frac{1}{x}dx = \frac{1}{t}dt$$

to obtain $x(t) = ct$. Substitute this into the second equation to get

$$y' + \frac{1}{t}y = ct,$$

a linear first-order differential eqaution. This equation can be written

$$ty' + y = ct^2,$$

or

$$(ty)' = ct^2.$$

Integrate to get

$$ty = \frac{c}{3}t^3 + d.$$

Hence

$$y(t) = \frac{c}{3}t^2 + d\frac{1}{t}.$$

Now observe that conclusion (2) of Theorem 11.2 fails for this system. For example, for any number t_0, the trajectory

$$x(t) = \frac{1}{t_0}t, \, y(t) = \frac{1}{3t_0}t^2 - \frac{t_0^2}{3}\frac{1}{t}.$$

passes through $(1, 0)$ at time t_0. Because t_0 is arbitrary, this gives many trajectories passing through $(1, 0)$ at different times, and these trajectories are not translations of each other. ∎

We now have the some of the vocabulary and tools needed to analyze 2×2 nonlinear autonomous systems of differential equations. First, however, we will reexamine linear systems, which we know how to solve explicitly. This will serve two purposes. It will give us some experience with phase portraits, as well as insight into significant features that solutions of a system might have. In addition, we will see shortly that some nonlinear systems can be thought of as perturbations of linear systems (that is, as linear systems with "small" nonlinear terms added). In such a case, knowledge of solutions of the linear system yields important information about solutions of the nonlinear system.

SECTION 11.2   PROBLEMS

In each of Problems 1 through 6, find the general solution of the system and draw a phase portrait containing at least six trajectories of the system.

1. $x' = 4x + y, y' = -17x - 4y$

2. $x' = 2x, y' = 8x + 2y$

3. $x' = 4x - 7y, y' = 2x - 5y$

4. $x' = 3x - 2y, y' = 10x - 5y$

5. $x' = 5x - 2y, y' = 4y$

6. $x' = -4x - 6y, y' = 2x - 11y$

In each of Problems 7 through 12, use the method of Examples 11.3 and 11.4 to draw some integral curves (at least six) for the system.

7. $x' = 9y, y' = -4x$

8. $x' = 2xy, y' = y^2 - x^2$

9. $x' = y + 2, y' = x - 1$

10. $x' = \csc(x), y' = y$

11. $x' = x, y' = x + y$

12. $x' = x^2, y' = y$

13. How would phase portraits for the following systems compare with each other?

    (a) $x' = F(x, y), y' = G(x, y)$

    (b) $x' = -F(x, y), y' = -G(x, y)$

11.3   Phase Portraits of Linear Systems

In preparation for studying the nonlinear autonomous system (11.4), we will thoroughly analyze the linear system

$$\mathbf{X}' = \mathbf{AX}, \tag{11.6}$$

in which $\mathbf{A}$ is a 2×2 real matrix and $\mathbf{X} = \begin{pmatrix} x \\ y \end{pmatrix}$. We assume that $\mathbf{A}$ is nonsingular, so the equation $\mathbf{AX} = \mathbf{O}$ has only the trivial solution.

For the linear system $\mathbf{X}' = \mathbf{AX}$, we actually have the solutions in hand. We will examine these solutions to prepare for the analysis of nonlinear systems, for which we are unlikely to have explicit solutions.

The origin $(0, 0)$ stands apart from other points in the plane in the following respect. The trajectory through the origin is the solution of:

$$\mathbf{X}' = \mathbf{AX}; \quad \mathbf{X}(0) = \mathbf{O} = \begin{pmatrix} 0 \\ 0 \end{pmatrix}$$

and this is the constant trajectory

$$x(t) = 0, y(t) = 0 \text{ for all } t.$$

The graph of this trajectory is the single point $(0, 0)$. For this reason, the origin is called an *equilibrium point* of the system, and the constant solution $\mathbf{X} = \mathbf{O}$ is called an *equilibrium solution*. The origin is also called a *critical point* of $\mathbf{X}' = \mathbf{AX}$. By Theorem 11.1, no other trajectory can pass through this point. As we proceed, observe how the behavior of trajectories of $\mathbf{X}' = \mathbf{AX}$ near this critical point is the key to understanding the behavior of trajectories throughout the entire plane. The critical point, then, will be the focal point in drawing a phase portrait of the system and analyzing the behavior of solutions.

We will draw the phase portrait for $\mathbf{X}' = \mathbf{AX}$ in all cases that can occur. Because the general solution of (11.6) is completely determined by the eigenvalues of $\mathbf{A}$, we will use these eigenvalues to distinguish cases.

Case 1—Real, distinct eigenvalues λ and μ of the same sign.

Let associated eigenvectors be, respectively, $\mathbf{E}_1$ and $\mathbf{E}_2$. Since λ and μ are distinct, $\mathbf{E}_1$ and $\mathbf{E}_2$ are linearly independent. The general solution is

$$\mathbf{X}(t) = \left(\begin{array}{c} x(t) \\ y(t) \end{array} \right) = c_1 \mathbf{E}_1 e^{\lambda t} + c_2 \mathbf{E}_2 e^{\mu t}.$$

Since $\mathbf{E}_1$ and $\mathbf{E}_2$ are vectors in the plane, we can represent them as arrows from the origin, as in Figure 11.7. Draw half-lines L_1 and L_2 from the origin along these eigenvectors, respectively, as shown. These half-lines lines are parts of trajectories, and so do not pass through the origin, which is itself a trajectory.

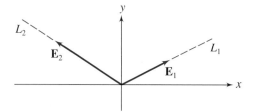

FIGURE 11.7 *Eigenvectors $\mathbf{E}_1$ and $\mathbf{E}_2$ of*
$\mathbf{X}' = \mathbf{AX}$, *for distinct eigenvalues of $\mathbf{A}$.*

Now consider subcases.

Case 1-(a)—The eigenvalues are negative, say $\lambda < \mu < 0$.

Since $e^{\lambda t} \to 0$ and $e^{\mu t} \to 0$ as $t \to \infty$, then $X(t) \to (0,0)$ and every trajectory approaches the origin as $t \to \infty$. However, this can happen in three ways, depending on an initial point $P_0 : (x_0, y_0)$ we choose for a trajectory to pass through at time $t = 0$. Here are the three possibilities.

If P_0 is on L_1, then $c_2 = 0$ and

$$\mathbf{X}(t) = c_1 \mathbf{E}_1 e^{\lambda t},$$

which for any t is a scalar multiple of $\mathbf{E}_1$. The trajectory through P_0 is the half-line from the origin along L_1 through P_0, and the arrows toward the origin indicate that points on this trajectory approach the origin along L_1 as t increases. This is the trajectory T_1 of Figure 11.8.

If P_0 is on L_2, then $c_1 = 0$ and now

$$\mathbf{X}(t) = c_2 \mathbf{E}_2 e^{\mu t}.$$

This trajectory is a half-line from the origin along L_2 through P_0. Again, the arrows indicate that points on this trajectory also approach the origin along L_2 as $t \to \infty$. This is the trajectory T_2 of Figure 11.8.

If P_0 is on neither L_1 or L_2, then the trajectory is a curve through P_0 having the parametric form

$$\mathbf{X}(t) = c_1 \mathbf{E}_1 e^{\lambda t} + c_2 \mathbf{E}_2 e^{\mu t}.$$

Write this as

$$\mathbf{X}(t) = e^{\mu t} \left[c_1 \mathbf{E}_1 e^{(\lambda - \mu)t} + c_2 \mathbf{E}_2 \right].$$

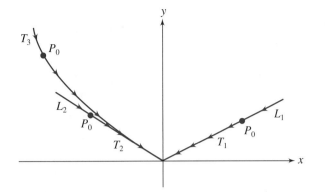

FIGURE 11.8 *Trajectories along* $\mathbf{E}_1$, *along* $\mathbf{E}_2$, *or asymptotic to* $\mathbf{E}_2$ *in the case* $\lambda < \mu < 0$.

Because $\lambda - \mu < 0$, $e^{(\lambda - \mu)t} \to 0$ as $t \to \infty$ and the term $c_1 \mathbf{E}_1 e^{(\lambda - \mu)t}$ exerts increasingly less influence on $\mathbf{X}(t)$. In this case, $\mathbf{X}(t)$ still approaches the origin, but also approaches the line L_2, as $t \to \infty$. A typical such trajectory is shown as the curve T_3 of Figure 11.8.

A phase portrait of $\mathbf{X}' = \mathbf{AX}$ in this case therefore has some trajectories approaching the origin along the lines through the eigenvectors of $\mathbf{A}$ and all others approaching the origin along curves that approach one of these lines asymptotically. In this case the origin is called a *nodal sink* of the system $\mathbf{X}' = \mathbf{AX}$. We can think of particles flowing along the trajectories and toward the origin.

The following example and phase portrait are typical of nodal sinks.

EXAMPLE 11.6

Consider the system $\mathbf{X}' = \mathbf{AX}$, in which

$$\mathbf{A} = \begin{pmatrix} -6 & -2 \\ 5 & 1 \end{pmatrix}.$$

$\mathbf{A}$ has engenvalues and corresponding eigenvectors

$$-1, \begin{pmatrix} 2 \\ -5 \end{pmatrix} \text{ and } -4, \begin{pmatrix} -1 \\ 1 \end{pmatrix}.$$

In the notation of the discussion, $\lambda = -4$ and $\mu = -1$. The general solution is

$$\mathbf{X}(t) = c_1 \begin{pmatrix} -1 \\ 1 \end{pmatrix} e^{-4t} + c_2 \begin{pmatrix} 2 \\ -5 \end{pmatrix} e^{-t}.$$

L_1 is the line through $(-1, 1)$, and L_2 the line through $(2, -5)$. Figure 11.9 shows a phase portrait for this system, with the origin a nodal sink. ∎

Case 1-(b)—The eigenvalues are positive, say $0 < \mu < \lambda$.
The discussion of Case 1-(a) can be replicated with one change. Now $e^{\lambda t}$ and $e^{\mu t}$ approach ∞ instead of zero as t increases. The phase portrait is like that of the previous case, except all the arrows are reversed and trajectories flow away from the origin instead of into the origin as time increases. As we might expect, now the origin is called a **nodal source**. Particles are flowing away from the origin.

Here is a typical example of a nodal source.

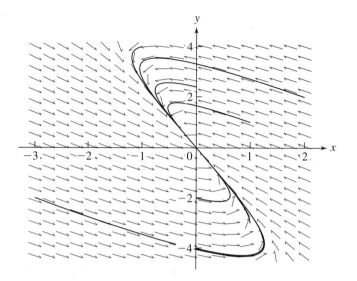

FIGURE 11.9 *Phase portrait showing a nodal sink*

$$of \begin{cases} x' = -6x - 2y \\ y' = 5x + y \end{cases}.$$

EXAMPLE 11.7

Consider the system

$$\mathbf{X}' = \begin{pmatrix} 3 & 3 \\ 1 & 5 \end{pmatrix}.$$

This has eigenvalues and eigenvectors

$$2, \begin{pmatrix} -3 \\ 1 \end{pmatrix} \text{ and } 6, \begin{pmatrix} 1 \\ 1 \end{pmatrix}.$$

Now $\lambda = 6$ and $\mu = 2$, and the general solution is

$$\mathbf{X}(t) = c_1 \begin{pmatrix} -3 \\ 1 \end{pmatrix} e^{2t} + c_2 \begin{pmatrix} 1 \\ 1 \end{pmatrix} e^{6t}.$$

Figure 11.10 shows a phase portrait for this system, exhibiting the behavior expected for a nodal source at the origin. ▪

Case 2—Real, distinct eigenvalues of opposite sign.

Suppose the eigenvalues are λ and μ with $\mu < 0 < \lambda$. The general solution still has the appearance

$$\mathbf{X}(t) = c_1 \mathbf{E}_1 e^{\lambda t} + c_2 \mathbf{E}_2 e^{\mu t},$$

and we start to draw a phase portrait by again drawing half-lines L_1 and L_2 from the origin along the eigenvectors.

If P_0 is on L_1, then $c_2 = 0$ and $\mathbf{X}(t)$ moves on this half-line away from the origin as t increases, because $\lambda > 0$ and $e^{\lambda t} \to \infty$ as $t \to \infty$.

But if P_0 is on L_2, then $c_1 = 0$ and $\mathbf{X}(t)$ moves along this half-line toward the origin, because $\mu < 0$ and $e^{\mu t} \to 0$ as $t \to \infty$.

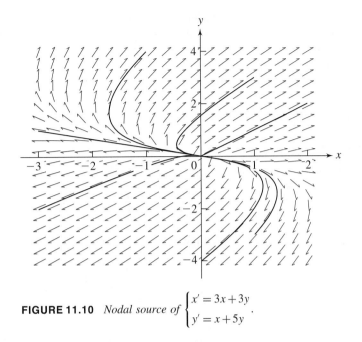

FIGURE 11.10 *Nodal source of* $\begin{cases} x' = 3x + 3y \\ y' = x + 5y \end{cases}$.

The arrows along the half-lines along the eigenvectors therefore have opposite directions, toward the origin along L_2 and away from the origin along L_1. This is in contrast to Case 1, in which solutions starting out on the half-lines through the eigenvectors either both approached the origin or both moved away from the origin as time increased.

If P_0 is on neither L_1 nor L_2, then the trajectory through P_0 does not come arbitrarily close to the origin for any times, but rather approaches the direction determined by the eigenvector $\mathbf{E}_1$ as $t \to \infty$ (in which case $e^{\mu t} \to 0$) or the direction determined by $\mathbf{E}_2$ as $t \to -\infty$ (in which case $e^{\lambda t} \to 0$). The phase portrait therefore has typical trajectories as shown in Figure 11.11. The

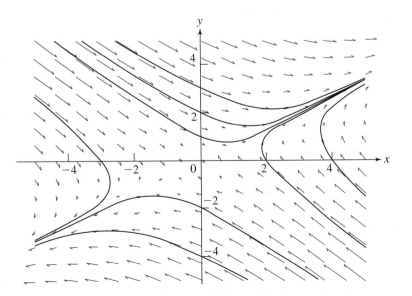

FIGURE 11.11 *Typical phase portrait for a saddle point at the origin.*

lines along the eigenvectors determine four trajectories that separate the plane into four regions. A trajectory starting in one of these regions must remain in it because distinct trajectories cannot cross each other, and such a trajectory is asymptotic to both of the lines bounding its region.

The origin in this case is called a *saddle point*.

EXAMPLE 11.8

Consider $\mathbf{X}' = \mathbf{AX}$ with

$$\mathbf{A} = \begin{pmatrix} -1 & 3 \\ 2 & -2 \end{pmatrix}.$$

Eigenvalues and eigenvectors of $\mathbf{A}$ are

$$-4, \begin{pmatrix} -1 \\ 1 \end{pmatrix} \text{ and } 1, \begin{pmatrix} 3 \\ 2 \end{pmatrix}$$

The general solution is

$$\mathbf{X}(t) = c_1 \begin{pmatrix} -1 \\ 1 \end{pmatrix} e^{-4t} + c_2 \begin{pmatrix} 3 \\ 2 \end{pmatrix} e^{t}$$

and a phase portrait is given in Figure 11.12. In this case of a saddle point at the origin, trajectories do not enter or leave the origin, but asymptotically approach the lines determined by the eigenvectors. ∎

Case 3—Equal eigenvalues.
Suppose $\mathbf{A}$ has the real eigenvalue λ of multiplicity 2. There are two possibilities.

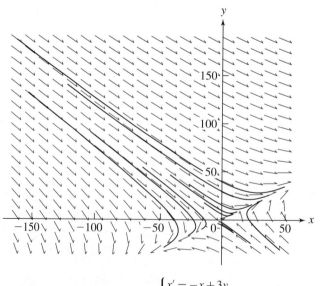

FIGURE 11.12 *Saddle point of* $\begin{cases} x' = -x + 3y \\ y' = 2x - 2y \end{cases}$.

Case 3-(a)—**A** has two linearly independent eigenvectors $\mathbf{E}_1$ and $\mathbf{E}_2$. Now the general solution of $\mathbf{X}' = \mathbf{AX}$ is

$$\mathbf{X}(t) = (c_1\mathbf{E}_1 + c_2\mathbf{E}_2)\,e^{\lambda t}.$$

If

$$\mathbf{E}_1 = \begin{pmatrix} a \\ b \end{pmatrix} \text{ and } \mathbf{E}_2 = \begin{pmatrix} h \\ k \end{pmatrix}$$

then, in terms of components,

$$x(t) = (c_1 a + c_2 h)e^{\lambda t}, \quad y(t) = (c_1 b + c_2 k)e^{\lambda t}.$$

Now

$$\frac{y(t)}{x(t)} = \text{constant}.$$

This means that all trajectories in this case are half-lines from the origin. If $\lambda > 0$, arrows along these trajectories are away from the origin, as in Figure 11.13. If $\lambda < 0$, they move toward the origin, reversing the arrows in Figure 11.13.

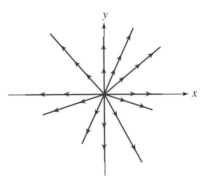

FIGURE 11.13 *Typical proper node with positive eigenvalue of* **A**.

The origin in case 3 - (a) is called a *proper node*.

Case 3-(b)—**A** does not have two linearly independent eigenvectors.
In this case there is an eigenvector $\mathbf{E}$ and the general solution has the form

$$\mathbf{X}(t) = c_1(\mathbf{E}t + \mathbf{W})e^{\lambda t} + c_2\mathbf{E}e^{\lambda t}$$

$$= [(c_1\mathbf{W} + c_2\mathbf{E}) + c_1\mathbf{E}t]\,e^{\lambda t}.$$

To visualize the trajectories, begin with arrows from the origin representing the vectors $\mathbf{W}$ and $\mathbf{E}$. Now, for selected constants c_1 and c_2, draw the vector $c_1\mathbf{W} + c_2\mathbf{E}$, which may have various orientations relative to $\mathbf{W}$ and $\mathbf{E}$, depending on the signs and magnitudes of c_1 and c_2. Some possibilities are displayed in Figure 11.14. For given c_1 and c_2, the vector

$$c_1\mathbf{W} + c_2\mathbf{E} + c_1\mathbf{E}t$$

drawn as an arrow from the origin, sweeps out a straight line L as t varies over all real values. For a given t, $\mathbf{X}(t)$ is the vector $c_1\mathbf{W} + c_2\mathbf{E} + c_1\mathbf{E}t$ from the origin to a point on L, with length adjusted by a factor $e^{\lambda t}$. If λ is negative, then this length goes to zero as $t \to \infty$ and the vector $\mathbf{X}(t)$ sweeps out a curve as shown in Figure 11.15, approaching the origin tangent to $\mathbf{E}$. If

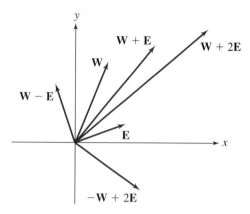

FIGURE 11.14 *Vectors $c_1\mathbf{W} + c_2\mathbf{E}$ in the case of an improper node.*

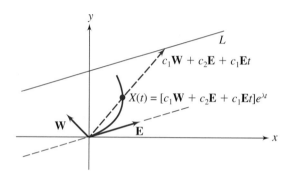

FIGURE 11.15 *Typical trajectory near an improper node.*

$\lambda > 0$, we have the same curve (now $e^{\lambda t} \to 0$ as $t \to -\infty$), except that the arrow indicating direction of the flow on the trajectory is reversed.

The origin in this case is called a *improper node* of the system $\mathbf{X}' = \mathbf{AX}$. The following example has a phase portrait that is typical of improper nodes.

EXAMPLE 11.9

Let

$$\mathbf{A} = \begin{pmatrix} -10 & 6 \\ -6 & 2 \end{pmatrix}.$$

Then $\mathbf{A}$ has eigenvalue -4, and every eigenvector is a real constant multiple of $\mathbf{E} = \begin{pmatrix} 1 \\ 1 \end{pmatrix}$. A routine calculation gives

$$\mathbf{W} = \begin{pmatrix} 1 \\ \frac{7}{6} \end{pmatrix},$$

and the general solution is

$$\mathbf{X}(t) = c_1 \begin{pmatrix} t+1 \\ t+\frac{7}{6} \end{pmatrix} e^{-4t} + c_2 \begin{pmatrix} 1 \\ 1 \end{pmatrix} e^{-4t}.$$

Figure 11.16 is a phase portrait for this system. We can see that the trajectories approach the origin tangent to $\mathbf{E}$ in this case of an improper node at the origin, with negative eigenvalue for $\mathbf{A}$. ▆

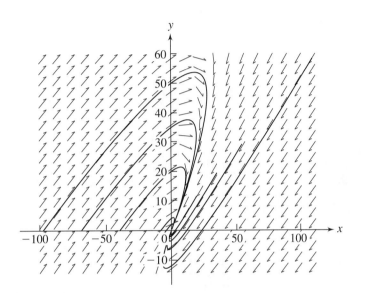

FIGURE 11.16 *Phase portrait for the improper node*

$$of \begin{cases} x' = -10x + 6y \\ y' = -6x + 2y \end{cases} . \quad .$$

Case 4—Complex eigenvalues with nonzero real part.

We know that the complex eigenvalues must be complex conjugates, say $\lambda = \alpha + i\beta$ and $\mu = \alpha - i\beta$. The complex eigenvectors are also conjugates. Write these, respectively, as $\mathbf{U} + i\mathbf{V}$ and $\mathbf{U} - i\mathbf{V}$. Then the general solution of $\mathbf{X}' = \mathbf{AX}$ is

$$\mathbf{X}(t) = c_1 e^{\alpha t}[\mathbf{U}\cos(\beta t) - \mathbf{V}\sin(\beta t)] + c_2 e^{\alpha t}[\mathbf{U}\sin(\beta t) + \mathbf{V}\cos(\beta t)].$$

Suppose first that $\alpha < 0$. The trigonometric terms in this solution cause $\mathbf{X}(t)$ to rotate about the origin as t increases, while the factor $e^{\alpha t}$ causes $\mathbf{X}(t)$ to move closer to the origin (or, equivalently, the length of the vector $\mathbf{X}(t)$ to decrease to zero) as $t \to \infty$. This suggests a trajectory that spirals inward toward the origin as t increases.

Since t varies over the entire real line, taking on both negative and positive values, the trajectories when $\alpha > 0$ have the same spiral appearance, but now the arrows are reversed and $\mathbf{X}(t)$ moves outward, away from the origin, as $t \to \infty$.

The origin in this case is called a *spiral point*. When $\alpha < 0$ the origin is a *spiral sink* because the flow defined by the trajectories is spiralling into the origin. When $\alpha > 0$ the origin is a *spiral source* because now the origin appears to be spewing material outward in a spiral pattern.

The phase portrait in the following example is typical of a spiral source.

EXAMPLE 11.10

Let

$$\mathbf{A} = \begin{pmatrix} -1 & -2 \\ 4 & 3 \end{pmatrix},$$

with eigenvalues $1+2i$ and $1-2i$ and eigenvectors, respectively, $\begin{pmatrix} -1+i \\ 2 \end{pmatrix}$ and $\begin{pmatrix} -1-i \\ 2 \end{pmatrix}$.
Let

$$\mathbf{U} = \begin{pmatrix} -1 \\ 2 \end{pmatrix} \text{ and } \mathbf{V} = \begin{pmatrix} 1 \\ 0 \end{pmatrix}$$

so that the eigenvectors are $\mathbf{U}+i\mathbf{V}$ and $\mathbf{U}-i\mathbf{V}$. The general solution of $\mathbf{X}' = \mathbf{AX}$ is

$$\mathbf{X}(t) = c_1 e^t \left[\begin{pmatrix} -1 \\ 2 \end{pmatrix} \cos(2t) - \begin{pmatrix} 1 \\ 0 \end{pmatrix} \sin(2t) \right]$$

$$+ c_2 e^t \left[\begin{pmatrix} -1 \\ 2 \end{pmatrix} \sin(2t) + \begin{pmatrix} 1 \\ 0 \end{pmatrix} \cos(2t) \right].$$

Figure 11.17 gives a phase portrait for this system, showing trajectories spiraling away from the spiral source at the origin because the real part of the eigenvalues is positive. ■

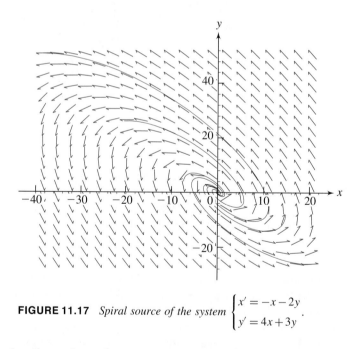

FIGURE 11.17 *Spiral source of the system* $\begin{cases} x' = -x - 2y \\ y' = 4x + 3y \end{cases}$.

Case 5—Pure imaginary eigenvalues.
Now trajectories have the form

$$\mathbf{X}(t) = c_1 \left[\mathbf{U}\cos(\beta t) - \mathbf{V}\sin(\beta t) \right] + c_2 \left[\mathbf{U}\sin(\beta t) + \mathbf{V}\cos(\beta t) \right].$$

Because of the trigonometric terms, this trajectory moves about the origin. Unlike the preceding case, however, there is no exponential factor to decrease or increase distance from the origin as t increases. This trajectory is a closed curve about the origin, representing a periodic solution of the system. The origin in this case is called a *center* of $\mathbf{X}' = \mathbf{AX}$. In general, any closed trajectory of $\mathbf{X}' = \mathbf{AX}$ represents a periodic solution of this system.

EXAMPLE 11.11

Let

$$\mathbf{A} = \begin{pmatrix} 3 & 18 \\ -1 & -3 \end{pmatrix}.$$

$\mathbf{A}$ has eigenvalues $3i$ and $-3i$, with respective eigenvectors, eigenvectors $\begin{pmatrix} -3 - 3i \\ 1 \end{pmatrix}$ and $\begin{pmatrix} -3 + 3i \\ 1 \end{pmatrix}$. A phase portrait is given in Figure 11.18, showing closed trajectories about the center (origin). If we wish, we can write the general solution

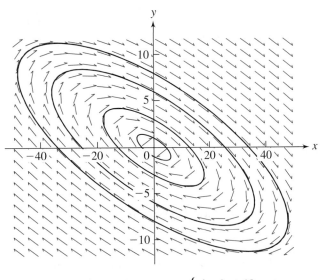

FIGURE 11.18 *Center of the system* $\begin{cases} x' = 3x + 18y \\ y' = -x - 3y \end{cases}$.

$$\mathbf{X}(t) = c_1 \left[\begin{pmatrix} -3 \\ 1 \end{pmatrix} \cos(3t) + \begin{pmatrix} 3 \\ 0 \end{pmatrix} \sin(3t) \right]$$

$$+ c_2 \left[\begin{pmatrix} -3 \\ 1 \end{pmatrix} \sin(3t) + \begin{pmatrix} -3 \\ 0 \end{pmatrix} \cos(3t) \right]. \ \blacksquare$$

We now have a complete description of the behavior of trajectories for the 2×2 constant coefficient system $\mathbf{X}' = \mathbf{AX}$. The general appearance of the phase portrait is completely determined by the eigenvalues of $\mathbf{A}$, and the critical point $(0, 0)$ is the primary point of interest, with the following correspondences:

Real, distinct eigenvalues of the same sign—$(0, 0)$ is a nodal source (Figure 11.10, p. 417) or sink (Figure 11.9, p. 416).

Real, distinct eigenvalues of opposite sign—$(0, 0)$ is a saddle point (Figure 11.12, p. 418).

Equal eigenvalues, two linearly independent eigenvectors—$(0,0)$ is a proper node (Figure 11.13, p. 419).

Equal eigenvalues, all eigenvectors a multiple of a single eigenvector—$(0,0)$ is an improper node (Figure 11.16, p. 421)

Complex eigenvalues with nonzero real part—$(0,0)$ is a spiral point (Figure 11.17, p. 422).

Pure imaginary eigenvalues—$(0,0)$ is a center (Figure 11.18, p. 423).

When we speak of a *classification* of the origin of a linear system, we mean a determination of the origin as a nodal source or sink, saddle point, proper or improper node, spiral point or center.

SECTION 11.3 PROBLEMS

In each of Problems 1 through 10, use the eigenvalues of the matrix of the system to classify the origin of the system. Draw a phase portrait for the system. It is assumed here that software is available to do this, and it is not necessary to solve the system to generate the phase portrait.

1. $x' = 3x - 5y, y' = 5x - 7y$

2. $x' = x + 4y, y' = 3x$

3. $x' = x - 5y, y' = x - y$

4. $x' = 9x - 7y, y' = 6x - 4y$

5. $x' = 7x - 17y, y' = 2x + y$

6. $x' = 2x - 7y, y' = 5x - 10y$

7. $x' = 4x - y, y' = x + 2y$

8. $x' = 3x - 5y, y' = 8x - 3y$

9. $x' = -2x - y, y' = 3x - 2y$

10. $x' = -6x - 7y, y' = 7x - 20y$

11.4 Critical Points and Stability

A complete knowledge of the possible phase portraits of linear 2×2 systems is good preparation for the analysis of nonlinear systems. In this section we will introduce the concept of critical point for a nonlinear system, define stability of critical points, and prepare for the qualitiative analysis of nonlinear systems, in which we attempt to draw conclusions about how solutions will behave, without having explicit solutions in hand.

We will consider the 2×2 autonomous system

$$x'(t) = f(x(t), y(t)),$$
$$y'(t) = g(x(t), y(t)),$$

or, more compactly,

$$x' = f(x, y),$$
$$y' = g(x, y).$$

This is the system (11.4) discussed in Section 11.2. We will assume that f and g are continuous with continuous first partial derivatives in some region D of the $x, y-$ plane. In specific cases D may be the entire plane.

This system can be written in matrix form as

$$\mathbf{X}' = \mathbf{F}(\mathbf{X}),$$

In August of 1999, the Petronas Towers was officially opened. Designed by the American firm of Cesar Pelli and Associates, in collaboration with Kuala Lumpur City Center architects, the graceful towers have an elegant slenderness (height to width) ratio of 9:4. This was made possible by modern materials and building techniques, featuring high-strength concrete that is twice as effective as steel in sway reduction. The towers are supported by 75-foot-by-75-foot concrete cores and an outer ring of super columns. The 88 floors stand 452 meters above street level, and include 65,000 square meters of stainless steel cladding and 77,000 square meters of vision glass. Computations of stability of structures involve the analysis of critical points of systems of nonlinear differential equations.

where

$$\mathbf{X}(t) = \begin{pmatrix} x(t) \\ y(t) \end{pmatrix} \quad \text{and} \quad \mathbf{F}(\mathbf{X}) = \begin{pmatrix} f(x, y) \\ g(x, y) \end{pmatrix}.$$

Taking the lead from the linear system $\mathbf{X}' = \mathbf{A}\mathbf{X}$, we make the following definition.

DEFINITION 11.1   *Critical Point*

A point (x_0, y_0) in D is a critical point (or equilibrium point) of $\mathbf{X}' = \mathbf{F}(\mathbf{X})$ if

$$f(x_0, y_0) = g(x_0, y_0) = 0.$$

We see immediately one significant difference between the linear and nonlinear cases. The linear system $\mathbf{X}' = \mathbf{A}\mathbf{X}$, with $\mathbf{A}$ nonsingular, has exactly one critical point, the origin. A nonlinear system $\mathbf{X}' = \mathbf{F}(\mathbf{X})$ can have any number of critical points. We will, however, only consider systems in which critical points are *isolated*. This means that, about any critical point, there is a circle that contains no other critical point of the system.

EXAMPLE 11.12

Consider the damped pendulum (Example 11.1), whose motion is governed by the system

$$x' = y$$

$$y' = -\omega^2 \sin(x) - \gamma y.$$

Here

$$f(x, y) = y$$

and

$$g(x, y) = -\omega^2 \sin(x) - \gamma y.$$

The critical points are solutions of

$$y = 0$$

and

$$-\omega^2 \sin(x) - \gamma y = 0.$$

These equations are satisfied by all points $(n\pi, 0)$, in which $n = 0, \pm 1, \pm 2, \ldots$. These critical points are isolated. About any point $(n\pi, 0)$, we can draw a circle (for example, of radius $1/4$) that does not contain any other critical point.

For this problem, the critical points split naturally into two classes. Recall that $x = \theta$ is the angle of displacement of the pendulum from the vertical downward position, with the bob at the bottom, and $y = d\theta/dt$. When n is even, then $x = \theta = 2k\pi$ for k any integer. Each critical point $(2k\pi, 0)$ corresponds to the bob pointing straight down, with zero velocity (because $y = x' = \theta' = 0$). When n is odd, then $x = \theta = (2k + 1)\pi$ for k any integer. The critical point $((2k + 1)\pi, 0)$ corresponds to the bob in the vertical upright position, with zero velocity.

Without any mathematical analysis, there is an obvious and striking difference between these two kinds of critical points. At, for example, $x = 0$, the bob hangs straight down from the point of suspension. If we displace it slightly from this position and then release it, the bob will go through some oscillations of decreasing amplitude, after which it will return to its downward position and remain there. This critical point, and all critical points $(2n\pi, 0)$, are what we will call stable. Solutions of the pendulum equation for initial values near this critical point remain close to the constant equilibrium solution for all later times.

By contrast, consider the critical point $(\pi, 0)$. This has the bob initially balanced vertically upward. If the bob is displaced, no matter how slightly, it will swing downward and oscillate back and forth some number of times, but never return to this vertical position. Solutions near this constant equilibrium solution (bob vertically up) do not remain near this position, but move away from it. This critical point, and any critical point $((2k + 1)\pi, 0)$, is unstable. ∎

EXAMPLE 11.13

Consider the damped nonlinear spring of Example 11.2. The system of differential equations governing the motion is

$$x' = y,$$

$$y' = -\frac{k}{m}x + \frac{\alpha}{m}x^3 - \frac{c}{m}y.$$

The critical points are $(0,0)$, $(\sqrt{k/\alpha}, 0)$ and $(-\sqrt{k/\alpha}, 0)$. Recall that x measures the position of the spring, from the equilibrium (rest) position, and $y = dx/dt$ is the velocity of the spring.

We will do a mathematical analysis of this system shortly, but for now look at these critical points from the point of view of our experience with how springs behave. If we displace the spring very slightly from the equilibrium solution $(0,0)$, and then release it, we expect it to undergo some motion back and forth and then come to rest, approaching the equilibrium point. In this sense $(0,0)$ is a stable critical point. However, if we displace the spring slightly from a position very nearly at distance $\sqrt{k/\alpha}$ to the right or left of the equilibrium position and then release it, the spring may or may not return to this position, depending on the relative sizes of the damping constant c and the coefficients in the nonlinear spring force function, particularly α. In this sense these equilibrium points may be stable or may not be. In the next section we will develop the tools for a more definitive analysis of these critical points. ▨

Taking a cue from these examples, we will define a concept of stability of critical points. Recall that

$$\|\mathbf{V}\| = \sqrt{v_1^2 + v_2^2}$$

is the length (or norm) of a vector $\mathbf{V} = (v_1, v_2)$ in the plane. If $\mathbf{W} = (w_1, w_2)$ is also a vector in the plane, then $\|\mathbf{V} - \mathbf{W}\|$ is the length of the vector from $\mathbf{W}$ to $\mathbf{V}$. If $\mathbf{W} = (w_1, w_2)$, then

$$\|\mathbf{V} - \mathbf{W}\| = \left((v_1 - w_1)^2 + (v_2 - w_2)^2\right)^{1/2}$$

is also the distance between the points (v_1, v_2) and (w_1, w_2).

Finally, if $\mathbf{X}_0$ is a given vector, then the locus of points (vectors) $\mathbf{X}$ such that

$$\|\mathbf{X} - \mathbf{X}_0\| < r$$

for any positive r, is the set of points $\mathbf{X}$ within the circle of radius r about $\mathbf{X}_0$. These are exactly the points at distance $< r$ from $\mathbf{X}_0$.

DEFINITION 11.2   *Stability of a Critical Point*

Let $\mathbf{X}_0 = (x_0, y_0)$ be a critical point of $\mathbf{X}' = \mathbf{F}(\mathbf{X})$. Then $\mathbf{X}_0$ is stable if and only if, given any positive number ϵ there exists a positive number δ_ϵ such, if $\mathbf{X} = \Phi(t)$ is a solution of $\mathbf{X}' = \mathbf{F}(\mathbf{X})$ and

$$\|\Phi(0) - \mathbf{X}_0\| < \delta_\epsilon,$$

then $\Phi(t)$ exists for all $t \geq 0$, and

$$\|\Phi(t) - \mathbf{X}_0\| < \epsilon \text{ for all } t \geq 0.$$

We say that $\mathbf{X}_0$ is unstable if this point is not stable.

Keep in mind that the constant solution $\mathbf{X}(t) = \mathbf{X}_0$ is the unique solution through this critical point. That is, the trajectory through a critical point is just this point itself. A critical point $\mathbf{X}_0$ is stable if solutions that are initially (at $t = 0$) close (within δ_ϵ) to $\mathbf{X}_0$, remain close

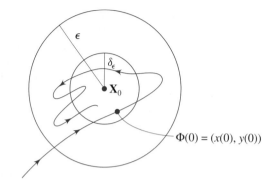

FIGURE 11.19 *Stable critical point of*
$\mathbf{X}' = \mathbf{F}(\mathbf{X})$.

(within ϵ) for all later times. In terms of trajectories, this means that a trajectory that starts out sufficiently close to $\mathbf{X}_0$ at time zero, must remain close to this equilibrium solution at all later times. Figure 11.19 illustrates this idea.

This does not imply that solutions that start near $\mathbf{X}_0$ approach this point as a limit as $t \to \infty$. They may simply remain within a small disk about $\mathbf{X}_0$, without approaching $\mathbf{X}_0$ in a limiting sense. If, however, solutions initially near $\mathbf{X}_0$ also approach $\mathbf{X}_0$ as a limit, then we call $\mathbf{X}_0$ an *asymptotically stable* critical point.

DEFINITION 11.3 *Asymptotically Stable Critical Point*

$\mathbf{X}_0$ is an asymptotically stable critical point of $\mathbf{X}' = \mathbf{F}(\mathbf{X})$ if and only if $\mathbf{X}_0$ is a stable critical point, and there exists a positive number δ such that, if a solution $\mathbf{X} = \Phi(t)$ satisfies $\|\Phi(0) - \mathbf{X}_0\| < \delta$, then $\lim_{t\to\infty} \Phi(t) = \mathbf{X}_0$.

This concept is illustrated in Figure 11.20. Stability does not imply asymptotic stability. It is less obvious that asymptotic stability does not imply stability. A solution might start "close

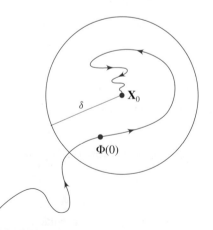

FIGURE 11.20 *Asymptotically stable critical point of* $\mathbf{X}' = \mathbf{F}(\mathbf{X})$.

enough" to the critical point and actually approach the critical point in the limit as $t \to \infty$, but for some arbitrarily large positive times move arbitrarily far from $\mathbf{X}_0$ (before bending back to approach it in the limit).

In the case of the damped pendulum, critical points $(2n\pi, 0)$ are asymptotically stable. If the bob is displaced slightly from the vertical downward position and then released, it will eventually approach this vertical downward position in the limit as $t \to \infty$.

To get some experience with stability and asymptotic stability, and also to prepare for nonlinear systems that are in some sense "nearly" linear, we will review the critical point $(0, 0)$ for the linear system $\mathbf{X}' = \mathbf{AX}$, in the context of stability.

Nodal Source or Sink   This occurs when the eigenvalues of $\mathbf{A}$ are real and distinct, but of the same sign—a nodal sink when they are negative, and a nodal source when they are positive. From the phase portrait in Figure 11.9, p. 416 $(0, 0)$ is stable and asymptotically stable when the eigenvalues are negative (nodal sink), because then all trajectories tend toward the origin as time increases. However, $(0, 0)$ is unstable when the eigenvalues are positive (nodal source), because in this case all trajectories move away from the origin with increasing time (Figure 11.10, p. 417).

Saddle Point   The origin is a saddle point when $\mathbf{A}$ has real eigenvalues of opposite sign. A saddle point is unstable.This is apparent in Figure 11.12, p. 418 in which we can see that trajectories do not remain near the origin as time increases, nor do they approach the origin as a limit.

Proper Node   The origin is a proper node when the eigenvalues of $\mathbf{A}$ are equal and $\mathbf{A}$ has two linearly independent eigenvectors. Figure 11.13, p. 419 shows a typical proper node. When the arrows are toward the origin (negative eigenvalues), this node is stable and asymptotically stable. When the trajectories are oriented away from the origin, this node is not stable.

Improper Node   The origin is an improper node when the eigenvalues of $\mathbf{A}$ are equal and $\mathbf{A}$ does not have two linearly independent eigenvectors. Now the origin is a stable and asymptotically stable critical point if the eigenvalue is negative, and unstable if the eigenvalue is positive. Figure 11.16 shows trajectories near a stable improper node (negative eigenvalue). If the eigenvalue is positive, the trajectories have orientation away from the origin, and then this node is unstable.

Spiral Point   The origin is a spiral point when the eigenvalues are complex conjugates with nonzero real part. When this real part is positive, the origin is a spiral source (trajectories spiral away from the origin, as in Figure 11.17), and in this case the origin is unstable. When this real part is negative, the origin is a stable and asymptotically stable spiral sink (trajectories spiralling into the origin). The phase portrait of such a sink has the same appearance as a spiral source, with arrows on the trajectories reversed.

Center   The origin is a center when the eigenvalues of $\mathbf{A}$ are pure imaginary. A center is stable, but not asymptotically stable (Figure 11.18).

There is a succinct graphical way of summarizing the classifications and stability type of the critical point $(0, 0)$ for the linear system $\mathbf{X}' = \mathbf{AX}$. Let

$$\mathbf{A} = \begin{pmatrix} a & b \\ c & d \end{pmatrix}.$$

The eigenvalues of **A** are solutions of

$$\lambda^2 - (a+d)\lambda + ad - bc = 0.$$

Let $p = -(a+d)$ and $q = ad - bc$ to write this equation as

$$\lambda^2 + p\lambda + q = 0.$$

The eigenvalues of **A** are

$$\frac{-p \pm \sqrt{p^2 - 4q}}{2}.$$

These are real or complex depending on whether $p^2 - 4q \geq 0$ or $p^2 - 4q < 0$. In the p, q plane of Figure 11.21, the boundary between these two cases is the parabola $p^2 = 4q$. Now the p, q plane gives a summary of conclusions as follows:

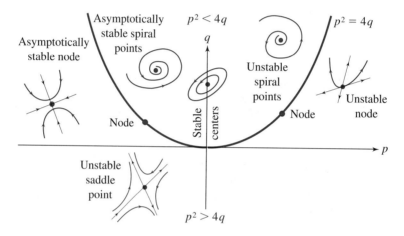

FIGURE 11.21   *Classification of $(0,0)$ for $\mathbf{X}' = \mathbf{AX}$.*

Above this parabola ($p^2 < 4q$) the eigenvalues are complex conjugates with nonzero real parts (spiral point).

On the parabola ($p^2 = 4q$) the eigenvalues are real and equal (proper or improper node).

On the q–axis, the eigenvalues are pure imaginary (center).

Between the p–axis and the parabola, the eigenvalues are real and distinct, with the same sign (nodal source or sink).

Below the p–axis, the eigenvalues are real and have opposite sign (saddle point).

It is interesting to observe how sensitive the classification and stability type of a critical point are to changes in the coefficients of the system. Suppose we begin with a linear system $\mathbf{X}' = \mathbf{AX}$, and then perturb one or more elements of **A** by "small" amounts to form a new system. How (if at all) will this change the classification and stability of the critical point? The classification and stability of $(0,0)$ are completely determined by the eigenvalues, so the issue is really how small changes in the matrix elements affect the eigenvalues. The eigenvalues of **A** are $(-p \pm \sqrt{p^2 - 4q})/2$, which is a continuous function of p and q. Thus small changes in p and q (caused by small changes in a, b, c and d) result in small changes in the eigenvalues. There are two cases in which arbitrarily small changes in **A** will change the nature of the critical point.

(1) If the origin is a center (pure imaginary eigenvalues), then $p = -a - d = 0$. Arbitrarily small changes in a and d can change this, resulting in a new matrix whose eigenvalues have positive or negative real parts. For the new, perturbed system, $(0, 0)$ is no longer a center. This means that centers are sensitive to arbitrarily small changes in **A**.

(2) The other sensitive case is that both eigenvalues are the same, which occurs when $p^2 - 4q = 0$. Again, arbitrarily small changes in **A** can result in this quantity becoming positive or negative, changing the classification of the critical point. However, the stability or instability of $(0, 0)$ is determined by the sign of p, and sufficiently small changes in **A** will leave this sign unchanged. Thus in this case the classification of kind of critical point the system has is more sensitive to change than its stability or instability.

These considerations should be kept in mind when we state Theorem 11.3 in the next section.

With this background on linear systems and the various characteristics of its critical point, we are ready to analyze systems that are in some sense approximated by linear systems.

SECTION 11.4   PROBLEMS

1.–10. For $j = 1, \ldots, 10$ classify the critical point of the system of Problem j of Section 11.3, as to being stable and asymptotically stable, stable and not asymptotically stable, or unstable.

11. Consider the system $\mathbf{X}' = \mathbf{AX}$, where $\mathbf{A} = \begin{pmatrix} 1 & -3 \\ 2 & -1+\epsilon \end{pmatrix}$, with $\epsilon > 0$.

(a) Show that, when $\epsilon = 0$, the critical point is a center, stable but not asymptotically stable. Generate a phase portrait for this system.

(b) Show that, when $\epsilon \neq 0$, the critical point is not a center, no matter how small ϵ is chosen. Generate a phase portrait for this system with $\epsilon = \dfrac{1}{10}$.

This problem illustrates the sensitivity of trajectories of the system to small changes in the coefficients, in the case of pure imaginary eigenvalues.

12. Consider the system $\mathbf{X}' = \mathbf{AX}$, where $\mathbf{A} = \begin{pmatrix} 2+\epsilon & 5 \\ -5 & -8 \end{pmatrix}$ and $\epsilon > 0$.

(a) Show that, when $\epsilon = 0$, **A** has equal eigenvalues and does not have two linearly independent eigenvectors. Classify the type of critical point at the origin and its stability characteristics. Generate a phase portrait for this system.

(b) Show that, if ϵ is not zero (but can be arbitrarily small in magnitude), then **A** has real and distinct eigenvalues. Classify the type of critical point at the origin in this case, as well as its stability characteristics. Generate a phase portrait for the case $\epsilon = \dfrac{1}{10}$.

This problem illustrates the sensitivity of trajectories to small changes in the coefficients, in the case of equal eigenvalues.

11.5   Almost Linear Systems

Suppose $\mathbf{X}' = \mathbf{F}(\mathbf{X})$ is a nonlinear system. We want to define a sense in which this system may be thought of as "almost linear."

Suppose the system has the special form

$$\mathbf{X}' = \mathbf{AX} + \mathbf{G}(\mathbf{X}). \tag{11.7}$$

This is a linear system $\mathbf{X}' = \mathbf{AX}$, with another term, $\mathbf{G}(\mathbf{X}) = \begin{pmatrix} p(x, y) \\ q(x, y) \end{pmatrix}$ added. Any nonlinearity of the system (11.7) is in $\mathbf{G}(\mathbf{X})$. We refer to the system $\mathbf{X}' = \mathbf{AX}$ as the *linear part* of the system (11.7).

Assume that

$$p(0,0) = q(0,0) = 0$$

so the system (11.7) has a critical point at the origin. The idea we want to pursue is that if the nonlinear term is "small enough", then the behavior of solutions of the linear system $\mathbf{X}' = \mathbf{AX}$ near the origin may give us information about the behavior of solutions of the original, nonlinear system near this critical point. The question is: how small is "small enough?"

We will assume in this discussion that $\mathbf{A}$ is a nonsingular, 2×2 matrix of real numbers, and that p and q are continuous at least within some disk about the origin. In the following definition, we refer to partial derivatives of $\mathbf{G}$, by which we mean

$$\mathbf{G}_x = \frac{\partial \mathbf{G}}{\partial x} = \begin{pmatrix} p_x \\ q_x \end{pmatrix} \text{ and } \mathbf{G}_y = \frac{\partial \mathbf{G}}{\partial y} = \begin{pmatrix} p_y \\ q_y \end{pmatrix}.$$

DEFINITION 11.4   *Almost Linear*

The system (11.7) is almost linear in a neighborhood of $(0,0)$ if $\mathbf{G}$ and its first partial derivatives are continuous within some circle about the origin, and

$$\lim_{\mathbf{X} \to \mathbf{0}} \frac{\|\mathbf{G}(\mathbf{X})\|}{\|\mathbf{X}\|} = 0. \tag{11.8}$$

This condition (11.8) means that, as $\mathbf{X}$ is chosen closer to the origin, $\mathbf{G}(\mathbf{X})$ must become small in magnitude faster than $\mathbf{X}$ does. This gives a precise measure of "how small" the nonlinear term must be near the origin for the system (11.7) to qualify as almost linear.

If we write

$$\mathbf{X} = \begin{pmatrix} x \\ y \end{pmatrix}, \mathbf{A} = \begin{pmatrix} a & b \\ c & d \end{pmatrix} \text{ and } \mathbf{G}(\mathbf{X}) = \mathbf{G}(x, y) = \begin{pmatrix} p(x, y) \\ q(x, y) \end{pmatrix},$$

then the system (11.7) is

$$x' = ax + by + p(x, y)$$

$$y' = cx + dy + q(x, y).$$

Condition (11.8) now becomes

$$\lim_{(x,y) \to (0,0)} \frac{p(x, y)}{\sqrt{x^2 + y^2}} = \lim_{(x,y) \to (0,0)} \frac{q(x, y)}{\sqrt{x^2 + y^2}} = 0.$$

These limits, in terms of the components of $\mathbf{G}(\mathbf{X})$, are sometimes easier to deal with than the limit of $\|\mathbf{G}(\mathbf{X})\| / \|\mathbf{X}\|$ as $\mathbf{X}$ approaches the origin, although the two formulations are equivalent.

EXAMPLE 11.14

The system

$$\mathbf{X}' = \begin{pmatrix} 4 & -2 \\ 1 & 6 \end{pmatrix} \mathbf{X} + \begin{pmatrix} -4xy \\ -8x^2y \end{pmatrix}$$

is almost linear. To verify this, compute

$$\lim_{(x,y)\to(0,0)} \frac{-4xy}{\sqrt{x^2+y^2}} \quad \text{and} \quad \lim_{(x,y)\to(0,0)} \frac{-8x^2y}{\sqrt{x^2+y^2}}.$$

There are various ways of showing that these limits are zero, but here is a device worth remembering. Express (x, y) in polar coordinates by putting $x = r\cos(\theta)$ and $y = r\sin(\theta)$. Then

$$\frac{-4xy}{\sqrt{x^2+y^2}} = -\frac{4r^2\cos(\theta)\sin(\theta)}{r} = -4r\cos(\theta)\sin(\theta) \to 0$$

as $r \to 0$, which must occur if $(x, y) \to (0, 0)$. Similarly,

$$\frac{-8x^2y}{\sqrt{x^2+y^2}} = -8\frac{r^3\cos^2(\theta)\sin(\theta)}{r} = -8r^2\cos^2(\theta)\sin(\theta) \to 0$$

as $r \to 0$. ∎

Figure 11.22(a) shows a phase portrait of this system. For comparison, a phase portrait of the linear part $\mathbf{X}' = \mathbf{AX}$ is given in Figure 11.22(b). Notice a qualitative similarity between the phase portraits near the origin. This is the rationale for the definition of almost linear systems. We will now display a correspondence between the type of critical point, and its stability properties, for the almost linear system $\mathbf{X}' = \mathbf{AX} + \mathbf{G}$ and its linear part $\mathbf{X}' = \mathbf{AX}$. The behavior is not always the same. Nevertheless, in some cases which we will identify, properties of the critical point for the linear system carry over to either the same properties for the almost linear system or, if not the same, at least to important information about the nonlinear system.

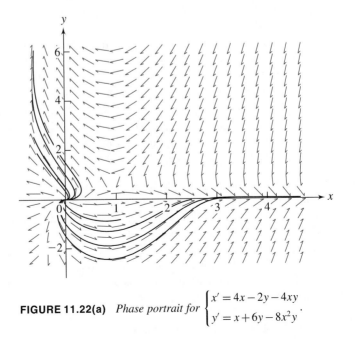

FIGURE 11.22(a) *Phase portrait for* $\begin{cases} x' = 4x - 2y - 4xy \\ y' = x + 6y - 8x^2y \end{cases}$.

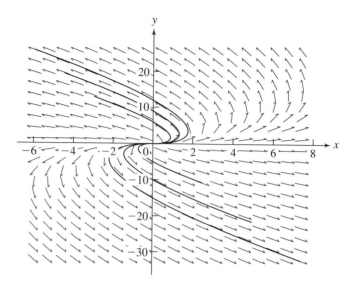

FIGURE 11.22(b)   *Phase portrait for the linear part of the system of Figure 11.22(a).*

THEOREM 11.3

Let λ and μ be the eigenvalues of **A**. Assume that $\mathbf{X}' = \mathbf{AX} + \mathbf{G}$ is almost linear. Then the following conclusions hold for the system $\mathbf{X}' = \mathbf{AX} + \mathbf{G}$.

1. If λ and μ are unequal and negative, then the origin is an asymptotically stable nodal sink of $\mathbf{X}' = \mathbf{AX} + \mathbf{G}$. If these eigenvalues are unequal and positive, then the origin is an unstable nodal source of $\mathbf{X}' = \mathbf{AX} + \mathbf{G}$.

2. If λ and μ are of opposite sign, then the origin is an unstable saddle point of $\mathbf{X}' = \mathbf{AX} + \mathbf{G}$.

3. If λ and μ are complex with negative real part, then the origin is an asymptotically stable spiral point of $\mathbf{X}' = \mathbf{AX} + \mathbf{G}$. If these eigenvalues have positive real part, then the origin is an unstable spiral point.

4. If λ and μ are equal and negative, then the linear system has an asymptotically stable proper or improper node, while the almost linear system has an asymptotically stable node or spiral point. If λ and μ are equal and positive, then the linear system has an unstable proper or improper node, while the almost linear system has an unstable node or spiral point.

5. If λ and μ are pure imaginary (conjugates of each other), then the origin is a center of $\mathbf{X}' = \mathbf{AX}$, but may be a center or spiral point of the almost linear system $\mathbf{X}' = \mathbf{AX} + \mathbf{G}$. Further, in the case of a spiral point of the almost linear system, the critical point may be unstable or asymptotically stable. ∎

The only case in which the linear system fails to provide definitive information of some kind about the almost linear system is that the eigenvalues of **A** are pure imaginary. In this event, the linear system has a stable center, while the almost linear system can have a stable center or a spiral point which may be stable or unstable.

In light of this theorem, when we ask for an analysis of a critical point of an almost linear system, we mean a determination of whether the point is an asymptotically stable nodal sink, an unstable nodal source, an unstable saddle point, an asymptotically stable spiral point or unstable spiral point, or, from (5) of the theorem, either a center or spiral point.

A proof of this theorem requires some delicate analysis that we will avoid. The rest of this section is devoted to examples and phase portraits.

EXAMPLE 11.15

The system

$$\mathbf{X}' = \begin{pmatrix} -1 & -1 \\ -1 & -3 \end{pmatrix} \mathbf{X} + \begin{pmatrix} x^2 y^2 \\ x^3 - y^2 \end{pmatrix}$$

is almost linear and has only one critical point, $(0, 0)$. The eigenvalues of $\mathbf{A}$ are $-2 + \sqrt{2}$ and $-2 - \sqrt{2}$, which are distinct and negative. The origin is an asymptotically stable nodal sink of the linear system $\mathbf{X}' = \mathbf{AX}$, and hence is also a stable and asymptotically stable nodal sink of the almost linear system. Figure 11.23 (a) and (b) shows a phase portrait of the almost linear system and its linear part, respectively. ■

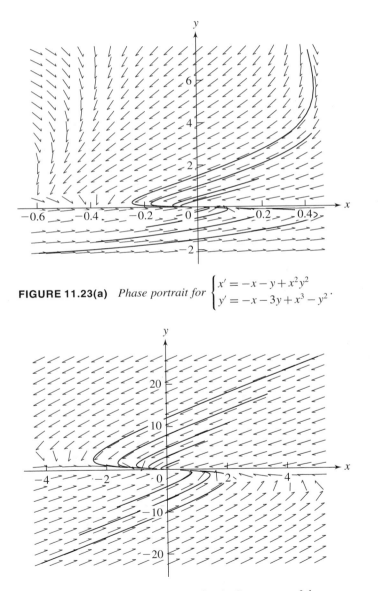

FIGURE 11.23(a) *Phase portrait for* $\begin{cases} x' = -x - y + x^2 y^2 \\ y' = -x - 3y + x^3 - y^2 \end{cases}$.

FIGURE 11.23(b) *Phase portrait for the linear part of the system of Figure 11.23(a).*

EXAMPLE 11.16

The system

$$\mathbf{X}' = \begin{pmatrix} 3 & -4 \\ 6 & 2 \end{pmatrix} \mathbf{X} + \begin{pmatrix} x^2 \cos(y) \\ y^3 \end{pmatrix}$$

is almost linear. The only critical point is $(0,0)$. The eigenvalues of $\mathbf{A}$ are $\frac{5}{2} + \frac{1}{2}i\sqrt{95}$ and $\frac{5}{2} - \frac{1}{2}i\sqrt{95}$. The linear part has an unstable spiral point at the origin. The origin is therefore an unstable spiral point of the almost linear system. Phase portraits for the given nonlinear system and its linear part are shown in Figure 11.24 (a) and (b), respectively. ∎

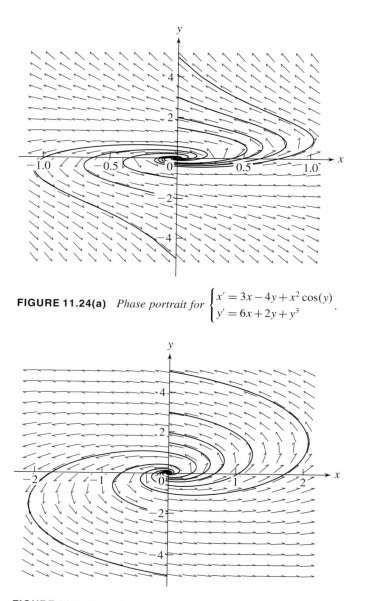

FIGURE 11.24(a) *Phase portrait for* $\begin{cases} x' = 3x - 4y + x^2\cos(y) \\ y' = 6x + 2y + y^3 \end{cases}$.

FIGURE 11.24(b) *Phase portrait for the linear part of the system of Figure 11.24(a).*

EXAMPLE 11.17

The system

$$\mathbf{X}' = \begin{pmatrix} -1 & 2 \\ 2 & 3 \end{pmatrix} \mathbf{X} + \begin{pmatrix} x\sin(y) \\ 8\sin(x) \end{pmatrix}$$

is almost linear, and its only critical point is the origin. The eigenvalues of $\mathbf{A}$ are $1 + 2\sqrt{2}$ and $1 - 2\sqrt{2}$, which are real and of opposite sign. The origin is an unstable saddle point of the linear part, hence also of the given system. Phase portraits of both systems are shown in Figure 11.25 (a) (nonlinear system) and (b) (linear part). ■

EXAMPLE 11.18

The system

$$\mathbf{X}' = \begin{pmatrix} 4 & 11 \\ -2 & -4 \end{pmatrix} \mathbf{X} + \begin{pmatrix} x\sin(y) \\ \sin(y) \end{pmatrix}$$

is almost linear, and its only critical point is $(0,0)$. The eigenvalues of $\mathbf{A}$ are $\sqrt{6}i$ and $-\sqrt{6}i$. The origin is a stable, but not asymptotically stable, center for the linear part. The theorem does not allow us to draw a definitive conclusion about the almost linear system, which might have a center or spiral point at the origin. Figure 11.26 (a) and (b) shows phase portraits for the almost linear system and its linear part, respectively. ■

EXAMPLE 11.19

Consider the system

$$\mathbf{X}' = \begin{pmatrix} \alpha & -1 \\ 1 & -\alpha \end{pmatrix} \mathbf{X} + \begin{pmatrix} hx(x^2 + y^2) \\ ky(x^2 + y^2) \end{pmatrix},$$

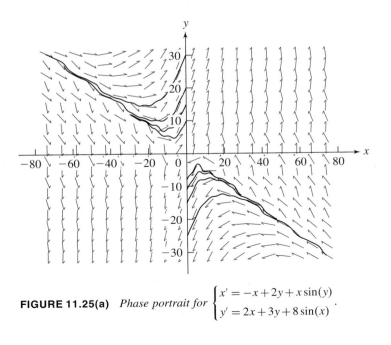

FIGURE 11.25(a) *Phase portrait for* $\begin{cases} x' = -x + 2y + x\sin(y) \\ y' = 2x + 3y + 8\sin(x) \end{cases}$.

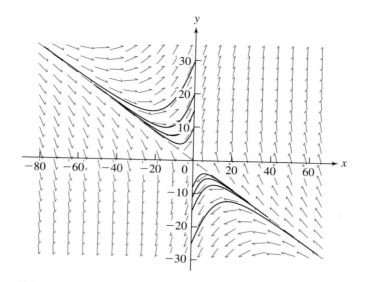

FIGURE 11.25(b) *Phase portrait for the linear part of the system of Figure 11.25(a).*

in which α, h and k are constants. The eigenvalues of the matrix of the linear part are $\sqrt{\alpha^2 - 1}$ and $-\sqrt{\alpha^2 - 1}$. Consider cases.

If $0 < |\alpha| < 1$, then these eigenvalues are pure imaginary. The origin is a center of the linear part but may be a center or spiral point of the almost linear system.

If $|\alpha| > 1$, then the eigenvalues are real and of opposite sign, so the origin is an unstable saddle point of both the linear part and the original almost linear system.

If $\alpha = \pm 1$, then $\mathbf{A}$ is singular and the system is not almost linear.

Figure 11.27 (a) shows a phase portrait for this system with $h = 0.4$, $k = 0.7$ and $\alpha = \frac{1}{3}$. Figure 11.27 (b) has $\alpha = 2$. ■

The next example demonstrates the sensitivity of case (5) of Theorem 11.3.

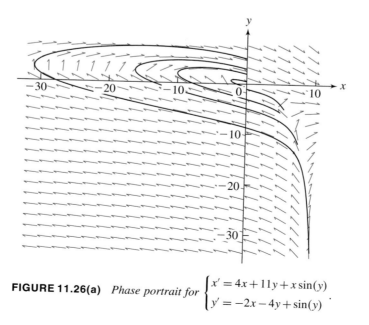

FIGURE 11.26(a) *Phase portrait for* $\begin{cases} x' = 4x + 11y + x\sin(y) \\ y' = -2x - 4y + \sin(y) \end{cases}$.

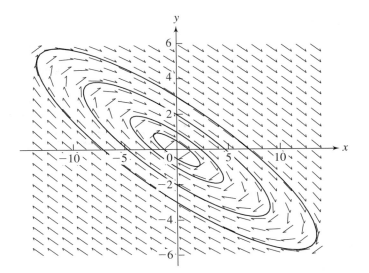

FIGURE 11.26(b) *Phase portrait for the linear part of the system of Figure 11.26(a).*

EXAMPLE 11.20

Let ϵ be a real number and consider the system

$$\mathbf{X}' = \begin{pmatrix} y + \epsilon x(x^2 + y^2) \\ -x + \epsilon y(x^2 + y^2) \end{pmatrix}.$$

We can write this in the form $\mathbf{X}' = \mathbf{AX} + \mathbf{G}$ as

$$\mathbf{X}' = \begin{pmatrix} 0 & 1 \\ -1 & 0 \end{pmatrix} \mathbf{X} + \begin{pmatrix} \epsilon x(x^2 + y^2) \\ \epsilon y(x^2 + y^2) \end{pmatrix}.$$

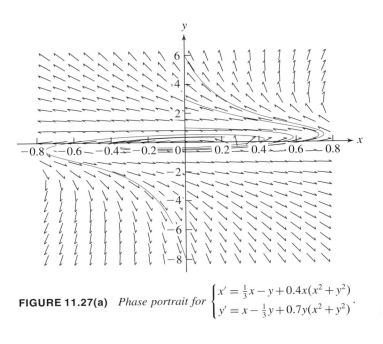

FIGURE 11.27(a) *Phase portrait for* $\begin{cases} x' = \frac{1}{3}x - y + 0.4x(x^2 + y^2) \\ y' = x - \frac{1}{3}y + 0.7y(x^2 + y^2) \end{cases}.$

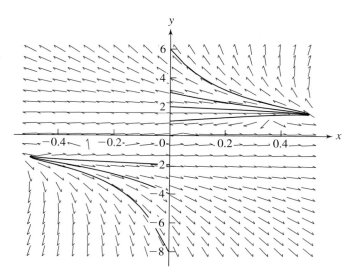

FIGURE 11.27(b)   *Phase portrait for*

$$\begin{cases} x' = 2x - y + 0.4x(x^2 + y^2) \\ y' = x - 2y + 0.7y(x^2 + y^2) \end{cases}.$$

The origin is a critical point of this almost linear system. The eigenvalues of **A** are i and $-i$, so the linear part of this system has a center at the origin. This is the case in which Theorem 11.3 does not give a definitive conclusion for the nonlinear system.

To analyze the nature of this critical point for the nonlinear system, use polar coordinates r and θ. Since

$$r^2 = x^2 + y^2$$

then

$$rr' = xx' + yy'$$
$$= x\left[y + \epsilon x(x^2 + y^2)\right] + y\left[-x + \epsilon y(x^2 + y^2)\right]$$
$$= \epsilon(x^2 + y^2)(x^2 + y^2) = \epsilon r^4.$$

Then

$$\frac{dr}{dt} = \epsilon r^3.$$

This is a separable equation for r, which we solve to get

$$r(t) = \frac{1}{\sqrt{k - 2\epsilon t}},$$

in which k is constant determined by initial conditions (a point the trajectory is to pass through). Now consider cases.

If $\epsilon < 0$, then

$$r(t) = \frac{1}{\sqrt{k + 2|\epsilon| t}} \to 0$$

as $t \to \infty$. In this case the trajectory approaches the origin in the limit as $t \to \infty$, and $(0, 0)$ is asymptotically stable.

However, watch what happens if $\epsilon > 0$. Say $r(0) = \rho$, so the trajectory starts at a point at a positive distance ρ from the origin. Then $k = 1/\rho^2$ and

$$r(t) = \frac{1}{\sqrt{(1/\rho^2) - 2\epsilon t}}.$$

In this case, as t increases from 0 and approaches $1/(2\epsilon\rho^2)$, $r(t) \to \infty$. This means that, at finite times, the trajectory is arbitrarily far away from $(0, 0)$, hence $(0, 0)$ is unstable when ϵ is positive.

A phase portrait for $\epsilon = -0.2$ is given in Figure 11.28 (a), and for $\epsilon = 0.2$ in Figure 11.28 (b). Figure 11.28 (c) gives a phase portrait for the linear part of this system. ■

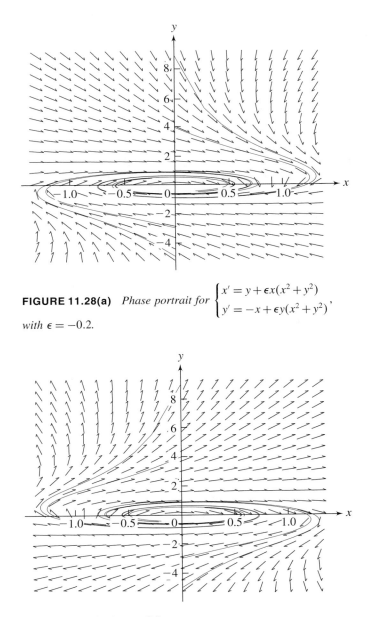

FIGURE 11.28(a) *Phase portrait for* $\begin{cases} x' = y + \epsilon x(x^2 + y^2) \\ y' = -x + \epsilon y(x^2 + y^2) \end{cases}$,

with $\epsilon = -0.2$.

FIGURE 11.28(b) $\epsilon = 0.2$.

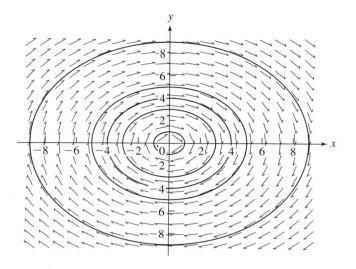

FIGURE 11.28(c)   *The linear part ($\epsilon = 0$).*

Example 11.20 shows how sensitive an almost linear system can be when the eigenvalues of the linear part are pure imaginary. In this example, ϵ can be chosen arbitrarily small. Still, when ϵ is negative, the origin is asymptotically stable, and when ϵ is positive, regardless of magnitude, the origin becomes unstable.

Thus far the discussion has been restricted to nonlinear systems in the special form $\mathbf{X}' = \mathbf{AX} + \mathbf{G}$, with the origin as the critical point. However, in general a nonlinear system comes in the form $\mathbf{X}' = \mathbf{F}(\mathbf{X})$, and there may be critical points other than the origin. We will now show how to translate a critical point (x_0, y_0) to the origin so that $\mathbf{X}' = \mathbf{F}(\mathbf{X})$ translates to a system $\mathbf{X}' = \mathbf{AX} + \mathbf{G}$. This makes the linear part of the translated system transparent. Further, since Theorem 11.3 is set up to deal with critical points at the origin, we can apply it to $\mathbf{X}' = \mathbf{AX} + \mathbf{G}$ whenever this system is almost linear.

Thus suppose (x_0, y_0) is a critical point of $\mathbf{X}' = \mathbf{F}(\mathbf{X})$, where $\mathbf{F} = \begin{pmatrix} f \\ g \end{pmatrix}$. Assume that f and g are continuous with continuous first and second partial derivatives at least within some circle about (x_0, y_0). By Taylor's theorem for functions of two variables, we can write, for (x, y) within some circle about (x_0, y_0) as

$$f(x, y) = f(x_0, y_0) + f_x(x_0, y_0)(x - x_0) + f_y(x_0, y_0)(y - y_0) + \alpha(x, y)$$

and

$$g(x, y) = g(x_0, y_0) + g_x(x_0, y_0)(x - x_0) + g_y(x_0, y_0)(y - y_0) + \beta(x, y),$$

where

$$\lim_{(x,y)\to(x_0,y_0)} \frac{\alpha(x, y)}{\sqrt{(x - x_0)^2 + (y - y_0)^2}} = \lim_{(x,y)\to(x_0,y_0)} \frac{\beta(x, y)}{\sqrt{(x - x_0)^2 + (y - y_0)^2}} = 0. \qquad (11.9)$$

Now (x_0, y_0) is assumed to be a critical point of $\mathbf{X}' = \mathbf{F}(\mathbf{X})$, so $f(x_0, y_0) = g(x_0, y_0) = 0$ and these expansions are

$$f(x, y) = f_x(x_0, y_0)(x - x_0) + f_y(x_0, y_0)(y - y_0) + \alpha(x, y)$$

and

$$g(x, y) = g_x(x_0, y_0)(x - x_0) + g_y(x_0, y_0)(y - y_0) + \beta(x, y).$$

Let

$$\widetilde{\mathbf{X}} = \begin{pmatrix} x - x_0 \\ y - y_0 \end{pmatrix}.$$

Then

$$\frac{d}{dt}\widetilde{\mathbf{X}} = \begin{pmatrix} \frac{d}{dt}(x - x_0) \\ \frac{d}{dt}(y - y_0) \end{pmatrix} = \begin{pmatrix} x' \\ y' \end{pmatrix} = \mathbf{X}' = \mathbf{F}(\mathbf{X})$$

$$= \begin{pmatrix} f(x, y) \\ g(x, , y) \end{pmatrix}$$

$$= \begin{pmatrix} f_x(x_0, y_0) & f_y(x_0, y_0) \\ g_x(x_0, y_0) & g_y(x_0, y_0) \end{pmatrix} \begin{pmatrix} x - x_0 \\ y - y_0 \end{pmatrix} + \begin{pmatrix} \alpha(x, y) \\ \beta(x, y) \end{pmatrix}$$

$$= \mathbf{A}_{(x_0, y_0)}\widetilde{\mathbf{X}} + \mathbf{G}.$$

Because of the condition (11.9), this system is almost linear. Omitting the tilda notation for simplicity, this puts the translated system into the form $\mathbf{X}' = \mathbf{A}_{(x_0, y_0)}\mathbf{X} + \mathbf{G}$, with the critical point (x_0, y_0) of $\mathbf{X}' = \mathbf{F}(\mathbf{X})$ translated to the origin as the critical point of the almost linear system $\mathbf{X}' = \mathbf{A}_{(x_0, y_0)}\mathbf{X} + \mathbf{G}$. Now we can apply the preceding discussion and Theorem 11.3 to the translated system $\mathbf{X}' = \mathbf{A}_{(x_0, y_0)}\mathbf{X} + \mathbf{G}$ at the origin, and hence draw conclusions about behavior of solutions of $\mathbf{X}' = \mathbf{F}(\mathbf{X})$ near (x_0, y_0). We use the notation $\mathbf{A}_{(x_0, y_0)}$ for the matrix of the linear part of the translated system for two reasons. First, it reminds us that this is the translated system (since we dropped the $\widetilde{\mathbf{X}}$ notation). Second, when we are analyzing several critical points of the same system, this notation reminds us which critical point is under consideration, and clearly distinguishes the linear part associated with one critical point from that associated with another.

In carrying out this strategy, it is important to realize that we do not have to explicitly compute $\alpha(x, y)$ or $\beta(x, y)$, which in some cases would be quite tedious, or not even practical. The point is that we know that the translated system $\mathbf{X}' = \mathbf{A}_{(x_0, y_0)}\mathbf{X} + \mathbf{G}$ is almost linear if $\mathbf{F}$ has continuous first and second partial derivatives, a condition that is usually easy to verify.

EXAMPLE 11.21

Consider the system

$$\mathbf{X}' = \mathbf{F}(\mathbf{X}) = \begin{pmatrix} \sin(\pi x) - x^2 + y^2 \\ \cos((x + y + 1)\frac{\pi}{2}). \end{pmatrix}$$

Here $f(x, y) = \sin(\pi x) - x^2 + y^2$ and $g(x, y) = \cos((x + y + 1)\pi/2)$. This is an almost linear system because f and g are continuous with continuous first and second partial derivatives throughout the plane.

For the critical points, solve

$$\sin(\pi x) - x^2 + y^2 = 0,$$

$$\cos((x + y + 1)\frac{\pi}{2}) = 0.$$

Certainly $x = y = n$ is a solution for every integer n. Every point (n, n) in the plane is a critical point. There may be other critical points as well, but other solutions of $f(x, y) = g(x, y) = 0$

are not obvious. We will need the partial derivatives

$$f_x = \pi \cos(\pi x) - 2x, \ f_y = 2y$$

$$g_x = -\frac{\pi}{2} \sin((x+y+1)\frac{\pi}{2}), \ g_y = -\frac{\pi}{2} \sin((x+y+1)\frac{\pi}{2}).$$

Now consider a typical critical point (n, n). We can translate this point to the origin and write the translated system as $\mathbf{X}' = \mathbf{A}_{(n,n)}\mathbf{X} + \mathbf{G}$ with

$$\mathbf{A}_{(n,n)} = \begin{pmatrix} f_x(n, n) & f_y(n, n) \\ g_x(n, n) & g_y(n, n) \end{pmatrix}$$

$$= \begin{pmatrix} \pi \cos(\pi n) - 2n & 2n \\ -\frac{\pi}{2} \sin((2n+1)\frac{\pi}{2}) & -\frac{\pi}{2} \sin((2n+1)\frac{\pi}{2}) \end{pmatrix}$$

$$= \begin{pmatrix} \pi(-1)^n - 2n & 2n \\ (-1)^{n+1}\frac{\pi}{2} & (-1)^{n+1}\frac{\pi}{2} \end{pmatrix}$$

and

$$\mathbf{G}(\mathbf{X}) = \begin{pmatrix} \alpha(x, y) \\ \beta(x, y) \end{pmatrix}.$$

We need not actually compute $\alpha(x, y)$ or $\beta(x, y)$. Because the system is almost linear, the qualitative behavior of trajectories of the nonlinear system near (n, n) is (with exceptions noted in Theorem 11.3) determined by the behavior of trajectories of the linear system $\mathbf{X}' = \mathbf{A}_{(n,n)}\mathbf{X}$. We are therefore led to consider the eigenvalues of $\mathbf{A}_{(n,n)}$, which are

$$\frac{1}{4}\pi(-1)^n - n \pm \frac{1}{4}\sqrt{9\pi^2 - 40n\pi(-1)^n + 16n^2}.$$

We will consider several values for n. For $n = 0$, the eigenvalues are π and $-\pi/2$, so the origin is an unstable saddle point of the linear system and also of the nonlinear system.

For $n = 1$, the eigenvalues of $A_{(1,1)}$ are

$$-\frac{1}{4}\pi - 1 \pm \frac{1}{4}\sqrt{9\pi^2 + 40\pi + 16},$$

which are approximately 2.0101 and -5.5809. Therefore $(1, 1)$ is also an unstable saddle point.

For $n = 2$, the eigenvalues are

$$\frac{1}{4}\pi - 2 \pm \frac{1}{4}\sqrt{9\pi^2 - 80\pi + 64},$$

which are approximately $-1.2146 + 2.4812i$ and $-1.2146 - 2.4812i$. These are complex conjugates with negative real part, so $(2, 2)$ is an asymptotically stable spiral point.

For $n = 3$, the eigenvalues are

$$-\frac{1}{4}\pi - 3 \pm \frac{1}{4}\sqrt{9\pi^2 + 120\pi + 144},$$

which are approximately -9.959 and 2.3882. Thus $(3, 3)$ is an unstable saddle point.

For $n = 4$, the eigenvalues are

$$\frac{1}{4}\pi - 4 \pm \frac{1}{4}\sqrt{9\pi^2 - 160\pi + 256},$$

approximately $-3.2146 + 3.1407i$ and $-3.2146 - 3.1407i$. We conclude that $(4, 4)$ is an asymptotically stable spiral point.

For $n = 5$,

$$-\frac{1}{4}\pi - 5 \pm \frac{1}{4}\sqrt{9\pi^2 + 200\pi + 400},$$

approximately 2.5705 and -14.141, so $(5, 5)$ is an unstable saddle point.

The pattern suggested by the cases $n = 2$ and $n = 4$ is broken with $n = 6$. Now the eigenvalues are

$$\frac{1}{4}\pi - 6 \pm \frac{1}{4}\sqrt{9\pi^2 - 240\pi + 576},$$

approximately $-5.2146 \pm 2.3606i$, so $(6, 6)$ is also an unstable spiral point. With $n = 7$ we get eigenvalues

$$-\frac{1}{4}\pi - 7 \pm \frac{1}{4}\sqrt{9\pi^2 + 280\pi + 784},$$

approximately 2.6802 and -18.251, so $(7, 7)$ is an unstable saddle point. The new pattern that seens to be forming is broken with the next case. If $n = 8$ the eigenvalues are

$$\frac{1}{4}\pi - 8 \pm \frac{1}{4}\sqrt{9\pi^2 - 320\pi + 16(64)},$$

approximately -9.8069 and -4.6223, so $(8, 8)$ is a stable node.

Figures 11.29, 11.30 and 11.31 show phase portraits of this system, focusing on trajectories near selected critical points. The student should experiment with phase portraits near some of the other critical points, for example, those with negative coordinates. ■

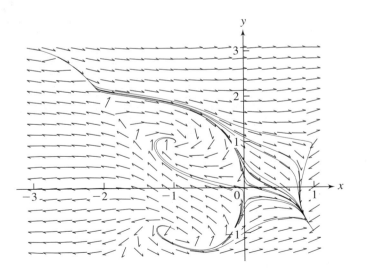

FIGURE 11.29 *Trajectories of the system of Example 11.21 near the origin.*

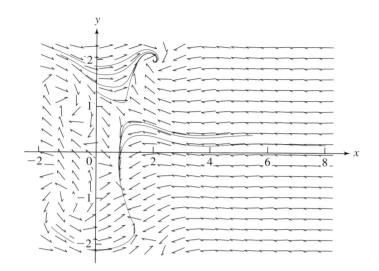

FIGURE 11.30 *Trajectories of the system of Example 11.21 near* $(1, 1)$.

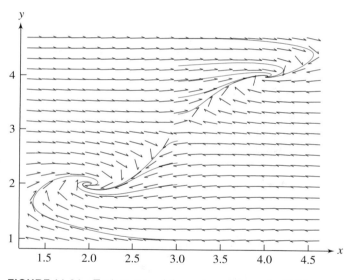

FIGURE 11.31 *Trajectories of the system of Example 11.21 near* $(2, 2)$ *and* $(4, 4)$.

EXAMPLE 11.22   Damped Pendulum

The system for the damped pendulum is

$$x' = y$$
$$y' = -\omega^2 \sin(x) - \gamma y.$$

In matrix form, this system is

$$\mathbf{X}' = \mathbf{F}(\mathbf{X}) = \begin{pmatrix} y \\ -\omega^2 \sin(x) - \gamma y \end{pmatrix}.$$

Here

$$f(x, y) = y \quad \text{and} \quad g(x, y) = -\omega^2 \sin(x) - \gamma y.$$

The partial derivatives are

$$f_x = 0, \quad f_y = 1, \quad g_x = -\omega^2 \cos(x), \quad g_y = -\gamma.$$

We saw in Example 11.12 that the critical points are $(n\pi, 0)$ with n any integer. When n is even, this corresponds to the pendulum bob hanging straight down, and when n is odd, to the bob initially pointing straight up. We will analyze these critical points.

Consider first the critical point $(0, 0)$. The linear part of the system has matrix

$$\mathbf{A}_{(0,0)} = \begin{pmatrix} f_x(0,0) & f_y(0,0) \\ g_x(0,0) & g_y(0,0) \end{pmatrix}$$

$$= \begin{pmatrix} 0 & 1 \\ -\omega^2 & -\gamma \end{pmatrix},$$

with eigenvalues $-\frac{1}{2}\gamma + \frac{1}{2}\sqrt{\gamma^2 - 4\omega^2}$ and $-\frac{1}{2}\gamma - \frac{1}{2}\sqrt{\gamma^2 - 4\omega^2}$. Recall that $\gamma = c/mL$ and $\omega^2 = g/L$. As we might expect, the relative sizes of the damping force, the mass of the bob and the length of the pendulum will determine the nature of the motion.

The following cases occur.

(1) If $\gamma^2 - 4\omega^2 > 0$, then the eigenvalues are real, unequal and negative, so the origin is an asymptotically stable nodal sink. This happens when $c > 2m\sqrt{gL}$. This gives a measure of how large the damping force must be, compared to the mass of the bob and length of the pendulum, to have trajectories spiralling toward the equilibrium solution $(0, 0)$. In this case, after release following a small displacement from the vertical downward position, the bob moves toward this position with decreasing velocity, oscillating back and forth through this position and eventually coming to rest in the limit as $t \to \infty$. Figure 11.32 shows a phase portrait for the pendulum with $\gamma^2 = 0.8$ and $\omega = 0.44$.

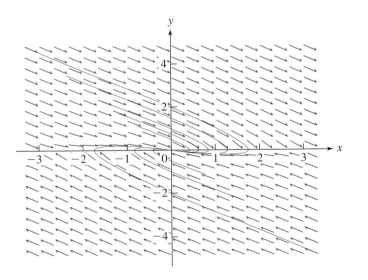

FIGURE 11.32 *Phase portrait for the damped pendulum with* $\gamma^2 = 0.8$ *and* $\omega = 0.44 (\gamma^2 - 4\omega^2 > 0).$

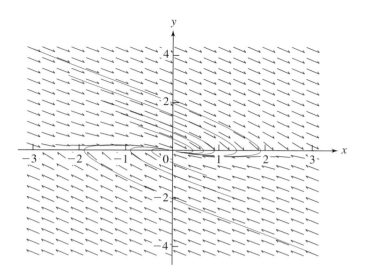

FIGURE 11.33 *Damped pendulum with* $\gamma^2 = 0.8$ *and* $\omega^2 = 0.2(\gamma^2 - 4\omega^2 = 0)$.

(2) If $\gamma^2 - 4\omega^2 = 0$, then the eigenvalues are equal and negative, corresponding to an asymptotically stable proper or improper node of the linear system. This is the case in which Theorem 11.3 does not give a definitive conclusion, and the origin could be an asymptotically stable node or spiral point of the nonlinear pendulum. This case occurs when $c = 2m\sqrt{gL}$, a delicate balance between the damping force, mass, and pendulum length. In the case of an asymptotically stable node, the bob, when released, moves with decreasing velocity toward the vertical equilibrium position, approaching it as $t \to \infty$ but not oscillating through it. Figure 11.33 gives a phase portrait for this case, in which $\gamma^2 = 0.8$ and $\omega^2 = 0.2$.

(3) If $\gamma^2 - 4\omega^2 < 0$, then the eigenvalues are complex conjugates with negative real part. Hence the origin is an asymptotically stable spiral point of both the linear part and the nonlinear pendulum system. This happens when $c < 2m\sqrt{gL}$. Figure 11.34 displays this case, with $\gamma^2 = 0.6$ and $\omega^2 = 0.3$.

It is routine to check that each critical point $(2n\pi, 0)$, in which the first coordinate is an even integer multiple of π, has the same characteristics as the origin.

Now consider critical points $((2n+1)\pi, 0)$, with first coordinate an odd integer multiple of π. To be specific, consider $(\pi, 0)$. Now the linear part of the system (with $(\pi, 0)$ translated to the origin) is

$$\mathbf{A}_{(\pi,0)} = \begin{pmatrix} f_x(\pi, 0) & f_y(\pi, 0) \\ g_x(\pi, 0) & g_y(\pi, 0) \end{pmatrix} = \begin{pmatrix} 0 & 1 \\ -\omega^2\cos(\pi) & -\gamma \end{pmatrix} = \begin{pmatrix} 0 & 1 \\ \omega^2 & -\gamma \end{pmatrix}.$$

The eigenvalues are $-\frac{1}{2}\gamma + \frac{1}{2}\sqrt{\gamma^2 + 4\omega^2}$ and $-\frac{1}{2}\gamma - \frac{1}{2}\sqrt{\gamma^2 + 4\omega^2}$. These are real and of opposite sign, so $(\pi, 0)$ is an unstable saddle point. The other critical points $((2n+1)\pi, 0)$ exhibit the same behavior. This is what we would expect of a pendulum in which the bob is initially in the vertical upward position, since arbitrarily small displacements will result in the bob moving away from this position, and it will never return to it. The analysis is the same for each critical point $((2n+1)\pi, 0)$. ∎

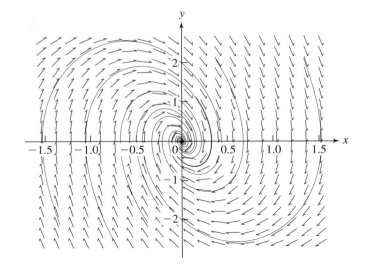

FIGURE 11.34 *Damped pendulum with $\gamma^2 = 0.6$ and $\omega^2 = 0.3(\gamma^2 - 4\omega^2 < 0)$.*

EXAMPLE 11.23 Nonlinear Damped Spring

The nonlinear damped spring equation is

$$x' = y,$$

$$y' = -\frac{k}{m}x + \frac{\alpha}{m}x^3 - \frac{c}{m}y.$$

This is

$$\mathbf{X}' = \mathbf{F}(\mathbf{X}) = \begin{pmatrix} y \\ -(k/m)x + (\alpha/m)x^3 - (c/m)y \end{pmatrix}.$$

Here

$$f(x, y) = y \quad \text{and} \quad g(x, y) = -\frac{k}{m}x + \frac{\alpha}{m}x^3 - \frac{c}{m}y.$$

There are three critical points, $(0, 0)$, $(\sqrt{k/\alpha}, 0)$ and $(-\sqrt{k/\alpha}, 0)$. The partial derivatives are

$$f_x = 0, f_y = 1, g_x = -\frac{k}{m} + 3\frac{\alpha}{m}x^2, g_y = -\frac{c}{m}.$$

First consider the behavior of trajectories near the origin. The linear part of the system has matrix

$$\mathbf{A}_{(0,0)} = \begin{pmatrix} 0 & 1 \\ -k/m & -c/m \end{pmatrix},$$

with eigenvalues $(1/2m)\left(-c+\sqrt{c^2-4mk}\right)$ and $(1/2m)\left(-c-\sqrt{c^2-4mk}\right)$. This yields three cases, depending, as we might expect, on the relative magnitudes of the mass, damping constant and spring constant.

1. If $c^2 - 4mk > 0$, then $\mathbf{A}_{(0,0)}$ has real, distinct, negative eigenvalues, so the origin is an asymptotically stable nodal sink. Small disturbances from the equilibrium position result in a motion that dies out with time, with the mass approaching the equilibrium position.

2. If $c^2 - 4mk = 0$, then $\mathbf{A}_{(0,0)}$ has equal real, negative eigenvalues, so the origin is an asymptotically stable proper or improper node of the linear system. Hence the origin is an asymptotically stable node or spiral point of the nonlinear system.

3. If $c^2 - 4mk < 0$, then $\mathbf{A}_{(0,0)}$ has complex conjugate eigenvalues with negative real part, and the origin is an asymptotically stable spiral point.

Figure 11.35 shows a phase portrait for case (3), with $c = 2$, $k = 5$, $\alpha = 1$ and $m = 3$. Next, consider the critical point $(\sqrt{k/\alpha}, 0)$. Now the linear part of the system obtained by translating this point to the origin is

$$\mathbf{A}_{(\sqrt{k/\alpha},0)} = \begin{pmatrix} 0 & 1 \\ k/m & -c/m \end{pmatrix},$$

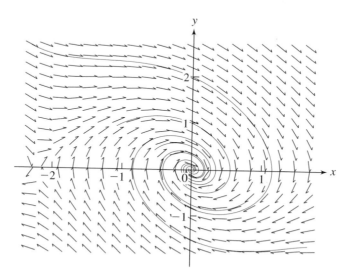

FIGURE 11.35 *Nonlinear spring system with $c = 2$, $k = 5$, $\alpha = 1$, and $m = 3 (c^2 - 4mk < 0)$.*

with eigenvalues $(1/2m)\left(-c+\sqrt{c^2+4mk}\right)$ and $(1/2m)\left(-c-\sqrt{c^2+4mk}\right)$. The first eigenvalue is positive and the second negative, so $(\sqrt{k/\alpha}, 0)$ is an unstable saddle point. A similar analysis holds for the critical point $(-\sqrt{k/\alpha}, 0)$. ∎

In each of Problems 1 through 10, (a) show that the system is almost linear, (b) determine the critical points, (c) use Theorem 11.3 to analyze the nature of the critical point, or state why no conclusion can be drawn, and (d) generate a phase portrait for the system.

1. $x' = x - y + x^2, y' = x + 2y$

2. $x' = x + 3y - x^2 \sin(y), y' = 2x + y - xy^2$

3. $x' = -2x + 2y, y' = x + 4y + y^2$

4. $x' = -2x - 3y - y^2, y' = x + 4y$

5. $x' = 3x + 12y, y' = -x - 3y + x^3$

6. $x' = 2x - 4y + 3xy, y' = x + y + x^2$

7. $x' = -3x - 4y + x^2 - y^2, y' = x + y$

8. $x' = -3x - 4y, y' = -x + y - x^2 y$

9. $x' = -2x - y + y^2, y' = -4x + y$

10. $x' = 2x - y - x^3 \sin(x), y' = -2x + y + xy^2$

11. Theorem 11.3 is inconclusive in the case that the critical point of an almost linear system is a center of the associated linear system. Verify that no conclusion

is possible in this case in general by considering the following two systems:

$$x' = y - x\sqrt{x^2 + y^2}, y' = -x - y\sqrt{x^2 + y^2}$$

and

$$x' = y + x\sqrt{x^2 + y^2}, y' = -x + y\sqrt{x^2 + y^2}.$$

(a) Show that the origin is a center for the associated linear system of both systems.

(b) Show that each system is almost linear.

(c) Introduce polar coordinates, with $x = r\cos(\theta)$ and $y = r\sin(\theta)$ and use the chain rule to obtain

$$x' = \frac{dx}{dr}\frac{dr}{dt} = \cos(\theta)r'(t)$$

and

$$y' = \frac{dy}{dr}\frac{dr}{dt} = \sin(\theta)r'(t).$$

Use these to evaluate $xx' + yy'$ in terms of r and r', where $r' = dr/dt$. Thus convert each system to a system in terms of $r(t)$ and $\theta(t)$.

(d) Use the polar coordinate version of the first system to obtain a separable differential equation for $r(t)$. Conclude from this that $r'(t) < 0$ for all t. Solve for $r(t)$ and show that $r(t) \to 0$ as $t \to \infty$. Thus conclude that for the first system the origin is asymptotically stable.

(e) Follow the procedure of (d), using the second system. However, now find that $r'(t) > 0$ for all t. Solve for $r(t)$ with the initial condition $r(t_0) = r_0$. Show that $r(t) \to \infty$ as $t \to t_0 + 1/r$ from the left. Conclude that the origin is unstable for the second system.

11.6   Lyapunov's Stability Criteria

There is a subtle criterion for stability due to the Russian engineer and mathematician Alexander M. Lyapunov (1857-1918). Suppose $\mathbf{X}' = \mathbf{F}(\mathbf{X})$ is a 2×2 autonomous system of first order differential equations (not necessarily almost linear), and that $(0, 0)$ is an isolated critical point. Lyapunov's insight was this. Suppose there is a function, commonly denoted V, such that closed curves $V(x, y) = c$ enclose the origin. Further, if the constants are chosen smaller, say $0 < k < c$, then the curve $V(x, y) = k$ lies within the region enclosed by the curve $V(x, y) = c$ (Figure 11.36 (a)). So far this has nothing to do with the system of differential equations. However, suppose it also happens that, if a trajectory intersects the curve $V(x, y) = c$ at some time, which we can take to be time zero, then it cannot escape from the region bounded by this curve, but must for all later times remain within this region (Figure 11.36 (b)). This would force trajectories starting out near the origin (meaning within $V(x, y) = c$) to forever lie at least this

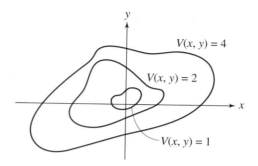

FIGURE 11.36(a) *Closed curves contracting about the origin.*

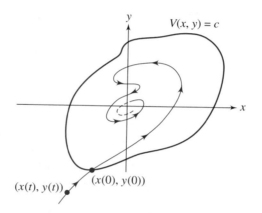

FIGURE 11.36(b) *Trajectories entering shrinking regions about the origin.*

close to the origin. But this would imply, by choosing c successively smaller, that the origin is a stable critical point!

If in addition trajectories starting at a point on $V(x, y) = c$ point into the region bounded by this curve, then we can further conclude that the trajectories are approaching the origin, hence that the origin is asymptotically stable.

This is the intuition behind an approach to determining whether a critical point is stable or asymptotically stable. We will now develop the vocabulary which will allow us to give substance to this approach. First, we will distinguish certain functions that have been found to serve the role of V in this discussion.

If $r > 0$, let N_r consist of all (x, y) within distance r from the origin. Thus, (x, y) is in N_r exactly when

$$x^2 + y^2 < r^2.$$

This set is called the *r-neighborhood* of the origin, or, if we need no explicit reference to r, just a neighborhood of the origin.

DEFINITION 11.5   *Positive Definite, Semidefinite*

Let $V(x, y)$ be defined for all (x, y) in some neighborhood N_r of the origin. Suppose V is continuous with continuous first partial derivatives. Then

1. V is positive definite on N_r if $V(0, 0) = 0$ and $V(x, y) > 0$ for all other points of N_r.
2. V is positive semidefinite on N_r if $V(0, 0) = 0$ and $V(x, y) \geq 0$ for all points of N_r.
3. V is negative definite on N_r if $V(0, 0) = 0$ and $V(x, y) < 0$ for all other points of N_r.
4. V is negative semidefinite on N_r if $V(0, 0) = 0$ and $V(x, y) \leq 0$ for all points of N_r.

For example, $V(x, y) = x^2 + 3xy + 9y^2$ is positive definite on N_r for any positive r, and $-3x^2 + 4xy - 5y^2$ is negative definite on any N_r. The function $(x - y)^4$ is positive semidefinite, being nonnegative but vanishing on the line $y = x$.

The following lemma is useful in producing examples of positive definite and negative definite functions.

LEMMA 11.2

Let $V(x, y) = ax^2 + bxy + cy^2$. Then V is positive definite (on any N_r) if and only if

$$a > 0 \text{ and } 4ac - b^2 > 0.$$

V is negative definite (on any N_r) if and only if

$$a < 0 \text{ and } 4ac - b^2 > 0. \quad \blacksquare$$

Proof   Certainly V is continuous with continuous partial derivatives in the entire x, y plane. Further, $V(0, 0) = 0$, and this is the only point at which $V(x, y)$ vanishes.

Now recall the second derivative test for extrema of a function of two variables. First,

$$V_x(0, 0) = V_y(0, 0) = 0,$$

so the origin is a candidate for a maximum or minimum of V. For a maximum or minimum, we need

$$V_{xx}(0, 0) V_{yy}(0, 0) - V_{xy}(0, 0)^2 > 0.$$

But this condition is the same as

$$(2a)(2c) - b^2 > 0,$$

or

$$4ac - b^2 > 0.$$

Satisfaction of this inequality requires that a and c have the same sign.

When $a > 0$, then $V_{xx}(0,0) > 0$ and the origin is a point where V has a minimum. In this event $V(x, y) > V(0,0) = 0$ for all (x, y) other than $(0, 0)$. Now V is positive definite.

When $a < 0$ then $V_{xx}(0,0) < 0$ and the origin is a point where V has a maximum. Now $V(x, y) < 0$ for all (x, y) other than $(0, 0)$, and V is negative definite. ∎

If $x = x(t)$, $y = y(t)$ defines a trajectory of $\mathbf{X}' = \mathbf{F}(\mathbf{X})$, and V is a differentiable function of two variables, then $V(x(t), y(t))$ is a differentiable function of t along this trajectory. We will denote the derivative of $V(x(t), y(t))$ with respect to t as $\dot{V}(x, y)$, or just $\dot{V}$. By the chain rule,

$$\dot{V}(x, y) = V_x(x(t), y(t))x'(t) + V_y(x(t), y(t))y'(t),$$

or, more succinctly,

$$\dot{V} = V_x x' + V_y y'.$$

This is called the derivative of V along the trajectory, or the *orbital derivative* of V.

The following two theorems show how these ideas about positive and negative definite functions relate to Lyapunov's approach to stable and asymptotically stable critical points. The criteria given in the first theorem constitute *Lyapunov's direct method* for determining the stability or asymptotic stability of a critical point.

THEOREM 11.4   *Lyapunov's Direct Method for Stability*

Let $(0, 0)$ be an isolated critical point of the autonomous 2×2 system $\mathbf{X}' = \mathbf{F}(\mathbf{X})$.

1. If a positive definite function V can be found for some neighborhood N_r of the origin, such that $\dot{V}$ is negative semidefinite on N_r, then the origin is stable.

2. If a positive definite function V can be found for some neighborhood N_r of the origin, such that $\dot{V}$ is negative definite on N_r, then the origin is asymptotically stable. ∎

On the other side of the issue, Lyapunov's second theorem gives a test to determine that a critical point is unstable.

THEOREM 11.5   *Lyapunov's Direct Method for Instability*

Let $(0, 0)$ be an isolated critical point of the autonomous 2×2 system $\mathbf{X}' = \mathbf{F}(\mathbf{X})$. Let V be continuous with continuous first partial derivatives in some neighborhood of the origin, and let $V(0, 0) = 0$.

1. Suppose $R > 0$, and that in every neighborhood N_r, with $0 < r \leq R$, there is a point at which $V(x, y)$ is positive. Suppose $\dot{V}$ is positive definite in N_R. Then $(0, 0)$ is unstable.

2. Suppose $R > 0$, and that in every neighborhood N_r, with $0 < r \leq R$, there is a point at which $V(x, y)$ is negative. Suppose $\dot{V}$ is negative definite in N_R. Then $(0, 0)$ is unstable. ∎

Any function V playing the role cited in these theorems is called a *Lyapunov function*. Theorems 11.4 and 11.5 give no suggestion at all as to how a Lyapunov function might be produced, and in attempting to apply them this is the difficult part. Lemma 11.2 is sometimes useful in providing candidates, but, as might be expected, if the differential equation is complicated the task of finding a Lyapunov function might be insurmountable. In spite of this potential difficulty, Lyapunov's theorems are useful because they do not require solving the system, nor do they require that the system be almost linear.

Adding to the mystique of the theorem is the nonobvious connection between V, $\dot{V}$, and stability characteristics of the critical point. We will give a plausibility argument intended to clarify this connection.

Consider Figure 11.37, which shows a typical curve $V(x, y) = c$ about the origin. Call this curve Γ. Here is how $\dot{V}$ enters the picture. At any point $P : (a, b)$ on this curve, the vector

$$\mathbf{N} = V_x\mathbf{i} + V_y\mathbf{j}$$

is normal (perpendicular) to Γ, by which we mean that it is normal to the tangent to Γ at this point. In addition, consider a trajectory $x = \varphi(t)$, $y = \psi(t)$ passing through P at time $t = 0$, also shown in Figure 11.37. Thus, $\varphi(0) = a$ and $\psi(0) = b$. The vector

$$\mathbf{T} = \varphi'(0)\mathbf{i} + \psi'(0)\mathbf{j}$$

is tangent to this trajectory (not to Γ) at (a, b). Now,

$$\dot{V}(a, b) = V_x(a, b)\varphi'(0) + V_y(a, b)\psi'(0) = \mathbf{N} \cdot \mathbf{T},$$

the dot product of the normal to Γ and the tangent to the trajectory at (a, b). Since the dot product of two vectors is equal to the product of their lengths and the cosine of the angle between them, we obtain

$$\dot{V}(a, b) = \|\mathbf{N}\| \, \|\mathbf{T}\| \cos(\theta),$$

with θ the angle between $\mathbf{T}$ and $\mathbf{N}$.

Now look at conclusions (1) and (2) of the first Lyapunov theorem. If $\dot{V}$ is negative semidefinite, then $\dot{V}(a, b) \leq 0$, so $\cos(\theta) \leq 0$. Then $\pi/2 \leq \theta \leq 3\pi/2$. This means that the trajectory at this point is moving at this point either into the region enclosed by Γ, or perhaps in the same direction as the tangent to Γ. The effect of this is that the trajectory cannot move away from the region enclosed by Γ. The trajectory cannot escape from this region, and so the origin is stable. If $\dot{V}$ is negative definite, then $\cos(\theta) < 0$, so $\pi/2 < \theta < 3\pi/2$ and now the trajectory actually moves into the region enclosed by Γ, and cannot simply trace out a path around the origin. In this case the origin is asymptotically stable.

We leave it for the student to make a similar geometric argument in support of the second Lyapunov theorem.

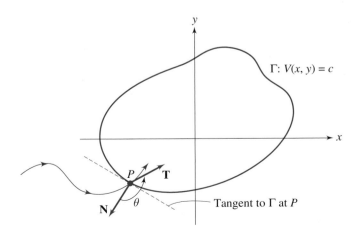

FIGURE 11.37 *Rationale for Lyapunov's direct method.*

EXAMPLE 11.24

Consider the nonlinear system

$$\mathbf{X}' = \begin{pmatrix} -x^3 \\ -4x^2 y \end{pmatrix}.$$

The origin is an isolated critical point. We will attempt to construct a Lyapunov function of the form $V(x, y) = ax^2 + bxy + cy^2$ that will tell us whether the origin is stable or unstable. We may not succeed in this, but it is a good first attempt because at least we know conditions on the coefficients of V to make this function positive definite or negative definite. The key lies in $\dot{V}$, so compute

$$\dot{V} = V_x x' + V_y y'$$
$$= (2ax + by)(-x^3) + (bx + 2cy)(-4x^2 y)$$
$$= -2ax^4 - bx^3 y - 4bx^3 y - 8cx^2 y^2.$$

Now observe that the $-2ax^4$ and $-8cx^2 y^2$ terms will be nonpositive if a and c are positive. The $x^3 y$ term will vary in sign, but we can make $bx^3 y$ vanish by choosing $b = 0$. We can choose a and c as any positive numbers, say $a = c = 1$. Then

$$V(x, y) = x^2 + y^2$$

is positive definite in any neighborhood of the origin , and

$$\dot{V} = -2x^4 - 8x^2 y^2$$

is negative semidefinite in any neighborhood of the origin. By Lyapunov's direct method (Theorem 11.4), the origin is stable. A phase portrait for this system is shown in Figure 11.38. ∎

We can draw no conclusion about asymptotic stability of the origin in the last example. If we had been able to find a Lyapunov function V so that $\dot{V}$ was negative definite (instead of

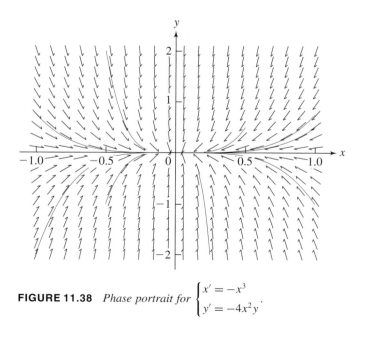

FIGURE 11.38 *Phase portrait for* $\begin{cases} x' = -x^3 \\ y' = -4x^2 y \end{cases}$.

negative semidefinite), then we could have concluded that the origin was asymptotically stable. But we cannot be sure, from the work done, whether there is no such function, or whether we simply did not find one.

EXAMPLE 11.25

It is instructive to consider Lyapunov's theorems as they relate to a simple physical problem, the undamped pendulum (put $c = 0$). The system is

$$x' = y,$$

$$y = -\frac{g}{L}\sin(x).$$

Recall that $x = \theta$, the displacement angle of the bob from the downward vertical rest position.

We have already characterized the critical points of this problem (with damping). However, this example makes an important point. In problems that are drawn from a physical setting, the total energy of the system can often serve as a Lyapunov function. This is a useful observation, since the search for a Lyapunov function constitutes the primary issue in attempting to apply Lyapunov's theorems.

Thus compute the total energy V of the pendulum. The kinetic energy is

$$\frac{1}{2}mL^2\left(\theta'(t)\right)^2,$$

which in the variables of the system is

$$\frac{1}{2}mL^2y^2.$$

The potential energy is the work done in lifting the bob above the lowest position. From Figure 11.1, this is

$$mgL(1 - \cos(\theta)),$$

or

$$mgL(1 - \cos(x)).$$

The total energy is therefore given by

$$V(x, y) = mgL(1 - \cos(x)) + \frac{1}{2}mL^2y^2.$$

Clearly $V(0, 0) = 0$. The rest position of the pendulum (pendulum arm vertical with bob at the low point) has zero energy. Next, compute

$$\dot{V}(x(t), y(t)) = V_x x'(t) + V_y y'(t)$$

$$= mgL\sin(x)x'(t) + mL^2 yy'(t).$$

Along any trajectory of the system, $x' = y$ and $y' = -(g/L)\sin(x)$, so the orbital derivative is

$$\dot{V}(x(t), y(t)) = mgL\sin(x)y + mL^2 y\left(-\frac{g}{L}\sin(x)\right) = 0.$$

This corresponds to the fact that, in a conservative physical setting, the total energy is a constant of the motion.

Now V is positive definite. This is expected because the energy should be a minimum in the rest position, where $V(0, 0) = 0$. Further, $\dot{V}$ is negative semidefinite. Therefore the origin is stable. ◼

As expected, Lyapunov's theorem did not tell us anything new about the pendulum, which we had already analyzed by other means. However, this example does provide some insight into a line of thought that could have motivated Lyapunov. In any conservative physical system, the total energy must be a constant of the motion, and we expect that any position with the system at rest should be stable if the potential energy is a minimum, and unstable if it is not. This suggests looking at the total energy as a candidate for a Lyapunov function V. In particular, for many mechanical systems the kinetic energy is a quadratic form. One then checks the orbital derivative $\dot{V}$ to see if it is negative definite or semidefinite in a neighborhood of the point of interest.

EXAMPLE 11.26

Consider the system

$$\mathbf{X}' = \begin{pmatrix} x^3 - xy^2 \\ y^3 + 6x^2 y \end{pmatrix}.$$

The origin is an isolated critical point. We do not know whether it is stable, asymptotically stable, or unstable, so we will begin by trying to construct a Lyapunov theorem that fits either of the Lyapunov theorems. Attempt a Lyapunov function

$$V(x, y) = ax^2 + bxy + cx^2.$$

We know how to choose the coefficients to make this positive definite. The question is what happens with the orbital derivative. Compute

$$\begin{aligned}
\dot{V} &= V_x x' + V_y y' \\
&= (2ax + by)(x^3 - xy^2) + (bx + 2cy)(y^3 + 6x^2 y) \\
&= 2ax^4 + 2cy^4 + (12c - 2a)x^2 y^2 + 7bx^3 y.
\end{aligned}$$

This looks promising because the first three terms can be made strictly positive for $(x, y) \neq (0, 0)$. Thus choose $b = 0$ and $a = c = 1$ to get

$$\dot{V}(x, y) = 2x^4 + 2y^4 + 10x^2 y^2 > 0$$

for $(x, y) \neq (0, 0)$. With this choice of the coefficients,

$$V(x, y) = x^2 + y^2$$

is positive definite on any neighborhood of the origin, and $\dot{V}$ is also positive definite. By Lyapunov's second theorem (Theorem 11.5), the origin is unstable. Figure 11.39 shows a phase portrait for this system. ∎

EXAMPLE 11.27

A nonlinear oscillator with linear damping can be modeled by the differential equation

$$z'' + \alpha z' + z + \beta z^2 + \gamma z^3 = 0,$$

in which β and γ are positive and $\alpha \neq 0$. To convert this to a system, let $z = x$ and $z' = y$ to obtain

$$x' = y,$$

$$y' = -\alpha y - x - \beta x^2 - \gamma x^3.$$

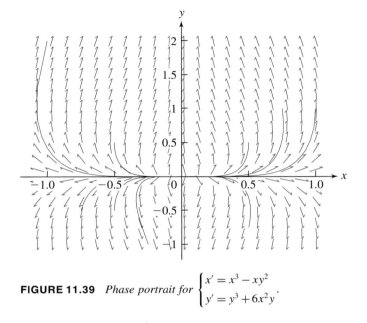

FIGURE 11.39 *Phase portrait for* $\begin{cases} x' = x^3 - xy^2 \\ y' = y^3 + 6x^2 y \end{cases}$.

This is the system

$$\mathbf{X}' = \begin{pmatrix} y \\ -\alpha y - x - \beta x^2 - \gamma x^3 \end{pmatrix}.$$

We can construct a Lyapunov function by a clever observation. Let

$$V(x, y) = \frac{1}{2}y^2 + \frac{1}{2}x^2 + \frac{1}{3}\beta x^3 + \frac{1}{4}\gamma x^4.$$

Then

$$\dot{V} = (x + \beta x^2 + \gamma x^3)y + (y)(-\alpha y - x - \beta x^2 - \gamma x^3)$$
$$= -\alpha y^2.$$

Since $\alpha > 0$, $\dot{V}$ is certainly negative semidefinite in any neighborhood of the origin. It may not be obvious whether V is positive definite in any neighborhood of the origin. Certainly the term $y^2/2$ in V is nonnegative. The other terms are

$$\frac{1}{2}x^2 + \frac{1}{3}\beta x^3 + \frac{1}{4}\gamma x^4,$$

which we can write as

$$x^2\left(\frac{1}{2} + \frac{1}{4}\gamma x^2 + \frac{1}{3}\beta x\right).$$

Since $g(x) = \frac{1}{2} + \frac{1}{4}\gamma x^2 + \frac{1}{3}\beta x$ is continuous for all x, and $g(0) = 1/2$, there is an interval $(-h, h)$ about the origin such that

$$g(x) > 0 \text{ for } -h < x < h.$$

Then, in N_h, $V(x, y) \geq 0$, and $V(x, y) > 0$ if $(x, y) \neq (0, 0)$. Therefore V is positive definite in this neighborhood.

We now have V positive definite and $\dot{V}$ negative semidefinite in N_h, hence the origin is stable. Figure 11.40 shows a phase portrait for the case $\alpha = 1$, $\beta = \frac{1}{4}$ and $\gamma = \frac{1}{6}$. It is instructive to try different values of β and γ to get some idea of effect of the nonlinear terms on the trajectories. ▧

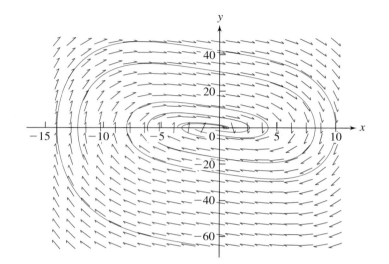

FIGURE 11.40 *Nonlinear oscillator with $\alpha = 1$, $\beta = \frac{1}{4}$, $\gamma = \frac{1}{6}$.*

EXAMPLE 11.28

Consider the system

$$x' = f(t)y + g(t)x(x^2 + y^2),$$
$$y' = -f(t)x + g(t)y(x^2 + y^2).$$

Assume that the origin is an isolated critical point.

If we attempt a Lyapunov function $V(x, y) = ax^2 + bxy + cy^2$, then

$$\dot{V} = (2ax + by)[f(t)y + g(t)x(x^2 + y^2)] + (bx + 2cy)[-f(t)x + g(t)y(x^2 + y^2)]$$
$$= (2a - 2c)f(t)xy + 2ax^2 g(t)(x^2 + y^2) + 2cy^2 g(t)(x^2 + y^2)$$
$$+ bf(t)y^2 + 2bg(t)xy(x^2 + y^2) - bf(t)x^2.$$

We can eliminate three terms in the orbital derivative by trying $b = 0$. The term $(2a - 2c) f(t)xy$ vanishes if we choose $a = c$. To have V positive definite we need a and c positive, so let $a = c = 1$. Then

$$V(x, y) = x^2 + y^2,$$

which is positive definite in any neighborhood of the origin, and

$$\dot{V} = 2(x^2 + y^2)^2 g(t).$$

This is negative definite if $g(t) < 0$ for all $t \geq 0$. In this case the origin is asymptotically stable. If $g(t) \leq 0$ for $t \geq 0$, then V is negative semidefinite and then the origin is stable. If $g(t) > 0$ for $t \geq 0$, then the origin is unstable. ∎

SECTION 11.6 PROBLEMS

In each of Problems 1 through 8, use Lyapunov's theorem to determine whether the origin is stable asymptotically stable, or unstable.

1. $x' = -2xy^2, \, y' = -x^2 y$

2. $x' = -x\cos^2(y), \, y' = (6-x)y^2$

3. $x' = -2x, \, y' = -3y^3$

4. $x' = -x^2 y^2, \, y' = x^2$

5. $x' = xy^2, \, y' = y^3$

6. $x' = x^5(1+y^2), \, y' = x^2 y + y^3$

7. $x' = x^3(1+y), \, y' = y^3(4+x^2)$

8. $x' = x^3\cot^2(y), \, y' = y^3(2+x^4)$

11.7 Limit Cycles and Periodic Solutions

Nonlinear systems of differential equations can give rise to curves called limit cycles which have particularly interesting properties. To see how a limit cycle occurs naturally in a physical setting, draw a circle C of radius R on pavement, with R exceeding the length L between the points where the front and rear wheel of a bicycle touch the ground. Now grab the handlebars and push the bicycle so that its front wheel moves around C. What path does the rear wheel follow?

If you tie a marker to the rear wheel so that it traces out the rear wheel's path as the front wheel moves along C, you find that this path does not approach a particular point. Instead, as the front wheel continues its path around C, the rear wheel asymptotically approaches a circle K concentric with C and having radius $\sqrt{R^2 - L^2}$. If the rear wheel begins outside C, it will spiral inward toward K, while if it begins inside C, it will work its way outward toward K. If the rear wheel begins on K, it will remain on K.

This inner circle K has two properties in common with a stable critical point. Trajectories beginning near K move toward it, and if a trajectory begins on K, it remains there. However, K is not a point, but is instead a closed curve. K is a *limit cycle* of this motion.

> **DEFINITION 11.6** *Limit Cycle*
>
> A limit cycle of a 2×2 system $\mathbf{X}' = \mathbf{F}(\mathbf{X})$ is a closed trajectory K having the property that there are trajectories $x = \varphi(t), \, y = \psi(t)$ of the system such that $(\varphi(t), \psi(t))$ spirals toward K in the limit as $t \to \infty$.

We have already pointed out the analogy between a limit cycle and a critical point. This analogy can be pushed further by defining a concept of stability and asymptotic stability for limit cycles that is modeled after stability and asymptotic stability for critical points.

DEFINITION 11.7

Let K be a limit cycle of $\mathbf{X}' = \mathbf{F}(\mathbf{X})$. Then,

1. K is stable if trajectories starting within a certain distance of K must remain within a fixed distance of K.

2. K is asymptotically stable if every trajectory that starts sufficiently close to K spirals toward K as $t \to \infty$.

3. K is semistable if every trajectory starting on one side of K spirals toward K as $t \to \infty$, while there are trajectories starting on the other side of K that spiral away from K as $t \to \infty$.

4. K is unstable if there are trajectories starting on both sides of K that spiral away from K as $t \to \infty$.

Keep in mind that a closed trajectory of $\mathbf{X}' = \mathbf{F}(\mathbf{X})$ represents a periodic solution. We have seen periodic solutions previously with centers, which are critical points about which trajectories form closed curves. A limit cycle is therefore a periodic solution, toward which other solutions approach spirally. Often we are interested in whether a system $\mathbf{X}' = \mathbf{F}(\mathbf{X})$ has a periodic solution, and we will shortly develop some tests to tell whether a system has such a solution, or sometimes to tell that it does not.

EXAMPLE 11.29 Limit Cycle

Consider the almost linear system

$$\mathbf{X}' = \begin{pmatrix} 1 & 1 \\ -1 & 1 \end{pmatrix} \mathbf{X} + \begin{pmatrix} -x\sqrt{x^2+y^2} \\ -y\sqrt{x^2+y^2} \end{pmatrix}. \tag{11.10}$$

$(0,0)$ is the only critical point of this system. The eigenvalues of

$$\begin{pmatrix} 1 & 1 \\ -1 & 1 \end{pmatrix}$$

are $1 \pm i$, so the origin is an unstable spiral point of the system $\mathbf{X}' = \mathbf{A}\mathbf{X} + \mathbf{G}$ and also of the linear system $\mathbf{X}' = \mathbf{A}\mathbf{X}$. Figure 11.41 shows a phase portrait of the linear system.

Up to this point, whenever we have seen trajectories spiraling outward, they have grown without bound. We will now see that this does not happen with this current system. This will be transparent if we convert the system to polar coordinates. Since

$$r^2 = x^2 + y^2,$$

then

$$rr' = xx' + yy'$$

$$= x\left[x + y - x\sqrt{x^2+y^2}\right] + y\left[-x + y - y\sqrt{x^2+y^2}\right]$$

$$= x^2 + y^2 - (x^2+y^2)\sqrt{x^2+y^2} = r^2 - r^3.$$

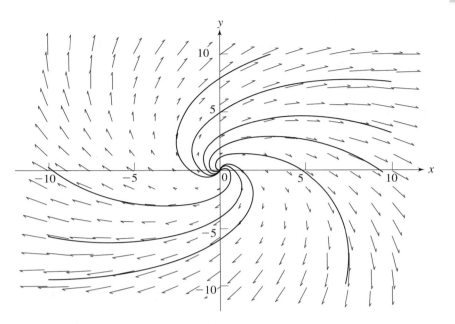

FIGURE 11.41 *Unstable spiral point for $x' = x + y$, $y' = -x + y$.*

Then

$$r' = r - r^2 = r(1 - r).$$

This tells us that, if $0 < r < 1$, then $r' > 0$ so the distance between a trajectory and the origin is increasing. Trajectories inside the unit circle are moving outward. But if $r > 1$, then $r' < 0$, so the distance between a trajectory and the origin is decreasing. Trajectories outside the unit circle are moving inward.

This does not yet tell us in detail how the trajectories are moving outward or inward. To determine this, we need to bring the polar angle θ into consideration. Differentiate $x = r\cos(\theta)$ and $y = r\sin(\theta)$ with respect to t:

$$x' = r'\cos(\theta) - r\sin(\theta)\theta',$$

$$y' = r'\sin(\theta) + r\cos(\theta)\theta'.$$

Now observe that

$$x'y - xy' = r\sin(\theta)\left[r'\cos(\theta) - r\sin(\theta)\theta'\right] - r\cos(\theta)\left[r'\sin(\theta) + r\cos(\theta)\theta'\right]$$

$$= -r^2\left[\cos^2(\theta) + \sin^2(\theta)\right]\theta' = -r^2\theta'.$$

But from the system $\mathbf{X}' = \mathbf{AX} + \mathbf{G}$ we have

$$x'y - xy' = y\left[x + y - x\sqrt{x^2 + y^2}\right] - x\left[-x + y - y\sqrt{x^2 + y^2}\right]$$

$$= x^2 + y^2 = r^2.$$

Therefore,

$$r^2 = -r^2\theta',$$

from which we conclude that

$$\theta' = -1.$$

We now have an uncoupled system of differential equations for r and θ:

$$r' = r(1 - r), \quad \theta' = -1.$$

This equation for r is separable. For the trajectory through (r_0, θ_0), solve these equations subject to the initial conditions

$$r(0) = r_0, \quad \theta(0) = \theta_0.$$

We get

$$r = \frac{1}{1 - ((r_0 - 1)/r_0)e^{-t}}, \theta = \theta_0 - t.$$

These explicit solutions enable us to conclude the following.

If $r_0 = 1$, then (r_0, θ_0) is on the unit circle. But then $r(t) = 1$ for all t, hence a trajectory that starts on the unit circle remains there for all times. Further, $\theta'(t) = -1$, so the point $(r(t), \theta(t))$ moves clockwise around this circle as t increases.

If $0 < r_0 < 1$, then (r_0, θ_0) is within the disk bounded by the unit circle. Now

$$r(t) = \frac{1}{1 + ((1 - r_0)/r_0)e^{-t}} < 1$$

for all $t > 0$. Therefore a trajectory starting at a point inside the unit disk remains there forever. Further, $r(t) \to 1$ as $t \to \infty$, so this trajectory approaches the unit circle from within.

Finally, if $r_0 > 1$, then (r_0, θ_0) is outside the unit circle. But now $r(t) > 1$ for all t, so a trajectory starting outside the unit circle remains outside for all time. However, it is still true that $r(t) \to 1$ as $t \to \infty$, so this trajectory approaches the unit circle from without.

In sum, trajectories tend in the limit to wrap around the unit circle, either from within or from without, depending on where they start. The unit circle is a an asymptotically stable limit cycle of $X' = F(X)$. A phase portrait is shown in Figure 11.42. ■

Here is an example of a system having infinitely many asymptotically stable limit cycles.

EXAMPLE 11.30

The system

$$X' = \begin{pmatrix} 0 & 1 \\ -1 & 0 \end{pmatrix} X + \begin{pmatrix} x \sin\left(\sqrt{x^2 + y^2}\right) \\ y \sin\left(\sqrt{x^2 + y^2}\right) \end{pmatrix}$$

has particularly interesting limit cycles, as can be seen in Figure 11.43. These occur as concentric circles about the origin. Trajectories originating within the innermost circle spiral toward this circle, as do trajectories beginning between this first circle and the second one. Trajectories beginning between the second and third circles spiral toward the third circle, as do trajectories originating between the third and fourth circles. This pattern continues throughout the plane. ■

We will now develop some facts about closed trajectories (periodic solutions) and limit cycles. For the remainder of this section,

$$X' = F(X) = \begin{pmatrix} f(x, y) \\ g(x, y) \end{pmatrix}$$

is a 2×2 autonomous system.

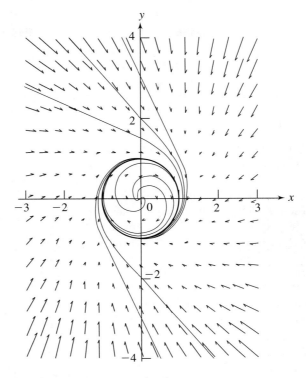

FIGURE 11.42 *Limit cycle of*

$$\begin{cases} x' = x + y - x\sqrt{x^2 + y^2} \\ y' = -x + y - y\sqrt{x^2 + y^2} \end{cases}.$$

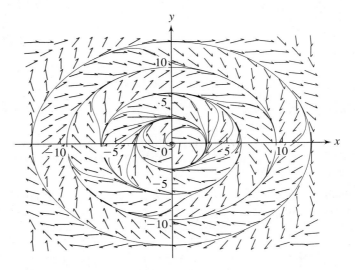

FIGURE 11.43 *Asymptotically stable limit cycles of*

$$\begin{cases} x' = y + x\sin(\sqrt{x^2 + y^2}) \\ y' = -x + y\sin(\sqrt{x^2 + y^2}) \end{cases}.$$

The first result states that, under commonly encountered conditions, a closed trajectory of $\mathbf{X}' = \mathbf{F}(\mathbf{X})$ must always enclose a critical point.

THEOREM 11.6   *Enclosure of Critical Points*

Let f and g be continuous with continuous first partial derivatives in a region of the plane containing a closed trajectory K of $\mathbf{X}' = \mathbf{F}(\mathbf{X})$. Then K must enclose at least one critical point of $\mathbf{X}' = \mathbf{F}(\mathbf{X})$. ∎

This kind of result can sometimes be used to tell that certain regions of the plane cannot contain closed trajectories of a system of differential equations. For example, suppose the origin is the only critical point of $\mathbf{X}' = \mathbf{F}(\mathbf{X})$. Then we automatically know that there can be no closed trajectory in, for example, one of the quadrants, because such a closed trajectory could not enclose the origin, contradicting the fact that it must enclose a critical point.

Bendixson's theorem, which follows, gives conditions under which $\mathbf{X}' = \mathbf{F}(\mathbf{X})$ has no closed trajectory in a part of the plane. A region of the plane is called *simply connected* if it contains all the points enclosed by any closed curve in the region. For example, the region bounded by the unit circle is simply connected. But the shaded region shown in Figure 11.44 between the curves C and K is not simply connected, because C encloses points not in the region. A simply connected region can have no "holes" in it, because then a closed curve wrapping around a hole encloses points not in the region.

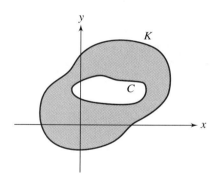

FIGURE 11.44   *Non-simply connected region.*

THEOREM 11.7   *Bendixson*

Let f and g be continuous with continuous first partial derivatives in a simply connected region R of the plane. Suppose $f_x + g_y$ has the same sign throughout points of R, either positive or negative. Then $\mathbf{X}' = \mathbf{F}(\mathbf{X})$ has no closed trajectory in R.

Proof   Suppose R contains a closed trajectory C representing the periodic solution $x = \varphi(t)$, $y = \psi(t)$. Suppose $(\varphi(t), \psi(t))$ traverses this curve exactly once as t varies from a to b, and let D be the region enclosed by C. Evaluate the line integral:

$$\oint_C -g(x, y)\,dx + f(x, y)\,dy = \int_a^b [-g(\varphi(t), \psi(t))\varphi'(t) + f(\varphi(t), \psi(t))\psi'(t)]\,dt.$$

So far we have not used the fact that $x = \varphi(t)$, $y = \psi(t)$ is a solution of $\mathbf{X}' = \mathbf{F}(\mathbf{X})$. Using this, we have

$$\varphi'(t) = x' = f(x, y) = f(\varphi(t), \psi(t))$$

and

$$\psi'(t) = y' = g(x, y) = g(\varphi(t), \psi(t)).$$

Then

$$-g(\varphi(t), \psi(t))\varphi'(t) + f(\varphi(t), \psi(t))\psi'(t) = -g(\varphi(t), \psi(t))f(\varphi(t), \psi(t))$$
$$+ f(\varphi(t), \psi(t))g(\varphi(t), \psi(t)) = 0.$$

Therefore

$$\oint_C -g(x, y)\,dx + f(x, y)\,dy = 0.$$

But by Green's theorem,

$$\oint_C -g(x, y)\,dx + f(x, y)\,dy = \iint_D \left(f_x + g_y\right) dx\,dy,$$

and this integral cannot be zero because the integrand is continuous and of the same sign throughout D. This contradiction implies that no such closed trajectory C can exist within the region R. ∎

EXAMPLE 11.31

Consider the system

$$\mathbf{X}' = \begin{pmatrix} 3x + 4y + x^3 \\ 5x - 2y + y^3 \end{pmatrix}.$$

Here f and g are continuous, with continuous first partial derivatives, throughout the plane. Further,

$$f_x + g_y = 3 + 3x^2 - 2 + 3y^2 > 0$$

for all (x, y). This system has no closed trajectory, hence no periodic solution. ∎

The last two theorems have been negative, in the sense of providing criteria for $\mathbf{X}' = \mathbf{F}(\mathbf{X})$ to have no periodic solution in some part of the plane. The next theorem, a major result credited dually to Henri Poincaré and Ivar Bendixson, gives a condition under which $\mathbf{X}' = \mathbf{F}(\mathbf{X})$ has a periodic solution.

THEOREM 11.8 *Poincaré-Bendixson*

Let f and g be continuous with continuous first partial derivatives in a closed, bounded region R of the plane that contains no critical point of $\mathbf{X}' = \mathbf{F}(\mathbf{X})$. Let C be a trajectory of $\mathbf{X}' = \mathbf{F}(\mathbf{X})$ that is in R for $t \geq t_0$. Then, C must be a periodic solution (closed trajectory), or else C spirals toward a closed trajectory as $t \to \infty$. ∎

In either case, as long as a trajectory enters R at some time, and R contains no critical point, then $\mathbf{X}' = \mathbf{F}(\mathbf{X})$ has a periodic solution, namely this trajectory itself, or, if not, a closed trajectory approached spirally by this trajectory.

On the face of it, this result may appear to contradict the conclusion of Theorem 11.6, since any periodic trajectory should enclose a critical point. However, this critical point need not be in the region R of the theorem. To illustrate, consider again the system (11.10). Let R be the region between the concentric circles $r = 1$ and $r = 3$ shown in Figure 11.45. The only critical point of $\mathbf{X}' = \mathbf{F}(\mathbf{X})$ is the origin, which is not in R. If we choose any trajectory

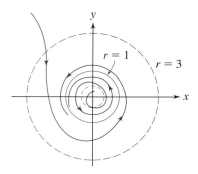

FIGURE 11.45 *Region between the circles $r = \frac{1}{2}$ and $r = 3$, with trajectories approaching the limit cycle $r = 1$.*

beginning at a point inside the unit circle, then, as we have seen, this trajectory approaches the unit circle, hence eventually enters R. The Poincaré-Bendixson theorem would allow us to assert just from this that R contains a periodic solution of the system.

We will conclude this section with Lienard's theorem, which gives conditions sufficient for a system to have a limit cycle.

THEOREM 11.9 *Lienard*

Let p and q be continuous and have continuous derivatives on the entire real line. Suppose:

1. $q(x) = -q(-x)$ for all x.
2. $q(x) > 0$ for all $x > 0$.
3. $p(x) = p(-x)$ for all x.

Suppose also the equation $F(x) = 0$ has exactly one positive root, where

$$F(x) = \int_0^x p(\xi) d\xi.$$

If this root is denoted γ, suppose $F(x) < 0$ for $0 < x < \gamma$, and $F(x)$ is positive and nondecreasing for $x > \gamma$. Then, the system

$$X' = \begin{pmatrix} y \\ -p(x)y - q(x) \end{pmatrix}$$

has a unique limit cycle enclosing the origin. Further, this limit cycle is asymptotically stable. ∎

Under the conditions of the theorem, the system has exactly one periodic solution, and every other trajectory spirals toward this closed curve as $t \to \infty$.

As an illustration, we will use Lienard's theorem to analyze the van der Pol equation.

EXAMPLE 11.32 van der Pol Equation

The second-order differential equation

$$z'' + \alpha(z^2 - 1)z' + z = 0,$$

in which α is a positive constant, is called van der Pol's equation. It was derived by the Dutch engineer Balthazar van der Pol in the 1920's in his studies of vacuum tubes. It was of great interest to know whether this equation has periodic solutions, a question to which the answer is not obvious.

First write van der Pol's equation as a system. Let $x = z$ and $y = z'$ to get

$$x' = y,$$

$$y' = -\alpha(x^2 - 1) - x.$$

This system has exactly one critical point, the origin. Further, this system matches the one in Lienard's theorem if we let

$$p(x) = \alpha(x^2 - 1) \text{ and } q(x) = x.$$

Now $q(-x) = -q(x)$, $q(x) > 0$ for $x > 0$, and $p(-x) = p(x)$, as required. Next, let

$$F(x) = \int_0^x p(\xi)d\xi = \alpha x\left(\frac{1}{3}x^2 - 1\right).$$

F has exactly one positive zero, $\gamma = \sqrt{3}$. For $0 < x < \sqrt{3}$, $F(x) < 0$. Further, for $x > \sqrt{3}$, $F(x)$ is positive and increasing (hence nondecreasing). By Lienard's theorem, the van der Pol equation has a unique limit cycle (hence periodic solution) enclosing the origin. This limit cycle is asymptotically stable, so trajectories beginning at points not on this closed trajectory spiral toward this limit cycle. Figures 11.46 through 11.49 show phase portraits for van der Pol's equation, for various choices of α. ∎

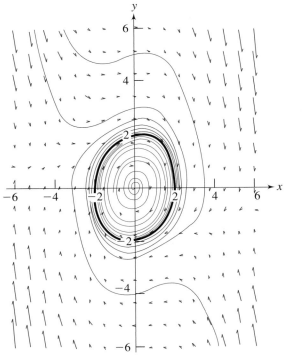

FIGURE 11.46 *Phase portrait for van der Pol's equation for* $\alpha = 0.2$.

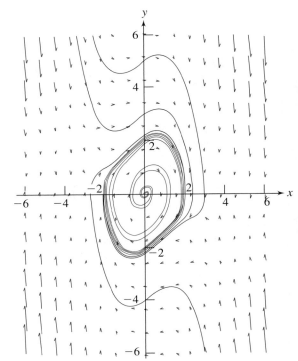

FIGURE 11.47 *Phase portrait for van der Pol's equation for* $\alpha = 0.5$.

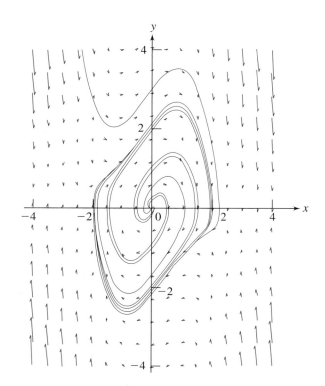

FIGURE 11.48 *Phase portrait for van der Pol's equation for $\alpha = 1$.*

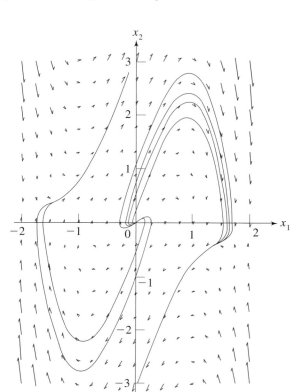

FIGURE 11.49 *Phase portrait for van der Pol's equation for $\alpha = 3$.*

SECTION 11.7 PROBLEMS

In each of Problems 1 through 4, use Bendixson's theorem to show that the system has no closed trajectory. Generate a phase portrait for the system.

1. $x' = -2x - y + x^3$, $y' = 10x + 5y + x^2 y - 2y \sin(x)$

2. $x' = -x - 3y + e^{2x}$, $y' = x + 2y + \cos(y)$

3. $x' = 3x - 7y + \sinh(x)$, $y' = -4y + 5e^{3y}$

4. $x' = y$, $y' = -x + y(9 - x^2 - y^2)$, for (x, y) in the elliptical region bounded by the graph of $x^2 + 9y^2 = 9$

5. Recall that with the transformation from rectangular to polar coordinates, we obtain

$$x \frac{dx}{dt} + y \frac{dy}{dt} = r \frac{dr}{dt}$$

and

$$y \frac{dx}{dt} - x \frac{dy}{dt} = -r^2 \frac{d\theta}{dt}.$$

Use these equations to show that the system

$$x' = y + \frac{x}{\sqrt{x^2 + y^2}} f(\sqrt{x^2 + y^2}),$$

$$y' = -x + \frac{y}{\sqrt{x^2 + y^2}} f(\sqrt{x^2 + y^2})$$

has closed trajectories associated with zeros of the function f (a given continuous function of one variable). If the closed trajectory is a limit cycle, what is its direction of orientation?

In each of Problems 6 through 9, use a conversion to polar coordinates (see Problem 5) to find all of the closed trajectories of the system, and determine which of these are limit cycles. Also classify the stability of each limit cycle. Generate a phase portrait for each system and attempt to identify the limit cycles.

6. $x' = 4y + x\sin(\sqrt{x^2 + y^2}), y' = -x + y\sin(\sqrt{x^2 + y^2})$

7. $x' = y(1 - x^2 - y^2), y' = -x(1 - x^2 - y^2)$

8. $x' = x(1 - x^2 - y^2), y' = y(1 - x^2 - y^2)$

9. $x' = y + x(1 - x^2 - y^2)(4 - x^2 - y^2)(9 - x^2 - y^2),$
$y' = -x + y(1 - x^2 - y^2)(4 - x^2 - y^2)(9 - x^2 - y^2)$

In each of Problems 10 through 13, use the Poincaré-Bendixson theorem to establish the existence of a closed trajectory of the system. In each problem, find an annular region R (region between two concentric circles) about the origin such that solutions within R remain within R. To do this, check the sign of $xx' + yy'$ on circles bounding the annulus. Generate a phase portrait of the system and attempt to identify closed trajectories.

10. $x' = x - y - x\sqrt{x^2 + y^2}, y' = x + y - y\sqrt{x^2 + y^2}$

11. $x' = 4x - 4y - x(x^2 + 9y^2), y' = 4x + 4y - y(x^2 + 9y^2)$

12. $x' = y, x' = -x + y - y(x^2 + 2y^2)$

13. $x' = 4x - 2y - y(4x^2 + y^2), y' = 2x + 4y - y(4x^2 + y^2)$

In each of Problems 14 through 22, determine whether the system has a closed trajectory. Generate a phase portrait for the system and attempt to find closed trajectories.

14. $x' = 3x + 4xy + xy^2, y' = -2y^2 + x^4y$

15. $x' = -y + x + x(x^2 + y^2), y' = x + y + y(x^2 + y^2)$

16. $x' = -y^2, y' = 3x + 2x^3$

17. $x' = y, y' = x^2 + e^{\sin(x)}$

18. $x' = y, y' = -x + y - x^2y$

19. $x' = x - 5y + y^3, y' = x - y + y^3 + 7y^5$

20. $x' = y, y' = -x + ye^{-y}$

21. $x' = y, y' = -x^3$

22. $x' = 9x - 5y + x(x^2 + 9y^2), y' = 5x + 9y - y(x^2 + 9y^2)$

A differential equation $x(t)$ has a periodic solution if there is a solution $x = \mu(t)$ and a positive number T such that $\mu(t + T) = \mu(t)$ for all t. In each of Problems 23 through 27, prove that the differential equation has a periodic solution by converting it to a system and using theorems from this section. Generate a phase portrait for this system and attempt to identify a closed trajectory, which represents a periodic solution.

23. $x'' + (x^2 - 1)x' + 2\sin(x) = 0$

24. $x'' + (5x^4 + 9x^2 - 4x)x' + \sinh(x) = 0$

25. $x'' + x^3 = 0$

26. $x'' + 4x = 0$

27. $x'' + \dfrac{x}{1 + x^2} = 0$

28. Use Bendixson's theorem to show that the van der Pol equation does not have a closed trajectory whose graph is completely contained in any of the following regions: (a) the infinite strip $-1 < x < 1$, (b) the half-plane $x \geq 1$, or (c) the half-plane $x \leq -1$.

PART 4

Vector Analysis

CHAPTER 12
Vector Differential Calculus

CHAPTER 13
Vector Integral Calculus

The next two chapters combine vector algebra and geometry with the processes of calculus to develop vector calculus, or vector analysis. We begin with vector differential calculus, and follow in the next chapter with vector integral calculus.

Much of science and engineering deals with the analysis of forces—the force of water on a dam, air turbulence on a wing, tension on bridge supports, wind and weight stresses on buildings, and so on. These forces do not occur in a static state, but vary with position, time and usually a variety of conditions. This leads to the use of vectors that are functions of one or more variables.

Our treatment of vectors is in two parts—vector differential calculus (Chapter 12), and vector integral calculus (Chapter 13).

Vector differential calculus extends out ability to analyze motion problems from the real line to curves and surfaces in 3-space. Tools such as the directional derivative, divergence and curl of a vector, and gradient play significant roles in many applications.

Vector integral calculus generalizes integration to curves and surfaces in 3-space. This will pay many dividends, including the computation of quantities such as mass, center of mass, work, and flux of a vector field, as well as physical interpretations of vector operations. The main results are the integral theorems of Green, Gauss, and Stokes, which have broad applications in such areas as potential theory and the derivation and solution of partial differential equations modeling physical processes.

CHAPTER 12

Vector Differential Calculus

12.1   Vector Functions of One Variable

In vector analysis we deal with functions involving vectors. We will begin with one such class of functions.

DEFINITION 12.1   *Vector Function of One Variable*

A vector function of one variable is a vector, each component of which is a function of the same single variable.

Such a function typically has the appearance

$$\mathbf{F}(t) = x(t)\mathbf{i} + y(t)\mathbf{j} + z(t)\mathbf{k},$$

in which $x(t)$, $y(t)$ and $z(t)$ are the component functions of $\mathbf{F}$. For each t such that the components are defined, $\mathbf{F}(t)$ is a vector. For example, if

$$\mathbf{F}(t) = \cos(t)\mathbf{i} + 2t^2\mathbf{j} + 3t\mathbf{k}, \qquad (12.1)$$

then $\mathbf{F}(0) = \mathbf{i}$, $\mathbf{F}(\pi) = -\mathbf{i} + 2\pi^2\mathbf{j} + 3\pi\mathbf{k}$, and $\mathbf{F}(-3) = \cos(-3)\mathbf{i} + 18\mathbf{j} - 9\mathbf{k}$.

A vector function is *continuous at* t_0 if each component function is continuous at t_0. A vector function is *continuous* if each component function is continuous (for those values of t for which they are all defined). For example,

$$\mathbf{G}(t) = \frac{1}{t-1}\mathbf{i} + \ln(t)\mathbf{k}$$

is continuous for all $t > 0$ with $t \neq 1$.

The derivative of a vector function is the vector function formed by differentiating each component. With the function **F** of (12.1),

$$\mathbf{F}'(t) = -\sin(t)\mathbf{i} + 4t\mathbf{j} + 3\mathbf{k}.$$

A vector function is differentiable if it has a derivative for all t for which it is defined. The vector function **G** defined above is differentiable for t positive and different from 1, and

$$\mathbf{G}'(t) = \frac{-1}{(t-1)^2}\mathbf{i} + \frac{1}{t}\mathbf{k}.$$

We may think of $\mathbf{F}(t)$ as an arrow extending from the origin to $(x(t), y(t), z(t))$. Since $\mathbf{F}(t)$ generally varies with t, we must think of this arrow as having adjustable length and pivoting at the origin to swing about as $(x(t), y(t), z(t))$ moves. In this way the arrow sweeps out a curve in 3-space as t varies. This curve has parametric equations $x = x(t)$, $y = y(t)$, $z = z(t)$. $\mathbf{F}(t)$ is called a *position vector* for this curve. Figure 12.1 shows a typical such curve.

FIGURE 12.1
Position vector
for a curve.

The derivative of the position vector is the tangent vector to this curve. To see why this is true, observe from Figure 12.2 and the parallelogram law that the vector

$$\mathbf{F}(t_0 + \Delta t) - \mathbf{F}(t_0)$$

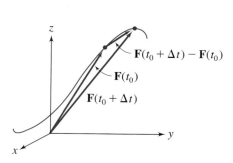

FIGURE 12.2

is represented by the arrow from $(x(t_0), y(t_0), z(t_0))$ to $(x(t_0 + \Delta t), y(t_0 + \Delta t), z(t_0 + \Delta t))$. Since Δt is a nonzero scalar, the vector

$$\frac{1}{\Delta t}[\mathbf{F}(t_0 + \Delta t) - \mathbf{F}(t_0)] \tag{12.2}$$

is along the line between these points. In terms of components, this vector is

$$\frac{x(t_0 + \Delta t) - x(t_0)}{\Delta t}\mathbf{i} + \frac{y(t_0 + \Delta t) - y(t_0)}{\Delta t}\mathbf{j} + \frac{z(t_0 + \Delta t) - z(t_0)}{\Delta t}\mathbf{k}.$$

In the limit as $\Delta t \to 0$, this vector approaches $x'(t_0)\mathbf{i} + y'(t_0)\mathbf{j} + z'(t_0)\mathbf{k}$, which is $\mathbf{F}'(t_0)$. In this limit, the vector (12.2) moves into a position tangent to the curve at $(x(t_0), y(t_0), z(t_0))$, as suggested by Figure 12.3. This leads us to interpret $\mathbf{F}'(t_0)$ as the tangent vector to the curve at $(x(t_0), y(t_0), z(t_0))$. This assumes that $\mathbf{F}'(t_0)$ is not the zero vector, which has no direction.

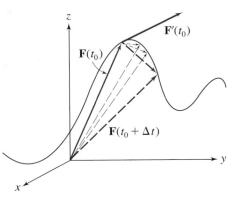

FIGURE 12.3 $\mathbf{F}'(t_0) = \displaystyle\lim_{\Delta t \to 0}$
$\dfrac{\mathbf{F}(t_0 + \Delta t) - \mathbf{F}(t_0)}{\Delta t}.$

We usually represent the tangent vector $\mathbf{F}'(t_0)$ as an arrow from the point $(x(t_0), y(t_0), z(t_0))$ on the curve having $\mathbf{F}(t)$ as position vector.

EXAMPLE 12.1

Let

$$\mathbf{H}(t) = t^2\mathbf{i} + \sin(t)\mathbf{j} - t^2\mathbf{k}.$$

$\mathbf{H}(t)$ is the position vector for the curve given parametrically by $x(t) = t^2$, $y(t) = \sin(t)$, $z(t) = -t^2$, part of whose graph is given in Figure 12.4. The tangent vector is

$$\mathbf{H}'(t) = 2t\mathbf{i} + \cos(t)\mathbf{j} - 2t\mathbf{k}.$$

The tangent vector at the origin is

$$\mathbf{H}'(0) = \mathbf{j}.$$

The tangent vector at $(1, \sin(1), -1)$ is

$$\mathbf{H}'(1) = 2\mathbf{i} + \cos(1)\mathbf{j} - 2\mathbf{k}. \quad\blacksquare$$

From calculus, we know that the length of a curve given parametrically by $x = x(t)$, $y = y(t)$, $z = z(t)$ for $a \le t \le b$, is

$$\text{length} = \int_a^b \sqrt{(x'(t))^2 + (y'(t))^2 + (z'(t))^2},$$

in which it is assumed that x', y' and z' are continuous on $[a, b]$. Now

$$\|\mathbf{F}'(t)\| = \sqrt{(x'(t))^2 + (y'(t))^2 + (z'(t))^2}$$

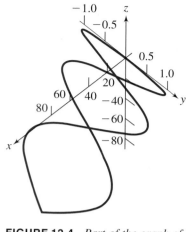

FIGURE 12.4 *Part of the graph of*
$x = t^2$, $y = \sin(t)$, $z = -t^2$.

is the length of the tangent vector. Thus, in terms of the position vector $\mathbf{F}(t) = x(t)\mathbf{i} + y(t)\mathbf{j} + z(t)\mathbf{k}$,

$$\text{length} = \int_a^b \|\mathbf{F}'(t)\| \, dt.$$

The length of a curve having a tangent at each point is the integral of the length of the tangent vector over the curve.

EXAMPLE 12.2

Consider the curve given by the parametric equations

$$x = \cos(t), \quad y = \sin(t), \quad z = \frac{t}{3}$$

for $-4\pi \le t \le 4\pi$. The position vector for this curve is

$$\mathbf{F}(t) = \cos(t)\mathbf{i} + \sin(t)\mathbf{j} + \frac{1}{3}t\mathbf{k}.$$

The graph of the curve is part of a helix wrapping around the cylinder $x^2 + y^2 = 1$, centered about the z-axis. The tangent vector at any point is

$$\mathbf{F}'(t) = -\sin(t)\mathbf{i} + \cos(t)\mathbf{j} + \frac{1}{3}\mathbf{k}.$$

Figure 12.5 shows part of the helix and tangent vectors at various points. The length of the tangent vector is

$$\|\mathbf{F}'(t)\| = \sqrt{\sin^2(t) + \cos^2(t) + \frac{1}{9}} = \frac{1}{3}\sqrt{10}.$$

The length of this curve is

$$\text{length} = \int_{-4\pi}^{4\pi} \|\mathbf{F}'(t)\| \, dt = \int_{-4\pi}^{4\pi} \frac{1}{3}\sqrt{10}\, dt = \frac{8\pi}{3}\sqrt{10}. \quad \blacksquare$$

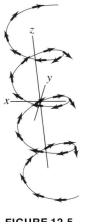

FIGURE 12.5
*Part of a
circular helix
and some
of its tangent
vectors.*

Sometimes it is convenient to write the position vector of a curve in such a way that the tangent vector at each point has length 1. Such a tangent is called a *unit tangent*. We will show how this can be done (at least in theory) if the coordinate functions of the curve have continuous derivatives. Let

$$\mathbf{F}(t) = x(t)\mathbf{i} + y(t)\mathbf{j} + z(t)\mathbf{k}$$

for $a \le t \le b$, and suppose x', y' and z' are continuous. Define the real-valued function

$$s(t) = \int_a^t \|\mathbf{F}'(\xi)\| \, d\xi.$$

As suggested by Figure 12.6, $s(t)$ is the length of the part of the curve from its initial point $(x(a), y(a), z(a))$ to $(x(t), y(t), z(t))$. As t moves from a to b, $s(t)$ increases from $s(a) = 0$ to $s(b) = L$, which is the total length of the curve. By the fundamental theorem of calculus, $s(t)$ is differentiable wherever $\mathbf{F}(t)$ is continuous, and

$$\frac{ds}{dt} = \|\mathbf{F}'(t)\| = \sqrt{x'(t)^2 + y'(t)^2 + z'(t)^2}.$$

Because s is strictly increasing as a function of t, we can, at least in theory, solve for t in terms of s, giving the inverse function $t(s)$ (see Figure 12.7). Now define

$$\mathbf{G}(s) = \mathbf{F}(t(s)) = x(t(s))\mathbf{i} + y(t(s))\mathbf{j} + z(t(s))\mathbf{k}$$

for $0 \le s \le L$. Then $\mathbf{G}$ is a position function for the same curve as $\mathbf{F}$. As t varies from a to b, $\mathbf{F}(t)$ sweeps out the same curve as $\mathbf{G}(s)$, as s varies from 0 to L. However, $\mathbf{G}$ has the advantage that the tangent vector $\mathbf{G}'$ always has length 1. To see this, use the chain rule to compute

$$\mathbf{G}'(s) = \frac{d}{ds}\mathbf{F}(t(s)) = \frac{d}{dt}\mathbf{F}(t)\frac{dt}{ds}$$

$$= \frac{1}{ds/dt}\mathbf{F}'(t) = \frac{1}{\|\mathbf{F}'(t)\|}\mathbf{F}'(t),$$

and this vector has length 1.

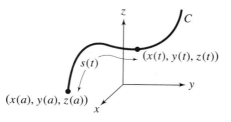

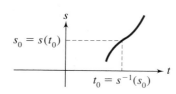

FIGURE 12.6 *Length function along a curve.*

FIGURE 12.7 *A length function has an inverse.*

EXAMPLE 12.3

Consider again the helix having position function

$$\mathbf{F}(t) = \cos(t)\mathbf{i} + \sin(t)\mathbf{j} + \frac{1}{3}t\mathbf{k}$$

for $-4\pi \leq t \leq 4\pi$. We have already calculated

$$\|\mathbf{F}'(t)\| = \frac{1}{3}\sqrt{10}.$$

Therefore the length function along this curve is

$$s(t) = \int_{-4\pi}^{t} \frac{1}{3}\sqrt{10}\,d\xi = \frac{1}{3}\sqrt{10}(t + 4\pi).$$

Solve for the inverse function to write

$$t = t(s) = \frac{3}{\sqrt{10}}s - 4\pi.$$

Substitute this into the position vector to define

$$\mathbf{G}(s) = \mathbf{F}(t(s)) = \mathbf{F}\left(\frac{3}{\sqrt{10}}s - 4\pi\right)$$

$$= \cos\left(\frac{3}{\sqrt{10}}s - 4\pi\right)\mathbf{i} + \sin\left(\frac{3}{\sqrt{10}}s - 4\pi\right)\mathbf{j} + \frac{1}{3}\left(\frac{3}{\sqrt{10}}s - 4\pi\right)\mathbf{k}$$

$$= \cos\left(\frac{3}{\sqrt{10}}s\right)\mathbf{i} + \sin\left(\frac{3}{\sqrt{10}}s\right)\mathbf{j} + \left(\frac{1}{\sqrt{10}}s - \frac{4}{3}\pi\right)\mathbf{k}.$$

Now compute

$$\mathbf{G}'(s) = -\frac{3}{\sqrt{10}}\cos\left(\frac{3}{\sqrt{10}}s\right)\mathbf{i} + \frac{3}{\sqrt{10}}\sin\left(\frac{3}{\sqrt{10}}s\right)\mathbf{j} + \frac{1}{\sqrt{10}}\mathbf{k}.$$

This is a tangent vector to the helix, and it has length 1. ∎

Assuming that the derivatives exist, then

1. $[\mathbf{F}(t) + \mathbf{G}(t)]' = \mathbf{F}'(t) + \mathbf{G}'(t).$
2. $[f(t)\mathbf{F}(t)]' = f'(t)\mathbf{F}(t) + f(t)\mathbf{F}'(t)$ if f is a differentiable real-valued function.
3. $[\mathbf{F}(t) \cdot \mathbf{G}(t)]' = \mathbf{F}'(t) \cdot \mathbf{G}(t) + \mathbf{F}(t) \cdot \mathbf{G}'(t).$

4. $[\mathbf{F}(t) \times \mathbf{G}(t)]' = \mathbf{F}'(t) \times \mathbf{G}(t) + \mathbf{F}(t) \times \mathbf{G}'(t)$.

5. $[\mathbf{F}(f(t))]' = f'(t)\mathbf{F}'(f(t))$.

Items (2), (3) and (4) are all "product rules". Rule (2) is for the derivative of a product of a scalar function with a vector function; (3) is for the derivative of a dot product; and (4) is for the derivative of a cross product. In each case the rule has the same form as the familiar calculus formula for the derivative of a product of two functions. However, in (4), order is important, since $\mathbf{F} \times \mathbf{G} = -\mathbf{G} \times \mathbf{F}$. Rule (5) is a vector version of the chain rule.

In the next section we will use vector functions to develop the concepts of velocity and acceleration, which we will apply to the geometry of curves in 3–space.

SECTION 12.1   PROBLEMS

In each of Problems 1 through 8, compute the requested derivative (a) by carrying out the vector operation and differentiating the resulting vector or scalar, and (b) by using one of the differentiation rules (1) through (5) stated at the end of this section.

1. $\mathbf{F}(t) = \mathbf{i} + 3t^2\mathbf{j} + 2t\mathbf{k}$, $f(t) = 4\cos(3t)$; $(d/dt)[f(t)\mathbf{F}(t)]$

2. $\mathbf{F}(t) = t\mathbf{i} - 3t^2\mathbf{k}$, $\mathbf{G}(t) = \mathbf{i} + \cos(t)\mathbf{k}$;
   $(d/dt)[\mathbf{F}(t) \cdot \mathbf{G}(t)]$

3. $\mathbf{F}(t) = t\mathbf{i} + \mathbf{j} + 4\mathbf{k}$, $\mathbf{G}(t) = \mathbf{i} - \cos(t)\mathbf{j} + t\mathbf{k}$;
   $(d/dt)[\mathbf{F}(t) \times \mathbf{G}(t)]$

4. $\mathbf{F}(t) = \sinh(t)\mathbf{j} - t\mathbf{k}$, $\mathbf{G}(t) = t\mathbf{i} + t^2\mathbf{j} - t^2\mathbf{k}$;
   $(d/dt)[\mathbf{F}(t) \times \mathbf{G}(t)]$

5. $\mathbf{F}(t) = t\mathbf{i} - \cosh(t)\mathbf{j} + e^t\mathbf{k}$, $f(t) = 1 - 2t^3$;
   $(d/dt)[f(t)\mathbf{F}(t)]$

6. $\mathbf{F}(t) = t\mathbf{i} - t\mathbf{j} + t^2\mathbf{k}$, $\mathbf{G}(t) = \sin(t)\mathbf{i} - 4\mathbf{j} + t^3\mathbf{k}$;
   $(d/dt)[\mathbf{F}(t) \cdot \mathbf{G}(t)]$

7. $\mathbf{F}(t) = -9\mathbf{i} + t^2\mathbf{j} + t^2\mathbf{k}$, $\mathbf{G}(t) = e^t\mathbf{i}$; $(d/dt)[\mathbf{F}(t) \times \mathbf{G}(t)]$

8. $\mathbf{F}(t) = -4\cos(t)\mathbf{k}$, $\mathbf{G}(t) = -t^2\mathbf{i} + 4\sin(t)\mathbf{k}$;
   $(d/dt)[\mathbf{F}(t) \cdot \mathbf{G}(t)]$

In each of Problems 9, 10, and 11, (a) write the position vector and tangent vector for the curve whose parametric equations are given, (b) find a length function $s(t)$ for the curve, (c) write the position vector as a function of s, and (d) verify that the resulting position vector has a derivative of length 1.

9. $x = \sin(t)$, $y = \cos(t)$, $z = 45t$; $(0 \le t \le 2\pi)$

10. $x = y = z = t^3$; $(-1 \le t \le 1)$

11. $x = 2t^2$, $y = 3t^2$, $z = 4t^2$; $(1 \le t \le 3)$

12. Let $\mathbf{F}(t) = x(t)\mathbf{i} + y(t)\mathbf{j} + z(t)\mathbf{k}$. Suppose x, y and z are differentiable functions of t. Think of $\mathbf{F}(t)$ as the position function of a particle moving along a curve in 3-space. Suppose $\mathbf{F} \times \mathbf{F}' = \mathbf{O}$. Prove that the particle always moves in the same direction.

12.2   Velocity, Acceleration, Curvature and Torsion

Imagine a particle moving along a path having position vector $\mathbf{F}(t) = x(t)\mathbf{i} + y(t)\mathbf{j} + z(t)\mathbf{k}$ as t varies from a to b. We want to relate $\mathbf{F}$ to the dynamics of the particle.

For calculations we will be doing, we assume that x, y and z are twice differentiable. We will also make use of the distance function along the curve,

$$s(t) = \int_a^t \|\mathbf{F}'(\xi)\| \, d\xi$$

> **DEFINITION 12.2** *Velocity, Speed*
>
> 1. The velocity $\mathbf{v}(t)$ of the particle at time t is defined to be
>
> $$\mathbf{v}(t) = \mathbf{F}'(t).$$
>
> 2. The speed $v(t)$ of the particle at time t is the magnitude of the velocity.

Velocity is therefore a vector, having magnitude and direction. If $\mathbf{v}(t)$ is not the zero vector, then the velocity is tangent to the curve of motion of the particle. Thus, at any instant the particle may be thought of as moving in the direction of the tangent to the path of motion.

The speed at time t is a real-valued function, given by

$$v(t) = \|\mathbf{v}(t)\| = \|\mathbf{F}'(t)\| = \frac{ds}{dt}.$$

This is consistent with the familiar idea of speed as the rate of change of distance (along the path of motion) with respect to time.

> **DEFINITION 12.3** *Acceleration*
>
> The acceleration $\mathbf{a}(t)$ of the particle is the rate of change of the velocity with respect to time:
>
> $$\mathbf{a}(t) = \mathbf{v}'(t).$$

Alternatively,

$$\mathbf{a}(t) = \mathbf{F}''(t).$$

As with velocity, acceleration is a vector.

EXAMPLE 12.4

Let

$$\mathbf{F}(t) = \sin(t)\mathbf{i} + 2e^{-t}\mathbf{j} + t^2\mathbf{k}.$$

The path of the particle is the curve whose parametric equations are

$$x = \sin(t), \quad y = 2e^{-t}, \quad z = t^2.$$

Part of the graph of this curve is shown in Figure 12.8. The velocity and acceleration are, respectively,

$$\mathbf{v}(t) = \cos(t)\mathbf{i} - 2e^{-t}\mathbf{j} + 2t\mathbf{k}$$

and

$$\mathbf{a}(t) = -\sin(t)\mathbf{i} + 2e^{-t}\mathbf{j} + 2\mathbf{k}.$$

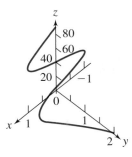

FIGURE 12.8 *Part of the graph of $x = \sin(t)$, $y = 2e^{-t}$, $z = t^2$.*

The speed of the particle is

$$v(t) = \sqrt{\cos^2(t) + 4e^{-2t} + 4t^2}. \quad \blacksquare$$

If $\mathbf{F}'(t)$ is not the zero vector, then this vector is tangent to the curve at $(x(t), y(t), z(t))$. We may obtain a unit tangent by dividing this vector by its length:

$$\mathbf{T}(t) = \frac{1}{\|\mathbf{F}'(t)\|} \mathbf{F}'(t) = \frac{1}{ds/dt} \mathbf{F}'(t).$$

Equivalently,

$$\mathbf{T}(t) = \frac{1}{\|\mathbf{v}(t)\|} \mathbf{v}(t) = \frac{1}{v(t)} \mathbf{v}(t),$$

the velocity divided by the speed. If arc length s along the path of motion is used as the parameter in the position function, then we have seen that $\|\mathbf{F}'(s)\| = 1$ automatically, so in this case the speed is identically 1 and this unit tangent is just the velocity vector. We will use this unit tangent to define a function that quantifies the "amount of bending" of a curve at a point.

DEFINITION 12.4 *Curvature*

The curvature κ of a curve is the magnitude of the rate of change of the unit tangent with respect to arc length along the curve:

$$\kappa(s) = \left\| \frac{d\mathbf{T}}{ds} \right\|.$$

The definition is motivated by the intuition (Figure 12.9) that the more a curve bends at a point, the faster the tangent vector is changing there.

If the unit tangent vector has been written using s as parameter, then computing $\mathbf{T}'(s)$ is straightforward. More often, however, the unit tangent is parametrized by some other variable, and then the derivative defining the curvature must be computed by the chain rule:

$$\kappa(t) = \left\| \frac{d\mathbf{T}}{dt} \frac{dt}{ds} \right\|.$$

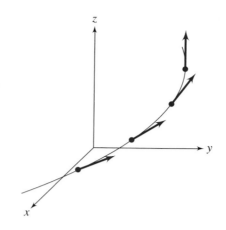

FIGURE 12.9 *Increasing curvature corresponds to an increasing rate of change of the tangent vector along the curve.*

This gives the curvature as a function of the parameter used in the position vector. Since

$$\frac{dt}{ds} = \frac{1}{ds/dt} = \frac{1}{\|\mathbf{F}'(t)\|},$$

we often write

$$\kappa(t) = \frac{1}{\|\mathbf{F}'(t)\|} \, \|\mathbf{T}'(t)\|. \tag{12.3}$$

EXAMPLE 12.5

Consider a straight line having parametric equations

$$x = a + bt, \quad y = c + dt, \quad z = e + ht,$$

in which a, b, c, d, e and h are constants. The position vector of this line is

$$\mathbf{F}(t) = (a + bt)\mathbf{i} + (c + dt)\mathbf{j} + (e + ht)\mathbf{k}.$$

We will compute the curvature using equation (12.3). First,

$$\mathbf{F}'(t) = b\mathbf{i} + d\mathbf{j} + h\mathbf{k},$$

so

$$\|\mathbf{F}'(t)\| = \sqrt{b^2 + d^2 + h^2}.$$

The unit tangent vector is

$$\mathbf{T}(t) = \frac{1}{\|\mathbf{F}'(t)\|} \mathbf{F}'(t)$$

$$= \frac{1}{\sqrt{b^2 + d^2 + h^2}} (b\mathbf{i} + d\mathbf{j} + h\mathbf{k}).$$

This is a constant vector, so $\mathbf{T}'(t) = \mathbf{O}$ and the curvature is

$$\kappa(t) = \frac{1}{\|\mathbf{F}'(t)\|} \, \|\mathbf{T}'(t)\| = 0.$$

This is consistent with our intuition that a straight line should have curvature zero. ∎

EXAMPLE 12.6

Let C be the circle of radius 4 about the origin in the plane $y = 3$. Using polar coordinates, this curve has parametric equations

$$x = 4\cos(\theta), \quad y = 3, \quad z = 4\sin(\theta)$$

for $0 \leq t \leq 2\pi$. The circle has position vector

$$\mathbf{F}(\theta) = 4\cos(\theta)\mathbf{i} + 3\mathbf{j} + 4\sin(\theta)\mathbf{k}.$$

Then

$$\mathbf{F}'(\theta) = -4\sin(\theta)\mathbf{i} + 4\cos(\theta)\mathbf{k},$$

so

$$\|\mathbf{F}'(\theta)\| = 4.$$

The unit tangent is

$$\mathbf{T}(\theta) = \frac{1}{4}[-4\sin(\theta)\mathbf{i} + 4\cos(\theta)\mathbf{k}] = -\sin(\theta)\mathbf{i} + \cos(\theta)\mathbf{k}.$$

Then

$$\mathbf{T}'(\theta) = -\cos(\theta)\mathbf{i} - \sin(\theta)\mathbf{k}.$$

The curvature is

$$\kappa(\theta) = \frac{1}{\|\mathbf{F}'(\theta)\|} \, \|\mathbf{T}'(\theta)\| = \frac{1}{4}.$$

The curvature of this circle is constant, again consistent with intuition. ∎

One can show that a circle of radius r has curvature $1/r$. Not only does a circle have constant curvature, but this curvature also decreases the larger the radius is chosen, as we should expect.

EXAMPLE 12.7

Let C have parametric representation

$$x = \cos(t) + t\sin(t), \quad y = \sin(t) - t\cos(t), \quad z = t^2$$

for $t > 0$. Figure 12.10 shows part of the graph of C. We will compute the curvature.

We can write the position vector

$$\mathbf{F}(t) = [\cos(t) + t\sin(t)]\mathbf{i} + [\sin(t) - t\cos(t)]\mathbf{j} + t^2\mathbf{k}.$$

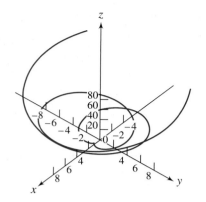

FIGURE 12.10 *Part of the graph of $x = \cos(t) + t\sin(t)$, $y = \sin(t) - t\cos(t)$, $z = t^2$.*

A tangent vector is given by

$$\mathbf{F}'(t) = t\cos(t)\mathbf{i} + t\sin(t)\mathbf{j} + 2t\mathbf{k}$$

and

$$\|\mathbf{F}'(t)\| = \sqrt{5}t.$$

Next, the unit tangent vector is

$$\mathbf{T}(t) = \frac{1}{\|\mathbf{F}'(t)\|}\mathbf{F}'(t) = \frac{1}{\sqrt{5}}\left[\cos(t)\mathbf{i} + \sin(t)\mathbf{j} + 2\mathbf{k}\right].$$

Compute

$$\mathbf{T}'(t) = \frac{1}{\sqrt{5}}\left[-\sin(t)\mathbf{i} + \cos(t)\mathbf{j}\right].$$

We can now use equation (12.3) to compute

$$\kappa(t) = \frac{1}{\|\mathbf{F}'(t)\|}\|\mathbf{T}'(t)\|$$

$$= \frac{1}{\sqrt{5}t}\sqrt{\frac{1}{5}\left[\sin^2(t) + \cos^2(t)\right]} = \frac{1}{5t}$$

for $t > 0$. ■

We will now introduce another vector of interest in studying motion along a curve.

DEFINITION 12.5 *Unit Normal Vector*

Using arc length s as parameter on the curve, the unit normal vector $\mathbf{N}(s)$ is defined by

$$\mathbf{N}(s) = \frac{1}{\kappa(s)}\mathbf{T}'(s),$$

provided that $\kappa(s) \neq 0$.

The name given to this vector is motivated by two observations. First, $\mathbf{N}(s)$ is a unit vector. Since $\kappa(s) = \|\mathbf{T}'(s)\|$, then

$$\|\mathbf{N}(s)\| = \frac{1}{\|\mathbf{T}'(s)\|}\|\mathbf{T}'(s)\| = 1.$$

Second, $\mathbf{N}(s)$ is orthogonal to the unit tangent vector. To see this, begin with the fact that $\mathbf{T}(s)$ is a unit tangent, hence $\|\mathbf{T}(s)\| = 1$. Then

$$\|\mathbf{T}(s)\|^2 = \mathbf{T}(s) \cdot \mathbf{T}(s) = 1.$$

Differentiate this equation to get

$$\mathbf{T}'(s) \cdot \mathbf{T}(s) + \mathbf{T}(s) \cdot \mathbf{T}'(s) = 2\mathbf{T}(s) \cdot \mathbf{T}'(s) = 0,$$

hence

$$\mathbf{T}(s) \cdot \mathbf{T}'(s) = 0,$$

which means that $\mathbf{T}(s)$ is orthogonal to $\mathbf{T}'(s)$. But $\mathbf{N}(s)$ is a positive scalar multiple of $\mathbf{T}'(s)$, and so is in the same direction as $\mathbf{T}'(s)$. We conclude that $\mathbf{N}(s)$ is orthogonal to $\mathbf{T}(s)$.

At any point of a curve with differentiable coordinate functions (not all vanishing for the same parameter value), we may now place a tangent vector to the curve, and a normal vector that is perpendicular to the tangent vector (Figure 12.11).

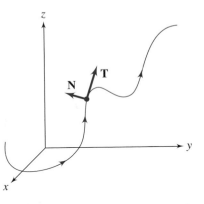

FIGURE 12.11 *Tangent and normal vector to a curve at a point.*

EXAMPLE 12.8

Consider again the curve with position function

$$\mathbf{F}(t) = [\cos(t) + t\sin(t)]\mathbf{i} + [\sin(t) - t\cos(t)]\mathbf{j} + t^2\mathbf{k}$$

for $t > 0$. In Example 12.7 we computed the unit tangent and the curvature as functions of t. We will write the position vector as a function of arc length, and compute the unit tangent $\mathbf{T}(s)$ and the unit normal $\mathbf{N}(s)$.

First, using $\|\mathbf{F}'(t)\| = \sqrt{5}t$ from Example 12.7,

$$s(t) = \int_0^t \|\mathbf{F}'(\xi)\| \, d\xi = \int_0^t \sqrt{5}\xi \, d\xi = \frac{\sqrt{5}}{2}t^2.$$

Solve for t as a function of s:

$$t = \frac{\sqrt{2}}{5^{1/4}}\sqrt{s} = \alpha\sqrt{s},$$

in which $\alpha = \sqrt{2}/5^{1/4}$. In terms of s, the position vector is

$$\mathbf{G}(s) = \mathbf{F}(t(s))$$

$$= \left[\cos(\alpha\sqrt{s}) + \alpha\sqrt{s}\sin(\alpha\sqrt{s})\right]\mathbf{i} + \left[\sin(\alpha\sqrt{s}) - \alpha\sqrt{s}\cos(\alpha\sqrt{s})\right]\mathbf{j} + \alpha^2 s\mathbf{k}.$$

The unit tangent is

$$\mathbf{T}(s) = \mathbf{G}'(s)$$

$$= \frac{1}{2}\alpha^2\cos(\alpha\sqrt{s})\mathbf{i} + \frac{1}{2}\alpha^2\sin(\alpha\sqrt{s})\mathbf{j} + \alpha^2\mathbf{k}.$$

This vector does indeed have length 1:

$$\|\mathbf{T}(s)\|^2 = \frac{1}{4}\alpha^4 + \alpha^4 = \frac{5}{4}\left(\frac{\sqrt{2}}{5^{1/4}}\right)^4 = 1.$$

Now

$$\mathbf{T}'(s) = -\frac{\alpha^3}{4\sqrt{s}}\sin(\alpha\sqrt{s})\mathbf{i} + \frac{\alpha^3}{4\sqrt{s}}\cos(\alpha\sqrt{s})\mathbf{j}$$

so the curvature is

$$\kappa(s) = \|\mathbf{T}'(s)\| = \left(\frac{\alpha^6}{16s}\right)^{1/2} = \frac{1}{4\sqrt{s}}\left(\frac{2^{1/2}}{5^{1/4}}\right)^3 = \frac{1}{5^{3/4}}\frac{1}{\sqrt{2}}\frac{1}{\sqrt{s}}$$

for $s > 0$. Since $s = \sqrt{5}t^2/2$, then in terms of t we have $\kappa = 1/5t$, consistent with Example 12.7. Now compute the unit normal vector

$$\mathbf{N}(s) = \frac{1}{\kappa(s)}\mathbf{T}'(s) = \frac{4\sqrt{s}}{\alpha^3}\left[-\frac{\alpha^3}{4\sqrt{s}}\sin(\alpha\sqrt{s})\mathbf{i} + \frac{\alpha^3}{4\sqrt{s}}\cos(\alpha\sqrt{s})\mathbf{j}\right]$$

$$= -\sin(\alpha\sqrt{s})\mathbf{i} + \cos(\alpha\sqrt{s})\mathbf{j}.$$

This is a unit vector orthogonal to $\mathbf{T}(s)$. ∎

12.2.1 Tangential and Normal Components of Acceleration

At any point on the trajectory of a particle, the tangent and normal vectors are orthogonal. We will now show how to write the acceleration at a point as a linear combination of the tangent and normal vectors there:

$$\mathbf{a} = a_T\mathbf{T} + a_N\mathbf{N}.$$

This is illustrated in Figure 12.12.

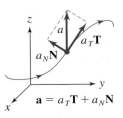

FIGURE 12.12

THEOREM 12.1

$$\mathbf{a} = \frac{dv}{dt}\mathbf{T} + v^2\kappa\mathbf{N}. \ \blacksquare$$

Thus $a_T = dv/dt$ and $a_N = v^2\kappa$. The tangential component of the acceleration is the derivative of the speed, while the normal component is the curvature at the point, times the square of the speed there.

Proof   First observe that

$$\mathbf{T}(t) = \frac{1}{\|\mathbf{F}'(t)\|}\mathbf{F}'(t) = \frac{1}{v}\mathbf{v}.$$

Therefore

$$\mathbf{v} = v\mathbf{T}.$$

Then

$$\mathbf{a} = \frac{d}{dt}\mathbf{v} = \frac{dv}{dt}\mathbf{T} + v\mathbf{T}'(t)$$

$$= \frac{dv}{dt}\mathbf{T} + v\frac{ds}{dt}\frac{d\mathbf{T}}{ds}$$

$$= \frac{dv}{dt}\mathbf{T} + v^2\mathbf{T}'(s)$$

$$= \frac{dv}{dt}\mathbf{T} + v^2\kappa\mathbf{N}. \ \blacksquare$$

Here is one use of this decomposition of the acceleration. Since $\mathbf{T}$ and $\mathbf{N}$ are orthogonal unit vectors, then

$$\|\mathbf{a}\|^2 = \mathbf{a} \cdot \mathbf{a} = (a_T\mathbf{T} + a_N\mathbf{N}) \cdot (a_T\mathbf{T} + a_N\mathbf{N})$$

$$= a_T^2\mathbf{T} \cdot \mathbf{T} + 2a_Ta_N\mathbf{T} \cdot \mathbf{N} + a_N^2\mathbf{N} \cdot \mathbf{N}$$

$$= a_T^2 + a_N^2.$$

From this, whenever two of $\|\mathbf{a}\|$, a_T and a_N are known, we can compute the third quantity.

EXAMPLE 12.9

Return again to the curve C having position function

$$\mathbf{F}(t) = [\cos(t) + t\sin(t)]\mathbf{i} + [\sin(t) - t\cos(t)]\mathbf{j} + t^2\mathbf{k}$$

for $t > 0$. We will compute the tangential and normal components of the acceleration. First,

$$\mathbf{v}(t) = \mathbf{F}'(t) = t\cos(t)\mathbf{i} + t\sin(t)\mathbf{j} + 2t\mathbf{k},$$

so the speed is

$$v(t) = \|\mathbf{F}'(t)\| = \sqrt{5}t.$$

The tangential component of the acceleration is therefore

$$a_T = \frac{dv}{dt} = \sqrt{5},$$

a constant for this curve. The acceleration vector is

$$\mathbf{a} = \mathbf{v}' = [\cos(t) - t\sin(t)]\mathbf{i} + [\sin(t) + t\cos(t)]\mathbf{j} + 2\mathbf{k},$$

and a routine calculation gives

$$\|\mathbf{a}\| = \sqrt{5 + t^2}.$$

Then

$$a_N^2 = \|\mathbf{a}\|^2 - a_T^2 = 5 + t^2 - 5 = t^2.$$

Since $t > 0$, the normal component of acceleration is

$$a_N = t.$$

The acceleration may therefore be written as

$$\mathbf{a} = \sqrt{5}\mathbf{T} + t\mathbf{N}.$$

If we know the normal component a_N and the speed v, it is easy to compute the curvature, since

$$a_N = t = \kappa v^2 = 5t^2\kappa$$

implies that

$$\kappa = \frac{1}{5t},$$

as we computed in Example 12.7 directly from the tangent vector.

Now the unit tangent and normal vectors are easy to compute in terms of t. First,

$$\mathbf{T}(t) = \frac{1}{v}\mathbf{v} = \frac{1}{\sqrt{5}}[\cos(t)\mathbf{i} + \sin(t)\mathbf{j} + 2\mathbf{k}].$$

This is usually easy to compute, since $\mathbf{v} = \mathbf{F}'(t)$ is a straightforward calculation. But in addition, we now have the unit normal vector (as a function of t)

$$\mathbf{N}(t) = \frac{1}{\kappa}\mathbf{T}'(s) = \frac{1}{\kappa}\frac{dt}{ds}\frac{d\mathbf{T}}{dt} = \frac{1}{\kappa v}\mathbf{T}'(t)$$

$$= \frac{5t}{\sqrt{5}t}\frac{1}{\sqrt{5}}[-\sin(t)\mathbf{i} + \cos(t)\mathbf{j}] = -\sin(t)\mathbf{i} + \cos(t)\mathbf{j}.$$

This calculation does not require the explicit computation of $s(t)$ and its inverse function. ∎

12.2.2 Curvature as a Function of *t*

Equation (12.3) gives the curvature in terms of the parameter t used for the position function:

$$\kappa(t) = \frac{1}{\|\mathbf{F}'(t)\|} \|\mathbf{T}'(t)\|.$$

This is a handy formula because it does not require introduction of the distance function $s(t)$. We will now derive another expression for the curvature that is sometimes useful in calculating κ directly from the position function.

THEOREM 12.2

Let $\mathbf{F}$ be the position function of a curve, and suppose that the components of $\mathbf{F}$ are twice differentiable functions. Then

$$\kappa = \frac{\|\mathbf{F}' \times \mathbf{F}''\|}{\|\mathbf{F}'\|^{3/2}}. \quad \blacksquare$$

This states that the curvature is the magnitude of the cross product of the first and second derivatives of $\mathbf{F}$, divided by the cube of the length of $\mathbf{F}'$.

Proof First write

$$\mathbf{a} = a_T \mathbf{T} + \kappa \left(\frac{ds}{dt}\right)^2 \mathbf{N}.$$

Take the cross product of this equation with the unit tangent vector:

$$\mathbf{T} \times \mathbf{a} = a_T \mathbf{T} \times \mathbf{T} + \kappa \left(\frac{ds}{dt}\right)^2 (\mathbf{T} \times \mathbf{N}) = \kappa \left(\frac{ds}{dt}\right)^2 (\mathbf{T} \times \mathbf{N}),$$

since the cross product of any vector with itself is the zero vector. Then

$$\|\mathbf{T} \times \mathbf{a}\| = \kappa \left(\frac{ds}{dt}\right)^2 \|\mathbf{T} \times \mathbf{N}\|$$

$$= \kappa \left(\frac{ds}{dt}\right)^2 \|\mathbf{T}\| \|\mathbf{N}\| \sin(\theta),$$

where θ is the angle between $\mathbf{T}$ and $\mathbf{N}$. But these are orthogonal unit vectors, so $\theta = \pi/2$ and $\|\mathbf{T}\| = \|\mathbf{N}\| = 1$. Therefore

$$\|\mathbf{T} \times \mathbf{a}\| = \kappa \left(\frac{ds}{dt}\right)^2.$$

Then

$$\kappa = \frac{\|\mathbf{T} \times \mathbf{a}\|}{(ds/dt)^2}.$$

But $\mathbf{T} = \mathbf{F}'/\|\mathbf{F}'\|$, $\mathbf{a} = \mathbf{T}' = \mathbf{F}''$, and $ds/dt = \|\mathbf{F}'\|$, so

$$\kappa = \frac{1}{\|\mathbf{F}'\|^2} \left\| \frac{1}{\|\mathbf{F}'\|} \mathbf{F}' \times \mathbf{F}'' \right\| = \frac{\|\mathbf{F}' \times \mathbf{F}''\|}{\|\mathbf{F}'\|^3}. \quad \blacksquare$$

EXAMPLE 12.10

Let C have position function

$$\mathbf{F}(t) = t^2\mathbf{i} - t^3\mathbf{j} + t\mathbf{k}.$$

We want the curvature of C. Compute

$$\mathbf{F}'(t) = 2t\mathbf{i} - 3t^2\mathbf{j} + \mathbf{k},$$

$$\mathbf{F}''(t) = 2\mathbf{i} - 6t\mathbf{j},$$

and

$$\mathbf{F}' \times \mathbf{F}'' = \begin{vmatrix} \mathbf{i} & \mathbf{j} & \mathbf{k} \\ 2t & -3t^2 & 1 \\ 2 & -6t & 0 \end{vmatrix}$$

$$= 6t\mathbf{i} + 2\mathbf{j} - 6t^2\mathbf{k}.$$

The curvature is

$$\kappa(t) = \frac{\|6t\mathbf{i} + 2\mathbf{j} - 6t^2\mathbf{k}\|}{\|2t\mathbf{i} - 3t^2\mathbf{j} + \mathbf{k}\|^3}$$

$$= \frac{\sqrt{36t^2 + 4 + 36t^4}}{(4t^2 + 9t^4 + 1)^{3/2}}. \ \blacksquare$$

12.2.3 The Frenet Formulas

If $\mathbf{T}$ and $\mathbf{N}$ are the unit tangent and normal vectors, the vector $\mathbf{B} = \mathbf{T} \times \mathbf{N}$ is also a unit vector, and is orthogonal to $\mathbf{T}$ and $\mathbf{N}$. At any point on the curve where these three vectors are defined and nonzero, the triple $\mathbf{T}, \mathbf{N}, \mathbf{B}$ forms a right-handed rectangular coordinate system (as in Figure 12.13). We can in effect put an x, y, z coordinate system at any point P on C, with the positive x-axis along $\mathbf{T}$, the positive y-axis along $\mathbf{N}$, and the positive z axis along $\mathbf{B}$. Of course, this system twists and changes orientation in space as P moves along C (Figure 12.14).

Since $\mathbf{N} = (1/\kappa)\mathbf{T}'(s)$, then

$$\frac{d\mathbf{T}}{ds} = \kappa\mathbf{N}.$$

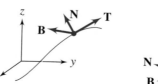

FIGURE 12.13

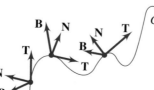

FIGURE 12.14

Further, it can be shown that there is a scalar-valued function τ such that

$$\frac{d\mathbf{N}}{ds} = -\kappa\mathbf{T} + \tau\mathbf{B},$$

and

$$\frac{d\mathbf{B}}{ds} = -\tau\mathbf{N}.$$

These three equations are called the *Frenet formulas*. The scalar quantity $\tau(s)$ is the *torsion* of C at $(x(s), y(s), z(s))$. If we look along C at the coordinate system formed at each point by $\mathbf{T}$, $\mathbf{N}$ and $\mathbf{B}$, the torsion measures how this system twists about the curve as the point moves along the curve.

SECTION 12.2   PROBLEMS

In each of Problems 1 through 10, a position vector is given. Determine the velocity, speed, acceleration, tangential and normal components of the acceleration, the curvature, the unit tangent, unit normal and binormal vectors.

1. $\mathbf{F} = 3t\mathbf{i} - 2\mathbf{j} + t^2\mathbf{k}$
2. $\mathbf{F} = t\sin(t)\mathbf{i} + t\cos(t)\mathbf{j} + \mathbf{k}$
3. $\mathbf{F} = 2t\mathbf{i} - 2t\mathbf{j} + t\mathbf{k}$
4. $\mathbf{F} = e^t\sin(t)\mathbf{i} - \mathbf{j} + e^t\cos(t)\mathbf{k}$
5. $\mathbf{F} = 3e^{-t}(\mathbf{i} + \mathbf{j} - 2\mathbf{k})$
6. $\mathbf{F} = \alpha\cos(t)\mathbf{i} + \beta t\mathbf{j} + \alpha\sin(t)\mathbf{k}$

7. $\mathbf{F} = 2\sinh(t)\mathbf{j} - 2\cosh(t)\mathbf{k}$
8. $\mathbf{F} = \ln(t)(\mathbf{i} - \mathbf{j} + 2\mathbf{k})$
9. $\mathbf{F} = \alpha t^2\mathbf{i} + \beta t^2\mathbf{j} + \gamma t^2\mathbf{k}$
10. $\mathbf{F} = 3t\cos(t)\mathbf{j} - 3t\sin(t)\mathbf{k}$

11. Suppose we are given the position vector of a curve and find that the unit tangent vector is a constant vector. Prove that the curve is a straight line.

12. It is easy to verify that the curvature of any straight line is zero. Suppose C is a curve with twice differentiable coordinate functions, and curvature zero. Does it follow that C is a straight line?

12.3   Vector Fields and Streamlines

We now turn to the analysis of vector functions of more than one variable.

> **DEFINITION 12.6   Vector Field**
>
> A vector field in 3-space is a 3-vector whose components are functions of three variables.
>   A vector field in the plane is a 2-vector whose components are functions of two variables.

A vector field in 3-space has the appearance

$$\mathbf{G}(x, y, z) = f(x, y, z)\mathbf{i} + g(x, y, z)\mathbf{j} + h(x, y, z)\mathbf{k},$$

and, in the plane,

$$\mathbf{K}(x, y) = f(x, y)\mathbf{i} + g(x, y)\mathbf{j}.$$

The term "vector field" is geometrically motivated. At each point P for which a vector field $\mathbf{G}$ is defined, we can represent the vector $\mathbf{G}(P)$ as an arrow from P. If is often useful in working with a vector field $\mathbf{G}$ to draw arrows $\mathbf{G}(P)$ at points through the region where $\mathbf{G}$ is defined. This drawing is also referred to as a vector field (think of arrows growing at points). The variations in length and orientation of these arrows gives some sense of the flow of the vector field, and its variations in strength, just as a direction field helps us visualize trajectories of a system $\mathbf{X}' = \mathbf{F}(\mathbf{X})$ of differential equations. Figures 12.15 and 12.16 show the vector fields $\mathbf{G}(x, y) = xy\mathbf{i} + (x - y)\mathbf{j}$ and $\mathbf{H}(x, y) = y\cos(x)\mathbf{i} + (x^2 - y^2)\mathbf{j}$, respectively, in the plane. Figures 12.17, 12.18 and 12.19 show the vector fields $\mathbf{F}(x, y, z) = \cos(x + y)\mathbf{i} - x\mathbf{j} + (x - z)\mathbf{k}$, $\mathbf{Q}(x, y, z) = -y\mathbf{i} + z\mathbf{j} + (x + y + z)\mathbf{k}$ and $\mathbf{M}(x, y, z) = \cos(x)\mathbf{i} + e^{-x}\sin(y)\mathbf{j} + (z - y)\mathbf{k}$, respectively, in 3-space.

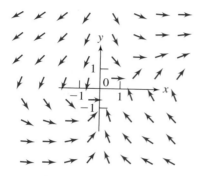

FIGURE 12.15 *Representation of the vector field* $\mathbf{G}(x, y) = xy\mathbf{i} + (x - y)\mathbf{j}$.

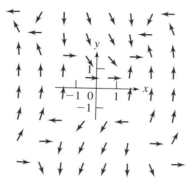

FIGURE 12.16 *Representation of the vector field* $\mathbf{H}(x, y) = y\cos(x)\mathbf{i} + (x^2 - y^2)\mathbf{j}$.

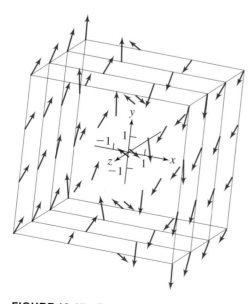

FIGURE 12.17 *Representation of the vector field* $\mathbf{F}(x, y, z) = \cos(x + y)\mathbf{i} - x\mathbf{j} + (x - z)\mathbf{k}$ *as arrows in planes* $z = $ *constant.*

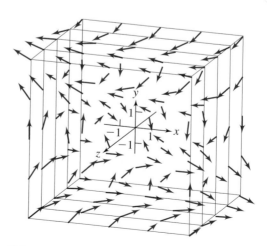

FIGURE 12.18 *Representation of the vector field* $\mathbf{Q}(x, y, z) = -y\mathbf{i} + z\mathbf{j} + (x + y + z)\mathbf{k}$ *in planes* $z = $ *constant.*

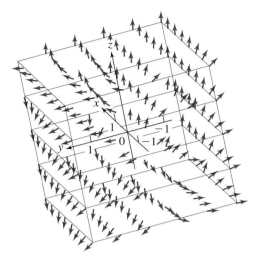

FIGURE 12.19 *The vector field*
$\mathbf{M}(x, y, z) = \cos(x)\mathbf{i} + e^{-x}\sin(y)\mathbf{j} + (z - y)\mathbf{k}$ *in*
planes $z = $ constant.

A vector field is continuous if each of its component functions is continuous. A partial derivative of a vector field is the vector field obtained by taking the partial derivative of each component function. For example, if

$$\mathbf{F}(x, y, z) = \cos(x + y)\mathbf{i} - x\mathbf{j} + (x - z)\mathbf{k},$$

then

$$\frac{\partial \mathbf{F}}{\partial x} = \mathbf{F}_x = -\sin(x + y)\mathbf{i} - \mathbf{j} + \mathbf{k}, \quad \frac{\partial \mathbf{F}}{\partial y} = \mathbf{F}_y = -\sin(x + y)\mathbf{i}, \quad \text{and} \quad \frac{\partial \mathbf{F}}{\partial z} = \mathbf{F}_z = -\mathbf{k}.$$

If

$$\mathbf{G}(x, y) = xy\mathbf{i} + (x - y)\mathbf{j},$$

then

$$\frac{\partial \mathbf{G}}{\partial x} = \mathbf{G}_x = y\mathbf{i} + \mathbf{j} \quad \text{and} \quad \frac{\partial \mathbf{G}}{\partial y} = \mathbf{G}_y = x\mathbf{i} - \mathbf{j}.$$

Streamlines of a vector field $\mathbf{F}$ are curves with the property that, at each point (x, y, z), the vector $\mathbf{F}(x, y, z)$ is tangent to the curve through this point.

DEFINITION 12.7   *Streamlines*

Let $\mathbf{F}$ be a vector field, defined for all (x, y, z) in some region Ω of 3-space. Let $\mathfrak{F}$ be a set of curves with the property that, through each point P of Ω, there passes exactly one curve from $\mathfrak{F}$. The curves in $\mathfrak{F}$ are streamlines of $\mathbf{F}$ if, at each (x, y, z) in Ω, the vector $\mathbf{F}(x, y, z)$ is tangent to the curve in $\mathfrak{F}$ passing through (x, y, z).

Streamlines are also called *flow lines* or *lines of force*, depending on context. If $\mathbf{F}$ is the velocity field for a fluid, the streamlines are often called *flow lines* (paths of particles in the fluid). If **F** is a magnetic field the streamlines are called *lines of force*. If you put iron filings on a piece of cardboard and then hold a magnet underneath, the filings will be aligned by the magnet along the lines of force of the field.

Given a vector field **F**, we would like to find the streamlines. This is the problem of constructing a curve through each point of a region, given the tangent to the curve at each point. Figure 12.20 shows typical streamlines of a vector field, together with some of the tangent vectors. We want to determine the curves from the tangents.

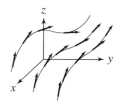

FIGURE 12.20
*Streamlines of a
vector field.*

To solve this problem, suppose C is a streamline of $\mathbf{F} = f\mathbf{i} + g\mathbf{j} + h\mathbf{j}$. Let C have parametric equations

$$x = x(\xi), y = y(\xi), z = z(\xi).$$

The position vector for this curve is

$$\mathbf{R}(\xi) = x(\xi)\mathbf{i} + y(\xi)\mathbf{j} + z(\xi)\mathbf{k}.$$

Now

$$\mathbf{R}'(\xi) = x'(\xi)\mathbf{i} + y'(\xi)\mathbf{j} + z'(\xi)\mathbf{k}$$

is tangent to C at $(x(\xi), y(\xi), z(\xi))$. But for C to be a streamline of **F**, $\mathbf{F}(x(\xi), y(\xi), z(\xi))$ is also tangent to C at this point, hence must be parallel to $\mathbf{R}'(\xi)$. These vectors must therefore be scalar multiples of each other. For some scalar t (which may depend on ξ),

$$\mathbf{R}'(\xi) = t\mathbf{F}(x(\xi), y(\xi), z(\xi)).$$

But then

$$\frac{dx}{d\xi}\mathbf{i} + \frac{dy}{d\xi}\mathbf{j} + \frac{dz}{d\xi}\mathbf{k} = tf(x(\xi), y(\xi), z(\xi))\mathbf{i} + tg(x(\xi), y(\xi), z(\xi))\mathbf{j} + th(x(\xi), y(\xi), z(\xi))\mathbf{k}.$$

This implies that

$$\frac{dx}{d\xi} = tf, \frac{dy}{d\xi} = tg, \frac{dz}{d\xi} = th. \tag{12.4}$$

Since f, g and h are given functions, these equations constitute a system of differential equations for the coordinate functions of the streamlines. If f, g and h are nonzero, then t can be eliminated to write the system in differential form as

$$\frac{dx}{f} = \frac{dy}{g} = \frac{dz}{h}. \tag{12.5}$$

EXAMPLE 12.11

We will find the streamlines of the vector field $\mathbf{F} = x^2\mathbf{i} + 2y\mathbf{j} - \mathbf{k}$.

The system (12.4) is

$$\frac{dx}{d\xi} = tx^2, \frac{dy}{d\xi} = 2ty, \frac{dz}{d\xi} = -t.$$

If x and y are not zero, this can be written in the form of equations (12.5):

$$\frac{dx}{x^2} = \frac{dy}{2y} = \frac{dz}{-1}.$$

These equations can be solved in pairs. To begin, integrate

$$\frac{dx}{x^2} = -dz$$

to get

$$-\frac{1}{x} = -z + c.$$

in which c is an arbitrary constant.

Next, integrate

$$\frac{dy}{2y} = -dz$$

to get

$$\frac{1}{2}\ln|y| = -z + k.$$

It is convenient to express two of the variables in terms of the third. If we solve for x and y in terms of z, we get

$$x = \frac{1}{z - c}, \quad y = ae^{-2z},$$

in which $a = e^{2k}$ is an arbitrary (positive) constant. This gives us parametric equations of the streamlines, with z as parameter:

$$x = \frac{1}{z - c}, \quad y = ae^{-2z}, \quad z = z.$$

To find the streamline through a particular point, we must choose c and a appropriately. For example, suppose we want the streamline through $(-1, 6, 2)$. Then $z = 2$ and we need to choose c and a so that

$$-1 = \frac{1}{2 - c} \quad \text{and } 6 = ae^{-4}.$$

Then $c = 3$ and $a = 6e^4$, so the streamline through $(-1, 6, 2)$ has parametric equations

$$x = \frac{1}{z - 3}, \quad y = 6e^{4-2z}, \quad z = z.$$

A graph of this streamline is shown in Figure 12.21. ∎

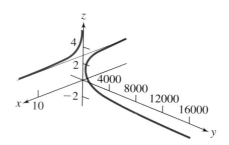

FIGURE 12.21   *Part of the graph of*
$x = 1/(z-3)$, $y = 6e^{4-2z}$, $z = z$.

EXAMPLE 12.12

Suppose we want the streamlines of $\mathbf{F}(x, y, z) = -y\mathbf{i} + z\mathbf{k}$. Here the $\mathbf{i}$ component is zero, so we must begin with equations (12.4), not (12.5). We have

$$\frac{dx}{d\xi} = 0, \quad \frac{dy}{d\xi} = -ty, \quad \frac{dz}{d\xi} = tz.$$

The first equation implies that $x = $ constant. This simply means that all the streamlines are in planes parallel to the y, z plane. The other two equations yield

$$\frac{dy}{-y} = \frac{dz}{z}$$

and an integration gives

$$-\ln(y) + c = \ln(z).$$

Then

$$\ln(zy) = c,$$

implying that

$$zy = k,$$

in which k is constant. The streamlines are given by the equations

$$x = c, \quad z = \frac{k}{y},$$

in which c and k are arbitrary constants and y is the parameter. For example, to find the streamline through $(-4, 1, 7)$, choose $c = -4$ and k so that $z = k/y$ passes through $y = 1$, $z = 7$. We need

$$7 = \frac{k}{1} = k,$$

and the streamline has equations

$$x = -4, z = \frac{7}{y}.$$

The streamline is a hyperbola in the plane $x = -4$ (Figure 12.22).

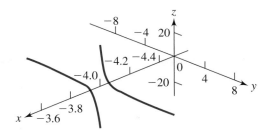

FIGURE 12.22 *Part of the graph of* $x = -4$, $z = 7/y$.

PROBLEMS

In each of Problems 1 through 5, compute the two first partial derivatives of the vector field and make a diagram in which each indicated vector is drawn as an arrow from the point at which the vector is evaluated.

1. $\mathbf{G}(x, y) = 3x\mathbf{i} - 4xy\mathbf{j}$; $\mathbf{G}(0, 1), \mathbf{G}(1, 3), \mathbf{G}(1, 4), \mathbf{G}(-1, -2), \mathbf{G}(-3, 2)$

2. $\mathbf{G}(x, y) = e^x\mathbf{i} - 2x^2y\mathbf{j}$; $\mathbf{G}(0, 0), \mathbf{G}(0, 1), \mathbf{G}(2, -3), \mathbf{G}(-1, -3)$

3. $\mathbf{G}(x, y) = 2xy\mathbf{i} + \cos(x)\mathbf{j}$; $\mathbf{G}(\pi/2, 0), \mathbf{G}(0, 0), \mathbf{G}(-1, 1), \mathbf{G}(\pi, -3), \mathbf{G}(-\pi/4, -2)$

4. $\mathbf{G}(x, y) = \sin(2xy)\mathbf{i} + (x^2 + y)\mathbf{j}$; $\mathbf{G}(-\pi/2, 0), \mathbf{G}(0, 2), \mathbf{G}(\pi/4, 4), \mathbf{G}(1, 1), \mathbf{G}(-2, 1)$

5. $\mathbf{G}(x, y) = 3x^2\mathbf{i} + (x - 2y)\mathbf{j}$; $\mathbf{G}(1, -1), \mathbf{G}(0, 2), \mathbf{G}(-3, 2), \mathbf{G}(-2, -2), \mathbf{G}(2, 5)$

In each of Problems 6 through 10, compute the three first partial derivatives of the vector field.

6. $\mathbf{F} = e^{xy}\mathbf{i} - 2x^2y\mathbf{j} + \cosh(z + y)\mathbf{k}$

7. $\mathbf{F} = 4z^2\cos(x)\mathbf{i} - x^3yz\mathbf{j} + x^3y\mathbf{k}$

8. $\mathbf{F} = 3xy^3\mathbf{i} + \ln(x + y + z)\mathbf{j} + \cosh(xyz)\mathbf{k}$

9. $\mathbf{F} = -z^4\sin(xy)\mathbf{i} + 3xy^4z\mathbf{j} + \cosh(z - x)\mathbf{k}$

10. $\mathbf{F} = (14x - 2y)\mathbf{i} + (x^2 - y^2 - z^2)\mathbf{j} + 5xy\mathbf{k}$

In each of Problems 11 through 16, find the streamlines of the vector field, then find the particular streamline through the given point.

11. $\mathbf{F} = \mathbf{i} - y^2\mathbf{j} + z\mathbf{k}$; $(2, 1, 1)$

12. $\mathbf{F} = \mathbf{i} - 2\mathbf{j} + \mathbf{k}$; $(0, 1, 1)$

13. $\mathbf{F} = (1/x)\mathbf{i} + e^x\mathbf{j} - \mathbf{k}$; $(2, 0, 4)$

14. $\mathbf{F} = \cos(y)\mathbf{i} + \sin(x)\mathbf{j}$; $(\pi/2, 0, -4)$

15. $\mathbf{F} = 2e^z\mathbf{j} - \cos(y)\mathbf{k}$; $(3, \pi/4, 0)$

16. $\mathbf{F} = 3x^2\mathbf{i} - y\mathbf{j} + z^3\mathbf{k}$; $(2, 1, 6)$

17. Construct a vector field whose streamlines are straight lines.

18. Construct a vector field in the x, y plane whose streamlines are circles about the origin.

12.4 The Gradient Field and Directional Derivatives

Let $\varphi(x, y, z)$ be a real-valued function of three variables. In the context of vectors, such a function is called a *scalar field*. We will define an important vector field manufactured from φ.

DEFINITION 12.8   Gradient

The gradient of a scalar field φ is the vector field $\nabla\varphi$ given by

$$\nabla\varphi = \frac{\partial\varphi}{\partial x}\mathbf{i} + \frac{\partial\varphi}{\partial y}\mathbf{j} + \frac{\partial\varphi}{\partial z}\mathbf{k},$$

wherever these partial derivatives are defined.

The symbol $\nabla\varphi$ is read "del phi", and ∇ is called the *del operator*. It operates on a scalar field to produce a vector field.

For example, if $\varphi(x, y, z) = x^2 y \cos(yz)$, then

$$\nabla\varphi = 2xy\cos(yz)\mathbf{i} + [x^2\cos(yz) - x^2 yz\sin(yz)]\mathbf{j} - x^2 y^2\sin(yz)\mathbf{k}.$$

The gradient field evaluated at a point P is denoted $\nabla\varphi(P)$. For the gradient just computed,

$$\nabla\varphi(1, -1, 3) = -2\cos(3)\mathbf{i} + [\cos(3) - 3\sin(3)]\mathbf{j} + \sin(3)\mathbf{k}.$$

If φ is a function of just x and y, then $\nabla\varphi$ is a vector in the x, y plane. For example, if $\varphi(x, y) = (x - y)\cos(y)$, then

$$\nabla\varphi(x, y) = \cos(y)\mathbf{i} + [-\cos(y) - (x - y)\sin(y)]\mathbf{j}.$$

At $(2, \pi)$ this gradient is

$$\nabla\varphi(2, \pi) = -\mathbf{i} + \mathbf{j}.$$

The gradient has the obvious properties

$$\nabla(\varphi + \psi) = \nabla\varphi + \nabla\psi$$

and, if c is a number, then

$$\nabla(c\varphi) = c\nabla\varphi.$$

We will now define the directional derivative, and relate this to the gradient. Suppose $\varphi(x, y, z)$ is a scalar field. Let $\mathbf{u} = a\mathbf{i} + b\mathbf{j} + c\mathbf{k}$ be a unit vector (length 1). Let $P_0 = (x_0, y_0, z_0)$. Represent $\mathbf{u}$ as an arrow from P_0, as in Figure 12.23. We want to define a quantity that measures the rate of change of $\varphi(x, y, z)$ as (x, y, z) varies from P_0, in the direction of $\mathbf{u}$. To do this, notice that, if $t > 0$, then the point

$$P : (x_0 + at, y_0 + bt, z_0 + ct)$$

is on the line through P_0 in the direction of $\mathbf{u}$. Further, the distance from P_0 to P along this direction is exactly t, because the vector from P_0 to P is

$$(x_0 + at - x_0)\mathbf{i} + (y_0 + bt - y_0)\mathbf{j} + (z_0 + ct - z_0)\mathbf{k},$$

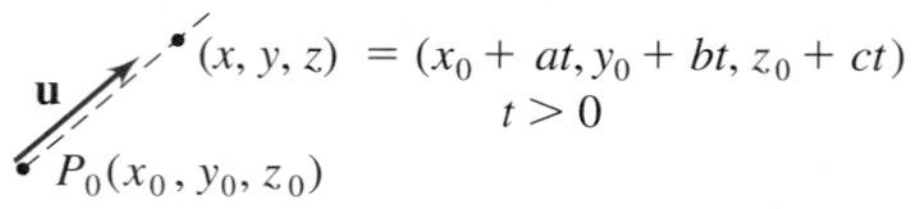

FIGURE 12.23

and this is just $t\mathbf{u}$. The derivative

$$\frac{d}{dt}\varphi(x+at, y+bt, z+ct)$$

is the rate of change of $\varphi(x+at, y+bt, z+ct)$ with respect to this distance t, and

$$\frac{d}{dt}\varphi(x+at, y+bt, z+ct)\Bigg]_{t=0}$$

is this rate of change evaluated at P_0. This derivative gives the rate of change of $\varphi(x, y, z)$ at P_0 in the direction of $\mathbf{u}$. We will summarize this discussion in the following definition.

DEFINITION 12.9 Directional Derivative

The directional derivative of a scalar field φ at P_0 in the direction of the unit vector $\mathbf{u}$ is denoted $D_{\mathbf{u}}\varphi(P_0)$, and is given by

$$D_{\mathbf{u}}\varphi(P_0) = \frac{d}{dt}\varphi(x+at, y+bt, z+ct)\Bigg]_{t=0}.$$

We usually compute a directional derivative using the following.

THEOREM 12.3

If φ is a differentiable function of two or three variables, and $\mathbf{u}$ is a constant unit vector, then

$$D_{\mathbf{u}}\varphi(P_0) = \nabla\varphi(P_0)\cdot\mathbf{u}.$$

Proof   Let $\mathbf{u} = a\mathbf{i} + b\mathbf{j} + c\mathbf{k}$. By the chain rule,

$$\frac{d}{dt}\varphi(x+at, y+bt, z+ct) = \frac{\partial\varphi}{\partial x}a + \frac{\partial\varphi}{\partial y}b + \frac{\partial\varphi}{\partial z}c.$$

Since $(x_0 + at, y_0 + bt, z_0 + ct) = (x_0, y_0, z_0)$ when $t = 0$, then

$$D_u\varphi(P_0) = \frac{\partial\varphi}{\partial x}(P_0)a + \frac{\partial\varphi}{\partial y}(P_0)b + \frac{\partial\varphi}{\partial z}(P_0)c$$

$$= \nabla\varphi(P_0)\cdot\mathbf{u}. \ \blacksquare$$

EXAMPLE 12.13

Let $\varphi(x, y, z) = x^2y - xe^z$, $P_0 = (2, -1, \pi)$ and $u = \frac{1}{\sqrt{6}}(\mathbf{i} - 2\mathbf{j} + \mathbf{k})$. Then the rate of change of $\varphi(x, y, z)$ at P_0 in the direction of $\mathbf{u}$ is

$$D_{\mathbf{u}}\varphi(2, -1, \pi) = \nabla\varphi(2, -1, \pi)\cdot\mathbf{u}$$

$$= \varphi_x(2, -1, \pi)\frac{1}{\sqrt{6}} + \varphi_y(2, -1, \pi)\left(-\frac{2}{\sqrt{6}}\right) + \varphi_z(2, -1, \pi)\frac{1}{\sqrt{6}}$$

$$= \frac{1}{\sqrt{6}}\left([2xy - e^z]_{(2,-1,\pi)} - 2[x^2]_{(-2,1,\pi)} + [-xe^z]_{(2,-1,\pi)}\right)$$

$$= \frac{1}{\sqrt{6}}(-4 - e^\pi - 8 - 2e^\pi) = \frac{-3}{\sqrt{6}}(4 + e^\pi). \ \blacksquare$$

In working with directional derivatives, care must be taken that the direction is given by a unit vector. If a vector **w** of length other than 1 is used to specify the direction, then use the unit vector $\mathbf{w}/\|\mathbf{w}\|$ in computing the directional derivative. Of course, **w** and $\mathbf{w}/\|\mathbf{w}\|$ have the same direction. A unit vector is used with directional derivatives so that the vector specifies only direction, without contributing a factor of magnitude.

Suppose now that $\varphi(x, y, z)$ is defined at least for all points within some sphere about P_0. Imagine standing at P_0 and looking in various directions. We may see $\varphi(x, y, z)$ increasing in some, decreasing in others, perhaps remaining constant in some directions. In what direction does $\varphi(x, y, z)$ have its greatest, or least, rate of increase from P_0? We will now show that the gradient vector $\nabla\varphi(P_0)$ points in the direction of maximum rate of increase at P_0, and $-\nabla\varphi(P_0)$ in the direction of minimum rate of increase.

THEOREM 12.4

Let φ and its first partial derivatives be continuous in some sphere about P_0, and suppose that $\nabla\varphi(P_0) \neq \mathbf{O}$. Then

1. At P_0, $\varphi(x, y, z)$ has its maximum rate of change in the direction of $\nabla\varphi(P_0)$. This maximum rate of change is $\|\nabla\varphi(P_0)\|$.

2. At P_0, $\varphi(x, y, z)$ has its minimum rate of change in the direction of $-\nabla\varphi(P_0)$. This minimum rate of change is $-\|\nabla\varphi(P_0)\|$.

Proof   Let **u** be any unit vector. Then

$$D_{\mathbf{u}}\varphi(P_0) = \nabla\varphi(P_0) \cdot \mathbf{u}$$

$$= \|\nabla\varphi(P_0)\|\,\|\mathbf{u}\|\cos(\theta) = \|\nabla\varphi(P_0)\|\cos(\theta),$$

because **u** has length 1. θ is the angle between **u** and $\nabla\varphi(P_0)$. The direction **u** in which φ has its greatest rate of increase from P_0 is the direction in which this directional derivative is a maximum. Clearly the maximum occurs when $\cos(\theta) = 1$, hence when $\theta = 0$. But this occurs when **u** is along $\nabla\varphi(P_0)$. Therefore this gradient is the direction of maximum rate of change of $\varphi(x, y, z)$ at P_0. This maximum rate of change is $\|\nabla\varphi(P_0)\|$.

For (2), observe that the directional derivative is a minimum when $\cos(\theta) = -1$, hence when $\theta = \pi$. This occurs when **u** is opposite $\nabla\varphi(P_0)$, and this minimum rate of change is $-\|\nabla\varphi(P_0)\|$. ∎

EXAMPLE 12.14

Let $\varphi(x, y, z) = 2xz + e^y z^2$. We will find the maximum and minimum rates of change of $\varphi(x, y, z)$ from $(2, 1, 1)$. First,

$$\nabla\varphi(x, y, z) = 2z\mathbf{i} + e^y z^2 \mathbf{j} + (2x + 2ze^y)\mathbf{k},$$

so

$$\nabla\varphi(P_0) = 2\mathbf{i} + e\mathbf{j} + (4 + 2e)\mathbf{k}.$$

The maximum rate of increase of $\varphi(x, y, z)$ at $(2, 1, 1)$ is in the direction of this gradient, and this maximum rate of change is

$$\sqrt{4 + e^2 + (4 + 2e)^2}.$$

The minimum rate of increase is in the direction of $-2\mathbf{i} - e\mathbf{j} - (4 + 2e)\mathbf{k}$, and is $-\sqrt{4 + e^2 + (4 + 2e)^2}$. ∎

12.4.1   Level Surfaces, Tangent Planes and Normal Lines

Depending on the function φ and the constant k, the locus of points $\varphi(x, y, z) = k$ may form a surface in 3-space. Any such surface is called a *level surface* of φ. For example, if $\varphi(x, y, z) = x^2 + y^2 + z^2$ and $k > 0$, then the level surface $\varphi(x, y, z) = k$ is a sphere of radius $\sqrt{k}$. If $k = 0$ this locus is just a single point, the origin. If $k < 0$ this locus is empty. There are no points whose coordinates satisfy this equation. The level surface $\varphi(x, y, z) = 0$ of $\varphi(x, y, z) = z - \sin(xy)$ is shown from three perspectives in Figures 12.24 (a), (b) and (c).

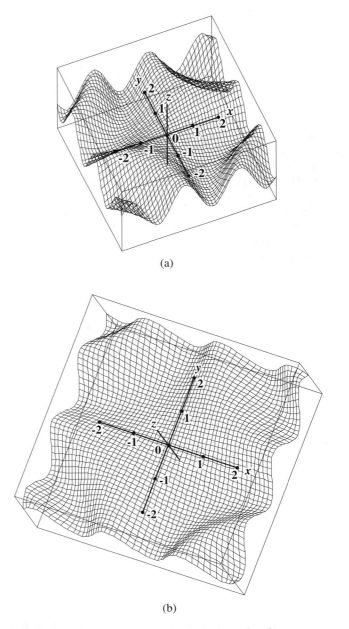

(a)

(b)

FIGURE 12.24 *Different perspectives of graphs of* $z = \sin(xy)$.

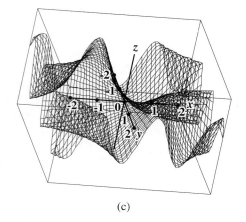

(c)

FIGURE 12.24 *(Continued).*

Now consider a point $P_0 : (x_0, y_0, z_0)$ on a level surface $\varphi(x, y, z) = k$. Assume that there are smooth (having continuous tangents) curves on the surface passing through P_0, such as C_1 and C_2 in Figure 12.25. Each such curve has a tangent vector at P_0. These tangent vectors determine a plane Π at P_0, called the *tangent plane* to the surface at P_0. A vector normal (perpendicular) to Π at P_0, in the sense of being normal to each of these tangent vectors, is called a *normal vector*, or just *normal*, to the surface at P_0. We would like to be able to determine the tangent plane and normal to a surface at a point. Recall that we can find the equation of a plane through a given point if we are given a normal vector to the plane. Thus the normal vector is the key to finding the tangent plane.

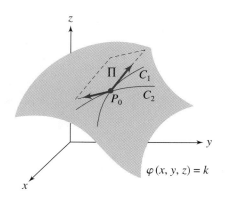

FIGURE 12.25 *Tangents to curves on the surface through P_0 determine the tangent plane Π.*

THEOREM 12.5 *Gradient As a Normal Vector*

Let φ and its first partial derivatives be continuous. Then $\nabla\varphi(P)$ is normal to the level surface $\varphi(x, y, z) = k$ at any point P on this surface at which this gradient vector is nonzero. ∎

We will outline an argument suggesting why this is true. Consider a point $P_0 : (x_0, y_0, z_0)$ on the level surface $\varphi(x, y, z) = k$. Suppose a smooth curve C on this surface passes through P_0, as in Figure 12.26 (a). Suppose C has parametric equations

$$x = x(t), y = y(t), z = z(t).$$

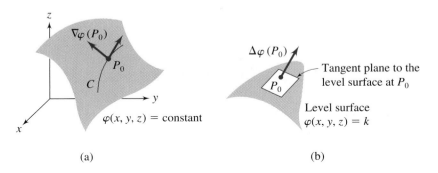

(a)   (b)

FIGURE 12.26 $\nabla\varphi(P_0)$ *is normal to the level surface at* P_0.

Since P_0 is on this curve, for some t_0,

$$x(t_0) = x_0, y(t_0) = y_0, z(t_0) = z_0.$$

Further, since the curve lies on the level surface, then

$$\varphi(x(t), y(t), z(t)) = k$$

for all t. Then

$$\frac{d}{dt}\varphi(x(t), y(t), z(t)) = 0$$
$$= \varphi_x x'(t) + \varphi_y y'(t) + \varphi_z z'(t)$$
$$= \nabla\varphi \cdot [x'(t)\mathbf{i} + y'(t)\mathbf{j} + z'(t)\mathbf{k}].$$

Now $x'(t)\mathbf{i} + y'(t)\mathbf{j} + z'(t)\mathbf{k} = \mathbf{T}(t)$ is a tangent vector to C. In particular, letting $t = t_0$, then $\mathbf{T}(t_0)$ is a tangent vector to C at P_0, and we have

$$\nabla\varphi(P_0) \cdot \mathbf{T}(t_0) = 0.$$

This means that $\nabla\varphi(P_0)$ is normal to the tangent to C at P_0. But this is true for any smooth curve on the surface and passing through P_0. Therefore $\nabla\varphi(P_0)$ is normal to the surface at P_0 (Figure 12.26 (b)).

Once we have this normal vector, finding the equation of the tangent plane is straightforward. If (x, y, z) is any other point on the tangent plane (Figure 12.27), then the vector

$$(x - x_0)\mathbf{i} + (y - y_0)\mathbf{j} + (z - z_0)\mathbf{k}$$

is in this plane, hence is orthogonal to the normal vector. Then

$$\nabla\varphi(P_0) \cdot [(x - x_0)\mathbf{i} + (y - y_0)\mathbf{j} + (z - z_0)\mathbf{k}] = 0.$$

Then

$$\frac{\partial\varphi}{\partial x}(P_0)(x - x_0) + \frac{\partial\varphi}{\partial y}(P_0)(y - y_0) + \frac{\partial\varphi}{\partial z}(P_0)(z - z_0) = 0. \tag{12.6}$$

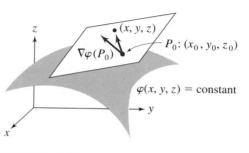

FIGURE 12.27

$$\nabla(P_0)\cdot[(x-x_0)\mathbf{i}+(y-y_0)\mathbf{j}+(z-z_0)\mathbf{k}]=0.$$

This equation is satisfied by every point on the tangent plane. Conversely, if (x, y, z) satisfies this equation, then $(x-x_0)\mathbf{i}+(y-y_0)\mathbf{j}+(z-z_0)\mathbf{k}$ is normal to the normal vector, hence lies in the tangent plane, implying that (x, y, z) is a point in this plane. We call equation (12.6) the *equation of the tangent plane* to $\varphi(x, y, z)=k$ at P_0.

EXAMPLE 12.15

Consider the level surface $\varphi(x, y, z)=z-\sqrt{x^2+y^2}=0$. This surface is the cone shown in Figure 12.28. We will find the normal vector and tangent plane to this surface at $(1, 1, \sqrt{2})$.
First compute the gradient vector:

$$\nabla\varphi = -\frac{x}{\sqrt{x^2+y^2}}\mathbf{i} - \frac{y}{\sqrt{x^2+y^2}}\mathbf{j}+\mathbf{k},$$

provided that x and y are not both zero. Figure 12.29 shows $\nabla\varphi$ at a point on the cone determined by the position vector

$$\mathbf{R}(x, y, z)=x\mathbf{i}+y\mathbf{j}+\sqrt{x^2+y^2}\mathbf{k}.$$

Then

$$\nabla\varphi(1, 1, \sqrt{2}) = -\frac{1}{\sqrt{2}}\mathbf{i} - \frac{1}{\sqrt{2}}\mathbf{j}+\mathbf{k}.$$

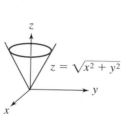

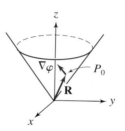

FIGURE 12.28

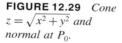

FIGURE 12.29 *Cone* $z=\sqrt{x^2+y^2}$ *and normal at P_0.*

This is the normal vector to the cone at $(1, 1, \sqrt{2})$. The tangent plane at this point has equation

$$-\frac{1}{\sqrt{2}}(x-1) - \frac{1}{\sqrt{2}}(y-1) + z - \sqrt{2} = 0,$$

or

$$x + y - \sqrt{2}z = 0.$$

The cone has no tangent plane or normal vector at the origin, where the surface has a "sharp point". This is analogous to a graph in the plane having no tangent vector where it has a sharp point (for example, $y = |x|$ at the origin). ■

EXAMPLE 12.16

Consider the surface $z = \sin(xy)$. If we let $\varphi(x, y, z) = \sin(xy) - z$, then this surface is the level surface $\varphi(x, y, z) = 0$. The gradient vector is

$$\nabla\varphi = y\cos(xy)\mathbf{i} + x\cos(xy)\mathbf{j} - \mathbf{k}.$$

This vector field is shown in Figure 12.30, with the gradient vectors drawn as arrows from selected points on the surface.

The tangent plane at any point (x_0, y_0, z_0) on this surface has equation

$$y_0\cos(x_0y_0)(x - x_0) + x_0\cos(x_0y_0)(y - y_0) - (z - z_0) = 0.$$

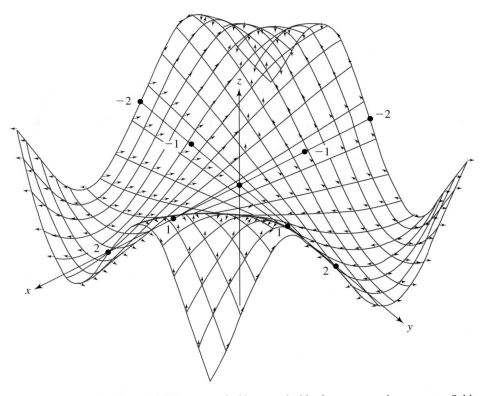

FIGURE 12.30 *Gradient field* $\nabla\varphi = y\cos(xy)\mathbf{i} + x\cos(xy)\mathbf{j} - \mathbf{k}$ *represented as a vector field on the surface* $z = \sin(xy)$.

For example, the tangent plane at $(2, 1, \sin(2))$ has equation

$$\cos(2)(x - 2) + 2\cos(2)(y - 1) - z + \sin(2) = 0,$$

or

$$\cos(2)x + 2\cos(2)y - z = 4\cos(2) - \sin(2).$$

A patch of this tangent plane is shown in Figure 12.31. Similarly, the tangent plane at $(-1, -2, \sin(2))$ has equation

$$2\cos(2)x + \cos(2)y + z = -4\cos(2) + \sin(2).$$

Part of this tangent plane is shown in Figure 12.32. ■

A straight line through P_0 and parallel to $\nabla\varphi(P_0)$ is called the *normal line* to the level surface $\varphi(x, y, z) = k$ at P_0, assuming that this gradient vector is not zero. This idea is illustrated in Figure 12.33.

To write the equation of the normal line, let (x, y, z) be any point on it. Then the vector

$$(x - x_0)\mathbf{i} + (y - y_0)\mathbf{j} + (z - z_0)\mathbf{k}$$

is along this line, hence is parallel to $\nabla\varphi(P_0)$. This means that, for some scalar t, either of these vectors is t times the other, say

$$(x - x_0)\mathbf{i} + (y - y_0)\mathbf{j} + (z - z_0)\mathbf{k} = t\nabla\varphi(P_0).$$

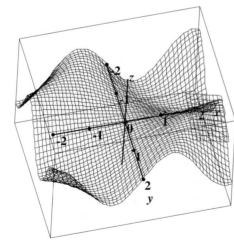

FIGURE 12.31 *Part of the tangent plane to* $z = \sin(xy)$ *at* $(2, 1, \sin(2))$.

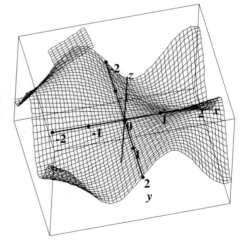

FIGURE 12.32 *Part of the tangent plane to* $z = \sin(xy)$ *at* $(-1, -2, \sin(2))$.

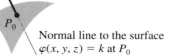

FIGURE 12.33

The components on the left must equal the respective components on the right:

$$x - x_0 = \frac{\partial \varphi}{\partial x}(P_0)t, \; y - y_0 = \frac{\partial \varphi}{\partial y}(P_0)t, \; z - z_0 = \frac{\partial \varphi}{\partial z}(P_0)t.$$

These are parametric equations of the normal line. As t varies over the real line, these equations give coordinates of points (x, y, z) on the normal line.

EXAMPLE 12.17

Consider again the cone $\varphi(x, y, z) = \sqrt{x^2 + y^2} - z = 0$. In Example 12.15 we computed the gradient vector at $(1, 1, \sqrt{2})$, obtaining

$$-\frac{1}{\sqrt{2}}\mathbf{i} - \frac{1}{\sqrt{2}}\mathbf{j} + \mathbf{k}.$$

The normal line through this point has parametric equations

$$x - 1 = -\frac{1}{\sqrt{2}}t, \, y - 1 = -\frac{1}{\sqrt{2}}t, z - \sqrt{2} = t.$$

We can also write

$$x = 1 - \frac{1}{\sqrt{2}}t, \, y = 1 - \frac{1}{\sqrt{2}}t, z = \sqrt{2} + t. \; \blacksquare$$

SECTION 12.4   PROBLEMS

In each of Problems 1 through 6, compute the gradient of the function and evaluate this gradient at the given point. Determine at this point the maximum and minimum rate of change of the function.

1. $\varphi(x, y, z) = xyz$; $(1, 1, 1)$

2. $\varphi(x, y, z) = x^2 y - \sin(xz)$; $(1, -1, \pi/4)$

3. $\varphi(x, y, z) = 2xy + xe^z$; $(-2, 1, 6)$

4. $\varphi(x, y, z) = \cos(xyz)$; $(-1, 1, \pi/2)$

5. $\varphi(x, y, z) = \cosh(2xy) - \sinh(z)$; $(0, 1, 1)$

6. $\varphi(x, y, z) = \sqrt{x^2 + y^2 + z^2}$; $(2, 2, 2)$

In each of Problems 7 through 10, compute the directional derivative of the function in the direction of the given vector.

7. $\varphi(x, y, z) = 8xy^2 - xz$; $(1/\sqrt{3})(\mathbf{i} + \mathbf{j} + \mathbf{k})$

8. $\varphi(x, y, z) = \cos(x - y) + e^z$; $\mathbf{i} - \mathbf{j} + 2\mathbf{k}$

9. $\varphi(x, y, z) = x^2 yz^3$; $2\bar{\mathbf{j}} + \mathbf{k}$

10. $\varphi(x, y, z) = yz + xz + xy$; $\mathbf{i} - 4\mathbf{k}$

In each of Problems 11 through 16, find the equations of the tangent plane and normal line to the surface at the point.

11. $x^2 + y^2 + z^2 = 4$; $(1, 1, \sqrt{2})$

12. $z = x^2 + y$; $(-1, 1, 2)$

13. $z^2 = x^2 - y^2$; $(1, 1, 0)$

14. $x^2 - y^2 + z^2 = 0$; $(1, 1, 0)$

15. $2x - \cos(xyz) = 3$; $(1, \pi, 1)$

16. $3x^4 + 3y^4 + 6z^4 = 12$; $(1, 1, 1)$

In each of Problems 17 through 20, find the angle between the two surfaces at the given point of intersection. (Compute this angle as the angle between the normals to the surfaces at this point).

17. $z = 3x^2 + 2y^2$, $-2x + 7y^2 - z = 0$; $(1, 1, 5)$

18. $x^2 + y^2 + z^2 = 4$, $z^2 + x^2 = 2$; $(1, \sqrt{2}, 1)$

19. $z = \sqrt{x^2 + y^2}$, $x^2 + y^2 = 8$; $(2, 2, \sqrt{8})$

20. $x^2 + y^2 + 2z^2 = 10$, $x + y + z = 5$; $(2, 2, 1)$

21. Suppose $\nabla \varphi = \mathbf{i} + \mathbf{k}$. What can be said about level surfaces of φ? Prove that the streamlines of $\nabla \varphi$ are orthogonal to the level surfaces of φ.

12.5   Divergence and Curl

The gradient operator ∇ produces a vector field from a scalar field. We will now discuss two other vector operations. One produces a scalar field from a vector field, and the other a vector field from a vector field.

DEFINITION 12.10   *Divergence*

The divergence of a vector field $\mathbf{F}(x, y, z) = f(x, y, z)\mathbf{i} + g(x, y, z)\mathbf{j} + h(x, y, z)\mathbf{k}$ is the scalar field

$$div\ \mathbf{F} = \frac{\partial f}{\partial x} + \frac{\partial g}{\partial y} + \frac{\partial h}{\partial z}.$$

For example, if $\mathbf{F} = 2xy\mathbf{i} + (xyz^2 - \sin(yz))\mathbf{j} + ze^{x+y}\mathbf{k}$, then

$$div\ \mathbf{F} = 2y + xz^2 - z\cos(yz) + e^{x+y}.$$

We read *div* $\mathbf{F}$ as the divergence of $\mathbf{F}$, or just "div $\mathbf{F}$".

DEFINITION 12.11   *Curl*

The curl of a vector field $\mathbf{F}(x, y, z) = f(x, y, z)\mathbf{i} + g(x, y, z)\mathbf{j} + h(x, y, z)\mathbf{k}$ is the vector field

$$curl\ \mathbf{F} = \left(\frac{\partial h}{\partial y} - \frac{\partial g}{\partial z}\right)\mathbf{i} + \left(\frac{\partial f}{\partial z} - \frac{\partial h}{\partial x}\right)\mathbf{j} + \left(\frac{\partial g}{\partial x} - \frac{\partial f}{\partial y}\right)\mathbf{k}.$$

This vector is read "curl of $\mathbf{F}$", or just "curl $\mathbf{F}$". For example, if $\mathbf{F} = y\mathbf{i} + 2xz\mathbf{j} + ze^x\mathbf{k}$, then

$$curl\ \mathbf{F} = -2x\mathbf{i} - ze^x\mathbf{j} + (2z - 1)\mathbf{k}.$$

Divergence, curl and gradient can all be thought of in terms of the vector operations of multiplication of a vector by a scalar, dot product and cross product, using the *del operator* ∇. This is defined by

$$\nabla = \frac{\partial}{\partial x}\mathbf{i} + \frac{\partial}{\partial y}\mathbf{j} + \frac{\partial}{\partial z}\mathbf{k}.$$

The symbol ∇, which is read "del", is treated like a vector in carrying out calculations, and the "product" of $\partial/\partial x$, $\partial/\partial y$ and $\partial/\partial z$ with a function $\varphi(x, y, z)$ is interpreted to mean, respectively,

$\partial\varphi/\partial x$, $\partial\varphi/\partial y$ and $\partial\varphi/\partial z$. In this way, the gradient of φ is the product of the vector ∇ with the scalar function φ:

$$\left(\frac{\partial}{\partial x}\mathbf{i}+\frac{\partial}{\partial y}\mathbf{j}+\frac{\partial}{\partial z}\mathbf{k}\right)\varphi = \frac{\partial\varphi}{\partial x}\mathbf{i}+\frac{\partial\varphi}{\partial y}\mathbf{j}+\frac{\partial\varphi}{\partial z}\mathbf{k}$$

$$= \nabla\varphi = \text{ gradient of } \varphi.$$

The divergence of a vector is the dot product of del with the vector:

$$\nabla \cdot \mathbf{F} = \left(\frac{\partial}{\partial x}\mathbf{i}+\frac{\partial}{\partial y}\mathbf{j}+\frac{\partial}{\partial z}\mathbf{k}\right)\cdot(f\mathbf{i}+g\mathbf{j}+h\mathbf{k})$$

$$= \frac{\partial f}{\partial x}+\frac{\partial g}{\partial y}+\frac{\partial h}{\partial z} = \text{ divergence of } \mathbf{F}.$$

And the curl of a vector is the cross product of del with the vector:

$$\nabla \times \mathbf{F} = \begin{vmatrix} \mathbf{i} & \mathbf{j} & \mathbf{k} \\ \partial/\partial x & \partial/\partial y & \partial/\partial z \\ f & g & h \end{vmatrix}$$

$$= \left(\frac{\partial h}{\partial y}-\frac{\partial g}{\partial z}\right)\mathbf{i}+\left(\frac{\partial f}{\partial z}-\frac{\partial h}{\partial x}\right)\mathbf{j}+\left(\frac{\partial g}{\partial x}-\frac{\partial f}{\partial y}\right)\mathbf{k}$$

$$= curl \ \mathbf{F}.$$

Informally,

$$\text{del times} = \text{gradient},$$

$$\text{del dot} = \text{divergence},$$

and

$$\text{del cross} = \text{curl}.$$

This provides a way of thinking of gradient, divergence and curl in terms of familiar vector operations involving del, and will prove to be an efficient tool in carrying out computations.

There are two fundamental relationships between gradient, divergence and curl. The first states that the curl of a gradient is the zero vector.

THEOREM 12.6   *Curl of a Gradient*

Let φ be continuous with continuous first and second partial derivatives. Then

$$\nabla \times (\nabla\varphi) = \mathbf{O}. \ \blacksquare$$

This conclusion can also be written

$$curl(\nabla\varphi) = \mathbf{O}.$$

The zero on the right is the zero vector, since the curl of a vector field is a vector.

Proof By direct computation,

$$\nabla \times (\nabla \varphi) = \nabla \times \left(\frac{\partial \varphi}{\partial x} \mathbf{i} + \frac{\partial \varphi}{\partial y} \mathbf{j} + \frac{\partial \varphi}{\partial z} \mathbf{k} \right)$$

$$= \begin{vmatrix} \mathbf{i} & \mathbf{j} & \mathbf{k} \\ \partial/\partial x & \partial/\partial y & \partial/\partial z \\ \partial \varphi/\partial x & \partial \varphi/\partial y & \partial \varphi/\partial z \end{vmatrix}$$

$$= \left(\frac{\partial^2 \varphi}{\partial y \partial z} - \frac{\partial^2 \varphi}{\partial z \partial y} \right) \mathbf{i} + \left(\frac{\partial^2 \varphi}{\partial z \partial x} - \frac{\partial^2 \varphi}{\partial x \partial z} \right) \mathbf{j} + \left(\frac{\partial^2 \varphi}{\partial x \partial y} - \frac{\partial^2 \varphi}{\partial y \partial x} \right) \mathbf{k} = \mathbf{O}$$

because the paired mixed partial derivatives in each set of parentheses are equal. ■

The second relationship states that the divergence of a curl is the number zero.

THEOREM 12.7

Let $\mathbf{F}$ be a continuous vector field whose components have continuous first and second partial derivatives. Then

$$\nabla \cdot (\nabla \times \mathbf{F}) = \mathbf{0}. \ ■$$

We may also write

$$div(curl \ \mathbf{F}) = 0.$$

Proof As with the preceding theorem, proceed by direct computation:

$$\nabla \cdot (\nabla \times \mathbf{F}) = \frac{\partial}{\partial x} \left(\frac{\partial h}{\partial y} - \frac{\partial g}{\partial z} \right) + \frac{\partial}{\partial y} \left(\frac{\partial f}{\partial z} - \frac{\partial h}{\partial x} \right) + \frac{\partial}{\partial z} \left(\frac{\partial g}{\partial x} - \frac{\partial f}{\partial y} \right)$$

$$= \frac{\partial^2 h}{\partial x \partial y} - \frac{\partial^2 g}{\partial x \partial z} + \frac{\partial^2 f}{\partial y \partial z} - \frac{\partial^2 h}{\partial y \partial x} + \frac{\partial^2 g}{\partial z \partial x} - \frac{\partial^2 f}{\partial z \partial y} = 0$$

because equal mixed partials appear in pairs with opposite signs. ■

Divergence and curl have physical interpretations, two of which we will now develop.

12.5.1 A Physical Interpretation of Divergence

Suppose $\mathbf{F}(x, y, z, t)$ is the velocity of a fluid at point (x, y, z) and time t. Time plays no role in computing divergence, but is included here because normally a velocity vector does depend on time.

Imagine a small rectangular box within the fluid, as in Figure 12.34. We would like some measure of the rate per unit volume at which fluid flows out of this box across its faces, at any given time.

First look at the front face II and the back face I in the diagram. The normal vector pointing out of the box from face II is $\mathbf{i}$. The flux of the flow out of the box across face II is the normal component of the velocity (dot product of $\mathbf{F}$ with $\mathbf{i}$), multiplied by the area of this face:

$$\text{flux outward across face II} = \mathbf{F}(x + \Delta x, y, z, t) \cdot \mathbf{i} \Delta y \Delta z.$$

$$= f(x + \Delta x, y, z, t) \Delta y \Delta z.$$

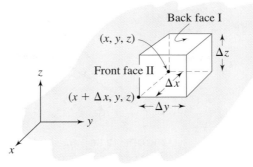

FIGURE 12.34

On face I, the unit outer normal is $-\mathbf{i}$, so

$$\text{flux outward across face I} = \mathbf{F}(x, y, z, t) \cdot (-\mathbf{i})\Delta y\Delta z = -f(x, y, z, t)\Delta y\Delta z.$$

The total outward flux across faces I and II is therefore

$$[f(x + \Delta x, y, z, t) - f(x, y, z, t)]\Delta y\Delta z.$$

A similar calculation can be done for the other two pairs of sides. The total flux of fluid out of the box across its faces is

$$[f(x + \Delta x, y, z, t) - f(x, y, z, t)]\Delta y\Delta z + [g(x, y + \Delta y, z, t) - g(x, y, z, t)]\Delta x\Delta z$$
$$+ [h(x, y, z + \Delta z, t) - h(x, y, z, t)]\Delta x\Delta y.$$

The flux per unit volume is obtained by dividing this flux by the volume $\Delta x\Delta y\Delta z$ of the box:

$$\text{flux per unit volume out of the box} = \frac{f(x + \Delta x, y, z, t) - f(x, y, z, t)}{\Delta x}$$
$$+ \frac{g(x, y + \Delta y, z, t) - g(x, y, z, t)}{\Delta y}$$
$$+ \frac{h(x, y, z + \Delta z, t) - h(x, y, z, t)}{\Delta z}.$$

Now take the limit as $\Delta x \to 0$, $\Delta y \to 0$ and $\Delta z \to 0$. The box shrinks to the point (x, y, z) and the flux per unit volume approaches

$$\frac{\partial f}{\partial x} + \frac{\partial g}{\partial y} + \frac{\partial h}{\partial z},$$

which is the divergence of $\mathbf{F}(x, y, z, t)$ at time t. We may therefore intrepret the divergence of $\mathbf{F}$ as a measure of the outward flow or expansion of the fluid from this point.

12.5.2 A Physical Interpretation of Curl

Suppose an object rotates with uniform angular speed ω about a line L as in Figure 12.35. The angular velocity vector Ω has magnitude ω and is directed along L as a right-handed screw would progress if given the same sense of rotation as the object.

Put L through the origin as a convenience, and let $\mathbf{R} = x\mathbf{i} + y\mathbf{j} + z\mathbf{k}$ for any point (x, y, z) on the rotating object. Let $\mathbf{T}(x, y, z)$ be the tangential linear velocity. Then

$$\|\mathbf{T}\| = \omega\|\mathbf{R}\|\sin(\theta) = \|\Omega \times \mathbf{R}\|,$$

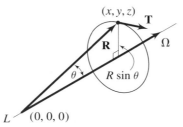

FIGURE 12.35 *Angular velocity as the curl of the linear velocity.*

where θ is the angle between $\mathbf{R}$ and Ω. Since $\mathbf{T}$ and $\Omega \times \mathbf{R}$ have the same direction and magnitude, we conclude that $\mathbf{T} = \Omega \times \mathbf{R}$. Now write $\Omega = a\mathbf{i} + b\mathbf{j} + c\mathbf{k}$ to obtain

$$\mathbf{T} = \Omega \times \mathbf{R} = (bz - cy)\mathbf{i} + (cx - az)\mathbf{j} + (ay - bx)\mathbf{k}.$$

Then

$$\nabla \times \mathbf{T} = \begin{vmatrix} \mathbf{i} & \mathbf{j} & \mathbf{k} \\ \partial/\partial x & \partial/\partial y & \partial/\partial z \\ bz - cy & cx - az & ay - bx \end{vmatrix}$$

$$= 2a\mathbf{i} + 2b\mathbf{j} + 2c\mathbf{k} = 2\Omega.$$

Therefore

$$\Omega = \frac{1}{2} \nabla \times \mathbf{T}.$$

The angular velocity of a uniformly rotating body is a constant times the curl of the linear velocity. Because of this interpretation, *curl* was once written *rot* (for rotation), particularly in British treatments of mechanics. This is also the motivation for the term *irrotational* for a vector field whose curl is zero.

Other interpretations of divergence and curl follow from vector integral theorems we will see in the next chapter.

SECTION 12.5 PROBLEMS

In each of Problems 1 through 6, compute $\nabla \cdot \mathbf{F}$ and $\nabla \times \mathbf{F}$ and verify explicitly that $\nabla \cdot (\nabla \times \mathbf{F}) = 0$.

1. $\mathbf{F} = x\mathbf{i} + y\mathbf{j} + 2z\mathbf{k}$

2. $\mathbf{F} = \sinh(xyz)\mathbf{j}$

3. $\mathbf{F} = 2xy\mathbf{i} + xe^y\mathbf{j} + 2z\mathbf{k}$

4. $\mathbf{F} = \sinh(x)\mathbf{i} + \cosh(xyz)\mathbf{j} - (x + y + z)\mathbf{k}$

5. $\mathbf{F} = x^2\mathbf{i} + y^2\mathbf{j} + z^2\mathbf{k}$

6. $\mathbf{F} = \sinh(x - z)\mathbf{i} + 2y\mathbf{j} + (z - y^2)\mathbf{k}$

In each of Problems 7 through 12, compute $\nabla\varphi$ and verify explicitly that $\nabla \times (\nabla\varphi) = \mathbf{O}$.

7. $\varphi(x, y, z) = x - y + 2z^2$

8. $\varphi(x, y, z) = 18xyz + e^x$

9. $\varphi(x, y, z) = -2x^3yz^2$

10. $\varphi(x, y, z) = \sin(xz)$

11. $\varphi(x, y, z) = x\cos(x + y + z)$

12. $\varphi(x, y, z) = e^{x+y+z}$

13. Let $\varphi(x, y, z)$ be a scalar field and $\mathbf{F}$ a vector field. Derive expressions for $\nabla \cdot (\varphi \mathbf{F})$ and $\nabla \times (\varphi \mathbf{F})$ in terms of operations applied to $\varphi(x, y, z)$ and $\mathbf{F}$.

14. Let $\mathbf{F} = f\mathbf{i} + g\mathbf{j} + h\mathbf{k}$ be a vector field. Define

$$\mathbf{F} \cdot \nabla = \left(f\frac{\partial}{\partial x} \right)\mathbf{i} + \left(g\frac{\partial}{\partial y} \right)\mathbf{j} + \left(h\frac{\partial}{\partial z} \right)\mathbf{k}.$$

Let $\mathbf{G}$ be a vector field. Show that

$$\nabla(\mathbf{F} \cdot \mathbf{G}) = (\mathbf{F} \cdot \nabla)\mathbf{G} + (\mathbf{G} \cdot \nabla)\mathbf{F} + \mathbf{F} \times (\nabla \times \mathbf{G}) + \mathbf{G} \times (\nabla \times \mathbf{F}).$$

15. Let $\mathbf{F}$ and $\mathbf{G}$ be vector fields. Prove that

$$\nabla \cdot (\mathbf{F} \times \mathbf{G}) = \mathbf{G} \cdot (\nabla \times \mathbf{G}) - \mathbf{F} \cdot (\nabla \times \mathbf{G}).$$

16. Let $\varphi(x, y, z)$ and $\psi(x, y, z)$ be scalar fields. Prove that $\nabla \cdot (\nabla\varphi \times \nabla\psi) = 0$.

CHAPTER 13

Vector Integral Calculus

This chapter is devoted to integrals of vector fields over curves and surfaces, and relationships between such integrals. These have important uses in solving partial differential equations and in constructing models used in the sciences and engineering.

13.1 Line Integrals

We begin with the integral of a vector field over a curve. This requires some background on curves.

Suppose a curve C in 3-space is given by parametric equations

$$x = x(t), y = y(t), z = z(t) \quad \text{for } a \le t \le b.$$

We call $x(t)$, $y(t)$ and $z(t)$ the *coordinate functions* of C.

We will think of C not only as a geometric locus of points $(x(t), y(t), z(t))$, but also as having an orientation or direction, given by the direction this point moves along C as t increases from a to b. Denote this orientation by putting arrows on the graph of the curve (Figure 13.1). Trajectories of a system of differential equations are also oriented curves, with the particle moving along the geometric locus in a direction dictated by the flow of the system. We call $(x(a), y(a), z(a))$ the *initial point* of C, and $(x(b), y(b), z(b))$ the *terminal point*. A curve is *closed* if the initial and terminal points are the same.

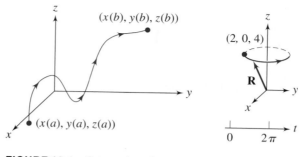

FIGURE 13.1   *Orientation along a curve.*   **FIGURE 13.2**

EXAMPLE 13.1

Let C be given by

$$x = 2\cos(t), \, y = 2\sin(t), \, z = 4; \quad 0 \le t \le 2\pi.$$

A graph of C is shown in Figure 13.2. This graph is the circle of radius 2 about the origin in the plane $z = 4$. The arrow on the curve indicates its orientation (the direction of motion of $(2\cos(t), 2\sin(t), 4)$ around the graph as t varies from 0 to 2π). The initial point is $(2, 0, 4)$, obtained at $t = 0$, and the terminal point is also $(2, 0, 4)$, obtained at $t = 2\pi$. This curve is closed.

Contrast C with the curve K given by

$$x = 2\cos(t), \, y = 2\sin(t), \, z = 4; \quad 0 \le t \le 3\pi.$$

K has the same graph and counterclockwise orientation as C, but is a different curve. K is not closed. The initial point of K is $(2, 0, 4)$, but its terminal point is $(-2, 0, 4)$. A particle moving about K goes around the circle once, and then makes another half-circle. It would presumably take more energy to move a particle about K than about C. K is also longer than C. ∎

A curve is:

- *continuous* if its coordinate functions are continuous on the parameter interval,
- *differentiable* if its coordinate functions are differentiable, and
- *smooth* if its coordinate functions have continuous derivatives, which are not all zero for the same value of t.

Because $x'(t)\mathbf{i} + y'(t)\mathbf{j} + z'(t)\mathbf{k}$ is tangent to the curve if this is not the zero vector, a smooth curve is one that has a continuous tangent vector.

The *graph* of a curve consists of all points $(x(t), y(t), z(t))$ as t varies over the parameter interval. As Example 13.1 shows, there is more to a curve than just its graph. We are dealing with curves both as geometric objects and as oriented objects, having a sense of direction along the graph.

We will now define the line integral of a vector field over a smooth curve.

DEFINITION 13.1   Line Integral

Suppose a smooth curve C has coordinate functions $x = x(t), \, y = y(t), \, z = z(t)$ for $a \le t \le b$. Let $f(x, y, z), \, g(x, y, z),$ and $h(x, y, z)$ be continuous at least on the graph of C. Then, the line integral

$$\int_C f(x, y, z)\,dx + g(x, y, z)\,dy + h(x, y, z)\,dz$$

is defined by

$$\int_C f(x, y, z)\, dx + g(x, y, z)\, dy + h(x, y, z)\, dz$$

$$= \int_a^b \left[f(x(t), y(t), z(t)) \frac{dx}{dt} + g(x(t), y(t), z(t)) \frac{dy}{dt} + h(x(t), y(t), z(t)) \frac{dz}{dt} \right] dt.$$

$$(13.1)$$

We can write this line integral more compactly as

$$\int_C f\, dx + g\, dy + h\, dz.$$

To evaluate $\int_C f\, dx + g\, dy + h\, dz$, substitute the coordinate functions $x = x(t)$, $y = y(t)$ and $z = z(t)$ into $f(x, y, z)$, $g(x, y, z)$ and $h(x, y, z)$, obtaining functions of t. Further, substitute

$$dx = \frac{dx}{dt}\, dt, \quad dy = \frac{dy}{dt}\, dt, \quad \text{and} \quad dz = \frac{dz}{dt}\, dt.$$

This results in the Riemann integral on the right side of equation (13.1) of a function of t over the range of values of this parameter.

EXAMPLE 13.2

Evaluate the line integral $\int_C x\, dx - yz\, dy + e^z\, dz$ if C is given by

$$x = t^3,\, y = -t,\, z = t^2;\, 1 \le t \le 2.$$

Here

$$f(x, y, z) = x, \quad g(x, y, z) = -yz \quad \text{and} \quad h(x, y, z) = e^z$$

and, on C,

$$dx = 3t^2 dt, \quad dy = -dt \quad \text{and} \quad dz = 2t\, dt.$$

Then

$$\int_C x\, dx - yz\, dy + e^z\, dz$$

$$= \int_1^2 \left[t^3 (3t^2) - (-t)(t^2)(-1) + e^{t^2}(2t) \right] dt$$

$$= \int_1^2 \left[3t^5 - t^3 + 2t e^{t^2} \right] dt = \frac{111}{4} + e^4 - e. \quad \blacksquare$$

EXAMPLE 13.3

Evaluate $\int_C xyz\,dx - \cos(yz)\,dy + xz\,dz$ over the straight line segment from $(1, 1, 1)$ to $(-2, 1, 3)$.

Here we are left to find the coordinate functions of the curve. Parametric equations of the line through these points are

$$x(t) = 1 - 3t, \quad y(t) = 1, \quad z(t) = 1 + 2t.$$

We must let t vary from 0 to 1 for the initial point to be $(1, 1, 1)$ and the terminal point to be $(-2, 1, 3)$.

Now

$$\int_C xyz\,dx - \cos(yz)\,dy + xz\,dz$$

$$= \int_0^1 [(1 - 3t)(1)(1 + 2t)(-3) - \cos(1 + 2t)(0) + (1 - 3t)(1 + 2t)(2)]\,dt$$

$$= \int_0^1 \left(-1 + t + 6t^2\right) dt = \frac{3}{2}. \ \blacksquare$$

If C is a smooth curve in the x, y plane (zero z-component), and $f(x, y)$ and $g(x, y)$ are continuous on C, then we can write a line integral

$$\int_C f(x, y)\,dx + g(x, y)\,dy,$$

which we refer to as a line integral in the plane. We evaluate this according to the Definition 13.1, except now there is no z-component.

EXAMPLE 13.4

Evaluate $\int_C xy\,dx - y\sin(x)\,dy$ if C is given by $x(t) = t^2$ and $y(t) = t$ for $-1 \leq t \leq 4$.

Proceed:

$$\int_C xy\,dx - y\sin(x)\,dy$$

$$= \int_{-1}^4 [t^2 t(2t) - t\sin(t^2)(1)]\,dt$$

$$= 410 + \frac{1}{2}\cos(16) - \frac{1}{2}\cos(1). \ \blacksquare$$

In these examples we have included all the terms to follow equation 13.1 very literally. However, with some experience there are obvious shortcuts one can take. In Example 13.3, for example, y is constant on the curve, so $dy = 0$ and the term $g(x(t), y(t), z(t))\frac{dy}{dt}$ could have been simply omitted.

Thus far we can integrate only over a smooth curve. This requirement can be relaxed as follows. A curve C is *piecewise smooth* if $x'(t)$, $y'(t)$ and $z'(t)$ are continuous, and not all zero for the same value of t, at all but possibly finitely many values of t. Since $x'(t)\mathbf{i} + y'(t)\mathbf{j} + z'(t)\mathbf{k}$ is the tangent vector to C if this is not the zero vector, this condition means that a piecewise smooth curve has a continuous tangent at all but finitely many points. Such a curve typically has the appearance of Figure 13.3, with smooth pieces $C_1, \ldots, C_n$ connected at points where the curve may have no tangent. We will refer to a piecewise smooth curve as a *path*.

In Figure 13.3 the terminal point of C_j is the initial point of C_{j+1} for $j = 1, \ldots, n - 1$. The segments $C_1, \ldots, C_n$ are in order as one moves from the initial to the terminal point of C. This

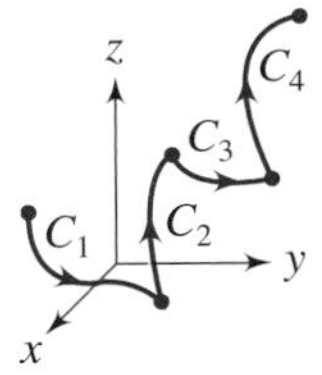

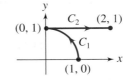

FIGURE 13.3 *Typical piecewise smooth curve (path).*

FIGURE 13.4

is indicated by the arrows showing orientation along the smooth pieces of C. If f, g and h are continuous over each C_j, then we define

$$\int_C f\,dx + g\,dy + h\,dz = \int_{C_1} f\,dx + g\,dy + h\,dz + \cdots + \int_{C_n} f\,dx + g\,dy + h\,dz.$$

This allows us to take line integrals over paths, rather than restricting the integral to smooth curves.

EXAMPLE 13.5

Let C be the curve consisting of the quarter circle $x^2 + y^2 = 1$ in the $x, y-$ plane, from $(1, 0)$ to $(0, 1)$, followed by the horizontal line segment from $(0, 1)$ to $(2, 1)$. Compute $\int_C x^2 y\,dx + y^2\,dy$.

C is piecewise smooth and consists of two smooth pieces (Figure 13.4). Parametrize these as follows. The quarter circle part is

$$C_1 : x = \cos(t), y = \sin(t); \quad 0 \le t \le \pi/2.$$

The straight segment is

$$C_2 : x = p, y = p; \quad 0 \le p \le 2.$$

We have used different names for the parameters on the curves to help distinguish them.

Now evaluate the line integral along each of the two curves making up the path. For the line integral over C_1, compute

$$\int_{C_1} x^2 y\,dx + y^2\,dy = \int_0^{\pi/2} [\cos^2(t)\sin(t)(-\sin(t)) + \sin^2(t)\cos(t)]\,dt$$

$$= \int_0^{\pi/2} \left(-\cos^2(t)\sin^2(t) + \sin^2(t)\cos(t)\right)\,dt = -\frac{1}{16}\pi + \frac{1}{3}.$$

Next evaluate the line integral over C_2. On C_2, $x = p$ and $y = 1$, so $dy = 0$ and

$$\int_{C_2} x^2 y\,dx + y^2\,dy = \int_0^2 p^2\,dp = \frac{8}{3}.$$

Then

$$\int_C x^2 y\,dx + y^2\,dy = -\frac{1}{16}\pi + \frac{1}{3} + \frac{8}{3} = -\frac{\pi}{16} + 3. \quad \blacksquare$$

It is sometimes useful to think of a line integral in terms of vector operations, particularly in the next section when we deal with potential functions. Consider $\int_C f\,dx + g\,dy + h\,dz$. Form a vector field

$$\mathbf{F}(x, y, z) = f(x, y, z)\mathbf{i} + g(x, y, z)\mathbf{j} + h(x, y, z)\mathbf{k}.$$

If C has coordinate functions $x = x(t)$, $y = y(t)$, $z = z(t)$, we can form the position vector, for C:

$$\mathbf{R}(t) = x(t)\mathbf{i} + y(t)\mathbf{j} + z(t)\mathbf{k}.$$

At any time t, the vector $\mathbf{R}(t)$ can be represented by an arrow from the origin to the point $(x(t), y(t), z(t))$ on C. As t varies, this vector pivots about the origin and adjusts its length to sweep out the curve. If C is smooth, then the tangent vector $\mathbf{R}'(t)$ is continuous. Now $d\mathbf{R} = dx\mathbf{i} + dy\mathbf{j} + dz\mathbf{k}$, so

$$\mathbf{F} \cdot d\mathbf{R} = f(x, y, z)\,dx + g(x, y, z)\,dy + h(x, y, z)\,dy$$

and

$$\int_C f(x, y, z)\,dx + g(x, y, z)\,dy + h(x, y, z)\,dz = \int_C \mathbf{F} \cdot d\mathbf{R}.$$

This is just another way of writing a line integral in terms of vector operations.

Line integrals arise in many contexts. For example, consider a force $\mathbf{F}$ causing a particle to move along a smooth curve C having position function $\mathbf{R}(t)$, where t varies from a to b. At any point $(x(t), y(t), z(t))$ of C, the particle may be thought of as moving in the direction of the tangent to its trajectory, and this tangent is $\mathbf{R}'(t)$. Now $\mathbf{F}(x(t), y(t), z(t)) \cdot \mathbf{R}'(t)$ is the dot product of a force with a direction, and so has the dimensions of work. By integrating this function from a to b, we "sum" the work being done by $\mathbf{F}$ over the entire path of motion. This suggests that $\int_C \mathbf{F} \cdot d\mathbf{R}$, or $\int_C f\,dx + g\,dy + h\,dz$, can be interpreted as the work done by $\mathbf{F}$ in moving the particle over the path.

EXAMPLE 13.6

Calculate the work done by $\mathbf{F} = \mathbf{i} - y\mathbf{j} + xyz\mathbf{k}$ in moving a particle from $(0, 0, 0)$ to $(1, -1, 1)$ along the curve $x = t$, $y = -t^2$, $z = t$ for $0 \le t \le 1$.

The work is

$$\text{work} = \int_C \mathbf{F} \cdot d\mathbf{R} = \int_C dx - y\,dy + xyz\,dz$$

$$= \int_0^1 \left(1 + t^2(-2t) - t^4\right) dt$$

$$= \int_0^1 \left(1 - 2t^3 - t^4\right) dt = \frac{3}{10}.$$

The correct units (such as foot-pounds) would have to be provided from context. ■

Line integrals have some of the usual properties we associate with integrals.

THEOREM 13.1

Let C be a path and let having position vector $\mathbf{R}$. Let $\mathbf{F}$ and $\mathbf{G}$ be vector fields that are continuous at points of C. Then

1.

$$\int_C (\mathbf{F} + \mathbf{G}) \cdot d\mathbf{R} = \int_C \mathbf{F} \cdot d\mathbf{R} + \int_C \mathbf{G} \cdot d\mathbf{R}.$$

2. For any number α,

$$\int_C \alpha\mathbf{F} \cdot d\mathbf{R} = \alpha \int_C \mathbf{F} \cdot d\mathbf{R}. \ \blacksquare$$

This theorem illustrates the efficiency of the vector notation for line integrals. We could also write the conclusion (1) as

$$\int_C (f + f^*)dx + (g + g^*)dy + (h + h^*)dz$$

$$= \int_C f\,dx + g\,dy + h\,dz + \int_C f^*dx + g^*dy + h^*dz.$$

For Riemann integrals, reversing the limits of integration changes the sign of the integral: $\int_a^b f(x)dx = -\int_b^a f(x)dx$. The analogous property for line integrals involves reversing orientation on C. Given C with an orientation from an initial point P to a terminal point Q, let $-C$ denote the curve obtained from C by reversing the orientation to go from Q to P (Figure 13.5). Here is a more careful definition of this orientation reversal.

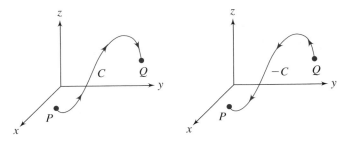

FIGURE 13.5 *Reversing orientation of a curve.*

DEFINITION 13.2

Let C be a smooth curve with coordinate functions $x = x(t)$, $y = y(t)$, $z = z(t)$, for $a \leq t \leq b$. Then $-C$ denotes the curve having coordinate functions

$$\widetilde{x}(t) = x(a+b-t), \quad \widetilde{y}(t) = y(a+b-t), \quad \widetilde{z}(t) = z(a+b-t)$$

for $a \leq t \leq b$.

The initial point of $-C$ is

$$(\widetilde{x}(a), \widetilde{y}(a), \widetilde{z}(a)) = (x(b), y(b), z(b)),$$

the terminal point of C. And the terminal point of $-C$ is

$$(\tilde{x}(b), \tilde{y}(b), \tilde{z}(b)) = (x(a), y(a), z(a)),$$

the initial point of C. By the chain rule, $-C$ is piecewise smooth if C is piecewise smooth.

We will now show that the line integral of a vector field over $-C$ is the negative of the line integral of the vector field over C.

THEOREM 13.2

Let C be a smooth curve with coordinate functions $x = x(t)$, $y = y(t)$, $z = z(t)$. Let f, g and h be continuous on C. Then

$$\int_{-C} f\,dx + g\,dy + h\,dz = -\int_{C} f\,dx + g\,dy + h\,dz. \quad \blacksquare$$

Proof   First,

$$\int_{C} f\,dx + g\,dy + h\,dz$$

$$= \int_{a}^{b} \left[f(x(t), y(t), z(t))\frac{dx}{dt} + g(x(t), y(t), z(t))\frac{dy}{dt} + h(x(t), y(t), z(t))\frac{dz}{dt} \right] dt.$$

Similarly,

$$\int_{-C} f\,dx + g\,dy + h\,dz$$

$$= \int_{a}^{b} \left[f(\tilde{x}(t), \tilde{y}(t), \tilde{z}(t))\frac{d\tilde{x}}{dt} + g(\tilde{x}(t), \tilde{y}(t), \tilde{z}(t))\frac{d\tilde{y}}{dt} + h(\tilde{x}(t), \tilde{y}(t), \tilde{z}(t))\frac{d\tilde{z}}{dt} \right] dt.$$

Change variables in the last integral by putting $s = a + b - t$. When $t = a$, $s = b$, and when $t = b$, $s = a$. Further,

$$\frac{d\tilde{x}}{dt} = \frac{d}{dt}x(a+b-t) = \frac{d}{dt}x(s) = \frac{dx}{ds}\frac{ds}{dt} = -\frac{dx}{ds}$$

and, similarly,

$$\frac{d\tilde{y}}{dt} = -\frac{dy}{ds}, \frac{d\tilde{z}}{dt} = -\frac{dz}{ds}.$$

Finally,

$$dt = -ds.$$

Then

$$\int_{-C} f\,dx + g\,dy + h\,dz$$

$$= \int_{b}^{a} \left[-f(x(s), y(s), z(x))\frac{dx}{ds} - g(x(s), y(s), z(s))\frac{dy}{ds} - h(x(s), y(s), z(s))\frac{dz}{ds} \right](-1)ds$$

$$= -\int_{a}^{b} \left[f(x(s), y(s), z(x))\frac{dx}{ds} + g(x(s), y(s), z(s))\frac{dy}{ds} + h(x(s), y(s), z(s))\frac{dz}{ds} \right] ds$$

$$= -\int_{C} f\,dx + g\,dy + h\,dz. \quad \blacksquare$$

In view of this theorem, the easiest way to evaluate $\int_{-C} f\,dx + g\,dy + h\,dz$ is usually to take the negative of $\int_C f\,dx + g\,dy + h\,dz$. We need not actually write the coordinate functions of $-C$, as was done in the proof.

EXAMPLE 13.7

A force $\mathbf{F}(x, y, z) = x^2\mathbf{i} - zy\mathbf{j} + x\cos(z)\mathbf{k}$ moves a particle along the path C given by $x = t^2$, $y = t$, $z = \pi t$ for $0 \le t \le 3$. The initial point is $P : (0, 0, 0)$ and the terminal point of C is $Q : (9, 3, 3\pi)$. Suppose we want the work done in moving the particle along this path from Q to P.

Since we want to go from the terminal to the initial point of C, the work done is $\int_{-C} \mathbf{F} \cdot d\mathbf{R}$. However, we do not need to formally define $-C$ in terms of new coordinate functions. We can simply calculate $\int_C \mathbf{F} \cdot d\mathbf{R}$, and take the negative of this. Calculate

$$\int_C \mathbf{F} \cdot d\mathbf{R} = \int_C f\,dx + g\,dy + h\,dz$$

$$= \int_0^3 \left[t^4(2t) - \pi t(t)(1) + t^2 \cos(\pi t)(\pi) \right] dt$$

$$= 243 - 9\pi - \frac{6}{\pi}.$$

The work done in moving the particle along the path from Q to P is

$$\frac{6}{\pi} + 9\pi - 243. \quad \blacksquare$$

13.1.1 Line Integral with Respect to Arc Length

Line integrals with respect to arc length occur in some uses of line integrals. Here is the definition of this kind of line integral.

DEFINITION 13.3   *Line Integral With Respect to Arc Length*

Let C be a smooth curve with coordinate functions $x = x(t)$, $y = y(t)$, $z = z(t)$ for $a \le t \le b$. Let φ be a real-valued function that is continuous on the graph of C. Then the integral of φ over C with respect to arc length is

$$\int_C \varphi(x, y, z)\,ds = \int_a^b \varphi(x(t), y(t), z(t))\sqrt{x'(t)^2 + y'(t)^2 + z'(t)^2}\,dt.$$

The rationale behind this definition is that the length function along C is

$$s(t) = \int_a^t \sqrt{x'(\xi)^2 + y'(\xi)^2 + z'(\xi)^2}\,d\xi.$$

Then

$$ds = \sqrt{x'(t)^2 + y'(t)^2 + z'(t)^2}\,dt,$$

suggesting the integral in the definition.

EXAMPLE 13.8

Evaluate $\int_C xy\,ds$ over the curve given by

$$x = 4\cos(t), \, y = 4\sin(t), \, z = -3 \quad \text{for } 0 \le t \le \pi/2.$$

Compute

$$\int_C xy\,ds = \int_0^{\pi/2} 4\cos(t)[4\sin(t)]\sqrt{16\sin^2(t) + 16\cos^2(t)}\,dt$$

$$= \int_0^{\pi/2} 64\cos(t)\sin(t)\,dt = 32. \quad \blacksquare$$

Line integrals with respect to arc length occur in calculations of mass, density, and various other quantities for one-dimensional objects. Suppose, for example, we want the mass of a thin wire bent into the shape of a piecewise smooth curve C having coordinate functions

$$x = x(t), \, y = y(t), \, z = z(t) \quad \text{for } a \le t \le b.$$

The wire is one-dimensional in the sense that (ideally) it has length but not area or volume.

We will derive an expression for the mass of the wire as follows. Let $\delta(x, y, z)$ be the density of the wire at any point. Partition $[a, b]$ into subintervals by inserting points

$$a = t_0 < t_1 < \cdots < t_{n-1} < t_n = b.$$

Choose these points Δt units apart, so $t_j - t_{j-1} = \Delta t$. These partition points of $[a, b]$ determine points

$$P_j : (x(t_j), y(t_j), z(t_j))$$

along C, as shown in Figure 13.6. Assuming that the density function is continuous, we can choose Δt sufficiently small that on the piece of wire between P_{j-1} and P_j, the values of the density function are approximated to whatever accuracy we wish by $\delta(P_j)$. The length of the segment of wire between P_{j-1} and P_j is $\Delta s = s(P_j) - s(P_{j-1})$, which is approximated by

$$ds = \sqrt{x'(t_j)^2 + (y'(t_j)^2 + z'(t_j)^2}\,\Delta t.$$

The density of this piece of wire between P_{j-1} and P_j is therefore approximately the "nearly" constant value of the density on this piece, times the length of this piece of wire, this product being

$$\delta(x(t_j), y(t_j), z(t_j))\sqrt{x'(t_j)^2 + (y'(t_j)^2 + z'(t_j)^2}\,\Delta t.$$

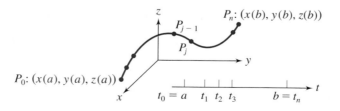

FIGURE 13.6

The mass of the entire length of wire is approximately the sum of the masses of these pieces:

$$\text{mass} \approx \sum_{j=1}^{n} \delta(x(t_j), y(t_j), z(t_j))\sqrt{x'(t_j)^2 + (y'(t_j)^2 + z'(t_j)^2}\,\Delta t,$$

in which $\approx$ means "approximately equal". Recognize this as the Riemann sum for a definite integral to obtain, in the limit as $\Delta t \to 0$,

$$\text{mass} = \int_C \delta(x(t), y(t), z(t))\sqrt{x'(t)^2 + y'(t)^2 + z'(t)^2}\,dt$$

$$= \int_C \delta(x, y, z)\,ds.$$

A similar argument leads to coordinates $(\bar{x}, \bar{y}, \bar{z})$ of the center of mass of the wire:

$$\bar{x} = \frac{1}{m}\int_C x\delta(x, y, z)\,ds, \quad \bar{y} = \frac{1}{m}\int_C y\delta(x, y, z)\,ds, \quad \bar{z} = \frac{1}{m}\int_C z\delta(x, y, z)\,ds.$$

in which m is the mass of the wire.

EXAMPLE 13.9

A wire is bent into the shape of the quarter circle C given by

$$x = 2\cos(t), y = 2\sin(t), z = 3 \quad \text{for } 0 \le t \le \pi/2.$$

The density function is $\delta(x, y, z) = xy^2$ grams/centimeter. We want the mass and center of mass of the wire.

The mass is

$$m = \int_C xy^2\,ds$$

$$= \int_0^{\pi/2} 2\cos(t)[2\sin(t)]^2\sqrt{4\sin^2(t) + 4\cos^2(t)}\,dt$$

$$= \int_0^{\pi/2} 16\cos(t)\sin^2(t)\,dt = \frac{16}{3} \text{ grams.}$$

Now compute the coordinates of the center of mass. First,

$$\bar{x} = \frac{1}{m}\int_C x\delta(x, y, z)\,ds$$

$$= \frac{3}{16}\int_0^{\pi/2} [2\cos(t)]^2[2\sin(t)]^2\sqrt{4\sin^2(t) + 4\cos^2(t)}\,dt$$

$$= 6\int_0^{\pi/2} \cos^2(t)\sin^2(t)\,dt = \frac{3\pi}{8}.$$

Next,

$$\bar{y} = \frac{1}{m}\int_C y\delta(x, y, z)\,ds$$

$$= \frac{3}{16}\int_0^{\pi/2} [2\cos(t)][2\sin(t)]^3\sqrt{4\sin^2(t) + 4\cos^2(t)}\,dt$$

$$= 6\int_0^{\pi/2} \cos(t)\sin^3(t)\,dt = \frac{3}{2}.$$

Finally,

$$\bar{z} = \frac{1}{m} \int_C z\delta(x, y, z)\, ds$$

$$= \frac{3}{16} \int_0^{\pi/2} 3[2\cos(t)][2\sin(t)]^2 \sqrt{4\sin^2(t) + 4\cos^2(t)}\, dt$$

$$= 9 \int_0^{\pi/2} \sin^2(t)\cos(t)\, dt = 3.$$

The last result could have been anticipated, since the z-component on the curve is constant. The center of mass is

$$(3\pi/8, 3/2, 3).\ \blacksquare$$

SECTION 13.1   PROBLEMS

In each of Problems 1 through 15, evaluate the line integral.

1. $\int_C x\, dx - dy + z\, dz$, with C given by $x(t) = t$, $y(t) = t$, $z(t) = t^3$ for $0 \le t \le 1$

2. $\int_C -4x\, dx + y^2\, dy - yz\, dz$, with C given by $x(t) = -t^2$, $y(t) = 0$, $z(t) = -3t$ for $0 \le t \le 1$

3. $\int_C (x + y)\, ds$, where C is given by $x = y = t$, $z = t^2$ for $0 \le t \le 2$

4. $\int_C x^2 z\, ds$, where C is the line segment from $(0, 1, 1)$ to $(1, 2, -1)$

5. $\int_C \mathbf{F} \cdot d\mathbf{R}$, where $\mathbf{F} = \cos(x)\mathbf{i} - y\mathbf{j} + xz\mathbf{k}$ and $\mathbf{R} = t\mathbf{i} - t^2\mathbf{j} + \mathbf{k}$ for $0 \le t \le 3$

6. $\int_C 4xy\, ds$, with C given by $x = y = t$, $z = 2t$ for $1 \le t \le 2$

7. $\int_C \mathbf{F} \cdot d\mathbf{R}$, with $\mathbf{F} = x\mathbf{i} + y\mathbf{j} - z\mathbf{k}$ and C the circle $x^2 + y^2 = 4$, $z = 0$, going around once counterclockwise.

8. $\int_C yz\, ds$, with C the parabola $z = y^2$, $x = 1$ for $0 \le y \le 2$

9. $\int_C -xyz\, dz$, with C the curve $x = 1$, $y = \sqrt{z}$ for $4 \le z \le 9$

10. $\int_C xz\, dy$, with C the curve $x = y = t$, $z = -4t^2$ for $1 \le t \le 3$

11. $\int_C 8z^2\, ds$, with C the curve $x = y = 2t^2$, $z = 1$ for $1 \le t \le 2$

12. $\int_C \mathbf{F} \cdot d\mathbf{R}$, with $\mathbf{F} = \mathbf{i} - x\mathbf{j} + \mathbf{k}$ and $\mathbf{R} = \cos(t)\mathbf{i} - \sin(t)\mathbf{j} + t\mathbf{k}$ for $0 \le t \le \pi$

13. $\int_C 8x^2\, dy$, with C given by $x = e^t$, $y = -t^2$, $z = t$ for $1 \le t \le 2$

14. $\int_C x\, dy - y\, dx$, C the curve $x = y = 2t$, $z = e^{-t}$ for $0 \le t \le 3$

15. $\int_C \sin(x)\, ds$, with C given by $x = t$, $y = 2t$, $z = 3t$ for $1 \le t \le 3$

16. Find the mass and center of mass of a thin, straight wire from the origin to $(3, 3, 3)$ if $\delta(x, y, z) = x + y + z$ grams per centimeter.

17. Find the work done by $\mathbf{F} = x^2\mathbf{i} - 2yz\mathbf{j} + z\mathbf{k}$ in moving an object along the line segment from $(1, 1, 1)$ to $(4, 4, 4)$.

18. Show that any Riemann integral $\int_a^b f(x)\, dx$ is equal to a line integral $\int_C \mathbf{F} \cdot d\mathbf{R}$ for appropriate choices of $\mathbf{F}$ and C. In this sense the line integral generalizes the Riemann integral.

13.2   Green's Theorem

Green's theorem was developed independently by the self-taught British amateur natural philosopher George Green and the Ukrainian mathematician Michel Ostrogradsky. They were studying potential theory (electric potentials, potential functions), and they obtained an important relationship between double integrals and line integrals in the plane.

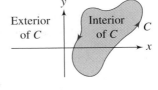

FIGURE 13.7 *Graph of a curve that is not simple.*

FIGURE 13.8 *The Jordan curve theorem.*

Let C be a piecewise smooth curve in the plane, having coordinate functions $x = x(t)$, $y = y(t)$ for $a \le t \le b$. We will be interested in this section in C being a closed curve, so the initial and terminal points coincide.

C is *positively oriented* if $(x(t), y(t))$ moves around C counterclockwise as t varies from a to b. If $(x(t), y(t))$ moves clockwise, then we say that C is *negatively oriented*. For example, let $x(t) = \cos(t)$ and $y(t) = \sin(t)$ for $0 \le t \le 2\pi$. Then $(x(t), y(t))$ moves counterclockwise once around the unit circle as t varies from 0 to 2π, so C is positively oriented. If, however, K has coordinate functions $x(t) = -\cos(t)$ and $y(t) = \sin(t)$ for $0 \le t \le 2\pi$, then K is negatively oriented, because now $(x(t), y(t))$ moves in a clockwise sense. However, C and K have the same graph. A closed curve in the plane is positively oriented if, as you walk around it, the region it encloses is over your left shoulder.

A curve is *simple* if the same point cannot be on the graph for different values of the parameter. This means that $x(t_1) = x(t_2)$ and $y(t_1) = y(t_2)$ can occur only if $t_1 = t_2$. If we envision the graph of a curve as a train track, this means that the train does not return to the same location at a later time. Figure 13.7 shows the graph of a curve that is not simple.

This would prevent a closed curve from being simple, but we make an exception of the initial and terminal points. If these are the only points obtained for different values of the parameter, then a closed curve is also called simple. For example, the equations $x = \cos(t)$ and $y = \sin(t)$ for $0 \le t \le 2\pi$, describe a simple closed curve. However, consider M given by $x = \cos(t)$, $y = \sin(t)$ for $0 \le t \le 4\pi$. This is a closed curve, beginning and ending at $(1, 0)$, but $(x(t), y(t))$ traverses the unit circle twice counterclockwise as t varies from 0 to 4π. M is a closed curve but it is not simple.

It is a subtle theorem of topology, the *Jordan curve theorem*, that a simple closed curve C in the plane separates the plane into two regions having C as common boundary. One region contains points arbitrarily far from the origin, and is called the exterior of C. The other region is called the interior of C. These regions are displayed for a typical closed curve in Figure 13.8. The interior of C has finite area, while the exterior does not.

Finally, when a line integral is taken around a closed curve, we often use the symbol $\oint_C$ in place of $\int_C$. This notation is optional, and is simply a reminder that C is closed. It does not alter in any way the meaning of the integral.

We are now ready to state the first fundamental theorem of vector integral calculus. Recall that a path is a piecewise smooth curve (having a continuous tangent at all but finitely many points).

THEOREM 13.3 *Green*

Let C be a simple closed positively oriented path in the plane. Let D consist of all points on C and in its interior. Let f, g, $\partial g/\partial x$ and $\partial f/\partial y$ be continuous on D. Then

$$\oint_C f(x, y)\,dx + g(x, y)\,dy = \iint_D \left(\frac{\partial g}{\partial x} - \frac{\partial f}{\partial y} \right) dA. \ \blacksquare$$

The significance of Green's theorem is that it relates an object that deals with a curve, which is one-dimensional, to an object related to a planar region, which is two-dimensional. This will have important implications when we discuss independence of path of line integrals in the next section, and later when we develop partial differential equations and complex analysis. Green's theorem will also lead shortly to Stokes's theorem and Gauss's theorem, which are its generalizations to 3-space.

We will prove the theorem under restricted conditions at the end of this section. For now, here are two computational examples.

EXAMPLE 13.10

Sometimes we use Green's theorem as a computational aid to convert one kind of integral into another, possibly simpler, one. As an illustration, suppose we want to compute the work done by the force

$$\mathbf{F}(x, y) = (y - x^2 e^x)\mathbf{i} + (\cos(2y^2) - x)\mathbf{j}$$

in moving a particle about the rectangular path C of Figure 13.9.

If you try to evaluate $\oint_C \mathbf{F} \cdot d\mathbf{R}$ as a sum of line integrals over the straight line sides of this rectangle, you will find that the integrations cannot be done in elementary form. However, apply Green's theorem, with D the region bounded by the rectangle. We obtain

$$\text{work} = \oint_C \mathbf{F} \cdot d\mathbf{R} = \iint_D \left(\frac{\partial}{\partial x}(\cos(2y^2) - x) - \frac{\partial}{\partial y}(y - x^2 e^x) \right) dA$$

$$= \iint_D -2 \, dA = (-2)(\text{area of } D) = -4. \quad \blacksquare$$

EXAMPLE 13.11

Another typical use of Green's theorem is in deriving very general results. To illustrate, suppose we want to evaluate

$$\oint_C 2x \cos(2y) dx - 2x^2 \sin(2y) dy$$

for every positively oriented simple closed path C in the plane.

This may appear to be a daunting task, since there are infinitely many different such paths. However, observe the form of $f(x, y)$ and $g(x, y)$ in the line integral. In particular,

$$\frac{\partial}{\partial x}(-2x^2 \sin(2y)) - \frac{\partial}{\partial y}(2x \cos(2y)) = -4x \sin(2y) + 4x \sin(2y) = 0$$

for all x and y. Therefore, Green's theorem gives us

$$\oint_C 2x \cos(2y) dx - 2x^2 \sin(2y) dy = \iint_D 0 \, dA = 0.$$

In the next section we will see how the vanishing of this line integral for any closed curve allows an important conclusion about line integrals $\int_K 2x \cos(2y) dx - 2x^2 \sin(2y) dy$ when K is not closed. $\blacksquare$

We will conclude this section with a proof of Green's theorem under special conditions on the region bounded by C. Assume that D can be described in two ways.

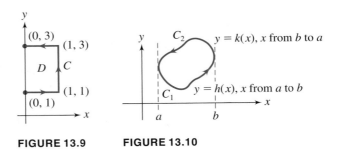

FIGURE 13.9   **FIGURE 13.10**

First, D consists of all points (x, y) with

$$a \leq x \leq b$$

and, for each x,

$$h(x) \leq y \leq k(x).$$

Graphs of the curves $y = h(x)$ and $y = k(x)$ form, respectively, the lower and upper parts of the boundary of D (see Figure 13.10).

Second, D consists of all points (x, y) with

$$c \leq y \leq d$$

and, for each y,

$$F(y) \leq x \leq G(y).$$

In this description, the graphs of $x = F(y)$ and $x = G(y)$ form, respectively, the left and right parts of the boundary of D (see Figure 13.11).

Using these descriptions of D and the boundary of D, we can demonstrate Green's theorem by evaluating the integrals involved. First, let C_1 be the lower part of C (graph of $y = h(x)$) and C_2 the upper part (graph of $y = k(x)$). Then

$$\oint_C f(x, y)dx = \int_{C_1} f(x, y)dx + \int_{C_2} f(x, y)dx$$

$$= \int_a^b f(x, h(x))dx + \int_b^a f(x, k(x))dx$$

$$= \int_a^b -[f(x, k(x)) - f(x, h(x))]dx.$$

The upper and lower limits of integration in the second line maintain a counterclockwise orientation on C.

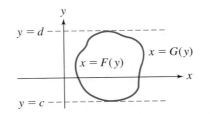

FIGURE 13.11

Now compute

$$\iint_D \frac{\partial f}{\partial y} dA = \int_a^b \int_{h(x)}^{k(x)} \frac{\partial f}{\partial y} dy dx$$

$$= \int_a^b [f(x, y)]_{h(x)}^{k(x)} dx$$

$$= \int_a^b [f(x, k(x)) - f(x, h(x))] dx.$$

Therefore

$$\oint_C f(x, y) dx = -\iint_D \frac{\partial f}{\partial y} dA.$$

Using the other description of D, a similar computation shows that

$$\oint_C g(x, y) dy = \iint_D \frac{\partial g}{\partial x} dA.$$

Upon adding the last two equations we obtain the conclusion of Green's theorem.

SECTION 13.2   PROBLEMS

1. A particle moves once counterclockwise about the triangle with vertices $(0, 0)$, $(4, 0)$ and $(1, 6)$, under the influence of the force $\mathbf{F} = xy\mathbf{i} + x\mathbf{j}$. Calculate the work done by this force.

2. A particle moves once counterclockwise about the circle of radius 6 about the origin, under the influence of the force $\mathbf{F} = (e^x - y + x\cosh(x))\mathbf{i} + (y^{3/2} + x)\mathbf{j}$. Calculate the work done.

3. A particle moves once counterclockwise about the rectangle with vertices $(1, 1)$, $(1, 7)$, $(3, 1)$ and $(3, 7)$, under the influence of the force $\mathbf{F} = (-\cosh(4x^4) + xy)\mathbf{i} + (e^{-y} + x)\mathbf{j}$. Calculate the work done.

In each of Problems 4 through 11, use Green's theorem to evaluate $\oint_C \mathbf{F} \cdot d\mathbf{R}$. All curves are oriented counterclockwise.

4. $\mathbf{F} = 2y\mathbf{i} - x\mathbf{j}$, C is the circle of radius 4 about $(1, 3)$

5. $\mathbf{F} = x^2\mathbf{i} - 2xy\mathbf{j}$, C is the triangle with vertices $(1, 1)$, $(4, 1)$, $(2, 6)$

6. $\mathbf{F} = (x + y)\mathbf{i} + (x - y)\mathbf{j}$, C is the ellipse $x^2 + 4y^2 = 1$

7. $\mathbf{F} = 8xy^2\mathbf{j}$, C is the circle of radius 4 about the origin

8. $\mathbf{F} = (x^2 - y)\mathbf{i} + (\cos(2y) - e^{3y} + 4x)\mathbf{j}$, with C any square with sides of length 5

9. $\mathbf{F} = e^x \cos(y)\mathbf{i} - e^x \sin(y)\mathbf{j}$, C is any simple closed piecewise smooth curve in the plane

10. $\mathbf{F} = x^2 y\mathbf{i} - xy^2\mathbf{j}$, C the boundary of the region $x^2 + y^2 \le 4$, $x \ge 0$, $y \ge 0$

11. $\mathbf{F} = xy\mathbf{i} + (xy^2 - e^{\cos(y)})\mathbf{j}$, C the triangle with vertices $(0, 0)$, $(3, 0)$, $(0, 5)$

12. Let C be a positively oriented simple closed path with interior D.

   (a) Show that the area of D equals $\oint_C -y \, dx$.

   (b) Show that the area of D equals $\oint_C x \, dy$.

   (c) Show that the area of D equals $\frac{1}{2} \oint -y \, dx + x \, dy$.

13. Let $u(x, y)$ be continuous with continuous first and second partial derivatives on a simple closed path C and throughout the interior D of C. Show that

$$\oint_C -\frac{\partial u}{\partial y} dx + \frac{\partial u}{\partial x} dy = \iint_D \left[\frac{\partial^2 u}{\partial x^2} + \frac{\partial^2 u}{\partial y^2} \right] dA.$$

13.2.1   An Extension of Green's Theorem

There is an extension of Green's theorem to include the case that there are finitely many points enclosed by C at which f, g, $\partial f / \partial y$ and/or $\partial g / \partial x$ are not continuous, or perhaps are not even defined. The idea is to excise the "bad points," as we will now describe.

Suppose C is a simple closed positively oriented path in the plane enclosing a region D. Suppose f, g, $\partial f/\partial y$ and $\partial g/\partial x$ are continuous on C, and throughout D except at points $P_1, \ldots, P_n$. Green's theorem does not apply to this region. But with a little imagination we can still draw an interesting conclusion.

Enclose each P_j with a circle K_j of sufficiently small radius that none of these circles intersects either C or each other (Figure 13.12). Next, cut a channel in D from C to K_1, then from K_1 to K_2, and so on until finally a channel is cut from K_{n-1} to K_n. A typical case is shown in Figure 13.13. Form the closed path C^* consisting of C (with a small segment cut out where the channel to K_1 was made), each of the $K'_j s$ (with small cuts removed where the channels entered and exited), and the segments forming the connections between C and the successive $K'_j s$. Figure 13.14 shows C^*, which encloses the region D^*.

By the way C^* was formed, the points $P_1, \ldots, P_n$ are *external* to C^* (Figure 13.15). Further, f, g, $\partial f/\partial y$ and $\partial g/\partial x$ are continuous on C^* and throughout D^*. We can therefore apply Green's theorem to C^* and D^* to conclude that

$$\oint_{C^*} f(x,y)dx + g(x,y)dy = \iint_{D^*} \left(\frac{\partial g}{\partial x} - \frac{\partial f}{\partial y} \right) dA. \tag{13.2}$$

Now imagine that the channels that were cut become narrower, merging to form segments between C and successive $K'_j s$. Then C^* approaches the curve $\hat{C}$ of Figure 13.16, and D^* approaches the region $\hat{D}$ shown in Figure 13.17. $\hat{D}$ consists of D with the disks bounded by $K_1, \ldots, K_n$ cut out. In this limit process, equation 13.2 approaches

$$\oint_C f(x,y)dx + g(x,y)dy + \sum_{j=1}^{n} \oint_{K_j} f(x,y)dx + g(x,y)dy = \iint_{\hat{D}} \left(\frac{\partial g}{\partial x} - \frac{\partial f}{\partial y} \right) dA.$$

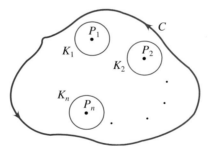

FIGURE 13.12

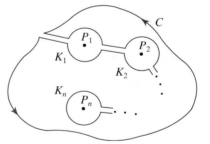

FIGURE 13.13

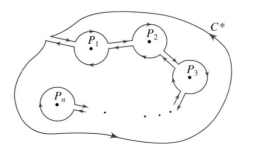

FIGURE 13.14

FIGURE 13.15

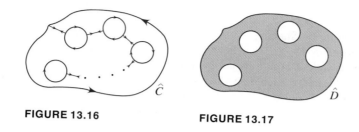

FIGURE 13.16   FIGURE 13.17

On the left side of this equation, line integrals over the internal segments connecting C and the $K_j's$ cancel because the integration is carried out twice over each segment, once in each direction. Further, the orientation on C is counterclockwise, but the orientation on each K_j is clockwise because of the way the boundaries were traversed (Figure 13.14). If we reverse the orientations on these circles the line integrals over them change sign and we can write

$$\oint_C f(x, y)\,dx + g(x, y)\,dy = \sum_{j=1}^{n} \oint_{K_j} f(x, y)\,dx + g(x, y)\,dy + \iint_{\hat{D}} \left(\frac{\partial g}{\partial x} - \frac{\partial f}{\partial y} \right) dA,$$

in which all the integrals are in the positive, counterclockwise sense about the curves C and $K_1, \ldots, K_n$. This is the generalization of Green's theorem that we sought.

EXAMPLE 13.12

Suppose we are interested in

$$\oint_C \frac{-y}{x^2 + y^2}\,dx + \frac{x}{x^2 + y^2}\,dy,$$

with C any simple closed positively oriented path in the plane, but not passing through the origin.

With

$$f(x, y) = \frac{-y}{x^2 + y^2} \quad \text{and} \quad g(x, y) = \frac{x}{x^2 + y^2},$$

we have

$$\frac{\partial g}{\partial x} = \frac{y^2 - x^2}{x^2 + y^2} = \frac{\partial f}{\partial y}.$$

f, g, $\partial f/\partial y$ and $\partial g/\partial x$ are continuous at every point of the plane except the origin. This leads us to consider two cases.

Case 1—C does not enclose the origin.
Now Green's theorem applies and

$$\oint_C \frac{-y}{x^2 + y^2}\,dx + \frac{x}{x^2 + y^2}\,dy = \iint_D \left(\frac{\partial g}{\partial x} - \frac{\partial f}{\partial y} \right) dA = 0.$$

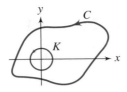

FIGURE 13.18

Case 2—*C* encloses the origin.

Draw a circle *K* centered at the origin, with radius sufficiently small that *K* does not intersect *C* (Figure 13.18). By the extension of Green's theorem,

$$\oint_C f(x, y)dx + g(x, y)dy$$

$$= \oint_K f(x, y)dx + g(x, y)dy + \iint_{\hat{D}} \left(\frac{\partial g}{\partial x} - \frac{\partial f}{\partial y} \right) dA$$

$$= \oint_K f(x, y)dx + g(x, y)dy,$$

where $\hat{D}$ is the region between *K* and *C*. Both of these line integrals are in the counterclockwise sense about the respective curves.

The last line integral can be evaluated explicitly because we know *K*. Parametrize *K* by

$$x = r\cos(\theta), y = r\sin(\theta) \text{ for } 0 \le \theta \le 2\pi.$$

Then

$$\oint_K f(x, y)dx + g(x, y)dy$$

$$= \int_0^{2\pi} \left(\frac{-r\sin(\theta)}{r^2}[-r\sin(\theta)] + \frac{r\cos(\theta)}{r^2}[r\cos(\theta)] \right) d\theta$$

$$= \int_0^{2\pi} d\theta = 2\pi.$$

We conclude that

$$\oint_C f(x, y)dx + g(x, y)dy = \begin{cases} 0 & \text{if } C \text{ does not enclose the origin} \\ 2\pi & \text{if } C \text{ encloses the origin} \end{cases}$$

SECTION 13.2   PROBLEMS

In each of Problems 1 through 5, evaluate $\oint_C \mathbf{F} \cdot d\mathbf{R}$ over any simple closed path in the *x, y* plane that does not pass through the origin.

1. $\mathbf{F} = \dfrac{x}{x^2 + y^2}\mathbf{i} + \dfrac{y}{x^2 + y^2}\mathbf{j}$

2. $\mathbf{F} = \left(\dfrac{1}{x^2 + y^2} \right)^{3/2} (x\mathbf{i} + y\mathbf{j})$

3. $\mathbf{F} = \left(\dfrac{-y}{x^2 + y^2} + x^2 \right)\mathbf{i} + \left(\dfrac{x}{x^2 + y^2} - 2y \right)\mathbf{j}$

4. $\mathbf{F} = \left(\dfrac{-y}{x^2 + y^2} + 3x \right)\mathbf{i} + \left(\dfrac{x}{x^2 + y^2} - y \right)\mathbf{j}$

5. $\mathbf{F} = \left(\dfrac{x}{\sqrt{x^2 + y^2}} + 2x \right)\mathbf{i} + \left(\dfrac{y}{\sqrt{x^2 + y^2}} - 3y^2 \right)\mathbf{j}$

13.3   Independence of Path and Potential Theory in the Plane

In physics, a conservative force field is one that is derivable from a potential. We will use the same terminology.

DEFINITION 13.4   Conservative Vector Field

Let D be a set of points in the plane. A vector field $\mathbf{F}(x, y)$ is conservative on D if for some real-valued $\varphi(x, y)$, $\mathbf{F} = \nabla\varphi$ for all (x, y) in D. In this event, φ is a potential function for $\mathbf{F}$ on D.

If φ is a potential function for $\mathbf{F}$, then so is $\varphi + c$ for any constant c, because $\nabla(\varphi + c) = \nabla\varphi$. For this reason we often speak of a potential function for $\mathbf{F}$, rather than the potential function.

Recall that, if $\mathbf{F}(x, y) = f(x, y)\mathbf{i} + g(x, y)\mathbf{j}$ and $\mathbf{R}(t) = x(t)\mathbf{i} + y(t)\mathbf{j}$ is a position function for C, then $\int_C \mathbf{F} \cdot d\mathbf{R}$ is another way of writing $\int_C f(x, y)dx + g(x, y)dy$. We will make frequent use of the notation $\int_C \mathbf{F} \cdot d\mathbf{R}$ throughout this section because we want to examine the effect on this integral when $\mathbf{F}$ has a potential function, and for this we will use vector notation.

First, the line integral of a conservative vector field can be evaluated directly in terms of a potential function. For suppose C is smooth, with coordinate functions $x = x(t)$, $y = y(t)$ for $a \leq t \leq b$. If $\mathbf{F} = \nabla\varphi$, then

$$\mathbf{F}(x, y) = \frac{\partial\varphi}{\partial x}\mathbf{i} + \frac{\partial\varphi}{\partial y}\mathbf{j}$$

and

$$\int_C \mathbf{F} \cdot d\mathbf{R} = \int_C \frac{\partial\varphi}{\partial x}dx + \frac{\partial\varphi}{\partial y}dy$$

$$= \int_a^b \left(\frac{\partial\varphi}{\partial x}\frac{dx}{dt} + \frac{\partial\varphi}{\partial y}\frac{dy}{dt}\right)dt$$

$$= \int_a^b \frac{d}{dt}\varphi(x(t), y(t))dt$$

$$= \varphi(x(b), y(b)) - \varphi(x(a), y(a)).$$

Denoting $P_1 = (x(b), y(b))$ and $P_0 = (x(a), y(a))$, this result states that

$$\int_C \mathbf{F} \cdot d\mathbf{R} = \varphi(P_1) - \varphi(P_0)$$

$$= \varphi(\text{terminal point of } C) - \varphi(\text{initial point of } C). \qquad (13.3)$$

The line integral of a conservative vector field over a path is the difference in values of a potential function at end points of the path. This is familiar from physics. If a particle moves along a path under the influence of a conservative force field, then the work done is equal to the difference in the potential energy at the ends of the path.

One ramification of equation (13.3) is that the actual path itself does not influence the outcome, only the end points of the path. If we chose a different path K between the same end points, we would obtain the same result for $\int_K \mathbf{F} \cdot d\mathbf{R}$. This suggests the concept of independence of path of a line integral.

DEFINITION 13.5   Independence of Path

$\int_C \mathbf{F} \cdot d\mathbf{R}$ is independent of path on a set D of points in the plane if for any points P_0 and P_1 in D, the line integral has the same value over any paths in D having initial point P_0 and terminal point P_1.

The discussion preceding the definition may now be summarized.

THEOREM 13.4

Let φ and its first partial derivatives be continuous for all (x, y) in a set D of points in the plane. Let $\mathbf{F} = \nabla \varphi$. Then $\int_C \mathbf{F} \cdot d\mathbf{R}$ is independent of path in D. Further, if C is a simple closed path in D, then $\oint_C \mathbf{F} \cdot d\mathbf{R} = 0$. ■

The independence of path follows from equation (13.3), which states that, when $\mathbf{F} = \nabla \varphi$, the value of $\int_C \mathbf{F} \cdot d\mathbf{R}$ depends only on the values of $\varphi(x, y)$ at the end points of the path, and not where the path goes in between. For the last conclusion of the theorem, if C is a closed path in D, then the initial and terminal points coincide, hence the difference between the values of φ at the terminal and initial points is zero.

EXAMPLE 13.13

Let $\mathbf{F}(x, y) = 2x \cos(2y)\mathbf{i} - 2x^2 \sin(2y)\mathbf{j}$. It is routine to check that $\varphi(x, y) = x^2 \cos(2y)$ is a potential function for $\mathbf{F}$. Since φ is continuous with continuous partial derivatives over the entire plane, we can let D consist of all points in the plane in the definition of independence of path. For example, if C is any path in the plane from $(0, 0)$ to $(1, \pi/8)$, then

$$\int_C \mathbf{F} \cdot d\mathbf{R} = \varphi(1, \pi/8) - \varphi(0, 0) = \frac{\sqrt{2}}{2}.$$

Further, if K is any simple closed path in D, then $\oint_K \mathbf{F} \cdot d\mathbf{R} = 0$. ■

It is clearly to our advantage to know whether a vector field is conservative, and, if it is, to be able to produce a potential function. Let

$$\mathbf{F}(x, y) = f(x, y)\mathbf{i} + g(x, y)\mathbf{j}.$$

$\mathbf{F}$ is conservative exactly when, for some φ,

$$\mathbf{F} = \nabla \varphi = \frac{\partial \varphi}{\partial x}\mathbf{i} + \frac{\partial \varphi}{\partial y}\mathbf{j},$$

and this requires that

$$\frac{\partial \varphi}{\partial x} = f(x, y) \text{ and } \frac{\partial \varphi}{\partial y} = g(x, y).$$

To attempt to find such a φ, begin with either of these equations and integrate with respect to the variable of the derivative, keeping the other variable fixed. The constant of integration is then actually a function of the other (fixed) variable. Finally, use the second equation to attempt to find this function.

EXAMPLE 13.14

Consider the vector field

$$\mathbf{F}(x, y) = 2x\cos(2y)\mathbf{i} - [2x^2\sin(2y) + 4y^2]\mathbf{j}.$$

We want a real-valued function φ such that

$$\frac{\partial\varphi}{\partial x} = 2x\cos(2y) \quad \text{and} \quad \frac{\partial\varphi}{\partial y} = -2x^2\sin(2y) - 4y^2.$$

Choose one of these equations. If we pick the first, then integrate with respect to x, holding y fixed:

$$\varphi(x, y) = \int 2x\cos(2y)dx = x^2\cos(2y) + g(y).$$

The "constant" of integration is allowed to involve y because we are reversing a partial derivative, and for any function of y,

$$\frac{\partial}{\partial x}[x^2\cos(2y) + g(y)] = 2x\cos(2y),$$

as we require. We now have $\varphi(x, y)$ to within some function $g(y)$. From the second equation we need

$$\frac{\partial\varphi}{\partial y} = -2x^2\sin(2y) - 4y^2 = \frac{\partial}{\partial y}[x^2\cos(2y) + g(y)].$$

Then

$$-2x^2\sin(2y) - 4y^2 = -2x^2\sin(2y) + g'(y),$$

so

$$g'(y) = -4y^2.$$

Choose $g(y) = -4y^3/3$ to obtain the potential function

$$\varphi(x, y) = x^2\cos(2y) - \frac{4}{3}y^3.$$

It is easy to check that $\mathbf{F} = \nabla\varphi$. ∎

Is every vector field in the plane conservative? As the following example shows, the answer is no.

EXAMPLE 13.15

Let $\mathbf{F}(x, y) = (2xy^2 + y)\mathbf{i} + (2x^2y + e^x y)\mathbf{j}$. If this vector field were conservative, there would be a potential φ such that

$$\frac{\partial\varphi}{\partial x} = 2xy^2 + y, \quad \frac{\partial\varphi}{\partial y} = 2x^2y + e^x y.$$

Integrate the first equation with respect to x to get

$$\varphi(x, y) = \int (2xy^2 + y)dx = x^2y^2 + xy + f(y).$$

From the second equation,

$$\frac{\partial \varphi}{\partial y} = 2x^2 y + e^x y = \frac{\partial}{\partial y}(x^2 y^2 + xy + f(y)) = 2x^2 y + x + f'(y).$$

But this would imply that

$$f'(y) = e^x y - x,$$

and we cannot find a function of y alone satisfying this equation. Therefore **F** has no potential. ∎

Because not every vector field is conservative, we need some test to determine whether or not a given vector field is conservative. The following theorem provides such a test.

THEOREM 13.5 *Test for a Convervative Field*

Let f and g be continuous in a region D bounded by a rectangle having its sides parallel to the axes. Then $\mathbf{F}(x, y) = f(x, y)\mathbf{i} + g(x, y)\mathbf{j}$ is conservative on D if and only if, for all (x, y) in D,

$$\frac{\partial g}{\partial x} = \frac{\partial f}{\partial y}. \quad ∎ \tag{13.4}$$

Sometimes the conditions of the theorem hold throughout the plane, and in this event the vector field is conservative for all (x, y) when equation (13.4) is satisfied.

EXAMPLE 13.16

Consider again $\mathbf{F}(x, y) = (2xy^2 + y)\mathbf{i} + (2x^2 y + e^x y)\mathbf{j}$, from Example 13.15. Compute

$$\frac{\partial f}{\partial y} = 4xy + 1 \quad \text{and} \quad \frac{\partial g}{\partial x} = 4xy + e^x y$$

and these are unequal on any rectangular region of the plane. This vector field is not conservative. We showed in Example 13.15 that no potential function can exist for this field. ∎

13.3.1 A More Critical Look at Theorem 13.5

The condition (13.4) derived in Theorem 13.5 can be written

$$\frac{\partial g}{\partial x} - \frac{\partial f}{\partial y} = 0.$$

But the combination

$$\frac{\partial g}{\partial x} - \frac{\partial f}{\partial y}$$

also occurs in Green's theorem. This must be more than coincidence. In this section we will explore connections between independence of path, Green's theorem, condition (13.4), and existence of a potential function.

The following example is instructive. Let D consist of all points in the plane except the origin. Thus, D is the plane with the origin punched out. Let

$$\mathbf{F}(x, y) = \frac{-y}{x^2 + y^2}\mathbf{i} + \frac{x}{x^2 + y^2}\mathbf{j} = f(x, y)\mathbf{i} + g(x, y)\mathbf{j}.$$

Then **F** is defined on D, and f and g are continuous with continuous partial derivatives on D. Further, we saw in Example 13.12 that

$$\frac{\partial f}{\partial y} - \frac{\partial g}{\partial x} = 0 \quad \text{for } (x, y) \text{ in } D.$$

Now evaluate $\int_C f(x, y) dx + g(x, y) dy$ over two paths from $(1, 0)$ to $(-1, 0)$. First, let C be the top half of the unit circle, given by

$$x = \cos(\theta), y = \sin(\theta) \quad \text{for } 0 \leq \theta \leq \pi.$$

Then

$$\int_C f(x, y) dx + g(x, y) dy$$

$$= \int_0^\pi [(-\sin(\theta))(-\sin(\theta)) + \cos(\theta)\cos(\theta)] d\theta = \int_0^\pi d\theta = \pi.$$

Next, let K be the path from $(1, 0)$ to $(-1, 0)$ along the bottom half of the unit circle, given by

$$x = \cos(\theta), y = -\sin(\theta) \quad \text{for } 0 \leq \theta \leq \pi.$$

Then

$$\int_K f(x, y) dx + g(x, y) dy$$

$$= \int_0^\pi [\sin(\theta)(-\sin(\theta)) + \cos(\theta)(-\cos(\theta))] d\theta = -\int_0^\pi d\theta = -\pi.$$

This means that $\int_C f(x, y) dx + g(x, y) dy$ is not independent of path in D. The path chosen between two given points makes a difference. This also means that **F** is not conservative over D. There is no potential function for **F** (by Theorem 13.4, if there were a potential function, then the line integral would have to be independent of path).

This example suggests that there is something about the conditions specified on the set D in Theorem 13.5 that make a difference. The rectangular set in the theorem, where condition (13.4) is necessary and sufficient for existence of a potential, must have some property or properties that the set in this example lacks. We will explore this line of thought.

Let D be a set of points in the plane. We call D a *domain* if it satisfies two conditions:

1. If P_0 is any point of D, there is a circle about P_0 such that every point enclosed by this circle is also in D.

2. Between any two points of D, there is a path lying entirely in D.

For example, the right quarter plane S consisting of points (x, y) with $x \geq 0$ and $y \geq 0$ enjoys property (2), but not (1). There is no circle that can be drawn about a point $(x, 0)$ with $x \geq 0$, that contains only points with nonnegative coordinates (Figure 13.19). Similarly, any circle drawn about a point $(0, y)$ in S must contains points outside of S.

The shaded set M of points in Figure 13.20 does not satisfy condition (2). Any path C connecting the indicated points P and Q must at some time go outside of M.

Figure 13.21 shows the set A of points between the circles of radius 1 and 3 about the origin. Thus, (x, y) is in A exactly when

$$1 < x^2 + y^2 < 9.$$

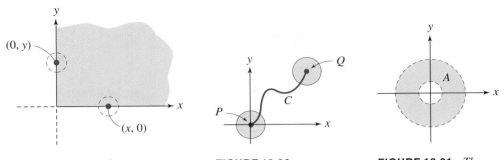

FIGURE 13.19 *Right quarter plane $x \geq 0$, $y \geq 0$.*

FIGURE 13.20

FIGURE 13.21 *The region between two concentric circles.*

This set satisfies conditions (1) and (2), and so is a domain. The boundary circles are drawn as dashed curves to emphasize that points on these curves are not in A.

The conditions defining a domain are enough for the first theorem.

THEOREM 13.6

Let **F** be a vector field that is continuous on a domain D. Then, $\int_C \mathbf{F} \cdot d\mathbf{R}$ is independent of path on D if and only if **F** is conservative. ∎

Proof We know that, if **F** is conservative, then $\int_C \mathbf{F} \cdot d\mathbf{R}$ is independent of path on D. It is the converse that uses the condition that D is a domain.

Conversely, suppose $\int_C \mathbf{F} \cdot d\mathbf{R}$ is independent of path on D. We will produce a potential function. Choose any point $P_0 : (x_0, y_0)$ in D. If $P : (x, y)$ is any point of D, define

$$\varphi(x, y) = \int_C \mathbf{F} \cdot d\mathbf{R},$$

in which C is any path in D from P_0 to P. There is such a path because D is a domain. Further, because this line integral is independent of path, $\varphi(x, y)$ depends only on (x, y) and P_0 and not on the curve chosen between them. Thus φ is a function. Because **F** is continuous on D, φ is also continuous on D.

Now let $\mathbf{F}(x, y) = f(x, y)\mathbf{i} + g(x, y)\mathbf{j}$ and select any point (a, b) in D. We will show that

$$\frac{\partial \varphi}{\partial x}(a, b) = f(a, b) \quad \text{and} \quad \frac{\partial \varphi}{\partial y}(a, b) = g(a, b).$$

For the first of these equations, recall that

$$\frac{\partial \varphi}{\partial x}(a, b) = \lim_{\Delta \to 0} \frac{\varphi(a + \Delta x, b) - \varphi(a, b)}{\Delta x}.$$

Because D is a domain, there is a circle about (a, b) enclosing only points of D. Let r be the radius of such a circle and restrict Δx so that $0 < \Delta x < r$. Let C_1 be any path in D from P_0 to (a, b) and C_2 the horizontal line segment from (a, b) to $(a + \Delta x, b)$, as shown in Figure 13.22. Let C be the path from P_0 to $(a + \Delta x, b)$ consisting of C_1 and then C_2. Now

$$\varphi(a + \Delta x, b) - \varphi(a, b) = \int_C \mathbf{F} \cdot d\mathbf{R} - \int_{C_1} \mathbf{F} \cdot d\mathbf{R} = \int_{C_2} \mathbf{F} \cdot dR.$$

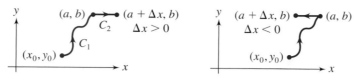

FIGURE 13.22   **FIGURE 13.23**

Parametrize C_2 by $x = a + t\Delta x$, $y = b$ for $0 \le t \le 1$. Then

$$\varphi(a + \Delta x, b) - \varphi(a, b)$$

$$= \int_{C_2} \mathbf{F} \cdot d\mathbf{R} = \int_{C_2} f(x, y)dx + g(x, y)dy$$

$$= \int_0^1 f(a + t\Delta x, b)(\Delta x)dt.$$

Then

$$\frac{\varphi(a + \Delta x, b) - \varphi(a, b)}{\Delta x} = \int_0^1 f(a + t\Delta x, b)dt.$$

By the mean value theorem for integrals, there is a number ϵ between 0 and 1, inclusive, such that

$$\int_0^1 f(a + t\Delta x, b)dt = f(a + \epsilon\Delta x, b).$$

Therefore

$$\frac{\varphi(a + \Delta x, b) - \varphi(a, b)}{\Delta x} = f(a + \epsilon\Delta x, b).$$

As $\Delta x \to 0$, $f(a + \epsilon\Delta x, b) \to f(a, b)$ by continuity of f, proving that

$$\lim_{\Delta x \to 0+} \frac{\varphi(a + \Delta x, b) - \varphi(a, b)}{\Delta x} = f(a, b).$$

By a similar argument, using the path of Figure 13.23, we can show that

$$\lim_{\Delta x \to 0-} \frac{\varphi(a + \Delta x, b) - \varphi(a, b)}{\Delta x} = f(a, b).$$

Therefore

$$\frac{\partial \varphi}{\partial x}(a, b) = f(a, b).$$

To prove that $(\partial\varphi/\partial y)(a, b) = g(a, b)$, the reasoning is similar except now use the paths of Figures 13.24 and 13.25.

This completes the proof of the theorem. ∎

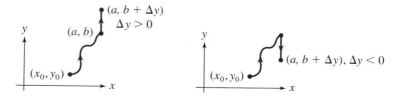

FIGURE 13.24   **FIGURE 13.25**

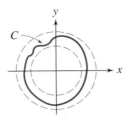

FIGURE 13.26 *The set of points between two concentric circles is not simply connected.*

We have seen that the condition (13.4) is necessary and sufficient for **F** to be conservative within a rectangular region (which is a domain). Although this result is strong enough for many purposes, it is possible to extend it to regions that are not rectangular in shape if another condition is added to the region.

A domain D is called *simply connected* if every simple closed path in D encloses only points of D. A simply connected domain is one that has no "holes" in it, because a simple closed path about the hole will enclose points not in the domain. If D is the plane with the origin removed, then D is not simply connected, because the unit circle about the origin encloses a point not in D. We have seen in Example 13.12 that condition (13.4) may be satisfied in this domain by a vector field having no potential function on D. Similarly, the region between two concentric circles is not simply connected, because a closed curve in this region may wrap around the inner circle, hence enclose points not in the region (Figure 13.26).

We will now show that simple connectivity is just what is needed to ensure that condition (13.4) is equivalent to existence of a potential function. The key is that simple connectivity allows the use of Green's theorem.

THEOREM 13.7

Let $\mathbf{F}(x, y) = f(x, y)\mathbf{i} + g(x, y)\mathbf{j}$ be a vector field and D a simply connected domain. Suppose f, g, $\partial f/\partial y$ and $\partial g/\partial x$ are continuous on D. Then, **F** is conservative on D if and only if

$$\frac{\partial f}{\partial y} = \frac{\partial g}{\partial x}$$

for all (x, y) in D. ■

Proof Suppose first that **F** is conservative, with potential φ. Then

$$f(x, y) = \frac{\partial \varphi}{\partial x} \quad \text{and} \quad g(x, y) = \frac{\partial \varphi}{\partial y}.$$

Then

$$\frac{\partial f}{\partial y} = \frac{\partial^2 \varphi}{\partial x \partial y} = \frac{\partial^2 \varphi}{\partial y \partial x} = \frac{\partial g}{\partial y}$$

for (x, y) in D.

For the converse, suppose that condition (13.4) holds throughout D. We will prove that $\int_C \mathbf{F} \cdot d\mathbf{R}$ is independent of path in D. By the previous theorem, this will imply that **F** is conservative. To this end, let P_0 and P_1 be any points of D, and let C and K be paths in D from P_0 to P_1. Suppose first that these paths have only their end points in common (Figure 13.27 (a)). We can then form a positively oriented simply closed path J from P_0 to P_0 by moving

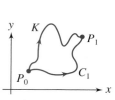

FIGURE 13.27(a)
Paths C and K from
P_0 to P_1.

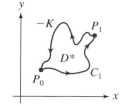

FIGURE 13.27(b)
A closed path formed
from C and −K.

from P_0 to P_1 along C, then back to P_0 along $-K$ (Figure 13.27 (b)). Let J enclose a region D^*. Since D is simply connected, every point in D^* is in D, over which f, g, $\partial f/\partial y$ and $\partial g/\partial x$ are continuous. Apply Green's theorem to write

$$\oint_J \mathbf{F} \cdot d\mathbf{R} = \iint_{D^*} \left(\frac{\partial g}{\partial x} - \frac{\partial f}{\partial y} \right) dA = 0.$$

But then

$$\oint_J \mathbf{F} \cdot d\mathbf{R} = \int_C \mathbf{F} \cdot d\mathbf{R} + \int_{-K} \mathbf{F} \cdot d\mathbf{R}$$

$$= \int_C \mathbf{F} \cdot d\mathbf{R} - \int_K \mathbf{F} \cdot d\mathbf{R} = 0,$$

so

$$\int_C \mathbf{F} \cdot d\mathbf{R} = \int_K \mathbf{F} \cdot d\mathbf{R}.$$

If C and K intersect each other between P_0 and P_1 as in Figure 13.28 then this conclusion can still be drawn by considering closed paths between successive points of intersection. We will not pursue this technical argument.

Once we have independence of path of $\int_C \mathbf{F} \cdot d\mathbf{R}$ on D, then $\mathbf{F}$ is conservative, and the theorem is proved. ∎

In sum:

$$\text{conservative vector field} \implies \text{independence of path of } \int_C \mathbf{F} \cdot d\mathbf{R} \text{ on a set } D,$$

$$\text{independence of path on a } \textit{domain} \iff \text{conservative vector field}$$

and

$$\text{conservative on a } \textit{simply connected domain} \iff \frac{\partial g}{\partial x} = \frac{\partial f}{\partial y}.$$

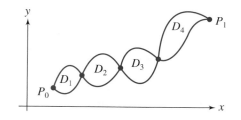

FIGURE 13.28

SECTION 13.3   PROBLEMS

In each of Problems 1 through 8, determine whether **F** is conservative in the given region D. If it is, find a potential function. If D is not defined, it is understood to be the entire plane.

1. $\mathbf{F} = y^3\mathbf{i} + (3xy^2 - 4)\mathbf{j}$

2. $\mathbf{F} = (6y + ye^{xy})\mathbf{i} + (6x + xe^{xy})\mathbf{j}$

3. $\mathbf{F} = 16x\mathbf{i} + (2 - y^2)\mathbf{j}$

4. $\mathbf{F} = 2xy\cos(x^2)\mathbf{i} + \sin(x^2)\mathbf{j}$

5. $\mathbf{F} = \left(\dfrac{2x}{x^2 + y^2}\right)\mathbf{i} + \left(\dfrac{2y}{x^2 + y^2}\right)\mathbf{j}$, D the plane with the origin removed

6. $\mathbf{F} = \sinh(x + y)(\mathbf{i} + \mathbf{j})$

7. $\mathbf{F} = 2\cos(2x)e^y\mathbf{i} + [e^y\sin(2x) - y]\mathbf{j}$

8. $\mathbf{F} = (3x^2y - \sin(x) + 1)\mathbf{i} + (x^3 + e^y)\mathbf{j}$

In each of Problems 9 through 16, evaluate $\oint_C \mathbf{F} \cdot d\mathbf{R}$ for C any path from the first given point to the second.

9. $\mathbf{F} = 3x^2(y^2 - 4y)\mathbf{i} + (2x^3y - 4x^3)\mathbf{j}$; $(-1, 1)$, $(2, 3)$

10. $\mathbf{F} = e^x\cos(y)\mathbf{i} - e^x\sin(y)\mathbf{j}$; $(0, 0)$, $(2, \pi/4)$

11. $\mathbf{F} = 2xy\mathbf{i} + (x^2 - 1/y)\mathbf{j}$; $(1, 3)$, $(2, 2)$ (the path cannot cross the x axis)

12. $\mathbf{F} = \mathbf{i} + (6y + \sin(y))\mathbf{j}$; $(0, 0)$, $(1, 3)$

13. $\mathbf{F} = (3x^2y^2 - 6y^3)\mathbf{i} + (2x^3y - 18xy^2)\mathbf{j}$; $(0, 0)$, $(1, 1)$

14. $\mathbf{F} = \dfrac{y}{x}\mathbf{i} + \ln(x)\mathbf{j}$; $(1, 1)$, $(2, 2)$ (the path must lie in the right half-plane $x > 0$)

15. $\mathbf{F} = (-8e^y + e^x)\mathbf{i} - 8xe^y\mathbf{j}$; $(-1, -1)$, $(3, 1)$

16. $\mathbf{F} = \left(4xy + \dfrac{3}{x^2}\right)\mathbf{i} + 2x^2\mathbf{j}$; $(1, 2)$, $(3, 3)$ (the path must lie in the half-plane $x > 0$)

17. Prove the law of conservation of energy: the sum of the kinetic and potential energies of an object acted on by a conservative force field is a constant. *Hint*: The kinetic energy is $(m/2)\|\mathbf{R}'(t)\|^2$, where m is the mass and $\mathbf{R}(t)$ the position vector of the particle. The potential energy is $-\varphi(x, y)$, where φ is a potential function for the force. Show that the derivative of the sum of the kinetic and potential energies is zero along any path of motion.

13.4   Surfaces in 3-Space and Surface Integrals

Analogous to the integral of a function over a curve, we would like to develop an integral of a function over a surface. This will require some background on surfaces.

A curve is often given by specifying coordinate functions, each of which is a function of a single variable or parameter. For this reason we think of a curve as a one-dimensional object, although the graph may be in 2-space or 3-space.

A *surface* may be defined by giving coordinate functions which depend on two independent variables, say

$$x = x(u, v), \quad y = y(u, v), \quad z = z(u, v),$$

with (u, v) varying over some set in the u, v plane. The locus of such points may form a two-dimensional object in the plane or in R^3.

EXAMPLE 13.17

Suppose a surface is given by the coordinate functions

$$x = au\cos(v), \quad y = bu\sin(v), \quad z = u,$$

with u and v any real numbers and a and b nonzero constants. In this case it is easy to write z in terms of x and y, a tactic that is sometimes useful in visualizing the surface. Notice that

$$\left(\frac{x}{au}\right)^2 + \left(\frac{y}{bu}\right)^2 = \cos^2(v) + \sin^2(v) = 1,$$

so

$$\frac{x^2}{a^2} + \frac{y^2}{b^2} = u^2 = z^2.$$

In the plane $y = 0$ (the x, z plane), $z = \pm x/a$, which are straight lines of slope $\pm 1/a$ through the origin. In the plane $x = 0$ (the y, z plane), $z = \pm y/b$, and these are straight lines of slope $\pm 1/b$ through the origin. The surface intersects a plane $z = c = $ constant $\neq 0$, in an ellipse

$$\frac{x^2}{a^2} + \frac{y^2}{b^2} = c^2, \quad z = c.$$

This surface is called an elliptical cone because it has elliptical cross sections parallel to the x, y plane. ∎

EXAMPLE 13.18

Consider the surface having coordinate functions

$$x = u\cos(v), \quad y = u\sin(v), \quad z = \frac{1}{2}u^2\sin(2v),$$

in which u and v can be any real numbers. Now

$$z = \frac{1}{2}u^2\sin(2v) = u^2\sin(v)\cos(v)$$

$$= [u\cos(v)][u\sin(v)] = xy.$$

This surface intersects any plane $z = c = $ constant $\neq 0$ in the hyperbola $xy = c, z = c$. However, the surface intersects a plane $y = \pm x$ in a parabola $z = \pm x^2$. For this reason this surface is called a hyperbolic paraboloid. ∎

Sometimes x and y are used as parameters, and the surface is defined by giving z as a function of x and y, say $z = S(x, y)$. Now the graph of the surface is the locus of points $(x, y, S(x, y))$, as (x, y) varies over some set of points in the x, y plane.

EXAMPLE 13.19

Consider $z = \sqrt{4 - x^2 - y^2}$ for $x^2 + y^2 \leq 4$. By squaring both sides of this equation, we can write

$$x^2 + y^2 + z^2 = 4.$$

This appears to be the equation of a sphere of radius 2 about the origin. However, in the original formulation with z given by the radical, we have $z \geq 0$, so in fact we have not the sphere, but the hemisphere (upper half of the sphere) of radius 2 about the origin. ∎

EXAMPLE 13.20

The equation $z = \sqrt{x^2 + y^2}$ for $x^2 + y^2 \leq 8$ determines a cone having circular cross sections parallel to the x, y plane. The "top" of the cone is the circle $x^2 + y^2 = 8$ in the plane $z = \sqrt{8}$. ∎

EXAMPLE 13.21

The equation $z = x^2 + y^2$ defines a parabolic bowl, extending to infinity in the positive z-direction because there is no restriction on x or y. ■

These surfaces are easy to visualize and sketch by hand. If the defining function is more complicated then we usually depend on a software package to sketch all or part of the surface. Examples are given in Figures 13.29 through 13.33.

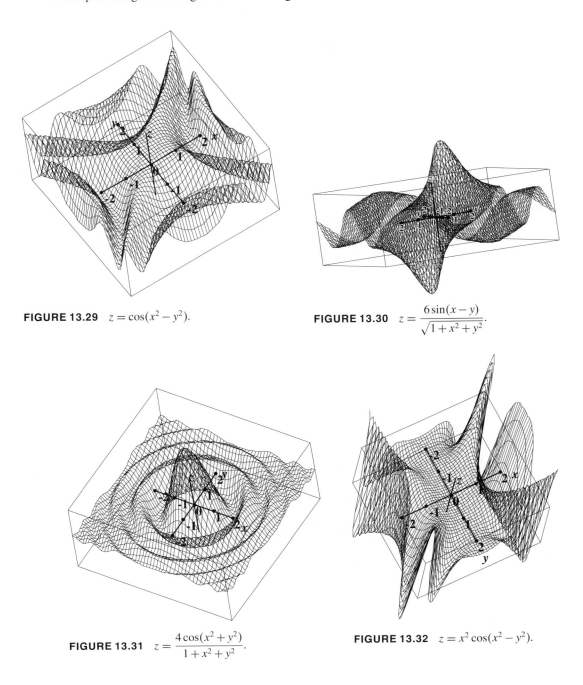

FIGURE 13.29 $z = \cos(x^2 - y^2)$.

FIGURE 13.30 $z = \dfrac{6\sin(x-y)}{\sqrt{1 + x^2 + y^2}}$.

FIGURE 13.31 $z = \dfrac{4\cos(x^2 + y^2)}{1 + x^2 + y^2}$.

FIGURE 13.32 $z = x^2 \cos(x^2 - y^2)$.

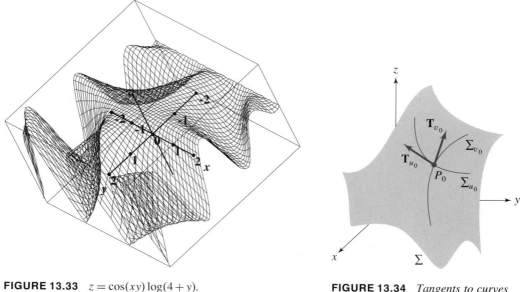

FIGURE 13.33 $z = \cos(xy)\log(4+y)$.

FIGURE 13.34 *Tangents to curves on $\sum$ at P_0 determine the tangent plane to the surface there.*

Just as we can write a position vector to a curve, we can write a position vector

$$\mathbf{R}(u, v) = x(u, v)\mathbf{i} + y(u, v)\mathbf{j} + z(u, v)\mathbf{k}$$

for a surface. For any u and v in the parameter domain, $\mathbf{R}(u, v)$ can be thought of as an arrow from the origin to the point $(x(u, v), y(u, v), z(u, v))$ on the surface.

A surface is *simple* if $\mathbf{R}(u_1, v_1) = \mathbf{R}(u_2, v_2)$ can occur only if $u_1 = u_2$ and $v_1 = v_2$. A simple surface is one that does not fold over and return to the same point for different values of the parameter pairs.

13.4.1 Normal Vector to a Surface

Let $\sum$ be a surface with coordinate functions $x = x(u, v)$, $y = y(u, v)$, $z = z(u, v)$. Assume that these functions are continuous with continuous first partial derivatives. Let $P_0 : (x(u_0, v_0), y(u_0, v_0), z(u_0, v_0))$ be a point on $\sum$.

If we fix $v = v_0$, we can define the curve $\sum_{v_0}$ on the surface, having coordinate functions

$$x = x(u, v_0), \quad y = y(u, v_0), \quad z = z(u, v_0).$$

(See Figure 13.34.) This is a curve because its coordinate functions are functions of the single variable u. The tangent vector to $\sum_{v_0}$ at P_0 is

$$\mathbf{T}_{v_0} = \frac{\partial x}{\partial u}(u_0, v_0)\mathbf{i} + \frac{\partial y}{\partial u}(u_0, v_0)\mathbf{j} + \frac{\partial z}{\partial u}(u_0, v_0)\mathbf{k}.$$

Similarly, if we fix $u = u_0$ and use v as parameter, we obtain the curve $\sum_{u_0}$ on the surface (also shown in Figure 13.34). This curve has coordinate functions

$$x = x(u_0, v), \quad y = y(u_0, v), \quad z = z(u_0, v).$$

The tangent vector to $\sum_{u_0}$ at P_0 is

$$\mathbf{T}_{u_0} = \frac{\partial x}{\partial v}(u_0, v_0)\mathbf{i} + \frac{\partial y}{\partial v}(u_0, v_0)\mathbf{j} + \frac{\partial z}{\partial v}(u_0, v_0)\mathbf{k}.$$

Assuming that neither of these tangent vectors is the zero vector, they both lie in the tangent plane to $\sum$ at P_0. Their cross product is therefore normal (orthogonal) to this tangent plane, and is the vector we define to be the *normal to $\sum$ at P_0*:

$$\mathbf{N}(P_0) = \left[\frac{\partial x}{\partial u}(u_0, v_0)\mathbf{i} + \frac{\partial y}{\partial u}(u_0, v_0)\mathbf{j} + \frac{\partial z}{\partial u}(u_0, v_0)\mathbf{k}\right]$$

$$\times \left[\frac{\partial x}{\partial v}(u_0, v_0)\mathbf{i} + \frac{\partial y}{\partial v}(u_0, v_0)\mathbf{j} + \frac{\partial z}{\partial v}(u_0, v_0)\mathbf{k}\right]$$

$$= \begin{vmatrix} \mathbf{i} & \mathbf{j} & \mathbf{k} \\ \frac{\partial x}{\partial u}(u_0, v_0) & \frac{\partial y}{\partial u}(u_0, v_0) & \frac{\partial z}{\partial u}(u_0, v_0) \\ \frac{\partial x}{\partial v}(u_0, v_0) & \frac{\partial y}{\partial v}(u_0, v_0) & \frac{\partial z}{\partial v}(u_0, v_0) \end{vmatrix}.$$

$$= \left(\frac{\partial y}{\partial u}\frac{\partial z}{\partial v} - \frac{\partial z}{\partial u}\frac{\partial y}{\partial v}\right)\mathbf{i} + \left(\frac{\partial z}{\partial u}\frac{\partial x}{\partial v} - \frac{\partial x}{\partial u}\frac{\partial z}{\partial v}\right)\mathbf{j} + \left(\frac{\partial x}{\partial u}\frac{\partial y}{\partial v} - \frac{\partial y}{\partial u}\frac{\partial x}{\partial v}\right)\mathbf{k}, \qquad (13.5)$$

in which all the partial derivatives are evaluated at (u_0, v_0). An expression that is easier to remember is obtained by introducing Jacobian notation. Define the Jacobian determinant (named for the German mathematician Karl Jacobi) of functions f and g to be the 2×2 determinant

$$\frac{\partial(f, g)}{\partial(u, v)} = \begin{vmatrix} \frac{\partial f}{\partial u} & \frac{\partial f}{\partial v} \\ \frac{\partial g}{\partial u} & \frac{\partial g}{\partial v} \end{vmatrix} = \frac{\partial f}{\partial u}\frac{\partial g}{\partial v} - \frac{\partial g}{\partial u}\frac{\partial f}{\partial v}.$$

In this notation, the normal vector to $\sum$ at P_0 is

$$\mathbf{N}(P_0) = \frac{\partial(y, z)}{\partial(u, v)}\mathbf{i} + \frac{\partial(z, x)}{\partial(u, v)}\mathbf{j} + \frac{\partial(x, y)}{\partial(u, v)}\mathbf{k},$$

with all the partial derivatives evaluated at (u_0, v_0). This notation helps in remembering the normal vector because of the cyclic pattern in the Jacobian symbols. Write

$$x, y, z$$

in this order. For the first component of $\mathbf{N}(P_0)$, omit the first letter, x, to obtain $\partial(y, z)/\partial(u, v)$. For the second component, omit y, but maintain the same cyclic direction, moving left to right through x, y, z. This means we start with z, the next letter after y, then back to x, obtaining $\partial(z, x)/\partial(u, v)$. For the third component, omit z, leaving x, y and the Jacobian $\partial(x, y)/\partial(u, v)$. Of course, any nonzero real multiple of $\mathbf{N}(P_0)$ is also a normal to $\sum$ at P_0.

EXAMPLE 13.22

Consider again the elliptical cone

$$x = au\cos(v), \quad y = bu\sin(v), \quad z = u.$$

Suppose we want the normal vector at $P_0 : (a\sqrt{3}/4, b/4, 1/2)$, obtained when $u = u_0 = 1/2$, $v = v_0 = \pi/6$. Compute the Jacobians:

$$\frac{\partial(y, z)}{\partial(u, v)}\bigg]_{(1/2, \pi/6)} = \left[\frac{\partial y}{\partial u}\frac{\partial z}{\partial v} - \frac{\partial z}{\partial u}\frac{\partial y}{\partial v}\right]_{(1/2, \pi/6)}$$

$$= [b\sin(v)(0) - bu\cos(v)]_{(1/2, \pi/6)} = -\sqrt{3}b/4,$$

$$\frac{\partial(z, x)}{\partial(u, v)}\bigg]_{(1/2, \pi/6)} = \left[\frac{\partial z}{\partial u}\frac{\partial x}{\partial v} - \frac{\partial x}{\partial u}\frac{\partial z}{\partial v}\right]_{(1/2, \pi/6)}$$

$$= [-au\sin(v) - a\cos(v)(0)]_{(1/2, \pi/6)} = -a/4$$

and

$$\frac{\partial(x, y)}{\partial(u, v)}\bigg]_{(1/2, \pi/6)} = \left[\frac{\partial x}{\partial u}\frac{\partial y}{\partial v} - \frac{\partial y}{\partial u}\frac{\partial x}{\partial v}\right]_{(1/2, \pi/6)}$$

$$= [a\cos(v)bu\cos(v) - b\sin(v)(-au\sin(v))]_{(1/2, \pi/6)}$$

$$= ab/2.$$

The normal vector at P_0 is

$$\mathbf{N}(P_0) = -\sqrt{3}\frac{b}{4}\mathbf{i} - \frac{a}{4}\mathbf{j} + \frac{ab}{2}\mathbf{k}. \blacksquare$$

Consider the special case that the surface is given explicitly as $z = S(x, y)$. We may think of $u = x$ and $v = y$ as the parameters for Σ and write the coordinate functions as

$$x = x, \quad y = y, \quad z = S(x, y).$$

Since $\partial x/\partial x = 1 = \partial y/\partial y$ and $\partial x/\partial y = \partial y/\partial x = 0$, we have

$$\frac{\partial(y, z)}{\partial(u, v)} = \frac{\partial(y, z)}{\partial(x, y)} = \begin{vmatrix} 0 & 1 \\ \frac{\partial S}{\partial x} & \frac{\partial S}{\partial y} \end{vmatrix} = -\frac{\partial S}{\partial x},$$

$$\frac{\partial(z, x)}{\partial(x, y)} = \begin{vmatrix} \frac{\partial S}{\partial x} & \frac{\partial S}{\partial y} \\ 1 & 0 \end{vmatrix} = -\frac{\partial S}{\partial y},$$

and

$$\frac{\partial(x, y)}{\partial(x, y)} = \begin{vmatrix} 1 & 0 \\ 0 & 1 \end{vmatrix} = 1.$$

The normal at a point $P_0 : (x_0, y_0, S(x_0, y_0))$ in this case is

$$\mathbf{N}(P_0) = -\frac{\partial S}{\partial x}(x_0, y_0)\mathbf{i} - \frac{\partial S}{\partial y}(x_0, y_0)\mathbf{j} + \mathbf{k} \tag{13.6}$$

$$= -\frac{\partial z}{\partial x}(x_0, y_0)\mathbf{i} - \frac{\partial z}{\partial y}(x_0, y_0)\mathbf{j} + \mathbf{k}.$$

We can also denote this vector as $\mathbf{N}(x_0, y_0)$.

EXAMPLE 13.23

Consider the cone given by $z = S(x, y) = \sqrt{x^2 + y^2}$. Then

$$\frac{\partial S}{\partial x} = \frac{x}{\sqrt{x^2 + y^2}} \quad \text{and} \quad \frac{\partial S}{\partial y} = \frac{y}{\sqrt{x^2 + y^2}},$$

except for $x = y = 0$. Take, for example, the point $(3, 1, \sqrt{10})$. The normal vector at this point is

$$\mathbf{N}(3, 1, \sqrt{10}) = -\frac{3}{\sqrt{10}}\mathbf{i} - \frac{1}{\sqrt{10}}\mathbf{j} + \mathbf{k}.$$

This normal vector is shown in Figure 13.35, and it points into the cone. In some contexts we want to know whether a normal vector is an inner normal (such as this one) or an outer normal (pointing out of the region bounded by the surface). If we wanted an outer normal at this point, we could take

$$-\mathbf{N}(P_0) = \frac{3}{\sqrt{10}}\mathbf{i} + \frac{1}{\sqrt{10}}\mathbf{j} - \mathbf{k}.$$

This cone does not have a normal vector at the origin, which is a "sharp point" of the surface. There is no tangent plane at the origin. ■

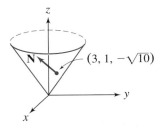

FIGURE 13.35 *Normal to the cone* $z = \sqrt{x^2 + y^2}$ *at* $(3, 1, \sqrt{10})$.

The normal vector (13.6) could also have been derived using the gradient vector. If $\sum$ is given by $z = S(x, y)$, then $\sum$ is a level surface of the function

$$\varphi(x, y, z) = z - S(x, y).$$

The gradient of this function is a normal vector, so compute

$$\nabla\varphi = \frac{\partial\varphi}{\partial x}\mathbf{i} + \frac{\partial\varphi}{\partial y}\mathbf{j} + \frac{\partial\varphi}{\partial z}\mathbf{k}$$

$$= -\frac{\partial S}{\partial x}\mathbf{i} - \frac{\partial S}{\partial y}\mathbf{j} + \mathbf{k} = \mathbf{N}(P).$$

13.4.2 The Tangent Plane to a Surface

If a surface $\sum$ has a normal vector $\mathbf{N}$ at a point P_0, then we can use $\mathbf{N}$ to determine the equation of the tangent plane to $\sum$ at P_0. Let (x, y, z) be any point on the tangent plane. Then the vector $(x - x_0)\mathbf{i} + (y - y_0)\mathbf{j} + (z - z_0)\mathbf{k}$ is in the tangent plane, hence is orthogonal to $\mathbf{N}$. Then

$$\mathbf{N} \cdot [(x - x_0)\mathbf{i} + (y - y_0)\mathbf{j} + (z - z_0)\mathbf{k}] = 0.$$

More explicitly,

$$\left[\frac{\partial(y, z)}{\partial(u, v)}\right]_{(u_0, v_0)}(x - x_0) + \left[\frac{\partial(z, x)}{\partial(u, v)}\right]_{(u_0, v_0)}(y - y_0) + \left[\frac{\partial(x, y)}{\partial(u, v)}\right]_{(u_0, v_0)}(z - z_0) = 0.$$

This is the equation of the tangent plane to $\sum$ at P_0.

EXAMPLE 13.24

Consider again the elliptical cone given by

$$x = au\cos(v), \quad y = bu\sin(v), \quad z = u.$$

We found in Example 13.22 that the normal vector at $P_0 : (a\sqrt{3}/4, b/4, 1/2)$ is $\mathbf{N} = -\sqrt{3}(b/4)\mathbf{i} - (a/4)\mathbf{j} + (ab/2)\mathbf{k}$. The tangent plane to $\sum$ at this point has equation

$$-\sqrt{3}\frac{b}{4}\left(x - \frac{a\sqrt{3}}{4}\right) - \frac{a}{4}\left(x - \frac{b}{4}\right) + \frac{ab}{2}\left(z - \frac{1}{2}\right) = 0. \quad \blacksquare$$

In the special case that $\sum$ is given by $z = S(x, y)$, then the normal vector at P_0 is $\mathbf{N} = -\partial S/\partial x(x_0, y_0)\mathbf{i} - \partial S/\partial y(x_0, y_0)\mathbf{j} + \mathbf{k}$, so the equation of the tangent plane becomes

$$-\frac{\partial S}{\partial x}(x_0, y_0)(x - x_0) - \frac{\partial S}{\partial y}(x_0, y_0)(y - y_0) + (z - z_0) = 0.$$

This equation is usually written

$$z - z_0 = \frac{\partial S}{\partial x}(x_0, y_0)(x - x_0) + \frac{\partial S}{\partial y}(x_0, y_0)(y - y_0).$$

13.4.3 Smooth and Piecewise Smooth Surfaces

Recall that a curve is smooth if it has a continuous tangent. Similarly, a surface is *smooth* if it has a continuous normal vector. A surface is *piecewise smooth* if it consists of a finite number of smooth surfaces. For example, a sphere is smooth, and the surface of a cube is piecewise smooth. A cube consists of six square pieces, which are smooth, but does not have a normal vector along any of its edges.

In calculus, it is shown that the area of a smooth surface $\sum$ given by $z = S(x, y)$ is the integral

$$\text{area of } \sum = \iint_D \sqrt{1 + \left(\frac{\partial S}{\partial x}\right)^2 + \left(\frac{\partial S}{\partial y}\right)^2}\, dA \tag{13.7}$$

where D is the set of points in the $x, y-$ plane for which S is defined. This may also be written

$$\text{area of } \sum = \iint_D \sqrt{1 + \left(\frac{\partial z}{\partial x}\right)^2 + \left(\frac{\partial z}{\partial y}\right)^2}\, dx\, dy.$$

Equation (13.7) is the integral of the length of the normal vector (13.6):

$$\text{area of } \sum = \iint_D \|\mathbf{N}(x, y)\|\, dx\, dy.$$

This is analogous to the formula for the length of a curve as the integral of the length of the tangent vector.

More generally, if Σ is given by coordinate functions $x = x(u, v)$, $y = y(u, v)$ and $z = z(u, v)$, with (u, v) varying over some set D in the u, v plane, then

$$\text{area of } \Sigma = \iint_D \|\mathbf{N}(u, v)\| \, du \, dv, \tag{13.8}$$

the integral of the length of the normal vector, which is given by equation (13.5).

EXAMPLE 13.25

We will illustrate these formulas for surface area for a simple case in which we know the area from elementary geometry. Let Σ be the upper hemisphere of radius 3 about the origin.

We can write Σ as the graph of $z = S(x, y) = \sqrt{9 - x^2 - y^2}$, with $x^2 + y^2 \leq 9$. D consists of all points on or inside the circle of radius 3 about the origin in the x, y-plane.

We can use equation (13.7). Compute

$$\frac{\partial z}{\partial x} = -\frac{x}{\sqrt{9 - x^2 - y^2}} = -\frac{x}{z}$$

and, by symmetry,

$$\frac{\partial z}{\partial y} = -\frac{y}{z}.$$

Then

$$\text{area of } \Sigma = \iint_D \sqrt{1 + \left(\frac{x}{z}\right)^2 + \left(\frac{y}{z}\right)^2} \, dx \, dy$$

$$= \iint_D \sqrt{\frac{z^2 + x^2 + y^2}{z^2}} \, dx \, dy = \iint_D \frac{3}{\sqrt{9 - x^2 - y^2}} \, dx \, dy.$$

This is an improper double integral which we can evaluate easily by converting it to polar coordinates. Let $x = r\cos(\theta)$, $y = r\sin(\theta)$. Since D is the disk of radius 3 about the origin, $0 \leq r \leq 3$ and $0 \leq \theta \leq 2\pi$. Then

$$\iint_D \frac{3}{\sqrt{9 - x^2 - y^2}} \, dx \, dy = \int_0^{2\pi} \int_0^3 \frac{3}{\sqrt{9 - r^2}} r \, dr \, d\theta$$

$$= 6\pi \int_0^3 \frac{r}{\sqrt{9 - r^2}} \, dr = 6\pi \left[-(9 - r^2)^{1/2} \right]_0^3$$

$$= 6\pi \left[9^{1/2} \right] = 18\pi.$$

This is the area of a hemisphere of radius 3. ∎

We are now prepared to define the integral of a function over a surface.

13.4.4   Surface Integrals

The notion of the integral of a function over a surface is modeled after the line integral, with respect to arc length, of a function over a curve. Recall that, if a smooth curve C is given by $x = x(t)$, $y = y(t)$, $z = z(t)$ for $a \leq t \leq b$, then the arc length along C is

$$s(t) = \int_a^t \sqrt{x'(\xi)^2 + y'(\xi)^2 + z'(\xi)^2} \, d\xi.$$

Then

$$ds = \sqrt{x'(t)^2 + y'(t)^2 + z'(t)^2} \, dt$$

and the line integral of a function f along C, with respect to arc length, is

$$\int_C f(x, y, z) \, ds = \int_a^b f(x(t), y(t), z(t)) \sqrt{x'(t)^2 + y'(t)^2 + z'(t)^2} \, dt.$$

We want to lift these ideas up one dimension to integrate over a surface instead of a curve. Now we have coordinate functions that are functions of two independent variables, say u and v, with (u, v) varying over some given set D in the u, v plane. This means that $\int_a^b$ will be replaced by $\iint_D$. The differential element of arc length, ds, which is used in the line integral, will be replaced by the differential element $d\sigma$ of surface area on the surface. By equation (13.8), $d\sigma = \|\mathbf{N}(u, v)\| \, du \, dv$, in which $\mathbf{N}(u, v)$ is the normal vector at the point $(x(u, v), y(u, v), z(u, v))$ on Σ.

DEFINITION 13.6   *Surface Integral*

Let Σ be a smooth surface having coordinate functions $x = x(u, v)$, $y = y(u, v)$, $z = z(u, v)$ for (u, v) in some set D of the u, v plane. Let f be continuous on Σ. Then the surface integral of f over Σ is denoted $\iint_\Sigma f(x, y, z) \, d\sigma$, and is defined by

$$\iint_\Sigma f(x, y, z) \, d\sigma = \iint_D f(x(u, v), y(u, v), z(u, v)) \, \|\mathbf{N}(u, v)\| \, du \, dv.$$

If Σ is a piecewise smooth surface having smooth components $\Sigma_1, \ldots, \Sigma_n$, with each component either disjoint from the others, or intersecting another component in a set of zero area (for example, along a curve), then

$$\iint_\Sigma f(x, y, z) \, d\sigma = \iint_{\Sigma_1} f(x, y, z) \, d\sigma + \cdots + \iint_{\Sigma_n} f(x, y, z) \, d\sigma.$$

For example, we would integrate over the surface of a cube by summing the surface integrals over the six faces. Two such faces either do not intersect, or intersect each other along a line segment having zero area. The intersection condition is to prevent the selection of surface components that overlap each other in significant ways. This is analogous to a piecewise smooth curve C formed as the join of smooth curves $C_1, \ldots, C_n$. When we do this, we assume that two of these component curves either do not intersect, or intersect just at an end point, not along an arc of both curves.

If Σ is described by $z = S(x, y)$, then

$$\iint_\Sigma f(x, y, z) \, d\sigma = \iint_D f(x, y, S(x, y)) \sqrt{1 + \left(\frac{\partial S}{\partial x}\right)^2 + \left(\frac{\partial S}{\partial y}\right)^2} \, dx \, dy.$$

We will look at some examples of evaluation of surface integrals, then consider uses of surface integrals.

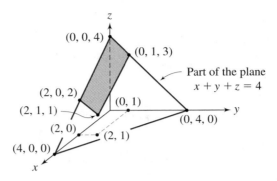

FIGURE 13.36

EXAMPLE 13.26

Evaluate $\iint_{\Sigma} z\,d\sigma$ if Σ is the part of the plane $x+y+z=4$ lying above the rectangle $0 \leq x \leq 2$, $0 \leq y \leq 1$.

The surface is shown in Figure 13.36. D consists of all (x, y) with $0 \leq x \leq 2$ and $0 \leq y \leq 1$. With $z = S(x, y) = 4 - x - y$ we have

$$\iint_{\Sigma} z\,d\sigma = \iint_{D} z\sqrt{1 + (-1)^2 + (-1)^2}\,dx\,dy$$

$$= \sqrt{3} \int_{0}^{2} \int_{0}^{1} (4 - x - y)\,dy\,dx.$$

First compute

$$\int_{0}^{1} (4 - x - y)\,dy = (4-x)y - \frac{1}{2}y^2 \Big]_{0}^{1}$$

$$= 4 - x - \frac{1}{2} = \frac{7}{2} - x.$$

Then

$$\iint_{\Sigma} z\,d\sigma = \sqrt{3} \int_{0}^{2} \left(\frac{7}{2} - x \right) dx = 5\sqrt{3}. \quad \blacksquare$$

EXAMPLE 13.27

Recall the hyperbolic paraboloid of Example 13.18 given by

$$x = u\cos(v), \quad y = u\sin(v), \quad z = \frac{1}{2}u^2\sin(2v).$$

We will compute the surface integral $\iint_{\Sigma} xyz\,d\sigma$ over the part of this surface corresponding to $1 \leq u \leq 2$, $0 \leq v \leq \pi$.

First we need the normal vector. The components of $\mathbf{N}(u, v)$ are the Jacobians:

$$\frac{\partial(y, z)}{\partial(u, v)} = \begin{vmatrix} \sin(v) & u\cos(v) \\ u\sin(2v) & u^2\cos(2v) \end{vmatrix}$$

$$= u^2 \left[\sin(v)\cos(2v) - \cos(v)\sin(2v) \right],$$

$$\frac{\partial(z, x)}{\partial(u, v)} = \begin{vmatrix} u\sin(2v) & u^2\cos(2v) \\ \cos(v) & -u\sin(v) \end{vmatrix}$$

$$= -u^2 \left[\sin(v)\sin(2v) + \cos(v)\cos(2v) \right],$$

and

$$\frac{\partial(x, y)}{\partial(u, v)} = \begin{vmatrix} \cos(v) & -u\sin(v) \\ \sin(v) & u\cos(v) \end{vmatrix} = u.$$

Then

$$\|\mathbf{N}(u, v)\|^2 = u^4 \left[\sin(v)\cos(2v) - \cos(v)\sin(2v) \right]^2$$

$$+ u^4 \left[\sin(v)\sin(2v) + \cos(v)\cos(2v) \right]^2 + u^2$$

$$= u^2(1 + u^2),$$

so

$$\|\mathbf{N}(u, v)\| = u\sqrt{1 + u^2}.$$

The surface integral is

$$\iint_{\Sigma} xyz\, d\sigma = \iint_D [u\cos(v)][u\sin(v)]\left[\frac{1}{2}u^2\sin(2v)\right]u\sqrt{1+u^2}\, dA$$

$$= \int_0^{\pi} \cos(v)\sin(v)\sin(2v)\, dv \int_1^2 u^5\sqrt{1+u^2}\, du$$

$$= \frac{\pi}{4}\left(\frac{100}{21}\sqrt{5} - \frac{11}{105}\sqrt{2}\right). \quad \blacksquare$$

As we expect of an integral,

$$\iint_{\Sigma} (f(x, y, z) + g(x, y, z))\, d\sigma = \iint_{\Sigma} (f(x, y, z)\, d\sigma + \iint_{\Sigma} g(x, y, z))\, d\sigma$$

and, for any real number α,

$$\iint_{\Sigma} \alpha f(x, y, z)\, d\sigma = \alpha \iint_{\Sigma} f(x, y, z)\, d\sigma.$$

The next section is devoted to some applications of surface integrals.

SECTION 13.4   PROBLEMS

In each of Problems 1 through 10, evaluate $\iint_{\Sigma} f(x, y, z)\, d\sigma$.

1. $f(x, y, z) = x$, Σ is the part of the plane $x + 4y + z = 10$ in the first octant

2. $f(x, y, z) = y^2$, Σ is the part of the plane $z = x$ for $0 \le x \le 2, 0 \le y \le 4$

3. $f(x, y, z) = 1$, Σ is the part of the paraboloid $z = x^2 + y^2$ lying between the planes $z = 2$ and $z = 7$

4. $f(x, y, z) = x + y$, Σ is the part of the plane $4x + 8y + 10z = 25$ lying above the triangle in the $x, y-$ plane having vertices $(0, 0)$, $(1, 0)$ and $(1, 1)$

5. $f(x, y, z) = z$, Σ is the part of the cone $z = \sqrt{x^2 + y^2}$ lying in the first octant and between the planes $z = 2$ and $z = 4$

6. $f(x, y, z) = xyz$, Σ is the part of the plane $z = x + y$ with (x, y) lying in the square with vertices $(0, 0)$, $(1, 0)$, $(0, 1)$ and $(1, 1)$

7. $f(x, y, z) = y$, $\sum$ is the part of the cylinder $z = x^2$ for $0 \leq x \leq 2, 0 \leq y \leq 3$

8. $f(x, y, z) = x^2$, $\sum$ is the part of the paraboloid $z = 4 - x^2 - y^2$ lying above the x, y plane

9. $f(x, y, z) = z$, $\sum$ is the part of the plane $z = x - y$ for $0 \leq x \leq 1, 0 \leq y \leq 5$

10. $f(x, y, z) = xyz$, $\sum$ is the part of the cylinder $z = 1 + y^2$ for $0 \leq x \leq 1, 0 \leq y \leq 1$

13.5   Applications of Surface Integrals

13.5.1   Surface Area

If $\sum$ is a piecewise smooth surface, then

$$\iint_{\sum} 1 \, d\sigma = \iint_D \|\mathbf{N}(u, v)\| \, du \, dv = \text{ area of } \sum.$$

(This assumes a bounded surface having finite area.) Clearly we do not need the notion of a surface integral to compute the integral and obtain the area of a surface. However, we mention this result because it is in the same spirit as other familiar mensuration formulas:

$$\int_C ds = \text{length of } C,$$

$$\iint_D dA = \text{area of } D,$$

and, if M is a solid region in 3-space enclosing a volume, then

$$\iiint_M dV = \text{volume of } M.$$

13.5.2   Mass and Center of Mass of a Shell

Imagine a thin shell of negligible thickness taking the shape of a smooth surface $\sum$. Let $\delta(x, y, z)$ be the density of the material of the shell at (x, y, z). Assume that δ is continuous. We want to compute the mass of the shell.

Suppose $\sum$ has coordinate functions $x = x(u, v)$, $y = y(u, v)$, $z = z(u, v)$ for (u, v) in D. Form a grid over D in the u, v plane by drawing lines (dashed lines in Figure 13.37) parallel to the axes, and retain only those rectangles $R_1, \ldots, R_N$ intersecting D. Let the vertical lines be Δu units apart, and the horizontal lines, Δv units apart. For (u, v) varying over R_j, we obtain a patch or surface element $\sum_j$ on the surface (Figure 13.38). That is, $\sum_j(u, v) = \sum(u, v)$ for (u, v) in R_j. Let (u_j, v_j) be a point in R_j, and approximate the density of the surface element $\sum_j$ by the constant

$$\delta_j = \delta(x(u_j, v_j), y(u_j, v_j), z(u_j, v_j)).$$

Because δ is continuous and $\sum_j$ has finite area, we can choose Δu and Δv sufficiently small that δ_j approximates $\delta(x, y, z)$ as closely as we like over $\sum_j$.

Approximate the mass of $\sum_j$ as δ_j times the area of $\sum_j$. Now this area is

$$\text{area of } \sum_j = \iint_{R_j} \|\mathbf{N}(u, v)\| \, du \, dv$$

$$\approx \|\mathbf{N}(u_j, v_j)\| \Delta u \Delta v,$$

so

$$\text{mass of } \sum_j \approx \delta_j \|\mathbf{N}(u_j, v_j)\| \Delta u \Delta v.$$

The mass of $\sum$ is approximately the sum of the masses of the surface elements:

$$\text{mass of } \sum \approx \sum_{j=1}^N \delta(x(u_j, v_j), y(u_j, v_j), z(u_j, v_j)) \|\mathbf{N}(u_j, v_j)\| \Delta u \Delta v.$$

In 1927, Congress approved construction of a dam to control the Colorado River for the purpose of fostering agriculture in the American southwest and as a source of hydroelectric power, spurring the growth of Las Vegas and southern California. Construction began in 1931. One major problem of construction was the cooling of concrete as it was poured. Engineers estimated that the amount of concrete required would take 100 years to cool. The solution was to pour it in rows and columns of blocks, through which cooled water was pumped in pipes. Hoover Dam was completed in 1935 and is 727 feet high, 1244 feet long, 660 feet thick at its base, and 45 feet thick at the top. It weighs about 5.5 million tons and contains 3,250,000 cubic yards of concrete. On one side of the dam, Lake Mead is over 500 feet deep. Computation of forces and stresses on parts of the dam surface involve a combination of material science, fluid flow, and vector analysis.

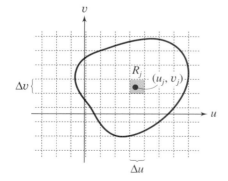

FIGURE 13.37 Grid over D in the u, v plane.

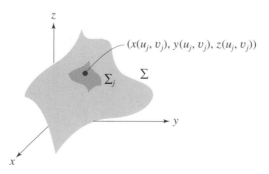

FIGURE 13.38 Surface element $\sum_j$ on $\sum$.

This is a Riemann sum for $\iint_D \delta(x(u,v), y(u,v), z(u,v)) \|\mathbf{N}(u,v)\| \, dudv$. Hence in the limit as $\Delta u \to 0$ and $\Delta v \to 0$ we obtain

$$\text{mass of } \Sigma = \iint_\Sigma \delta(x,y,z) d\sigma.$$

The mass of the shell is the surface integral of the density function. This is analogous to the mass of a wire being the line integral of the density function over the wire.

The center of mass of the shell is $(\overline{x}, \overline{y}, \overline{z})$, where

$$\overline{x} = \frac{1}{m} \iint_\Sigma x\delta(x,y,z) d\sigma, \overline{y} = \frac{1}{m} \iint_\Sigma y\delta(x,y,z) d\sigma,$$

and

$$\overline{z} = \frac{1}{m} \iint_\Sigma z\delta(x,y,z) d\sigma,$$

in which m is the mass of the shell.

EXAMPLE 13.28

We will find the mass and center of mass of the cone $z = \sqrt{x^2 + y^2}$, where $x^2 + y^2 \leq 4$ and the density function is $\delta(x,y,z) = x^2 + y^2$.

First calculate the mass m. We will need

$$\frac{\partial z}{\partial x} = \frac{x}{z} \quad \text{and} \quad \frac{\partial z}{\partial y} = \frac{y}{z}.$$

Then

$$m = \iint_\Sigma (x^2 + y^2) d\sigma$$

$$= \iint_D (x^2 + y^2) \sqrt{1 + \frac{x^2}{z^2} + \frac{y^2}{z^2}} \, dydx$$

$$= \int_0^{2\pi} \int_0^2 r^2 \sqrt{2} r \, drd\theta$$

$$= 2\sqrt{2}\pi \frac{1}{4} r^4 \Big]_0^2 = 8\sqrt{2}\pi.$$

By symmetry of the surface and of the density function, we expect the center of mass to lie on the z axis, so $\overline{x} = \overline{y} = 0$. Finally,

$$\overline{z} = \frac{1}{8\sqrt{2}\pi} \iint_\Sigma z(x^2 + y^2) d\sigma$$

$$= \frac{1}{8\sqrt{2}\pi} \iint_D \sqrt{x^2 + y^2}(x^2 + y^2) \sqrt{1 + \frac{x^2}{z^2} + \frac{y^2}{z^2}} \, dydx$$

$$= \frac{1}{8\pi} \int_0^{2\pi} \int_0^2 r(r^2) r \, drd\theta$$

$$= \frac{1}{8\pi} (2\pi) \left[\frac{1}{5} r^5\right]_0^2 = \frac{8}{5}.$$

The center of mass is $(0, 0, \frac{8}{5})$. ∎

13.5.3 Flux of a Vector Field Across a Surface

Suppose a fluid moves in some region of 3-space (for example, through a pipeline), with velocity $\mathbf{V}(x, y, z, t)$. Consider an imaginary surface $\sum$ within the fluid, with continuous *unit* normal vector $\mathbf{N}(u, v, t)$. The flux of $\mathbf{V}$ across $\sum$ is the net volume of fluid, per unit time, flowing across $\sum$ in the direction of $\mathbf{N}$. We would like to calculate this flux.

In a time interval Δt the volume of fluid flowing across a small piece $\sum_j$ of $\sum$ equals the volume of the cylinder with base $\sum_j$ and altitude $V_N \Delta t$, where V_N is the component of $\mathbf{V}$ in the direction of $\mathbf{N}$, evaluated at some point of $\sum_j$. This volume (Figure 13.39) is $(V_N \Delta t) A_j$, where A_j is the area of $\sum_j$. Because $\|\mathbf{N}\| = 1$, $V_N = \mathbf{V} \cdot \mathbf{N}$. The volume of fluid flowing across $\sum_j$ per unit time is

$$\frac{V_N (\Delta t) A_j}{\Delta t} = V_N A_j = \mathbf{V} \cdot \mathbf{N} A_j.$$

Sum these quantities over all the pieces of the surface and take the limit as the pieces are chosen smaller, as we did for the mass of the shell. We get

$$\text{flux of } \mathbf{V} \text{ across } \sum \text{ in the direction of } \mathbf{N} = \iint_{\sum} \mathbf{V} \cdot \mathbf{N} d\sigma.$$

The flux of a vector across a surface is therefore computed as the surface integral of the normal component of the vector to the surface.

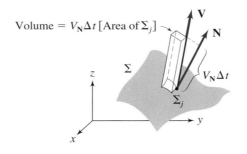

Volume $= V_{\mathbf{N}} \Delta t \, [\text{Area of } \Sigma_j]$

FIGURE 13.39

EXAMPLE 13.29

Find the flux of $\mathbf{F} = x\mathbf{i} + y\mathbf{j} + z\mathbf{k}$ across the part of the sphere $x^2 + y^2 + z^2 = 4$ lying between the planes $z = 1$ and $z = 2$.

The surface $\sum$ is shown in Figure 13.40, along with the normal vector (computed below) at a point. We may think of $\sum$ as defined by $z = S(x, y)$, where S is defined by the equation of the sphere and (x, y) varies over a set D in the x, y plane. To determine D, observe that the plane $z = 2$ hits $\sum$ only at its "north pole" $(0, 0, 2)$. The plane $z = 1$ intersects the sphere in the circle $x^2 + y^2 = 3$, $z = 1$. This circle projects onto the x, y plane to the circle of radius $\sqrt{3}$ about the origin. Thus D consists of points (x, y) satisfying $x^2 + y^2 \leq 3$ (shaded in Figure 13.41).

To compute the partial derivatives $\partial z / \partial x$ and $\partial z / \partial y$, we can implicitly differentiate the equation of the sphere to get

$$2x + 2z \frac{\partial z}{\partial x} = 0,$$

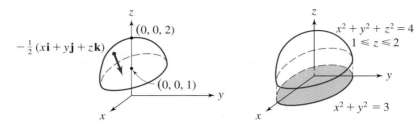

FIGURE 13.40 **FIGURE 13.41**

so

$$\frac{\partial z}{\partial x} = -\frac{x}{z}$$

and, similarly,

$$\frac{\partial z}{\partial y} = -\frac{y}{z}.$$

A normal vector to the sphere is therefore

$$-\frac{x}{z}\mathbf{i} - \frac{y}{z}\mathbf{j} - \mathbf{k}.$$

Since we need a unit normal in computing flux, we must divide this vector by its length, which is

$$\sqrt{\frac{x^2}{z^2} + \frac{y^2}{z^2} + 1} = \sqrt{\frac{x^2 + y^2 + z^2}{z^2}} = \frac{2}{z}.$$

A unit normal is therefore

$$\mathbf{N} = \frac{z}{2}\left(-\frac{x}{z}\mathbf{i} - \frac{y}{z}\mathbf{j} - \mathbf{k}\right) = -\frac{1}{2}(x\mathbf{i} + y\mathbf{j} + z\mathbf{k}).$$

This points into the sphere. If we want the flux across Σ from the outside of the sphere toward the inside, this is the normal to use. If we want the flux across Σ from within the sphere, use $-\mathbf{N}$ instead. Now,

$$\mathbf{F} \cdot (-\mathbf{N}) = \frac{1}{2}(x^2 + y^2 + z^2).$$

There

$$\text{flux} = \iint_{\Sigma} \frac{1}{2}(x^2 + y^2 + z^2)d\sigma$$

$$= \frac{1}{2}\iint_{D}(x^2 + y^2 + z^2)\sqrt{1 + \frac{x^2}{z^2} + \frac{y^2}{z^2}}\,dA$$

$$= \frac{1}{2}\iint_{D}(x^2 + y^2 + z^2)\sqrt{\frac{x^2 + y^2 + z^2}{z^2}}\,dA$$

$$= \frac{1}{2}\iint_{D}(x^2 + y^2 + z^2)^{3/2}\frac{1}{\sqrt{4 - x^2 - y^2}}\,dA$$

$$= 4\iint_{D}\frac{1}{\sqrt{4 - x^2 - y^2}}\,dA$$

because $x^2 + y^2 + z^2 = 4$ on Σ. Converting to polar coordinates, we have

$$\text{flux} = 4 \int_0^{2\pi} \int_0^{\sqrt{3}} \frac{1}{\sqrt{4-r^2}} r\, dr\, d\theta$$

$$= 8\pi \left[-(4-r^2)^{1/2} \right]_0^{\sqrt{3}} = 8\pi. \; \blacksquare$$

We will see other applications of surface integrals when we discuss the integral theorems of Gauss and Stokes, and again when we study partial differential equations.

SECTION 13.5   PROBLEMS

1. Find the mass and center of mass of the triangular shell having vertices $(1, 0, 0)$, $(0, 3, 0)$ and $(0, 0, 2)$ if $\delta(x, y, z) = xz + 1$.

2. Find the center of mass of the portion of the homogeneous sphere $x^2 + y^2 + z^2 = 9$ lying above the plane $z = 1$. (Homogeneous means that the density function is constant).

3. Find the center of mass of the homogeneous cone $z = \sqrt{x^2 + y^2}$ for $x^2 + z^2 \le 9$.

4. Find the center of mass of the part of the paraboloid $z = 16 - x^2 - y^2$ lying in the first octant and be-

tween the cylinders $x^2 + y^2 = 1$ and $x^2 + y^2 = 9$, if $\delta(x, y, z) = xy/\sqrt{1 + 4x^2 + 4y^2}$.

5. Find the mass and center of mass of the paraboloid $z = 6 - x^2 - y^2$ if $\delta(x, y, z) = \sqrt{1 + 4x^2 + 4y^2}$.

6. Find the center of mass of the part of the homogeneous sphere $x^2 + y^2 + z^2 = 1$ lying in the first octant.

7. Find the flux of $\mathbf{F} = x\mathbf{i} + y\mathbf{j} - z\mathbf{k}$ across the part of the plane $x + 2y + z = 8$ lying in the first octant.

8. Find the flux of $\mathbf{F} = xz\mathbf{i} - y\mathbf{k}$ across the part of the sphere $x^2 + y^2 + z^2 = 4$ lying above the plane $z = 1$.

13.6   Preparation for the Integral Theorems of Gauss and Stokes

The fundamental results of vector integral calculus are the theorems of Gauss and Stokes. In this section we will begin with Green's theorem and explore how natural generalizations lead to these results.

With appropriate conditions on the curve and the functions, the conclusion of Green's theorem is

$$\oint_C f(x, y)\, dx + g(x, y)\, dy = \iint_D \left(\frac{\partial g}{\partial x} - \frac{\partial f}{\partial y} \right) dA$$

in which D is the region on and enclosed by the simple closed smooth curve C. Define the vector field

$$\mathbf{F}(x, y) = g(x, y)\mathbf{i} - f(x, y)\mathbf{j}.$$

Then

$$\nabla \cdot \mathbf{F} = \frac{\partial g}{\partial x} - \frac{\partial f}{\partial y}.$$

Now parametrize C by arc length, so the coordinate functions are $x = x(s)$, $y = y(s)$ for $0 \le s \le L$. The unit tangent vector to C is $\mathbf{T}(s) = x'(s)\mathbf{i} + y'(s)\mathbf{j}$, and the unit normal vector is $\mathbf{N}(s) = y'(s)\mathbf{i} - x'(s)\mathbf{j}$. These are shown in Figure 13.42. This normal points away from the interior D of C, and so is an *outer normal*. Now

$$\mathbf{F} \cdot \mathbf{N} = g(x, y)\frac{dy}{ds} + f(x, y)\frac{dx}{ds},$$

so

$$\oint_C f(x, y)dx + g(x, y)dy = \oint_C \left[f(x, y)\frac{dx}{ds} + g(x, y)\frac{dy}{ds} \right] ds$$

$$= \oint_C \mathbf{F} \cdot \mathbf{N} ds.$$

We may therefore write the conclusion of Green's theorem in vector form as

$$\oint_C \mathbf{F} \cdot \mathbf{N} ds = \iint_D \nabla \cdot \mathbf{F} dA. \tag{13.9}$$

This is a conservation of energy equation. Recall from Section 12.4.1 that the divergence of a vector field at a point is a measure of the flow of the field from that point. Equation (13.9) states that the flux of the vector field outward from D across C (because $\mathbf{N}$ is an outer normal) exactly balances the flow of the field from each point in D.

The reason for writing Green's theorem in this form is that it suggests a generalization to three dimensions. Replace the closed curve C in the plane with a closed surface Σ in 3-space (closed meaning bounding a volume). Replace the line integral over C with a surface integral over Σ, and allow the vector field $\mathbf{F}$ to be a function of three variables. We conjecture that equation (13.9) generalizes to

$$\iint_\Sigma \mathbf{F} \cdot \mathbf{N} d\sigma = \iiint_M \nabla \cdot \mathbf{F} dV,$$

in which $\mathbf{N}$ is a unit normal to Σ pointing away from the solid region M bounded by Σ. We will see that, under suitable conditions on Σ and $\mathbf{F}$, this is the conclusion of Gauss's divergence theorem.

Now begin again with Green's theorem. We will pursue a different generalization to three dimensions. This time let

$$\mathbf{F}(x, y, z) = f(x, y)\mathbf{i} + g(x, y)\mathbf{j} + 0\mathbf{k}.$$

The reason for adding the third component is to be able to take the curl:

$$\nabla \times \mathbf{F} = \begin{vmatrix} \mathbf{i} & \mathbf{j} & \mathbf{k} \\ \frac{\partial}{\partial x} & \frac{\partial}{\partial y} & \frac{\partial}{\partial z} \\ f & g & 0 \end{vmatrix} = \left(\frac{\partial g}{\partial x} - \frac{\partial f}{\partial y} \right) \mathbf{k}.$$

Then

$$(\nabla \times \mathbf{F}) \cdot \mathbf{k} = \frac{\partial g}{\partial x} - \frac{\partial f}{\partial y}.$$

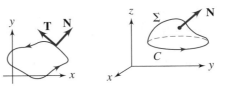

FIGURE 13.42   **FIGURE 13.43**

Further, with unit tangent $\mathbf{T}(s) = x'(s)\mathbf{i} + y'(s)\mathbf{j}$ to C, we can write

$$\mathbf{F} \cdot \mathbf{T} ds = [f(x, y)\mathbf{i} + g(x, y)\mathbf{j}] \cdot \left(\frac{dx}{ds}\mathbf{i} + \frac{dy}{ds}\mathbf{j}\right) ds$$

$$= f(x, y)dx + g(x, y)dy$$

so the conclusion of Green's theorem can also be written

$$\oint_C \mathbf{F} \cdot \mathbf{T} ds = \iint_D (\nabla \times \mathbf{F}) \cdot \mathbf{k} dA. \tag{13.10}$$

Now think of D as a flat surface in the x, y plane, with unit normal vector $\mathbf{k}$, and bounded by the closed curve C. To generalize this, allow C to be a curve in 3-space bounding a surface $\sum$ having unit outer normal vector $\mathbf{N}$, as shown in Figure 13.43. Now equation (13.10) suggests that

$$\oint_C \mathbf{F} \cdot \mathbf{T} ds = \iint_{\sum} (\nabla \times \mathbf{F}) \cdot \mathbf{N} d\sigma.$$

We will see this equation shortly as the conclusion of Stokes's theorem.

SECTION 13.6   PROBLEMS

1. Let C be a simple closed path in the x, y plane, with interior D. Let $\varphi(x, y)$ and $\psi(x, y)$ be continuous with continuous first and second partial derivatives on C and throughout D. Let

$$\nabla^2 \psi = \frac{\partial^2 \psi}{\partial x^2} + \frac{\partial^2 \psi}{\partial y^2}.$$

Prove that

$$\iint_D \varphi \nabla^2 \psi \, dA$$

$$= \oint_C -\varphi \frac{\partial \psi}{\partial y} dx + \varphi \frac{\partial \psi}{\partial x} dy - \iint_D \nabla\varphi \cdot \nabla\psi \, dA.$$

2. Under the conditions of Problem 1, show that

$$\iint_D \left(\varphi \nabla^2 \psi - \psi \nabla^2 \varphi\right) dA$$

$$= \oint_C \left[\psi \frac{\partial \varphi}{\partial y} - \varphi \frac{\partial \psi}{\partial y}\right] dx + \left[\varphi \frac{\partial \psi}{\partial x} - \psi \frac{\partial \varphi}{\partial x}\right] dy.$$

3. Let C be a simple closed path in the x, y plane, with interior D. Let φ be continuous with continuous first and second partial derivatives on C and at all points of D. Let $\mathbf{N}(x, y)$ be the unit outer normal to C (outer meaning pointing away from D if drawn as an arrow at (x, y) on C). Prove that

$$\oint_C \varphi_{\mathbf{N}}(x, y) ds = \iint_D \nabla^2 \varphi(x, y) dA.$$

(Recall that $\varphi_{\mathbf{N}}(x, y)$ is the directional derivative of φ in the direction of $\mathbf{N}$).

13.7   The Divergence Theorem of Gauss

We have seen that, under certain conditions, the conclusion of Green's theorem is

$$\oint_C \mathbf{F} \cdot \mathbf{N} ds = \iint_D \nabla \cdot \mathbf{F} dA.$$

Now make the following generalizations from the plane to 3-space:

set D in the plane $\rightarrow$ a 3-dimensional solid M

a closed curve C bounding $D \rightarrow$ a surface $\sum$ enclosing M

a unit outer normal $\mathbf{N}$ to $C \rightarrow$ a unit outer normal $\mathbf{N}$ to $\sum$

a vector field $\mathbf{F}$ in the plane $\rightarrow$ a vector field $\mathbf{F}$ in 3-space

a line integral $\oint_C \mathbf{F} \cdot \mathbf{N} ds \rightarrow$ a surface integral $\iint_{\sum} \mathbf{F} \cdot \mathbf{N} d\sigma$

a double integral $\iint_D \nabla \cdot \mathbf{F} dA \rightarrow$ a triple integral $\iiint_M \nabla \cdot \mathbf{F} dV.$

With these correspondences and some terminology, Green's theorem suggests a theorem named for the great nineteenth-century German mathematician and scientist Carl Friedrich Gauss.

A surface $\sum$ is *closed* if it encloses a volume. For example, a sphere is closed, as is a cube, while a hemisphere is not. A surface consisting of the top part of the sphere $x^2 + y^2 + z^2 = a^2$, together with the disk $x^2 + y^2 \leq a^2$ in the x, y plane, is closed. If filled with water (through some opening that is then sealed off), it will hold the water.

A normal vector $\mathbf{N}$ to $\sum$ is an *outer normal* if, when represented as an arrow from a point of the surface, it points away from the region enclosed by the surface (Figure 13.44). If $\mathbf{N}$ is also a unit vector, then it is a *unit outer normal*.

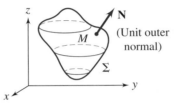

FIGURE 13.44

THEOREM 13.8　Gauss's Divergence Theorem

Let $\sum$ be a piecewise smooth closed surface. Let M be the set of points on and enclosed by $\sum$. Let $\sum$ have unit outer normal vector $\mathbf{N}$. Let $\mathbf{F}$ be a vector field whose components are continuous with continuous first and second partial derivatives on $\sum$ and throughout M. Then

$$\iint_{\sum} \mathbf{F} \cdot \mathbf{N} d\sigma = \iiint_M \nabla \cdot \mathbf{F} dV. \blacksquare \tag{13.11}$$

$\nabla \cdot \mathbf{F}$ is the divergence of the vector field, hence the name "divergence theorem". In the spirit of Green's theorem, Gauss's theorem relates vector operations over objects of different dimensions. A surface is a two-dimensional object (it has area but no volume), while a solid region in 3-space is three-dimensional.

Gauss's theorem has several kinds of applications. One is to replace one of the integrals in equation (13.11) with the other, in the event that this simplifies an integral evaluation. A second is to suggest interpretations of vector operations. A third is to serve as a tool in deriving physical laws. Finally, we will use the theorem in developing relationships to be used in solving partial differential equations.

Before looking at uses of the theorem, here are two purely computational examples to provide some feeling for equation (13.11).

EXAMPLE 13.30

Let $\sum$ be the piecewise smooth closed surface consisting of the surface $\sum_1$ of the cone $z = \sqrt{x^2 + y^2}$ for $x^2 + y^2 \le 1$, together with the flat cap $\sum_2$ consisting of the disk $x^2 + y^2 \le 1$ in the plane $z = 1$. This surface is shown in Figure 13.45. Let $\mathbf{F}(x, y, z) = x\mathbf{i} + y\mathbf{j} + z\mathbf{k}$. We will calculate both sides of equation (13.11).

The unit outer normal to $\sum_1$ is

$$\mathbf{N}_1 = \frac{1}{\sqrt{2}} \left(\frac{x}{z}\mathbf{i} + \frac{y}{z}\mathbf{j} - \mathbf{k} \right).$$

Then

$$\mathbf{F} \cdot \mathbf{N}_1 = (x\mathbf{i} + y\mathbf{j} + z\mathbf{k}) \cdot \frac{1}{\sqrt{2}} \left(\frac{x}{z}\mathbf{i} + \frac{y}{z}\mathbf{j} - \mathbf{k} \right)$$

$$= \frac{1}{\sqrt{2}} \left(\frac{x^2}{z} + \frac{y^2}{z} - z \right) = 0$$

because on $\sum_1$, $z^2 = x^2 + y^2$. (One can also see geometrically that $\mathbf{F}$ is orthogonal to $\mathbf{N}_1$.) Then

$$\iint_{\sum_1} \mathbf{F} \cdot \mathbf{N}_1 \, d\sigma = 0.$$

The unit outer normal to $\sum_2$ is $\mathbf{N}_2 = \mathbf{k}$, so

$$\mathbf{F} \cdot \mathbf{N}_2 = z.$$

Since $z = 1$ on $\sum_2$, then

$$\iint_{\sum_2} \mathbf{F} \cdot \mathbf{N}_2 \, d\sigma = \iint_{\sum_2} z \, d\sigma = \iint_{\sum_2} d\sigma$$

$$= \text{area of } \sum_2 = \pi.$$

Therefore

$$\iint_{\sum} \mathbf{F} \cdot \mathbf{N} \, d\sigma = \iint_{\sum_1} \mathbf{F} \cdot \mathbf{N}_1 \, d\sigma + \iint_{\sum_2} \mathbf{F} \cdot \mathbf{N}_2 \, d\sigma = \pi.$$

Now compute the triple integral. The divergence of $\mathbf{F}$ is

$$\nabla \cdot \mathbf{F} = \frac{\partial}{\partial x}x + \frac{\partial}{\partial y}y + \frac{\partial}{\partial z}z = 3,$$

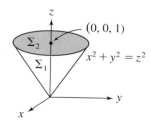

FIGURE 13.45

so

$$\iiint_M \nabla \cdot \mathbf{F} \, dV = \iiint_M 3 \, dV$$

$$= 3 \, [\text{volume of the cone of height 1, radius 1}]$$

$$= 3 \frac{1}{3} \pi = \pi. \quad \blacksquare$$

EXAMPLE 13.31

Let $\sum$ be the piecewise smooth surface of the cube having vertices

$$(0, 0, 0), (1, 0, 0), (0, 1, 0), (0, 0, 1),$$

$$(1, 1, 0), (0, 1, 1), (1, 0, 1), (1, 1, 1).$$

Let $\mathbf{F}(x, y, z) = x^2 \mathbf{i} + y^2 \mathbf{j} + z^2 \mathbf{k}$. We would like to compute the flux of this vector field across the faces of the cube.

The flux is $\iint_{\sum} \mathbf{F} \cdot \mathbf{N} d\sigma$. This integral can certainly be calculated directly, but it requires performing the integration over each of the six smooth faces of $\sum$. It is easier to use the triple integral from Gauss's theorem. Compute the divergence

$$\nabla \cdot \mathbf{F} = 2x + 2y + 2z$$

and then

$$\text{flux} = \iint_{\sum} \mathbf{F} \cdot \mathbf{N} d\sigma$$

$$= \iiint_M \nabla \cdot \mathbf{F} \, dV = 2 \iiint_M (x + y + z) \, dV$$

$$= \int_0^1 \int_0^1 \int_0^1 (2x + 2y + 2z) \, dz \, dy \, dx$$

$$= \int_0^1 \int_0^1 (2x + 2y + 1) \, dy \, dx$$

$$= \int_0^1 (2x + 2) \, dx = 3. \quad \blacksquare$$

Now we will move to more substantial uses of the theorem.

13.7.1 Archimedes's Principle

Archimedes's Principle states that the buoyant force a fluid exerts on a solid object immersed in it, is equal to the weight of the fluid displaced. A bar of soap floats or sinks in a full bathtub for the same reason a battleship floats or sinks in the ocean. The issue rests with the weight of the fluid displaced by the object. We will derive this principle.

Consider a solid object M bounded by a piecewise smooth surface $\sum$. Let ρ be the constant density of the fluid. Draw a coordinate system as in Figure 13.46, with M below the surface of the fluid. Using the fact that pressure is the product of depth and density, the pressure $p(x, y, z)$ at a point on $\sum$ is given by $p(x, y, z) = -\rho z$. The negative sign is used because z is negative in the downward direction and we want pressure to be positive.

Now consider a piece $\sum_j$ of the surface, also shown in Figure 13.46. The force of the pressure on this surface element has magnitude approximately $-\rho z$ times the area A_j of $\sum_j$.

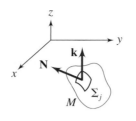

FIGURE 13.46
Pressure force on
$\sum_j \approx \rho z \mathbf{N} \cdot A_j.$
Vertical component
$= \rho z \mathbf{N} \cdot \mathbf{k} A_j.$

If $\mathbf{N}$ is the unit outer normal to $\sum_j$, then the force caused by the pressure on $\sum_j$ is approximately $\rho z \mathbf{N} A_j$. The vertical component of this force is the magnitude of the buoyant force acting upward on $\sum_j$. This vertical component is $\rho z \mathbf{N} \cdot \mathbf{k} A_j$. Sum these vertical components over the entire surface to obtain approximately the net buoyant force on the object, then take the limit as the surface elements are chosen smaller (areas tending to zero). We obtain in this limit that

$$\text{net buoyant force on } \sum = \iint_{\sum} \rho z \mathbf{N} \cdot \mathbf{k} d\sigma.$$

Write this integral as $\iint_{\sum} \rho z \mathbf{k} \cdot \mathbf{N} d\sigma$ and apply Gauss's theorem to convert the surface integral into a triple integral:

$$\text{net buoyant force on } \sum = \iiint_{M} \nabla \cdot (\rho z \mathbf{k}) dV.$$

But $\nabla \cdot (\rho z \mathbf{k}) = \rho$, so

$$\text{net buoyant force on } \sum = \iiint_{M} \rho dV = \rho \, [\text{volume of } M].$$

But this is exactly the weight of the fluid displaced, establishing Archimedes's Principle.

13.7.2 The Heat Equation

We will derive a partial differential equation that models heat conduction. Suppose some medium (for example, a metal bar, the air in a room or water in a pool) has density $\rho(x, y, z)$, specific heat $\mu(x, y, z)$, and coefficient of thermal conductivity $K(x, y, z)$. Let $u(x, y, z, t)$ be the temperature of the medium at time t and point (x, y, z). We want to derive an equation for u.

We will employ a device used frequently in deriving mathematical models. Consider an imaginary smooth closed surface $\sum$ within the medium, bounding a solid region M. The amount of heat energy leaving M across $\sum$ in a time interval Δt is

$$\left(\iint_{\sum} (K \nabla u) \cdot \mathbf{N} d\sigma \right) \Delta t.$$

This is the flux of the vector (K times the gradient of u) across this surface, multiplied by the length of the time interval.

But, the change in temperature at (x, y, z) in M in this time interval is approximately $(\partial u / \partial t) \Delta t$, so the resulting heat loss in M is

$$\left(\iiint_{M} \mu \rho \frac{\partial u}{\partial t} dV \right) \Delta t.$$

Assuming that there are no heat sources or losses within M (for example, chemical reactions or radioactivity), the change in heat energy in M over this time interval must equal the heat exchange across Σ. Then

$$\left(\iint_{\Sigma} (K\nabla u) \cdot \mathbf{N} d\sigma \right) \Delta t = \left(\iiint_{M} \mu\rho \frac{\partial u}{\partial t} dV \right) \Delta t.$$

Therefore

$$\iint_{\Sigma} (K\nabla u) \cdot \mathbf{N} d\sigma = \iiint_{M} \mu\rho \frac{\partial u}{\partial t} dV.$$

Apply Gauss's theorem to the surface integral to obtain

$$\iiint_{M} \nabla \cdot (K\nabla u) dV = \iiint_{M} \mu\rho \frac{\partial u}{\partial t} dV.$$

The role of Gauss's theorem here is to convert the surface integral to a triple integral, thus obtaining an equation with the same kind of integral on both sides. This allows us to combine terms and write the last equation as

$$\iiint_{M} \left(\mu\rho \frac{\partial u}{\partial t} - \nabla \cdot (K\nabla u) \right) dV = 0.$$

Now keep in mind a crucial point—Σ is *any* smooth closed surface within the medium. Assume that the integrand in the last equation is continuous. If this integrand were nonzero at any point P_0 of the medium, then it would be positive or negative at P_0, say positive. By continuity of this integrand, there would be a sphere S, centered at P_0, of small enough radius that the integrand would be strictly positive on and within S. But then we would have

$$\iiint_{M} \left(\mu\rho \frac{\partial u}{\partial t} - \nabla \cdot (K\nabla u) \right) dV > 0,$$

in which M is the solid ball bounded by S. By choosing $\Sigma = S$, this is a contradiction. We conclude that

$$\mu\rho \frac{\partial u}{\partial t} - \nabla \cdot (K\nabla u) = 0$$

at all points in the medium, for all times. This gives us the partial differential equation

$$\mu\rho \frac{\partial u}{\partial t} = \nabla \cdot (K\nabla u)$$

for the temperature function at any point and time. This equation is called the *heat equation*.

We can expand

$$\nabla \cdot (K\nabla u) = \nabla \cdot \left(K\frac{\partial u}{\partial x}\mathbf{i} + K\frac{\partial u}{\partial y}\mathbf{j} + K\frac{\partial u}{\partial z}\mathbf{k} \right)$$

$$= \frac{\partial}{\partial x}(K\frac{\partial u}{\partial x}) + \frac{\partial}{\partial y}(K\frac{\partial u}{\partial y}) + \frac{\partial}{\partial z}(K\frac{\partial u}{\partial z})$$

$$= \frac{\partial K}{\partial x}\frac{\partial u}{\partial x} + \frac{\partial K}{\partial y}\frac{\partial u}{\partial y} + \frac{\partial K}{\partial z}\frac{\partial u}{\partial z} + K\left(\frac{\partial^2 u}{\partial x^2} + \frac{\partial^2 u}{\partial y^2} + \frac{\partial^2 u}{\partial z^2} \right)$$

$$= \nabla K \cdot \nabla u + K\nabla^2 u,$$

in which

$$\nabla^2 u = \frac{\partial^2 u}{\partial x^2} + \frac{\partial^2 u}{\partial y^2} + \frac{\partial^2 u}{\partial z^2}$$

is called the Laplacian of u. (∇^2 is read "del squared"). Now the heat equation can be written

$$\mu\rho\frac{\partial u}{\partial t} = \nabla K \cdot \nabla u + K\nabla^2 u.$$

If K is constant, then its gradient is the zero vector and this equation simplifies to

$$\frac{\partial u}{\partial t} = \frac{K}{\mu\rho}\nabla^2 u.$$

In the case of one space dimension (for example, if $u(x, t)$ is the temperature distribution in a thin bar lying along a segment of the x axis), this is

$$\frac{\partial u}{\partial t} = k\frac{\partial^2 u}{\partial x^2}.$$

with $k = K/\mu p.$K

The steady-state case occurs when u does not change with time. In this case $\partial u/\partial t = 0$, and the last equation becomes

$$\nabla^2 u = 0,$$

a partial differential equation called Laplace's equation. In Chapters 18 and 19 we will write solutions of the heat equation and Laplace's equation under various conditions.

13.7.3 The Divergence Theorem as a Conservation of Mass Principle

We will derive a model providing a physical interpretation of the divergence of a vector.

Let $\mathbf{F}(x, y, z, t)$ be the velocity of a fluid moving in a region of 3-space at point (x, y, z) and time t. Let P_0 be a point in this region. Place an imaginary sphere Σ_r of radius r about P_0, as in Figure 13.47. Σ_r bounds a solid ball M_r. Let $\mathbf{N}$ be the unit outer normal to Σ_r. We know that $\iint_{\Sigma_r} \mathbf{F} \cdot \mathbf{N} d\sigma$ is the flux of $\mathbf{F}$ out of M_r across Σ_r.

If r is sufficiently small, then for a given time, $\nabla \cdot \mathbf{F}(x, y, z, t)$ is approximated by $\nabla \cdot \mathbf{F}(P_0, t)$ at all points (x, y, z) of M_r, to within any desired tolerance. Therefore

$$\iiint_{M_r} \nabla \cdot \mathbf{F}(x, y, z, t)dV \approx \iiint_{M_r} \nabla \cdot \mathbf{F}(P_0, t)dV$$

$$= [\nabla \cdot \mathbf{F}(P_0, t)][\text{volume of } M_r] = \frac{4}{3}\pi r^3 \nabla \cdot \mathbf{F}(P_0, t).$$

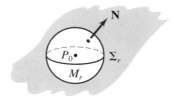

FIGURE 13.47

Then

$$\nabla \cdot \mathbf{F}(P_0, t) \approx \frac{3}{4\pi r^3} \iiint_{M_r} \nabla \cdot \mathbf{F}(x, y, z, t) dV$$

$$= \frac{3}{4\pi r^3} \iint_{\Sigma} \mathbf{F} \cdot \mathbf{N} d\sigma,$$

by Gauss's theorem. Let $r \to 0$. Then Σ_r contracts to its center P_0 and this approximation becomes an equality:

$$\nabla \cdot \mathbf{F}(P_0, t) = \lim_{r \to 0} \frac{3}{4\pi r^3} \iint_{\Sigma_r} \mathbf{F} \cdot \mathbf{N} d\sigma.$$

On the right is the limit, as $r \to 0$, of the flux of $\mathbf{F}$ across the sphere of radius r, divided by the volume of this sphere. This is the amount per unit volume of fluid flowing out of M_r across Σ_r. Since the sphere contracts to P_0 in this limit, we interpret the right side, hence also the divergence of $\mathbf{F}$ at P_0, as a measure of fluid flow away from P_0. This provides a physical sense of the divergence of a vector field.

In view of this interpretation, the equation

$$\iint_{\Sigma} \mathbf{F} \cdot \mathbf{N} d\sigma = \iiint_{M} \nabla \cdot \mathbf{F} dV$$

states that the flux of $\mathbf{F}$ out of M across its bounding surface exactly balances the divergence of fluid away from the points of M. This is a conservation of mass statement, in the absence of fluid produced or destroyed within M, and provides a model for the divergence theorem.

SECTION 13.7 PROBLEMS

In each of Problems 1 through 8, evaluate $\iint_{\Sigma} \mathbf{F} \cdot \mathbf{N} d\sigma$ or $\iiint_M div(\mathbf{F}) dV$, whichever is most convenient.

1. $\mathbf{F} = x\mathbf{i} + y\mathbf{j} - z\mathbf{k}$, Σ the sphere of radius 4 about $(1, 1, 1)$

2. $\mathbf{F} = 4x\mathbf{i} - 6y\mathbf{j} + \mathbf{k}$, Σ the surface of the solid cylinder $x^2 + y^2 \leq 4$, $0 \leq z \leq 2$ (the surface includes the end caps of the cylinder)

3. $\mathbf{F} = 2yz\mathbf{i} - 4xz\mathbf{j} + xy\mathbf{k}$, Σ the sphere of radius 5 about $(-1, 3, 1)$

4. $\mathbf{F} = x^3\mathbf{i} + y^3\mathbf{j} + z^3\mathbf{k}$, Σ the sphere of radius 1 about the origin

5. $\mathbf{F} = 4x\mathbf{i} - z\mathbf{j} + x\mathbf{k}$, Σ the hemisphere $x^2 + y^2 + z^2 = 1$, $z \geq 0$, including the base consisting of points (x, y) with $x^2 + y^2 \leq 1$

6. $\mathbf{F} = (x - y)\mathbf{i} + (y - 4xz)\mathbf{j} + xz\mathbf{k}$, Σ the surface of the rectangular box bounded by the coordinate planes $x = 0$, $y = 0$ and $z = 0$ and by the planes $x = 4$, $y = 2$ and $z = 3$.

7. $\mathbf{F} = x^2\mathbf{i} + y^2\mathbf{j} + z^2\mathbf{k}$, Σ the cone $z = \sqrt{x^2 + y^2}$ for $x^2 + y^2 \leq 2$, together with the top cap consisting of points $(x, y, \sqrt{2})$ with $x^2 + y^2 \leq 2$.

8. $\mathbf{F} = x^2\mathbf{i} - e^z\mathbf{j} + z\mathbf{k}$, Σ the surface bounding the cylinder $x^2 + y^2 \leq 4$, $0 \leq z \leq 2$ (including the top and bottom caps of the cylinder)

9. Let Σ be a smooth closed surface and $\mathbf{F}$ a vector field with components that are continuous with continuous first and second partial derivatives. through Σ and its interior. Evaluate $\iint_{\Sigma} (\nabla \times \mathbf{F}) \cdot \mathbf{N} d\sigma$.

10. Let $\varphi(x, y, z)$ and $\psi(x, y, z)$ be continuous with continuous first and second partial derivatives on a smooth closed surface Σ and its interior M. Suppose $\nabla \varphi = \mathbf{O}$ in M. Prove that $\iiint_M \varphi \nabla^2 \psi dV = 0$.

11. Show that under the conditions of Problem 10, if $\nabla \varphi = \nabla \psi = \mathbf{O}$, then $\iiint_M (\varphi \nabla^2 \psi - \psi \nabla^2 \varphi) dV = 0$.

12. Let Σ be a smooth closed surface bounding an interior M. Show that

$$\text{volume of } M = \frac{1}{3} \iint_{\Sigma} \mathbf{R} \cdot \mathbf{N} d\sigma,$$

where $\mathbf{R} = x\mathbf{i} + y\mathbf{j} + z\mathbf{k}$ is a position vector for Σ.

13. Suppose f and g satisfy Laplace's equation in a region M bounded by a smooth closed surface Σ. Suppose $\partial f / \partial \eta = \partial g / \partial \eta$ on Σ. Prove that for some constant k, $f(x, y, z) = g(x, y, z) + k$ for all (x, y, z) in M.

13.8 The Integral Theorem of Stokes

We have seen that the conclusion of Green's theorem can be written

$$\oint_C \mathbf{F} \cdot \mathbf{T}\, ds = \iint_D (\nabla \times \mathbf{F}) \cdot \mathbf{k}\, dA,$$

in which $\mathbf{T}$ is the unit tangent to C, a simple positively oriented closed curve enclosing a region D.

Think of D as a flat surface with unit normal vector $\mathbf{k}$ and bounded by C. To generalize to three dimensions, allow C to be a closed curve in 3-space, bounding a smooth surface Σ as in Figure 13.48. Here Σ need not be a closed surface. Let $\mathbf{N}$ be a unit normal to Σ.

This raises a subtle point. At any point of Σ there are two normal vectors, as shown in Figure 13.49. Which should we choose? In addition to this decision, we must choose a direction on C. In the plane we chose counterclockwise as positive orientation, but this has no meaning in three dimensions.

First we will give a rule for choosing a particular unit normal to Σ at each point. If Σ has coordinate functions $x = x(u, v)$, $y = y(u, v)$, $z = z(u, v)$, then the normal vector

$$\frac{\partial(y, z)}{\partial(u, v)}\mathbf{i} + \frac{\partial(z, x)}{\partial(u, v)}\mathbf{j} + \frac{\partial(x, y)}{\partial(u, v)}\mathbf{k},$$

divided by its length, yields a unit normal to Σ. The negative of this unit normal is also a unit normal at the same point. Choose either this vector or its negative to use as the normal to Σ, and call it $\mathbf{n}$. Whichever is chosen as $\mathbf{n}$, use it at all points of Σ. That is, do not use $\mathbf{n}$ at one point and $-\mathbf{n}$ at another.

Now use the choice of $\mathbf{n}$ to determine an orientation or direction on C to be called the positive orientation. Referring to Figure 13.50, at any point on C, if you stand along $\mathbf{n}$ (that is, your head is at the tip of $\mathbf{n}$), then the positive direction on C is the one in which you walk to have Σ over your left shoulder. The arrow shows the orientation on C obtained in this way. Although this is not a rigorous definition, it is sufficient for our purpose, without becoming enmeshed in topological details. With this direction, we say that C has been *oriented coherently* with $\mathbf{n}$. If we had chosen the normal in the opposite direction, then we would have reached the opposite orientation on C. The choice of the normal determines the orientation on the curve. There is no intrinsic positive or negative orientation of the curve—simply an orientation coherent with the choice of normal.

With this understanding, we can state Stokes's theorem.

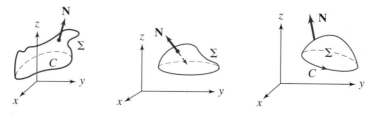

FIGURE 13.48   **FIGURE 13.49**   **FIGURE 13.50**

Normals to a surface at a point.

THEOREM 13.9 *Stokes*

Let $\sum$ be a piecewise smooth surface bounded by a piecewise smooth curve C. Suppose a unit normal $\mathbf{n}$ has been chosen on $\sum$ and that C is oriented coherently with $\mathbf{n}$. Let $\mathbf{F}(x, y, z)$ be a vector field whose component functions are continuous with continuous first and second partial derivatives on $\sum$. Then,

$$\oint_C \mathbf{F} \cdot d\mathbf{R} = \iint_{\sum} (\nabla \times \mathbf{F}) \cdot \mathbf{n} d\sigma. \quad \blacksquare$$

We will write this conclusion in terms of coordinates and component functions. Let the component functions of $\mathbf{F}$ be, respectively, f, g and h. Then

$$\oint_C \mathbf{F} \cdot d\mathbf{R} = \oint_C f(x, y, z)dx + g(x, y, z)dy + h(x, y, z)dz.$$

Next,

$$\nabla \times \mathbf{F} = \begin{vmatrix} \mathbf{i} & \mathbf{j} & \mathbf{k} \\ \partial/\partial x & \partial/\partial y & \partial/\partial z \\ f & g & h \end{vmatrix} = \left(\frac{\partial h}{\partial y} - \frac{\partial g}{\partial z} \right)\mathbf{i} + \left(\frac{\partial f}{\partial z} - \frac{\partial h}{\partial x} \right)\mathbf{j} + \left(\frac{\partial g}{\partial x} - \frac{\partial f}{\partial y} \right)\mathbf{k}.$$

The normal to the surface is given by equation (13.5) as

$$\mathbf{N} = \frac{\partial(y, z)}{\partial(u, v)}\mathbf{i} + \frac{\partial(z, x)}{\partial(u, v)}\mathbf{j} + \frac{\partial(x, y)}{\partial(u, v)}\mathbf{k}.$$

Use this to define the unit normal

$$\mathbf{n}(u, v) = \frac{\mathbf{N}(u, v)}{\|\mathbf{N}(u, v)\|}.$$

Then

$$(\nabla \times \mathbf{F}) \cdot \mathbf{n} = (\nabla \times \mathbf{F}) \cdot \frac{\mathbf{N}(u, v)}{\|\mathbf{N}(u, v)\|}$$

$$= \frac{1}{\|\mathbf{N}(u, v)\|} \left[\left(\frac{\partial h}{\partial y} - \frac{\partial g}{\partial z} \right) \frac{\partial(y, z)}{\partial(u, v)} + \left(\frac{\partial f}{\partial z} - \frac{\partial h}{\partial x} \right) \frac{\partial(z, x)}{\partial(u, v)} \right.$$

$$\left. + \left(\frac{\partial g}{\partial x} - \frac{\partial f}{\partial y} \right) \frac{\partial(x, y)}{\partial(u, v)} \right].$$

Then

$$\iint_{\sum} (\nabla \times \mathbf{F}) \cdot \mathbf{n} d\sigma$$

$$= \iint_D \frac{1}{\|\mathbf{N}(u, v)\|} \left[\left(\frac{\partial h}{\partial y} - \frac{\partial g}{\partial z} \right) \frac{\partial(y, z)}{\partial(u, v)} + \left(\frac{\partial f}{\partial z} - \frac{\partial h}{\partial x} \right) \frac{\partial(z, x)}{\partial(u, v)} \right.$$

$$\left. + \left(\frac{\partial g}{\partial x} - \frac{\partial f}{\partial y} \right) \frac{\partial(x, y)}{\partial(u, v)} \right] \|\mathbf{N}(u, v)\| \, dudv$$

$$= \iint_D \left[\left(\frac{\partial h}{\partial y} - \frac{\partial g}{\partial z} \right) \frac{\partial(y, z)}{\partial(u, v)} + \left(\frac{\partial f}{\partial z} - \frac{\partial h}{\partial x} \right) \frac{\partial(z, x)}{\partial(u, v)} \right.$$

$$\left. + \left(\frac{\partial g}{\partial x} - \frac{\partial f}{\partial y} \right) \frac{\partial(x, y)}{\partial(u, v)} \right] dudv.$$

in which the coordinate functions $x(u, v)$, $y(u, v)$ and $z(u, v)$ from Σ are substituted into the integral, and D is set of points (u, v) over which these coordinate functions are defined. Keep in mind that the function to be integrated in Stokes's theorem is $(\nabla \times \mathbf{F}) \cdot \mathbf{n}$, in which $\mathbf{n} = \mathbf{N}/\|\mathbf{N}\|$ is a unit normal. However, in converting the surface integral to a double integral over D, using the definition of surface integral, $(\nabla \times \mathbf{F}) \cdot \mathbf{n}$ must be multiplied by $\|\mathbf{N}(u, v)\|$, with $\mathbf{N}(u, v)$ determined by equation (13.5).

EXAMPLE 13.32

Let $\mathbf{F}(x, y, z) = -y\mathbf{i} + xy\mathbf{j} - xyz\mathbf{k}$ and let Σ consist of the part of the cone $z = \sqrt{x^2 + y^2}$ for $x^2 + y^2 \le 9$. We will compute both sides of the conclusion of Stokes's theorem to illustrate the various terms and integrals involved.

The cone is shown in Figure 13.51. Its boundary curve C is the circle around the top of the cone, the curve $x^2 + y^2 = 9$ in the plane $z = 3$. In this example the surface is described by $z = S(x, y)$. Here x and y are the parameters, varying over the disk D given by $x^2 + y^2 \le 9$. We can compute a normal vector

$$\mathbf{N} = -\frac{\partial z}{\partial x}\mathbf{i} - \frac{\partial z}{\partial y}\mathbf{j} + \mathbf{k}$$

$$= -\frac{x}{z}\mathbf{i} - \frac{y}{z}\mathbf{j} + \mathbf{k}.$$

For $(\nabla \times \mathbf{F}) \cdot \mathbf{n}$ in Stokes's theorem, $\mathbf{n}$ is a unit normal, so compute the norm of $\mathbf{N}$:

$$\|\mathbf{N}\| = \left\| -\frac{x}{z}\mathbf{i} - \frac{y}{z}\mathbf{j} + \mathbf{k} \right\| = \sqrt{\frac{x^2}{z^2} + \frac{y^2}{z^2} + 1}$$

$$= \sqrt{\frac{x^2 + y^2 + (x^2 + y^2)}{x^2 + y^2}} = \sqrt{2}.$$

Use the unit normal

$$\mathbf{n} = \frac{\mathbf{N}}{\|\mathbf{N}\|} = \frac{1}{\sqrt{2}z}(-x\mathbf{i} - y\mathbf{j} + z\mathbf{k}).$$

This normal is defined at all points of the cone except the origin, where there is no normal. $\mathbf{n}$ is an inner normal, pointing from any point on the cone into the region bounded by the cone.

If we stand along $\mathbf{n}$ at points of C and imagine walking along C in the direction of the arrow in Figure 13.52, then the surface is over our left shoulder. Therefore this arrow orients

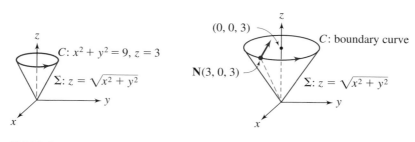

FIGURE 13.51   **FIGURE 13.52**

C coherently with $\mathbf{n}$. If we had used $-\mathbf{n}$ as normal vector, we would orient C in the other direction. We can parametrize C by

$$x = 3\cos(t), \quad y = 3\sin(t), \quad z = 3 \quad \text{for } 0 \le t \le 2\pi.$$

The point $(3\cos(t), 3\sin(t), 3)$ traverses C in the positive direction (as determined by $\mathbf{n}$) as t increases from 0 to 2π.

This completes the preliminary work and we can evaluate the integrals. For the line integral,

$$
\begin{aligned}
\oint_C \mathbf{F} \cdot d\mathbf{R} &= \oint_C -y\,dx + x\,dy - xyz\,dz \\
&= \int_0^{2\pi} [-3\sin(t)(-3\sin(t)) + 3\cos(t)3\cos(t)]\,dt \\
&= \int_0^{2\pi} 9\,dt = 18\pi.
\end{aligned}
$$

For the surface integral, first compute the curl of $\mathbf{F}$:

$$
\nabla \times \mathbf{F} = \begin{vmatrix} \mathbf{i} & \mathbf{j} & \mathbf{k} \\ \partial/\partial x & \partial/\partial y & \partial/\partial z \\ -y & x & -xyz \end{vmatrix}
$$

$$= -xz\mathbf{i} + yz\mathbf{j} + 2\mathbf{k}.$$

Then

$$
\begin{aligned}
(\nabla \times \mathbf{F}) \cdot \mathbf{n} &= \frac{1}{\sqrt{2}z}(x^2 z - y^2 z + 2z) \\
&= \frac{1}{\sqrt{2}}(x^2 - y^2 + 2).
\end{aligned}
$$

Then

$$
\begin{aligned}
\iint_\Sigma (\nabla \times \mathbf{F}) \cdot \mathbf{n}\,d\sigma &= \iint_D [(\nabla \times \mathbf{F}) \cdot \mathbf{n}]\,\|\mathbf{N}\|\,dx\,dy \\
&= \iint_D \frac{1}{\sqrt{2}}(x^2 - y^2 + 2)\sqrt{2}\,dx\,dy \\
&= \iint_D (x^2 - y^2 + 2)\,dx\,dy.
\end{aligned}
$$

Use polar coordinates on D to write this integral as

$$
\begin{aligned}
\int_0^{2\pi}\!\!\int_0^3 &\left(r^2 \cos^2(\theta) - r^2 \sin^2(\theta) + 2\right) r\,dr\,d\theta \\
&= \int_0^{2\pi}\!\!\int_0^3 r^3 \cos(2\theta)\,dr\,d\theta + \int_0^{2\pi}\!\!\int_0^3 2r\,dr\,d\theta \\
&= \left[\frac{1}{2}\sin(2\theta)\right]_0^{2\pi}\left[\frac{1}{4}r^4\right]_0^3 + 2\pi\left[r^2\right]_0^3 = 18\pi. \quad \blacksquare
\end{aligned}
$$

The following are two applications of Stokes's theorem.

13.8.1 An Interpretation of Curl

We will use Stokes's theorem to argue for a physical interpretation of the curl operation. Think of $\mathbf{F}(x, y, z)$ as the velocity of a fluid and let P_0 be any point in the fluid. Consider a disk $\sum_r$ of radius r about P_0, with unit normal vector $\mathbf{n}$ and boundary circle C_r coherently oriented, as in Figure 13.53. For the disk the normal vector is constant. By Stokes's theorem,

$$\oint_{C_r} \mathbf{F} \cdot d\mathbf{R} = \iint_{\sum_r} (\nabla \times \mathbf{F}) \cdot \mathbf{n} d\sigma.$$

Since $\mathbf{R}'(t)$ is a tangent vector to C_r, then $\mathbf{F} \cdot \mathbf{R}'$ is the tangential component of the velocity about C_r and $\oint_{C_r} \mathbf{F} \cdot d\mathbf{R}$ measures the circulation of the fluid about C_r.

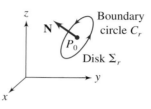

FIGURE 13.53

By choosing r sufficiently small, $\nabla \times \mathbf{F}(x, y, z)$ is approximated by $\nabla \times \mathbf{F}(P_0)$ as closely as we like on $\sum_r$. Further, since $\mathbf{n}$ is constant,

$$\text{circulation of } \mathbf{F} \text{ about } C_r \approx \iint_{\sum_r} (\nabla \times \mathbf{F})(P_0) \cdot \mathbf{n} d\sigma$$

$$= (\nabla \times \mathbf{F})(P_0) \cdot \mathbf{n}(\text{area of the disk } \sum_r)$$

$$= \pi r^2 (\nabla \times \mathbf{F})(P_0) \cdot \mathbf{n}.$$

Therefore

$$\nabla \times \mathbf{F}(P_0) \cdot \mathbf{n} \approx \frac{1}{\pi r^2} (\text{circulation of } \mathbf{F} \text{ about } C_r).$$

As $r \to 0$, the disk contracts to its center P_0 and we obtain

$$\nabla \times \mathbf{F}(P_0) \cdot \mathbf{n} = \lim_{r \to 0} \frac{1}{\pi r^2} (\text{circulation of } \mathbf{F} \text{ about } C_r).$$

Since $\mathbf{n}$ is normal to the plane of C_r, this equation can be read

$$\nabla \times \mathbf{F}(P_0) \cdot \mathbf{n} = \text{circulation of } \mathbf{F} \text{ per unit area in the plane normal to } \mathbf{n}.$$

Thus the curl of $\mathbf{F}$ is a measure of rotation of the fluid at a point. This is the reason why a fluid is called irrotational if the curl of the velocity vector is zero. For example, any conservative vector field is irrotational, because if $\mathbf{F} = \nabla \varphi$, then $\nabla \times \mathbf{F} = \nabla \times (\nabla \varphi) = \mathbf{O}$.

13.8.2 Potential Theory in 3-Space

As in the plane, a vector field $\mathbf{F}(x, y, z)$ in 3-space is conservative if for some potential function φ, $\mathbf{F} = \nabla \varphi$. By exactly the same reasoning as applied in the two-dimensional case, we get

$$\int_C \mathbf{F} \cdot d\mathbf{R} = \varphi(P_1) - \varphi(P_0),$$

if P_0 is the initial point of C and P_1 the terminal point. Therefore the line integral of a conservative vector field in 3-space is independent of path.

If a potential function exists, we attempt to find it by integration just as in the plane.

EXAMPLE 13.33

Let

$$\mathbf{F}(x, y, z) = (yze^{xyz} - 4x)\mathbf{i} + (xze^{xyz} + z + \cos(y))\mathbf{j} + (xye^{xyz} + y)\mathbf{k}.$$

For this to be the gradient of a scalar field φ, we must have

$$\frac{\partial \varphi}{\partial x} = yze^{xyz} - 4x, \qquad \frac{\partial \varphi}{\partial y} = xze^{xyz} + z + \cos(y),$$

and

$$\frac{\partial \varphi}{\partial z} = xye^{xyz} + y.$$

Begin with one of these equations, say the last, and integrate with respect to z to get

$$\varphi(x, y, z) = e^{xyz} + yz + k(x, y),$$

where the "constant" of integration may involve the other two variables. Now we need

$$\frac{\partial \varphi}{\partial x} = yze^{xyz} - 4x$$

$$= \frac{\partial}{\partial x}[e^{xyz} + yz + k(x, y)] = yze^{xyz} + \frac{\partial k}{\partial x}.$$

This will be satisfied if

$$\frac{\partial k}{\partial x} = -4x,$$

so $k(x, y)$ must have the form

$$k(x, y) = -2x^2 + c(y).$$

Thus far $\varphi(x, y, z)$ must have the appearance

$$\varphi(x, y, z) = e^{xyz} + yz - 2x^2 + c(y).$$

Finally, we must satisfy

$$\frac{\partial \varphi}{\partial y} = xze^{xyz} + z + \cos(y)$$

$$= \frac{\partial}{\partial y}[e^{xyz} + yz - 2x^2 + c(y)]$$

$$= xze^{xyz} + z + c'(y).$$

Then

$$c'(y) = \cos(y)$$

and we may choose

$$c(y) = \sin(y).$$

A potential function is given by

$$\varphi(x, y, z) = e^{xyz} + yz - 2x^2 + \sin(y).$$

Of course, for any number a, $\varphi(x, y, z) + a$ is also a potential function for **F**. ∎

As in the plane, in 3-space there are vector fields that are not conservative. We would like to develop a test to determine when **F** has a potential function. The discussion follows that in Section 13.3.1 for the plane. As we saw in the plane, the test requires conditions not only on **F**, but on the set D of points on which we want to find a potential function. We define a set D of points in 3-space to be a *domain* if

1. about every point of D there exists a sphere containing only points of D, and
2. between any two points of D there is a path lying entirely in D.

This definition is analogous to the definition made for sets in the plane. For example, the set of points bounded by two disjoint spheres is not a domain because it fails to satisfy (2), while the set of points on or inside the solid unit sphere about the origin fails to be a domain because of condition (1). The set of points (x, y, z) with $x \geq 0$, $y \geq 0$ and $z \geq 0$ is not a domain because it fails condition (1). For example, there is no sphere about the origin containing only points with nonnegative coordinates. The set of points (x, y, z) with $x > 0$, $y > 0$ and $z > 0$ is a domain.

On a domain, existence of a potential function is equivalent to independence of path.

THEOREM 13.10

Let D be a domain in 3-space, and let **F** be continuous on D. Then $\int_C \mathbf{F} \cdot d\mathbf{R}$ is independent of path on D if and only if **F** is conservative. ∎

We already know that existence of a potential function implies independence of path. For the converse, suppose $\int_C \mathbf{F} \cdot d\mathbf{R}$ is independent of path in D. Choose any P_0 in D. If P is any point of D, there is a path C in D from P_0 to P, and we can define

$$\varphi(P) = \int_C \mathbf{F} \cdot d\mathbf{R}.$$

Because this line integral depends only on the end points of any path in D, this defines a function for all (x, y, z) in D. Now the argument used in the proof of Theorem 13.6 can be essentially duplicated to show that $\mathbf{F} = \nabla \varphi$.

With one more condition on the domain D, we can derive a simple test for a vector field to be conservative. A set D of points in 3-space is *simply connected* if every simple closed path in D is the boundary of a piecewise smooth surface lying in D. This condition enables us to use Stokes's theorem to derive the condition we want.

THEOREM 13.11

Let D be a simply connected domain in 3-space. Let **F** and $\nabla \times \mathbf{F}$ be continuous on D. Then, **F** is conservative if and only if $\nabla \times \mathbf{F} = \mathbf{O}$ in D. ∎

Thus, in simply connected domains, the conservative vector fields are the ones having curl zero—that is, the irrotational vector fields.

In one direction, the proof is simple. If $\mathbf{F} = \nabla \varphi$, then $\nabla \times \mathbf{F} = \nabla \times (\nabla \varphi) = \mathbf{O}$, without the requirement of simple connectivity.

In the other direction, suppose $\nabla \times \mathbf{F} = \mathbf{O}$. To prove that **F** is conservative, it is enough to prove that $\int_C \mathbf{F} \cdot d\mathbf{R}$ is independent of path in D. Let C and K be two paths from P_0 to P_1 in D.

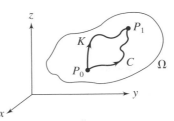

FIGURE 13.54

Form a closed path L in D consisting of C and $-K$, as in Figure 13.54. Since D is simply connected, there is a piecewise smooth surface $\sum$ in D having boundary C. Then

$$\oint_L \mathbf{F} \cdot d\mathbf{R} = \int_C \mathbf{F} \cdot d\mathbf{R} - \int_K \mathbf{F} \cdot d\mathbf{R}$$

$$= \iint_\Sigma (\nabla \times \mathbf{F}) \cdot \mathbf{n} \, d\sigma = 0,$$

so

$$\int_C \mathbf{F} \cdot d\mathbf{R} = \int_K \mathbf{F} \cdot d\mathbf{R}$$

and the line integral is independent of path, hence conservative.

If $\mathbf{G}(x, y) = f(x, y)\mathbf{i} + g(x, y)\mathbf{j}$, then we can think of $\mathbf{G}$ as a vector field in 3-space by writing

$$\mathbf{G}(x, y) = f(x, y)\mathbf{i} + g(x, y)\mathbf{j} + 0\mathbf{k}.$$

Then

$$\nabla \times \mathbf{G} = \begin{vmatrix} \mathbf{i} & \mathbf{j} & \mathbf{k} \\ \partial/\partial x & \partial/\partial y & \partial/\partial z \\ f(x, y) & g(x, y) & 0 \end{vmatrix} = \left(\frac{\partial g}{\partial x} - \frac{\partial f}{\partial y} \right)\mathbf{k},$$

so the condition $\nabla \times \mathbf{G} = \mathbf{O}$ in this two-dimensional case is exactly the condition of Theorem 13.5.

SECTION 13.8 PROBLEMS

In each of Problems 1 through 5, use Stokes's theorem to evaluate $\oint_C \mathbf{F} \cdot d\mathbf{R}$ or $\iint_\Sigma (\nabla \times \mathbf{F}) \cdot \mathbf{N} d\sigma$, whichever appears easier.

1. $\mathbf{F} = yx^2\mathbf{i} - xy^2\mathbf{j} + z^2\mathbf{k}$, $\sum$ the hemisphere $x^2 + y^2 + z^2 = 4$, $z \geq 0$

2. $\mathbf{F} = xy\mathbf{i} + yz\mathbf{j} + xz\mathbf{k}$, $\sum$ the paraboloid $z = x^2 + y^2$ for $x^2 + y^2 \leq 9$

3. $\mathbf{F} = z\mathbf{i} + x\mathbf{j} + y\mathbf{k}$, $\sum$ the cone $z = \sqrt{x^2 + y^2}$ for $0 \leq z \leq 4$

4. $\mathbf{F} = z^2\mathbf{i} + x^2\mathbf{j} + y^2\mathbf{k}$, $\sum$ the part of the paraboloid $z = 6 - x^2 - y^2$ above the x, y plane

5. $\mathbf{F} = xy\mathbf{i} + yz\mathbf{j} + xy\mathbf{k}$, $\sum$ the part of the plane $2x + 4y + z = 8$ in the first octant

6. Calculate the circulation of $\mathbf{F} = (x - y)\mathbf{i} + x^2y\mathbf{j} + xza\mathbf{k}$ counterclockwise about the circle $x^2 + y^2 = 1$. Here a is a positive constant. *Hint*: Use Stokes's theorem, with $\sum$ any smooth surface having the circle as boundary.

7. Use Stokes's theorem to evaluate $\oint_C \mathbf{F} \cdot \mathbf{T} ds$, where C is the boundary of the part of the plane $x + 4y + z = 12$ lying in the first octant, and $\mathbf{F} = (x - z)\mathbf{i} + (y - x)\mathbf{j} + (z - y)\mathbf{k}$.

In each of Problems 8 through 14, let Ω be all of 3-space (so Ω is a simply connected domain). Test to see if $\mathbf{F}$ is conservative. If it is, find a potential function.

8. $\mathbf{F} = 2x\mathbf{i} - 2y\mathbf{j} + 2z\mathbf{k}$

9. $\mathbf{F} = \mathbf{i} - 2\mathbf{j} + \mathbf{k}$

10. $\mathbf{F} = yz\cos(x)\mathbf{i} + (z\sin(x) + 1)\mathbf{j} + y\sin(x)\mathbf{k}$

11. $\mathbf{F} = (x^2 - 2)\mathbf{i} + xyz\mathbf{j} - yz^2\mathbf{k}$

12. $\mathbf{F} = e^{xyz}(1 + xyz)\mathbf{i} + x^2z\mathbf{j} + x^2y\mathbf{k}$

13. $\mathbf{F} = (\cos(x) + y\sin(x))\mathbf{i} + x\sin(xy)\mathbf{j} + \mathbf{k}$

14. $\mathbf{F} = (2x^2 + 3y^2z)\mathbf{i} + 6xyz\mathbf{j} + 3xy^2\mathbf{k}$

In each of Problems 15 through 20, evaluate the line integral of the vector field on any path from the first point to the second by finding a potential function.

15. $\mathbf{F} = \mathbf{i} - 9y^2z\mathbf{j} - 3y^2\mathbf{k}$; $(1, 1, 1), (0, 3, 5)$

16. $\mathbf{F} = (y\cos(xz) - xyz\sin(xz))\mathbf{i} + x\cos(xz)\mathbf{j}$
    $\quad -x^2\sin(xz)\mathbf{k}$; $(1, 0, \pi), (1, 1, 7)$

17. $\mathbf{F} = 6x^2e^{yz}\mathbf{i} + 2x^3ze^{yz}\mathbf{j} + 2x^3ye^{yz}\mathbf{k}$; $(0, 0, 0), (1, 2, -1)$

18. $\mathbf{F} = -8y^2\mathbf{i} - (16xy + 4z)\mathbf{j} - 4y\mathbf{k}$; $(-2, 1, 1), (1, 3, 2)$

19. $\mathbf{F} = -\mathbf{i} + 2z^2\mathbf{j} + 4yz\mathbf{k}$; $(0, 0, -4), (1, 1, 6)$

20. $\mathbf{F} = (y - 4xz)\mathbf{i} + x\mathbf{j} + (3z^2 - 2x^2)\mathbf{k}$; $(1, 1, 1), (3, 1, 4)$

$$a_n = \frac{2}{p} \int_{-p/2}^{p/2} f(x) \cos\left(\frac{2n\pi x}{p}\right) dx = \frac{2}{p} \int_{-p/2}^{p/2} f(x) \cos(n\omega_0 x)\, dx$$

PART 5

Fourier Analysis, Orthogonal Expansions, and Wavelets

In 1807 the French mathematician Joseph Fourier (1768–1830) submitted a paper to the Academy of Sciences in Paris. In it he presented a mathematical treatment of problems involving heat conduction. Although the paper was rejected for lack of rigor, it contained ideas that were so rich and widely applicable that they would occupy mathematicians in research to the present day.

One surprising implication of Fourier's work was that many functions can be expanded in infinite series or integrals involving sines and cosines. This revolutionary idea sparked a heated debate among leading mathematicians of the day and led to important advances in mathematics (Cantor's work on cardinals and ordinals, orders of infinity, measure theory, real and complex analysis, differential equations), science and engineering (data compression, signal analysis), and applications undreamed of in Fourier's day (CAT scans, PET scans, nuclear magnetic resonance).

Today the term Fourier analysis refers to many extensions of Fourier's original insights, including various kinds of Fourier series and integrals, real and complex Fourier transforms, discrete and finite transforms, and, because of their wide applicability, a variety of computer

581

programs for efficiently computing Fourier coefficients and transforms. The ideas behind Fourier series have also found important generalizations in a broad theory of eigenfunction expansions, in which functions are expanded in series of special functions (Bessel functions, orthogonal polynomials, and other functions generated by differential equations). More recently, wavelet expansions have been developed to provide additional tools in areas such as filtering and signal analysis.

This part is devoted to some of these ideas and their applications.

CHAPTER 14

Fourier Series

14.1   Why Fourier Series?

A Fourier series is a representation of a function as a series of constants times sine and/or cosine functions of different frequencies. In order to see why such a series might be interesting, we will look at a problem of the type that led Fourier to consider them.

Consider a thin bar of length π, constant density and uniform cross section. Let $u(x, t)$ be the temperature at time t in the cross section of the bar at x, for $0 \leq x \leq \pi$. In Section 13.7.2 we derived a partial differential equation for u:

$$\frac{\partial u}{\partial t} = k\frac{\partial^2 u}{\partial x^2} \quad \text{for} \quad 0 < x < \pi, t > 0, \tag{14.1}$$

in which k is a constant depending on the material of the bar. Suppose the left and right ends of the bar are kept at zero temperature,

$$u(0, t) = u(\pi, t) = 0 \quad \text{for} \quad t > 0, \tag{14.2}$$

and that the temperature throughout the bar at time $t = 0$ is specified

$$u(x, 0) = f(x) = x(\pi - x). \tag{14.3}$$

Intuitively, the heat equation, together with the initial temperature distribution throughout the bar, and the information that the ends are kept at zero degrees for all time, are enough to determine the temperature distribution $u(x, t)$ throughout the bar at any time.

By a process that now bears his name, and which we will develop when we study partial differential equations, Fourier found functions satisfying the heat equation (14.1) and the conditions at the ends of the bar, equations (14.2), and having the form

$$u_n(x, t) = b_n \sin(nx)e^{-kn^2 t}, \tag{14.4}$$

in which n can be any positive integer, and b_n can be any real number. We will use these functions to find a function that also satisfies the condition (14.3).

583

Periodic phenomena have long fascinated mankind; our ancient ancestors were aware of the recurrence of phases of the moon and certain planets, the tides of lakes and oceans, and cycles in the weather. Isaac Newton's calculus and law of gravitation enabled him to explain the periodicities of the tides, but it was left to Joseph Fourier and his successors to develop Fourier analysis, which has had profound applications in the study of natural phenomena and the analysis of signals and data.

A single choice of positive integer n_0 and constant b_{n_0} will not do. If we let $u(x, t) = b_{n_0} \sin(n_0 x) e^{-k n_0^2 t}$, then we would need

$$u(x, 0) = x(\pi - x) = b_{n_0} \sin(n_0 x) \text{ for } 0 \le x \le \pi,$$

an impossibility. A polynomial cannot equal a constant multiple of a sine function over $[0, \pi]$ (or over any nontrivial interval).

The next thing to try is a finite sum of the functions (14.4), say

$$u(x, t) = \sum_{n=1}^{N} b_n \sin(nx) e^{-k n^2 t}. \tag{14.5}$$

Such a function will still satisfy the heat equation and the conditions (14.2). To satisfy the condition (14.3), we must choose N and $b_n's$ so that

$$u(x, 0) = x(\pi - x) = \sum_{n=1}^{N} b_n \sin(nx) \quad \text{for} \quad 0 \le x \le \pi.$$

But this is also impossible. A finite sum of constant multiples of sine functions cannot equal a polynomial over $[0, \pi]$.

At this point Fourier had a brilliant insight. Since no finite sum of functions (14.4) can be a solution, attempt an infinite series:

$$u(x, t) = \sum_{n=1}^{\infty} b_n \sin(nx) e^{-kn^2 t}. \tag{14.6}$$

This function will satisfy the heat equation, as well as the conditions $u(x, 0) = u(\pi, 0) = 0$. To satisfy condition (14.3) we must choose the $b_n's$ so that

$$u(x, 0) = x(\pi - x) = \sum_{n=1}^{\infty} b_n \sin(nx) \quad \text{for} \quad 0 \le x \le \pi. \tag{14.7}$$

This is quite different from attempting to represent the polynomial $x(\pi - x)$ by the finite trigonometric sum (14.5). Fourier claimed that equation (14.7) is valid for $0 \le x \le \pi$ if the coefficients are chosen as

$$b_n = \frac{2}{\pi} \int_0^\pi x(\pi - x) \sin(nx) dx = \frac{4}{\pi} \frac{1 - (-1)^n}{n^3}.$$

By inserting these coefficients into the proposed solution (14.6), Fourier thus claimed that the solution of this heat conduction problem, with the given initial temperature, is

$$u(x, t) = \frac{4}{\pi} \sum_{n=1}^{\infty} \frac{1 - (-1)^n}{n^3} \sin(nx) e^{-kn^2 t}.$$

The claim that

$$\sum_{n=1}^{\infty} \frac{4}{\pi} \frac{1 - (-1)^n}{n^3} \sin(nx) = x(\pi - x) \quad \text{for} \quad 0 \le x \le \pi$$

was too much for mathematicians of Fourier's time to accept. The mathematics of this time was not adequate to proving this kind of assertion. This was the lack of rigor that led the Academy to reject publication of Fourier's paper. But the implications were not lost on Fourier's colleagues. There is nothing unique about $x(\pi - x)$ as an initial temperature distribution, and many different functions could be used. What Fourier was actually claiming was that, for a broad class of functions f, coefficients b_n could be chosen so that $f(x) = \sum_{n=1}^{\infty} b_n \sin(nx)$ on $[0, \pi]$.

Eventually this and even more general claims for these series proposed by Fourier were proved. We will now begin an analysis of Fourier's ideas and some of their ramifications.

SECTION 14.1 PROBLEMS

1. On the same set of axes, generate a graph of $x(\pi - x)$ and $\sum_{n=1}^{5}(4/\pi)([1 - (-1)^n]/n^3) \sin(nx)$ for $0 \le x \le \pi$. Repeat this for the partial sums $\sum_{n=1}^{10}(4/\pi)([1 - (-1)^n]/n^3) \sin(nx)$ and $\sum_{n=1}^{20}(4/\pi)([1 - (-1)^n]/n^3) \sin(nx)$. This will give a sense of the correctness of Fourier's intuition in asserting that $x(\pi - x)$ can be accurately represented by $\sum_{n=1}^{\infty}(4/\pi)([1 - (-1)^n]/n^3) \sin(nx)$ on this interval.

2. Prove that a polynomial cannot be a constant multiple of $\sin(nx)$ over $[0, \pi]$, for any positive integer n. *Hint*: One way is to proceed by induction on the degree of the polynomial.

3. Prove that a polynomial cannot be equal to a nonzero sum of the form $\sum_{j=0}^{n} c_j \sin(jx)$ for $0 \le x \le \pi$, where the $c_j's$ are real numbers.

14.2   The Fourier Series of a Function

Let $f(x)$ be defined for $-L \leq x \leq L$. For the time being, we assume only that $\int_{-L}^{L} f(x)dx$ exists. We want to explore the possibility of choosing numbers $a_0, a_1, \ldots, b_1, b_2, \ldots$ such that

$$f(x) = \frac{1}{2}a_0 + \sum_{n=1}^{\infty} a_n \cos\left(\frac{n\pi x}{L}\right) + b_n \sin\left(\frac{n\pi x}{L}\right) \tag{14.8}$$

for $-L \leq x \leq L$. We will see that this is sometimes asking too much, but that under certain conditions on f it can be done. However, to get started, we will assume the best of all worlds and suppose for the moment that equation (14.8) holds. What does this tell us about how to choose the coefficients? There is clever device used to answer this question, which was known to Fourier and others of his time. We will need the following elementary lemma.

LEMMA 14.1

Let n and m be nonnegative integers. Then

1.

$$\int_{-L}^{L} \cos\left(\frac{n\pi x}{L}\right) \sin\left(\frac{m\pi x}{L}\right) dx = 0.$$

2. If $n \neq m$, then

$$\int_{-L}^{L} \cos\left(\frac{n\pi x}{L}\right) \cos\left(\frac{m\pi x}{L}\right) dx = \int_{-L}^{L} \sin\left(\frac{n\pi x}{L}\right) \sin\left(\frac{m\pi x}{L}\right) dx = 0.$$

3. If $n \neq 0$, then

$$\int_{-L}^{L} \cos^2\left(\frac{n\pi x}{L}\right) dx = \int_{-L}^{L} \sin^2\left(\frac{n\pi x}{L}\right) dx = L. \blacksquare$$

The lemma is proved by straightforward integration.

Now, to find a_0, integrate the series (14.8) term by term (supposing for now that we can do this):

$$\int_{-L}^{L} f(x)dx = \frac{1}{2}a_0 \int_{-L}^{L} dx$$
$$+ \sum_{n=1}^{\infty} a_n \int_{-L}^{L} \cos\left(\frac{n\pi x}{L}\right) dx + b_n \int_{-L}^{L} \sin\left(\frac{n\pi x}{L}\right) dx.$$

All of the integrals on the right are zero and this equation reduces to

$$\int_{-L}^{L} f(x)dx = La_0.$$

Therefore

$$a_0 = \frac{1}{L} \int_{-L}^{L} f(x)dx.$$

Next, we will determine a_k for any positive integer k. Multiply equation (14.8) by $\cos(k\pi x/L)$ and integrate each term of the resulting series to get

$$\int_{-L}^{L} f(x)\cos\left(\frac{k\pi x}{L}\right) dx = \frac{1}{2}a_0 \int_{-L}^{L} \cos\left(\frac{k\pi x}{L}\right) dx$$
$$+ \sum_{n=1}^{\infty} a_n \int_{-L}^{L} \cos\left(\frac{n\pi x}{L}\right) \cos\left(\frac{k\pi x}{L}\right) dx + b_n \int_{-L}^{L} \sin\left(\frac{n\pi x}{L}\right) \cos\left(\frac{k\pi x}{L}\right) dx.$$

By the lemma, all of the integrals on the right are zero except for $\int_{-L}^{L} \cos(k\pi x/L)\cos(k\pi x/L)dx$, which occurs when $n = k$, and in this case this integral equals L. The right side of this equation therefore collapses to just one term, and the equation becomes

$$\int_{-L}^{L} f(x)\cos\left(\frac{k\pi x}{L}\right) dx = a_k L,$$

whereupon

$$a_k = \frac{1}{L} \int_{-L}^{L} f(x)\cos\left(\frac{k\pi x}{L}\right) dx.$$

To determine b_k, return to equation (14.8). This time multiply the equation by $\sin(k\pi x/L)$ and integrate each term to get

$$\int_{-L}^{L} f(x)\sin\left(\frac{kx}{L}\right) dx = \frac{1}{2}a_0 \int_{-L}^{L} \sin\left(\frac{k\pi x}{L}\right) dx$$
$$+ \sum_{n=1}^{\infty} a_n \int_{-L}^{L} \cos\left(\frac{n\pi x}{L}\right) \sin\left(\frac{k\pi x}{L}\right) dx + b_n \int_{-L}^{L} \sin\left(\frac{n\pi x}{L}\right) \sin\left(\frac{k\pi x}{L}\right) dx.$$

Again, by the lemma, all terms on the right are zero except for $\int_{-L}^{L} \sin(n\pi x/L)\sin(k\pi x/L)dx$ when $n = k$, and this equation reduces to

$$\int_{-L}^{L} f(x)\sin\left(\frac{kx}{L}\right) dx = b_k L.$$

Therefore

$$b_k = \frac{1}{L} \int_{-L}^{L} f(x)\sin\left(\frac{kx}{L}\right) dx.$$

We have now "solved" for the coefficients in the trigonometric series expansion 14.8. Of course, this analysis is flawed by the interchange of series and integrals, which is not always justified. However, the argument does tell us how the constants should be chosen, at least under certain conditions, and suggests the following definition.

DEFINITION 14.1   *Fourier Coefficients and Series*

Let f be a Riemann integrable function on $[-L, L]$.

1. The numbers

$$a_n = \frac{1}{L} \int_{-L}^{L} f(x)\cos\left(\frac{n\pi x}{L}\right) dx, \quad \text{for} \quad n = 0, 1, 2, \ldots$$

and

$$b_n = \frac{1}{L} \int_{-L}^{L} f(x) \sin\left(\frac{n\pi x}{L}\right) dx \quad \text{for} \quad n = 1, 2, 3, \ldots$$

are the Fourier coefficients of f on $[-L, L]$.

2. The series

$$\frac{1}{2}a_0 + \sum_{n=1}^{\infty} a_n \cos\left(\frac{n\pi x}{L}\right) + b_n \sin\left(\frac{n\pi x}{L}\right)$$

is the Fourier series of f on $[-L, L]$ when the constants are chosen to be the Fourier coefficients of f on $[-L, L]$.

EXAMPLE 14.1

Let $f(x) = x$ for $-\pi \le x \le \pi$. We will write the Fourier series of f on $[-\pi, \pi]$. The coefficients are:

$$a_0 = \frac{1}{\pi} \int_{-\pi}^{\pi} x\,dx = 0,$$

$$a_n = \frac{1}{\pi} \int_{-\pi}^{\pi} x \cos(nx)\,dx$$

$$= \left[\frac{1}{n^2\pi}\cos(nx) + \frac{x}{n\pi}\sin(nx)\right]_{-\pi}^{\pi} = 0,$$

and

$$b_n = \frac{1}{\pi} \int_{-\pi}^{\pi} x \sin(nx)\,dx$$

$$= \left[\frac{1}{n^2\pi}\sin(nx) - \frac{x}{n\pi}\cos(nx)\right]_{-\pi}^{\pi}$$

$$= -\frac{2}{n}\cos(n\pi) = \frac{2}{n}(-1)^{n+1},$$

since $\cos(n\pi) = (-1)^n$ if n is an integer. The Fourier series of x on $[-\pi, \pi]$ is

$$\sum_{n=1}^{\infty} \frac{2}{n}(-1)^{n+1}\sin(nx) = 2\sin(x) - \sin(2x) + \frac{2}{3}\sin(3x) - \frac{1}{2}\sin(4x) + \frac{2}{5}\sin(5x) - \cdots.$$

In this example the constant term and cosine coefficients are all zero, and the Fourier series contains only sine terms. ■

EXAMPLE 14.2

Let

$$f(x) = \begin{cases} 0 & \text{for } -3 \le x < 0 \\ x & \text{for } 0 \le x \le 3 \end{cases}.$$

Here $L = 3$ and the Fourier coefficients are:

$$a_0 = \frac{1}{3} \int_{-3}^{3} f(x)\,dx = \frac{1}{3} \int_{0}^{3} x\,dx = \frac{3}{2},$$

$$a_n = \frac{1}{3} \int_{-3}^{3} f(x) \cos\left(\frac{n\pi x}{3}\right) dx$$

$$= \frac{1}{3} \int_{0}^{3} x \cos\left(\frac{n\pi x}{3}\right) dx$$

$$= \frac{3}{n^2 \pi^2} \cos\left(\frac{n\pi x}{3}\right) + \frac{x}{n\pi} \sin\left(\frac{n\pi x}{3}\right)\bigg]_{0}^{3}$$

$$= \frac{3}{n^2 \pi^2}[(-1)^n - 1],$$

and

$$b_n = \frac{1}{3} \int_{-3}^{3} f(x) \sin\left(\frac{n\pi x}{3}\right) dx = \frac{1}{3} \int_{0}^{3} x \sin\left(\frac{n\pi x}{3}\right) dx$$

$$= \frac{3}{n^2 \pi^2} \sin\left(\frac{n\pi x}{3}\right) - \frac{x}{n\pi} \cos\left(\frac{n\pi x}{3}\right)\bigg]_{0}^{3}$$

$$= \frac{3}{n\pi}(-1)^{n+1}.$$

The Fourier series of f on $[-3, 3]$ is

$$\frac{3}{4} + \sum_{n=1}^{\infty} \left(\frac{3}{n^2 \pi^2}[(-1)^n - 1] \cos\left(\frac{n\pi x}{3}\right) + \frac{3}{n\pi}(-1)^{n+1} \sin\left(\frac{n\pi x}{3}\right)\right). \ \blacksquare$$

Even when $f(x)$ is fairly simple, $\int_{-L}^{L} f(x) \cos(n\pi x/L)\,dx$ and $\int_{-L}^{L} f(x) \sin(n\pi x/L)\,dx$ can involve considerable labor if done by hand. Use of a software package to evaluate definite integrals is highly recommended.

In these examples, we wrote the Fourier series of f, but did not claim that it equalled $f(x)$. For most x it is not obvious what the sum of the Fourier series is. However, in some cases it is obvious that the series does not equal $f(x)$. Consider again $f(x) = x$ on $[-\pi, \pi]$ in Example 14.1. At $x = \pi$ and at $x = -\pi$, every term of the Fourier series is zero, even though $f(\pi) = \pi$ and $f(-\pi) = -\pi$. Even for very simple functions, then, there may be points where the Fourier series does not converge to $f(x)$. Shortly we will determine the sum of the Fourier series of a function. Until this is done, we do not know the relationship between the Fourier series and the function itself.

14.2.1 Even and Odd Functions

Sometimes we can save some work in computing Fourier coefficients by observing special properties of $f(x)$.

DEFINITION 14.2

Even Function
f is an even function on $[-L, L]$ if $f(-x) = f(x)$ for $-L \leq x \leq L$.

Odd Function
f is an odd function on $[-L, L]$ if $f(-x) = -f(x)$ for $-L \leq x \leq L$.

For example, x^2, x^4, $\cos(n\pi x/L)$ and $e^{-|x|}$ are even functions on any interval $[-L, L]$. Graphs of $y = x^2$ and $y = \cos(5\pi x/3)$ are given in Figure 14.1. The graph of such a function for $-L \leq x \leq 0$ is the reflection across the y-axis of the graph for $0 \leq x \leq L$ (Figure 14.2).

The functions x, x^3, x^5 and $\sin(n\pi x/L)$ are odd functions on any interval $[-L, L]$. Graphs of $y = x$, $y = x^3$ and $y = \sin(5\pi x/2)$ are shown in Figure 14.3. The graph of an odd function for $-L \leq x \leq 0$ is the reflection across the vertical axis, and then across the horizontal axis, of the graph for $0 \leq x \leq L$ (Figure 14.4). If f is odd, then $f(0) = 0$, since

$$f(-0) = f(0) = -f(0).$$

Of course, "most" functions are neither even nor odd. For example, $f(x) = e^x$ is not even or odd on any interval $[-L, L]$.

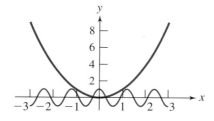

FIGURE 14.1 *Graphs of even functions* $y = x^2$ *and* $y = \cos(5\pi x/3)$.

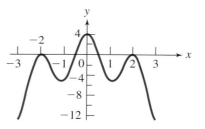

FIGURE 14.2 *Graph of a typical even function, symmetric about the y axis.*

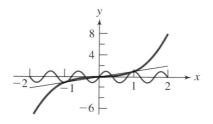

FIGURE 14.3 *Graphis of odd functions* $y = x$, $y = x^3$, *and* $y = \sin(5\pi x/2)$.

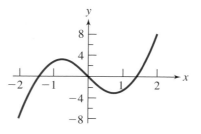

FIGURE 14.4 *Graph of a typical odd function, symmetric through the origin.*

Even and odd functions behave as follows under multiplication:

$$\text{even} \cdot \text{even} = \text{even},$$

$$\text{odd} \cdot \text{odd} = \text{even},$$

and

$$\text{even} \cdot \text{odd} = \text{odd}.$$

For example, $x^2 \cos(n\pi x/L)$ is an even function (product of two even functions); $x^2 \sin(n\pi x/L)$ is odd (product of an even function with an odd function); and $x^3 \sin(n\pi x/L)$ is even (product of two odd functions).

Now recall from calculus that

$$\int_{-L}^{L} f(x)dx = 0 \quad \text{if} \quad f \text{ is odd on } [-L, L]$$

and

$$\int_{-L}^{L} f(x)dx = 2\int_{0}^{L} f(x)dx \quad \text{if} \quad f \text{ is even on } [-L, L].$$

These integrals are suggested by Figures 14.2 and 14.4. In Figure 14.4, f is odd on $[-L, L]$, and the "area" bounded by the graph and the horizontal axis for $-L \le x \le 0$ is exactly the negative of that bounded by the graph and the horizontal axis for $0 \le x \le L$. This makes $\int_{-L}^{L} f(x)dx = 0$. In Figure 14.2, where f is even, the area to the left of the vertical axis, for $-L \le x \le 0$, equals that to the right, for $0 \le x \le L$, so $\int_{-L}^{L} f(x)dx = 2\int_{0}^{L} f(x)dx$.

One ramification of these ideas for Fourier coefficients is that, if f is an even or odd function, then some of the Fourier coefficients can be seen immediately to be zero, and we need not carry out the integrations explicitly. We saw this in Example 14.1 with $f(x) = x$, which is an odd function on $[-\pi, \pi]$. There we found that the cosine coefficients were all zero, since $x\cos(nx)$ is an odd function.

EXAMPLE 14.3

We will find the Fourier series of $f(x) = x^4$ on $[-1, 1]$. Since f is an even function, $x^4\sin(n\pi x)$ is odd and we know immediately that all the sine coefficients b_n are zero. For the other coefficients, compute:

$$a_0 = \int_{-1}^{1} x^4 dx = 2\int_{0}^{1} x^4 dx = \frac{2}{5},$$

and

$$a_n = \int_{-1}^{1} x^4 \cos(n\pi x)dx$$

$$= 2\int_{0}^{1} x^4 \cos(n\pi x)dx = 8\frac{n^2\pi^2 - 6}{\pi^4 n^4}(-1)^n.$$

The Fourier series of x^4 on $[-1, 1]$ is

$$\frac{1}{5} + \sum_{n=1}^{\infty} 8\frac{n^2\pi^2 - 6}{\pi^4 n^4}(-1)^n \cos(n\pi x). \quad \blacksquare$$

To again make the point about convergence, notice that $f(0) = 0$ in this example, but the Fourier series at $x = 0$ is

$$\frac{1}{5} + \sum_{n=1}^{\infty} 8 \frac{n^2 \pi^2 - 6}{\pi^4 n^4}(-1)^n.$$

It is not clear whether or not this series sums to the function value 0.

EXAMPLE 14.4

Let $f(x) = x^3$ for $-4 \leq x \leq 4$. Because f is odd on $[-4, 4]$, its Fourier cosine coefficients are all zero. Its Fourier sine coefficients are

$$b_n = \frac{1}{4} \int_{-4}^{4} x^3 \sin\left(\frac{n\pi x}{4}\right) dx$$

$$= \frac{1}{2} \int_{0}^{4} x^3 \sin\left(\frac{n\pi x}{4}\right) dx = (-1)^{n+1} 128 \frac{n^2 \pi^2 - 6}{n^3 \pi^3}.$$

The Fourier series of x^3 on $[-4, 4]$ is

$$\sum_{n=1}^{\infty} (-1)^{n+1} 128 \frac{n^2 \pi^2 - 6}{n^3 \pi^3} \sin\left(\frac{n\pi x}{4}\right). \ \blacksquare$$

We will make use of this discussion later, so here is a summary of its conclusions: If f is even on $[-L, L]$, then its Fourier series on this interval is

$$\frac{1}{2} a_0 + \sum_{n=1}^{\infty} a_n \cos\left(\frac{n\pi x}{L}\right), \tag{14.9}$$

in which

$$a_n = \frac{2}{L} \int_{0}^{L} f(x) \cos\left(\frac{n\pi x}{L}\right) dx \quad \text{for} \quad n = 0, 1, 2, \ldots. \tag{14.10}$$

If f is odd on $[-L, L]$, then its Fourier series on this interval is

$$\sum_{n=1}^{\infty} b_n \sin\left(\frac{n\pi x}{L}\right), \tag{14.11}$$

where

$$b_n = \frac{2}{L} \int_{0}^{L} f(x) \sin\left(\frac{n\pi x}{L}\right) dx \quad \text{for} \quad n = 1, 2, \ldots. \tag{14.12}$$

SECTION 14.2   PROBLEMS

In each of Problems 1 through 12, find the Fourier series of the function on the interval.

1. $f(x) = 4, -3 \leq x \leq 3$

2. $f(x) = -x, -1 \leq x \leq 1$

3. $f(x) = \cosh(\pi x), = 1 \leq x \leq 1$

4. $f(x) = 1 - |x|, -2 \leq x \leq 2$

5. $f(x) = \begin{cases} -4 & \text{for } -\pi \leq x \leq 0 \\ 4 & \text{for } 0 < x \leq \pi \end{cases}$

6. $f(x) = \sin(2x), -\pi \leq x \leq \pi$

7. $f(x) = x^2 - x + 3, -2 \leq x \leq 2$

8. $f(x) = \begin{cases} -x & \text{for } -5 \leq x < 0 \\ 1 + x^2 & \text{for } 0 \leq x \leq 5 \end{cases}$

9. $f(x) = \begin{cases} 1 & \text{for } -\pi \leq x < 0 \\ 2 & \text{for } 0 \leq x \leq \pi \end{cases}$

10. $f(x) = \cos(x/2) - \sin(x), -\pi \leq x \leq \pi$

11. $f(x) = \cos(x), -3 \leq x \leq 3$

12. $f(x) = \begin{cases} 1 - x & \text{for } -1 \leq x \leq 0 \\ 0 & \text{for } 0 < x \leq 1 \end{cases}$

13. Suppose f and g are integrable on $[-L, L]$ and that $f(x) = g(x)$ except for $x = x_0$, a given point in the interval. How are the Fourier series of f and g related? What does this suggest about the relationship between a function and its Fourier series on an interval?

14. Prove that $\int_{-L}^{L} f(x) dx = 0$ if f is odd on $[-L, L]$.

15. Prove that $\int_{-L}^{L} f(x) dx = 2 \int_{0}^{L} f(x) dx$ if f is even on $[-L, L]$.

14.3 Convergence of Fourier Series

It is one thing to be able to write the Fourier coefficients of a function f on an interval $[-L, L]$. This requires only existence of $\int_{-L}^{L} f(x) \cos(n\pi x/L) dx$ and $\int_{-L}^{L} f(x) \sin(n\pi x/L) dx$. It is another issue entirely to determine whether the resulting Fourier series converges to $f(x)$—or even that it converges at all! The subtleties of this question were dramatized in 1873 when the French mathematician Paul Du Bois-Reymond gave an example of a function which is continuous on $(-\pi, \pi)$, but whose Fourier series fails to converge at any point of this interval.

However, the obvious utility of Fourier series in solving partial differential equations led in the nineteenth century to an intensive effort to determine their convergence properties. About 1829, Peter Gustav Lejeune-Dirichlet gave conditions on the function f which were sufficient for convergence of the Fourier series of f. Further, Dirichlet's theorem actually gave the sum of the Fourier series at each point, whether or not this sum is $f(x)$.

This section is devoted to conditions on a function that enable us to determine the sum of its Fourier series on an interval. These conditions center about the concept of piecewise continuity.

DEFINITION 14.3 *Piecewise Continuous Function*

Let $f(x)$ be defined on $[a, b]$, except possibly at finitely many points. Then f is piecewise continuous on $[a, b]$ if:

1. f is continuous on $[a, b]$ except perhaps at finitely many points.

2. Both $\lim_{x \to a+} f(x)$ and $\lim_{x \to b-} f(x)$ exist and are finite.

3. If x_0 is in (a, b) and f is not continuous at x_0, then $\lim_{x \to x_0+} f(x)$ and $\lim_{x \to x_0-} f(x)$ exist and are finite.

Figures 14.5 and 14.6 shows graphs of typical piecewise continuous functions. At a point of discontinuity (which we assume are finite in number), the function must have finite one-sided limits. This means that the graph experiences at worst a finite gap at a discontinuity. Points where these occur are called *jump discontinuities* of the function.

As an example of a simple function that is not piecewise continuous, let

$$f(x) = \begin{cases} 0 & \text{for } x = 0 \\ 1/x & \text{for } 0 < x \leq 1 \end{cases} .$$

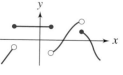

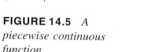

FIGURE 14.5 *A piecewise continuous function.*

FIGURE 14.6 *Graph of a typical piecewise continuous function.*

Then f is continuous on $(0, 1]$, and discontinuous at 0. However, $\lim_{x \to 0+} f(x) = \infty$, so the discontinuity is not a finite jump discontinuity, and f is not piecewise continuous on $[0, 1]$.

EXAMPLE 14.5

Let

$$
f(x) = \begin{cases} 5 & \text{for } x = -\pi \\ x & \text{for } -\pi < x < 1 \\ 1 - x^2 & \text{for } 1 \le x < 2 \\ 4 & \text{for } 2 \le x \le \pi \end{cases}.
$$

A graph of f is shown in Figure 14.7. This function is discontinuous at $-\pi$, and

$$
\lim_{x \to -\pi+} f(x) = -\pi.
$$

f is also discontinuous at 1, interior to $[-\pi, \pi]$, and

$$
\lim_{x \to 1-} f(x) = 1 \quad \text{and} \quad \lim_{x \to 1+} f(x) = 0.
$$

Finally, f is discontinuous at 2, and

$$
\lim_{x \to 2-} f(x) = -3 \quad \text{and} \quad \lim_{x \to 2+} f(x) = 4.
$$

At each point of discontinuity interior to the interval, the function has finite one sided limits from both sides. At the point of discontinuity at the end point $-\pi$, the function has a finite limit

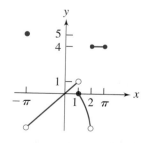

FIGURE 14.7 *Graph of the function of Example 14.5.*

from within the interval. In this example, the other end point is not an issue, as f is continuous (from the left) there. Therefore f is piecewise continuous on $[-\pi, \pi]$. ∎

We will use the following notation for left and right limits of a function at a point:

$$f(x_0+) = \lim_{x \to x_0+} f(x) \quad \text{and} \quad f(x_0-) = \lim_{x \to x_0-} f(x).$$

In Example 14.5,

$$f(1-) = 1 \quad \text{and} \quad f(1+) = 0$$

and

$$f(2-) = -3 \quad \text{and} \quad f(2+) = 4.$$

At the end points of an interval, we can still use this notation, except at the left end point we consider only the right limit (from inside the interval), and at the right end point we use only the left limit (again, so that the limit is taken from within the interval). Again referring to Example 14.5,

$$f(-\pi+) = -\pi \quad \text{and} \quad f(\pi-) = 4.$$

DEFINITION 14.4   *Piecewise Smooth Function*

f is piecewise smooth on $[a, b]$ if f and f' are piecewise continuous on $[a, b]$.

A piecewise smooth function is therefore one that is continuous except possibly for finitely many jump discontinuities, and has a continuous derivative at all but finitely many points, where the derivative may not exist but must have finite one-sided limits.

EXAMPLE 14.6

Let

$$f(x) = \begin{cases} 1 & \text{for } -4 \leq x < 1 \\ -2x & \text{for } 1 \leq x < 2 \\ 9e^{-x} & \text{for } 2 \leq x \leq 3 \end{cases}.$$

Figure 14.8 shows a graph of f. The function is continuous except for finite jump discontinuities at 1 and 2. Therefore f is piecewise continuous on $[-4, 3]$. The derivative of f is

$$f'(x) = \begin{cases} 0 & \text{for } -4 < x < 1 \\ -2 & \text{for } 1 < x < 2 \\ -9e^{-x} & \text{for } 2 < x < 3 \end{cases}.$$

The derivative is continuous on $[-4, 3]$ except at the points of discontinuity 1 and 2 of f, where $f'(x)$ does not exist. However, at these points $f'(x)$ has finite one-sided limits. Thus f' is piecewise continuous on $[-4, 3]$, so f is piecewise smooth. ∎

As suggested by Figure 14.8, a piecewise smooth function is one that has a continuous tangent at all but finitely many points.

We will now state our first convergence theorem.

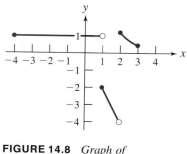

FIGURE 14.8 *Graph of*

$$f(x) = \begin{cases} 1 & \text{for } -4 \le x < 1 \\ -2x & \text{for } 1 \le x < 2 \\ 9e^{-x} & \text{for } 2 \le x \le 3 \end{cases}$$

THEOREM 14.1 *Convergence of Fourier Series*

Let f be piecewise smooth on $[-L, L]$. Then for $-L < x < L$, the Fourier series of f on $[-L, L]$ converges to

$$\frac{1}{2}\left(f(x+) + f(x-)\right). \quad \blacksquare$$

This means that, at each point between $-L$ and L, the function converges to the average of its left and right limits. If f is continuous at x, then these left and right limits both equal $f(x)$, so the Fourier series converges to the function value at x. If f has a jump discontinuity at x, then the Fourier series may not converge to $f(x)$, but will converge to the point midway between the ends of the gap in the graph at x (Figure 14.9).

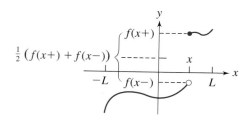

FIGURE 14.9 *Convergence of a Fourier series at a jump discontinuity.*

EXAMPLE 14.7

Let

$$f(x) = \begin{cases} 5\sin(x) & \text{for } -2\pi \le x < -\pi/2 \\ 4 & \text{for } x = -\pi/2 \\ x^2 & \text{for } -\pi/2 < x < 2 \\ 8\cos(x) & \text{for } 2 \le x < \pi \\ 4x & \text{for } \pi \le x \le 2\pi \end{cases}$$

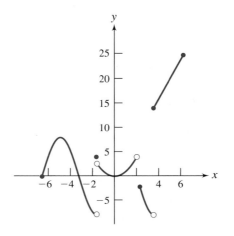

FIGURE 14.10

$$\text{Graph of } f(x) = \begin{cases} 5\sin(x) & \text{for } -2\pi \le x < -\pi/2 \\ 4 & \text{for } x = -\pi/2 \\ x^2 & \text{for } -\pi/2 < x < 2 \\ 8\cos(x) & \text{for } 2 \le x < \pi \\ 4x & \text{for } \pi \le x \le 2\pi \end{cases}$$

A graph of f is given in Figure 14.10. Since f is piecewise smooth on $[-2\pi, 2\pi]$, we can determine the sum of its Fourier series on this interval. In applying the theorem, we do not actually have to compute this Fourier series. We could do this, but it is not necessary to determine the sum of the Fourier series.

For $-2\pi < x < -\pi/2$, f is continuous and the Fourier series converges to $f(x) = 5\sin(x)$.

At $x = -\pi/2$, f has a jump discontinuity and the Fourier series will converge to the average of the left and right limits of $f(x)$ at $-\pi/2$. Compute

$$f(-\pi/2-) = \lim_{x \to -\pi/2-} f(x) = \lim_{x \to -\pi/2-} 5\sin(x) = 5\sin(-\pi/2) = -5$$

and

$$f(-\pi/2+) = \lim_{x \to -\pi/2+} f(x) = \lim_{x \to -\pi/2+} x^2 = \frac{\pi^2}{4}.$$

Therefore, at $x = -\pi/2$, the Fourier series of f converges to

$$\frac{1}{2}\left(\frac{\pi^2}{4} - 5\right).$$

On $(-\pi/2, 2)$ the function is continuous, so the Fourier series converges to x^2 for $-\pi/2 < x < 2$.

At $x = 2$ the function the function has another jump discontinuity. Compute

$$f(2-) = \lim_{x \to 2-} x^2 = 4$$

and

$$f(2+) = \lim_{x \to 2+} 8\cos(x) = 8\cos(2).$$

At $x = 2$ the Fourier series converges to

$$\frac{1}{2}(4 + 8\cos(2)).$$

On $(2, \pi)$, f is continuous. At each x with $2 < x < \pi$, the Fourier series converges to $f(x) = 8\cos(x)$.

At $x = \pi$, f has a jump discontinuity. Compute

$$f(\pi-) = \lim_{x \to \pi-} 8\cos(x) = 8\cos(\pi) = -8$$

and

$$f(\pi+) = \lim_{x \to \pi+} 4x = 4\pi.$$

At $x = \pi$ the Fourier series of f converges to

$$\frac{1}{2}(4\pi - 8).$$

Finally, on $(\pi, 2\pi)$, f is continuous and the Fourier series converges to $f(x) = 4x$. These conclusions can be summarized:

$$\text{Fourier series converges to}
\begin{cases}
5\sin(x) & \text{for } -2\pi < x < \dfrac{-\pi}{2} \\[2mm]
\dfrac{1}{2}\left(\dfrac{\pi^2}{4} - 5\right) & \text{for } x = \dfrac{-\pi}{2} \\[2mm]
x^2 & \text{for } -\pi/2 < x < 2 \\[2mm]
\dfrac{1}{2}(4 + 8\cos(2)) & \text{for } x = 2 \\[2mm]
8\cos(x) & \text{for } 2 < x < \pi \\[2mm]
\dfrac{1}{2}(4\pi - 8) & \text{for } x = \pi \\[2mm]
4x & \text{for } \pi < x < 2\pi
\end{cases}.$$

Figure 14.11 shows a graph of this sum of the Fourier series, differing from the function itself on $(-2\pi, 2\pi)$ at the jump discontinuities, where the series converges to the average of the left and right limits. ∎

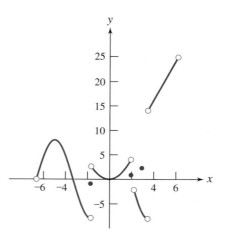

FIGURE 14.11 *Graph of the Fourier series of the function of Figure 14.10.*

If f is piecewise smooth on $[-L, L]$ and actually continuous on $[-L, L]$, then the Fourier series converges to $f(x)$ for $-L < x < L$.

EXAMPLE 14.8

Let

$$f(x) = \begin{cases} x & \text{for } -2 \leq x \leq 1 \\ 2 - x^2 & \text{for } 1 < x \leq 2 \end{cases}.$$

Then f is continuous on $[-2, 2]$ (Figure 14.12). f is differentiable except at $x = 1$, where $f'(x)$ has finite left and right limits, so f is piecewise smooth. For $-2 < x < 2$, the Fourier series of f converges to $f(x)$. In this example the Fourier series is an exact representation of the function on $(-2, 2)$. ∎

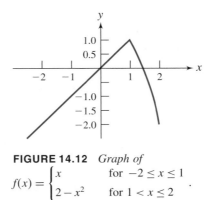

FIGURE 14.12 *Graph of*
$$f(x) = \begin{cases} x & \text{for } -2 \leq x \leq 1 \\ 2 - x^2 & \text{for } 1 < x \leq 2 \end{cases}.$$

14.3.1 Convergence at the End Points

Theorem 14.1 does not address convergence of a Fourier series at the end points of the interval. There is a subtlety here that we will now discuss.

The problem is that, while the function f of interest may be defined only on $[-L, L]$, its Fourier series

$$\frac{1}{2}a_0 + \sum_{n=1}^{\infty} a_n \cos\left(\frac{n\pi x}{L}\right) + b_n \sin\left(\frac{n\pi x}{L}\right) \tag{14.13}$$

is defined for all real x for which the series converges. Further, the Fourier series is periodic, of period $2L$. The value of the series is unchanged if x is replaced with $x + 2L$. How do we reconcile representing a function that is defined only on an interval by a function that is periodic and may be defined over the entire real line?

The reconciliation lies in a periodic extension of f over the real line. Take the graph of $f(x)$ on $[-L, L)$ and replicate it over successive intervals of length $2L$. This defines a new function f_p that agrees with $f(x)$ for $-L \leq x < L$, and has period $2L$. This process is illustrated in Figure 14.13 for the function $f(x) = x^2$ for $-2 \leq x < 2$. This graph is simply repeated for

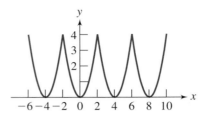

FIGURE 14.13 *Part of the periodic extension, of period 4, of $f(x) = x^2$ for $-2 \leq x < 2$.*

$2 \leq x < 6, 6 \leq x < 10, \ldots, -6 \leq x < -2, -10 \leq x < -6$, and so on. The reason for using the half-open interval $[-L, L)$ in this extension is that, if f_p is to have period $2L$, then

$$f_p(x + 2L) = f_p(x)$$

for all x. But this requires that $f(-L) = f(-L + 2L) = f(L)$, so once $f_p(-L)$ is defined, $f_p(L)$ must equal this value.

If we make this extension, then the convergence theorem applies to $f_p(x)$ at all x. In particular, at $-L$, the series converges to

$$\frac{1}{2} \left(f_p(-L-) + f_p(-L+) \right),$$

which is

$$\frac{1}{2} \left(f(L-) + f(-L+) \right).$$

Similarly, at L, the Fourier series converges to

$$\frac{1}{2} \left(f_p(L-) + f_p(L+) \right),$$

which is

$$\frac{1}{2} \left(f(L-) + f(-L+) \right).$$

The Fourier series converges to the same value at both L and at $-L$. This can also be seen directly from the series (14.13). If $x = L$, all the sine terms are $\sin(n\pi)$, which vanish, and the cosine terms are $\cos(n\pi)$, so the series at $x = L$ is

$$\frac{1}{2} a_0 + \sum_{n=1}^{\infty} a_n \cos(n\pi).$$

At $x = -L$, again all the sine terms vanish, and because $\cos(-n\pi) = \cos(n\pi)$, the series at $x = -L$ is also

$$\frac{1}{2} a_0 + \sum_{n=1}^{\infty} a_n \cos(n\pi).$$

14.3.2   A Second Convergence Theorem

A second convergence theorem can be framed in terms of one-sided derivatives.

DEFINITION 14.5   *Right Derivative*

Suppose $f(x)$ is defined at least for $c < x < c + r$ for some positive number r. Suppose $f(c+)$ is finite. Then the right derivative of f at c is

$$f'_{\mathcal{R}}(c) = \lim_{h \to 0+} \frac{f(c+h) - f(c+)}{h},$$

if this limit exists and is finite. ∎

DEFINITION 14.6   *Left Derivative*

Suppose $f(x)$ is defined at least for $c - r < x < c$ for some positive number r. Suppose $f(c-)$ is finite. Then the left derivative of f at c is

$$f'_{\mathcal{L}}(c) = \lim_{h \to 0-} \frac{f(c+h) - f(c-)}{h},$$

if this limit exists and is finite.

If $f'(c)$ exists, then f is continuous at c, so $f(c-) = f(c+) = f(c)$, and in this case the left and right derivative are both equal to $f'(c)$. However, Figure 14.14 shows the significance of the left and right derivatives when f has a jump discontinuity at c. The left derivative is the slope of the graph at $x = c$ if we cover up the part of the graph to the right of c and keep only the left side. The right derivative is the slope at c if we cover up the left part and just keep the right part.

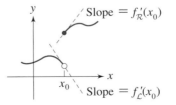

FIGURE 14.14   *One-sided derivatives as slopes from the right or left.*

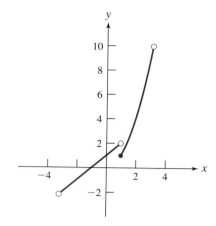

FIGURE 14.15 *Graph of*

$$f(x) = \begin{cases} 1+x & \text{for } -\pi < x < 1 \\ x^2 & \text{for } 1 \leq x < \pi \end{cases}.$$

EXAMPLE 14.9

Let

$$f(x) = \begin{cases} 1+x & \text{for } -\pi < x < 1 \\ x^2 & \text{for } 1 \leq x < \pi \end{cases}.$$

Then f is continuous on $(-\pi, \pi)$ except at 1, where there is a jump discontinuity (Figure 14.15). Further, f is differentiable except at this point of discontinuity. Indeed,

$$f'(x) = \begin{cases} 1 & \text{for } -\pi < x < 1 \\ 2x & \text{for } 1 < x < \pi \end{cases}.$$

From the graph and the slopes of the "left and right pieces" at $x = 1$, we would expect the left derivative at $x = 1$ to be 1, and the right derivative to be 2. Check this from the definition. First,

$$f'_{\mathcal{L}}(0) = \lim_{h \to 0-} \frac{f(1+h) - f(1-)}{h}$$

$$= \lim_{h \to 0-} \frac{1 + (1+h) - 2}{h} = \lim_{h \to 0-} \frac{h}{h} = 1,$$

and

$$f'_{\mathcal{R}}(c) = \lim_{h \to 0+} \frac{f(1+h) - f(1+)}{h}$$

$$= \lim_{h \to 0+} \frac{(1+h)^2 - 1}{h} = \lim_{h \to 0+} (2+h) = 2. \quad \blacksquare$$

Using the one-sided derivatives, we can state the following convergence theorem.

THEOREM 14.2

Let f be piecewise continuous on $[-L, L]$. Then,

1. If $-L < x < L$ and f has a left and right derivative at x, then the Fourier series of f on $[-L, L]$ converges at x to

$$\frac{1}{2} (f(x+) + f(x-)).$$

2. If $f'_{\mathcal{R}}(-L)$ and $f'_{\mathcal{L}}(L)$ exist, then at both L and $-L$, the Fourier series of f on $[-L, L]$ converges to

$$\frac{1}{2}\left(f(-L+)+f(L-)\right). \; \blacksquare$$

As with the first convergence theorem, we need not compute the Fourier series to determine its sum.

EXAMPLE 14.10

Let

$$f(x) = \begin{cases} e^{-x} & \text{for } -2 \le x < 1 \\ -2x^2 & \text{for } 1 \le x < 2 \\ 4 & \text{for } x = 2 \end{cases}.$$

We want to determine the sum of the Fourier series of f on $[-2, 2]$. A graph of f is shown in Figure 14.16.

f is piecewise continuous, being continuous except for jump discontinuities at 1 and 2.

For $-2 < x < 1$, f is continuous, and the Fourier series converges to $f(x) = e^{-x}$.

For $1 < x < 2$, f is also continuous and the Fourier series converges to $f(x) = -2x^2$.

At the jump discontinuity $x = 1$, the left and right derivatives exist ($-e^{-1}$ and -4, respectively). We can determine these from the limits in the definitions, but these derivatives are also apparent from looking at the graph of f to the right and left of 1. Therefore the Fourier series converges at $x = 1$ to

$$\frac{1}{2}\left(f(1-)+f(1+)\right),$$

which is

$$\frac{1}{2}\left(e^{-1}-2\right).$$

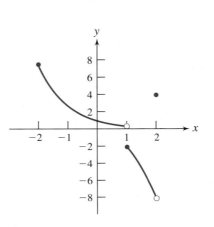

FIGURE 14.16 *Graph of*
$$f(x) = \begin{cases} e^{-x} & \text{for } -2 \le x < 1 \\ -2x^2 & \text{for } 1 \le x < 2 \\ 4 & \text{for } x = 2 \end{cases}.$$

This takes care of each point in $(-2, 2)$. Now consider the end points. The left derivative of f at 2 is -8 and the right derivative at -2 is $-e^2$. Therefore, at both 2 and at -2, the Fourier series converges to

$$\frac{1}{2}(f(2-) + f(-2+)) = \frac{1}{2}(-8 + e^2).$$

Figure 14.17 shows a graph of the sum of the Fourier series on $[-2, 2]$, and can be compared with the graph of f. The two graphs agree except at the end points and at the jump discontinuity. The fact that $f(2) = 9$ does not affect convergence of the Fourier series of $f(x)$ at $x = 2$. ∎

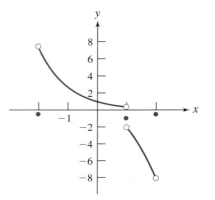

FIGURE 14.17 *Graph of the Fourier series of the function of Figure 14.16.*

A note of caution is warranted in applying the second convergence theorem. The left and right derivatives of a function at a point are relevant only to verify that the hypotheses of the theorem are satisfied at a jump discontinuity of the function. However, these derivatives play no role in the value to which the Fourier series converges at a point. That value involves the left and right limits of the function itself.

14.3.3 Partial Sums of Fourier Series

Fourier's claims for his series were counterintuitive in the sense that functions such as polynomials and exponentials do not seem to be likely candidates to be represented by series of sines and cosines. It is instructive to watch graphs of partial sums of some Fourier series converge to the graph of the function.

EXAMPLE 14.11

Let $f(x) = x$ for $-\pi \leq x \leq \pi$. We saw in Example 14.1 that the Fourier series is

$$\sum_{n=1}^{\infty} \frac{2}{n}(-1)^{n+1}\sin(nx).$$

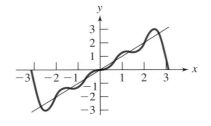

FIGURE 14.18(a) *Fourth partial sum* $S_4(x) = \sum_{n=1}^{4} \frac{2(-1)^{n+1}}{n} \sin(nx)$ *of the Fourier series of* $f(x) = x$ *on* $-\pi \le x \le \pi$.

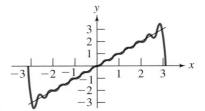

FIGURE 14.18(b) *Tenth partial sum of the Fourier series of* $f(x) = x$ *on* $[-\pi, \pi]$.

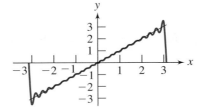

FIGURE 14.18(c) *Twentieth partial sum of the Fourier series of* $f(x) = x$ *on* $[-\pi, \pi]$.

We can apply either convergence theorem to show that this series converges to

$$\begin{cases} x & \text{for } -\pi < x < \pi \\ 0 & \text{for } x = \pi \text{ and for } x = -\pi \end{cases}.$$

Figures 14.18 (a), (b) and (c) show, respectively the fourth, tenth and twentieth partial sums of this series, suggesting how they approach nearer to $f(x) = x$ on $(-\pi, \pi)$ as more terms are included. ■

EXAMPLE 14.12

Let $f(x) = e^x$ for $-1 \le x \le 1$. The Fourier series of f on $[-1, 1]$ is

$$\frac{1}{2}\left(e - e^{-1}\right) + \left(e - e^{-1}\right) \sum_{n=1}^{\infty} \left(\frac{(-1)^n}{1 + n^2 \pi^2} \cos(n\pi x) - n\pi \frac{(-1)^n}{1 + n^2 \pi^2} \sin(n\pi x) \right).$$

This series converges to

$$\begin{cases} e^x & \text{for } -1 < x < 1 \\ \dfrac{1}{2}(e + e^{-1}) & \text{for } x = 1 \text{ and for } x = -1 \end{cases}.$$

Figures 14.19 (a) and (b) show the tenth and thirtieth partial sums of this series, compared with the graph of f. ■

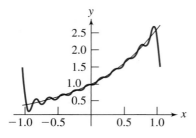

FIGURE 14.19(a) *Tenth partial sum of the Fourier series of* $f(x) = e^x$ *on* $[-1, 1]$.

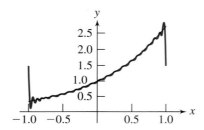

FIGURE 14.19(b) *Thirtieth partial sum of the Fourier series of* $f(x) = e^x$ *on* $[-1, 1]$.

EXAMPLE 14.13

Let $f(x) = \sin(x)$ for $-1 \le x \le 1$. The Fourier series of f on $[-1, 1]$ is

$$\sum_{n=1}^{\infty} 2 \frac{n\pi \sin(1)(-1)^{n+1}}{n^2 \pi^2 - 1} \sin(n\pi x).$$

This series converges to

$$\begin{cases} \sin(x) & \text{for } -1 < x < 1 \\ 0 & \text{for } x = 1 \text{ and for } x = -1 \end{cases}.$$

Figures 14.20 (a) and (b) show two partial sums of this series compared with the graph of f. ■

14.3.4 The Gibbs Phenomenon

In 1881 the Michelson-Morley experiment revolutionized physics and helped pave the way for Einstein's theory of general relativity. In a brilliant experiment using their adaptation of the interferometer, Michelson and Morley showed by careful measurements that the postulated "ether", which physicists at that time believed permeated all of space, had no effect on the velocity of light as seen from different directions.

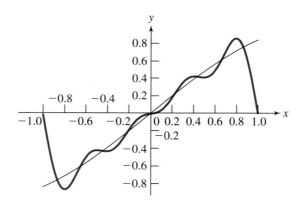

FIGURE 14.20(a) *Fourth partial sum of the Fourier series of* $f(x) = \sin(x)$ *for* $-1 \le x \le 1$.

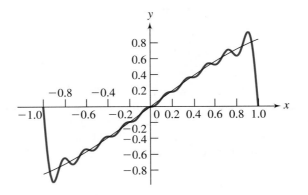

FIGURE 14.20(b) *Tenth partial sum of the function*
$f(x) = \sin(x)$ *for* $-1 \le x \le 1$.

Some years later Michelson was testing a mechanical device he had invented for computing Fourier coefficients and for constructing a function from its Fourier coefficients. In one test he used eighty Fourier coefficients for the function $f(x) = x$ for $-\pi \le x \le \pi$. The machine responded with a graph having unexpected jumps near the end points π and $-\pi$. At first Michelson assumed that there was some problem with his machine. Eventually, however, it was found that this behavior is characteristic of Fourier series at jump discontinuities of the function. This became known as the Gibbs phenomenon, after the Yale mathematician Josiah Willard Gibbs, who was the first to satisfactorily define and explain it. The phenomenon had also been noticed some sixty years before by the English mathematician Wilbraham, who was, however, unable to analyze it.

To illustrate the phenomenon, consider the function defined by

$$f(x) = \begin{cases} -\pi/4 & \text{for } -\pi \le x < 0 \\ 0 & \text{for } x = 0 \\ \pi/4 & \text{for } 0 < x \le \pi \end{cases}.$$

Figure 14.21 shows a graph of this function, whose Fourier series is

$$\sum_{n=1}^{\infty} \frac{1}{2n-1} \sin((2n-1)x).$$

By either convergence theorem this series converges to $f(x)$ for $-\pi < x < \pi$. There is a jump discontinuity at 0, but

$$\frac{1}{2}(f(0+) + f(0-)) = \frac{1}{2}\left(-\frac{\pi}{4} + \frac{\pi}{4}\right) = 0 = f(0).$$

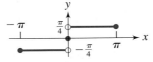

FIGURE 14.21 *Function illustrating the Gibbs phenomenon.*

The Nth partial sum of this Fourier series is

$$S_N(x) = \sum_{n=1}^{N} \frac{1}{2n-1} \sin((2n-1)x),$$

and Figure 14.22 shows graphs of $S_5(x)$, $S_{14}(x)$ and $S_{22}(x)$. Each of these partial sums shows a peak near zero. Intuitively, since the partial sums approach $f(x)$ as $N \to \infty$, we might expect these peaks to flatten out and become smaller as N is chosen larger. But they don't. Instead, the peaks maintain roughly the same height, but move closer to the y axis as N increases. The partial sums do indeed have the function as a limit, but not in quite the way mathematicians expected.

As another example, consider

$$f(x) = \begin{cases} 0 & \text{for } -2 \le x < 0 \\ 2-x & \text{for } 0 \le x \le 2 \end{cases}.$$

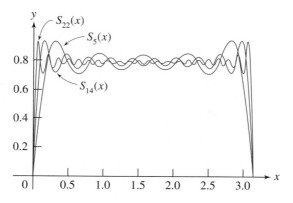

FIGURE 14.22 *Partial sums (for $0 \le x \le \pi/4$) showing the Gibbs phenomenon for the function of Figure 14.21.*

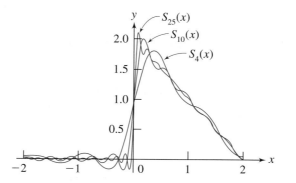

FIGURE 14.23 *Fourth, tenth, and twenty-fifth partial sums of the Fourier series of*
$$f(x) = \begin{cases} 0 & \text{for } -2 \le x < 0 \\ 2-x & \text{for } 0 \le x \le 2 \end{cases}.$$

This function has a jump discontinuity at 0, and Fourier series

$$\frac{1}{2} + \sum_{n=1}^{\infty} \left(\frac{2}{n^2 \pi^2} (1 - (-1)^n)) \cos(n\pi x/2) + \frac{2}{n\pi} \sin(n\pi x/2) \right).$$

Figure 14.23 shows the fourth, tenth and twenty-fifth partial sum of this series. Again, the Gibbs phenomenon shows up at the jump discontinuity. Gibbs showed that this behavior occurs in the Fourier series of a function at every point where it has a jump discontinuity.

SECTION 14.3   PROBLEMS

In each of Problems 1 through 10, use a convergence theorem to determine the sum of the Fourier series of the function on the interval. Whichever theorem is used, verify that the hypotheses are satisfied, assuming familiar facts from calculus about continuous and differentiable functions. It is not necessary to write the series itself to do this.

Next, find the Fourier series of the function and graph f and, for $N = 5, 10, 15, 25$, graph the Nth partial sum of the series, together with the function on the interval. Point out any places where the Gibbs phenomenon is apparent in these graphs.

1. $f(x) = \begin{cases} 2x & \text{for } -3 \le x < -2 \\ 0 & \text{for } -2 \le x < 1 \\ x^2 & \text{for } 1 \le x \le 3 \end{cases}$

2. $f(x) = x^2$ for $-2 \le x \le 2$

3. $f(x) = x^2 e^{-x}$ for $-3 \le x \le 3$

4. $f(x) = \begin{cases} 2x - 2 & \text{for } -\pi \le x \le 1 \\ 3 & \text{for } 1 < x \le \pi \end{cases}$

5. $f(x) = \begin{cases} x^2 & \text{for } -\pi \le x \le 0 \\ 2 & \text{for } 0 < x \le \pi \end{cases}$

6. $f(x) = \begin{cases} \cos(x) & \text{for } -2 \le x < 0 \\ \sin(x) & \text{for } 0 \le x \le 2 \end{cases}$

7. $f(x) = \begin{cases} -1 & \text{for } -4 \le x < 0 \\ 1 & \text{for } 0 \le x \le 4 \end{cases}$

8. $f(x) = \begin{cases} 0 & \text{for } -1 \le x < \frac{1}{2} \\ 1 & \text{for } \frac{1}{2} \le x \le \frac{3}{4} \\ 2 & \text{for } \frac{3}{4} < x \le 1 \end{cases}$

9. $f(x) = e^{-|x|}$ for $-\pi \le x \le \pi$

10. $f(x) = \begin{cases} -2 & \text{for } -4 \le x \le -2 \\ 1 + x^2 & \text{for } -2 < x \le 2 \\ 0 & \text{for } 2 < x \le 4 \end{cases}$

11. Let $f(x) = x^2/2$ for $-\pi \le x \le \pi$. Find the Fourier series of $f(x)$ and evaluate it at an appropriately chosen value of x to sum the series $\sum_{n=1}^{\infty} 1/n^2$.

12. Use the Fourier series of Problem 11 to sum the series $\sum_{n=1}^{\infty} (-1)^n / n^2$.

14.4   Fourier Cosine and Sine Series

If $f(x)$ is defined on $[-L, L]$, we may be able to write its Fourier series. The coefficients of this series are completely determined by the function and the interval.

We will now show that, if $f(x)$ is defined on the half-interval $[0, L]$, then we have a choice, and can write a series containing just cosines or just sines in attempting to represent $f(x)$ on this half-interval.

14.4.1 The Fourier Cosine Series of a Function

Let f be integrable on $[0, L]$. We want to expand $f(x)$ in a series of cosine functions.

We already have the means to do this. Figure 14.24 shows a graph of a typical f. Fold this graph across the $y-$ axis to obtain an function f_e defined for $-L \leq x \leq L$:

$$f_e(x) = \begin{cases} f(x) & \text{for } 0 \leq x \leq L \\ f(-x) & \text{for } -L \leq x < 0 \end{cases}.$$

f_e is an even function,

$$f_e(-x) = f(x),$$

and agrees with f on $[0, L]$,

$$f_e(x) = f(x) \text{ for } 0 \leq x \leq L.$$

We call f_e the *even extension* of f to $[-L, L]$.

EXAMPLE 14.14

Let $f(x) = e^x$ for $0 \leq x \leq 2$. Then

$$f_e(x) = \begin{cases} e^x & \text{for } 0 \leq x \leq 2 \\ e^{-x} & \text{for } -2 \leq x < 0 \end{cases}.$$

Here we put $f_e(-x) = f(x) = e^x$ for $0 < x \leq 2$, meaning that $f_e(x) = e^{-x}$ for $-2 \leq x < 0$. A graph of f_e is given in Figure 14.25. ■

Because f_e is an even function on $[-L, L]$, its Fourier series on $[-L, L]$ is

$$\frac{1}{2}a_0 + \sum_{n=1}^{\infty} a_n \cos\left(\frac{n\pi x}{L}\right), \tag{14.14}$$

in which

$$a_n = \frac{2}{L} \int_0^L f_e(x) \cos\left(\frac{n\pi x}{L}\right) dx = \frac{2}{L} \int_0^L f(x) \cos\left(\frac{n\pi x}{L}\right) dx, \tag{14.15}$$

since $f_e(x) = f(x)$ for $0 \leq x \leq L$. We call the series (14.14) the *Fourier cosine series of f on* $[0, L]$. The coefficients (14.15) are the *Fourier cosine coefficients of f on* $[0, L]$.

The even extension f_e was introduced only to be able to make use of earlier work to derive a series containing just cosines. When we actually write a Fourier cosine series, we just use (14.14) to calculate the coefficients, without defining f_e.

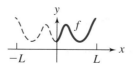

FIGURE 14.24 *Even extension of f to* $[-L, L]$.

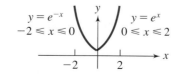

FIGURE 14.25

The other point to having f_e in the background, however, is that we can use the Fourier convergence theorems to write a convergence theorem for cosine series.

THEOREM 14.3   *Convergence of Fourier Cosine Series*

Let f be piecewise continuous on $[0, L]$. Then,

1. If $0 < x < L$, and f has left and right derivatives at x, then the Fourier cosine series for $f(x)$ on $[0, L]$ converges at x to

$$\frac{1}{2}\left(f(x-) + f(x+)\right).$$

2. If f has a right derivative at 0, then the Fourier cosine series for $f(x)$ on $[0, L]$ converges at 0 to $f(0+)$.

3. If f has a left derivative at L, then the Fourier cosine series for $f(x)$ on $[0, L]$ converges at L to $f(L-)$. ∎

Conclusions (2) and (3) follow from Theorem 14.2, applied to f_e. Consider first $x = 0$. The Fourier series of f_e converges at 0 to

$$\frac{1}{2}\left(f_e(0-) + f_e(0+)\right).$$

But

$$f_e(0+) = f(0+)$$

and

$$f_e(0-) = f(0+),$$

so at 0 the series converges to

$$\frac{1}{2}\left(f(0+) + f(0+)\right) = f(0+).$$

A similar argument proves conclusion (3).

EXAMPLE 14.15

Let $f(x) = e^{2x}$ for $0 \leq x \leq 1$. We will write the Fourier cosine series of f. Compute

$$a_0 = 2\int_0^1 e^{2x}\,dx = e^2 - 1$$

and

$$a_n = 2\int_0^1 e^{2x}\cos(n\pi x)\,dx$$

$$= 4\frac{e^2(-1)^n - 1}{4 + n^2\pi^2}.$$

The cosine expansion of f is

$$\frac{1}{2}(e^2 - 1) + \sum_{n=1}^{\infty} 4\frac{e^2(-1)^n - 1}{4 + n^2\pi^2}\cos(n\pi x).$$

This series converges to

$$\begin{cases} e^{2x} & \text{for } 0 < x < 1 \\ 1 & \text{for } x = 0 \\ e^2 & \text{for } x = 1 \end{cases}.$$

Thus this cosine series converges to e^{2x} for $0 \le x \le 1$. Figures 14.26 (a) and (b) show a graph of f compared with the fifth and tenth partial sums of this cosine expansion, respectively. ■

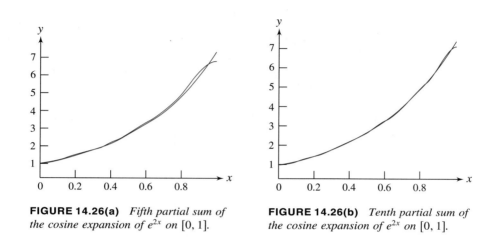

FIGURE 14.26(a)   *Fifth partial sum of the cosine expansion of e^{2x} on $[0, 1]$.*

FIGURE 14.26(b)   *Tenth partial sum of the cosine expansion of e^{2x} on $[0, 1]$.*

14.4.2   The Fourier Sine Series of a Function

By duplicating the strategy just used for writing a cosine series, except now extending f to an odd function f_o over $[-L, L]$, we can write a Fourier sine series for $f(x)$ on $[0, L]$. In particular, if $f(x)$ is defined on $[0, L]$, let

$$f_o(x) = \begin{cases} f(x) & \text{for } 0 \le x \le L \\ -f(-x) & \text{for } -L \le x < 0 \end{cases}.$$

Then f_o is an odd function, and $f_o(x) = f(x)$ for $0 \le x \le L$. This is the *odd extension* of f to $[-L, L]$. For example, if $f(x) = e^{2x}$ for $0 \le x \le 1$, let

$$f_o(x) = \begin{cases} e^{2x} & \text{for } 0 \le x \le 1 \\ -e^{-2x} & \text{for } -1 \le x < 0 \end{cases}$$

This amounts to folding the graph of f over the vertical axis, then over the horizontal axis (Figure 14.27).

Now write the Fourier series for $f_o(x)$ on $[-L, L]$. By equations (14.11) and (14.12), the Fourier series of f_o is

$$\sum_{n=1}^{\infty} b_n \sin\left(\frac{n\pi x}{L}\right) \tag{14.16}$$

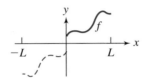

FIGURE 14.27 *Odd extension of f to [−L, L].*

with coefficients

$$b_n = \frac{2}{L} \int_0^L f_o(x) \sin\left(\frac{n\pi x}{L}\right) dx = \frac{2}{L} \int_0^L f(x) \sin\left(\frac{n\pi x}{L}\right) dx. \qquad (14.17)$$

We call the series (14.16) the *Fourier sine series* of f on $[0, L]$. The coefficients given by equation (14.17) are the Fourier sine coefficients of f on $[0, L]$. As with cosine series, we do not need to explicitly make the extension to f_o to write the Fourier sine series for f on $[0, L]$.

Again, as with the cosine expansion, we can write a convergence theorem for sine series using the convergence theorem for Fourier series.

THEOREM 14.4   *Convergence of Fourier Sine Series*

Let f be piecewise continuous on $[0, L]$. Then,

1. If $0 < x < L$, and f has left and right derivatives at x, then the Fourier sine series for $f(x)$ on $[0, L]$ converges at x to

$$\frac{1}{2}\left(f(x-) + f(x+)\right).$$

2. At 0 and at L, the Fourier sine series for $f(x)$ on $[0, L]$ converges to 0. ∎

Conclusion (2) is immediate because each term of the sine series (14.16) is zero for $x = 0$ and for $x = L$.

EXAMPLE 14.16

Let $f(x) = e^{2x}$ for $0 \le x \le 1$. We will write the Fourier sine series of f on $[0, 1]$. The coefficients are

$$b_n = 2 \int_0^1 e^{2x} \sin(n\pi x) dx$$

$$= 2 \frac{n\pi(1 - (-1)^n e^2)}{4 + n^2 \pi^2}.$$

The sine series is

$$\sum_{n=1}^{\infty} 2 \frac{n\pi(1 - (-1)^n e^2)}{4 + n^2 \pi^2} \sin(n\pi x).$$

This series converges to e^{2x} for $0 < x < 1$, and to zero for $x = 0$ and for $x = 1$. Figures 14.28 (a) and (b) show graphs of the tenth and fortieth partial sums of this series. ∎

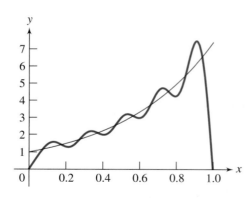

FIGURE 14.28(a) *Tenth partial sum of the sine expansion of e^{2x} on $[0, 1]$.*

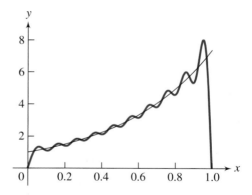

FIGURE 14.28(b) *Fortieth partial sum of the sine expansion of e^{2x} on $[0, 1]$.*

SECTION 14.4 PROBLEMS

In each of Problems 1 through 10, write the Fourier cosine series and the Fourier sine series of the function on the interval. Determine the sum of each series.

1. $f(x) = 4, 0 \leq x \leq 3$

2. $f(x) = \begin{cases} 1 & \text{for } 0 \leq x \leq 1 \\ -1 & \text{for } 1 < x \leq 2 \end{cases}$

3. $f(x) = \begin{cases} 0 & \text{for } 0 \leq x < \pi \\ \cos(x) & \text{for } \pi \leq x \leq 2\pi \end{cases}$

4. $f(x) = 2x$ for $0 \leq x \leq 1$

5. $f(x) = x^2$ for $0 \leq x \leq 2$

6. $f(x) = e^{-x}$ for $0 \leq x \leq 1$

7. $f(x) = \begin{cases} x & \text{for } 0 \leq x \leq 2 \\ 2-x & \text{for } 2 < x \leq 3 \end{cases}$

8. $f(x) = \begin{cases} 1 & \text{for } 0 \leq x < 1 \\ 0 & \text{for } 1 \leq x \leq 3 \\ -1 & \text{for } 3 < x \leq 5 \end{cases}$

9. $f(x) = \begin{cases} x^2 & \text{for } 0 \leq x < 1 \\ 1 & \text{for } 1 \leq x \leq 4 \end{cases}$

10. $f(x) = 1 - x^3$ for $0 \leq x \leq 2$

11. Let $f(x)$ be defined on $[-L, L]$. Prove that f can be written as the sum of an even and an odd function on this interval.

12. Find all functions defined on $[-L, L]$ that are both even and odd.

13. Find the sum of the series $\sum_{n=1}^{\infty}(-1)^n/(4n^2 - 1)$. *Hint*: Expand $\sin(x)$ in a cosine series on $[0, \pi]$ and choose an appropriate value of x.

14.5 Integration and Differentiation of Fourier Series

In this section we will take a closer look at Fourier coefficients, and consider term by term differentiation and integration of Fourier series.

Differentiation of Fourier series term-by-term generally leads to absurd results, even for extremely well behaved functions. Consider, for example, $f(x) = x$ for $-\pi \leq x \leq \pi$. The Fourier series is

$$\sum_{n=1}^{\infty} \frac{2}{n}(-1)^{n+1} \sin(nx),$$

which converges to x for $-\pi < x < \pi$. Of course, $f'(x) = 1$ for $-\pi < x < \pi$, so f is piecewise smooth. However, if we differentiate the Fourier series term-by-term, we get

$$\sum_{n=1}^{\infty} 2(-1)^{n+1} \cos(nx),$$

which does not even converge on $(-\pi, \pi)$. The term by term derivative of this Fourier series is unrelated to the derivative of $f(x)$.

Integration of Fourier series has better prospects.

THEOREM 14.5 *Integration of Fourier Series*

Let f be piecewise continuous on $[-L, L]$, with Fourier series

$$\frac{1}{2}a_0 + \sum_{n=1}^{\infty} a_n \cos\left(\frac{n\pi x}{L}\right) + b_n \sin\left(\frac{n\pi x}{L}\right).$$

Then, for any x with $-L \leq x \leq L$,

$$\int_{-L}^{x} f(t)\,dt = \frac{1}{2}a_0(x + L) + \frac{L}{\pi}\sum_{n=1}^{\infty}\frac{1}{n}\left[a_n \sin\left(\frac{n\pi x}{L}\right) - b_n\left(\cos\left(\frac{n\pi x}{L}\right) - (-1)^n\right)\right]. \quad \blacksquare$$

The expression on the right in this equation is exactly what we get by integrating the Fourier series term by term, from $-L$ to x. This means that, for any piecewise continuous function, we can integrate f from $-L$ to x by integrating its Fourier series term-by-term. This holds even if the Fourier series does not converge to $f(x)$ at this particular x (for example, f might have a jump discontinuity at x).

Proof Define

$$F(x) = \int_{-L}^{x} f(t)\,dt - \frac{1}{2}a_0 x$$

for $-L \leq x \leq L$. Then F is continuous on $[-L, L]$ and $F(L) = F(-L) = La_0/2$. Further, $F'(x) = f(x) - \frac{1}{2}a_0$ at every point of $[-L, L]$ where f is continuous. Hence F' is piecewise continuous on $[-L, L]$. Therefore the Fourier series of $F(x)$ converges to $F(x)$ on $[-L, L]$:

$$F(x) = \frac{1}{2}A_0 + \sum_{n=1}^{\infty} A_n \cos\left(\frac{n\pi x}{L}\right) + B_n \sin\left(\frac{n\pi x}{L}\right), \quad (14.18)$$

in which we will use upper case letters for Fourier coefficients of F, and lower case letters for those of f. Now compute the A_n's and B_n's for $n = 1, 2, \ldots$ by integrating by parts. First,

$$A_n = \frac{1}{L}\int_{-L}^{L} F(t) \cos\left(\frac{n\pi t}{L}\right) dt$$

$$= \frac{1}{L}\left[F(t)\frac{L}{n\pi}\sin\left(\frac{n\pi t}{L}\right)\right]_{-L}^{L} - \frac{1}{L}\int_{-L}^{L}\frac{L}{n\pi}\sin\left(\frac{n\pi t}{L}\right)F'(t)\,dt$$

$$= -\frac{1}{n\pi}\int_{-L}^{L}\left(f(t) - \frac{1}{2}a_0\right)\sin\left(\frac{n\pi t}{L}\right)dt$$

$$= -\frac{1}{n\pi}\int_{-L}^{L} f(t)\sin\left(\frac{n\pi t}{L}\right)dt + \frac{1}{2n\pi}a_0\int_{-L}^{L}\sin\left(\frac{n\pi t}{L}\right)dt$$

$$= -\frac{L}{n\pi}b_n,$$

in which b_n is the sine coefficient in the Fourier series of f on $[-L, L]$. Similarly,

$$B_n = \frac{1}{L} \int_{-L}^{L} F(t) \sin\left(\frac{n\pi t}{L}\right) dt$$

$$= \frac{1}{L}\left[F(t)\left(-\frac{L}{n\pi}\cos\left(\frac{n\pi t}{L}\right)\right)\right]_{-L}^{L} - \frac{1}{L}\int_{-L}^{L} F'(t)\left(-\frac{L}{n\pi}\right)\cos\left(\frac{n\pi t}{L}\right) dt$$

$$= \frac{1}{n\pi}\int_{-L}^{L}\left(f(t) - \frac{1}{2}a_0\right)\cos\left(\frac{n\pi t}{L}\right) dt$$

$$= \frac{1}{n\pi}\int_{-L}^{L} f(t)\cos\left(\frac{n\pi t}{L}\right) dt - \frac{1}{2n\pi}a_0\int_{-L}^{L}\cos\left(\frac{n\pi t}{L}\right) dt$$

$$= \frac{L}{n\pi}a_n.$$

Therefore the Fourier series of F is

$$F(x) = \frac{1}{2}A_0 + \frac{L}{\pi}\sum_{n=1}^{\infty}\left(\frac{1}{n}\right)\left(-b_n\cos\left(\frac{n\pi x}{L}\right) + a_n\sin\left(\frac{n\pi x}{L}\right)\right)$$

for $-L \le x \le L$. Now we must determine A_0. But

$$F(L) = \frac{L}{2}a_0 = \frac{1}{2}A_0 - \frac{L}{\pi}\sum_{n=1}^{\infty}\left(\frac{1}{n}\right)b_n\cos(n\pi)$$

$$= \frac{1}{2}A_0 - \frac{L}{\pi}\sum_{n=1}^{\infty}\left(\frac{1}{n}\right)b_n(-1)^n.$$

This gives us

$$A_0 = La_0 + \frac{2L}{\pi}\sum_{n=1}^{\infty}\left(\frac{1}{n}\right)b_n(-1)^n.$$

Upon substituting these expressions for A_0, A_n and B_n into the series (14.18), we obtain the conclusion of the theorem. ∎

EXAMPLE 14.17

Let $f(x) = x$ for $-\pi \le x \le \pi$. This function is continuous on $[-\pi, \pi]$, and its Fourier series is

$$\sum_{n=1}^{\infty}\frac{2}{n}(-1)^{n+1}\sin(nx).$$

We have seen that we get nonsense if we differentiate this series term by term. However, we can integrate it term by term to obtain, for any x in $[-\pi, \pi]$,

$$\int_{-\pi}^{x} t\, dt = \frac{1}{2}(x^2 - \pi^2)$$

$$= \sum_{n=1}^{\infty}\frac{2}{n}(-1)^{n+1}\int_{-\pi}^{x}\sin(nt)\, dt$$

$$= \sum_{n=1}^{\infty} \frac{2}{n}(-1)^{n+1} \left[-\frac{1}{n}\cos(nx) + \frac{1}{n}\cos(n\pi) \right]$$

$$= \sum_{n=1}^{\infty} \frac{2}{n^2}(-1)^n \left[\cos(nx) - (-1)^n \right]. \ \blacksquare$$

With stronger conditions on f, we can derive a result on term by term differentiation of Fourier series.

THEOREM 14.6   *Differentiation of Fourier Series*

Let f be continuous on $[-L, L]$ and suppose $f(L) = f(-L)$. Let f' be piecewise continuous on $[-L, L]$. Then $f(x)$ equals its Fourier series for $-L \le x \le L$,

$$f(x) = \frac{1}{2}a_0 + \sum_{n=1}^{\infty} a_n \cos\left(\frac{n\pi x}{L}\right) + b_n \sin\left(\frac{n\pi x}{L}\right),$$

and, at each point in $(-L, L)$ where $f''(x)$ exists,

$$f'(x) = \sum_{n=1}^{\infty} \frac{n\pi}{L}\left(-na_n \sin(\pi x/L) + b_n \cos\left(\frac{n\pi x}{L}\right)\right). \ \blacksquare$$

We leave a proof of this to the student. The idea is to write the Fourier series of $f'(x)$, noting that this Fourier series converges to $f'(x)$ wherever $f''(x)$ exists. Use integration by parts, as in the proof of Theorem 14.5, to relate the Fourier coefficients of $f'(x)$ to those of $f(x)$.

EXAMPLE 14.18

Let $f(x) = x^2$ for $-2 \le x \le 2$. The hypotheses of Theorem 14.6 are satisfied. The Fourier series of f on $[-2, 2]$ is

$$f(x) = \frac{4}{3} + \frac{16}{\pi^2} \sum_{n=1}^{\infty} \frac{(-1)^n}{n^2} \cos\left(\frac{n\pi x}{2}\right),$$

with equality between $f(x)$ and its Fourier series. Because $f'(x) = 2x$ is continuous, and $f''(x) = 2$ exists throughout the interval, then for $-2 < x < 2$,

$$f'(x) = 2x = \frac{8}{\pi} \sum_{n=1}^{\infty} \frac{(-1)^{n+1}}{n} \sin\left(\frac{n\pi x}{2}\right).$$

For example, putting $x = 1$, we get

$$\frac{8}{\pi} \sum_{n=1}^{\infty} \frac{(-1)^{n+1}}{n} \sin\left(\frac{n\pi}{2}\right) = 2,$$

or

$$\sum_{n=1}^{\infty} \frac{(-1)^{n+1}}{n} \sin\left(\frac{n\pi}{2}\right) = \frac{\pi}{4}.$$

Manipulations on Fourier series can sometimes be used to sum series such as this. $\blacksquare$

We now have conditions under which we can differentiate or integrate a Fourier series term by term. We will next consider conditions sufficient for a Fourier series to converge uniformly. First we will derive a set of important inequalities for Fourier coefficients, called Bessel's inequalities.

THEOREM 14.7 *Bessel's Inequalities*

Let f be integrable on $[0, L]$. Then

1. The coefficients in the Fourier sine expansion of f on $[0, L]$ satisfy

$$\sum_{n=1}^{\infty} b_n^2 \leq \frac{2}{L} \int_{-L}^{L} f(x)^2 \, dx.$$

2. The coefficients in the Fourier cosine expansion of f on $[0, L]$ satisfy

$$\frac{1}{2} a_0^2 + \sum_{n=1}^{\infty} a_n^2 \leq \frac{2}{L} \int_0^L f(x)^2 \, dx.$$

3. If f is integrable on $[-L, L]$, then the Fourier coefficients of f on $[-L, L]$ satisfy

$$\frac{1}{2} a_0^2 + \sum_{n=1}^{\infty} (a_n^2 + b_n^2) \leq \frac{1}{L} \int_{-L}^{L} f(x)^2 \, dx. \quad \blacksquare$$

In particular, the sum of the squares of the (sine, cosine, or Fourier series) coefficients of f converges. We will prove (1), which is notationally simpler than the other two inequalities, but contains the idea of the argument.

Proof Since $\int_0^L f(x) \, dx$ exists, we can compute the Fourier sine coefficients and write the sine series

$$\sum_{n=1}^{\infty} b_n \sin\left(\frac{n\pi x}{L}\right),$$

where

$$b_n = \frac{2}{L} \int_0^L f(x) \sin\left(\frac{n\pi x}{L}\right) dx.$$

The Nth partial sum of this series is

$$S_N(x) = \sum_{n=1}^{N} b_n \sin\left(\frac{n\pi x}{L}\right).$$

Now consider

$$0 \leq \int_0^L (f(x) - S_N(x))^2 \, dx$$

$$= \int_0^L f(x)^2 \, dx - 2 \int_0^L f(x) S_N(x) \, dx + \int_0^L S_N(x)^2 \, dx$$

$$= \int_0^L f(x)^2 \, dx - 2 \int_0^L f(x) \left(\sum_{n=1}^{N} b_n \sin\left(\frac{n\pi x}{L}\right)\right) dx$$

$$+ \int_0^L \left(\sum_{n=1}^{N} b_n \sin\left(\frac{n\pi x}{L}\right)\right) \left(\sum_{m=1}^{N} b_m \sin\left(\frac{m\pi x}{L}\right)\right) dx$$

$$= \int_0^L f(x)^2 \, dx - 2 \sum_{n=1}^{N} b_n \int_0^L f(x) \sin\left(\frac{n\pi x}{L}\right) dx$$

$$+ \sum_{n=1}^{N} \sum_{m=1}^{N} b_n b_m \int_0^L \sin\left(\frac{n\pi x}{L}\right) \sin\left(\frac{m\pi x}{L}\right) dx$$

$$= \int_0^L f(x)^2 \, dx - \sum_{n=1}^{N} b_n (Lb_n) + \sum_{n=1}^{N} b_n b_n \frac{L}{2},$$

in which we have used the fact that

$$\int_0^L \sin\left(\frac{n\pi x}{L}\right) \sin\left(\frac{m\pi x}{L}\right) dx = \begin{cases} 0 & \text{if } n \neq m \\ L/2 & \text{if } n = m \end{cases}.$$

We therefore have

$$0 \le \int_0^L f(x)^2 \, dx - L \sum_{n=1}^{N} b_n^2 + \frac{L}{2} \sum_{n=1}^{N} b_n^2,$$

or

$$\sum_{n=1}^{N} b_n^2 \le \frac{2}{L} \int_0^L f(x)^2 \, dx.$$

Since the right side is independent of N, we can let $N \to \infty$ to get

$$\sum_{n=1}^{\infty} b_n^2 \le \frac{2}{L} \int_0^L f(x)^2 \, dx,$$

proving conclusion (1). Conclusions (2) and (3) have similar proofs. ∎

EXAMPLE 14.19

We will use Bessel's inequality to derive an upper bound for an infinite series. Let $f(x) = x^2$ for $-\pi \le x \le \pi$. The Fourier series of f converges to $f(x)$ for all x in $[-\pi, \pi]$:

$$x^2 = \frac{1}{3}\pi^2 + \sum_{n=1}^{\infty} 4\frac{(-1)^n}{n^2} \cos(nx).$$

Here $a_0 = 2\pi^2/3$, $a_n = 4(-1)^n/n^2$ and $b_n = 0$ (x^2 is an even function). By Bessel's inequality (3) of Theorem 14.7,

$$\frac{1}{2}\left(\frac{2\pi^2}{3}\right)^2 + \sum_{n=1}^{\infty} \left(\frac{4(-1)^n}{n^2}\right)^2 \le \frac{1}{\pi} \int_{-\pi}^{\pi} x^4 \, dx = \frac{2}{5}\pi^4.$$

Then

$$16 \sum_{n=1}^{\infty} \frac{1}{n^4} \le \left(\frac{2}{5} - \frac{2}{9}\right) \pi^4 = \frac{8\pi^4}{45},$$

so

$$\sum_{n=1}^{\infty} \frac{1}{n^4} \le \frac{\pi^4}{90},$$

which is approximately 1.0823232. ∎

Using Bessel's inequality for coefficients in a Fourier expansion on $[-L, L]$, we can prove a result on uniform convergence of Fourier series.

THEOREM 14.8 *Uniform and Absolute Convergence of Fourier Series*

Let f be continuous on $[-L, L]$ and let f' be piecewise continuous. Suppose $f(-L) = f(L)$. Then, the Fourier series of f on $[-L, L]$ converges absolutely and uniformly to $f(x)$ on $[-L, L]$. ∎

Proof Denote the Fourier coefficients of f by lower case letters, and those of f' by upper case. Then

$$A_0 = \frac{1}{L} \int_{-L}^{L} f'(\xi)d\xi = f(L) - f(-L) = 0.$$

For positive integer n, we find by integration by parts, as in the proof of Theorem 14.5, that

$$A_n = \frac{n\pi}{L} b_n \text{ and } B_n = -\frac{n\pi}{L} a_n.$$

Now

$$0 \le \left(|A_n| - \frac{1}{n}\right)^2 = A_n^2 - \frac{2}{n}|A_n| + \frac{1}{n^2}$$

and, similarly,

$$0 \le B_n^2 - \frac{2}{n}|B_n| + \frac{1}{n^2}.$$

Then

$$\frac{1}{n}|A_n| + \frac{1}{n}|B_n| \le \frac{1}{2}\left(A_n^2 + B_n^2\right) + \frac{1}{n^2}.$$

Therefore

$$\frac{\pi}{L}|a_n| + \frac{\pi}{L}|b_n| \le \frac{1}{2}\left(A_n^2 + B_n^2\right) + \frac{1}{n^2},$$

hence

$$|a_n| + |b_n| \le \frac{L}{2\pi}\left(A_n^2 + B_n^2\right) + \frac{L}{\pi}\frac{1}{n^2}.$$

Now $\sum_{n=1}^{\infty}(1/n^2)$ converges, and $\sum_{n=1}^{\infty}\left(A_n^2 + B_n^2\right)$ converges by applying Bessel's inequality to the Fourier coefficients of f'. Therefore, by comparison, $\sum_{n=1}^{\infty}\left(|a_n| + |b_n|\right)$ converges also.

But, for $-L \le x \le L$,

$$|a_n \cos(n\pi x/L) + b_n \sin(n\pi x/L)| \le |a_n| + |b_n|.$$

By a theorem of Weierstrass, this implies that the Fourier series of f converges uniformly on $[-L, L]$. Further, the convergence is absolute, since the series of absolute values of terms of the series converges. Finally, by the Fourier convergence theorem, the Fourier series of f converges to $f(x)$ on $[-L, L]$. This completes the proof. ∎

EXAMPLE 14.20

Let $f(x) = e^{-|x|}$ for $-1 \le x \le 1$. Then

$$f(x) = \begin{cases} e^x & \text{for } -1 \le x < 0 \\ e^{-x} & \text{for } 0 \le x \le 1 \end{cases}.$$

f is continuous on $[-1, 1]$, and

$$f'(x) = \begin{cases} -e^{-x} & \text{for } 0 < x \le 1 \\ e^x & \text{for } -1 \le x < 0 \end{cases}.$$

f has no derivative at $x = 0$, which is a cusp of the graph (Figure 14.29). Thus f' is piecewise continuous on $[-1, 1]$. Finally, $f(1) = f(-1) = e^{-1}$. Therefore the Fourier series of f converges uniformly and absolutely to $f(x)$ on $[-1, 1]$:

$$f(x) = 1 - e^{-1} + 2 \sum_{n=1}^{\infty} \frac{1 - e^{-1}(-1)^n}{1 + \pi^2 n^2} \cos(n\pi x)$$

for $-1 \le x \le 1$.

We can integrate this series term by term. For example,

$$\int_{-1}^{x} f(t)dt = \int_{-1}^{x} (1 - e^{-1})dt + 2 \sum_{n=1}^{\infty} \frac{1 - e^{-1}(-1)^n}{1 + \pi^2 n^2} \int_{-1}^{x} \cos(n\pi t)dt$$

$$= (1 - e^{-1})(x + 1) + 2 \sum_{n=1}^{\infty} \frac{1 - e^{-1}(-1)^n}{1 + \pi^2 n^2} \frac{1}{n\pi} \sin(n\pi x).$$

This is a correct equation, but it is not a Fourier series (the right side includes the polynomial term x). We may always integrate a Fourier series term by term, and the result may be a convergent series, but not necessarily a Fourier series.

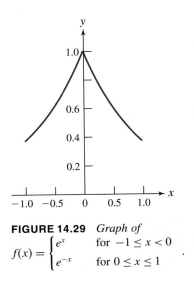

FIGURE 14.29 *Graph of*
$$f(x) = \begin{cases} e^x & \text{for } -1 \le x < 0 \\ e^{-x} & \text{for } 0 \le x \le 1 \end{cases}.$$

We can also differentiate the Fourier series for $f(x)$ term by term at any point in $(-1, 1)$ at which $f''(x)$ exists. Thus we can differentiate term by term for $-1 < x < 0$ and for $0 < x < 1$. For such x,

$$f'(x) = -2 \sum_{n=1}^{\infty} \frac{1 - e^{-1}(-1)^n}{1 + \pi^2 n^2} n\pi \sin(n\pi x). \ \blacksquare$$

We will conclude this section with Parseval's theorem. Recall that Bessel's inequality for Fourier coefficients on $[-L, L]$ requires only that we be able to compute these coefficients. If, however, we place continuity conditions on the function, as in Theorem 14.8, then we turn Bessel's inequality into an equality.

THEOREM 14.9   *Parseval*

Let f be continuous on $[-L, L]$ and let f' be piecewise continuous. Suppose $f(-L) = f(L)$. Then the Fourier coefficients of f on $[-L, L]$ satisfy

$$\frac{1}{2}a_0^2 + \sum_{n=1}^{\infty}(a_n^2 + b_n^2) = \frac{1}{L} \int_{-L}^{L} f(x)^2 dx. \ \blacksquare$$

Proof   The Fourier series of f on $[-L, L]$ converges to $f(x)$ at each point of this interval:

$$f(x) = \frac{1}{2}a_0 + \sum_{n=1}^{\infty} a_n \cos\left(\frac{n\pi x}{L}\right) + b_n \sin\left(\frac{n\pi x}{L}\right).$$

Then

$$f(x)^2 = \frac{1}{2}a_0 f(x) + \sum_{n=1}^{\infty} a_n f(x) \cos\left(\frac{n\pi x}{L}\right) + b_n f(x) \sin\left(\frac{n\pi x}{L}\right).$$

We can integrate this Fourier series term by term, and multiplication of the series by the continuous function $f(x)$ does not change this. Therefore

$$\int_{-L}^{L} f(x)^2 dx = \frac{1}{2}a_0 \int_{-L}^{L} f(x) dx$$

$$+ \sum_{n=1}^{\infty} a_n \int_{-L}^{L} f(x) \cos\left(\frac{n\pi x}{L}\right) dx + b_n \int_{-L}^{L} f(x) \sin\left(\frac{n\pi x}{L}\right) dx.$$

Recalling the integral formulas for the Fourier coefficients, this equation can be written

$$\int_{-L}^{L} f(x)^2 dx = \frac{1}{2}a_0 L a_0 + \sum_{n=1}^{\infty}(a_n L a_n + b_n L b_n),$$

and this is equivalent to the conclusion of the theorem. $\blacksquare$

EXAMPLE 14.21

Parseval's theorem has various applications in deriving other properties of Fourier series. We will encounter it later when we discuss completeness of sets of eigenfunctions. However, one immediate use is in summing certain infinite series. To illustrate, the Fourier coefficients of $\cos(x/2)$ on $[-\pi, \pi]$ are

$$a_0 = \frac{1}{\pi} \int_{-\pi}^{\pi} \cos(x/2) dx = \frac{4}{\pi}$$

and

$$a_n = \frac{1}{\pi} \int_{-\pi}^{\pi} \cos(x/2) \cos(nx)\,dx = -\frac{4}{\pi} \frac{(-1)^n}{4n^2 - 1}.$$

By Parseval's theorem,

$$\frac{1}{2} \left(\frac{4}{\pi} \right)^2 + \sum_{n=1}^{\infty} \left(\frac{4}{\pi} \frac{(-1)^n}{4n^2 - 1} \right)^2 = \frac{1}{\pi} \int_{-\pi}^{\pi} \cos^2(x/2)\,dx = 1.$$

Then,

$$\sum_{n=1}^{\infty} \frac{1}{(4n^2 - 1)^2} = \frac{\pi^2 - 8}{16}. \quad \blacksquare$$

SECTION 14.5   PROBLEMS

1. Prove Theorem 14.6. An argument can be formulated along the lines discussed following the statement of the theorem.

2. Let $f(x) = |x|$ for $-1 \le x \le 1$.

(a) Write the Fourier series for $f(x)$ on $[-1, 1]$.

(b) Show that this series can be differentiated term by term by yield the Fourier expansion of $f'(x)$ on $[-1, 1]$.

(c) Determine $f'(x)$ and write its Fourier series on $[-1, 1]$. Compare this series with that obtained in (b).

3. Let $f(x) = \begin{cases} 0 & \text{for } -\pi \le x \le 0 \\ x & \text{for } 0 < x \le \pi. \end{cases}$

(a) Write the Fourier series of $f(x)$ on $[-\pi, \pi]$ and show that this series converges to $f(x)$ on $(-\pi, \pi)$.

(b) Show that this series can be integrated term by term.

(c) Use the results of (a) and (b) to obtain a trigonometric series expansion for $\int_{-\pi}^{x} f(t)\,dt$ on $[-\pi, \pi]$.

4. Let $f(x) = x^2$ for $-3 \le x \le 3$.

(a) Write the Fourier series for $f(x)$ on $[-3, 3]$.

(b) Show that this series can be differentiated term-by-term and use this fact to obtain the Fourier expansion of $2x$ on $[-3, 3]$.

(c) Write the Fourier series of $2x$ on $[-3, 3]$ by computation of the Fourier coefficients and compare the result with that of (b).

5. Let $f(x) = x \sin(x)$ for $-\pi \le x \le \pi$.

(a) Write the Fourier series for $f(x)$ on $[-\pi, \pi]$.

(b) Show that this series can be differentiated term by term and use this fact to obtain the Fourier expansion of $\sin(x) + x \cos(x)$ on $[-\pi, \pi]$.

(c) Write the Fourier series of $\sin(x) + x \cos(x)$ on $[-\pi, \pi]$ by computation of the Fourier coefficients and compare the result with that of (b).

14.6   The Phase Angle Form of a Fourier Series

A function is *periodic* with period p if $f(x+p) = f(x)$ for all real x. If a function has a period, it has many periods. For example, $\cos(x)$ has periods 2π, 4π, 6π, -2π, -4π, and, in fact, $2n\pi$ for any integer n. The smallest positive period of a function is called its *principal period*. The principal period of $\sin(x)$ and $\cos(x)$ is 2π.

If f has period p, then for any x, and any integer n,

$$f(x + np) = f(x).$$

For example,

$$\cos\left(\frac{\pi}{6}\right) = \cos\left(\frac{\pi}{6} + 2\pi\right) = \cos\left(\frac{\pi}{6} + 4\pi\right) = \cos\left(\frac{\pi}{6} + 6\pi\right) = \cdots$$

$$= \cos\left(\frac{\pi}{6} - 2\pi\right) = \cos\left(\frac{\pi}{6} - 4\pi\right) = \cdots.$$

The graph of periodic $f(x)$ repeats itself over every interval of length p (Figure 14.30). This means that we need only specify $f(x)$ on an interval of length p, say on $[-p/2, p/2)$, to determine $f(x)$ for all x. This specification of function values can be made on any interval $[\alpha, \alpha + p)$ of length p. Since $f(\alpha + p) = f(\alpha)$, the function must have the same value at the end points of this interval. This is why we specify values on the half-open interval $[\alpha, \alpha + p)$, since $f(\alpha + p)$ is determined once $f(\alpha)$ is defined.

EXAMPLE 14.22

Let $g(x) = 2x$ for $-1 \leq x < 1$, and suppose g has period 2. Then the graph of g on $[-1, 1)$ is repeated to cover the entire real line, as in Figure 14.31. Knowing the period, and the function values on $[-1, 1)$, are enough to determine the function for all x.

As a specific example, suppose we want to know $g\left(\frac{7}{2}\right)$. Because g has period 2, $g(x + 2n) = g(x)$ for any x and any integer n. Then

$$g\left(\frac{7}{2}\right) = g\left(\frac{-1}{2} + 4\right) = g\left(\frac{-1}{2}\right) = 2\left(\frac{-1}{2}\right) = -1.$$

Similarly,

$$g(48.3) = g(0.3 + 2(24)) = g(0.3) = 0.6. \ \blacksquare$$

If f has period p, and is integrable, then we can calculate its Fourier coefficients on $[-p/2, p/2]$ and write the Fourier series

$$\frac{1}{2}a_0 + \sum_{n=1}^{\infty}\left(a_n \cos\frac{2n\pi x}{p}\right) + b_n \sin\left(\frac{2n\pi x}{p}\right).$$

Here $L = p/2$, so $n\pi x/L = 2n\pi x/p$ in the previous discussion of Fourier series on $[-L.L]$. The Fourier coefficients are

$$a_n = \frac{2}{p}\int_{-p/2}^{p/2} f(x)\cos\left(\frac{2n\pi x}{p}\right) dx \text{ for } n = 0, 1, 2, \ldots$$

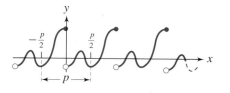

FIGURE 14.30 *Graph of a periodic function of fundamental period p.*

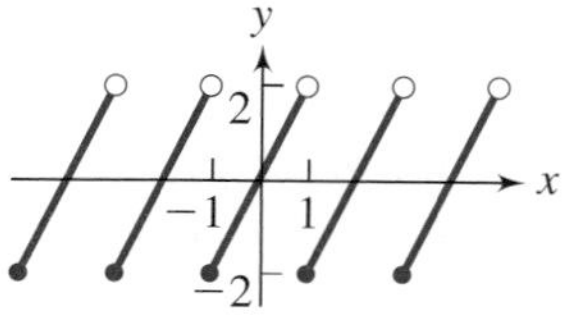

FIGURE 14.31

and

$$b_n = \frac{2}{p} \int_{-p/2}^{p/2} f(x) \sin\left(\frac{2n\pi x}{p}\right) dx \text{ for } n = 1, 2, \dots.$$

Actually, because of the periodicity, we could choose any convenient number α and write

$$a_n = \frac{2}{p} \int_{\alpha}^{\alpha+p} f(x) \cos\left(\frac{2n\pi x}{p}\right) dx \text{ for } n = 0, 1, 2, \dots \qquad (14.19)$$

and

$$b_n = \frac{2}{p} \int_{\alpha}^{\alpha+p} f(x) \sin\left(\frac{2n\pi x}{p}\right) dx \text{ for } n = 1, 2, \dots. \qquad (14.20)$$

Once we compute the coefficients, we can use a convergence theorem to determine where this series represents $f(x)$.

EXAMPLE 14.23

The function f shown in Figure 14.32 has fundamental period 6, and

$$f(x) = \begin{cases} 0 & \text{for } -3 \le x < 0 \\ 1 & \text{for } 0 \le x < 3 \end{cases}.$$

This function is called a square wave. It's Fourier series on $[-3, 3]$ is

$$\frac{1}{2} + \sum_{n=1}^{\infty} \frac{1}{n\pi} (1 - (-1)^n) \sin\left(\frac{n\pi x}{3}\right).$$

This series converges to 0 for $-3 < x < 0$, to 1 for $0 < x < 3$, and to $1/2$ at $x = 0$ and $x = \pm 3$. Because of the periodicity, this series also converges to $f(x)$ on $(-6, -3)$ and on $(3, 6)$, on $(-6, -9)$ and on $(6, 9)$, and so on. ∎

Sometimes we write

$$\omega_0 = \frac{2\pi}{p}.$$

Now the Fourier series of f on $[-p/2, p/2]$ is

$$\frac{1}{2} a_0 + \sum_{n=1}^{\infty} (a_n \cos(n\omega_0 x) + b_n \sin(n\omega_0 x)), \qquad (14.21)$$

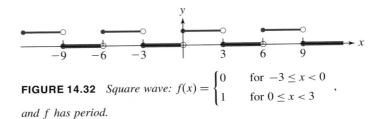

FIGURE 14.32 *Square wave:* $f(x) = \begin{cases} 0 & \text{for } -3 \le x < 0 \\ 1 & \text{for } 0 \le x < 3 \end{cases}$,

and f has period.

where

$$a_n = \frac{2}{p} \int_{-p/2}^{p/2} f(x) \cos(n\omega_0 x)dx \quad \text{for } n = 0, 1, 2, \ldots$$

and

$$b_n = \frac{2}{p} \int_{-p/2}^{p/2} f(x) \sin(n\omega_0 x)dx \quad \text{for } n = 1, 2, \ldots.$$

It is sometimes useful to write the Fourier series (14.21) in a different way. We will look for numbers c_n and δ_n so that

$$a_n \cos(n\omega_0 x) + b_n \sin(n\omega_0 x) = c_n \cos(n\omega_0 x + \delta_n).$$

To solve for these constants, write the last equation as

$$a_n \cos(n\omega_0 x) + b_n \sin(n\omega_0 x) = c_n \cos(n\omega_0 x) \cos(\delta_n) - c_n \sin(n\omega_0 x) \sin(\delta_n).$$

One way to satisfy this equation is to have

$$c_n \cos(\delta_n) = a_n$$

and

$$c_n \sin(\delta_n) = -b_n.$$

Solve these for c_n and δ_n. First square both equations and add to obtain

$$c_n^2 = a_n^2 + b_n^2,$$

so

$$c_n = \sqrt{a_n^2 + b_n^2}. \tag{14.22}$$

Next, write

$$\frac{c_n \sin(\delta_n)}{c_n \cos(\delta_n)} = \tan(\delta_n) = -\frac{b_n}{a_n},$$

so

$$\delta_n = \tan^{-1}\left(\frac{-b_n}{a_n}\right),$$

assuming that $a_n \neq 0$. The numbers c_n and δ_n allow us to write the phase angle form of the Fourier series (14.21).

DEFINITION 14.7 *Phase Angle Form*

Let f have fundamental period p. Then the phase angle form of the Fourier series (14.21) of f is

$$\frac{1}{2}a_0 + \sum_{n=1}^{\infty} c_n \cos(n\omega_0 x + \delta_n),$$

in which $\omega_0 = 2\pi/p$, $c_n = \sqrt{a_n^2 + b_n^2}$, and $\delta_n = \tan^{-1}(-b_n/a_n)$ for $n = 1, 2, \ldots.$

The phase angle form of the Fourier series is also called its *harmonic form*. This expression displays the composition of a periodic function (satisfying certain continuity conditions) as a superposition of cosine waves. The term $\cos(n\omega_0 x + \delta_n)$ is the nth harmonic of f, c_n is the nth *harmonic amplitude* , and δ_n is the nth *phase angle of f*.

EXAMPLE 14.24

Suppose f has fundamental period $p = 3$, and

$$f(x) = x^2 \text{ for } 0 \le x < 3.$$

Since f has fundamental period 3, defining $f(x)$ on any interval $[a, b]$ of length 3 determines $f(x)$ for all x. For example,

$$f(-1) = f(-1+3) = f(2) = 4,$$

$$f(5) = f(2+3) = f(2) = 2^2 = 4,$$

(or observe that $f(5) = f(-1+6) = f(-1+2\cdot 3) = f(-1) = 4$), and

$$f(7) = f(1+6) = f(1) = 1.$$

A graph of f is shown in Figure 14.33.

Care must be taken if we want to write an algebraic expression for $f(x)$ on a different interval. For example, on the symmetric interval $\left[\frac{-3}{2}, \frac{3}{2}\right)$ about the origin,

$$f(x) = \begin{cases} x^2 & \text{for } 0 \le x < \frac{3}{2} \\ (x+3)^2 & \text{for } \frac{-3}{2} \le x < 0 \end{cases}.$$

To find the Fourier coefficients of f, it is convenient to use equations (14.19) and (14.20) with $\alpha = 0$, since f is given explicitly on $[0, 3)$. Compute

$$a_0 = \frac{2}{3} \int_0^3 x^2 dx = 6,$$

$$a_n = \frac{2}{3} \int_0^3 x^2 \cos\left(\frac{2n\pi x}{3}\right) dx = \frac{9}{n^2 \pi^2}$$

and

$$b_n = \frac{2}{3} \int_0^3 x^2 \sin\left(\frac{2n\pi x}{3}\right) dx = -\frac{9}{n\pi}.$$

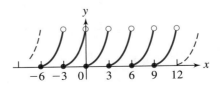

FIGURE 14.33 *Graph of $f(x) = x^2$ for $0 \le x < 3$, with $f(x+3) = f(x)$ for all x.*

The Fourier series of f is.

$$3 + \sum_{n=1}^{\infty} \frac{9}{n\pi} \left(\frac{1}{n\pi} \cos\left(\frac{2n\pi x}{3} \right) - \sin\left(\frac{2n\pi x}{3} \right) \right). \tag{14.23}$$

We can think of this as the Fourier series of f on the symmetric interval $\left[\frac{-3}{2}, \frac{3}{2} \right]$ about the origin. By the Fourier convergence theorem, this series converges to

$$\begin{cases} \frac{1}{2}\left(\frac{9}{4} + \frac{9}{4} \right) = \frac{9}{4} & \text{for } x = \frac{\pm 3}{2} \\ \frac{9}{2} & \text{for } x = 0 \\ (x+3)^2 & \text{for } -\frac{3}{2} < x < 0 \\ x^2 & \text{for } 0 < x < \frac{3}{2} \end{cases}$$

For the phase angle, or harmonic form, of this Fourier series, compute

$$c_n = \sqrt{a_n^2 + b_n^2} = \frac{9}{n^2 \pi^2} \sqrt{1 + n^2 \pi^2} \quad \text{for } n = 1, 2, \dots$$

and

$$\delta_n = \tan^{-1}\left(-\frac{-9/n\pi}{9/n^2\pi^2} \right) = \tan^{-1}(n\pi).$$

Since $\omega_0 = 2\pi/3$, the phase angle form of the series (14.23)

$$3 + \sum_{n=1}^{\infty} \frac{9}{n^2 \pi^2} \sqrt{1 + n^2 \pi^2} \cos\left(\frac{2n\pi x}{3} + \tan^{-1}(n\pi) \right). \quad \blacksquare$$

The *amplitude spectrum* of a periodic function f is a plot of values of $n\omega_0$ on the horizontal axis versus $c_n/2$ on the horizontal axis, for $n = 1, 2, \dots$. Thus the amplitude spectrum consists of points $(n\omega_0, c_n/2)$ for $n = 1, 2, \dots$. It is also common to include the point $(0, |a_0|)$ on the vertical axis. Figure 14.34 shows the amplitude spectrum for the function of Example 13.24, consisting of points $(0, 3)$ and, for $n = 1, 2, \dots$,

$$\left(\frac{2n\pi}{3}, \frac{9}{2n^2 \pi^2} \sqrt{1 + n^2 \pi^2} \right).$$

This graph allows us to envision the magnitude of the harmonics of which the periodic function is composed and clarifies which harmonics dominate in the function. This is useful in signal analysis, in which the function is the signal.

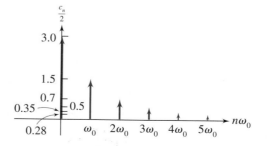

FIGURE 14.34 *Amplitude spectrum of the function of Figure 14.33.*

SECTION 14.6   *PROBLEMS*

1. Let f and g have period p. Show that $\alpha f + \beta g$ has period p for any constants α and β.

2. Let f have period p and let α and β be positive constants. Show that $g(t) = f(\alpha t)$ has period p/α, and that $h(t) = f(t/\beta)$ has period βp.

3. Let $f(x)$ be differentiable and have period p. Show that $f'(x)$ has period p.

4. Suppose f has period p. Show that, for any real number α,

$$\int_{\alpha}^{\alpha+p} f(x)\,dx = \int_{0}^{p} f(x)\,dx = \int_{-p/2}^{p/2} f(x)\,dx.$$

In each of Problems 5 through 9, find the phase angle form of the Fourier series of the function. Plot some points of the amplitude spectrum of the function.

5. $f(x) = x$ for $0 \le x < 2$ and $f(x+2) = f(x)$ for all x.

6. $f(x) = \begin{cases} 1 & \text{for } 0 \le x < 1 \\ 0 & \text{for } 1 \le x < 2 \\ f(x+2) & \text{for all } x. \end{cases}$

7. $f(x) = 3x^2$ for $0 \le x < 4$ and $f(x+4) = f(x)$ for all x.

8. $f(x) = \begin{cases} 1+x & \text{for } 0 \le x < 3 \\ 2 & \text{for } 3 \le x < 4 \\ f(x+4) & \text{for all } x. \end{cases}$

9. $f(x) = \cos(\pi x)$ for $0 \le x < 1$ and $f(x) = f(x+1)$ for all x.

In each of Problems 10 through 14, find the phase angle form of the Fourier series of the function, part of whose graph is given in the indicated diagram. Plot some points of the amplitude spectrum of the function.

10. Figure 14.35

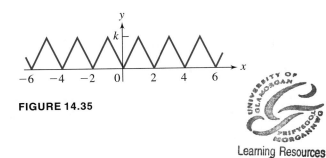

FIGURE 14.35

11. Figure 14.36

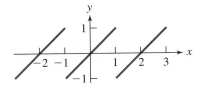

FIGURE 14.36

12. Figure 14.37

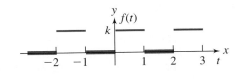

FIGURE 14.37

13. Figure 14.38

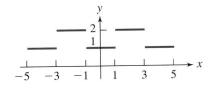

FIGURE 14.38

14. Figure 14.39

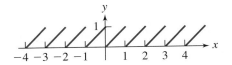

FIGURE 14.39

15. Determine the Fourier series representation of the steady-state current in the circuit of Figure 14.40 if

$$E(t) = \begin{cases} 100t(\pi^2 - t^2) & \text{for } -\pi \le t < \pi \\ E(t + 2\pi) & \text{for all } t. \end{cases}$$

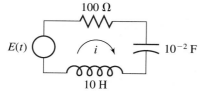

100 Ω

$E(t)$ i 10^{-2} F

10 H

FIGURE 14.40

16. Determine the Fourier series representation of the steady-state current in the circuit shown in Figure 14.41 if $E(t) = |10\sin(800\pi t)|$. *Hint:* First show that

$$E(t) = \frac{20}{\pi} \left[1 - 2 \sum_{n=1}^{\infty} \frac{\cos(1600n\pi t)}{4n^2 - 1} \right].$$

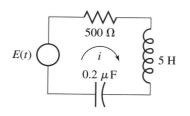

500 Ω

$E(t)$ i 5 H

0.2 μF

FIGURE 14.41

14.7 Complex Fourier Series and the Frequency Spectrum

It is often convenient to work in terms of complex numbers, even when the quantities of interest are real. For example, electrical engineers often use equations having complex quantities to compute currents, realizing that at the end the current is the real part of a certain complex expression.

We will cast Fourier series in this setting. Later, complex Fourier series and their coefficients will provide a natural starting point for the development of discrete Fourier transforms.

14.7.1 Review of Complex Numbers

Given a complex number $a + bi$, its *conjugate* is $\overline{a + bi} = a - bi$. If we identify $a + bi$ with the point (a, b) in the plane, then $a - bi$ is $(a, -b)$, the reflection of (a, b) across the horizontal (real) axis (Figure 14.42).

The conjugate of a product is the product of the conjugates:

$$\overline{zw} = \overline{z}\ \overline{w}$$

for any complex numbers z and w.

The *magnitude*, or modulus, of $a + bi$ is $|a + bi| = \sqrt{a^2 + b^2}$, the distance from the origin to (a, b). It is useful to observe that

$$(a + bi)\overline{(a + bi)} = a^2 + b^2 = |a + bi|^2.$$

If we denote the complex number as z, this equation is

$$z\overline{z} = |z|^2.$$

Introduce polar coordinates $x = r\cos(\theta)$, $y = r\sin(\theta)$ to write

$$z = x + iy = r[\cos(\theta) + i\sin(\theta)] = re^{i\theta},$$

by Euler's formula. Then $r = |z|$ and θ is called an *argument* of z. It is the angle between the positive x axis and the point (x, y), or $x + iy$, in the plane (Figure 14.43). The argument is

FIGURE 14.42
Complex conjugate as a reflection across the horizontal axis.

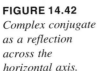

FIGURE 14.43
Polar form of a complex number.

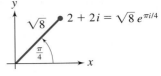

FIGURE 14.44 *Polar form of $2+2i$.*

determined to within integer multiples of 2π. For example, $|2+2i| = \sqrt{8}$ and the arguments of $2+2i$ are the angles $\pi/4 + 2n\pi$, with n any integer (Figure 14.44). Thus we can write

$$2+2i = \sqrt{8}e^{i\pi/4}.$$

This is the *polar form* of $2+2i$. We can actually write $2+2i = \sqrt{8}e^{i(\pi/4+2n\pi)}$, but this doesn't contribute anything new to the polar form of $2+2i$, since

$$e^{i(\pi/4+2n\pi)} = e^{\pi i/4}e^{2n\pi i},$$

and

$$e^{2n\pi i} = \cos(2n\pi) + i\sin(2n\pi) = 1.$$

If we use Euler's formula twice, we can write

$$e^{ix} = \cos(x) + i\sin(x)$$

and

$$e^{-ix} = \cos(x) - i\sin(x).$$

Solve these equations for $\sin(x)$ and $\cos(x)$ to write

$$\cos(x) = \frac{1}{2}\left(e^{ix} + e^{-ix}\right) \text{ and } \sin(x) = \frac{1}{2i}\left(e^{ix} - e^{-ix}\right). \tag{14.24}$$

Finally, we will use the fact that, if x is a real number, then $\overline{e^{ix}} = e^{-ix}$. This is true because

$$\overline{e^{ix}} = \overline{\cos(x) + i\sin(x)} = \cos(x) - i\sin(x) = e^{-ix}.$$

14.7.2 Complex Fourier Series

We will use these ideas to formulate the Fourier series of a function in complex terms. Let f be a real-valued, periodic function with fundamental period p. Assume that f is integrable on $[-p/2, p/2]$. As we did with the phase angle form of a Fourier series, write the Fourier series of $f(x)$ on this interval as

$$\frac{1}{2}a_0 + \sum_{n=1}^{\infty}[a_n\cos(n\omega_0 x) + b_n\sin(n\omega_0 x)],$$

with $\omega_0 = 2\pi/p$. Use equations (14.24) to write this series as

$$\frac{1}{2}a_0 + \sum_{n=1}^{\infty}\left[a_n\frac{1}{2}\left(e^{in\omega_0 x} + e^{-in\omega_0 x}\right) + b_n\frac{1}{2i}\left(e^{in\omega_0 x} - e^{-in\omega_0 x}\right)\right]$$

$$= \frac{1}{2}a_0 + \sum_{n=1}^{\infty}\left[\frac{1}{2}(a_n - ib_n)e^{in\omega_0 x} + \frac{1}{2}(a_n + ib_n)e^{-in\omega_0 x}\right]. \tag{14.25}$$

In the series (14.25), let

$$d_0 = \frac{1}{2}a_0$$

and, for each positive integer n,

$$d_n = \frac{1}{2}(a_n - ib_n).$$

Then the series (14.25) becomes

$$d_0 + \sum_{n=1}^{\infty}[d_n e^{in\omega_0 x} + \overline{d_n}e^{-in\omega_0 x}]$$

$$= d_0 + \sum_{n=1}^{\infty}d_n e^{in\omega_0 x} + \sum_{n=1}^{\infty}\overline{d_n}e^{-in\omega_0 x}. \tag{14.26}$$

Now consider the coefficients. First,

$$d_0 = \frac{1}{2}a_0 = \frac{1}{p}\int_{-p/2}^{p/2}f(t)\,dt.$$

And, for $n = 1, 2, \ldots$,

$$d_n = \frac{1}{2}(a_n - ib_n)$$

$$= \frac{1}{2}\frac{2}{p}\int_{-p/2}^{p/2}f(t)\cos(n\omega_0 t)\,dt - \frac{i}{2}\frac{2}{p}\int_{-p/2}^{p/2}f(t)\sin(n\omega_0 t)\,dt$$

$$= \frac{1}{p}\int_{-p/2}^{p/2}f(t)[\cos(n\omega_0 t) - i\sin(n\omega_0 t)]\,dt$$

$$= \frac{1}{p}\int_{-p/2}^{p/2}f(t)e^{-in\omega_0 t}\,dt.$$

Then

$$\overline{d_n} = \frac{1}{p}\int_{-p/2}^{p/2}f(t)\overline{e^{-in\omega_0 t}}\,dt = \frac{1}{p}\int_{-p/2}^{p/2}f(t)e^{in\omega_0 t}\,dt = d_{-n}.$$

Put these results into the series (14.26) to get

$$d_0 + \sum_{n=1}^{\infty}d_n e^{in\omega_0 x} + \sum_{n=1}^{\infty}\overline{d_n}e^{-in\omega_0 x}$$

$$= \frac{1}{2}d_0 + \sum_{n=1}^{\infty}d_n e^{in\omega_0 x} + \sum_{n=1}^{\infty}d_{-n}e^{-in\omega_0 x}$$

$$= d_0 + \sum_{n=-\infty, n\neq 0}^{\infty}d_n e^{in\omega_0 x} = \sum_{n=-\infty}^{\infty}d_n e^{in\omega_0 x}.$$

We have reached this expression by rearranging terms in the Fourier series of a periodic function f. This suggests the following definition.

DEFINITION 14.8 *Complex Fourier Series*

Let f have fundamental period p. Let $\omega_0 = 2\pi/p$. Then the complex Fourier series of f is

$$\sum_{n=-\infty}^{\infty} d_n e^{in\omega_0 x},$$

where

$$d_n = \frac{1}{p} \int_{-p/2}^{p/2} f(t) e^{-in\omega_0 t} dt$$

for $n = 0, \pm 1, \pm 2, \ldots$. The numbers d_n are the complex Fourier coefficients of f.

In the formula for d_n, the integration can actually be carried out over any interval of length p, because of the periodicity of f. Thus, for any real number α,

$$d_n = \frac{1}{p} \int_{\alpha}^{\alpha+p} f(t) e^{-in\omega_0 t} dt.$$

Since the complex Fourier series is just another way of writing the Fourier series, the convergence theorems (14.1) and (14.2) apply without any adjustments.

THEOREM 14.10

Let f be periodic with fundamental period p. Let f be piecewise smooth on $[-p/2, p/2]$. Then at each x the complex Fourier series converges to $\frac{1}{2}(f(x+) + f(x-))$. ∎

The *amplitude spectrum* of the complex Fourier series of a periodic function is a graph of the points $(n\omega_0, |d_n|)$, in which $|d_n|$ is the magnitude of the complex coefficient d_n. Sometimes this amplitude spectrum is referred to as a *frequency spectrum*.

EXAMPLE 14.25

We will compute the complex Fourier series of the full-wave rectification of $E\sin(\lambda t)$, in which E and λ are positive constants.

This means that we want the complex Fourier series of $|E\sin(\lambda t)|$, whose graph is shown in Figure 14.45. This function has fundamental period π/λ (even though $E\sin(\lambda t)$ has period $2\pi/\lambda$). In this example, $\omega_0 = 2\pi/(\pi/\lambda) = 2\lambda$. The complex Fourier coefficients are

$$d_n = \frac{\lambda}{\pi} \int_0^{\pi/\lambda} |E\sin(\lambda t)| e^{-2n\lambda it} dt$$

$$= \frac{E\lambda}{\pi} \int_0^{\pi/\lambda} \sin(\lambda t) e^{-2n\lambda it} dt.$$

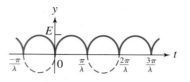

FIGURE 14.45 *Graph of* $|E \sin(\lambda t)|$.

When $n = 0$ we get

$$d_0 = \frac{E\lambda}{\pi} \int_0^{\pi/\lambda} \sin(\lambda t)dt = \frac{2E}{\pi}.$$

When $n \neq 0$, the integration is simplified by putting the sine term in exponential form:

$$d_n = \frac{E\lambda}{\pi} \int_0^{\pi/\lambda} \frac{1}{2i} \left(e^{\lambda it} - e^{-\lambda it}\right) e^{-2n\lambda it} dt$$

$$= \frac{E\lambda}{2i\pi} \int_0^{\pi/\lambda} e^{(1-2n)\lambda it} dt - \frac{E\lambda}{2i\pi} \int_0^{\pi/\lambda} e^{-(1+2n)\lambda it} dt$$

$$= \frac{E\lambda}{2i\pi} \left[\frac{1}{(1-2n)\lambda i} e^{(1-2n)\lambda it} \right]_0^{\pi/\lambda} + \frac{E\lambda}{2i\pi} \left[\frac{1}{(1+2n)\lambda i} e^{-(1+2n)\lambda it} \right]_0^{\pi/\lambda}$$

$$= -\frac{E}{2\pi} \left[\frac{e^{(1-2n)\pi i}}{1-2n} - \frac{1}{1-2n} + \frac{e^{-(1+2n)\pi i}}{1+2n} - \frac{1}{1+2n} \right].$$

Now

$$e^{(1-2n)\pi i} = \cos((1-2n)\pi) + i\sin((1-2n)\pi)$$

$$= (-1)^{1-2n} = -1$$

and

$$e^{-(1+2n)\pi i} = \cos((1+2n)\pi) - i\sin((1+2n)\pi)$$

$$= (-1)^{1+2n} = -1.$$

Therefore

$$d_n = -\frac{E}{2\pi} \left[\frac{-1}{1-2n} - \frac{1}{1-2n} + \frac{-1}{1+2n} + \frac{-1}{1+2n} \right]$$

$$= -\frac{2E}{\pi} \frac{1}{4n^2 - 1}.$$

When $n = 0$ this yields the correct value for d_0 as well. The complex Fourier series of $|E\sin(\lambda t)|$ is

$$-2\frac{E}{\pi} \sum_{n=-\infty}^{\infty} \frac{1}{4n^2 - 1} e^{2n\lambda it}.$$

The amplutide spectrum is a plot of the points

$$\left(2n\lambda, \left| \frac{2E}{(4n^2 - 1)\pi} \right| \right).$$

Part of this plot is shown in Figure 14.46. ∎

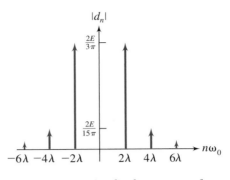

FIGURE 14.46 *Amplitude spectrum of* $|E\sin(\lambda t)|$.

SECTION 14.7 PROBLEMS

In each of Problems 1 through 7, write the complex Fourier series of f, determine what this series converges to, and plot some points of the frequency spectrum. Keep in mind that, in specifying a function of period p, it is sufficient to define $f(p)$ on any interval of length p.

1. f has period 3 and $f(x) = 2x$ for $0 \le x < 3$

2. f has period 2 and $f(x) = x^2$ for $0 \le x < 2$

3. f has period 4 and $f(x) = \begin{cases} 0 & \text{for } 0 \le x < 1 \\ 1 & \text{for } 1 \le x < 4 \end{cases}$

4. f has period 6 and $f(x) = 1 - x$ for $0 \le x < 6$

5. f has period 4 and $f(x) = \begin{cases} -1 & \text{for } 0 \le x < 2 \\ 2 & \text{for } 2 \le x < 4 \end{cases}$

6. f has period 5 and $f(x) = e^{-x}$ for $0 \le x < 5$

7. f has period 2 and $f(x) = \begin{cases} x & \text{for } 0 \le x < 1 \\ 2 - x & \text{for } 1 \le x < 2 \end{cases}$

8. Let f be the periodic function, part of whose graph is shown in Figure 14.47. Find the complex Fourier series of f and plot some points of its frequency spectrum.

The next problem involves the phase spectrum of f, which is a plot of points $(\varphi_n, n\omega_0)$ for $n = 0, 1, 2, \ldots$. Here $\varphi_n = \tan^{-1}(-b_n/a_n)$ is the nth phase angle of f.

9. The graphs of Figures 14.48 and 14.49 define two periodic functions f and g, respectively. Calculate the complex Fourier series of each function. Determine a relationship between the frequency spectra of these functions and also between their phase spectra.

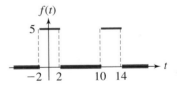

FIGURE 14.48

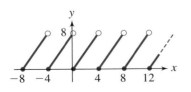

FIGURE 14.47

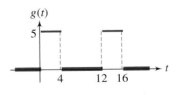

FIGURE 14.49

CHAPTER 15

The Fourier Integral and Fourier Transforms

15.1   The Fourier Integral

If $f(x)$ is defined on an interval $[-L, L]$, we may be able to represent it, at least at "most" points on this interval, by a Fourier series. If f is periodic, then we may be able to represent it by a Fourier series on intervals along the entire real line.

Now suppose $f(x)$ is defined for all x, but is not periodic. Then we cannot represent $f(x)$ by a Fourier series over the entire line. However, we may still be able to write a representation in terms of sines and cosines, using an integral instead of a summation. To see how this might be done, suppose f is absolutely integrable, which means that $\int_{-\infty}^{\infty} |f(x)|\, dx$ converges, and that f is piecewise smooth on every interval $[-L, L]$. Write the Fourier series of f on an arbitrary interval $[-L, L]$, with the integral formulas for the coefficients included:

$$\frac{1}{2} \int_{-L}^{L} f(\xi)d\xi + \sum_{n=1}^{\infty} \left[\left(\frac{1}{L} \int_{-L}^{L} f(\xi) \cos(n\pi\xi/L)d\xi \right) \cos(n\pi x/L) \right.$$
$$\left. + \left(\frac{1}{L} \int_{-L}^{L} f(\xi) \sin(n\pi\xi/L)d\xi \right) \sin(n\pi x/L) \right].$$

We want to let $L \to \infty$ to obtain a representation of $f(x)$ over the whole line. To see what limit, if any, this Fourier series approaches, let

$$\omega_n = \frac{n\pi}{L}$$

and

$$\omega_n - \omega_{n-1} = \frac{\pi}{L} = \Delta\omega.$$

637

Then the Fourier series on $[-L, L]$ can be written

$$\frac{1}{2\pi}\left(\int_{-L}^{L} f(\xi)d\xi\right)\Delta\omega + \frac{1}{\pi}\sum_{n=1}^{\infty}\left[\left(\frac{1}{L}\int_{-L}^{L} f(\xi)\cos(\omega_n\xi)d\xi\right)\cos(\omega_n x)\right.$$

$$\left. + \left(\frac{1}{L}\int_{-L}^{L} f(\xi)\sin(\omega_n\xi)d\xi\right)\sin(\omega_n x)\right]\Delta\omega. \tag{15.1}$$

Now let $L \to \infty$, causing $\Delta\omega \to 0$. In the last expression,

$$\frac{1}{2\pi}\left(\int_{-L}^{L} f(\xi)d\xi\right)\Delta\omega \to 0$$

because by assumption $\int_{-L}^{L} f(\xi)d\xi$ converges. The other terms in the expression (15.1) resemble a Riemann sum for a definite integral, and we assert that, in the limit as $L \to \infty$ and $\Delta\omega \to 0$, this expression approaches the limit

$$\frac{1}{\pi}\int_{0}^{\infty}\left[\left(\int_{-\infty}^{\infty} f(\xi)\cos(\omega\xi)d\xi\right)\cos(\omega x)\right.$$

$$\left. + \left(\int_{-\infty}^{\infty} f(\xi)\sin(\omega\xi)d\xi\right)\sin(\omega x)\right]d\omega.$$

This is the *Fourier integral* of f on the real line. Under the assumptions made about f, this integral converges to

$$\frac{1}{2}(f(x-)+f(x+))$$

at each x. In particular, if f is continuous at x, then this integral converges to $f(x)$.

Often this Fourier integral is written

$$\int_{0}^{\infty}[A_\omega\cos(\omega x) + B_\omega\sin(\omega x)]d\omega, \tag{15.2}$$

in which the *Fourier integral coefficients of* f are

$$A_\omega = \frac{1}{\pi}\int_{-\infty}^{\infty} f(\xi)\cos(\omega\xi)d\xi$$

and

$$B_\omega = \frac{1}{\pi}\int_{-\infty}^{\infty} f(\xi)\sin(\omega\xi)d\xi.$$

This Fourier integral representation of $f(x)$ is entirely analogous to a Fourier series on an interval, with $\int_{0}^{\infty}\ldots d\omega$ replacing $\sum_{n=1}^{\infty}$, and having integral formulas for the coefficients. These coefficients are functions of ω, which is the integration variable in the Fourier integral (15.2).

EXAMPLE 15.1

Let

$$f(x) = \begin{cases} 1 & \text{for } -1 \le x \le 1 \\ 0 & \text{for } |x| > 1 \end{cases}.$$

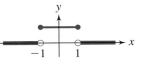

FIGURE 15.1

$$f(x) = \begin{cases} 1 & \text{for } -1 \le x \le 1 \\ 0 & \text{for } |x| > 1 \end{cases}.$$

Figure 15.1 is a graph of f. Certainly f is piecewise smooth, and $\int_{-\infty}^{\infty} |f(x)|\, dx$ converges. The Fourier coefficients of f are

$$A_\omega = \frac{1}{\pi} \int_{-1}^{1} \cos(\omega\xi)d\xi = \frac{2\sin(\omega)}{\pi\omega}$$

and

$$B_\omega = \frac{1}{\pi} \int_{-\infty}^{\infty} f(\xi)\sin(\omega\xi)d\xi = 0.$$

The Fourier integral of f is

$$\int_{0}^{\infty} \frac{2\sin(\omega)}{\pi\omega} \cos(\omega x)d\omega.$$

Because f is piecewise smooth, this converges to $\frac{1}{2}(f(x+)+f(x-))$ for all x. More explicitly,

$$\int_{0}^{\infty} \frac{2\sin(\omega)}{\pi\omega} \cos(\omega x)d\omega = \begin{cases} 1 & \text{for } -1 < x < 1 \\ \dfrac{1}{2} & \text{for } x = \pm 1 \\ 0 & \text{for } |x| > 1 \end{cases}. \quad \blacksquare$$

There is an another expression for the Fourier integral of a function that we will sometimes find convenient. Write

$$\int_{0}^{\infty} [A_\omega \cos(\omega x) + B_\omega \sin(\omega x)]\, d\omega = \int_{0}^{\infty} \left[\left(\frac{1}{\pi} \int_{-\infty}^{\infty} f(\xi)\cos(\omega\xi)d\xi \right) \cos(\omega x) \right.$$

$$\left. + \left(\frac{1}{\pi} \int_{-\infty}^{\infty} f(\xi)\sin(\omega\xi)d\xi \right) \sin(\omega x) \right] d\omega$$

$$= \frac{1}{\pi} \int_{0}^{\infty} \int_{-\infty}^{\infty} f(\xi)[\cos(\omega\xi)\cos(\omega x)$$

$$+ \sin(\omega\xi)\sin(\omega x)]d\xi d\omega$$

$$= \frac{1}{\pi} \int_{0}^{\infty} \int_{-\infty}^{\infty} f(\xi)\cos(\omega(\xi - x))d\xi d\omega. \quad (15.3)$$

Of course, this integral has the same convergence properties as the integral expression (15.2), since it is just a rearrangement of that integral.

In each of Problems 1 through 10, expand the function in a Fourier integral and determine what this integral converges to.

1. $f(x) = \begin{cases} x & \text{for } -\pi \le x \le \pi \\ 0 & \text{for } |x| > \pi \end{cases}$

2. $f(x) = \begin{cases} k & \text{for } -10 \le x \le 10 \\ 0 & \text{if } |x| > 10 \end{cases}$

3. $f(x) = \begin{cases} -1 & \text{for } -\pi \le x \le 0 \\ 1 & \text{for } 0 < x \le \pi \\ 0 & \text{for } |x| > \pi \end{cases}$

4. $f(x) = \begin{cases} \sin(x) & \text{for } -4 \le x \le 0 \\ \cos(x) & \text{for } 0 < x \le 4 \\ 0 & \text{for } |x| > 4 \end{cases}$

5. $f(x) = \begin{cases} x^2 & \text{for } -100 \le x \le 100 \\ 0 & \text{for } |x| > 100 \end{cases}$

6. $f(x) = \begin{cases} |x| & \text{for } -\pi \le x \le 2\pi \\ 0 & \text{for } x < -\pi \text{ and for } x > 2\pi \end{cases}$

7. $f(x) = \begin{cases} \sin(x) & \text{for } -3\pi \le x \le \pi \\ 0 & \text{for } x < -3\pi \text{ and for } x > \pi \end{cases}$

8. $f(x) = \begin{cases} 1/2 & \text{for } -5 \le x < 1 \\ 1 & \text{for } 1 \le x \le 5 \\ 0 & \text{for } |x| > 5 \end{cases}$

9. $f(x) = e^{-|x|}$

10. $f(x) = xe^{-|4x|}$

11. Show that the Fourier integral of f can be written

$$\lim_{\omega \to \infty} \frac{1}{\pi} \int_{-\infty}^{\infty} f(t) \frac{\sin(\omega(t-x))}{t-x} dt.$$

15.2   Fourier Cosine and Sine Integrals

If f is piecewise smooth on the half-line $[0, \infty)$, and $\int_0^\infty |f(\xi)| \, d\xi$ converges, then we can write a Fourier cosine or sine integral for f that is completely analogous to sine and cosine expansions of a function on an interval $[0, L]$.

To write a cosine integral, extend f to an even function f_e defined on the whole line by setting

$$f_e(x) = \begin{cases} f(x) & \text{for } x \ge 0 \\ f(-x) & \text{for } x < 0 \end{cases}.$$

This reflects the graph for $x \ge 0$ back across the vertical axis. Since f_e is an even function, its Fourier integral has only cosine terms. Since $f_e(x) = f(x)$ for $x \ge 0$, this cosine integral can be defined to be the Fourier cosine integral of f on $[0, \infty)$.

The coefficient of f_e in its Fourier integral expansion is

$$\frac{1}{\pi} \int_{-\infty}^{\infty} f_e(\xi) \cos(\omega\xi) d\xi$$

and this is

$$\frac{2}{\pi} \int_0^{\infty} f(\xi) \cos(\omega\xi) d\xi.$$

This suggests the following definition.

DEFINITION 15.1 *Fourier Cosine Integral*

Let f be defined on $[0, \infty)$ and let $\int_0^\infty |f(\xi)| \, d\xi$ converge. The Fourier cosine integral of f is

$$\int_0^\infty A_\omega \cos(\omega x) \, d\omega,$$

in which

$$A_\omega = \frac{2}{\pi} \int_0^\infty f(\xi) \cos(\omega \xi) \, d\xi.$$

By applying the convergence theorem to the integral expansion of f_e, we find that, if f is piecewise continuous on each interval $[0, L]$, then its cosine integral expansion converges to $\frac{1}{2}(f(x+) + f(x-))$ for each $x > 0$, and to $f(0)$ for $x = 0$. In particular, at any positive x at which f is continuous, the cosine integral converges to $f(x)$.

By extending f to an odd function f_o, similar to what we did with series, we obtain a Fourier integral for f_o containing only sine terms. Since $f_o(x) = f(x)$ for $x \geq 0$, this gives a sine integral for f on $[0, \infty)$.

DEFINITION 15.2 *Fourier Sine Integral*

Let f be defined on $[0, \infty)$ and let $\int_0^\infty |f(\xi)| \, d\xi$ converge. The Fourier sine integral of f is

$$\int_0^\infty A_\omega \sin(\omega x) \, d\omega,$$

in which

$$A_\omega = \frac{2}{\pi} \int_0^\infty f(\xi) \sin(\omega \xi) \, d\xi.$$

If f is piecewise smooth on every interval $[0, L]$, then this integral converges to $\frac{1}{2}(f(x+) + f(x-))$ on $(0, \infty)$. As with Fourier sine series on a bounded interval, this Fourier sine integral converges to 0 at $x = 0$.

EXAMPLE 15.2 Laplace's Integrals

Let $f(x) = e^{-kx}$ for $x \geq 0$, with k a positive constant. Then f is continuously differentiable on any interval $[0, L]$, and

$$\int_0^\infty e^{-kx} \, dx = \frac{1}{k}.$$

For the Fourier cosine integral, compute the coefficients

$$A_\omega = \frac{2}{\pi} \int_0^\infty e^{-k\xi} \cos(\omega \xi) \, d\xi = \frac{2}{\pi} \frac{k}{k^2 + \omega^2}.$$

The Fourier cosine integral representation of f converges to e^{-kx} for $x \geq 0$:

$$e^{-kx} = \frac{2k}{\pi} \int_0^\infty \frac{1}{k^2 + \omega^2} \cos(\omega x)\, d\omega.$$

For the sine integral, compute

$$B_\omega = \frac{2}{\pi} \int_0^\infty e^{-k\xi} \sin(k\xi)\, d\xi = \frac{2}{\pi} \frac{\omega}{k^2 + \omega^2}.$$

The sine integral converges to e^{-kx} for $x > 0$ and to 0 for $x = 0$:

$$e^{-kx} = \frac{2}{\pi} \int_0^\infty \frac{\omega}{k^2 + \omega^2} \sin(\omega x)\, d\omega \text{ for } x > 0.$$

These integral representations are called Laplace's integrals because A_ω is $2/\pi$ times the Laplace transform of $\sin(kx)$, while B_ω is $2/\pi$ times the Laplace transform of $\cos(kx)$. ▨

SECTION 15.2   PROBLEMS

In each of Problems 1 through 10, find the Fourier sine integral and Fourier cosine integral representations of the function. Determine to what each integral converges.

1. $f(x) = \begin{cases} x^2 & \text{for } 0 \leq x \leq 10 \\ 0 & \text{for } x > 10 \end{cases}$

2. $f(x) = \begin{cases} \sin(x) & \text{for } 0 \leq x \leq 2\pi \\ 0 & \text{for } x > 2\pi \end{cases}$

3. $f(x) = \begin{cases} 1 & \text{for } 0 \leq x \leq 1 \\ 2 & \text{for } 1 < x < 4 \\ 0 & \text{for } x > 4 \end{cases}$

4. $f(x) = \begin{cases} \cosh(x) & \text{for } 0 \leq x \leq 5 \\ 0 & \text{for } x > 5 \end{cases}$

5. $f(x) = \begin{cases} 2x+1 & \text{for } 0 \leq x \leq \pi \\ 2 & \text{for } \pi < x \leq 3\pi \\ 0 & \text{for } x > 3\pi \end{cases}$

6. $f(x) = \begin{cases} x & \text{for } 0 \leq x \leq 1 \\ x+1 & \text{for } 1 < x \leq 2 \\ 0 & \text{for } x > 2 \end{cases}$

7. $f(x) = e^{-x}\cos(x)$ for $x \geq 0$

8. $f(x) = xe^{-3x}$ for $x \geq 0$

9. $f(x) = \begin{cases} k & \text{for } 0 \leq x \leq c \\ 0 & \text{for } x > c \end{cases}$

in which k is constant and c is a positive constant

10. $f(x) = e^{-2x}\cos(x)$ for $x \geq 0$

11. Use the Laplace integrals to compute the Fourier cosine integral of $f(x) = 1/(1+x^2)$ and the Fourier sine integral of $g(x) = x/(1+x^2)$.

15.3   The Complex Fourier Integral and the Fourier Transform

It is sometimes convenient to have a complex form of the Fourier integral. This complex setting will prove a natural platform from which to develop the Fourier transform.

Suppose f is piecewise smooth on each interval $[-L, L]$, and that $\int_{-\infty}^\infty |f(x)|\, dx$ converges. Then, at any x,

$$\frac{1}{2}(f(x+) + f(x-)) = \frac{1}{\pi} \int_0^\infty \int_{-\infty}^\infty f(\xi)\cos(\omega(\xi - x))\, d\xi\, d\omega,$$

by the expression (15.3). Insert the complex exponential form of the cosine function into this expression to write

$$\frac{1}{2}(f(x+) + f(x-)) = \frac{1}{\pi} \int_0^\infty \int_{-\infty}^\infty f(\xi) \frac{1}{2} \left(e^{i\omega(\xi-x)} + e^{-i\omega(\xi-x)} \right) d\xi d\omega$$

$$= \frac{1}{2\pi} \int_0^\infty \int_{-\infty}^\infty f(\xi) e^{i\omega(\xi-x)} d\xi d\omega + \frac{1}{2\pi} \int_0^\infty \int_{-\infty}^\infty f(\xi) e^{-i\omega(\xi-x)} d\xi d\omega.$$

In the first integral on the last line, put $\omega = -w$ to get

$$\frac{1}{2}(f(x+) + f(x-)) = \frac{1}{2\pi} \int_{-\infty}^0 \int_{-\infty}^\infty f(\xi) e^{-iw(\xi-x)} d\xi dw + \frac{1}{2\pi} \int_0^\infty \int_{-\infty}^\infty f(\xi) e^{-i\omega(\xi-x)} d\xi d\omega.$$

Now write the variable of integration in the next to last integral as ω again and combine these two integrals to write

$$\frac{1}{2}(f(x+) + f(x-)) = \frac{1}{2\pi} \int_{-\infty}^\infty \int_{-\infty}^\infty f(\xi) e^{-i\omega(\xi-x)} d\xi d\omega. \tag{15.4}$$

This is the *complex Fourier integral representation* of f on the real line. If we let $C_\omega = \int_{-\infty}^\infty f(t) e^{-i\omega t} dt$, then this integral is

$$\frac{1}{2}(f(x+) + f(x-)) = \frac{1}{2\pi} \int_{-\infty}^\infty C_\omega e^{i\omega x} d\omega.$$

We call C_ω the *complex Fourier integral coefficient of* f.

EXAMPLE 15.3

Let $f(x) = e^{-a|x|}$ for all real x, with a a positive constant. We will compute the complex Fourier integral representation of f. First, we have

$$f(x) = \begin{cases} e^{-ax} & \text{for } x \geq 0 \\ e^{ax} & \text{for } x < 0 \end{cases}.$$

Further,

$$\int_{-\infty}^\infty f(x) dx = \int_{-\infty}^0 e^{ax} dx + \int_0^\infty e^{-ax} dx = \frac{2}{a}.$$

Now compute

$$C_\omega = \int_{-\infty}^\infty e^{-a|t|} e^{-i\omega t} dt$$

$$= \int_{-\infty}^0 e^{at} e^{-i\omega t} dt + \int_0^\infty e^{-at} e^{-i\omega t} dt$$

$$= \int_{-\infty}^0 e^{(a-i\omega)t} dt + \int_0^\infty e^{-(a+i\omega)t} dt$$

$$= \left[\frac{1}{a-i\omega} e^{(a-i\omega)t} \right]_{-\infty}^0 + \left[\frac{-1}{a+i\omega} e^{-(a+i\omega)t} \right]_0^\infty$$

$$= \left(\frac{1}{a+i\omega} + \frac{1}{a-i\omega} \right) = \frac{2a}{a^2 + \omega^2}.$$

The complex Fourier integral representation of f is

$$e^{-a|x|} = \frac{a}{\pi} \int_{-\infty}^{\infty} \frac{1}{a^2 + \omega^2} e^{i\omega x} d\omega. \quad \blacksquare$$

The expression on the right side of equation (15.4) leads naturally into the Fourier transform. To emphasize a certain term, write equation (15.4) as

$$\frac{1}{2}(f(x+) + f(x-)) = \frac{1}{2\pi} \int_{-\infty}^{\infty} \left(\int_{-\infty}^{\infty} f(\xi) e^{-i\omega\xi} d\xi \right) e^{i\omega x} d\omega. \tag{15.5}$$

The term in parentheses is what we will call the Fourier transform of f.

DEFINITION 15.3 *Fourier Transform*

Suppose $\int_{-\infty}^{\infty} |f(x)| \, dx$ converges. Then the Fourier transform of f is defined to be the function

$$\mathfrak{F}[f](\omega) = \int_{-\infty}^{\infty} f(t) e^{-i\omega t} dt.$$

Thus the Fourier transform of f is the coefficient C_ω in the complex Fourier integral representation of f.

$\mathfrak{F}$ turns a function f into a new function called $\mathfrak{F}[f]$. Because the transform is used in signal analysis, we will often use t (for time) as the variable with f, and ω the variable of the transformed function $\mathfrak{F}[f]$. The value of the function $\mathfrak{F}[f]$ at ω is $\mathfrak{F}[f](\omega)$, and this number is computed for a given ω by evaluating the integral $\int_{-\infty}^{\infty} f(t) e^{-i\omega t} dt$. If we want to keep the variable t before our attention, we sometimes write $\mathfrak{F}[f]$ as $\mathfrak{F}[f(t)]$.

Engineers refer to the variable ω in the transformed function as the *frequency* of the signal f. Later we will discuss how the Fourier transform, and a truncated version called the windowed Fourier transform, are used to determine information about the frequency content of a signal.

Because the symbol $\mathfrak{F}[f(t)]$ may be clumsy to use in calculations, we sometimes write the Fourier transform of f as $\hat{f}$. In this notation,

$$\mathfrak{F}[f](\omega) = \hat{f}(\omega).$$

EXAMPLE 15.4

Let a be a positive constant. Then

$$\mathfrak{F}\left[e^{-a|t|}\right](\omega) = \frac{2a}{a^2 + \omega^2}.$$

This follows immediately from Example 15.3, where we calculated the Fourier integral coefficient C_ω of $e^{-a|t|}$. This coefficient is the Fourier transform of f. $\blacksquare$

EXAMPLE 15.5

Let a and k be positive numbers, and let

$$f(t) = \begin{cases} k & \text{for } -a \leq t < a \\ 0 & \text{for } t < -a \text{ and for } t \geq a \end{cases}.$$

This pulse function can be written in terms of the Heaviside function as

$$f(t) = k[H(t+a) - H(t-a)],$$

and is graphed in Figure 15.2. The Fourier transform of f is

$$\hat{f}(\omega) = \int_{-\infty}^{\infty} f(t)e^{-i\omega t}\,dt$$

$$= \int_{-a}^{a} ke^{-i\omega t}\,dt = \left[\frac{-k}{i\omega}e^{-i\omega t}\right]_{-a}^{a}$$

$$= -\frac{k}{i\omega}\left[e^{-i\omega a} - e^{i\omega a}\right] = \frac{2k}{\omega}\sin(a\omega).$$

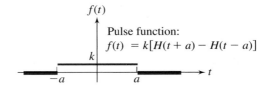

Pulse function:
$$f(t) = k[H(t+a) - H(t-a)]$$

FIGURE 15.2

Again, we can also write

$$\mathfrak{F}[f](\omega) = \frac{2k}{\omega}\sin(a\omega),$$

or

$$\mathfrak{F}[f(t)](\omega) = \frac{2k}{\omega}\sin(a\omega). \quad\blacksquare$$

In view of equation (15.5), the Fourier integral representation of f is

$$\frac{1}{2\pi}\int_{-\infty}^{\infty}\hat{f}(\omega)e^{i\omega t}\,d\omega.$$

If f is continuous, and f' piecewise continuous on every interval $[-L, L]$, then the Fourier integral of f represents f:

$$f(t) = \frac{1}{2\pi}\int_{-\infty}^{\infty}\hat{f}(\omega)e^{i\omega t}\,d\omega. \tag{15.6}$$

We can therefore use equation (15.6) as an inverse Fourier transform, retrieving f from $\hat{f}$. This is important because, in applications, we use the Fourier transform to change a problem involving f from one form to another, presumably easier one, which is solved for $\hat{f}(\omega)$. We must then have some way of getting back to the $f(t)$ that we want, and equation (15.6) is the vehicle that is often used. We write $\mathfrak{F}^{-1}[\hat{f}] = f$ if $\mathfrak{F}[f] = \hat{f}$.

As we expect of any integral transform, $\mathfrak{F}$ is linear:

$$\mathfrak{F}[\alpha f + \beta g] = \alpha\mathfrak{F}[f] + \beta\mathfrak{F}[g].$$

The integral defining the transform, and the integral (15.6) giving its inverse, are said to constitute a *transform pair* for the Fourier transform. Under certain conditions on f,

$$\hat{f}(\omega) = \int_{-\infty}^{\infty} f(t)e^{-i\omega t}\,dt \text{ and } f(t) = \frac{1}{2\pi}\int_{-\infty}^{\infty}\hat{f}(\omega)e^{i\omega t}\,dt.$$

EXAMPLE 15.6

Let

$$f(t) = \begin{cases} 1 - |t| & \text{for } -1 \le t \le 1 \\ 0 & \text{for } t > 1 \text{ and for } t < -1 \end{cases}.$$

Then f is continuous and absolutely integrable, and f' is piecewise continuous. Compute

$$\hat{f}(\omega) = \int_{-\infty}^{\infty} f(t)e^{-i\omega t}\,dt$$

$$= \int_{-1}^{1}(1-|t|)e^{-i\omega t}\,dt = \frac{2(1-\cos(\omega))}{\omega^2}.$$

This is the Fourier coefficient C_ω in the complex Fourier expansion of $f(t)$.

If we want to go the other way, then by equation (15.6),

$$f(t) = \frac{1}{2\pi}\int_{-\infty}^{\infty}\hat{f}(\omega)e^{i\omega t}\,d\omega$$

$$= \frac{1}{\pi}\int_{-\infty}^{\infty}\frac{(1-\cos(\omega))}{\omega^2}e^{i\omega t}\,d\omega.$$

We can verify this by explicitly carrying out this integration. A software package yields

$$\frac{1}{\pi}\int_{-\infty}^{\infty}\frac{(1-\cos(\omega))}{\omega^2}e^{i\omega t}\,d\omega$$

$$= \pi t \operatorname{signum}(t+1) + \pi \operatorname{signum}(t+1) + \pi t \operatorname{signum}(t-1)$$

$$- \pi \operatorname{signum}(t-1) - 2\operatorname{signum}(t),$$

in which

$$\operatorname{signum}(\omega) = \begin{cases} 1 & \text{for } \omega > 0 \\ 0 & \text{for } \omega = 0 \\ -1 & \text{for } \omega < 0 \end{cases}.$$

This expression is equal to $1 - |t|$ for $-1 \le t \le 1$, and 0 for $t > 1$ and for $t < -1$, verifying the integral for the inverse. ∎

In the context of the Fourier transform, the *amplitude spectrum* is often taken to be a graph of $\left|\hat{f}(\omega)\right|$. This is in the same spirit as the use of this term in connection with the Fourier integral.

EXAMPLE 15.7

If $f(t) = H(t)e^{-at}$, then $\hat{f}(\omega) = 1/(a + i\omega)$, so

$$\left|\hat{f}(\omega)\right| = \frac{1}{\sqrt{a^2 + \omega^2}}.$$

Figure 15.3 shows a graph of $\left|\hat{f}(\omega)\right|$. This graph is the amplitude spectrum of f. ▩

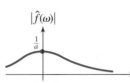

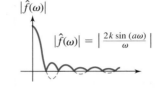

FIGURE 15.3 *Graph of* $|\hat{f}(\omega)| = \frac{1}{\sqrt{a^2 + \omega^2}}$, *with* $f(t) = H(t)e^{-at}$.

FIGURE 15.4

EXAMPLE 15.8

The amplitude spectrum of the function f of Example 15.5 is a graph of

$$\left|\hat{f}(\omega)\right| = 2k\left|\frac{\sin(\omega)}{\omega}\right|,$$

shown in Figure 15.4. ▩

We will now develop some of the important properties and computational rules for the Fourier transform. With each rule, there is also an inverse transform version which we will also state. Throughout, we assume that $\int_{-\infty}^{\infty} |f(t)|\, dt$ converges, and, for the inverse version, that f is continuous and f' piecewise continuous on each $[-L, L]$.

THEOREM 15.1 *Time Shifting*

If t_0 is a real number, then

$$\mathfrak{F}[f(t - t_0)](\omega) = e^{-i\omega t_0}\hat{f}(t). ■$$

That is, if we shift time back t_0 units and replace $f(t)$ by $f(t - t_0)$, then the Fourier transform of this shifted function is the Fourier transform of f, multiplied by the exponential factor $e^{-i\omega t_0}$.

Proof

$$\mathfrak{F}[f(t - t_0)](\omega) = \int_{-\infty}^{\infty} f(t - t_0)e^{-i\omega t}\, dt$$

$$= e^{-i\omega t_0} \int_{-\infty}^{\infty} f(t - t_0)e^{-i\omega(t - t_0)}\, dt.$$

Let $u = t - t_0$ to write

$$\mathfrak{F}[f(t-t_0)](\omega) = e^{-i\omega t_0} \int_{-\infty}^{\infty} f(u) e^{-i\omega u} du = e^{-i\omega t_0} \hat{f}(\omega). \ \blacksquare$$

EXAMPLE 15.9

Suppose we want the Fourier transform of the pulse of amplitude 6 which turns on at time 3 and off at time 7. This is the function

$$g(t) = \begin{cases} 0 & \text{for } t < 3 \text{ and for } t \geq 7 \\ 6 & \text{for } 3 \leq t < 7 \end{cases},$$

shown in Figure 15.5. We can certainly compute $\hat{g}(\omega)$ by integration. But we can also observe that the midpoint of the pulse (that is, of the nonzero part) occurs when $t = 5$. Shift the graph 5 units to the left to center the pulse at zero (Figure 15.6). Calling this shifted pulse f, then $f(t) = g(t+5)$. Shifting f five units to the right again just gets us back to g:

$$g(t) = f(t-5).$$

The point to this is that we already know the Fourier transform of f from Example 15.5:

$$\mathfrak{F}[f(t)](\omega) = 12 \frac{\sin(2\omega)}{\omega}.$$

By the time-shifting theorem,

$$\mathfrak{F}[g(t)](\omega) = \mathfrak{F}[f(t-5)](\omega) = 12 e^{-5i\omega} \frac{\sin(2\omega)}{\omega}. \ \blacksquare$$

The inverse version of the time-shifting theorem is:

$$\mathfrak{F}^{-1}[e^{-i\omega t_0} F(\omega)](t) = f(t-t_0). \tag{15.7}$$

EXAMPLE 15.10

Suppose we want

$$\mathfrak{F}^{-1}\left[\frac{e^{2i\omega}}{5+i\omega}\right].$$

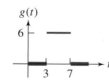

FIGURE 15.5

$$g(x) = \begin{cases} 6 & \text{for } 3 \leq t < 7 \\ 0 & \text{for } t < 3 \\ & \text{and for } t \geq 7 \end{cases}.$$

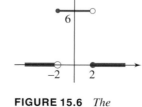

FIGURE 15.6 *The function of Figure 15.5 shifted five units to the left.*

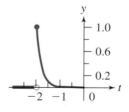

FIGURE 15.7 *Graph of* $H(t+2)e^{-5(t+2)}$.

The presence of the exponential factor suggests the inverse version of the time-shifting theorem. Put $t_0 = -2$ in equation (15.7) to write

$$\mathfrak{F}^{-1}\left[\frac{e^{2i\omega}}{5+i\omega}\right] = f(t-(-2)) = f(t+2),$$

where

$$f(t) = \mathfrak{F}^{-1}\left[\frac{1}{5+i\omega}\right] = H(t)e^{-5t}.$$

Therefore

$$\mathfrak{F}^{-1}\left[\frac{e^{2i\omega}}{5+i\omega}\right] = f(t+2) = H(t+2)e^{-5(t+2)}.$$

A graph of this function is shown in Figure 15.7. ■

The next result is reminiscent of the first shifting theorem for the Laplace transform (Theorem 3.7).

THEOREM 15.2 *Frequency Shifting*

If ω_0 is any real number, then

$$\mathfrak{F}[e^{i\omega t}f(t)] = \hat{f}(\omega - \omega_0). ■$$

Proof

$$\mathfrak{F}[e^{i\omega t}f(t)](\omega) = \int_{-\infty}^{\infty} e^{i\omega_0 t}f(t)e^{-i\omega t}\,dt$$

$$= \int_{-\infty}^{\infty} f(t)e^{-i(\omega-\omega_0)t}\,dt = \hat{f}(\omega - \omega_0). ■$$

The inverse version of the frequency-shifting theorem is

$$\mathfrak{F}^{-1}[\hat{f}(\omega - \omega_0)](t) = e^{i\omega_0 t}f(t).$$

THEOREM 15.3 *Scaling*

If a is a nonzero real number, then

$$\mathfrak{F}[f(at)](\omega) = \frac{1}{|a|}\hat{f}(\omega/a). ■$$

This can be proved by a straightforward calculation proceeding from the definition. The inverse transform version of this result is

$$\mathfrak{F}^{-1}[\hat{f}(\omega/a)](t) = |a|\,f(at).$$

This conclusion is called a scaling theorem because we want the transform not of $f(t)$, but of $f(at)$, in which a can be thought of as a scaling factor. The theorem says that we can compute the transform of the scaled function by replacing ω by ω/a in the transform of the original function, and dividing by the magnitude of the scaling factor.

EXAMPLE 15.11

We know from Example 15.6 that, if

$$f(t) = \begin{cases} 1 - |t| & \text{for } -1 \le t \le 1 \\ 0 & \text{for } t > 1 \text{ and for } t < -1 \end{cases},$$

then

$$\hat{f}(\omega) = 2\frac{1 - \cos(\omega)}{\omega^2}.$$

Let

$$g(t) = f(7t) = \begin{cases} 1 - |7t| & \text{for } -\frac{1}{7} \le t \le \frac{1}{7} \\ 0 & \text{for } t > \frac{1}{7} \text{ and for } t < \frac{-1}{7} \end{cases}.$$

Then

$$\hat{g}(\omega) = \mathfrak{F}[f(7t)](\omega) = \frac{1}{7}\hat{f}\left(\frac{\omega}{7}\right)$$

$$= \frac{2}{7}\frac{1 - \cos(\omega/7)}{(\omega/7)^2} = 14\frac{1 - \cos\left(\frac{\omega}{7}\right)}{\omega^2}. \quad \blacksquare$$

THEOREM 15.4 *Time Reversal*

$$\mathfrak{F}[f(-t)](\omega) = \hat{f}(-\omega). \quad \blacksquare$$

This result is called time reversal because we replace t by $-t$ in $f(t)$ to get $f(-t)$. The transform of this new function is obtained by simply replacing ω by $-\omega$ in the transform of $f(t)$. This conclusion follows immediately from the scaling theorem by putting $a = -1$. The inverse version of time reversal is

$$\mathfrak{F}^{-1}[\hat{f}(-\omega)](t) = f(-t).$$

THEOREM 15.5 *Symmetry*

$$\mathfrak{F}[\hat{f}(t)](\omega) = 2\pi f(-\omega). \quad \blacksquare$$

To understand this conclusion, begin with $f(t)$ and take its Fourier transform $\hat{f}(\omega)$. Replace ω by t and take the transform of the function $\hat{f}(t)$. The symmetry property of the Fourier transform states that the transform of $\hat{f}(t)$ is just the original function $f(t)$ with t replaced by $-\omega$, and then this new function multiplied by 2π.

EXAMPLE 15.12

Let

$$f(t) = \begin{cases} 4 - t^2 & \text{for } -2 \le t \le 2 \\ 0 & \text{for } t > 2 \text{ and for } t < -2 \end{cases}.$$

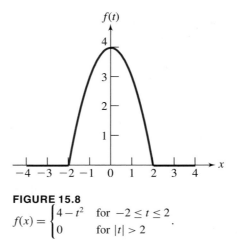

FIGURE 15.8

$$f(x) = \begin{cases} 4 - t^2 & \text{for } -2 \le t \le 2 \\ 0 & \text{for } |t| > 2 \end{cases}.$$

Figure 15.8 shows a graph of f. The Fourier transform of f is

$$\hat{f}(\omega) = \int_{-\infty}^{\infty} f(t)e^{-i\omega t}\,d\omega = \int_{-2}^{2}(4 - t^2)e^{-i\omega t}\,dt$$

$$= 4\frac{\sin(2\omega) - 2\omega\cos(2\omega)}{\omega^3}.$$

In this example, $f(-t) = f(t)$, so exchanging $-\omega$ for ω should not make any difference in $\hat{f}(\omega)$, and we can see that this is indeed the case. ∎

THEOREM 15.6   *Modulation*

If ω_0 is a real number, then

$$\mathfrak{F}[f(t)\cos(\omega_0 t)](\omega) = \frac{1}{2}\left[\hat{f}(\omega + \omega_0) + \hat{f}(\omega - \omega_0)\right]$$

and

$$\mathfrak{F}[f(t)\sin(\omega_0 t)](\omega) = \frac{1}{2}i\left[\hat{f}(\omega + \omega_0) - \hat{f}(\omega - \omega_0)\right]. \quad ∎$$

Proof   Put $\cos(\omega t) = \frac{1}{2}\left(e^{i\omega_0 t} + e^{-i\omega_0 t}\right)$ and use the linearity of $\mathfrak{F}$ and the frequency-shifting theorem to get

$$\mathfrak{F}[f(t)\cos(\omega_0 t)](\omega) = \mathfrak{F}\left[\frac{1}{2}e^{i\omega_0 t}f(t) + \frac{1}{2}e^{-i\omega_0 t}f(t)\right](\omega)$$

$$= \frac{1}{2}\mathfrak{F}[e^{i\omega_0 t}f(t)](\omega) + \frac{1}{2}\mathfrak{F}[e^{-i\omega_0 t}f(t)](\omega)$$

$$= \frac{1}{2}\hat{f}(\omega - \omega_0) + \frac{1}{2}\hat{f}(\omega + \omega_0).$$

The second conclusion is proved similarly, using $\sin(\omega t) = \frac{1}{2i}\left(e^{i\omega_0 t} - e^{-i\omega_0 t}\right)$. ∎

SECTION 15.3   PROBLEMS

In each of Problems 1 through 8, find the complex Fourier integral of the function and determine what this integral converges to.

1. $f(x) = xe^{-|x|}$

2. $f(x) = \begin{cases} 1 - x & \text{for } -1 \leq x \leq 1 \\ 0 & \text{for } |x| > 1 \end{cases}$

3. $f(x) = \begin{cases} \sin(\pi x) & \text{for } -5 \leq x \leq 5 \\ 0 & \text{for } |x| > 5 \end{cases}$

4. $f(x) = \begin{cases} |x| & \text{for } -2 \leq x \leq 2 \\ 0 & \text{for } |x| > 2 \end{cases}$

5. $f(x) = \begin{cases} x & \text{for } -1 \leq x \leq 1 \\ e^{-|x|} & \text{for } |x| > 1 \end{cases}$

6. $f(x) = \begin{cases} 1 & \text{for } 0 \leq x \leq k \\ -1 & \text{for } -k \leq x < 0 \\ 0 & \text{for } |x| > k, \end{cases}$

in which k is a positive constant

7. $f(x) = \begin{cases} \cos(x) & \text{for } 0 \leq x \leq \dfrac{\pi}{2} \\ \sin(x) & \text{for } -\dfrac{\pi}{2} \leq x < 0 \\ 0 & \text{for } |x| > \dfrac{\pi}{2} \end{cases}$

8. $f(x) = x^2 e^{-3|x|}$

In each of Problems 9 through 18, find the Fourier transform of the function and graph the amplitude spectrum. Wherever k appears, it is a positive constant. For some problems one or more theorems from this section can be used in conjunction with the following transforms, which can be assumed:

$$\mathfrak{F}[e^{-a|t|}](\omega) = \frac{2a}{a^2 + \omega^2}, \quad \mathfrak{F}[e^{-at^2}](\omega) = \sqrt{\frac{\pi}{a}}\, e^{-\omega^2/4a},$$

and

$$\mathfrak{F}\left[\frac{1}{a^2 + t^2}\right](\omega) = \frac{\pi}{a}e^{-a|\omega|}.$$

9. $f(t) = \begin{cases} 1 & \text{for } 0 \leq t \leq 1 \\ -1 & \text{for } -1 \leq t < 0 \\ 0 & \text{for } |t| > 1 \end{cases}$

10. $f(t) = \begin{cases} \sin(t) & \text{for } -k \leq t \leq k \\ 0 & \text{for } |t| > k, \end{cases}$

11. $f(t) = 5[H(t-3) - H(t-11)]$

12. $f(t) = 5e^{-3(t-5)^2}$

13. $f(t) = H(t-k)e^{-t/4}$

14. $f(t) = H(t-k)t^2$

15. $f(t) = 1/(1 + t^2)$

16. $f(t) = 3H(t-2)e^{-3t}$

17. $f(t) = 3e^{-4|t+2|}$

18. $f(t) = H(t-3)e^{-2t}$

In each of Problems 19 through 24, find the inverse Fourier transform of the function.

19. $9e^{-(\omega+4)^2/32}$

20. $\dfrac{e^{(20-4\omega)i}}{3 - (5 - \omega)i}$

21. $\dfrac{e^{(2\omega-6)i}}{5 - (3 - \omega)i}$

22. $\dfrac{10\sin(3\omega)}{\omega + \pi}$

23. $\dfrac{1 + i\omega}{6 - \omega^2 + 5i\omega}$

Hint: Factor the denominator and use partial fractions.

24. $\dfrac{10(4 + i\omega)}{9 - \omega^2 + 8i\omega}$

15.4   Additional Properties and Applications of the Fourier Transform

15.4.1   The Fourier Transform of a Derivative

In using the Fourier transform to solve differential equations, we need an expression relating the transform of f' to that of f. The following theorem provides such a relationship for derivatives of any order, and is called the *operational rule* for the Fourier transform. A similar issue arises for any integral transform when it is to be used in connection with differential equations (as in Theorems 3.5 and 3.6 for the Laplace transform).

Recall that the kth derivative of f is denoted $f^{(k)}$. As a convenience we may let $k = 0$ in this symbol, with the understanding that $f^{(0)} = f$.

THEOREM 15.7   *Differentiation in the Time Variable*

Let n be a positive integer. Suppose $f^{(n-1)}$ is continuous, and $f^{(n)}$ is piecewise continuous on each interval $[-L, L]$. Suppose $\int_{-\infty}^{\infty} |f^{(n-1)}(t)| \, dt$ converges. Suppose

$$\lim_{t \to \infty} f^{(k)}(t) = \lim_{t \to -\infty} f^{(k)}(t) = 0$$

for $k = 0, 1, \ldots, n - 1$. Then

$$\mathfrak{F}[f^{(n)}(t)](\omega) = (i\omega)^n \hat{f}(\omega). \quad \blacksquare$$

Proof   Begin with the first derivative. Integrating by parts, we have

$$\mathfrak{F}[f'](\omega) = \int_{-\infty}^{\infty} f'(t) e^{-i\omega t} \, dt$$

$$= \left[f(t) e^{-i\omega t} \right]_{-\infty}^{\infty} - \int_{-\infty}^{\infty} f(t)(-i\omega) e^{-i\omega t} \, dt.$$

Now $e^{-i\omega t} = \cos(\omega t) - i\sin(\omega t)$ has magnitude 1, and by assumption,

$$\lim_{t \to \infty} f(t) = \lim_{t \to -\infty} f(t) = 0.$$

Therefore

$$\mathfrak{F}[f^{(n)}(t)](\omega) = i\omega \int_{-\infty}^{\infty} f(t) e^{-i\omega t} \, dt = i\omega \hat{f}(\omega).$$

The conclusion for higher derivatives follows by inducation on n and the fact that.

$$f^{(n)}(t) = \frac{d}{dt} f^{(n-1)}(t). \quad \blacksquare$$

The assumption that f is continuous in the operational rule can be relaxed to allow for a finite number of jump discontinuities, if we allow for these in the conclusion by adding appropriate terms. We will state this result for the transform of f'.

THEOREM 15.8

Suppose f is continuous on the real line, except for jump discontinuities at $t_1, \ldots, t_M$. Let f' be piecewise continuous on every $[-L, L]$. Assume that $\int_{-\infty}^{\infty} |f(t)| \, dt$ converges, and that

$$\lim_{t \to \infty} f(t) = \lim_{t \to -\infty} f(t) = 0.$$

Then

$$\mathfrak{F}[f'](\omega) = i\omega \hat{f}(\omega) - \sum_{j=1}^{M} [f(t_j+) - f(t_j-)] e^{-it_j \omega}. \quad \blacksquare$$

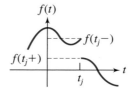

FIGURE 15.9 *The function f has a jump discontinuity at t_j.*

Each term $f(t_j+) - f(t_j-)$ is the difference between the one-sided limits of $f(t)$ at the jump discontinuity t_j. This shows up in Figure 15.9 as the size of the jump between ends of the graph at this point.

Proof Suppose first that f has a single jump discontinuity, at t_1. In the event of more jump discontinuities, the argument proceeds along the same lines, but includes more of the type of calculation we are about to do.

Integrate by parts:

$$\mathfrak{F}[f'](\omega) = \int_{-\infty}^{\infty} f'(t)e^{-i\omega t}\,dt$$

$$= \int_{-\infty}^{t_1} f'(t)e^{-i\omega t}\,dt + \int_{t_1}^{\infty} f'(t)e^{-i\omega t}\,dt$$

$$= \left[f(t)e^{-i\omega t}\right]_{-\infty}^{t_1} - \int_{-\infty}^{t_1} f(t)(-i\omega)e^{-i\omega t}\,dt$$

$$\quad + \left[f(t)e^{-i\omega t}\right]_{t_1}^{\infty} - (-i\omega)\int_{t_1}^{\infty} f(t)e^{-i\omega t}\,dt$$

$$= f(t_1-)e^{-it_1\omega} - f(t_1+)e^{-it_1\omega} + i\omega\int_{-\infty}^{\infty} f(t)e^{-i\omega t}\,dt$$

$$= i\omega\hat{f}(\omega) - [f(t_1+) - f(t_1-)]e^{-it_1\omega}. \ \blacksquare$$

Here is an example of the use of the operational rule in solving a differential equation.

EXAMPLE 15.13

Solve

$$y' - 4y = H(t)e^{-4t},$$

in which H is the Heaviside function. Thus the differential equation is

$$y' - 4y = \begin{cases} e^{-4t} & \text{for } t \geq 0 \\ 0 & \text{for } t < 0 \end{cases}.$$

Apply the Fourier transform to the differential equation to get

$$\mathfrak{F}[y'](\omega) - 4\hat{y}(\omega) = \mathfrak{F}[H(t)e^{-4t}](\omega).$$

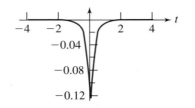

FIGURE 15.10 $y(t) = -\frac{1}{8}e^{-4|t|}$.

Using Theorem 15.7 and the fact that $F[H(t)e^{-4t}](\omega) = \frac{1}{4+i\omega}$, write this equation as

$$i\omega\hat{y}(\omega) - 4\hat{y}(\omega) = \frac{1}{4+i\omega}.$$

Solve for $\hat{y}(\omega)$ to obtain

$$\hat{y}(\omega) = \frac{-1}{16+\omega^2}.$$

The solution is

$$y(t) = \mathfrak{F}^{-1}\left[\frac{-1}{16+\omega^2}\right](t) = -\frac{1}{8}e^{-4|t|},$$

which is graphed in Figure 15.10.

The inverse transform just obtained can be derived in several ways. We can use a table of Fourier transforms, or a software package that contains this transform. We can also see from Example 15.4 that

$$\mathfrak{F}\left[e^{-a|t|}\right](\omega) = \frac{2a}{a^2+\omega^2}$$

and choose $a = 4$. ∎

There is no arbitrary constant in this solution because the Fourier transform has returned the only solution that is continuous and bounded for all real t. Boundedness is assumed when we use the transform because of the required convergence of $\int_{-\infty}^{\infty}|y(t)|\,dt$.

15.4.2   Frequency Differentiation

The variable ω used for the Fourier transform is the frequency of $f(t)$, since it occurs in the complex exponential $e^{i\omega t}$, which is $\cos(\omega t) + i\sin(\omega t)$. In this context, differentiation of $\hat{f}(\omega)$ with respect to ω is called *frequency differentiation*. We will now relate derivatives of $\hat{f}(\omega)$ and $f(t)$.

THEOREM 15.9   *Frequency Differentiation*

Let n be a positive integer. Let f be piecewise continuous on $[-L, L]$ for every positive number L, and assume that $\int_{-\infty}^{\infty}|t^n f(t)|\,dt$ converges. Then

$$\mathfrak{F}[t^n f(t)](\omega) = i^n \frac{d^n}{d\omega^n}\hat{f}(\omega). \quad∎$$

In particular, under the conditions of the theorem,

$$\mathfrak{F}[tf(t)](\omega) = i\frac{d}{d\omega}\hat{f}(\omega) \quad \text{and} \quad \mathfrak{F}[t^2 f(t)](\omega) = -\frac{d^2}{d\omega^2}\hat{f}(\omega).$$

Proof We will prove the theorem for $n = 1$. The argument for larger n is similar. Apply Leibniz's rule for differentiation under the integral to write

$$\frac{d}{d\omega}\hat{f}(\omega) = \frac{d}{d\omega}\int_{-\infty}^{\infty} f(t)e^{-i\omega t}\,dt = \int_{-\infty}^{\infty}\frac{\partial}{\partial\omega}\left[f(t)e^{-i\omega t}\right]dt$$

$$= \int_{-\infty}^{\infty} f(t)(-it)e^{-i\omega t}\,dt = -i\int_{-\infty}^{\infty}[tf(t)]e^{-i\omega t}\,dt$$

$$= -i\mathfrak{F}[tf(t)](\omega). \quad \blacksquare$$

EXAMPLE 15.14

Suppose we want to compute $\mathfrak{F}[t^2 e^{-5|t|}]$. Recall from Example 15.4 that

$$\mathfrak{F}[e^{-5|t|}](\omega) = \frac{10}{25 + \omega^2}.$$

By the frequency differentiation theorem,

$$\mathfrak{F}[t^2 e^{-5|t|}](\omega) = i^2 \frac{d^2}{d\omega^2}\left[\frac{10}{25 + \omega^2}\right] = 20\frac{25 - 3\omega^2}{(25 + \omega^2)^3}. \quad \blacksquare$$

15.4.3 The Fourier Transform of an Integral

The following enables us to take the transform of a function defined by an integral.

THEOREM 15.10

Let f be piecewise continuous on every interval $[-L, L]$. Suppose $\int_{-\infty}^{\infty} |f(t)|\,dt$ converges. Suppose $\hat{f}(0) = 0$. Then

$$\mathfrak{F}\left[\int_{-\infty}^{t} f(\tau)d\tau\right](\omega) = \frac{1}{i\omega}\hat{f}(\omega). \quad \blacksquare$$

Proof Let $g(t) = \int_{-\infty}^{t} f(\tau)d\tau$. Then $g'(t) = f(t)$ for any t at which f is continuous, and $g(t) \to 0$ as $t \to -\infty$. Further,

$$\lim_{t \to \infty} g(t) = \int_{-\infty}^{\infty} f(\tau)d\tau = \hat{f}(0) = 0.$$

We can therefore apply Theorem 15.7 to g to obtain

$$\hat{f}(\omega) = \mathfrak{F}[f(t)](\omega) = \mathfrak{F}[g'(t)](\omega)$$

$$= i\omega\mathfrak{F}[g(t)](\omega) = i\omega\mathfrak{F}\left[\int_{-\infty}^{t} f(\tau)d\tau\right](\omega).$$

This is equivalent to the conclusion to be proved. $\quad \blacksquare$

15.4.4 Convolution

There are many transforms defined by integrals, and it is common for such a transformation to have a convolution operation. We saw a convolution for the Laplace transform in Chapter 3. We will now discuss convolution for the Fourier transform.

DEFINITION 15.4 *Convolution*

Let f and g be functions defined on the real line. Then f has a convolution with g if

1. $\int_a^b f(t)dt$ and $\int_a^b g(t)dt$ exist for every interval $[a, b]$.
2. For every real number t,

$$\int_{-\infty}^{\infty} |f(t - \tau)g(\tau)| \, d\tau$$

converges. In this event, we define the convolution $f * g$ of f with g to be the function given by

$$(f * g)(t) = \int_{-\infty}^{\infty} f(t - \tau)g(\tau)d\tau.$$

In this definition, we wrote $(f * g)(t)$ for emphasis. However, the convolution is a function denoted $f * g$, so we can write just $f * g(t)$ to indicate $f * g$ evaluated at t.

THEOREM 15.11

Suppose f has a convolution with g. Then

1. (**Commutativity of Convolution**) g has a convolution with f, and $f * g = g * f$.
2. (**Linearity**) If f and g both have convolutions with h, and α and β are real numbers, then $\alpha f + \beta g$ also has a convolution with h, and

$$(\alpha f + \beta g) * h = \alpha(f * g) + \beta(g * h).$$

Proof   For (1), let $z = t - \tau$ to write

$$f * g(t) = \int_{-\infty}^{\infty} f(t - \tau)g(\tau)d\tau$$
$$= \int_{\infty}^{-\infty} f(z)g(t - z)(-1)dz = \int_{-\infty}^{\infty} g(t - z)f(z)dz = g * f(t).$$

Conclusion (2) follows from elementary properties of integrals, given that the integrals involved converge. ∎

We are now ready for the main results on convolution.

THEOREM 15.12

Suppose f and g are bounded and continuous on the real line, and that $\int_{-\infty}^{\infty} |f(t)| \, dt$ and $\int_{-\infty}^{\infty} |g(t)| \, dt$ both converge. Then,

1.

$$\int_{-\infty}^{\infty} f * g(t)\,dt = \int_{-\infty}^{\infty} f(t)\,dt \int_{-\infty}^{\infty} g(t)\,dt.$$

2. (**Time Convolution**)

$$\widehat{f * g}(\omega) = \hat{f}(\omega)\hat{g}(\omega).$$

3. (**Frequency Convolution**)

$$\widehat{f(t)g(t)}(\omega) = \frac{1}{2\pi}(\hat{f} * \hat{g})(\omega). \quad \blacksquare$$

The first conclusion is that the integral, over the real line, of the convolution of f with g, is equal to the product of the integrals of f and of g over the line.

Time convolution states that the Fourier transform of a convolution is the product of the transforms of the functions. This formula can be stated

$$\mathfrak{F}[f * g](\omega) = \hat{f}(\omega)\hat{g}(\omega).$$

That is, the Fourier transform of the convolution of f with g, is equal to the product of the transform of f with the transform of g. This has the important inverse version

$$\mathfrak{F}^{-1}\left[\hat{f}(\omega)\hat{g}(\omega)\right](t) = f * g(t).$$

The inverse Fourier transform of the product of two transformed functions, is equal to the convolution of these functions. This is sometimes of use in evaluating an inverse Fourier transform. If we want $\mathfrak{F}^{-1}[h(\omega)]$, and are able to factor $h(\omega)$ into $\hat{f}(\omega)\hat{g}(\omega)$, a product of the transforms of two known functions, then the inverse transform of h is the convolution of these known functions.

Frequency convolution can be stated

$$\mathfrak{F}[f(t)g(t)](\omega) = \frac{1}{2\pi}(\hat{f} * \hat{g})(\omega).$$

The Fourier transform of a product of two functions is equal to $\left(\frac{1}{2\pi}\right)$ times the convolution of the transforms of these functions.

The inverse version of frequency convolution is

$$\mathfrak{F}^{-1}[\hat{f}(\omega) * \hat{g}(\omega)](t) = 2\pi f(t)g(t).$$

Proof   For (1), write

$$\int_{-\infty}^{\infty} f * g(t)\,dt = \int_{-\infty}^{\infty}\left(\int_{-\infty}^{\infty} f(t-\tau)g(\tau)\,d\tau\right)dt$$

$$= \int_{-\infty}^{\infty}\left(\int_{-\infty}^{\infty} f(t-\tau)g(\tau)\,dt\right)d\tau = \int_{-\infty}^{\infty}\left(\int_{-\infty}^{\infty} f(t-\tau)\,dt\right)g(\tau)\,d\tau,$$

assuming the validity of this interchange of the order of integration. Now,

$$\int_{-\infty}^{\infty} f(t-\tau)\,dt = \int_{-\infty}^{\infty} f(t)\,dt$$

for any real number τ. Therefore

$$\int_{-\infty}^{\infty} f * g(t)dt = \int_{-\infty}^{\infty} \left(\int_{-\infty}^{\infty} f(t)dt \right) g(\tau)d\tau$$

$$= \int_{-\infty}^{\infty} f(t)dt \int_{-\infty}^{\infty} g(\tau)d\tau = \int_{-\infty}^{\infty} f(t)dt \int_{-\infty}^{\infty} g(t)dt.$$

For (2), begin by letting $F(t) = e^{-i\omega t} f(t)$ and $G(t) = e^{-i\omega t} g(t)$ for real t and ω. Then

$$\widehat{f * g}(\omega) = \int_{-\infty}^{\infty} f * g(t)e^{-i\omega t} dt$$

$$= \int_{-\infty}^{\infty} \left(\int_{-\infty}^{\infty} f(t-\tau)g(\tau)d\tau \right) e^{-i\omega t} dt$$

$$= \int_{-\infty}^{\infty} \left(\int_{-\infty}^{\infty} e^{-i\omega t} f(t-\tau)g(\tau)d\tau \right) dt$$

$$= \int_{-\infty}^{\infty} \left(\int_{-\infty}^{\infty} e^{-i\omega(t-\tau)} f(t-\tau)e^{-i\omega\tau} g(\tau)d\tau \right) dt.$$

Now recognize that the integral in large parentheses in the last line is the convolution of F with G. Then, by (1) of this theorem applied to F and G,

$$\widehat{f * g}(\omega) = \int_{-\infty}^{\infty} F * G(t)dt = \int_{-\infty}^{\infty} F(t)dt \int_{-\infty}^{\infty} G(t)dt$$

$$= \int_{-\infty}^{\infty} f(t)e^{-i\omega t} dt \int_{-\infty}^{\infty} g(t)e^{-i\omega t} dt = \hat{f}(\omega)\hat{g}(\omega).$$

We leave conclusion (3) to the student. ∎

EXAMPLE 15.15

Suppose we want to compute

$$\mathfrak{F}^{-1}\left[\frac{1}{(4+\omega^2)(9+\omega^2)} \right].$$

Recognize the problem as one of computing the inverse transform of a product of functions whose individual transforms we know:

$$\frac{1}{4+\omega^2} = \mathfrak{F}\left(\frac{1}{4} e^{-2|t|} \right) = \hat{f}(\omega) \quad \text{with } f(t) = \frac{1}{4} e^{-2|t|},$$

and

$$\frac{1}{9+\omega^2} = \mathfrak{F}\left(\frac{1}{6} e^{-3|t|} \right) = \hat{g}(\omega) \quad \text{with } g(t) = \frac{1}{6} e^{-3|t|}.$$

The inverse version of conclusion (2) tells us that

$$\mathfrak{F}^{-1}\left[\frac{1}{(4+\omega^2)(9+\omega^2)} \right](t) = \mathfrak{F}^{-1}[\hat{f}(\omega)\hat{g}(\omega)](t) = f * g(t)$$

$$= \frac{1}{4} e^{-2|t|} * \frac{1}{6} e^{-3|t|} = \frac{1}{24} \int_{-\infty}^{\infty} e^{-2|t-\tau|} e^{-3|\tau|} d\tau.$$

We must be careful in evaluating this integral because of the absolute values in the exponents. First, if $t > 0$, then

$$24[f * g(t)] = \int_{-\infty}^{0} e^{-2|t-\tau|} e^{-3|\tau|} d\tau + \int_{0}^{t} e^{-2|t-\tau|} e^{-3|\tau|} d\tau + \int_{t}^{\infty} e^{-2|t-\tau|} e^{-3|\tau|} d\tau$$

$$= \int_{-\infty}^{0} e^{-2(t-\tau)} e^{3\tau} d\tau + \int_{0}^{t} e^{-2(t-\tau)} e^{-3\tau} d\tau + \int_{t}^{\infty} e^{-2(\tau-t)} e^{-3\tau} d\tau$$

$$= \frac{6}{5} e^{-2t} - \frac{4}{5} e^{-3t}.$$

If $t < 0$, then

$$24[f * g(t)] = \int_{-\infty}^{t} e^{-2|t-\tau|} e^{-3|\tau|} d\tau + \int_{t}^{0} e^{-2|t-\tau|} e^{-3|\tau|} d\tau + \int_{0}^{\infty} e^{-2|t-\tau|} e^{-3|\tau|} d\tau$$

$$= \int_{-\infty}^{t} e^{-2(t-\tau)} e^{3\tau} d\tau + \int_{t}^{0} e^{2(t-\tau)} e^{3\tau} d\tau + \int_{0}^{\infty} e^{2(t-\tau)} e^{-3\tau} d\tau$$

$$= -\frac{4}{5} e^{3t} + \frac{6}{5} e^{2t}.$$

Finally, compute

$$24[f * g](0) = \int_{-\infty}^{\infty} e^{-2|\tau|} e^{-3|\tau|} d\tau = \frac{2}{5}.$$

Therefore

$$\mathfrak{F}^{-1}\left[\frac{1}{(4+\omega^2)(9+\omega^2)}\right](t) = \frac{1}{24}\left(\frac{6}{5} e^{-2|t|} - \frac{4}{5} e^{-3|t|}\right)$$

$$= \frac{1}{20} e^{-2|t|} - \frac{1}{30} e^{-3|t|}.$$

15.4.5 Filtering and the Dirac Delta Function

A Dirac delta function is a pulse of infinite magnitude having infinitely short duration. One way to describe such an object mathematically is to form a short pulse

$$\frac{1}{2a}[H(t+a) - H(t-a)],$$

as shown in Figure 15.11, and take the limit as the width of the pulse approaches zero:

$$\delta(t) = \lim_{a \to 0} \frac{1}{2a}[H(t+a) - H(t-a)].$$

This is not a function in the standard sense, but is an object called a distribution. Distributions are generalizations of the function concept. For this reason many theorems do not apply to $\delta(t)$.

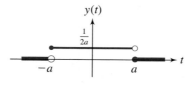

FIGURE 15.11
$y = \frac{1}{2a}[H(t+a) - H(t-a)]$.

However, there are some formal manipulations that yield useful results. First, if we take the Fourier transform of the pulse, we get

$$\mathfrak{F}[H(t+a) - H(t-a)] = \int_{-a}^{a} e^{-i\omega t} dt = -\frac{1}{i\omega} e^{-i\omega t} \Big]_{-a}^{a}$$

$$= \frac{1}{i\omega} \left(e^{ia\omega} - e^{-ia\omega}\right) = 2\frac{\sin(a\omega)}{\omega}.$$

By interchanging the limit and the operation of taking the transform, we have

$$\mathfrak{F}[\delta(t)](\omega) = \mathfrak{F}\left[\lim_{a \to 0} \frac{1}{2a}[H(t+a) - H(t-a)]\right](\omega)$$

$$= \lim_{a \to 0} \frac{1}{2a} \mathfrak{F}[H(t+a) - H(t-a)](\omega)$$

$$= \lim_{a \to 0} \frac{\sin(a\omega)}{a\omega} = 1.$$

This leads us to consider the Fourier transform of the delta function to be the function that is identically 1.

Further, putting $\delta(t)$ formally through the convolution, we have

$$\mathfrak{F}[\delta * f] = \mathfrak{F}[\delta]\mathfrak{F}[f] = \mathfrak{F}[f]$$

and

$$\mathfrak{F}[f * \delta] = \mathfrak{F}[f]\mathfrak{F}[\delta] = \mathfrak{F}[f],$$

suggesting that

$$\delta * f = f * \delta = f.$$

The delta function behaves like the identity under convolution.

The following filtering property enables us to recover a function value by "summing" its values when hit with a shifted delta function.

THEOREM 15.13 *Filtering*

If f has a Fourier transform and is continuous at t_0, then

$$\int_{-\infty}^{\infty} f(t)\delta(t - t_0) dt = f(t_0). \quad \blacksquare$$

This result can be modified to allow for a jump discontinuity of f at t_0. In this event we get

$$\int_{-\infty}^{\infty} f(t)\delta(t - t_0) dt = \frac{1}{2}(f(t_0+) + f(t_0-)).$$

15.4.6 The Windowed Fourier Transform

Suppose f is a signal. This means that f is a function that is defined over the real line, and has finite energy $\int_{-\infty}^{\infty} |f(t)|^2 dt$.

In analyzing $f(t)$, we sometimes want to localize its frequency content with respect to the time variable. We have mentioned that $\hat{f}(\omega)$ carries information about the frequencies of the signal. However, $\hat{f}(\omega)$ does not particularize information to specific time intervals, since

$$\hat{f}(\omega) = \int_{-\infty}^{\infty} f(t)e^{-i\omega t}\,dt,$$

and this integration is over all time. Hence the picture we obtain does not contain information about specific times, but instead enables us only to compute the total amplitude spectrum $\left|\hat{f}(\omega)\right|$. If we think of $f(t)$ as a piece of music being played over time, we would have to wait until the entire piece was done before even computing this amplitude spectrum. However, we can obtain a picture of the frequency content of $f(t)$ within given time intervals by windowing the function before taking its Fourier transform.

To do this, we first need a *window function g*, which is a function taking on nonzero values only on some closed interval, often $[0, T]$ or $[-T, T]$. Figures 15.12 and 15.13 show typical graphs of such functions, one on $[0, T]$ and the other on $[-T, T]$. The interval is called the *support* of g, and in this case that we are dealing with closed intervals, we say that g has *compact support*. The function g has zero values outside of this support interval. We window a function f with g by forming the product $g(t)f(t)$, which vanishes outside of $[-T, T]$.

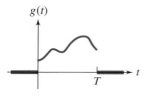

FIGURE 15.12 *Typical window function with compact support* $[0, T]$.

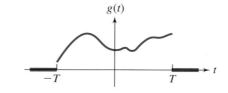

FIGURE 15.13 *Typical window function with compact support* $[-T, T]$.

EXAMPLE 15.16

Consider the window function

$$g(t) = \begin{cases} 1 & \text{for } -4 \leq t \leq 4 \\ 0 & \text{for } |t| > 4 \end{cases},$$

having compact support $[-4, 4]$. This function is graphed in Figure 15.14 (a), with the vertical segments at $t = \pm 4$ included to emphasize this interval. Let $f(t) = t\sin(t)$, shown in Figure 15.14 (b). To window f with g, form the product $g(t)f(t)$, shown in Figure 15.14 (c). This windowed function vanishes outside the support of g. For this choice of g, windowing has the effect of turning the signal $f(t)$ on at time -4 and turning it off at $t = 4$. ∎

The *windowed Fourier transform* (with respect to the choice of g) is

$$\mathfrak{F}_{win}[f])\omega) = \widehat{f_{win}}(\omega) = \int_{-\infty}^{\infty} f(t)g(t)e^{-i\omega t}\,dt$$

$$= \int_{-T}^{T} f(t)g(t)e^{-i\omega t}\,dt.$$

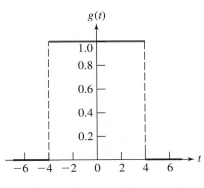

FIGURE 15.14(a) *Window function*

$$g(t) = \begin{cases} 1 & \text{for } |t| \le 4 \\ 0 & \text{for } |t| > 4 \end{cases}.$$

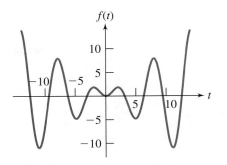
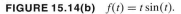

FIGURE 15.14(b) $f(t) = t\sin(t)$.

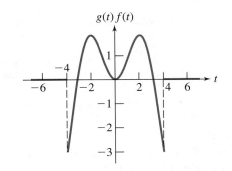

FIGURE 15.14(c) *f windowed with g.*

EXAMPLE 15.17

Let $f(t) = 6e^{-|t|}$. Then

$$\hat{f}(\omega) = \int_{-\infty}^{\infty} 6e^{-|t|}e^{-i\omega t}\,dt = \frac{12}{1+\omega^2}.$$

Use the window function

$$g(t) = \begin{cases} 1 & \text{for } -2 \le t \le 2 \\ 0 & \text{for } |t| > 2 \end{cases}.$$

Figure 15.15 shows a graph of the windowed function $g(t)f(t)$. The windowed Fourier transform of f is

$$\widehat{f_{win}}(\omega) = \int_{-\infty}^{\infty} 6e^{-|t|}g(t)e^{-i\omega t}\,dt$$

$$= \int_{-2}^{2} 6e^{-|t|}e^{-i\omega t}\,dt$$

$$= 12\frac{-2e^{-2}\cos^2(\omega) + e^{-2} + e^{-2}\omega\sin(2\omega) + 1}{1+\omega^2}.$$

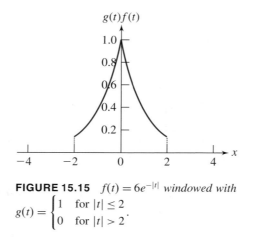

FIGURE 15.15 $f(t) = 6e^{-|t|}$ windowed with
$$g(t) = \begin{cases} 1 & \text{for } |t| \le 2 \\ 0 & \text{for } |t| > 2 \end{cases}.$$

This gives the frequency content of the signal f in the time interval $-2 \le t \le 2$. ∎

Often we use a shifted window function. Suppose the support of g is $[-T, T]$. If $t_0 > 0$, then the graph of $g(t - t_0)$ is the graph of $g(t)$ shifted t_0 units to the right. Now

$$f(t)g(t - t_0) = \begin{cases} f(t)g(t - t_0) & \text{for } t_0 - T \le t \le t_0 + T \\ 0 & \text{for } t < t_0 - T \text{ and for } t > t_0 + T \end{cases}.$$

Figures 15.16 (a) through (d) illustrates this process. In this case we take the Fourier transform of the shifted windowed signal to be

$$\widehat{f_{win,t_0}}(\omega) = \Im[f(t)g(t - t_0)](\omega)$$
$$= \int_{t_0 - T}^{t_0 + T} f(t)g(t - t_0)e^{-i\omega t}\, dt.$$

This gives the frequency content of the signal in the time interval $[t_0 - T, t_0 + T]$.

Engineers sometimes refer to the windowing process is known as *time-frequency localization*. If g is the window function, the *center* of g is defined to be the point

$$t_C = \frac{\int_{-\infty}^{\infty} t\,|g(t)|^2\, dt}{\int_{-\infty}^{\infty} |g(t)|^2\, dt}.$$

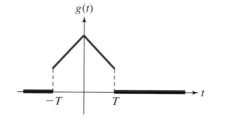

FIGURE 15.16(a) *A window function g on $[-T, T]$.*

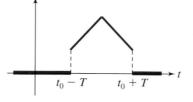

FIGURE 15.16(b) *Shifted window function $g(t - t_0)$.*

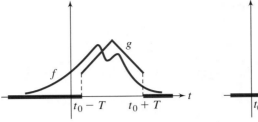 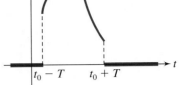

FIGURE 15.16(c) *Typical signal* $f(t)$.

FIGURE 15.16(d) $g(t - t_0)f(t)$.

The number

$$t_R = \left(\frac{\int_{-\infty}^{\infty} (t - t_C)^2 |g(t)|^2 \, dt}{\int_{-\infty}^{\infty} |g(t)|^2 \, dt} \right)^{1/2}$$

is the *radius* of the window function. The width of the window function is $2t_R$, and is referred to as the *RMS duration of the window*. It is assumed in this terminology that the integrals involved all converge.

When we deal with the Fourier transform of the window function, then similar terminology applies:

$$\text{center of } \hat{g} = \omega_C = \frac{\int_{-\infty}^{\infty} \omega |\hat{g}(\omega)|^2 \, d\omega}{\int_{-\infty}^{\infty} |\hat{g}(\omega)|^2 \, d\omega}$$

and

$$\text{radius of } \hat{g} = \omega_R = \left(\frac{\int_{-\infty}^{\infty} (\omega - \omega_C)^2 |\hat{g}(\omega)|^2 \, d\omega}{\int_{-\infty}^{\infty} |\hat{g}(\omega)|^2 \, d\omega} \right)^{1/2}.$$

The width of $\hat{g}$ is $2\omega_R$, a number referred to as the *RMS bandwidth* of the window function.

15.4.7 The Shannon Sampling Theorem

We will derive the Shannon sampling theorem, which states that a band-limited signal can be reconstructed from certain sampled values.

A signal f is *band-limited* if its Fourier transform $\hat{f}$ has compact support (has nonzero values only on a closed interval of finite length). This means that, for some L,

$$\hat{f}(\omega) = 0 \text{ if } |\omega| > L.$$

Usually we choose L to be the smallest number for which this condition holds. In this event L is the *bandwidth* of the signal. The total frequency content of such a signal f lies in the band $[-L, L]$.

We will now show that we can reconstruct a band-limited signal from samples taken at appropriately chosen times. Begin with the integral for the inverse Fourier transform, assuming that we can recover $f(t)$ for all real t from its transform:

$$f(t) = \frac{1}{2\pi} \int_{-\infty}^{\infty} \hat{f}(\omega) e^{i\omega t} \, d\omega.$$

Because f is band-limited,

$$f(t) = \frac{1}{2\pi} \int_{-L}^{L} \hat{f}(\omega) e^{i\omega t} \, d\omega. \tag{15.8}$$

Put this aside for the moment and write the complex Fourier series for $\hat{f}(\omega)$ on $[-L, L]$:

$$\hat{f}(\omega) = \sum_{n=-\infty}^{\infty} c_n e^{n\pi i \omega/L}, \tag{15.9}$$

where

$$c_n = \frac{1}{2L} \int_{-L}^{L} \hat{f}(\omega) e^{-n\pi i \omega/L} \, d\omega.$$

Comparing c_n with $f(t)$ in equation (15.8), we conclude that

$$c_n = \frac{\pi}{L} f\left(\frac{-n\pi}{L}\right).$$

Substitute this into equation (15.9) to get

$$\hat{f}(\omega) = \sum_{n=-\infty}^{\infty} \frac{\pi}{L} f\left(\frac{-n\pi}{L}\right) e^{n\pi i \omega/L}.$$

Since n takes on all integer values in this summation, we can replace n with $-n$ to write

$$\hat{f}(\omega) = \frac{\pi}{L} \sum_{n=-\infty}^{\infty} f\left(\frac{n\pi}{L}\right) e^{-n\pi i \omega/L}.$$

Now substitute this series for $\hat{f}(\omega)$ into equation (15.8) to get

$$f(t) = \frac{1}{2\pi} \frac{\pi}{L} \int_{-\pi}^{\pi} \sum_{n=-\infty}^{\infty} f\left(\frac{n\pi}{L}\right) e^{-n\pi i \omega/L} e^{i\omega t} \, d\omega.$$

Interchange the sum and the integral to get

$$f(t) = \frac{1}{2L} \sum_{n=-\infty}^{\infty} f\left(\frac{n\pi}{L}\right) \int_{-L}^{L} e^{i\omega(t - n\pi/L)} \, d\omega$$

$$= \frac{1}{2L} \sum_{n=-\infty}^{\infty} f(n\pi/L) \frac{1}{i(t - n\pi/L)} \left[e^{i\omega(t - n\pi/L)} \right]_{-L}^{L}$$

$$= \frac{1}{2L} \sum_{n=-\infty}^{\infty} f(n\pi/L) \frac{1}{i(t - n\pi/L)} \left(e^{i(Lt - n\pi)} - e^{-i(Lt - n\pi)} \right)$$

$$= \sum_{n=-\infty}^{\infty} f(n\pi/L) \frac{1}{Lt - n\pi} \frac{1}{2i} \left(e^{i(Lt - n\pi)} - e^{-i(Lt - n\pi)} \right)$$

$$= \sum_{n=-\infty}^{\infty} f(n\pi/L) \frac{\sin(Lt - n\pi)}{Lt - n\pi}. \tag{15.10}$$

This means that $f(t)$ is known for all times t if just the function values $f(n\pi/L)$ are determined for all integer values of n. An engineer would sample the signal $f(t)$ at times $0, \pm\pi/L, \pm 2\pi/L$, ... Once the values of $f(t)$ are known for these times, then equation (15.10) reconstructs the entire signal. This is actually the way engineers convert digital signals to analog signals, with application to technology such as that involved in making compact disks.

Equation (15.10) is known as the *Shannon sampling theorem*. We will encounter it again when we discuss wavelets. In the case $L = \pi$, the sampling theorem has the simple form

$$f(t) = \sum_{n=-\infty}^{\infty} f(n) \frac{\sin(\pi(t-n))}{\pi(t-n)} \tag{15.11}$$

15.4.8 Lowpass and Bandpass Filters

Consider a signal f, not necessarily band-limited. However, we assume that the signal has finite energy, so

$$\int_{-\infty}^{\infty} |f(t)|^2 \, dt$$

is finite. Such functions are called *square integrable*, and we will also encounter them later with wavelet expansions.

The spectrum of f is given by its Fourier transform

$$\hat{f}(\omega) = \int_{-\infty}^{\infty} f(t) e^{-i\omega t} \, dt.$$

If f is not band-limited, we can replace f with a band-limited signal f_{ω_0} with bandwidth not exceeding a positive number ω_0 by applying a low pass filter which cuts off $\hat{f}(\omega)$ at frequencies outside the range $[-\omega_0, \omega_0]$. That is, let

$$\widehat{f_{\omega_0}}(\omega) = \begin{cases} \hat{f}(\omega) & \text{for } -\omega_0 \leq \omega \leq \omega_0 \\ 0 & \text{for } |\omega| > \omega_0 \end{cases}.$$

This defines the transform of the function f_{ω_0}, from which we recover f_{ω_0} by the inverse Fourier transform:

$$f_{\omega_0}(t) = \frac{1}{2\pi} \int_{-\infty}^{\infty} \widehat{f_{\omega_0}}(\omega) e^{i\omega t} \, d\omega = \frac{1}{2\pi} \int_{-\omega_0}^{\omega_0} \widehat{f_{\omega_0}}(\omega) e^{i\omega t} \, d\omega.$$

The process of applying the lowpass filter is carried out mathematically by multiplying by an appropriate function (essentially windowing). Define the characteristic function χ_I of an interval I by

$$\chi_I(t) = \begin{cases} 1 & \text{if } t \text{ is in } I \\ 0 & \text{if } t \text{ is a real number that is not in } I \end{cases}.$$

Now observe that

$$\widehat{f_{\omega_0}}(\omega) = \chi_{[-\omega_0,\omega_0]}(\omega)\hat{f}(\omega), \tag{15.12}$$

or, more succinctly,

$$\widehat{f_{\omega_0}} = \chi_{[-\omega_0,\omega_0]}\hat{f}.$$

In this context, $\chi_{[-\omega_0,\omega_0]}$ is called the *transfer function*. Its graph is shown in Figure 15.17. The inverse Fourier transform of the transfer function is

$$\mathcal{F}^{-1}[\chi_{[-\omega_0,\omega_0]}](t) = \frac{1}{2\pi} \int_{-\omega_0}^{\omega_0} e^{i\omega t} \, d\omega = \frac{\sin(\omega_0 t)}{\pi t},$$

whose graph is given in Figure 15.18. In the case that $\omega_0 = \pi$, this is the function, evaluated at $t - n$ instead of t, which occurs in the Shannon sampling formula (15.11) that reconstructs $f(t)$ from sampled values $f(n)$ on the integers. For this reason $\sin(\omega_0 t)/\pi t$ is called the *Shannon sampling function*.

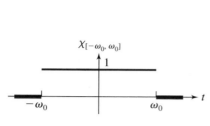

FIGURE 15.17 *Graph of* $\chi_{[-\omega_0,\omega_0]}$.

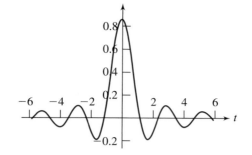

FIGURE 15.18 *Graph of* $\sin(\omega_0 t)/\pi t$ *for* $\omega_0 = 2.7$.

Now recall Theorem 15.12(2) and (3) of Section 15.4.4. Analog filtering in the time variable t is done by convolution. If $\varphi(t)$ is the filter function, then the effect of filtering a function f by φ is a new function g defined by

$$g(t) = (\varphi * f)(t) = \int_{-\infty}^{\infty} \varphi(\xi)f(t-\xi)d\xi.$$

Taking the Fourier transform of this equation, we have

$$\hat{g}(\omega) = \hat{\varphi}(\omega)\hat{f}(\omega).$$

We therefore filter in the frequency variable by taking a product of the Fourier transform of the filter function with the transform of the function being filtered.

We can now formulate equation (15.12) as

$$f_{\omega_0}(t) = \left(\frac{\sin(\omega_0 t)}{\pi t} * f(t)\right).$$

This gives the lowpass filtering of f as the convolution of the Shannon sampling function with f.

In lowpass filtering, we produce from the signal f a new signal f_{ω_0} that is band-limited. That is, we filter out the frequencies of the signal outside of $[-\omega_0, \omega_0]$. In a similar kind of filtering, called *bandpass filtering*, we want to filter out the effects of the signal outside of given bandwidths. A band-limited signal f can be decomposed into a sum of signals, each of which carries the information content of f within a certain given frequency band. To see how to do this, let f be a band-limited signal of bandwidth Ω. Consider a finite increasing sequence of frequencies,

$$0 < \omega_1 < \omega_2 < \cdots < \omega_N = \Omega.$$

For $j = 1, \ldots, N$, define a bandwidth filter function β_j by means of its transfer function:

$$\hat{\beta}_j = \chi_{[-\omega_j,-\omega_{j-1}]} + \chi_{[\omega_{j-1},\omega_j]}.$$

This transfer function, which is a sum of characteristic functions of frequency intervals, is graphed in Figure 15.19. The bandwidth filter function $\beta_j(t)$, which filters the frequency

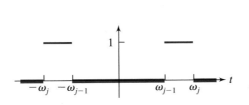

FIGURE 15.19 $\chi_{[-\omega_j, -\omega_{j-1}]} + \chi_{[\omega_{j-1}, \omega_j]}.$

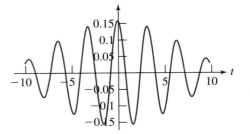

FIGURE 15.20

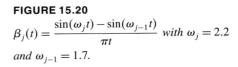

$$\beta_j(t) = \frac{\sin(\omega_j t) - \sin(\omega_{j-1} t)}{\pi t} \text{ with } \omega_j = 2.2$$

$$\text{and } \omega_{j-1} = 1.7.$$

content of $f(t)$ outside of the frequency range $[\omega_{j-1}, \omega_j]$, is obtained by taking the inverse Fourier transform of $\hat{\beta}_j(\omega)$. We get

$$\beta_j(t) = \frac{\sin(\omega_j t) - \sin(\omega_{j-1} t)}{\pi t},$$

whose graph is shown in Figure 15.20.

Now define functions

$$f_0(t) = \left(\frac{\sin(\omega_0 t)}{\pi t} * f\right)(t)$$

and, for for $j = 1, 2, \ldots, N$,

$$f_j(t) = (\beta_j * f)(t)$$

Then, for $j = 1, 2, \ldots, N$, each $f_j(t)$ carries the content of the signal $f(t)$ in the frequency range $\omega_{j-1} \le \omega \le \omega_j$, while $f_0(t)$ carries the content in $[0, \omega_0]$, which is the low-frequency range of $f(t)$. Further,

$$f(t) = f_0(t) + f_1(t) + f_2(t) + \cdots + f_N(t), \tag{15.13}$$

giving a decomposition of the signal into components carrying the information of the signal for specific frequency intervals.

SECTION 15.4   PROBLEMS

In each of Problems 1 through 8, determine the Fourier transform of the function

1. $\dfrac{t}{9 + t^2}$

2. $3te^{-9t^2}$

3. $26H(t)te^{-2t}$

4. $H(t-3)(t-3)e^{-4t}$

5. $\dfrac{d}{dt}[H(t)e^{-3t}]$

6. $t[H(t+1) - H(t-1)]$

7. $\dfrac{5e^{3it}}{t^2 - 4t + 13}$

8. $H(t-3)e^{-2t}$

In each of Problems 9, 10 and 11, use convolution to find the inverse Fourier transform of the function.

9. $\dfrac{1}{(1+i\omega)^2}$

10. $\dfrac{1}{(1+i\omega)(2+i\omega)}$

11. $\dfrac{\sin(3\omega)}{\omega(2+i\omega)}$

In each of Problems 12, 13 and 14, find the inverse Fourier transform of the function.

12. $\dfrac{6e^{4i\omega}\sin(2\omega)}{9+\omega^2}$

13. $e^{-3|\omega+4|}\cos(2\omega+8)$

14. $e^{-\omega^2/9}\sin(8\omega)$

15. Prove the following form of Parseval's theorem:

$$\int_{-\infty}^{\infty}|f(t)|^2\,dt = \frac{1}{2\pi}\int_{-\infty}^{\infty}\left|\hat{f}(\omega)\right|^2\,d\omega.$$

16. The *power content* of a signal $f(t)$ is defined to be $\int_{-\infty}^{\infty}|f(t)|^2\,dt$, assuming that this integral converges. Determine the power content of $H(t)e^{-2t}$.

17. Determine the power content of $(1/t)\sin(3t)$. *Hint:* Use the result of Problem 15.

18. Use the Fourier transform to solve

$$y'' + 6y' + 5y = \delta(t-3).$$

In each of Problems 19 through 24, compute the windowed Fourier transform of the given function f, using the windowing function g. Also compute the center and RMS bandwidth of the window function.

19. $f(t) = t^2$, $g(t) = \begin{cases} 1 & \text{for } -5 \le t \le 5 \\ 0 & \text{for } |t| > 5 \end{cases}$.

20. $f(t) = \cos(at)$, $g(t) = \begin{cases} 1 & \text{for } -4\pi \le t \le 4\pi \\ 0 & \text{for } |t| > 4\pi \end{cases}$.

21. $f(t) = e^{-t}$, $g(t) = \begin{cases} 1 & \text{for } 0 \le t \le 4 \\ 0 & \text{for } t < 0 \text{ and for } t > 4 \end{cases}$.

22. $f(t) = e^t\sin(\pi t)$, $g(t) = \begin{cases} 1 & \text{for } -1 \le t \le 1 \\ 0 & \text{for } |t| > 1 \end{cases}$.

23. $f(t) = (t+2)^2$, $g(t) = \begin{cases} 1 & \text{for } -2 \le t \le 2 \\ 0 & \text{for } |t| > 2 \end{cases}$.

24. $f(t) = H(t-\pi)$, $g(t) = \begin{cases} 1 & \text{for } 3\pi \le t \le 5\pi \\ 0 & \text{for } t < 3\pi \text{ and for } t > 5\pi \end{cases}$.

15.5 The Fourier Cosine and Sine Transforms

We saw in Section 15.3 how the Fourier integral representation of a function suggested its Fourier transform. We will now show how the Fourier cosine and sine integrals of a function suggest cosine and sine transforms.

Suppose $f(t)$ is piecewise smooth on each interval $[0, L]$ and $\int_0^\infty |f(t)|\,dt$ converges. Then for each t at which f is continuous,

$$f(t) = \int_0^\infty a_\omega\cos(\omega t)d\omega,$$

where

$$a_\omega = \frac{2}{\pi}\int_0^\infty f(t)\cos(\omega t)dt.$$

Based on these two equations, we make the following.

DEFINITION 15.5 *Fourier Cosine Transform*

The Fourier cosine transform of f is defined by

$$\mathfrak{F}_c[f](\omega) = \int_0^\infty f(t)\cos(\omega t)dt. \qquad (15.14)$$

Often we will denote $\mathfrak{F}_c[f](\omega) = \hat{f}_C(\omega)$.

Notice that

$$\hat{f}_C(\omega) = \frac{\pi}{2}a_\omega$$

and that

$$f(t) = \frac{2}{\pi}\int_0^\infty \hat{f}_C(\omega)\cos(\omega t)d\omega. \tag{15.15}$$

The integrals in expressions (15.14) and (15.15) form the transform pair for the Fourier cosine transform. The latter enables us, under certain conditions, to recover $f(t)$ from $\hat{f}_C(\omega)$.

EXAMPLE 15.18

Let K be a positive number, and let

$$f(t) = \begin{cases} 1 & \text{for } 0 \le t \le K \\ 0 & \text{for } t > K \end{cases}.$$

The Fourier transform of f is

$$\hat{f}_C(\omega) = \int_0^\infty f(t)\cos(\omega t)dt$$

$$= \int_0^K \cos(\omega t)dt = \frac{\sin(K\omega)}{\omega}. \quad \blacksquare$$

The Fourier sine transform is defined in the same spirit.

DEFINITION 15.6 *Fourier Sine Transform*

The Fourier sine transform of f is defined by

$$\mathfrak{F}_S[f](\omega) = \int_0^\infty f(t)\sin(\omega t)dt.$$

We also denote this as $\hat{f}_S(\omega)$.

If f is continuous at $t > 0$, then the Fourier integral sine representation is

$$f(t) = \int_0^\infty b_\omega \sin(\omega t)d\omega,$$

where

$$b_\omega = \frac{2}{\pi}\int_0^\infty f(t)\sin(\omega t)dt.$$

Since

$$\hat{f}_S(\omega) = \frac{\pi}{2}b_\omega$$

then

$$f(t) = \frac{2}{\pi}\int_0^\infty \hat{f}_S(\omega)\sin(\omega t)d\omega,$$

and this is the means by which we retrieve $f(t)$ from $\hat{f}_S(\omega)$.

EXAMPLE 15.19

With f the function of Example 15.18,

$$\hat{f}_S(\omega) = \int_0^\infty f(t)\sin(\omega t)dt$$

$$= \int_0^K \sin(\omega t)dt = \frac{1}{\omega}[1 - \cos(K\omega)]. \ \blacksquare$$

Both of these transforms are linear:

$$\mathfrak{F}_C[\alpha f + \beta g] = \alpha\mathfrak{F}_C[f] + \beta\mathfrak{F}_C[g]$$

and

$$\mathfrak{F}_S[\alpha f + \beta g] = \alpha\mathfrak{F}_S[f] + \beta\mathfrak{F}_S[g],$$

whenever all of these transforms are defined.

When these transforms are used to solve differential equations, the following operational rules play a key role.

THEOREM 15.14 *Operational Rules*

Let f and f' be continuous on every $[0, L]$, and let $\int_0^\infty |f(t)|\, dt$ converge. Suppose $f(t) \to 0$ and $f'(t) \to 0$ as $t \to \infty$. Suppose f'' is piecewise continuous on every interval $[0, L]$. Then,

1.
$$\mathfrak{F}_C[f''(t)](\omega) = -\omega^2 \hat{f}_C(\omega) - f'(0)$$

and

2.
$$\mathfrak{F}_S[f''(t)](\omega) = -\omega^2 \hat{f}_S(\omega) + \omega f(0). \ \blacksquare$$

The theorem is proved by integrating by parts twice for each rule, and we leave the details to the student.

The operational formula dictates which transform is used to solve a given problem. If we seek a function $f(t)$, for $0 \le t < \infty$, and $f(0)$ is specified, then we might consider a Fourier sine transform. If, however, information is given about $f'(0)$, then the cosine transform might be appropriate. When we solve partial differential equations we will encounter examples where this strategy is invoked.

SECTION 15.5 PROBLEMS

In each of Problems 1 through 6, determine the Fourier cosine transform and the Fourier sine transform of the function.

1. $f(t) = e^{-t}$

2. $f(t) = te^{-at}$, with a any positive number

3. $f(t) = \begin{cases} \cos(t) & \text{for } 0 \le t \le K \\ 0 & \text{for } t > K, \end{cases}$

with K any positive number

4. $f(t) = \begin{cases} 1 & \text{for } 0 \le t < K \\ -1 & \text{for } K \le t < 2K \\ 0 & \text{for } t \ge 2K \end{cases}$.

5. $f(t) = e^{-t}\cos(t)$

6. $f(t) = \begin{cases} \sinh(t) & \text{for } K \le t < 2K \\ 0 & \text{for } 0 \le t < K \text{ and for } t \ge 2K \end{cases}$.

7. Show that, under appropriate conditions on f and its derivatives,

$$\mathfrak{F}_S[f^{(4)}(t)](\omega) = \omega^4 \hat{f}_S(\omega) - \omega^3 f(0) + \omega f''(0).$$

Hint: Consider conditions that allow application of the operational formula to $(f''(t))''$.

8. Show that, under appropriate conditions on f and its derivatives,

$$\mathfrak{F}_C[f^{(4)}(t)](\omega) = \omega^4 \hat{f}_C(\omega) + \omega^2 f'(0) - f^{(3)}(0).$$

15.6 The Finite Fourier Cosine and Sine Transforms

The Fourier transform, cosine transform and sine transform are all motivated by the respective integral representations of a function. If we employ essentially the same line of reasoning, but using Fourier cosine and sine series instead of integrals, we obtain what are called finite transforms.

Suppose f is piecewise smooth on $[0, \pi]$.

DEFINITION 15.7 *Finite Fourier Cosine Transform*

The finite Fourier cosine transform of f is defined by

$$\mathfrak{C}[f](n) = \tilde{f}_C(n) = \int_0^\pi f(x) \cos(nx) \, dx$$

for $n = 0, 1, 2, \ldots$.

If f is continuous at x in $[0, \pi]$, then $f(x)$ has the Fourier cosine series representation

$$f(x) = \frac{1}{2} a_0 + \sum_{n=1}^\infty a_n \cos(nx),$$

where

$$a_n = \frac{2}{\pi} \int_0^\pi f(x) \cos(nx) \, dx = \frac{2}{\pi} \tilde{f}_C(n).$$

Then

$$f(x) = \frac{1}{\pi} \tilde{f}_C(0) + \frac{2}{\pi} \sum_{n=1}^\infty \tilde{f}_C(n) \cos(nx),$$

an inversion-type of expression from which we can recover $f(x)$ from the finite Fourier cosine transform of f.

By the same token, we can define a finite sine transform.

DEFINITION 15.8 *Finite Fourier Sine Transform*

The finite Fourier sine transform of f is defined by

$$\mathfrak{S}[f](n) = \tilde{f}_S(n) = \int_0^\pi f(x) \sin(nx) \, dx$$

for $n = 1, 2, \ldots$.

For $0 < x < \pi$, if f is continuous at x, then the sine series representation is

$$f(x) = \frac{2}{\pi} \sum_{n=1}^{\infty} \widetilde{f}_S(n) \sin(nx),$$

an inversion formula for the finite sine transform.

EXAMPLE 15.20

Let $f(x) = x^2$ for $0 \le x \le \pi$. For the finite cosine transform, compute

$$\widetilde{f}_C(0) = \int_0^{\pi} x^2 \, dx = \frac{1}{3} \pi^3$$

and, for $n = 1, 2, \ldots$,

$$\widetilde{f}_C(n) = \int_0^{\pi} x^2 \cos(nx) \, dx = 2\pi \frac{(-1)^n}{n^2}.$$

For the finite sine transform, compute

$$\widetilde{f}_S(n) = \int_0^{\pi} x^2 \sin(nx) \, dx = \frac{(-1)^n [2 - n^2 \pi^2] - 2}{n^3}. \quad \blacksquare$$

Here are the fundamental operational rules for these transforms.

THEOREM 15.15   *Operational Rules*

Let f and f' be continuous on $[0, \pi]$, and let f'' be piecewise continuous. Then

1. $$\mathfrak{C}[f''](n) = -n^2 \widetilde{f}_C(n) - f'(0) + (-1)^n f'(\pi),$$

    for $n = 1, 2, \ldots$, and

2. $$\mathfrak{S}[f''](n) = -n^2 \widetilde{f}_S(n) + n f(0) - n(-1)^n f(\pi)$$

    for $n = 1, 2, \ldots$. $\quad \blacksquare$

We will see applications of these finite transforms when we discuss partial differential equations.

SECTION 15.6   PROBLEMS

In each of Problems 1 through 7, find the finite Fourier sine transform of the function.

1. K (any constant)

2. x

3. x^2

4. x^5

5. $\sin(ax)$

6. $\cos(ax)$

7. e^{-x}

In each of Problems 8 through 14, find the finite Fourier cosine transform of the function.

8. $f(x) = \begin{cases} 1 & \text{for } 0 \le x < \dfrac{1}{2} \\ -1 & \text{for } \dfrac{1}{2} \le x \le \pi \end{cases}$

9. x

10. x^2

11. x^3

12. $\cosh(ax)$

13. $\sin(ax)$

14. e^{-x}

15. Suppose f is continuous on $[0, \pi]$ and f' is piecewise continuous. Prove that

$$(\widetilde{f'})_S(n) = -n\widetilde{f}_C(n)$$

for $n = 1, 2, \ldots$.

16. Let f be continuous and f' piecewise continuous on $[0, \pi]$. Prove that

$$(\widetilde{f'})_c(n) = n\widetilde{f}_S(n) - f(0) + (-1)^n f(\pi)$$

for $n = 0, 1, 2, \ldots$.

15.7 The Discrete Fourier Transform

If f has period p, its complex Fourier series is

$$\sum_{k=-\infty}^{\infty} d_k e^{ik\omega_0 t}.$$

Here $\omega_0 = 2\pi/p$ and the complex Fourier coefficients are given by

$$d_k = \frac{1}{p} \int_{\alpha}^{\alpha+p} f(t) e^{-ik\omega_0 t} \, dt,$$

in which, because of the periodicity of f, α can be any number. If we substitute the value of ω_0, the complex Fourier series of f is

$$\sum_{k=-\infty}^{\infty} d_k e^{2\pi ikt/p}.$$

Under certain conditions on f, this series converges to $\frac{1}{2}(f(t+) + f(t-))$ at any number t.

We will choose $\alpha = 0$ in the formula for the coefficients, so

$$d_k = \frac{1}{p} \int_{0}^{p} f(t) e^{-2\pi ikt/p} \, dt \text{ for } n = 0, \pm 1, \pm 2, \ldots.$$

To motivate the definition of the discrete Fourier transform, suppose we want to approximate d_k. One way is to subdivide $[0, p]$ into N subintervals of equal length p/N, and choose a point t_j in each $[jp/N, (j+1)p/N]$ for $j = 0, 1, \ldots, N-1$. Now approximate d_k by a Riemann sum:

$$d_k \approx \frac{1}{p} \sum_{j=0}^{N-1} f\left(t_j\right) e^{-2\pi ikt_j/p} \frac{p}{N}$$

$$= \frac{1}{N} \sum_{j=0}^{N-1} f\left(t_j\right) e^{-2\pi ikj/N}. \tag{15.16}$$

The N-point Fourier transform is a rule that acts on a given sequence of N complex numbers and produces an infinite sequence of complex numbers, one for each integer k (although with periodic repetitions, as we will see later). We will define the transform in such a way that, except for the $1/N$ factor, the approximating sum 15.16 is exactly the N-point discrete Fourier transform of the numbers $f(t_0), f(t_1), \cdots, f(t_{N-1})$.

DEFINITION 15.9 *N-Point Discrete Fourier Transform*

Let N be a positive integer. Let $u = \{u_j\}_{j=0}^{N-1}$ be a sequence of N complex numbers. Then the N-point discrete Fourier transform of u is the sequence $\mathbb{D}[u]$ defined by

$$\mathbb{D}[u](k) = \sum_{j=0}^{N-1} u_j e^{-2\pi ijk/N}$$

for $k = 0, \pm 1, \pm 2, \ldots$.

To simplify the notation, we will use a convention used with the Laplace transform and denote the N-point discrete Fourier transform of a sequence u by U (lower case for the given sequence of N numbers, upper case of the same letter for its N-point discrete Fourier transform). In this notation, if $u = \{u_j\}_{j=0}^{N-1}$, then

$$U_k = \sum_{j=0}^{N-1} u_j e^{-2\pi ijk/N}.$$

We will also abbreviate the phrase "discrete Fourier transform" to DFT.

EXAMPLE 15.21

Consider the constant sequence $u = \{c\}_{j=0}^{N-1}$, in which c is complex number. The N-point DFT is given by

$$U_k = \sum_{j=0}^{N-1} c e^{-2\pi ijk/N} = c \sum_{j=0}^{N-1} \left(e^{-2\pi ik/N}\right)^j.$$

Now recall that the sum of a finite geometric series is

$$\sum_{j=0}^{N-1} r^j = \frac{1 - r^N}{1 - r}. \tag{15.17}$$

Applying this to U_k, we have

$$U_k = c \frac{1 - \left(e^{-2\pi ik/N}\right)^N}{1 - e^{-2\pi ik/N}}$$

$$= c \frac{1 - e^{-2\pi ik}}{1 - e^{-2\pi ik/N}} = 0 \text{ for } k = 0, \pm 1, \pm 2, \ldots$$

because, for any integer k,

$$e^{-2\pi ik} = \cos(2\pi k) - i\sin(2\pi k) = 1.$$

For any positive integer N, the N-point DFT of a constant sequence of N numbers, is an infinite sequence of zeros. In more relaxed terms, the N-point DFT of a constant sequence is zero. ∎

EXAMPLE 15.22

Let a be a complex number and N a positive integer. To avoid trivialities, suppose a is not an integer multiple of π. We will find the N-point DFT of the sequence $u = \{\sin(ja)\}_{j=0}^{N-1}$. Denoting this transform by the upper case letter, we have

$$U_k = \sum_{j=0}^{N-1} \sin(ja) e^{-2\pi ijk/N}.$$

Use the fact that

$$\sin(ja) = \frac{1}{2i}\left(e^{ija} - e^{-ija}\right)$$

to write

$$U_k = \frac{1}{2i}\sum_{j=0}^{N-1} e^{ija} e^{-2\pi ijk/N} - \frac{1}{2i}\sum_{j=0}^{N-1} e^{-ija} e^{-2\pi ijk/N}$$

$$= \frac{1}{2i}\sum_{j=0}^{N-1}\left(e^{ia-2\pi ik/N}\right)^j - \frac{1}{2i}\sum_{j=0}^{N-1}\left(e^{-ia-2\pi ik/N}\right)^j.$$

Upon using equation (15.17) on each sum, we have

$$U_k = \frac{1}{2i}\frac{1-\left(e^{ia-2\pi ik/N}\right)^N}{1-e^{ia-2\pi ik/N}} - \frac{1}{2i}\frac{1-\left(e^{-ia-2\pi ik/N}\right)^N}{1-e^{-ia-2\pi ik/N}}$$

$$= \frac{1}{2i}\frac{1-e^{iaN}e^{-2\pi ik}}{1-e^{ia-2\pi ik/N}} - \frac{1}{2i}\frac{1-e^{-iaN}e^{-2\pi ik}}{1-e^{-ia-2\pi ik/N}}$$

$$= \frac{1}{2i}\frac{1-e^{iaN}}{1-e^{ia-2\pi ik/N}} - \frac{1}{2i}\frac{1-e^{-iaN}}{1-e^{-ia-2\pi ik/N}}, \qquad (15.18)$$

since $e^{-2\pi ik} = 1$.

To make the example more explicit, suppose $N = 5$ and $a = \sqrt{2}$. Then the given sequence u is

$$u_0 = 0, \quad u_1 = \sin(\sqrt{2}), \quad u_2 = \sin(2\sqrt{2}), \quad u_3 = \sin(3\sqrt{2}), \quad u_4 = \sin(4\sqrt{2}).$$

The 5-point DFT U has k^{th} term

$$U_k = \frac{1}{2i}\frac{1-e^{5i\sqrt{2}}}{1-e^{i\sqrt{2}-2\pi ik/5}} - \frac{1}{2i}\frac{1-e^{-5i\sqrt{2}}}{1-e^{-i\sqrt{2}-2\pi ik/5}}.$$

For example,

$$U_0 = \frac{1}{2i}\frac{1-e^{5i\sqrt{2}}}{1-e^{i\sqrt{2}}} - \frac{1}{2i}\frac{1-e^{-5i\sqrt{2}}}{1-e^{-i\sqrt{2}}}$$

$$= \frac{\sin(4\sqrt{2})+\sin(\sqrt{2})-\sin(5\sqrt{2})}{2-2\cos(\sqrt{2})},$$

$$U_1 = \frac{1}{2i}\frac{1-e^{5i\sqrt{2}}}{1-e^{i\sqrt{2}-2\pi i/5}} - \frac{1}{2i}\frac{1-e^{-5i\sqrt{2}}}{1-e^{-i\sqrt{2}-2\pi i/5}}$$

and

$$U_2 = \frac{1}{2i}\frac{1-e^{5i\sqrt{2}}}{1-e^{i\sqrt{2}-4\pi i/5}} - \frac{1}{2i}\frac{1-e^{-5i\sqrt{2}}}{1-e^{-i\sqrt{2}-4\pi i/5}}. \quad \blacksquare$$

We will develop some properties of this transform.

15.7.1   Linearity and Periodicity

If $u = \{u_j\}_{j=0}^{N-1}$ and $v = \{v_j\}_{j=0}^{N-1}$ are sequences of complex numbers, and a and b are complex numbers, then

$$au + bv = \{au_j + bv_j\}_{j=0}^{N-1}.$$

Linearity of the N-point DFT is the property:

$$\mathbb{D}[au + bv](k) = aU_k + bV_k.$$

This follows immediately from the definition of the transform, since

$$\mathbb{D}[au + bv](k) = \sum_{j=0}^{N-1}(au_j + bv_j)e^{-2\pi ijk/N}$$

$$= a\sum_{j=0}^{N-1}u_je^{-2\pi ijk/N} + b\sum_{j=0}^{N-1}v_je^{-2\pi ijk/N} = aU_k + bV_k.$$

Next we will show that the N-point DFT is periodic of period N. This means that, if the given sequence is $u = \{u_j\}_{j=0}^{N-1}$, then for any integer k,

$$U_{k+N} = U_k.$$

This can be seen in the DFT calculated in Example 15.22. In equation (15.18), replace k by $k+N$. In this example, this change shows up only in the term $e^{ia-2\pi ik/N}$ in the denominator. But, if k is replaced by $k+N$ in this exponential, no change results, since

$$e^{ia-2\pi i(k+N)/N} = e^{ia}e^{-2\pi ik}e^{-2\pi i} = e^{ia}e^{-2\pi ik} = e^{ia-2\pi ik}.$$

The argument in general proceeds as follows:

$$U_{k+N} = \sum_{j=0}^{N-1}u_je^{-2\pi ij(k+N)/N}$$

$$= \sum_{j=0}^{N-1}u_je^{-2\pi ijk/N}e^{-2\pi ijk} = \sum_{j=0}^{N-1}u_je^{-2\pi ijk/N} = U_k,$$

since $e^{-2\pi ijk} = 1$.

15.7.2   The Inverse N-Point DFT

Suppose we have an N-point DFT

$$U_k = \sum_{j=0}^{N-1}u_je^{-2\pi ijk/N}$$

of a sequence $\{u_j\}_{j=0}^{N-1}$ of N numbers. We claim that

$$u_j = \frac{1}{N}\sum_{k=0}^{N-1}U_ke^{2\pi ijk/N} \quad \text{for } j = 0, 1, \ldots, N-1. \tag{15.19}$$

Because this expression retrieves the original N-point sequence from its discrete transform, equation (15.19) is called the *inverse N-point discrete Fourier transform*.

To verify equation (15.19), it is convenient to put $W = e^{-2\pi i/N}$. Then

$$W^N = 1 \quad \text{and} \quad W^{-1} = e^{2\pi i/N}.$$

Now write

$$\frac{1}{N} \sum_{k=0}^{N-1} U_k e^{2\pi ijk/N} = \frac{1}{N} \sum_{k=0}^{N-1} U_k W^{-jk}$$

$$= \frac{1}{N} \sum_{k=0}^{N-1} \left(\sum_{r=0}^{N-1} u_r e^{-2\pi irk/N} \right) W^{-jk} = \frac{1}{N} \sum_{k=0}^{N-1} \sum_{r=0}^{N-1} u_r W^{rk} W^{-jk}$$

$$= \frac{1}{N} \sum_{r=0}^{N-1} u_r \sum_{k=0}^{N-1} W^{rk} W^{-jk}. \tag{15.20}$$

In the last summation, observe that

$$W^{rk} W^{-jk} = e^{-2\pi irk/N} e^{2\pi ijk/N} = e^{-2\pi(r-j)k/N} = W^{(r-j)k}.$$

For given j, if $r \neq j$, then by equation (15.17) for the finite sum of a geometric series,

$$\sum_{k=0}^{N-1} W^{rk} W^{-jk} = \sum_{k=0}^{N-1} W^{(r-j)k} = \sum_{k=0}^{N-1} (W^{r-j})^k = \frac{1 - (W^{r-j})^N}{1 - W^{r-j}} = 0$$

because $(W^{(r-j)})^N = e^{-2\pi i(r-j)} = 1$ and $W^{r-j} = e^{-2\pi i(r-j)/N} \neq 1$. But if $r = j$, then

$$\sum_{k=0}^{N-1} W^{rk} W^{-jk} = \sum_{k=0}^{N-1} W^{jk} W^{-jk} = \sum_{k=0}^{N-1} 1 = N.$$

Therefore, in the last double sum in equation (15.20), we need retain only the term when $r = j$ in the summation with respect to r, yielding

$$\frac{1}{N} \sum_{r=0}^{N-1} u_r \sum_{k=0}^{N-1} W^{rk} W^{-jk} = \frac{1}{N} u_j \sum_{k=0}^{N-1} W^{jk} W^{-jk} = \frac{1}{N} u_j N = u_j,$$

and verifying equation (15.19).

15.7.3 DFT Approximation of Fourier Coefficients

We began this section by defining the N-point DFT so that Riemann sums approximating the Fourier coefficients of a periodic function were $1/N$ times the N-point DFT of the sequence of function values at partition points of the interval. We will now pursue more closely the idea of approximating Fourier coefficients by a discrete Fourier transform, with the idea of sampling partial sums of Fourier series. This approximation also allows the application of DFT software to the approximation of Fourier coefficients.

We will consider a specific example, $f(t) = \sin(t)$ for $0 \leq t < 4$, with the understanding that f is extended over the entire real line with period 4. A graph of part of f is shown in Figure 15.21. With $p = 4$, the Fourier coefficients are

$$d_k = \frac{1}{4} \int_0^4 \sin(\xi) e^{-2\pi ik\xi/4} d\xi = \frac{1}{4} \int_0^4 \sin(\xi) e^{-\pi ik\xi/2} d\xi$$

$$= \frac{\cos(4) - 1}{\pi^2 k^2 - 4} + \frac{1}{2} i \frac{\pi k \sin(4)}{\pi^2 k^2 - 4}. \tag{15.21}$$

for $k = 0, \pm 1, \pm 2, \ldots$.

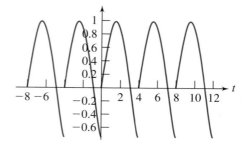

FIGURE 15.21 $f(t) = \sin(t)$ for $0 \le t < 4$, *extended periodically over the real line.*

Now let N be a positive integer and subdivide $[0,4]$ into N subintervals of equal length $4/N$. These subintervals are $[4j/N, 4(j+1)/N]$ for $j = 0, 1, \ldots, N-1$. Form N numbers by evaluating $f(t)$ at the left end point of each of these subintervals. These points are $4j/N$, so we obtain the N-point sequence

$$u = \left\{ \sin\left(\frac{4j}{N}\right) \right\}_{j=0}^{N-1}.$$

Form the N-point DFT of this sequence:

$$U_k = \sum_{j=0}^{N-1} \sin\left(\frac{4j}{N}\right) e^{-2\pi ijk/4} = \sum_{j=0}^{N-1} \sin\left(\frac{4j}{N}\right) e^{-\pi ijk/2}.$$

Then

$$\frac{1}{N} U_k = \frac{1}{N} \sum_{j=0}^{N-1} \sin\left(\frac{4j}{N}\right) e^{-\pi ijk/2}$$

is a Riemann sum for the integral defining d_k. We ask: to what extent does $(1/N)U_k$ approximate d_k? In this example we have an explicit expression (15.21) for d_k. We will explicitly evaluate $(1/N)U_k$, using $a = 4/N$ in the DFT of $\{\sin(ja)\}_{j=0}^{N-1}$ determined in Example 15.22 This gives us

$$\frac{1}{N} U_k = \frac{1}{N} \left[\frac{1}{2i} \frac{1 - e^{4i}}{1 - e^{4i/N - 2k\pi i/N}} - \frac{1}{2i} \frac{1 - e^{-4i}}{1 - e^{-4i/N - 2k\pi i/N}} \right].$$

Now approximate the exponential terms in the denominator by using the approximation

$$e^x \approx 1 + x$$

for $|x| << 1$. Then

$$\frac{1}{N} U_k \approx \frac{1}{N} \left[\frac{1}{2i} \frac{1 - e^{4i}}{1 - [1 + (4i/N - 2k\pi i/N)]} - \frac{1}{2i} \frac{1 - e^{-4i}}{1 - [1 + (-4i/N - 2k\pi i/N)]} \right]$$

$$= -\frac{1}{4} \left[\frac{1 - e^{4i}}{-2 + k\pi} - \frac{1 - e^{-4i}}{2 + k\pi} \right]$$

$$= -\frac{1}{4} \frac{1}{\pi^2 k^2 - 4} \left[4 - \pi k(e^{4i} - e^{-4i}) - 2(e^{4i} + e^{-4i}) \right]$$

$$= -\frac{1}{4}\frac{1}{\pi^2 k^2 - 4}[4 - 2\pi ki\sin(4) - 4\cos(4)]$$

$$= \frac{\cos(4) - 1}{\pi^2 k^2 - 4} + \frac{1}{2}i\frac{\pi k \sin(4)}{\pi^2 k^2 - 4}.$$

The approximation $e^x \approx 1 + x$ has therefore led to an approximate expression for $(1/N)U_k$ that is exactly equal to d_k. This approximation cannot be valid for all k, however. First, the approximation used for e^x assumes that $|x| << 1$, and second, the N-point DFT is periodic of period N, so $U_{k+N} = U_k$, while there is no such periodicity in the $d_k's$.

In general it would be very difficult to derive an estimate on relative sizes of $|k|$ and N that would result in $(1/N)U_k$ approximating d_k to within a given tolerance, and which would hold for a reasonable class of functions. However, for many science and engineering applications, the empirical rule $|k| \leq N/8$ has proved effective.

SECTION 15.7 PROBLEMS

In each of Problems 1 through 6, compute $\mathbb{D}[u](k)$ for $k = 0, \pm1, \ldots, \pm4$ for the given sequence u.

1. $\{\cos(j)\}_{j=0}^5$

2. $\{e^{ij}\}_{j=0}^5$

3. $\{1/(j+1)\}_{j=0}^5$

4. $\{1/(j+1)^2\}_{j=0}^5$

5. $\{j^2\}_{j=0}^5$

6. $\{\cos(j) - \sin(j)\}_{j=0}^4$

In each of 7 through 12, a sequence $\{U_k\}_{k=0}^N$ is given. Determine the N-point inverse discrete Fourier transform of this sequence.

7. $U_k = (1+i)^k, N = 6$

8. $U_k = i^{-k}, N = 5$

9. $U_k = e^{-ik}, N = 7$

10. $U_k = k^2, N = 5$

11. $U_k = \cos(k), N = 5$

12. $U_k = \ln(k+1), N = 6$

In each of Problems 13 through 16, compute the first seven complex Fourier coefficients $d_0, d_{\pm1}, d_{\pm2}$ and $d_{\pm3}$ of f (see Section 14.7). Then use the DFT to approximate these coefficients, with $N = 128$.

13. $f(t) = \cos(t)$ for $0 \leq t \leq 2$, f has period 2

14. $f(t) = e^{-t}$ for $0 \leq t \leq 3$, f has period 3

15. $f(t) = t^2$ for $0 \leq t \leq 1$, f has period 1

16. $f(t) = te^{2t}$ for $0 \leq t \leq 4$, f has period 4

15.8 Sampled Fourier Series

In the preceding subsection we discussed approximation of Fourier coefficients of a periodic function f. This was done by approximating terms of an N-point discrete Fourier transform formed by sampling $f(t)$ at N points of $[0, p]$. We will now discuss the use of an inverse DFT to approximate sampled partial sums of the Fourier series of a periodic function (that is, partial sums evaluated at chosen points).

Consider the partial sum

$$S_M(t) = \sum_{k=-M}^M d_k e^{2\pi ikt/p}.$$

Subdivide $[0, p]$ into N subintervals, and choose sample points $t_j = jp/N$ for $j = 0, 1, \ldots, N-1$.

Form the N-point sequence $u = \{f(jp/N)\}_{j=0}^{N-1}$ and approximate

$$d_k \approx \frac{1}{N} U_k,$$

where

$$U_k = \sum_{j=0}^{N-1} f(jp/N) e^{-2\pi ijk/N}$$

In order to have $|k| \leq N/8$, as mentioned at the end of the preceding subsection, we will require that $M \leq N/8$. Thus,

$$S_M(t) \approx \sum_{k=-M}^{M} \frac{1}{N} U_k e^{2\pi ikt/p}.$$

In particular, if we sample this partial sum at the partition points jp/N, then

$$S_M(jp/N) \approx \frac{1}{N} \sum_{k=-M}^{M} U_k e^{2\pi ijk/N}.$$

We will show that the sum on the right is actually an N-point inverse DFT for a particular N-point sequence, which we will now determine. We will exploit the periodicity of the N-point DFT—that is, $U_{k+N} = U_k$ for all integers k. Write

$$S_M(jp/N) \approx \frac{1}{N} \sum_{k=-M}^{-1} U_k e^{2\pi ijk/N} + \frac{1}{N} \sum_{k=0}^{M} U_k e^{2\pi ijk/N}$$

$$= \frac{1}{N} \sum_{k=1}^{M} U_{-k} e^{-2\pi ijk/N} + \frac{1}{N} \sum_{k=0}^{M} U_k e^{2\pi ijk/N}$$

$$= \frac{1}{N} \sum_{k=1}^{M} U_{-k+N} e^{2\pi ij(-k+N)/N} + \frac{1}{N} \sum_{k=0}^{M} U_k e^{2\pi ijk/N}$$

$$= \frac{1}{N} \sum_{k=N-M}^{N-1} U_k e^{2\pi ijk/N} + \frac{1}{N} \sum_{k=0}^{M} U_k e^{2\pi ijk/N}. \tag{15.22}$$

In these summations, we use the $2M+1$ numbers

$$U_{N-M}, \ldots, U_{N-1}, U_0, \ldots, U_M.$$

Since $M < N/8$, we must fill in other values to obtain an N-point sequence. One way to do this is to fill in the other places with zeros. Thus define

$$V_k = \begin{cases} U_k & \text{for } k = 0, 1, \ldots M \\ 0 & \text{for } k = M+1, \ldots, N-M-1 \\ U_k & \text{for } k = N-M, \ldots, N-1 \end{cases}.$$

Then the Mth partial sum of the Fourier series of f, sampled at jp/N, is approximated by

$$S_M(jp/N) \approx \frac{1}{N} \sum_{k=0}^{N-1} V_k e^{2\pi ijk/N}.$$

EXAMPLE 15.23

Let $f(x) = t$ for $0 \leq t < 2$, and extend f over the entire real line with period 2. Part of the graph of f is shown in Figure 15.22.

The Fourier coefficients of f are

$$d_k = \frac{1}{2} \int_0^2 te^{-2\pi ikt/2}\,dt = \begin{cases} \frac{i}{\pi k} & \text{for } k \neq 0 \\ 1 & \text{for } k = 0 \end{cases}.$$

and the complex Fourier series is

$$1 + \sum_{k=-\infty, k\neq 0}^{\infty} \frac{i}{\pi k}e^{\pi ikt}.$$

This converges to t on $0 < t < 2$ and on periodic extensions of this interval. The Mth partial sum is

$$S_M(t) = 1 + \sum_{k=-M, k\neq 0}^{M} \frac{i}{\pi k}e^{\pi ikt}.$$

To be specific, choose $N = 2^7 = 128$ and $M = 10$, so $M \leq N/8$. Sample the partial sum at points $jp/N = j/64$ for $j = 0, 1, \ldots, 127$. Then

$$u = \left\{ f\left(\frac{jp}{N}\right) \right\}_{j=0}^{N-1} = \left\{ \frac{j}{64} \right\}_{j=0}^{127}.$$

The 128-point DFT of u has k^{th} term

$$U_k = \sum_{j=0}^{127} \frac{j}{64}e^{-\pi ijk/64}.$$

Define

$$V_k = \begin{cases} U_k & \text{for } k = 0, 1, \ldots 10 \\ 0 & \text{for } k = 11, \ldots, 117 \\ U_k & \text{for } k = 118, \ldots, 127. \end{cases}$$

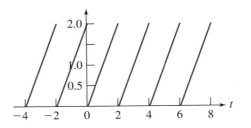

FIGURE 15.22 $f(t) = t$ *for* $0 \leq t < 2$, *periodically extended over the real line.*

Then

$$S_{10}(jp/N) = S_{10}(j/64) = 1 + \sum_{k=-10, k\neq 0}^{10} \frac{i}{\pi k} e^{\pi ijk/64}$$

$$\approx \frac{1}{128} \sum_{k=0}^{127} V_k e^{\pi ijk/64}. \tag{15.23}$$

In understanding this discussion of approximation of sampled partial sums of a Fourier series, it is worthwhile to see the numbers actually play out in an example. We will do the computation $S_{10}(1/2)$, and then of the approximation (15.23) with $j = 32$.

First,

$$S_{10}(1/2) = 1 + \sum_{k=-10, k\neq 0}^{10} \frac{i}{\pi k} e^{\pi ik/2} = .45847.$$

Now we must compute the $V_k's$. For these, we need the numbers

$$U_0 = \sum_{j=0}^{127} \frac{j}{64} = 127, U_1 = \sum_{j=0}^{127} \frac{j}{64} e^{-\pi ij/64} = -1.0 + 40.735i,$$

$$U_2 = \sum_{j=0}^{127} \frac{j}{64} e^{-\pi ij/32} = -1.0 + 20.355i, U_3 = -1.0 + 13.557i,$$

$$U_4 = -1.0 + 10.153i, U_5 = -1.0 + 8.1078i, U_6 = -1.0 + 6.7415i,$$

$$U_7 = -1.0 + 5.7631i, U_8 = -1.0 + 5.0273i, U_9 = -1.0 + 4.4532i,$$

$$U_{10} = -1.0 + 3.9922i, U_{118} = -1.0 - 3.9922i, U_{119} = -1.0 - 4.4532i,$$

$$U_{120} = -1.0 - 5.0273i, U_{121} = -1.0 - 5.7631i, U_{122} = -1.0 - 6.7415i,$$

$$U_{123} = -1.0 - 8.1078i, U_{124} = -1.0 - 10.153i, U_{125} = -1.0 - 13.557i,$$

$$U_{126} = -1.0 - 20.355i, U_{127} = -1.0 - 40.735i.$$

Now compute

$$\sum_{k=0}^{127} V_k e^{\pi ik/2} = 127 + (-1.0 + 40.735i)e^{\pi i/2} + (-1.0 + 20.355i) e^{\pi i}$$

$$+ (-1.0 + 13.557i) e^{3\pi i/2} + (-1.0 + 10.153i) e^{2\pi i} + (-1.0 + 8.1078i) e^{5\pi i/2}$$

$$+ (-1.0 + 6.7415i) e^{3\pi i} + (-1.0 + 5.7631i) e^{7\pi i/2} + (-1.0 + 5.0273i) e^{4\pi i}$$

$$+ (-1.0 + 4.4532i) e^{9\pi i/2} + (-1.0 + 3.9922i) e^{5\pi i}$$

$$+ (-1.0 - 3.9922i) e^{118\pi i/2} + (-1.0 - 4.4532i) e^{119\pi i/2} + (-1.0 - 5.0273i) e^{120\pi i/2}$$

$$+ (-1.0 - 5.7631i) e^{121\pi i/2} + (-1.0 - 6.7415i) e^{122\pi i/2} + (-1.0 - 8.1078i) e^{123\pi i/2}$$

$$+ (-1.0 - 10.153i) e^{124\pi i/2} + (-1.0 - 13.557i) e^{125\pi i/2} + (-1.0 - 20.355i) e^{126\pi i/2}$$

$$+ (-1.0 - 40.735i) e^{127\pi i/2}$$

$$= 61.04832.$$

Then

$$\frac{1}{128} \sum_{k=0}^{127} V_k e^{\pi i j k/64} = .47694.$$

This gives the 128-point DFT approximation 0.47694 to the sampled partial sum $S_{10}\left(\frac{1}{2}\right)$, which we computed to be 0.45847. The difference is 0.0185. The actual sum of the complex Fourier series at $t = \frac{1}{2}$ is $f\left(\frac{1}{2}\right) = 0.50000$.

In practice, we would obtain greater accuracy by using much larger N (allowing larger M), and a software routine to do the computations. ∎

15.8.1   Approximation of a Fourier Transform by an N-Point DFT

We will show how the discrete Fourier transform can be used to approximate the Fourier transform of a function, under certain conditions. Suppose, to begin, that $\hat{f}(\omega)$ can be approximated to within some acceptable tolerance by an integral over a finite interval:

$$\hat{f}(\omega) = \int_{-\infty}^{\infty} f(\xi) e^{-i\omega\xi} d\xi \approx \int_0^{2\pi L} f(\xi) e^{-i\omega\xi} d\xi.$$

Here we have written the length of the interval as $2\pi L$ for a reason that will reveal itself shortly. Subdivide $[0, 2\pi L]$ into N subintervals of length $2\pi L/N$ and choose partition points $\xi_j = 2\pi j L/N$ for $j = 0, 1, \ldots N$. We can then approximate the integral on the right by a Riemann sum, obtaining

$$\hat{f}(\omega) \approx \sum_{j=0}^{N-1} f(2\pi j L/N) e^{-2\pi i j L\omega/N} \left(\frac{2\pi L}{N}\right)$$

$$= \frac{2\pi L}{N} \sum_{j=0}^{N-1} f(2\pi j L/N) e^{-2\pi i j L\omega/N}.$$

The sum on the right is nearly in the form of a DFT. If we put $\omega = k/L$, with k any integer, then we have

$$\hat{f}(k/L) \approx \frac{2\pi L}{N} \sum_{j=0}^{N-1} f(2\pi j L/N) e^{-2\pi i j k/N}. \tag{15.24}$$

This gives $\hat{f}(k/L)$, the Fourier transform of f sampled at points k/L, approximated by $2\pi L/N$ times the N-point DFT of the sequence

$$\left\{ f\left(\frac{2\pi j L}{N}\right) \right\}_{j=0}^{N-1}.$$

As noted previously, the DFT is periodic of period N, while $\hat{f}(k/L)$ is not, so we again make the restriction that $|k| \leq N/8$.

EXAMPLE 15.24

We will test the approximation (15.24) for a simple case. Let

$$f(t) = \begin{cases} e^{-t} & \text{for } t \geq 0 \\ 0 & \text{for } t < 0 \end{cases}.$$

Then f has Fourier transform

$$\hat{f}(\omega) = \int_{-\infty}^{\infty} f(\xi)e^{-i\omega\xi}\,d\xi$$

$$= \int_{0}^{\infty} e^{-\xi}e^{-i\omega\xi}\,d\xi = \frac{1-i\omega}{1+\omega^2}.$$

Choose $L = 1$, $N = 2^7 = 128$ and $k = 3$ (keep in mind that we want $|k| \leq N/8$). Now $k/L = 3$ and

$$\hat{f}(k/L) = \hat{f}(3) \approx \frac{2\pi}{128} \sum_{j=0}^{127} e^{-\pi j/64} e^{-6\pi ij/128}$$

$$= \frac{\pi}{64} \sum_{j=0}^{127} e^{-\pi j/64} e^{-3\pi ij/64} = 0.124\,51 - 0.298\,84i.$$

For comparison,

$$\hat{f}(3) = \frac{1-3i}{10} = 0.1 - 0.3i.$$

Suppose we try a larger N, say $N = 2^9 = 512$. Now

$$\hat{f}(3) \approx \frac{2\pi}{512} \sum_{j=0}^{511} e^{-2\pi j/512} e^{-6\pi ij/512}$$

$$= \frac{\pi}{256} \sum_{j=0}^{511} e^{-\pi j/256} e^{-3\pi ij/256} = 0.105\,95 - 0.299\,4i,$$

a better approximation than obtained with $N = 128$. ∎

EXAMPLE 15.25

We will continue from the preceding example. There the emphasis was on detailing the idea of approximating a value of $\hat{f}(\omega)$. Now we will use the same function, but carry out the approximation at enough points to sketch approximate graphs of $\text{Re}[\hat{f}(\omega)]$, $\text{Im}[\hat{f}(\omega)]$ and $|\hat{f}(\omega)|$. Using $L = 4$ and $N = 2^8 = 256$, we obtain the approximation

$$\hat{f}(k/4) \approx \frac{\pi}{32} \sum_{j=0}^{255} e^{-\pi j/32} e^{-\pi ijk/128}.$$

We should have $|k| \le N/8 = 32$, although we will only compute approximate values of $\hat{f}(k/4)$ for $k = 1, \ldots, 13$. Because in this example we can compute $\hat{f}(\omega)$ exactly, these values are included in the table to allow comparison.

	DFT approx. of $\hat{f}(\omega)$	$\hat{f}(\omega)$
$(k = 1) \ \hat{f}(\frac{1}{4})$	$.99107 - .23509i$	$.94118 - .23529i$
$(k = 2) \ \hat{f}(\frac{1}{2})$	$.84989 - .3996i$	$.8 - .4i$
$(k = 3) \ \hat{f}(\frac{3}{4})$	$.68989 - .4794i$	$.64 - .48i$
$(k = 4) \ \hat{f}(1)$	$.54989 - .4992i$	$.5 - .5i$
$(k = 5) \ \hat{f}(\frac{5}{4})$	$.44013 - .4868i$	$.39024 - .4878i$
$(k = 6) \ f(\frac{3}{2})$	$0.35758 - 0.46033i$	$0.3077 - 0.4615i$
$(k = 7) \ \hat{f}(\frac{7}{4})$	$.29605 - .42936i$	$.24615 - .43077i$
$(k = 8) \ \hat{f}(2)$	$.24989 - .39839i$	$.2 - .4i$
$(k = 9) \ \hat{f}(\frac{9}{4})$	$.21484 - .36933i$	$.16495 - .37113i$
$(k = 10) \ \hat{f}(\frac{5}{2})$	$.18782 - .34282i$	$.13793 - .34483i$
$(k = 11) \ \hat{f}(\frac{11}{4})$	$.16668 - .31896i$	$.11679 - .32117i$
$(k = 12) \ \hat{f}(3)$	$.14989 - .29759i$	$.1 - .3i$
$(k = 13) \ \hat{f}(\frac{13}{4})$	$.13638 - .27847i$	$.086486 - .28108i$

The real part of $\hat{f}(\omega)$ is consistently approximated in this scheme with an error of about .05, while the imaginary part is approximated in many cases with an error of about .002. Improved accuracy can be achieved by choosing N larger.

In Figures 15.23, 15.24 and 15.25, the approximate values of $\text{Re}[\hat{f}(\omega)]$, $\text{Im}[\hat{f}(\omega)]$ and $\left|\hat{f}(\omega)\right|$, respectively, are compared with the values obtained from the exact expression for $\hat{f}(\omega)$. The squares represent approximate values, and the dots are actual values. In Figure 15.24 the approximation is sufficiently close that the points are nearly indistinguishable (within the resolution of the diagram). ▩

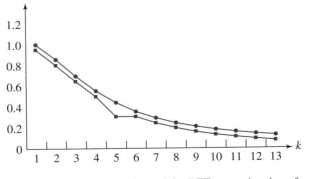

FIGURE 15.23 *Comparison of the DFT approximation of* $\text{Re}[\hat{f}(\omega)]$ *with actual values for*

$$f(t) = \begin{cases} e^{-t} & \text{for } t \ge 0 \\ 0 & \text{for } t < 0 \end{cases}.$$

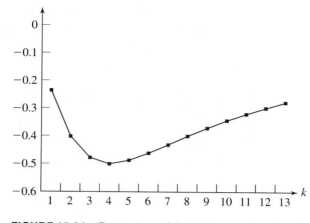

FIGURE 15.24 *Comparison of the DFT approximation of*
$\text{Im}[\hat{f}(\omega)]$ *with actual values for*
$$f(t) = \begin{cases} e^{-t} & \text{for } t \geq 0 \\ 0 & \text{for } t < 0 \end{cases}.$$

Thus far the discussion has centered on functions f for which $\hat{f}(\omega)$ can be approximated by an integral $\int_0^{2\pi L} f(\xi)e^{-i\omega\xi}\,d\xi$. We can extend this idea to the case that $\hat{f}(\omega)$ is approximated by an integral $\int_{-\pi L}^{\pi L} f(\xi)e^{-i\omega\xi}\,d\xi$, over a symmetric interval of length $2\pi L$:

$$\hat{f}(\omega) \approx \int_{-\pi L}^{\pi L} f(\xi)e^{-i\omega\xi}\,d\xi.$$

Then,

$$\hat{f}(k/L) \approx \int_{-\pi L}^{\pi L} f(\xi)e^{-ik\xi/L}\,d\xi$$
$$= \int_{-\pi L}^{0} f(\xi)e^{-ik\xi/L}\,d\xi + \int_{0}^{\pi L} f(\xi)e^{-ik\xi/L}\,d\xi.$$

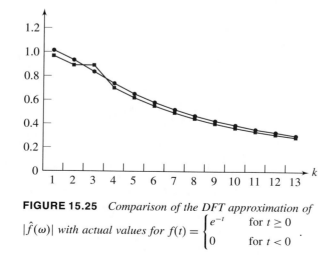

FIGURE 15.25 *Comparison of the DFT approximation of*
$|\hat{f}(\omega)|$ *with actual values for* $f(t) = \begin{cases} e^{-t} & \text{for } t \geq 0 \\ 0 & \text{for } t < 0 \end{cases}.$

Upon letting $\zeta = \xi + 2\pi L$ in the first integral of the last line, we have

$$\hat{f}(k/L) \approx \int_{\pi L}^{2\pi L} f(\zeta - 2\pi L)e^{-ik(\zeta - 2\pi L)/L}\,d\zeta + \int_0^{\pi L} f(\xi)e^{-ik\xi/L}\,d\xi$$

$$= \int_{\pi L}^{2\pi L} f(\zeta - 2\pi L)e^{-ik\zeta/L}\,d\zeta + \int_0^{\pi L} f(\xi)e^{-ik\xi/L}\,d\xi,$$

since $e^{-2\pi ik} = 1$ if k is an integer. Write ξ for ζ as variable of integration, obtaining

$$\hat{f}(k/L) = \int_{\pi L}^{2\pi L} f(\xi - 2\pi L)e^{-ik\xi/L}\,d\xi + \int_0^{\pi L} f(\xi)e^{-ik\xi/L}\,d\xi.$$

Now define

$$g(t) = \begin{cases} f(t) & \text{for } 0 \le t < \pi L \\ \frac{1}{2}(f(\pi L) + f(-\pi L)) & \text{for } t = \pi L \\ f(t - 2\pi L) & \text{for } \pi L < t \le 2\pi L \end{cases} \qquad (15.25)$$

Then

$$\hat{f}(k/L) \approx \int_0^{2\pi L} g(\xi)e^{-ik\xi/L}\,d\xi$$

$$= \int_0^L g(2\pi t)e^{-2\pi ikt/L}(2\pi)\,dt \quad (\text{let } \xi = 2\pi t)$$

$$= 2\pi \int_0^L g(2\pi t)e^{-2\pi ikt/L}.$$

Finally, approximate the last integral by a Riemann sum, subdividing $[0, L]$ into L/N subintervals and choosing $t_j = jL/N$ for $j = 0, 1, \ldots, N-1$. Then

$$\hat{f}\left(\frac{k}{L}\right) \approx \frac{2\pi L}{N} \sum_{j=0}^{N-1} g\left(\frac{2\pi jL}{N}\right) e^{-2\pi ijk/N}.$$

As before, we assume in using this approximation that $|k| \le N/8$. This approximates $\hat{f}(k/L)$ by a constant multiple of the $N-$ point DFT of the sequence

$$\left\{ g\left(\frac{2\pi jL}{N}\right) \right\}_{j=0}^{N-1}$$

in which points of the sequence are obtained from the function g manufactured from f according to equation (15.25).

15.8.2 Filtering

A periodic signal $f(t)$, of period $2L$, is often filtered for the purpose of cancelling out, or diminishing, certain unwanted effects, or perhaps for emphasizing certain effects one wants to study. Suppose $f(t)$ has complex Fourier series

$$\sum_{n=-\infty}^{\infty} d_n e^{n\pi it/L},$$

where

$$d_n = \frac{1}{2L} \int_{-L}^{L} f(t)e^{-n\pi it/L}\,dt.$$

Consider the Nth partial sum

$$S_N(t) = \sum_{j=-N}^{N} d_j e^{\pi i j t / L}.$$

A *filtered partial sum* of the Fourier series of f is a sum of the form

$$\sum_{j=-N}^{N} Z\left(\frac{j}{N}\right) d_j e^{\pi i j t / L}, \tag{15.26}$$

in which the filter function Z is a continuous, even function on $[-1, 1]$. In particular applications the object is to choose Z to serve some specific purpose. By way of introduction, we will illustrate filtering for a filter that actually forms a basic approach to the entire issue of convergence of Fourier series.

In the nineteenth century, there was an intense effort to understand the subtleties of convergence of Fourier series. An example of Du Bois-Reymond showed that it is possible for the Fourier series of a continuous function to diverge at every point. In the course of delving into the convergence question, it was observed that in many cases the sequence of averages of partial sums of a Fourier series is better behaved than the sequence of partial sums itself. This led to a consideration of averages of partial sums:

$$\sigma_N(t) = \frac{1}{N} \sum_{k=0}^{N-1} S_k(t) = \frac{1}{N} [S_0(t) + S_1(t) + \cdots + S_{N-1}(t)].$$

The quantity $\sigma_N(t)$ is called the Nth *Cesàro sum* of f, after the Italian mathematician who studied their properties. It was found that, if the partial sums of the Fourier series approach a particular limit at t, then $\sigma_N(t)$ must approach the same limit as $N \rightarrow \infty$, but not conversely. It is possible for the Cesàro sums to have a limit for some t, but for the Fourier series to diverge there. It was the 19-year-old prodigy Fejér who proved that, if f is periodic of period 2π, and $\int_0^{2\pi} f(t)\,dt$ exists, then $\sigma_N(t) \rightarrow f(t)$ wherever f is continuous. This is a stronger result than holds for the partial sums of the Fourier series.

With this as background, write

$$\sigma_N(t) = \frac{1}{N} \sum_{k=0}^{N-1} \left(\sum_{j=-k}^{k} d_j e^{\pi i j t / L} \right).$$

We leave it as an exercise for the student to show that the terms in this double sum can be rearranged to write

$$\sigma_N(t) = \sum_{n=-N}^{N} \left(1 - \left| \frac{n}{N} \right| \right) d_n e^{\pi i n t / L}.$$

This is of the form of equation 15.26 with the *Cesàro filter function*

$$Z(t) = 1 - |t| \quad \text{for} \ -1 \le t \le 1.$$

The sequence

$$\left\{ Z\left(\frac{n}{N}\right) \right\}_{n=-N}^{N} = \left\{ 1 - \left| \frac{n}{N} \right| \right\}_{n=-N}^{N}$$

is called the *sequence of filter factors for the Cesàro filter.*

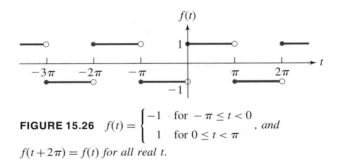

FIGURE 15.26 $f(t) = \begin{cases} -1 & \text{for } -\pi \le t < 0 \\ 1 & \text{for } 0 \le t < \pi \end{cases}$, *and*

$f(t+2\pi) = f(t)$ *for all real t.*

One effect of the Cesaro filter is to damp out the Gibbs phenomenon, which is seen in the convergence of the Fourier series of a function at a point of discontinuity. As an example that displays the Gibbs phenomenon very clearly, consider

$$f(t) = \begin{cases} -1 & \text{for } -\pi \le t < 0 \\ 1 & \text{for } 0 \le t < \pi \end{cases},$$

with periodic extension to the real line. Figure 15.26 shows a graph of this periodic extension. Its complex Fourier coefficients are

$$d_0 = \frac{1}{2\pi}\int_{-\pi}^{0} -1\,dt + \frac{1}{2\pi}\int_{0}^{\pi} dt = 0$$

and

$$d_n = \frac{1}{2\pi}\int_{-\pi}^{0} -e^{-nit}\,dt + \frac{1}{2\pi}\int_{0}^{\pi} e^{nit}\,dt = \frac{i}{\pi}\frac{-1+(-1)^n}{n}.$$

The Nth partial sum of this series is

$$S_N(t) = \sum_{n=-N, n\neq 0}^{N} \frac{i}{\pi}\frac{-1+(-1)^n}{n}e^{nit}.$$

If N is odd, then

$$S_N(t) = \frac{4}{\pi}\left(\sin(t) + \frac{1}{3}\sin(3t) + \frac{1}{5}\sin(5t) + \cdots + \frac{1}{N}\sin(Nt)\right).$$

The Nth Cesàro sum (with $L = \pi$) is

$$\sigma_N(t) = \sum_{n=-N}^{N} \left(1 - \left|\frac{n}{N}\right|\right)\frac{i}{\pi}\frac{-1+(-1)^n}{n}e^{int}.$$

This can be written

$$\sigma_N(t) = \sum_{n=1}^{N}\left(1 - \frac{n}{N}\right)\left(\frac{-2}{\pi}\right)\left(\frac{(-1)+(-1)^n}{n}\right)\sin(nt).$$

Figure 15.27 shows graphs of $S_{10}(t)$ and $\sigma_{10}(t)$, and Figure 15.28 shows graphs of $S_{20}(t)$ and $\sigma_{20}(t)$. In the partial sums $S_N(t)$, the Gibbs phenomenon is readily apparent near $t = 0$, where f has a jump discontinuity. Even though $S_N(t) \to f(t)$ for $0 < t < \pi$ and for $-\pi < t < 0$, the graphs of $S_N(t)$ have relatively high peaks near zero which remain at nearly constant height even as N increases (although these peaks move toward the vertical axis as N increases). However, this phenomenon is not seen in the graphs of $\sigma_N(t)$, which accelerates and "smooths out" the convergence of the Fourier series.

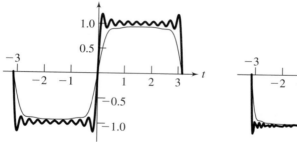

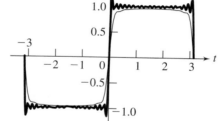

FIGURE 15.27 $S_{10}(t)$ and $\sigma_{10}(t)$ for the function of Figure 15.26.

FIGURE 15.28 $S_{20}(t)$ and $\sigma_{20}(t)$ for the function of Figure 15.26.

The Cesáro filter also damps the effects of the higher frequency terms in the Fourier series, because the Cesáro filter factor $1 - |n/N|$ tends to zero as n increases toward N. This effect is also seen in the graphs of the Cesáro sums.

There are many filters that are used in signal analysis. Two of the more commonly encountered ones are the Hamming and Gauss filters. The *Hamming filter* is named for Richard Hamming, who was for many years a senior scientist and researcher at Bell Labs. It is given by

$$Z(t) = .54 + .46\cos(\pi t).$$

The filtered N^{th} partial sum of the complex Fourier series of f, using the Hamming filter, is

$$\sum_{n=-N}^{N} (.54 + .46\cos(\pi n/N)) \, d_n e^{\pi nit/L}.$$

Another filter frequently used to filter out background noise in a signal is the *Gauss filter*, named for the nineteenth century mathematician and scientist Carl Friedrich Gauss. It is given by

$$Z(t) = e^{-a\pi^2 t^2},$$

in which a is a positive constant. The Gauss filtered partial sum of the complex Fourier series of f is

$$\sum_{n=-N}^{N} e^{-a\pi^2 n^2/N^2} d_n e^{\pi nit/L}.$$

Filtering is also applied to Fourier transforms. The filtered Fourier transform of f, using the filter function $Z(t)$, is

$$\int_{-\infty}^{\infty} Z(\xi) f(\xi) e^{-i\omega\xi} d\xi.$$

If this integral is approximated by an integral over a finite interval,

$$\int_{-\infty}^{\infty} Z(\xi) f(\xi) e^{-i\omega\xi} d\xi \approx \int_{-L}^{L} Z(\xi) f(\xi) e^{-i\omega\xi} d\xi,$$

then it is standard practice to approximate the integral on the right using a DFT. The Cesàro, Hamming and Gauss filters for this integral are, respectively,

$$Z(t) = 1 - \left|\frac{t}{L}\right| \quad \text{(Cesàro)}$$

$$Z(t) = 0.54 + 0.46\cos(\pi t/L) \quad \text{(Hamming)}$$

and

$$Z(t) = e^{-a(\pi t/L)^2} \text{ (Gauss)}.$$

SECTION 15.8   PROBLEMS

In each of Problems 1 through 6, a function is given, having period p. Compute the complex Fourier series of the function, and then the 10*th* partial sum of this series at the indicated point t_0. Then, using $N = 128$, compute a DFT approximation to this partial sum at the point.

1. $f(t) = 1 + t$ for $0 \le t \le 2$, $p = 2$, $t_0 = \dfrac{1}{8}$

2. $f(t) = t^2$ for $0 \le t \le 1$, $p = 1$, $t_0 = \dfrac{1}{2}$

3. $f(t) = \cos(t)$ for $0 \le t \le 2$, $p = 2$, $t_0 = \dfrac{1}{8}$

4. $f(t) = e^{-t}$ for $0 \le t \le 4$, $p = 4$, $t_0 = \dfrac{1}{4}$

5. $f(t) = t^3$ for $0 \le t \le 1$, $p = 1$, $t_0 = \dfrac{1}{4}$

6. $f(t) = t\sin(t)$ for $0 \le t \le 4$, $p = 4$, $t_0 = \dfrac{1}{8}$

In each of Problems 7 through 10, make a DFT approximation to the Fourier transform of f at the given point, using $N = 512$ and the given value of L.

7. $f(t) = \begin{cases} e^{-4t} & \text{for } t \ge 0 \\ 0 & \text{for } t < 0, \end{cases}$
$L = 3$; $\hat{f}(4)$

8. $f(t) = \begin{cases} \cos(2t) & \text{for } t \ge 0 \\ 0 & \text{for } t < 0, \end{cases}$
$L = 6$, $\hat{f}(2)$

9. $f(t) = \begin{cases} te^{-2t} & \text{for } t \ge 0 \\ 0 & \text{for } t < 0, \end{cases}$
$L = 3$, $\hat{f}(12)$

10. $f(t) = \begin{cases} t^2\cos(t) & \text{for } t \ge 0 \\ 0 & \text{for } t < 0, \end{cases}$
$L = 4$, $\hat{f}(4)$

In each of Problems 11 through 14, use the DFT to approximate graphs of $\text{Re}[\hat{f}(\omega)]$, $\text{Im}[\hat{f}(\omega)]$ and $\left|\hat{f}(\omega)\right|$ for $0 \le \omega \le 3$, using $N = 256$. For these functions, $\hat{f}(\omega)$ can be computed exactly. Graph each of the approximations of $\text{Re}[\hat{f}(\omega)]$, $\text{Im}[\hat{f}(\omega)]$ and $\left|\hat{f}(\omega)\right|$ on the same of axes with, respectively, the actual function itself.

11. $f(t) = t[H(t-1) - H(t-2)]$

12. $f(t) = 2e^{-4|t|}$

13. $f(t) = H(t) - H(t-1)$

14. $f(t) = e^t[H(t) - H(t-2)]$

In each of Problems 15 through 19, graph the function, the fifth partial sum of its Fourier series on the interval, and the fifth Cesàro sum, using the same set of axes. Repeat this process for the tenth and twenty-fifth partial sums. Notice in particular the graphs at points of discontinuity of the function, where the Gibbs phenomenon shows up in the partial sums.

15. $f(t) = \begin{cases} 1 & \text{for } 0 \le t < 2 \\ -1 & \text{for } -2 \le t < 0 \end{cases}$

16. $f(t) = \begin{cases} t^2 & \text{for } -2 \le t < 1 \\ 2+t & \text{for } 1 \le t < 2 \end{cases}$

17. $f(t) = \begin{cases} -1 & \text{for } -1 \le t < \dfrac{-1}{2} \\ 0 & \text{for } -1/2 \le t < \dfrac{1}{2} \\ 1 & \text{for } 1/2 \le t < 1 \end{cases}$

18. $f(t) = \begin{cases} e^{-t} & \text{for } -3 \le t < 1 \\ \cos(t) & \text{for } 1 \le t < 3 \end{cases}$

19. $f(t) = \begin{cases} 2+t & \text{for } -1 \le t < 0 \\ 7 & \text{for } 0 < t < 1 \end{cases}$

20. Let $f(t) = \begin{cases} 1 & \text{for } 0 \le t < 2 \\ -1 & \text{for } -2 \le t < 0. \end{cases}$

Plot the fifth partial sum of the Fourier series for $f(t)$ on $[-2, 2]$, together with the fifth Cesàro sum, the fifth Hamming filtered partial sum, and the fifth Gauss filtered partial sum on the same set of axes. Repeat this for the tenth sums, and the twenty-fifth sums.

21. Let $f(t) = \begin{cases} t & \text{for } -2 \le t < 0 \\ 2+t & \text{for } 0 \le t < 2. \end{cases}$

Plot the fifth partial sum of the Fourier series for $f(t)$ on $[-\pi, \pi]$, together with the fifth Cesàro sum, the fifth Hamming filtered partial sum, and the fifth Gauss filtered partial sum on the same set of axes. Repeat this for the tenth sums, and the twenty-fifth sums.

15.9 The Fast Fourier Transform

The discrete Fourier transform is a powerful tool for approximating Fourier coefficients, partial sums of Fourier series and Fourier transforms. However, such a tool is only useful if there are efficient computing techniques for carrying out the large numbers of calculations involved in typical applications. This is where the Fast Fourier Transform, or FFT, comes in. The FFT is not a transform at all, but rather an efficient procedure for computing discrete Fourier transforms. Its impact in engineering and science over the past 35 years has been profound, because it makes the DFT a practical tool in analyzing data.

The FFT first appeared formally in 1965 in a five-page paper, "An Algorithm for the Machine Calculation of Complex Fourier Coefficients", by James W. Cooley of IBM and John W. Tukey of Princeton University. The catalyst behind preparation and publication of the paper was Richard Garwin, a physicist who has consulted for federal agencies on questions involving weapons and defense policies. Garwin became aware that Tukey had developed an algorithm for computing Fourier transforms, a tool that Garwin needed for his own work. When Garwin took Tukey's ideas to the computer center at IBM Research in Yorktown Heights for the purpose of having them programmed, James Cooley was assigned to assist him. Because of the importance of an efficient method for computing Fourier transforms, word of Cooley's program quickly spread and it became so much in demand that the Cooley–Tukey paper resulted.

After the paper's publication it was found that some of the concepts underlying the method, or similar to it, had already appeared in other contexts. Tukey himself has related that Phillip Rudnick of the Scripps Oceanographic Institute had reported programming a special case of the algorithm, using ideas from a paper by G.D. Danielson and Cornelius Lanczos. Lanczos, a Hungarian born physicist/mathematician whose career spanned many areas, had developed the essential ideas around 1938 and in the years following, when he was working on problems in numerical methods and Fourier analysis. Much earlier, Gauss had essentially discovered discrete Fourier analysis in calculating the orbit of Pallas, but of course there were no computers in the Napoleonic era.

Today the FFT has become a standard part of certain instrumentation software. For example, FT-NMR, which stands for Fourier Transform-Nuclear Magnetic Resonance, uses the FFT as part of its data analysis system.

The reason for this widespread use is the FFT's efficiency, which can be illustrated by a simple example. It can be shown that, if N is a positive integer power of 2, then $\hat{f}(k/L)$ as given by equation (15.24), can be computed using no more than $4N \log_2(N)$ arithmetic operations. If we simply compute all of the sums and products involved in computing $\hat{f}(k/L)$, we must perform $N-1$ additions and $N+1$ multiplications, each duplicated N times to get the approximations at N points. This is a total of

$$N(N-1) + N(N+1) = 2N^2$$

operations. Suppose, to be specific, $N = 2^{20} = 1,048,576$. Now $2N^2 = 2.1990(10^{12})$. If the computer we are using performs one million operations per second, this calculation will require about 2,199,023 seconds, or about 25.45 days of computer time. Since a given project may require computation of the Fourier transform of many functions, this is intolerable in terms of both time and money.

By contrast, if $N = 2^n$, then

$$4N \log_2(N) = 2^{n+2} \log_2(2^n) = n2^{n+2}.$$

With $n = 20$, this is 83,886,080 operations. At one million operations per second, this will take a little under 84 seconds, a very substantial improvement over 25.45 days.

15.9.1 Use of the FFT in Analyzing Power Spectral Densities of Signals

The FFT is routinely used to display graphs of the power spectral densities of signals. For example, consider the relatively simple signal

$$f(t) = \sin(2\pi(50)t) + 2\sin(2\pi(120)t) + \sin(2\pi(175)t) + \sin(2\pi(210)t).$$

$f(t)$ is written in this way to make the frequencies of the components readily identifiable. By writing $\sin(100\pi t)$ as $\sin(2\pi(50)t)$, we immediately see that this function has frequency 50. Figure 15.29 shows a plot of the power spectral density versus frequency in Hz.

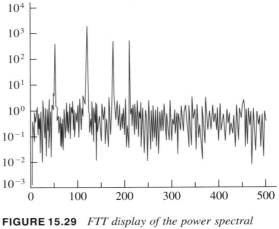

FIGURE 15.29 *FTT display of the power spectral density graph of* $y = \sin(100\pi t) + 2\sin(240\pi t) + \sin(350\pi t) + \sin(420\pi t).$

Where is the FFT in this? It is in the software that produced the plot. For this example, the graph was drawn using MATLAB and an FFT with $N = 2^{10} = 1024$. Using the same program and choice of N, Figure 15.30 shows the power spectral density graph of

$$g(t) = \cos(2\pi(25)t) + \cos(2\pi(80)t) + \cos(2\pi(125)t) + \cos(2\pi(240)t) + \cos(2\pi(315)t).$$

In both graphs the peaks occur at the primary frequencies of the function.

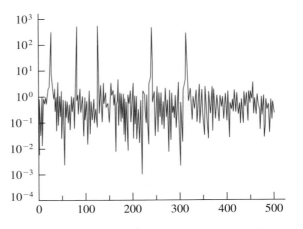

FIGURE 15.30 *FFT display of the power spectral density graph of* $y = \cos(50\pi t) + \cos(160\pi t) + \cos(250\pi t) + \cos(480\pi t) + \cos(630\pi t).$

15.9.2 Filtering Noise From a Signal

The FFT is used sometimes to filter noise from a signal. We discussed filtering previously, but the FFT is the tool for actually carrying it out. To illustrate, consider the signal

$$f(t) = \sin(2\pi(25)t) + \sin(2\pi(80)t) + \sin(2\pi(125)t) + \sin(2\pi(240)t) + \sin(2\pi(315)t).$$

This is a simple signal. However, the signal shown in Figure 15.31 corresponds more closely to reality, and was obtained from the graph of $f(t)$ by introducing zero-mean random noise. If we did not know the original signal $f(t)$, it would be difficult to identify from Figure 15.31 the main frequency components of $f(t)$ because of the effect of the noise. However, the Fourier transform sorts out the frequencies. The power spectral density of the noisy signal of Figure 15.31 is shown in Figure 15.32, where the five main frequencies can be identified easily. This particular plot does not reliably give the amplitudes, but the frequencies stand out very well. Figure 15.32 was done using the FFT via MATLAB, with $N = 2^9 = 512$.

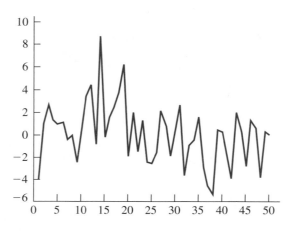

FIGURE 15.31 *A portion of the signal* $y = \sin(50\pi t) + \sin(160\pi t) + \sin(250\pi t) + \sin(480\pi t) + \sin(630\pi t)$ *corrupted with zero-mean random noise.*

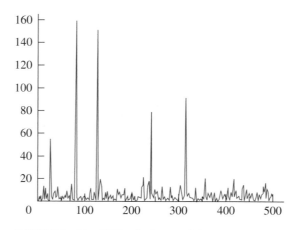

FIGURE 15.32 *FFT calculation of the power spectral density of the signal of Figure 15.31.*

15.9.3   Analysis of the Tides in Morro Bay

We will use the DFT and FFT to analyze a set of tidal data, seeking correlations between high and low tides and the relative positions of the sun, earth, and moon.

The forces that cause the tides were of great interest to Isaac Newton as he struggled to understand the world around him, and he devoted considerable space in the *Principia* to this topic. At one point, Newton required new tables of lunar positions from then Royal Astronomer Flamsteed, who, because of a busy schedule coupled with a personal feud with Newton, was not forthcoming with the data. Newton responded by exerting both professional and political pressure on Flamsteed, through his connections at court, finally forcing Flamsteed to publish the data at his own expense. Years later Flamsteed came into possession of the remaining copies of this book, and is reported to have given vent to his anger with Newton by burning every copy.

It was a triumph of Newton's theory of gravitation, applied to the system consisting of the earth, moon and sun, that enabled Newton to account for two of the primary tides that occur each day. He was also able to explain why the tides have a twice-monthly maximum and minimum and why the extremes are greatest when the moon is farthest from the earth's equatorial plane. The elliptical orbit of the moon about the earth also accounts for the monthly variation in tide heights resulting from the change in the distance between the earth and moon throughout the month.

Morro Bay is near San Luis Obispo in California. Extensive data have been collected as the Pacific Ocean rolls in and out of the bay and tides wash up on the shore. Figure 15.33 shows a curve drawn through data points giving hourly tide heights for May 1993. We will analyze this data to determine the primary forces causing these tidal variations. As a curiosity, comparison with Figure 2.12 even suggests the presence of beats in periodic tide oscillation! Before carrying out this analysis, we need some background information.

The length of a solar day is 24 hours. This is the time it takes the earth to spin once relative to the sun. The lunar day is 50 minutes longer than this. It takes the earth about 24.8 hours to spin once relative to the moon because the moon is traveling in the direction of the earth's rotation (Figure 15.34).

The sun exerts its primary tidal forces at a point on the earth twice each day, and the moon, twice each 24-hour-and-50-minute period. It is fairly clear why the tide should have a local maximum at a particular location when either the sun or moon is nearly above that point. It is not as obvious, however, that the tide will also rise at a point when either of these bodies is on the opposite side of the earth, as is observed. Newton was able to show that, as the earth/moon system travels about its center of mass (which is always interior to the earth), the moon actually exerts an outward force on the opposite side of the earth. The same is true of the earth/sun system. Hence both the sun and moon cause two daily tides.

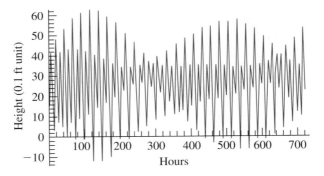

FIGURE 15.33 *Tide profile in Morro Bay from hourly data collected May 1993.*

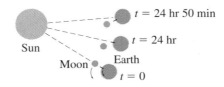

FIGURE 15.34

Tidal forces are proportional to the product of the masses of the bodies involved, and inversely proportional to the cube of the distance between them. This enables us to determine the relative tidal forces of the moon and sun on the earth and its waters. Since the sun has a mass of approximately $27(10^6)$ that of the moon and is about 390 times as far from the earth as the earth is from the moon, the sun's influence on the earth's tides is only about 0.46 times that of the moon's influence.

The semidiurnal (twice daily) tides caused by the sun and moon do not just vary between the same highs and lows each day. Other forces change the amplitudes of these highs and lows. These forces are periodic and are responsible for the beats that seem to be present in Figure 15.33. Authorities on tides claim that there are actually about 390 measurably significant partial tides. Depending on the application of the data, usually only seven to twelve of these are used in computing tables of high and low tides. We will focus for the rest of this discussion on three major contributing forces.

First, as the moon orbits the earth, the distance between the two changes from about 222,000 miles at perigee to 253,000 miles at apogee. With the inverse cube law of tidal forces this difference is significant. The time from perigee to apogee is about 27.55 days.

Next, since the moon gains on the sun by about 50 minutes each day, if the three bodies are in conjunction at some time then they will be in quadrature about seven days later. The twice daily tides will have large amplitudes when everything is aligned and the smallest variations when the earth/moon/sun angle is 90 degrees. The change from these greatest to smallest tide variations and back again is periodic with a period of 14.76 days, half the time it takes the moon to circle the earth.

The last tidal force we will consider is that resulting from the moon's orbit being tilted about 5 degrees from the plane containing the earth's orbit about the sun. The result of this deviation can be seen by observing the moon's location in the sky over a 1-month period. As the moon traverses the earth in its orbit, it will be above the Northern Hemisphere for a while, helping create high tides in that region. Then it will move in a southerly direction, and while it is in the Southern Hemisphere there is little variation in the tides in the north. It takes 13.66 days for the moon to move from the most northerly point to that farthest south.

The principal periods resulting from these forces are the solar semidiurnal period of 12 hours, the lunar semidiurnal period of 12 hours, 50 minutes, 14 seconds; a lunar-solar diurnal period of 23 hours, 56 minutes, 4 seconds; and a lunar diurnal period of 25 hours, 49 minutes, 10 seconds.

Now consider the actual data used to generate the graph in Figure 15.33, and look for this information. Apply the FFT to calculate the DFT of this set of 720 data points, take absolute values, and plot the resulting points. This results in the amplitude spectrum of Figure 15.35. The units along the horizontal (frequency) axis are cycles per 720 hours.

Begin from the right side of the amplitude spectrum in Figure 15.35 and move left. The first place we see a high point is at about 60, which indicates a term in the data at a frequency of 60/720, or 1/12 cycles per hour. Equivalently, this point denotes the presence of a force that is felt about every 12 hours. This is the solar semidiurnal force.

The next high point in the amplitude spectrum occurs almost immediately to the left of the first, at 58. The height of this data point indicates that this is the largest contribution to the

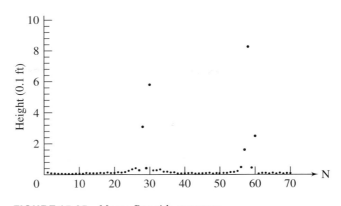

FIGURE 15.35 *Morro Bay tide spectrum.*

tides. It occurs every 720/58, or 12.4 hours. This is the lunar semidiurnal tide. There is also some other small amplitude activity near this point, about which we will comment shortly.

Continuing to move left in Figure 15.35, there is a large contribution at about 30, indicating a force with a frequency of 30/720, or 1/24, hence a period of about 24 hours. This is the lunar-solar diurnal period.

The only other term of influence that stands out occurs at 28, indicating a frequency of 28/720. This translates into a period of 25.7 hours, and indicates the lunar diurnal period.

Thus all of the dominant periods are accounted for and no other significant information occurs in the amplitude spectrum, except for the small scattering noted previously in the region around 58. Since the lunar day is not an exact multiple of 1 hour and the data samples were taken hourly, some of the data associated with the moon's tidal forces have leaked onto adjacent points. This also skews the amplitudes, hindering our ability to accurately determine the sun/moon ratio of forces. The same rationale could account for some of the data near 28.

No other discernible information shows up in the amplitude spectrum because all of the remaining forces have periods longer than 1 month, and this is longer than the time over which the data was taken.

It is interesting to speculate on what Newton would have thought of this graphical verification of his theory. Given his personality, it is possible that he would not have been impressed, having worked it all out to his own satisfaction with his calculus.

SECTION 15.9   PROBLEMS

In each of Problems 1 through 4, use a software package with the FFT to produce a graph of the power spectrum of the function. Use $N = 2^{10}$.

1. $y(t) = 4\sin(80\pi t) - \sin(20\pi t)$

2. $y(t) = 2\cos(40\pi t) + \sin(90\pi t)$

3. $y(t) = 3\cos(90\pi t) - \sin(30\pi t)$

4. $y(t) = \cos(220\pi t) + \cos(70\pi t)$

In each of Problems 5 through 8, corrupt the signal with zero-mean random noise and use the FFT to plot the power density spectrum to identify the frequency components of the original signal.

5. $y(t) = \cos(30\pi t) + \cos(70\pi t) + \cos(140\pi t)$

6. $y(t) = \sin(60\pi t) + 4\sin(130\pi t) + \sin(2405\pi t)$

7. $y(t) = \cos(20\pi t) + \sin(140\pi t) + \cos(240\pi t)$

8. $y(t) = \sin(30\pi t) + 3\sin(40\pi t) + \sin(130\pi t) + \sin(196\pi t) + \sin(220\pi t)$

CHAPTER 16

Special Functions, Orthogonal Expansions, and Wavelets

A function is designated as *special* when it has some distinctive characterics that make it worthwhile determining and recording its properties and behavior. Perhaps the most familiar examples of special functions are $\sin(kx)$ and $\cos(kx)$, which are solutions of an important differential equation, $y'' + k^2 y = 0$, and arise in many other contexts as well.

For us, the primary motivation for studying certain special functions is that they arise in solving ordinary and partial differential equations that model many physical phenomena. Like Fourier series, they constitute necessary items in the toolkit of anyone who wishes to understand and work with such models.

We will begin with Legendre polynomials and Bessel functions. These are important in their own right, but also form a model of how to approach special functions and the kinds of properties we should look for. Following these, we will develop parts of Sturm–Liouville theory, which will provide a template for studying certain aspects special functions in general, for example, eigenfunction expansions, of which Fourier series are a special case. The chapter concludes with a brief introduction to wavelets, in the setting of eigenfunction expansions.

16.1   Legendre Polynomials

There are many different approaches to Legendre polynomials. We will begin with Legendre's differential equation

$$(1 - x^2)y'' - 2xy' + \lambda y = 0 \qquad (16.1)$$

in which $-1 \le x \le 1$ and λ is a real number. This equation has the equivalent form

$$[(1 - x^2)y']' + \lambda y = 0,$$

which we will encounter in Chapter 17 in solving for the steady-state temperature distribution over a solid sphere.

We seek values of λ for which Legendre's equation has nontrivial solutions. Writing Legendre's equation as

$$y'' - \frac{2x}{1-x^2}y' + \frac{\lambda}{1-x^2}y = 0,$$

we conclude that 0 is an ordinary point. There are therefore power series solutions

$$y(x) = \sum_{n=0}^{\infty} a_n x^n.$$

Substitute this series into the differential equation to get

$$\sum_{n=2}^{\infty} a_n n(n-1)a_n x^{n-2} - \sum_{n=2}^{\infty} n(n-1)a_n x^n - \sum_{n=1}^{\infty} 2na_n x^n + \sum_{n=0}^{\infty} \lambda a_n x^n = 0.$$

Shift indices in the first summation to write the last equation as

$$\sum_{n=0}^{\infty} (n+2)(n+1)a_{n+2} x^n - \sum_{n=2}^{\infty} n(n-1)a_n x^n - \sum_{n=1}^{\infty} 2na_n x^n + \sum_{n=0}^{\infty} \lambda a_n x^n = 0.$$

Now combine terms for $n \geq 2$ under one summation, writing the $n = 0$ and $n = 1$ terms separately:

$$2a_2 + 6a_3 x - 2a_1 x + \lambda a_0 + \lambda a_1 x + \sum_{n=2}^{\infty} [(n+2)(n+1)a_{n+2} - (n^2 + n - \lambda)a_n]x^n = 0.$$

The coefficient of each power of x must be zero, hence

$$2a_2 + \lambda a_0 = 0, \qquad (16.2)$$

$$6a_3 - 2a_1 + \lambda a_1 = 0, \qquad (16.3)$$

and, for $n = 2, 3, \ldots,$

$$(n+1)(n+2)a_{n+2} - [n(n+1) - \lambda]a_n = 0$$

from which we get the recurrence relation

$$a_{n+2} = \frac{n(n+1) - \lambda}{(n+1)(n+2)}a_n \text{ for } n = 2, 3, \ldots. \qquad (16.4)$$

From equation (16.2) we have

$$a_2 = -\frac{\lambda}{2}a_0.$$

From equation (16.4),

$$a_4 = \frac{6-\lambda}{3\cdot 4}a_2 = -\frac{\lambda}{2}\frac{6-\lambda}{3\cdot 4}a_0 = \frac{-\lambda(6-\lambda)}{4!}a_0,$$

$$a_6 = \frac{20-\lambda}{5\cdot 6}a_4 = \frac{-\lambda(6-\lambda)(20-\lambda)}{6!}a_0,$$

and so on. Every even-indexed coefficient a_{2n} is a multiple, involving n and λ, of a_0. Here we have used the factorial notation, in which $n!$ is the product of the integers from 1 through n, if n is a positive integer. For example, $6! = 720$. By convention, $0! = 1$.

From equation (16.3),

$$a_3 = \frac{2-\lambda}{6}a_1 = \frac{2-\lambda}{3!}a_1.$$

Then, from the recurrence relation (16.4),

$$a_5 = \frac{12-\lambda}{4\cdot5}a_3 = \frac{(2-\lambda)(12-\lambda)}{5!}a_1,$$

$$a_7 = \frac{30-\lambda}{6\cdot7}a_5 = \frac{(2-\lambda)(12-\lambda)(30-\lambda)}{7!}a_1,$$

and so on. Every odd-indexed coefficient a_{2n+1} is a multiple, also involving n and λ, of a_1.

In this way we can write the solution

$$y(x) = \sum_{n=0}^{\infty} a_n x^n = a_0\left(1 - \frac{\lambda}{2}x^2 - \frac{\lambda(6-\lambda)}{4!}x^4 - \frac{\lambda(6-\lambda)(20-\lambda)}{6!}x^6 + \cdots\right)$$

$$+ a_1\left(x + \frac{2-\lambda}{3!}x^3 + \frac{(2-\lambda)(12-\lambda)}{5!}x^5 + \frac{(2-\lambda)(12-\lambda)(30-\lambda)}{7!}x^7 + \cdots\right).$$

The two series in large parentheses are linearly independent, one containing only even powers of x, the other only odd powers. Put

$$y_e(x) = 1 - \frac{\lambda}{2}x^2 - \frac{\lambda(6-\lambda)}{4!}x^4 - \frac{\lambda(6-\lambda)(20-\lambda)}{6!}x^6 + \cdots$$

and

$$y_o(x) = x + \frac{2-\lambda}{3!}x^3 + \frac{(2-\lambda)(12-\lambda)}{5!}x^5 + \frac{(2-\lambda)(12-\lambda)(30-\lambda)}{7!}x^7 + \cdots.$$

The general solution of Legendre's differential equation is

$$y(x) = a_0 y_e(x) + a_1 y_o(x),$$

in which a_0 and a_1 are arbitrary constants. Some particular solutions are:

with $\lambda = 0$ and $a_1 = 0$,

$$y(x) = a_0.$$

with $\lambda = 2$ and $a_0 = 0$,

$$y(x) = a_1 x.$$

with $\lambda = 6$ and $a_1 = 0$,

$$y(x) = a_0(1 - 3x^2).$$

with $\lambda = 12$ and $a_0 = 0$,

$$y(x) = a_1\left(x - \frac{5}{3}x^3\right).$$

with $\lambda = 20$ and $a_1 = 0$,

$$y(x) = a_0\left(1 - 10x^2 + \frac{35}{3}x^4\right),$$

and so on.

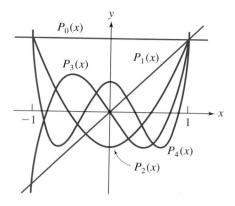

FIGURE 16.1 *The first five Legendre polynomials.*

The values of λ for which solutions are polynomial (finite series) solutions are $\lambda = n(n+1)$ for $n = 0, 1, 2, 3, \ldots$. This should not be surprising, since the recurrence relation (16.4) contains $n(n+1) - \lambda$ in its numerator. If for some nonnegative integer N we choose $\lambda = N(N+1)$, then $a_{N+2} = 0$, hence also $a_{N+4} = a_{N+6} = \cdots = 0$, and one of $y_e(x)$ or $y_o(x)$ will contain only finitely many nonzero terms, hence is a polynomial.

These polynomial solutions of Legendre's differential equation have many applications, for example, in astronomy, analysis of heat conduction, and approximation of solutions of equations $f(x) = 0$. To standardize and tabulate these polynomial solutions, a_0 or a_1 is chosen for each $\lambda = n(n+1)$ so that the polynomial solution has the value 1 at $x = 1$. The resulting polynomials are called *Legendre polynomials*, and are usually denoted $P_n(x)$. The first six Legendre polynomials are

$$P_0(x) = 1, \; P_1(x) = x, \; P_2(x) = \frac{1}{2}(3x^2 - 1), \; P_3(x) = \frac{1}{2}\left(5x^3 - 3x\right),$$

$$P_4(x) = \frac{1}{8}\left(35x^4 - 30x^2 + 3\right), \; P_5(x) = \frac{1}{8}\left(63x^5 - 70x^3 + 15x\right).$$

Graphs of these polynomials are given in Figure 16.1. $P_n(x)$ is of degree n, and contains only even powers of x if n is even, and only odd powers if n is odd. Although these polynomials are defined for all real x, the relevant interval for Legendre's differential equation is $-1 < x < 1$.

It will also be useful to keep in mind that, if $q(x)$ is any polynomial solution of Legendre's equation with $\lambda = n(n+1)$, then $q(x)$ must be a constant multiple of $P_n(x)$.

16.1.1 A Generating Function for the Legendre Polynomials

Many properties of Legendre polynomials can be derived by using a *generating function*, a concept we will now develop. Let

$$L(x, t) = \frac{1}{\sqrt{1 - 2xt + t^2}}.$$

We claim that, if $L(x, t)$ is expanded in a power series in powers of t, then the coefficient of t^n is exactly the nth Legendre polynomial.

THEOREM 16.1   *Generating Function for the Legendre Polynomials*

$$L(x, t) = \sum_{n=0}^{\infty} P_n(x)t^n. \quad \blacksquare$$

We will give an argument suggesting why this is true. Write the Maclaurin series for $(1 - w)^{-1/2}$:

$$\frac{1}{\sqrt{1 - w}} = 1 + \frac{1}{2}w + \frac{3}{8}w^2 + \frac{15}{48}w^3 + \frac{105}{384}w^4 + \frac{945}{3840}w^5 + \cdots$$

for $-1 < w < 1$. Put $w = 2xt - t^2$ to obtain

$$\frac{1}{\sqrt{1 - 2xt + t^2}} = 1 + \frac{1}{2}(2xt - t^2) + \frac{3}{8}(2xt - t^2)^2 + \frac{15}{48}(2xt - t^2)^3$$

$$+ \frac{105}{384}(2xt - t^2)^4 + \frac{945}{3840}(2xt - t^2)^5 + \cdots.$$

Now expand each of these powers of $2xt - t^2$ and collect the coefficient of each power of t in the resulting expression:

$$\frac{1}{\sqrt{1 - 2xt + t^2}} = 1 + xt - \frac{1}{2}t^2 + \frac{3}{2}x^2t^2 - \frac{3}{2}xt^3 + \frac{3}{8}t^4 + \frac{5}{2}x^3t^3 - \frac{15}{4}x^2t^4$$

$$+ \frac{15}{8}xt^5 - \frac{5}{16}t^6 + \frac{35}{8}x^4t^4 - \frac{35}{4}x^3t^5 + \frac{105}{16}x^2t^6 - \frac{35}{16}xt^7$$

$$+ \frac{35}{128}t^8 + \frac{63}{8}x^5t^5 - \frac{315}{16}x^4t^6 + \frac{315}{16}x^3t^7 - \frac{315}{32}x^2t^8 + \frac{315}{128}xt^9 - \frac{63}{256}t^{10} + \cdots$$

$$= 1 + xt + \left(-\frac{1}{2} + \frac{3}{2}x^2\right)t^2 + \left(-\frac{3}{2}x + \frac{5}{2}x^3\right)t^3$$

$$+ \left(\frac{3}{8} - \frac{15}{4}x^2 + \frac{35}{8}x^4\right)t^4 + \left(\frac{15}{8}x - \frac{35}{4}x^3 + \frac{63}{8}x^5\right)t^5 + \cdots$$

$$= P_0(x) + P_1(x)t + P_2(x)t^2 + P_3(x)t^3 + P_4(x)t^4 + P_5(x)t^5 + \cdots.$$

The generating function provides an efficient way of deriving many properties of Legendre polynomials. We will begin by using it to show that

$$P_n(1) = 1 \quad \text{and} \quad P_n(-1) = (-1)^n$$

for $n = 0, 1, 2, \ldots$. First, setting $x = 1$ we have

$$L(1, t) = \frac{1}{\sqrt{1 - 2t + t^2}} = \frac{1}{\sqrt{(1 - t)^2}} = \frac{1}{1 - t} = \sum_{n=0}^{\infty} P_n(1)t^n.$$

But, for $-1 < r < 1$,

$$\frac{1}{1 - t} = \sum_{n=0}^{\infty} t^n.$$

Since $1/(1 - t)$ has only one Maclaurin expansion, the coefficients in these two series must be the same, hence each $P_n(1) = 1$.

Similarly,

$$L(-1, t) = \frac{1}{\sqrt{1 + 2t + t^2}} = \frac{1}{\sqrt{(1+t)^2}} = \frac{1}{1+t} = \sum_{n=0}^{\infty} P_n(-1)t^n.$$

But, $-1 < t < 1$,

$$\frac{1}{1+t} = \sum_{n=0}^{\infty} (-1)^n t^n,$$

so $P_n(-1) = (-1)^n$.

16.1.2   A Recurrence Relation for the Legendre Polynomials

We will use the generating function to derive a recurrence relation for Legendre polynomials.

THEOREM 16.2   *Recurrence Relation for Legendre Polynomials*

For any positive integer n,

$$(n+1)P_{n+1}(x) - (2n+1)xP_n(x) + nP_{n-1}(x) = 0. \tag{16.5}$$

Proof   Begin by differentiating the generating function with respect to t:

$$\frac{\partial L(x, t)}{\partial t} = -\frac{1}{2}(1 - 2xt + t^2)^{-3/2}(-2x + 2t) = \frac{x - t}{(1 - 2xt + t^2)^{3/2}}.$$

Now notice that

$$(1 - 2xt + t^2)\frac{\partial L(x, t)}{\partial t} - (x - t)L(x, t) = 0.$$

Substitute $L(x, t) = \sum_{n=0}^{\infty} P_n(x)t^n$ into the last equation to obtain

$$(1 - 2xt + t^2)\sum_{n=1}^{\infty} nP_n(x)t^{n-1} - (x - t)\sum_{n=0}^{\infty} P_n(x)t^n = 0.$$

Carry out the indicated multiplications to write

$$\sum_{n=1}^{\infty} nP_n(x)t^{n-1} - \sum_{n=1}^{\infty} 2nxP_n(x)t^n + \sum_{n=1}^{\infty} nP_n(x)t^{n+1} - \sum_{n=0}^{\infty} xP_n(x)t^n + \sum_{n=0}^{\infty} P_n(x)t^{n+1} = 0.$$

Rearrange these series to have like powers of t in each summation:

$$\sum_{n=0}^{\infty}(n+1)P_{n+1}(x)t^n - \sum_{n=1}^{\infty} 2nxP_n(x)t^n + \sum_{n=2}^{\infty}(n-1)P_{n-1}(x)t^n$$

$$- \sum_{n=0}^{\infty} xP_n(x)t^n + \sum_{n=1}^{\infty} P_{n-1}(x)t^n = 0.$$

Combine summations from $n = 2$ on, writing the terms for $n = 0$ and $n = 1$ separately:

$$P_1(x) + 2P_2(x)t - 2xP_1(x)t - xP_0(x) - xP_1(x)t + P_0(x)t$$

$$+ \sum_{n=2}^{\infty} \left[(n+1)P_{n+1}(x) - 2nxP_n(x) + (n-1)P_{n-1}(x) - xP_n(x) + P_{n-1}(x) \right] t^n = 0.$$

For this power series in t to be zero for all t in some interval about 0, the coefficient of t^n must be zero for $n = 0, 1, 2, \ldots$. Then

$$P_1(x) - xP_0(x) = 0,$$

$$2P_2(x) - 2xP_1(x) - xP_1(x) + P_0(x) = 0,$$

and, for $n = 2, 3, \ldots$,

$$(n+1)P_{n+1}(x) - 2nxP_n(x) + (n-1)P_{n-1}(x) - xP_n(x) + P_{n-1}(x) = 0.$$

These give us

$$P_1(x) = xP_0(x),$$

$$P_2(x) = \frac{1}{2}(3xP_1(x) - P_0(x))$$

and, for $n = 2, 3, \ldots$,

$$(n+1)P_{n+1}(x) - (2n+1)xP_n(x) + nP_{n-1}(x) = 0.$$

Since this equation is also valid for $n = 1$, this establishes the recurrence relation for all positive integers. ∎

Later we will need to know the coefficient of x^n in $P_n(x)$. We will use the recurrence relation to derive a formula for this number.

THEOREM 16.3

For $n = 1, 2, \ldots$, let A_n be the coefficient of x^n in $P_n(x)$. Then

$$A_n = \frac{1 \cdot 3 \cdots \cdots (2n-1)}{n!}. \quad ∎$$

For example,

$$A_1 = 1, \quad A_2 = \frac{1 \cdot 3}{2!} = \frac{3}{2}, \quad \text{and} \quad A_3 = \frac{1 \cdot 3 \cdot 5}{3!} = \frac{5}{2},$$

as can be verified from the explicit expressions derived previously for $P_1(x)$, $P_2(x)$ and $P_3(x)$.

Proof In the recurrence relation (16.5), the highest power of x that occurs is x^{n+1}, and this term appears in $P_{n+1}(x)$ and in $xP_n(x)$. Thus the coefficient of x^{n+1} in the recurrence relation is

$$(n+1)A_{n+1} - (2n+1)A_n.$$

This must equal zero (because the other side of this recurrence equation is zero). Therefore

$$A_{n+1} = \frac{2n+1}{n+1}A_n,$$

and this holds for $n = 0, 1, 2, \ldots$. Now we can work back:

$$
\begin{aligned}
A_{n+1} &= \frac{2n+1}{n+1} A_n = \frac{2n+1}{n+1} \frac{2(n-1)+1}{(n-1)+1} A_{n-1} \\
&= \frac{2n+1}{n+1} \frac{2n-1}{n} A_{n-1} = \frac{2n+1}{n+1} \frac{2n-1}{n} \frac{2(n-2)+1}{(n-2)+1} A_{n-2} \\
&= \frac{2n+1}{n+1} \frac{2n-1}{n} \frac{2n-3}{n-1} A_{n-2} = \cdots = \frac{2n+1}{n+1} \frac{2n-1}{n} \frac{2n-3}{n-1} \cdots \frac{3}{2} A_0.
\end{aligned}
$$

But $A_0 = 1$ because $P_0(x) = 1$, so

$$
A_{n+1} = \frac{1 \cdot 3 \cdot 5 \cdots (2n-1)(2n+1)}{(n+1)!} \tag{16.6}
$$

for $n = 0, 1, 2, \ldots$. The conclusion of the theorem simply states this conclusion in terms of A_n instead of A_{n+1}. ∎

16.1.3   Orthogonality of the Legendre Polynomials

We will prove the following.

THEOREM 16.4   *Orthogonality of the Legendre Polynomials on $[-1, 1]$*

If n and m are nonnegative integers, then

$$
\int_{-1}^{1} P_n(x) P_m(x) dx = 0 \text{ if } n \neq m. \ \blacksquare \tag{16.7}
$$

This integral relationship is called *orthogonality* of the Legendre polynomials on $[-1, 1]$. We have seen this kind of behavior before, with the functions

$$
1, \cos(x), \cos(2x), \ldots, \sin(x), \sin(2x), \ldots
$$

on the interval $[-\pi, \pi]$. The integral, from $-\pi$ to π, of the product of any two of these (distinct) functions is zero. Because of this property, we were able to find the Fourier coefficients of a function (recall the argument given in Section 14.2). We will pursue a similar idea for Legendre polynomials after establishing equation (16.7).

Proof   Begin with the fact that $P_n(x)$ is a solution of Legendre's equation (16.1) for $\lambda = n(n+1)$. In particular, if n and m are distinct nonnegative integers, then

$$
[(1-x^2)P_n'(x)]' + n(n+1)P_n(x) = 0
$$

and

$$
[(1-x^2)P_m'(x)]' + m(m+1)P_m(x) = 0.
$$

Multiply the first equation by $P_m(x)$ and the second by $P_n(x)$ and subtract the resulting equations to get

$$
[(1-x^2)P_n'(x)]'P_m(x) - [(1-x^2)P_m'(x)]'P_n(x) + [n(n+1) - m(m+1)]P_n(x)P_m(x) = 0.
$$

Integrate this equation:

$$\int_{-1}^{1}[(1-x^2)P_n'(x)]'P_m(x)dx - \int_{-1}^{1}[(1-x^2)P_m'(x)]'P_n(x)dx$$

$$= [m(m+1)-n(n+1)]\int_{-1}^{1}P_n(x)P_m(x)dx.$$

Since $n \neq m$, equation (16.7) will be proved if we can show that the left side of the last equation is zero. But, by integrating the left side by parts, we have

$$\int_{-1}^{1}[(1-x^2)P_n'(x)]'P_m(x)dx - \int_{-1}^{1}[(1-x^2)P_m'(x)]'P_n(x)dx$$

$$= \left[(1-x^2)P_n'(x)P_m(x)\right]_{-1}^{1} - \int_{-1}^{1}(1-x^2)P_n'(x)P_m'(x)dx$$

$$- \left[(1-x^2)P_m'(x)P_n(x)\right]_{-1}^{1} + \int_{-1}^{1}(1-x^2)P_n'(x)P_m'(x)dx = 0,$$

and the orthogonality of the Legendre polynomials on $[-1, 1]$ is proved. ∎

16.1.4   Fourier–Legendre Series

Suppose $f(x)$ is defined for $-1 \le x \le 1$. We want to explore the possibility of expanding $f(x)$ in a series of Legendre polynomials:

$$f(x) = \sum_{n=0}^{\infty} c_n P_n(x). \tag{16.8}$$

We were in a similar situation in Section 14.2, except there we wanted to expand a function defined on $[-\pi, \pi]$ in a series of sines and cosines. We will follow the same reasoning that led to success then. Pick a nonnegative integer m and multiply the proposed expansion by $P_m(x)$, and then integrate the resulting equation, interchanging the series and the integral:

$$\int_{-1}^{1} f(x)P_m(x)dx = \sum_{n=0}^{\infty} c_n \int_{-1}^{1} P_n(x)P_m(x)dx.$$

Because of equation (16.7), all terms in the summation on the right are zero except when $n = m$. The preceding equation reduces to

$$\int_{-1}^{1} f(x)P_m(x)dx = c_m \int_{-1}^{1} P_m^2(x)dx.$$

Then

$$c_m = \frac{\int_{-1}^{1} f(x)P_m(x)dx}{\int_{-1}^{1} P_m^2(x)dx}. \tag{16.9}$$

Taking the lead from Fourier series, we call the expansion $\sum_{n=0}^{\infty} c_n P_n(x)$ *the Fourier–Legendre series*, or expansion, of $f(x)$, when the coefficients are chosen according to equation (16.9). We call these $c_n's$ the *Fourier–Legendre coefficients* of f.

As with Fourier series, we must address the question of convergence of the Fourier–Legendre series of a function. This is done in the following theorem, which is similar in form to the Fourier convergence theorem. As we will see later, this is not a coincidence.

THEOREM 16.5

Let f be piecewise smooth on $[-1, 1]$. Then, for $-1 < x < 1$,

$$\sum_{n=0}^{\infty} c_n P_n(x) = \frac{1}{2}\left(f(x+) + f(x-)\right),$$

if the $c_n's$ are the Fourier–Legendre coefficients of f. ∎

This means that, under the conditions on f, the Fourier–Legendre expansion of $f(x)$ converges to the average of the left and right limits of $f(x)$ at x, for $-1 < x < 1$. This is midway between the gap at the ends of the graph at x if $f(x)$ has a jump discontinuity there (Figure 16.2). We saw this behavior previously with convergence of Fourier (trigonometric) series. If f is continuous at x, then $f(x+) = f(x-) = f(x)$ and the Fourier–Legendre series converges to $f(x)$.

As a special case of general Fourier–Legendre expansions, any polynomial $q(x)$ is a linear combination of Legendre polynomials. In the case of a polynomial, this linear combination can be obtained by just solving for x^n in terms of $P_n(x)$ and writing each power of x in $q(x)$ in terms of Legendre polynomials.

For example, let

$$q(x) = -4 + 2x + 9x^2.$$

We can begin with

$$x = P_1(x)$$

and then solve for x^2 in $P_2(x)$:

$$P_2(x) = \frac{3}{2}x^2 - \frac{1}{2},$$

so

$$x^2 = \frac{2}{3}P_2(x) + \frac{1}{3} = \frac{2}{3}P_2(x) + \frac{1}{3}P_0(x).$$

Then

$$-4 + 2x + 9x^2 = -4P_0(x) + 2P_1(x) + 9\left(\frac{2}{3}P_2(x) + \frac{1}{3}P_0(x)\right)$$

$$= -P_0(x) + 2P_1(x) + 6P_2(x).$$

We can now prove the perhaps surprising result that every Legendre polynomial is orthogonal to every polynomial of lower degree.

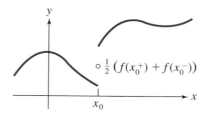

FIGURE 16.2 *Convergence of a Fourier–Legendre expansion at a jump discontinuity of the function.*

THEOREM 16.6

Let $q(x)$ be a polynomial of degree m, and let $n > m$. Then

$$\int_{-1}^{1} q(x)P_n(x)\,dx = 0. \quad \blacksquare$$

Proof Write

$$q(x) = c_0 P_0(x) + c_1 P_1(x) + \cdots + c_m P_m(x).$$

Then

$$\int_{-1}^{1} q(x)P_n(x)\,dx = \sum_{k=0}^{m} c_k \int_{-1}^{1} P_k(x)P_n(x)\,dx = 0,$$

since for $0 \le k \le m < n$, $\int_{-1}^{1} P_k(x)P_n(x)\,dx = 0$. $\quad \blacksquare$

This result will be useful shortly in obtaining information about the zeros of the Legendre polynomials.

16.1.5   Computation of Fourier–Legendre Coefficients

The equation (16.9) for the Fourier–Legendre coefficients of f has $\int_{-1}^{1} P_n^2(x)\,dx$ in the denominator. We will derive a simple expression for this integral.

THEOREM 16.7

If n is a nonnegative integer, then

$$\int_{-1}^{1} P_n^2(x)\,dx = \frac{2}{2n+1}. \quad \blacksquare$$

Proof   As before, denote the coefficient of x^n in $P_n(x)$ as A_n. We will also denote

$$p_n = \int_{-1}^{1} P_n^2(x)\,dx.$$

The highest power term in $P_n(x)$ is $A_n x^n$, while the highest power term in $P_{n-1}(x)$ is $A_{n-1} x^{n-1}$. This means that all terms involving x^n cancel in the polynomial

$$q(x) = P_n(x) - \frac{A_n}{A_{n-1}} x P_{n-1},$$

and so $q(x)$ has degree at most $n-1$. Write

$$P_n(x) = q(x) + \frac{A_n}{A_{n-1}} x P_{n-1}(x).$$

Then

$$p_n = \int_{-1}^{1} P_n(x)P_n(x)\,dx = \int_{-1}^{1} P_n(x)\left(q(x) + \frac{A_n}{A_{n-1}} x P_{n-1}(x) \right) dx$$

$$= \frac{A_n}{A_{n-1}} \int_{-1}^{1} x P_n(x)P_{n-1}(x)\,dx,$$

because $\int_{-1}^{1} q(x)P_n(x)dx = 0$. Now invoke the recurrence relation 16.5 to write

$$xP_n(x) = \frac{n+1}{2n+1}P_{n+1}(x) + \frac{n}{2n+1}P_{n-1}(x).$$

Then

$$xP_n(x)P_{n-1}(x) = \frac{n+1}{2n+1}P_{n+1}(x)P_{n-1}(x) + \frac{n}{2n+1}P_{n-1}^2(x),$$

so

$$p_n = \frac{A_n}{A_{n-1}}\int_{-1}^{1} xP_n(x)P_{n-1}(x)dx$$

$$= \frac{A_n}{A_{n-1}}\left[\frac{n+1}{2n+1}\int_{-1}^{1} P_{n+1}(x)P_{n-1}(x)dx + \frac{n}{2n+1}\int_{-1}^{1} P_{n-1}^2(x)dx\right].$$

Since $\int_{-1}^{1} P_{n+1}(x)P_{n-1}(x)dx = 0$, we are left with

$$p_n = \frac{A_n}{A_{n-1}}\frac{n}{2n+1}\int_{-1}^{1} P_{n-1}^2 dx = \frac{A_n}{A_{n-1}}\frac{n}{2n+1}p_{n-1}.$$

Using the previously obtained value for A_n, we have

$$p_n = \frac{1\cdot3\cdot5\cdots(2n-3)\cdot(2n-1)}{n!}\frac{(n-1)!}{1\cdot3\cdot5\cdots(2n-3)}\frac{n}{2n+1}p_{n-1} = \frac{2n-1}{2n+1}p_{n-1}.$$

Now work forward:

$$p_1 = \frac{1}{3}p_0 = \frac{1}{3}\int_{-1}^{1} P_0(x)^2 dx = \frac{1}{3}\int_{-1}^{1} dx = \frac{2}{3},$$

$$p_2 = \frac{3}{5}p_1 = \frac{3}{5}\frac{2}{3} = \frac{2}{5}, p_3 = \frac{5}{7}p_2 = \frac{2}{7}, p_4 = \frac{7}{9}p_3 = \frac{2}{9},$$

and so on. By induction, we find that

$$p_n = \frac{2}{2n+1},$$

proving the theorem. ∎

This means that the nth Fourier–Legendre coefficient of f is

$$c_n = \frac{\int_{-1}^{1} f(x)P_n(x)dx}{\int_{-1}^{1} P_n^2(x)dx} = \frac{2n+1}{2}\int_{-1}^{1} f(x)P_n(x)dx.$$

EXAMPLE 16.1

Let $f(x) = \cos(\pi x/2)$ for $-1 \le x \le 1$. Then f and f' are continuous on $[-1, 1]$, so the Fourier–Legendre expansion of f converges to $\cos(\pi x/2)$ for $-1 < x < 1$. The coefficients are

$$c_n = \frac{2n+1}{2}\int_{-1}^{1} \cos\left(\frac{\pi x}{2}\right)P_n(x)dx.$$

Because $\cos(x/2)$ is an even function, $\cos(\pi x/2)P_n(x)$ is an odd function for n odd. This means that $c_n = 0$ if n is odd. We need only compute even-indexed coefficients. Some of these are:

$$c_0 = \frac{1}{2}\int_{-1}^{1}\cos\left(\frac{\pi x}{2}\right)dx = \frac{2}{\pi},$$

$$c_2 = \frac{5}{2}\int_{-1}^{1}\cos\left(\frac{\pi x}{2}\right)\frac{1}{2}\left(3x^2 - 1\right)dx = 10\frac{\pi^2 - 12}{\pi^3},$$

$$c_4 = \frac{9}{2}\int_{-1}^{1}\cos\left(\frac{\pi x}{2}\right)\frac{1}{8}\left(35x^4 - 30x^2 + 3\right)dx = 18\frac{\pi^4 + 1680 - 180\pi^2}{\pi^5}.$$

Then, for $-1 < x < 1$,

$$\cos\left(\frac{\pi x}{2}\right) = \frac{2}{\pi} + 10\frac{\pi^2 - 12}{\pi^3}P_2(x) + 18\frac{\pi^4 + 1680 - 180\pi^2}{\pi^5}P_4(x) + \cdots$$

$$= \frac{2}{\pi} + 5\frac{\pi^2 - 12}{\pi^3}(3x^2 - 1) + \frac{9}{4}\frac{\pi^4 + 1680 - 180\pi^2}{\pi^5}\left(35x^4 - 30x^2 + 3\right) + \cdots.$$

Although in this example, $f(x)$ is simple enough to compute some Fourier–Legendre coefficients exactly, in a typical application we would use a software package to compute coefficients. The terms we have computed yield the approximation

$$\cos(\pi x/2) \approx 0.63662 - 0.34355(3x^2 - 1) + 0.0064724\left(35x^4 - 30x^2 + 3\right) + \cdots$$

$$= 0.99959 - 1.2248x^2 + 0.22653x^4 + \cdots.$$

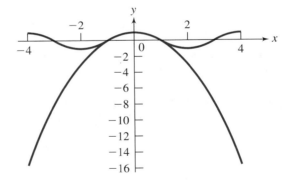

FIGURE 16.3 *Comparison of $\cos(\pi x/2)$ with a partial sum of a series expansion in Legendre polynomials.*

Figure 16.3 shows a graph of $\cos(\pi x/2)$ and the first three nonzero terms of its Fourier–Legendre expansion. This series agrees very well with $\cos(\pi x/2)$ for $-1 < x < 1$, but the two diverge from each other outside this interval. This emphasizes the fact that the Fourier–Legendre expansion is only for $-1 \le x \le 1$. ■

16.1.6 Zeros of the Legendre Polynomials

$P_0(x) = 1$, and has no zeros, while $P_1(x) = x$ has exactly one zero, namely $x = 0$. $P_2(x) = \frac{1}{2}(3x^2 - 1)$ has two real zeros, $\pm 1/\sqrt{3}$. $P_3(x)$ has three real zeros, namely 0 and $\pm\sqrt{3/5}$. After

$n = 3$, finding zeros of Legendre polynomials quickly becomes complicated. For example, $P_4(x)$ has four real zeros, and they are

$$\pm \frac{1}{35}\sqrt{525 + 70\sqrt{30}} \quad \text{and} \quad \pm \frac{1}{35}\sqrt{525 - 70\sqrt{30}}.$$

These are approximately ± 0.8611 and ± 0.3400.

Each $P_n(x)$ just tested has n real roots, all lying in the interval $(-1, 1)$. We will show that this is true for all the Legendre polynomials. This includes $P_0(x)$, which of course has no roots. The proof of this assertion is based on the orthogonality of the Legendre polynomials.

THEOREM 16.8 *Zeros of $P_n(x)$*

Let n be a positive integer. Then $P_n(x)$ has n real, distinct roots, all lying in $(-1, 1)$. ∎

Proof We first show that, if $P_n(x)$ has a real root x_0 in $(-1, 1)$, then this root must be simple (that is, not repeated). For suppose x_0 is a repeated root. Then $P_n(x_0) = P_n'(x_0) = 0$. Then $P_n(x)$ is a solution of the initial value problem

$$((1 - x^2)y')' + n(n+1)y = 0; \quad y(x_0) = y'(x_0) = 0.$$

But this problem has a unique solution, and the trivial function $y(x) = 0$ is a solution. This implies that $P_n(x)$ is the zero function on an interval containing x_0, and this is false. Hence $P_n(x)$ cannot have a repeated root in $(-1, 1)$.

Now suppose n is a positive integer. Then $P_n(x)$ and $P_0(x)$ are orthogonal on $[-1, 1]$, so

$$\int_{-1}^{1} P_n(x)P_0(x)dx = \int_{-1}^{1} P_n(x)dx = 0.$$

Therefore $P_n(x)$ cannot be strictly positive or strictly negative on $(-1, 1)$, hence must change sign in this interval. Since $P_n(x)$ is continuous, there must exist some x_1 in $(-1, 1)$ with $P_n(x_1) = 0$. So far, this gives us one real zero in this interval.

Let $x_1, \ldots, x_m$ be all the zeros of $P_n(x)$ in $(-1, 1)$, with $-1 < x_1 < \cdots < x_m < 1$. Then $1 \le m \le n$. Suppose $m < n$. Then the polynomial

$$q(x) = (x - x_1)(x - x_2) \cdots (x - x_m)$$

has degree less than n, and so is orthogonal to $P_n(x)$:

$$\int_{-1}^{1} q(x)P_n(x)dx = 0.$$

But $q(x)$ and $P_n(x)$ change sign at exactly the same points in $(-1, 1)$, namely at $x_1, \ldots, x_m$. Therefore $q(x)$ and $P_n(x)$ are either of the same sign on each interval $(-1, x_1), (x_1, x_2), \ldots, (x_m, 1)$, or of opposite sign on each of these intervals. This means that $q(x)P_n(x)$ is either strictly positive or strictly negative on $(-1, 1)$ except at the finitely many points $x_1, \ldots, x_m$ where this product vanishes. But then $\int_{-1}^{1} q(x)P_n(x)dx$ must be either positive or negative, a contradiction.

We conclude that $m = n$, hence $P_n(x)$ has n simple zeros in $(-1, 1)$. ∎

Referring back to the graphs of $P_0(x)$ through $P_4(x)$ in Figure 16.1, we can see that each of these Legendre polynomials crosses the x-axis exactly n times between -1 and 1.

16.1.7 Derivative and Integral Formulas for $P_n(x)$

We will derive two additional formulas for $P_n(x)$ that are sometimes used to further analyze Legendre polynomials. The first gives the nth Legendre polynomial in terms of the nth derivative of $(x^2 - 1)^n$.

THEOREM 16.9 *Rodrigues's Formula*

For $n = 0, 1, 2, \ldots,$

$$P_n(x) = \frac{1}{2^n n!} \frac{d^n}{dx^n}((x^2 - 1)^n). \quad \blacksquare$$

In this statement, it is understood that the zero-order derivative of a function is the function itself. Thus, when $n = 0$, the proposed formula gives

$$\frac{1}{2^0 0!} \frac{d^0}{dx^0}((x^2 - 1)^0) = (x^2 - 1)^0 = 1 = P_0(x).$$

For $n = 1$ it gives

$$\frac{1}{2(1!)} \frac{d}{dx}(x^2 - 1) = \frac{1}{2}(2x) = x = P_1(x),$$

and for $n = 2$, it gives

$$\frac{1}{2^2(2!)} \frac{d^2}{dx^2}((x^2 - 1)^2) = \frac{1}{8}\left(12x^2 - 4\right) = \frac{3}{2}x^2 - \frac{1}{2} = P_2(x).$$

Proof Let $w = (x^2 - 1)^n$. Then

$$w' = n(x^2 - 1)^{n-1}(2x).$$

Then

$$(x^2 - 1)w' - 2nxw = 0.$$

If this equation is differentiated $k + 1$ times, it is a routine exercise to verify that we obtain

$$(x^2 - 1)\frac{d^{k+2}w}{dx^{k+2}} - (2n - 2k - 2)x\frac{d^{k+1}w}{dx^{k+1}}$$

$$- [2n + (2n - 2) + \cdots + (2n - 2(k - 1)) + 2n - 2k]\frac{d^k w}{dx^k} = 0.$$

Putting $k = n$, we have

$$(x^2 - 1)\frac{d^{n+2}w}{dx^{n+2}} + 2x\frac{d^{n+1}w}{dx^{n+1}}$$

$$- [2n + (2n - 2) + \cdots + (2n - 2(n - 1)) + (2n - 2n)]\frac{d^n w}{dx^n} = 0.$$

The quantity in square brackets in this equation is

$$2n + (2n - 2) + \cdots + 2,$$

which is the same as

$$2(1 + 2 + \cdots + n).$$

But this quantity is equal to $n(n+1)$. (Recall that $\sum_{j=1}^{n} j = \frac{1}{2}n(n+1)$). Therefore

$$(x^2 - 1)\frac{d^{n+2}w}{dx^{n+2}} + 2x\frac{d^{n+1}w}{dx^{n+1}} - n(n+1)\frac{d^n w}{dx^n} = 0.$$

Upon multiplying this equation by -1, we have

$$(1 - x^2)\frac{d^{n+2}w}{dx^{n+2}} - 2x\frac{d^{n+1}w}{dx^{n+1}} + n(n+1)\frac{d^n w}{dx^n} = 0.$$

But this means that $d^n w/dx^n$ is a solution of Legendre's equation with $\lambda = n(n+1)$. Further, repeated differentiation of the polynomial $(x^2 - 1)^n$ yields a polynomial. Therefore, the polynomial solution $d^n w/dx^n$ must be a constant multiple of $P_n(x)$:

$$\frac{d^n w}{dx^n} = cP_n(x). \tag{16.10}$$

Now, the highest order term in $(x^2 - 1)^n$ is x^{2n}, and the nth derivative of x^{2n} is

$$2n(2n-1)\cdots(n+1)x^n.$$

Therefore the coefficient of the highest power of x in $d^n w/dx^n$ is $2n(2n-1)\cdots(n+1)$. The highest order term in $cP_n(x)$ is cA_n, where A_n is the coefficient of x^n in $P_n(x)$. We know A_n, so equation (16.10) gives us

$$2n(2n-1)\cdots(n+1) = cA_n = c\frac{1\cdot3\cdot5\cdots(2n-1)}{n!}.$$

Then

$$c = \frac{n!(n+1)\cdots(2n-1)(2n)}{1\cdot3\cdot5\cdots(2n-1)} = \frac{(2n)!}{1\cdot3\cdot5\cdots(2n-1)}$$

$$= 2\cdot4\cdot6\cdots2n = 2^n n!.$$

But now equation (16.10) becomes

$$\frac{d^n}{dx^n}((x^2 - 1)^n) = 2^n n! P_n(x),$$

which is equivalent to Rodrigues's formula. ∎

Next we will derive an integral formula for $P_n(x)$.

THEOREM 16.10

For $n = 0, 1, 2, \ldots$,

$$P_n(x) = \frac{1}{\pi}\int_0^{\pi} \left(x + \sqrt{x^2 - 1}\cos(\theta)\right)^n d\theta. \quad ∎$$

For example, with $n = 0$ we get

$$\frac{1}{\pi}\int_0^{\pi} d\theta = 1 = P_0(x).$$

With $n = 1$ we get

$$\frac{1}{\pi} \int_0^{\pi} \left(x + \sqrt{x^2 - 1} \cos(\theta) \right) d\theta = x = P_1(x),$$

and with $n = 2$ we get

$$\frac{1}{\pi} \int_0^{\pi} \left(x + \sqrt{x^2 - 1} \cos(\theta) \right)^2 d\theta$$

$$= \frac{1}{\pi} \int_0^{\pi} \left(x^2 + 2x\sqrt{x^2 - 1} \cos(\theta) + (x^2 - 1)\cos^2(\theta) \right) d\theta$$

$$= \frac{3}{2}x^2 - \frac{1}{2} = P_2(x).$$

Proof   Let

$$Q_n(x) = \frac{1}{\pi} \int_0^{\pi} \left(x + \sqrt{x^2 - 1} \cos(\theta) \right)^n d\theta.$$

The strategy behind the proof is to show that Q_n satisfies the same recurrence relation as the Legendre polynomials. Since $Q_0 = P_0$ and $Q_1 = P_1$, this will imply that $Q_n = P_n$ for all nonnegative integers n. Proceed

$$(n+1)Q_{n+1}(x) - (2n+1)xQ_n(x) + nQ_{n-1}(x)$$

$$= \frac{n+1}{\pi} \int_0^{\pi} \left(x + \sqrt{x^2 - 1} \cos(\theta) \right)^{n+1} d\theta$$

$$- \frac{2n+1}{\pi} \int_0^{\pi} x \left(x + \sqrt{x^2 - 1} \cos(\theta) \right)^n d\theta$$

$$+ \frac{n}{\pi} \int_0^{\pi} \left(x + \sqrt{x^2 - 1} \cos(\theta) \right)^{n-1} d\theta.$$

After a straightforward but lengthy computation, we find that

$$(n+1)Q_{n+1}(x) - (2n+1)xQ_n(x) + nQ_{n-1}(x)$$

$$= \frac{n}{\pi} \int_0^{\pi} \left(x + \sqrt{x^2 - 1} \cos(\theta) \right)^{n-1} (1 - x^2) \sin^2(\theta) d\theta$$

$$+ \frac{1}{\pi} \int_0^{\pi} \left(x + \sqrt{x^2 - 1} \cos(\theta) \right)^n \sqrt{x^2 - 1} \cos(\theta) d\theta.$$

Integrate the second integral by parts, with $u = \left(x + \sqrt{x^2 - 1} \cos(\theta) \right)^n$ and $dv = \sqrt{x^2 - 1} \cos(\theta) d\theta$ to get

$$(n+1)Q_{n+1}(x) - (2n+1)xQ_n(x) + nQ_{n-1}(x)$$

$$= \frac{n}{\pi} \int_0^{\pi} \left(x + \sqrt{x^2 - 1} \cos(\theta) \right)^{n-1} (1 - x^2) \sin^2(\theta) d\theta$$

$$+ \left[\frac{1}{\pi} \left(x + \sqrt{x^2 - 1} \cos(\theta) \right)^n \sqrt{x^2 - 1} \sin(\theta) \right]_0^{\pi}$$

$$- \frac{1}{\pi} \int_0^{\pi} \sqrt{x^2 - 1} \sin(\theta) n \left(x + \sqrt{x^2 - 1} \cos(\theta) \right)^{n-1} \sqrt{x^2 - 1}(-\sin(\theta)) d\theta$$

$$= 0,$$

completing the proof. ∎

SECTION 16.1   PROBLEMS

1. For $n = 0, 1, 3, 4, 5$, verify by substitution that $P_n(x)$ is a solution of Legendre's equation corresponding to $\lambda = n(n+1)$.

2. Use the recurrence relation (Theorem 16.2), and the list of $P_0(x), \ldots, P_5(x)$ given previously, to determine $P_6(x)$ through $P_{10}(x)$. Graph these functions and observe the location of their zeros in $[-1, 1]$.

3. Use Rodrigues's formula to obtain $P_1(x)$ through $P_5(x)$.

4. Use Theorem 16.10 to obtain $P_3(x)$, $P_4(x)$ and $P_5(x)$.

5. It can be shown that

$$P_n(x) = \sum_{k=0}^{[n/2]} (-1)^k \frac{(2n-2k)!}{2^n k!(n-k)!(n-2k)!} x^{n-2k}.$$

Use this formula to generate $P_0(x)$ through $P_5(x)$. The symbol $[n/2]$ denotes the largest integer not exceeding $n/2$.

6. Show that

$$P_n(x) = \sum_{k=0}^{n} \frac{n!}{k!(n-k)!} \frac{d^k}{dx^k}[(x+1)^n] \frac{d^{n-k}}{dx^{n-k}}[(x-1)^n].$$

Hint: Put $x^2 - 1 = (x-1)(x+1)$ in Rodrigues's formula.

7. Let n be a nonnegative integer. Use reduction of order (Section 2.2) and the fact that $P_n(x)$ is one solution of Legendre's equation with $\lambda = n(n+1)$ to obtain a second, linearly independent solution

$$Q_n(x) = P_n(x) \int \frac{1}{[P_n(x)]^2(1-x^2)} dx.$$

8. Use the result of Problem 7 to show that

$$Q_0(x) = -\frac{1}{2} \ln\left(\frac{1+x}{1-x}\right),$$

$$Q_1(x) = 1 - \frac{x}{2} \ln\left(\frac{1+x}{1-x}\right),$$

and

$$Q_2(x) = \frac{1}{4}(3x^2 - 1) \ln\left(\frac{1+x}{1-x}\right) - \frac{3}{2}x$$

for $-1 < x < 1$.

9. The gravitational potential at a point $P : (x, y, z)$ due to a unit mass at (x_0, y_0, z_0) is

$$\varphi(x, y, z) = \frac{1}{\sqrt{(x-x_0)^2 + (y-y_0)^2 + (z-z_0)^2}}.$$

For some purposes (such as in astronomy) it is convenient to expand $\varphi(x, y, z)$ in powers of r or $1/r$,

where $r = \sqrt{x^2 + y^2 + z^2}$. To do this, introduce the angle shown in Figure 16.4. Let $d = \sqrt{x_0^2 + y_0^2 + z_0^2}$ and $R = \sqrt{(x-x_0)^2 + (y-y_0)^2 + (z-z_0)^2}$.

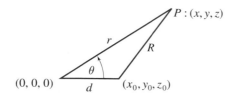

FIGURE 16.4

(a) Use the law of cosines to write

$$\varphi(x, y, z) = \frac{1}{d\sqrt{1 - 2(r/d)\cos(\theta) + (r/d)^2}}.$$

(b) From our discussion of the generating function for Legendre polynomials, recall that, if $1/\sqrt{1 - 2at + t^2}$ is expanded in a series about 0, convergent for $|t| < 1$, then the coefficient of t^n is $P_n(a)$.

(c) If $r < d$, let $a = \cos(\theta)$ and $t = r/d$ to obtain

$$\varphi(r) = \sum_{n=0}^{\infty} \frac{1}{d^{n+1}} P_n(\cos(\theta)) r^n.$$

(d) If $r > d$, show that

$$\varphi(r) = \frac{1}{r} \sum_{n=0}^{\infty} d^n P_n(\cos(\theta)) r^{-n}.$$

10. Show that $\displaystyle\sum_{n=0}^{\infty} \left(\frac{1}{2^{n+1}}\right) P_n\left(\frac{1}{2}\right) = \frac{1}{\sqrt{3}}$.

11. Let n be a nonnegative integer. Prove that

$$P_{2n+1}(0) = 0 \quad \text{and} \quad P_{2n}(0) = (-1)^n \frac{(2n)!}{2^{2n}(n!)^2}.$$

12. Expand each of the following in a series of Legendre polynomials.

(a) $1 + 2x - x^2$

(b) $2x + x^2 - 5x^3$

(c) $2 - x^2 + 4x^4$

In each of Problems 13 through 18, find the first five coefficients in the Fourier–Legendre expansion of the function. Graph the function and the sum of the first five terms of this expansion on the same set of axes, for $-3 \leq x \leq 3$.

The expansion is only valid on $[-1, 1]$, but it is instructive to see how the partial sum of the Fourier–Legendre expansion are generally unrelated outside this interval.

13. $f(x) = \sin(\pi x/2)$

14. $f(x) = e^{-x}$

15. $f(x) = \sin^2(x)$

16. $f(x) = \cos(x) - \sin(x)$

17. $f(x) = \begin{cases} -1 & \text{for } -1 \le x \le 0 \\ 1 & \text{for } 0 < x \le 1 \end{cases}$

18. $f(x) = (x+1)\cos(x)$

16.2   Bessel Functions

We will now develop the second kind of special function we will use to introduce the general topic of special functions.

Recall from Chapter 4 that the second-order differential equation

$$x^2 y'' + xy' + (x^2 - \nu^2)y = 0$$

is called Bessel's equation of order ν. Thus the term *order* is used in two senses here—the differential equation is of second order, but traditionally we say that the equation has order ν to refer to the parameter ν occurring in the coefficient of y.

In Example 4.12 of Section 4.3, we used the method of Frobenius to find a series solution

$$y(x) = c_0 \sum_{n=0}^{\infty} \frac{(-1)^n}{2^{2n} n!(1+\nu)(2+\nu)\cdots(n+\nu)} x^{2n+\nu},$$

in which c_0 is a nonzero constant and $\nu \ge 0$. This solution is valid in some interval $(0, R)$, depending on ν.

It will be useful to write this solution in terms of the gamma function, which we will now develop.

16.2.1   The Gamma Function

For $x > 0$, the *gamma function* Γ is defined by

$$\Gamma(x) = \int_0^{\infty} t^{x-1} e^{-t} dt.$$

This integral converges for all $x > 0$. The gamma function has a fascinating history and many interesting properties. For us, the most useful is the following.

THEOREM 16.11   *Factorial Property of the Gamma Function*

If $x > 0$, then

$$\Gamma(x+1) = x\Gamma(x).$$

Proof   If $0 < a < b$, then we can integrate by parts, with $u = t^x$ and $dv = e^{-t}dt$, to get

$$\int_a^b t^x e^{-t} dt = [t^x(-e^{-t})]_a^b - \int_a^b xt^{x-1}(-1)e^{-t} dt$$

$$= -b^x e^{-b} + a^x e^{-a} + x\int_a^b t^{x-1} e^{-t} dt.$$

Take the limit of this equation as $a \to 0+$ and $b \to \infty$ to get

$$\int_0^{\infty} t^x e^{-t} dt = \Gamma(x+1) = x\int_0^{\infty} t^{x-1} e^{-t} dt = x\Gamma(x). \quad \blacksquare$$

The reason why this is called the factorial property can be seen by letting $x = n$, a positive integer. By repeated application of the theorem, we get

$$\Gamma(n+1) = n\Gamma(n) = n\Gamma((n-1)+1) = n(n-1)\Gamma(n-1)$$
$$= n(n-1)\Gamma((n-2)+1) = n(n-1)(n-2)\Gamma(n-2)$$
$$= \cdots = n(n-1)(n-2)\cdots(2)(1)\Gamma(1) = n!\Gamma(1).$$

But

$$\Gamma(1) = \int_0^\infty e^{-t}dt = 1,$$

so

$$\Gamma(n+1) = n!$$

for any positive integer n. This is the reason for the term *factorial property* of the gamma function.

It is possible to extend $\Gamma(x)$ to negative (but noninteger) values of x by using the factorial property. For $x > 0$, write

$$\Gamma(x) = \frac{1}{x}\Gamma(x+1). \tag{16.11}$$

If $-1 < x < 0$, then $x+1 > 0$ so $\Gamma(x+1)$ is defined and we use the right side of equation (16.11) to define $\Gamma(x)$.

Once we have extended $\Gamma(x)$ to $-1 < x < 0$, we can let $-2 < x < -1$. Then $-1 < x+1 < 0$ so $\Gamma(x+1)$ has been defined and we can again use equation 16.11 to define $\Gamma(x)$. In this way we can walk to the left along the real line, defining $\Gamma(x)$ on $(-n-1, -n)$ as soon as it has been defined on the interval $(-n, -n+1)$ immediately to the right.

For example,

$$\Gamma\left(-\frac{1}{2}\right) = \frac{1}{-\frac{1}{2}}\Gamma\left(-\frac{1}{2}+1\right) = -2\Gamma\left(\frac{1}{2}\right),$$

and

$$\Gamma\left(-\frac{3}{2}\right) = \frac{1}{-\frac{3}{2}}\Gamma\left(-\frac{3}{2}+1\right) = -\frac{2}{3}\Gamma\left(-\frac{1}{2}\right) = \frac{4}{3}\Gamma\left(\frac{1}{2}\right).$$

Figure 16.5 (a) shows a graph of $y = \Gamma(x)$ for $0 < x < 5$. Graphs for $-1 < x < 0$, $-2 < x < -1$ and $-3 < x < -2$, respectively, are given in Figures 16.5(b), (c) and (d).

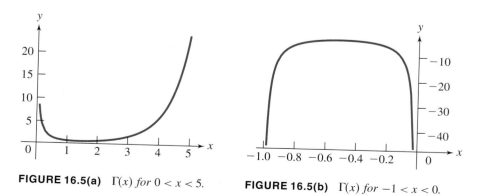

FIGURE 16.5(a) $\Gamma(x)$ for $0 < x < 5$.

FIGURE 16.5(b) $\Gamma(x)$ for $-1 < x < 0$.

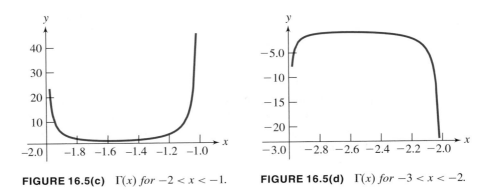

FIGURE 16.5(c) $\Gamma(x)$ *for* $-2 < x < -1$.   FIGURE 16.5(d) $\Gamma(x)$ *for* $-3 < x < -2$.

16.2.2 Bessel Functions of the First Kind and Solutions of Bessel's Equation

Now return to the Frobenius solution $y(x)$ of Bessel's equation, given previously. Part of the denominator in this solution is

$$(1+\nu)(2+\nu)\cdots(n+\nu),$$

in which we assume that $\nu \geq 0$. Now use the factorial property of the gamma function to write

$$\Gamma(n+\nu+1) = (n+\nu)\Gamma(n+\nu) = (n+\nu)(n+\nu-1)\Gamma(n+\nu-1)$$
$$= \cdots = (n+\nu)(n+\nu-1)\cdots(n+\nu-(n-1))\Gamma(n+\nu-(n-1))$$
$$= (1+\nu)(2+\nu)\cdots(n-1+\nu)(n+\nu)\Gamma(\nu+1).$$

Therefore

$$(1+\nu)(2+\nu)\cdots(n+\nu) = \frac{\Gamma(n+\nu+1)}{\Gamma(\nu+1)}$$

and we can write the solution as

$$y(x) = c_0 \sum_{n=0}^{\infty} \frac{(-1)^n \Gamma(\nu+1)}{2^{2n} n! \Gamma(n+\nu+1)} x^{2n+\nu}.$$

It is customary to choose

$$c_0 = \frac{1}{2^{\nu}\Gamma(\nu+1)}$$

to obtain the solution we will denote as $J_\nu(x)$:

$$J_\nu(x) = \sum_{n=0}^{\infty} \frac{(-1)^n}{2^{2n+\nu} n! \Gamma(n+\nu+1)} x^{2n+\nu}.$$

J_ν is called a *Bessel function of the first kind of order* ν. The series defining $J_\nu(x)$ converges for all x.

Because Bessel's equation is of second order (as a differential equation), we need a second solution, linearly independent from J_ν, to write the general solution. Theorem 4.4 in Section 4.4 tells us how to proceed to a second solution. In Example 4.12 we found that the indicial equation of Bessel's equation is $r^2 - \nu^2 = 0$, with roots $\pm\nu$. The key lies in the difference 2ν between these roots. Omitting the details of the analysis, here are the conclusions.

1. If 2ν is not an integer, then J_ν and $J_{-\nu}$ are linearly independent (neither is a constant multiple of the other), and the general solution of Bessel's equation of order ν is

$$y(x) = aJ_\nu(x) + bJ_{-\nu}(x),$$

with a and b arbitrary constants.

2. If 2ν is an odd positive integer, say $2\nu = 2n+1$, then $\nu = n + \frac{1}{2}$ for some positive integer n. In this case, J_ν and $J_{-\nu}$ are still linearly independent. It can be shown that in this case $J_{n+1/2}(x)$ and $J_{n-1/2}(x)$ can be expressed in closed form as finite sums of terms involving square roots, sines and cosines. For example, by manipulating the series for $J_\nu(x)$, we find that

$$J_{1/2}(x) = \sqrt{\frac{2}{\pi x}} \sin(x), \quad J_{-1/2}(x) = \sqrt{\frac{2}{\pi x}} \cos(x), \quad J_{3/2}(x) = \sqrt{\frac{2}{\pi x}} \left[\frac{\sin(x)}{x} - \cos(x) \right],$$

and

$$J_{-3/2}(x) = \sqrt{\frac{2}{\pi x}} \left[-\sin(x) - \frac{\cos(x)}{x} \right].$$

In this case, the general solution of Bessel's equation of order ν is

$$y(x) = aJ_{n+1/2}(x) + bJ_{n-1/2}(x),$$

with a and b arbitrary constants.

3. 2ν is an integer, but is not of the form $n + \frac{1}{2}$ for any positive integer n. In this case $J_\nu(x)$ and $J_{-\nu}(x)$ are solutions of Bessel's equation, but they are linearly dependent. Indeed, one can check from the series that in this case,

$$J_{-\nu}(x) = (-1)^\nu J_\nu(x).$$

In this case we must construct a second solution of Bessel's equation, linearly independent from $J_\nu(x)$. This leads us to Bessel functions of the second kind.

16.2.3 Bessel Functions of the Second Kind

In Section 4.4 we derived a second solution for Bessel's equation for the case $\nu = 0$. It was

$$y_2(x) = J_0(x)\ln(x) + \sum_{n=1}^\infty \frac{(-1)^{n+1}}{2^{2n}(n!)^2} \emptyset(n) x^{2n},$$

in which

$$\emptyset(n) = 1 + \frac{1}{2} + \cdots + \frac{1}{n}.$$

Instead of using this solution as it is written, it is customary to use a linear combination of $y_2(x)$ and $J_0(x)$, which will of course also be a solution. This combination is denoted $Y_0(x)$, and is defined for $x > 0$ by

$$Y_0(x) = \frac{2}{\pi} \left[y_2(x) + (\gamma - \ln(2)) J_0(x) \right],$$

where γ is Euler's constant, defined by

$$\gamma = \lim_{n \to \infty} (\emptyset(n) - \ln(n)) = 0.577215664901533\ldots.$$

J_0 and Y_0 are linearly independent because of the $\ln(x)$ term in $Y_0(x)$, and the general solution of Bessel's equation of order zero is therefore

$$y(x) = aJ_0(x) + bY_0(x),$$

with a and b arbitrary constants. Y_0 is called a *Bessel function of the second kind of order zero*. With the choice made for the constants in defining Y_0, this function is also called *Neumann's function of order zero*.

If ν is a positive integer, say $\nu = n$, a derivation similar to that of $Y_0(x)$, but with more computational details, yields the second solution

$$Y_n(x) = \frac{2}{\pi}\left[J_n(x)[\ln\left(\frac{x}{2}\right) + \gamma] + \sum_{k=1}^{\infty} \frac{(-1)^{k+1}[\O(k) + \O(k+1)]}{2^{2k+n+1}k!(k+n)!}x^{2k+n}\right]$$

$$-\frac{2}{\pi}\sum_{k=0}^{n-1}\frac{(n-k-1)!}{2^{2k-n+1}k!}x^{2k-n}.$$

This agrees with $Y_0(x)$ if $n = 0$, with the understanding that in this case the last summation does not appear.

The general solution of Bessel's equation of positive integer order n is therefore

$$y(x) = aJ_n(x) + bY_n(x).$$

Thus far we only have $Y_\nu(x)$ for ν a nonnegative integer. We did not need this Bessel function of the second kind for the general solution of Bessel's equation in other cases. However, it is possible to extend this definition of $Y_\nu(x)$ to include all real values of ν by letting

$$Y_\nu(x) = \frac{1}{\sin(\nu\pi)}[J_\nu(x)\cos(\nu\pi) - J_{-\nu}(x)].$$

For any nonnegative integer n, one can show that

$$Y_n(x) = \lim_{\nu \to n} Y_\nu(x).$$

Y_ν is *Neumann's Bessel function of order ν*. This function is linearly independent from $J_\nu(x)$ for $x > 0$, and it enables us to write the general solution of Bessel's equation of order ν in all cases as

$$y(x) = aJ_\nu(x) + bY_\nu(x).$$

Graphs of some Bessel functions of both kinds are shown in Figures 16.6 and 16.7.

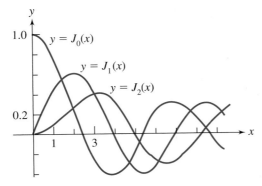

FIGURE 16.6 *Bessel functions of the first kind.*

FIGURE 16.7 *Bessel functions of the second kind.*

Is interesting to notice that solutions of Bessel's equation illustrate all of the cases of the Frobenius theorem (Theorem 4.4). Case 1 occurs if 2ν is not an integer, case 2 if $\nu = 0$, case 3 with no logarithm term if $\nu = n + \frac{1}{2}$ for some nonnegative integer n, and case 3 with a logarithm term if ν is a positive integer.

In applications and models of physical systems, Bessel's equation often occurs in disguised form, requiring a change of variables to write the solution in terms of Bessel functions.

EXAMPLE 16.2

Consider the differential equation

$$9x^2 y'' - 27xy' + (9x^2 + 35)y = 0.$$

Let $y = x^2 u$ and compute

$$y' = 2xu + x^2 u', \quad y'' = 2u + 4xu' + x^2 u''.$$

Substitute these into the differential equation to get

$$18x^2 u + 36x^3 u' + 9x^4 u'' - 54x^2 u - 27x^3 u' + 9x^4 u + 35x^2 u = 0.$$

Collect terms to write

$$9x^4 u'' + 9x^3 u' + (9x^4 - x^2)u = 0.$$

Divide by $9x^2$ to get

$$x^2 u'' + xu' + \left(x^2 - \frac{1}{9} \right) u = 0,$$

which is Bessel's equation of order $\nu = \frac{1}{3}$. Since 2ν is not an integer, the general solution for u is

$$u(x) = aJ_{1/3}(x) + bJ_{-1/3}(x).$$

Therefore the original differential equation has general solution

$$y(x) = ax^2 J_{1/3}(x) + bx^2 J_{-1/3}(x)$$

for $x > 0$. ∎

If a, b and c are constants and n is any nonnegative integer, then it is routine to show that $x^a J_\nu(bx^c)$ and $x^a Y_\nu(bx^c)$ are solutions of the general differential equation

$$y'' - \left(\frac{2a-1}{x} \right) y' + \left(b^2 c^2 x^{2c-2} + \frac{a^2 - \nu^2 c^2}{x^2} \right) y = 0. \tag{16.12}$$

EXAMPLE 16.3

Consider the differential equation

$$y'' - \left(\frac{2\sqrt{3}-1}{x} \right) y' + \left(784x^6 - \frac{61}{x^2} \right) y = 0.$$

To fit this into the template of equation 16.12, we must clearly choose $a = \sqrt{3}$. Because of the x^6 term, try putting $2c - 2 = 6$, hence $c = 4$. Now we must choose b and ν so that

$$784 = b^2 c^2 = 16b^2,$$

so $b = 7$, and

$$a^2 - \nu^2 c^2 = 3 - 16\nu^2 = -61.$$

This equation is satisfied by $\nu = 2$. The general solution of the differential equation is therefore

$$y(x) = c_1 x^{\sqrt{3}} J_2\left(7x^4\right) + c_2 x^{\sqrt{3}} Y_2(7x^4),$$

for $x > 0$. Here c_1 and c_2 are arbitrary constants. ■

16.2.4 Modified Bessel Functions

Sometimes a model of a physical phenomenon will require a modified Bessel function for its solution. We will show how these are obtained. Begin with the general solution

$$y(x) = c_1 J_0(kx) + c_2 Y_0(kx)$$

of the zero-order Bessel function

$$y'' + \frac{1}{x}y' + k^2 y = 0.$$

Let $k = i$. Then

$$y(x) = c_1 J_0(ix) + c_2 Y_0(ix)$$

is the general solution of

$$y'' + \frac{1}{x}y' - y = 0$$

for $x > 0$. This is a *modified Bessel equation of order zero*, and $J_0(ix)$ is a *modified Bessel function of the first kind of order zero*. Usually this is denoted

$$I_0(x) = J_0(ix) = 1 + \frac{1}{2^2}x^2 + \frac{1}{2^2 4^2}x^4 + \frac{1}{2^2 4^2 6^2}x^6 + \cdots.$$

Normally $Y_0(ix)$ is not used, but instead the second solution is chosen to be

$$K_0(x) = [\ln(2) - \gamma]I_0(x) - I_0(x)\ln(x) + \frac{1}{4}x^2 + \cdots$$

for $x > 0$. Here γ is Euler's constant. K_0 is a *modified Bessel function of the second kind of order zero*. Figure 16.8 shows graphs of $I_0(x)$ and $K_0(x)$.

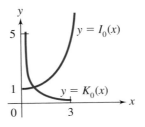

FIGURE 16.8 *Modified Bessel functions.*

The general solution of

$$y'' + \frac{1}{x}y' - y = 0$$

is therefore

$$y(x) = c_1 I_0(x) + c_2 K_0(x)$$

for $x > 0$. The general solution of

$$y'' + \frac{1}{x}y' - b^2 y = 0 \tag{16.13}$$

is

$$y(x) = c_1 I_0(bx) + c_2 K_0(bx) \tag{16.14}$$

for $x > 0$.

By a routine calculation using the series expansion, we find that

$$\int x I_0(\alpha x) dx = \frac{x}{\alpha} I_0'(x) + c$$

for any nonzero constant α.

Often we are interested in the behavior of a function when the variable assumes increasing large values. This is called *asymptotic behavior*, and we will treat it later in some detail for Bessel functions in general. However, with just a few lines of work we can get some idea of how $I_0(x)$ behaves for large x. Begin with

$$y'' + \frac{1}{x}y' - y = 0,$$

of which $cI_0(x)$ is a solution for any constant c. Under the change of variables $y = ux^{-1/2}$, this equation transforms to

$$u'' = \left(1 - \frac{1}{4x^2}\right)u,$$

with solution $u(x) = c\sqrt{x} I_0(x)$ for $x > 0$ and c any constant. Transform further by putting $u = ve^x$, obtaining

$$v'' + 2v' + \frac{1}{4x^2}v = 0,$$

with solution $v(x) = c\sqrt{x}e^{-x}I_0(x)$. Since we are interested in the behavior of solutions for large x, attempt a series solution of this differential equation for v of the form

$$v(x) = 1 + c_1\frac{1}{x} + c_2\frac{1}{x^2} + c_3\frac{1}{x^2} + \cdots.$$

Substitute into the differential equation and arrange terms to obtain

$$\left(-2c_1 + \frac{1}{4}\right)\frac{1}{x^2} + \left(2c_1 - 4c_2 + \frac{1}{4}c_1\right)\frac{1}{x^3}$$

$$+ \left(6c_2 - 6c_3 + \frac{1}{4}c_2\right)\frac{1}{x^4} + \left(12c_3 - 8c_4 + \frac{1}{4}c_3\right)\frac{1}{x^5} + \cdots = 0.$$

Each coefficient must vanish, hence

$$-2c_1 + \frac{1}{4} = 0,$$

$$2c_1 - 4c_2 + \frac{1}{4}c_1 = 0,$$

$$6c_2 - 6c_3 + \frac{1}{4}c_2 = 0,$$

$$12c_3 - 8c_4 + \frac{1}{4}c_3 = 0,$$

and so on. Then

$$c_1 = \frac{1}{8},$$

$$c_2 = \frac{9}{16}c_1 = \frac{9}{16}\frac{1}{8} = \frac{3^2}{2 \cdot 8^2},$$

$$c_3 = \frac{25}{24}c_2 = \frac{25}{24}\frac{3^2}{2 \cdot 8^2} = \frac{3^2 5^2}{3!8^3},$$

$$c_4 = \frac{49}{32}c_3 = \frac{49}{32}\frac{3^2 5^2}{3!8^3} = \frac{3^2 5^2 7^2}{4!8^4},$$

and the pattern is clear:

$$v(x) = 1 + \frac{1}{8}\frac{1}{x} + \frac{3^2}{2 \cdot 8^2}\frac{1}{x^2} + \frac{3^2 5^2}{3!8^3}\frac{1}{x^3} + \frac{3^2 5^2 7^2}{4!8^4}\frac{1}{x^4} + \cdots.$$

Then, for some constant c,

$$I_0(x) = c\frac{e^x}{\sqrt{x}}\left(1 + \frac{1}{8}\frac{1}{x} + \frac{3^2}{2 \cdot 8^2}\frac{1}{x^2} + \frac{3^2 5^2}{3!8^3}\frac{1}{x^3} + \frac{3^2 5^2 7^2}{4!8^4}\frac{1}{x^4} + \cdots\right).$$

The series on the right actually diverges, but the sum of the first N terms approximates $I_0(x)$ as closely as we want, for x sufficiently large. This is called an *asymptotic expansion* of $I_0(x)$. By an analysis we will not carry out, it can be shown that $c = 1/\sqrt{2\pi}$.

These results about modified Bessel functions will be applied shortly to a description of the skin effect in the flow of an alternating current through a wire of circular cross section.

16.2.5   Some Applications of Bessel Functions

We will use Bessel functions in the next chapter to solve certain partial differential equations. However, Bessel functions arise in many different contexts. We will discuss two such settings here.

The Critical Length of a Vertical Rod   Consider a thin elastic rod of uniform density and circular cross section, clamped in a vertical position as in Figure 16.9. If the rod is long enough, and the upper end is given a displacement and held in that position until the rod is at rest, the rod will remain bent or displaced when released. Such a length is referred to as an *unstable length*. At some shorter lengths, however, the rod will return to the vertical position when released, after some small oscillations. These lengths are referred to as *stable lengths* for the rod. We would like to determine the *critical length* L_C, the transition point from stable to unstable.

Suppose the rod has length L and weight w per unit length. Let a be the radius of its circular cross section and E the Young's modulus for the material of the rod. (This is the ratio of stress

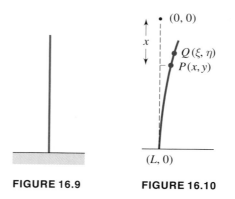

FIGURE 16.9   **FIGURE 16.10**

to the corresponding strain, for an elongation or linear compression). The moment of inertia about a diameter is $I = \pi a^4/4$. Assume that the rod is in equilibrium and is then displaced slightly from the vertical, as in Figure 16.10. The x axis is vertical along the original position of the rod, with downward as positive and the origin at the upper end of the rod at equilibrium. Let $P(x, y)$ and $Q(\xi, \eta)$ be points on the displaced rod, as shown. The moment about P of the weight of an element $w\Delta x$ at Q is $w\Delta x[y(\xi) - y(x)]$. By integrating this expression we obtain the moment about P of the weight of the rod above P. Assume from the theory of elasticity that this moment about P is $EIy''(x)$. Since the part of the rod above P is in equilibrium, then

$$EIy''(x) = \int_0^x w[y(\xi) - y(x)]d\xi.$$

Differentiate this equation with respect to x:

$$EIy^{(3)}(x) = w[y(x) - y(x)] - \int_0^x wy'(x)d\xi = -wxy'(x).$$

Then

$$y^{(3)}(x) + \frac{w}{EI}xy'(x) = 0.$$

Let $u = y'$ to obtain the second order differential equation

$$u'' + \frac{w}{EI}xu = 0.$$

Compare this equation with equation 16.12. We need

$$2a - 1 = 0, \quad a^2 - v^2c = 0, \quad 2c - 2 = 1 \quad \text{and} \quad b^2c^2 = \frac{w}{EI}.$$

This leads us to choose

$$a = \frac{1}{2}, \quad c = \frac{3}{2}, \quad v = \frac{1}{3}, \quad b = \frac{2}{3}\sqrt{\frac{w}{EI}}.$$

The general solution for $u(x)$ is

$$u(x) = y'(x) = c_1\sqrt{x}J_{1/3}\left(\frac{2}{3}\sqrt{\frac{w}{EI}}x^{3/2}\right) + c_2\sqrt{x}J_{-1/3}\left(\frac{2}{3}\sqrt{\frac{w}{EI}}x^{3/2}\right).$$

Since there is no bending moment at the top of the rod,

$$y''(0) = 0.$$

We leave it for the student to show that this condition requires $c_1 = 0$. Then

$$y'(x) = c_2 \sqrt{x} J_{-1/3}\left(\frac{2}{3}\sqrt{\frac{w}{EI}}x^{3/2}\right).$$

Since the lower end of the rod is clamped vertically, $y'(L) = 0$, so

$$c_2 \sqrt{L} J_{-1/3}\left(\frac{2}{3}\sqrt{\frac{w}{EI}}L^{3/2}\right) = 0.$$

Since c_2 must be nonzero to avoid a trivial solution, we need

$$J_{-1/3}\left(\frac{2}{3}\sqrt{\frac{w}{EI}}L^{3/2}\right) = 0.$$

The critical length L_C is the smallest positive number which can be substituted for L in this equation. From a table of Bessel functions we find that the smallest positive number α such that $J_{-1/3}(\alpha) = 0$ is approximately 1.8663. Therefore

$$\frac{2}{3}\sqrt{\frac{w}{EI}}L_C^{3/2} \approx 1.8663,$$

so

$$L_C \approx 1.9863\left(\frac{EI}{w}\right)^{1/3}.$$

Alternating Current in a Wire   We will analyze alternating current in a wire of circular cross section, culminating in a mathematical description of the skin effect (at high frequencies, "most" of the current flows through a thin layer at the surface of the wire).

Begin with general principles named for Ampère and Faraday. Ampère's law states that the line integral of the magnetic force around a closed curve (circuit) is equal to 4π times the integral of the electric current through the circuit. Faraday's law states that the line integral of the electric force around a closed circuit equals the negative of the time derivative of the magnetic induction through the circuit.

We want to use these laws to determine the current density at radius r in a wire of circular cross section and radius a. Let ρ be the specific resistance of the wire, μ its permeability, and $x(r, t)$ and $H(r, t)$ the current density and magnetic intensity, respectively at radius r and time t.

To begin, apply Ampère's law to a circle of radius r having its axis along the axis of the wire. We get

$$2\pi r H = 4\pi \int_0^r x(2\pi\xi)d\xi,$$

or

$$rH = 4\pi \int_0^r x\xi d\xi. \tag{16.15}$$

Then

$$\frac{\partial}{\partial r}(rH) = 4\pi x r,$$

so

$$\frac{1}{r}\frac{\partial}{\partial r}(rH) = 4\pi x(r, t). \tag{16.16}$$

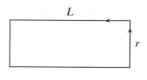

FIGURE 16.11

Now apply Faraday's law to the rectangular circuit of Figure 16.11, having one side of length L along the axis of the cylinder. We get

$$\rho L x(0, t) - \rho L x(r, t) = -\frac{\partial}{\partial t} \int_0^r \mu L H(\xi, t) \, d\xi.$$

Differentiate this equation with respect to r to get

$$\rho \frac{\partial x}{\partial r} = \mu \frac{\partial H}{\partial t}. \tag{16.17}$$

We want to use equations 16.16 and 16.17 to eliminate H. First multiply equation (16.17) by r to get

$$\rho r \frac{\partial x}{\partial r} = \mu r \frac{\partial H}{\partial t}.$$

Differentiate with respect to r:

$$\rho \frac{\partial}{\partial r} \left(r \frac{\partial x}{\partial r} \right) = \mu \frac{\partial}{\partial r} \left(r \frac{\partial H}{\partial t} \right) = \mu \frac{\partial}{\partial t} \left(\frac{\partial}{\partial r} (rH) \right) = \mu \frac{\partial}{\partial t} (4\pi x r) = 4\pi \mu r \frac{\partial x}{\partial t},$$

in which we substituted from equation (16.16) at the next to last step. Then

$$\rho \frac{\partial}{\partial r} \left(r \frac{\partial x}{\partial r} \right) = 4\pi \mu r \frac{\partial x}{\partial t}. \tag{16.18}$$

The idea is to solve this partial differential equation for $x(r, t)$, then obtain $H(r, t)$ from equation (16.15). To do this, assume that the current through the wire is an alternating current given by $C \cos(\omega t)$, with C constant. Thus the period of the current is $2\pi/\omega$. It is convenient to write $z(r, t) = x(r, t) + iy(r, t)$, so $x(r, t) = \text{Re}(z(r, t))$, and to think of the current as the real part of the complex exponential $Ce^{i\omega t}$. The differential equation (16.18), with z in place of x, is

$$\rho \frac{\partial}{\partial r} \left(r \frac{\partial z}{\partial r} \right) = 4\pi \mu r \frac{\partial z}{\partial t}. \tag{16.19}$$

To solve this equation, we will attempt a solution of the form

$$z(r, t) = f(r)e^{i\omega t}.$$

Substitute this proposed solution into equation (16.19) to get

$$\rho \frac{\partial}{\partial r} \left(rf'(r)e^{i\omega t} \right) = 4\pi \mu r f(r) i\omega e^{i\omega t}.$$

Divide by $e^{i\omega t}$ and carry out the differentiations to get

$$f''(r) + \frac{1}{r} f'(r) - b^2 f(r) = 0,$$

where

$$b^2 = \frac{4\pi \mu \omega}{\rho} i.$$

Comparing this equation with equation (16.13), we can write the general solution for $f(r)$ in terms of modified Bessel functions:

$$f(r) = c_1 I_0(br) + c_2 K_0(br),$$

where

$$b = \sqrt{\frac{4\pi\mu\omega}{\rho}} \frac{1+i}{\sqrt{2}}.$$

Because of the logarithm term in $K_0(r)$, which has infinite limit as $r \to 0$ (center of the wire), choose $c_2 = 0$. Thus $f(r)$ has the form

$$f(r) = c_1 I_0(br)$$

and

$$z(r, t) = c_1 I_0(br) e^{i\omega t}.$$

To determine the constant, use the fact that (the real part of) $Ce^{i\omega t}$ is the total current, hence, using equation (16.14),

$$C = 2\pi c_1 \int_0^a r I_0(br) dr = \frac{2\pi a c_1}{b} I_0'(ba).$$

Then

$$c_1 = \frac{bC}{2\pi a} \frac{1}{I_0'(ba)}$$

and

$$z(r, t) = \frac{bC}{2\pi a} \frac{1}{I_0'(ba)} I_0(br) e^{i\omega t}.$$

Then $x(r, t) = \text{Re}(z(r, t))$, and we leave it for the student to show that

$$H(r, t) = \text{Re}\left(\frac{2C}{aI_0'(ba)} I_0(br) e^{i\omega t}\right).$$

We can use the solution for $z(r, t)$ to model the skin effect. The entire current flowing through a cylinder of radius r within the wire (and having the same central axis as the wire), is the real part of

$$\frac{b}{2\pi a I_0'(ba)} Ce^{i\omega t} \int_0^r I_0(br) 2\pi r \, dr,$$

and some computation shows that this is the real part of

$$\frac{r I_0'(br)}{a I_0'(ba)} Ce^{i\omega t}.$$

Therefore

$$\frac{\text{current in the cylinder of radius } r}{\text{total current in the wire}} = \frac{r}{a} \frac{I_0'(br)}{I_0'(ba)}.$$

When the frequency ω is large, then the magnitude of b is large, and we can use the asymptotic expansion of $I_0(x)$ given in Section 16.2.4 to write

$$\frac{r}{a} \frac{I_0'(br)}{I_0'(ba)} \approx \frac{r}{a} \frac{e^{br}}{\sqrt{br}} \frac{\sqrt{ba}}{e^{ba}} = \sqrt{\frac{r}{a}} e^{-b(a-r)}.$$

For any r, with $0 < r < a$, we can make $\sqrt{\frac{r}{a}}e^{-b(a-r)}$ as small as we like by taking the frequency ω sufficiently large. This means that for large frequencies, most of the current is flowing near the outer surface of the wire. This is the skin effect.

16.2.6   A Generating Function for $J_n(x)$

We now return to a development of general properties of Bessel functions.

For the Legendre polynomials, we produced a generating function $L(x, t)$ with the property that

$$L(x, t) = \sum_{n=0}^{\infty} P_n(x)t^n.$$

In the same spirit, we will now produce a generating function for the integer order Bessel functions of the first kind.

THEOREM 16.12   *Generating Function for Bessel Functions*

$$e^{x(t-1/t)/2} = \sum_{n=-\infty}^{\infty} J_n(x)t^n. \tag{16.20}$$

To understand why equation (16.20) is true, begin with the familiar Maclaurin expansion of the exponential function to write

$$e^{x(t-1/t)/2} = e^{xt/2}e^{-x/2t}$$

$$= \left(\sum_{m=0}^{\infty} \frac{1}{m!} \left(\frac{xt}{2} \right)^m \right) \left(\sum_{k=0}^{\infty} \frac{1}{k!}(-1)^k \left(\frac{x}{2t} \right)^k \right)$$

$$\left(1 + \frac{xt}{2} + \frac{1}{2!}\frac{x^2t^2}{2^2} + \frac{1}{3!}\frac{x^3t^3}{2^3} + \cdots \right) \left(1 - \frac{x}{2t} + \frac{1}{2!}\frac{x^2}{2^2t^2} - \frac{1}{3!}\frac{x^3}{2^3t^3} + \cdots \right).$$

To illustrate the idea, look for the coefficient of t^4 in this product. We obtain t^4 when $x^4t^4/2^4 4!$ on the left is multiplied by 1 on the right, and when $x^5t^5/2^5 5!$ is multiplied by $-x/2t$ on the right, and when $x^6t^6/2^6 6!$ is multiplied by $x^2/2^2 2!t^2$ on the right, and so on. In this way we find that the coefficient of t^4 in this product is

$$\frac{1}{2^4 4!}x^4 - \frac{1}{2^6 5!}x^5 + \frac{1}{2^8 2!6!}x^6 - \frac{1}{2^{10} 3!7!}x^7 + \cdots = \sum_{n=0}^{\infty} \frac{(-1)^n}{2^{2n+4}n!(n+4)!}x^{2n+4}.$$

Now compare this series with

$$J_4(x) = \sum_{n=0}^{\infty} \frac{(-1)^n}{2^{2n+4}n!\Gamma(n+4+1)}x^{2n+4} = \sum_{n=0}^{\infty} \frac{(-1)^n}{2^{2n+4}n!(n+4)!}x^{2n+4}.$$

Similar reasoning establishes that the coefficient of t^n in equation (16.20) is $J_n(x)$ for any nonnegative integer n. For negative integers, we can use the fact that

$$J_{-n}(x) = (-1)^n J_n(x).$$

16.2.7   An Integral Formula for $J_n(x)$

Using the generating function, we can derive an integral formula for $J_n(x)$ when n is a positive integer.

THEOREM 16.13   *Bessel's Integral*

If n is a nonnegative integer, then

$$J_n(x) = \frac{1}{\pi} \int_0^\pi \cos(n\theta - x\sin(\theta))d\theta. \quad \blacksquare$$

Proof   Begin with the fact that

$$e^{xt/2}e^{-x/2t} = \sum_{n=-\infty}^\infty J_n(x)t^n.$$

Since $J_{-n}(x) = (-1)^n J_n(x)$,

$$e^{xt/2}e^{-x/2t} = e^{x(t-1/t)/2} = \sum_{n=-\infty}^{-1} J_n(x)t^n + J_0(x) + \sum_{n=1}^\infty J_n(x)t^n$$

$$= \sum_{n=1}^\infty (-1)^n J_n(x)t^{-n} + J_0(x) + \sum_{n=0}^\infty J_n(x)t^n$$

$$= J_0(x) + \sum_{n=1}^\infty J_n(x)\left(t^n + (-1)^n \frac{1}{t^n}\right)$$

$$= J_0(x) + \sum_{n=1}^\infty J_{2n}(x)\left(t^{2n} + \frac{1}{t^{2n}}\right) + \sum_{n=1}^\infty J_{2n-1}(x)\left(t^{2n-1} - \frac{1}{t^{2n-1}}\right). \quad (16.21)$$

Now let

$$t = e^{i\theta} = \cos(\theta) + i\sin(\theta).$$

Then

$$t^{2n} + \frac{1}{t^{2n}} = e^{2in\theta} + e^{-2in\theta} = 2\cos(2n\theta)$$

and

$$t^{2n-1} - \frac{1}{t^{2n-1}} = e^{i(2n-1)\theta} - e^{-i(2n-1)\theta} = 2i\sin((2n-1)\theta).$$

Therefore equation (16.21) becomes

$$e^{x(t-1/t)/2} = e^{ix\sin(\theta)}$$

$$= \cos(x\sin(\theta)) + i\sin(x\sin(\theta))$$

$$= J_0(x) + 2\sum_{n=1}^\infty J_{2n}(x)\cos(2n\theta) + 2i\sum_{n=1}^\infty J_{2n-1}(x)\sin((2n-1)\theta).$$

The real part of the left side of this equation must equal the real part of the right side, and similarly for the imaginary parts:

$$\cos(x\sin(\theta)) = J_0(x) + 2\sum_{n=1}^\infty J_{2n}(x)\cos(2n\theta) \quad (16.22)$$

and

$$\sin(x\sin(\theta)) = 2\sum_{n=1}^{\infty} J_{2n-1}(x)\sin((2n-1)\theta). \tag{16.23}$$

Now recognize that the series on the right in equations (16.22) and (16.23) are Fourier series. Focusing on equation (16.22) for the moment, its Fourier series is therefore

$$\cos(x\sin(\theta)) = \frac{1}{2}a_0 + \sum_{k=1}^{\infty} a_k\cos(k\theta) + b_k\sin(k\theta)$$

$$= J_0(x) + 2\sum_{n=1}^{\infty} J_{2n}(x)\cos(2n\theta).$$

Since we know the coefficients in a Fourier expansion, we conclude that

$$a_k = \frac{1}{\pi}\int_{-\pi}^{\pi}\cos(x\sin(\theta))\cos(k\theta)d\theta = \begin{cases} 0 & \text{if } k \text{ is odd} \\ 2J_k(x) & \text{if } k \text{ is even} \end{cases} \tag{16.24}$$

and

$$b_k = \frac{1}{\pi}\int_{-\pi}^{\pi}\cos(x\sin(\theta))\sin(k\theta)d\theta = 0 \text{ for } k = 1, 2, 3, \ldots. \tag{16.25}$$

Similarly, from equation (16.23),

$$\sin(x\sin(\theta)) = \frac{1}{2}A_0 + \sum_{k=1}^{\infty} A_k\cos(k\theta) + B_k\sin(k\theta)$$

$$= 2\sum_{n=1}^{\infty} J_{2n-1}(x)\sin((2n-1)\theta),$$

so these Fourier coefficients are

$$A_k = \frac{1}{\pi}\int_{-\pi}^{\pi}\sin(x\sin(\theta))\cos(k\theta)d\theta = 0 \quad \text{for} \quad k = 0, 1, 2, \tag{16.26}$$

and

$$B_k = \frac{1}{\pi}\int_{-\pi}^{\pi}\sin(x\sin(\theta))\sin(k\theta)d\theta = \begin{cases} 0 & \text{if } k \text{ is even} \\ 2J_k(x) & \text{if } k \text{ is odd} \end{cases}. \tag{16.27}$$

Upon adding equations (16.24) and (16.27), we have

$$\frac{1}{\pi}\int_{-\pi}^{\pi}\cos(x\sin(\theta))\cos(k\theta)d\theta + \frac{1}{\pi}\int_{-\pi}^{\pi}\sin(x\sin(\theta))\sin(k\theta)d\theta$$

$$= \frac{1}{\pi}\int_{-\pi}^{\pi}\cos(k\theta - x\sin(\theta))d\theta = \begin{cases} 2J_k(x) & \text{if } k \text{ is even} \\ 2J_k(x) & \text{if } k \text{ is odd} \end{cases}.$$

Thus

$$J_k(x) = \frac{1}{2\pi}\int_{-\pi}^{\pi}\cos(k\theta - x\sin(\theta))d\theta \quad \text{for} \quad k = 0, 1, 2, 3, \ldots.$$

To complete the proof, we have only to observe that $\cos(k\theta - x\sin(\theta))$ is an even function, hence $\int_{-\pi}^{\pi} = 2\int_0^{\pi}$, so

$$J_k(x) = \frac{1}{\pi}\int_0^{\pi}\cos(k\theta - x\sin(\theta))d\theta \quad \text{for} \quad k = 0, 1, 2, 3, \ldots. \ \blacksquare$$

16.2.8   A Recurrence Relation for $J_\nu(x)$

We will derive three recurrence-type relationships involving Bessel functions of the first kind. These provide information about the function or its derivative in terms of functions of the same type, but lower index. We begin with two relationships involving derivatives.

THEOREM 16.14

If ν is a real number, then

$$\frac{d}{dx}(x^\nu J_\nu(x)) = x^\nu J_{\nu-1}(x).$$

(16.28)

Proof   Begin with the case that ν is not a negative integer. By direct computation,

$$\frac{d}{dx}(x^\nu J_\nu(x)) = \frac{d}{dx}\left[x^\nu \sum_{n=0}^\infty \frac{(-1)^n}{2^{2n+\nu}n!\Gamma(n+\nu+1)}x^{2n+\nu}\right]$$

$$= \frac{d}{dx}\left[\sum_{n=0}^\infty \frac{(-1)^n}{2^{2n+\nu}n!\Gamma(n+\nu+1)}x^{2n+2\nu}\right]$$

$$= \sum_{n=0}^\infty \frac{(-1)^n 2(n+\nu)}{2^{2n+\nu}n!(n+\nu)\Gamma(n+\nu)}x^{2n+2\nu-1}$$

$$= x^\nu \sum_{n=0}^\infty \frac{(-1)^n}{2^{2n+\nu-1}n!\Gamma(n+\nu)}x^{2n+\nu-1} = x^\nu J_{\nu-1}(x).$$

Now extend this result to the case that ν is a negative integer, say $\nu = -m$ with m a positive integer, by using the fact that

$$J_{-m}(x) = (-1)^m J_m(x).$$

We leave this detail to the student. ■

THEOREM 16.15

If ν is a real number, then

$$\frac{d}{dx}(x^{-\nu}J_\nu(x)) = -x^{-\nu}J_{\nu+1}(x). \quad ■$$

(16.29)

Verification of this relationship is similar to that of equation (16.28).

Using these two recurrence formulas involving derivatives, we can derive the following relationship between Bessel functions of the first kind of different orders.

THEOREM 16.16

Let ν be a real number. Then for $x > 0$,

$$\frac{2\nu}{x}J_\nu(x) = J_{\nu+1}(x) + J_{\nu-1}(x).$$

(16.30)

Proof   Carry out the differentiations in equations (16.28) and (16.29) to write

$$x^\nu J_\nu'(x) + \nu x^{\nu-1}J_\nu(x) = x^\nu J_{\nu-1}(x)$$

and

$$x^{-\nu}J_{\nu}'(x) - \nu x^{-\nu-1}J_{\nu}(x) = -x^{\nu}J_{\nu+1}(x).$$

Multiply the first equation by $x^{-\nu}$ and the second by x^{ν} to obtain

$$J_{\nu}'(x) + \frac{\nu}{x}J_{\nu}(x) = J_{\nu-1}(x)$$

and

$$J_{\nu}'(x) - \frac{\nu}{x}J_{\nu}(x) = -J_{\nu+1}(x).$$

Upon subtracting the second of these equations from the first, we obtain the conclusion of the theorem. ∎

EXAMPLE 16.4

Previously we stated that

$$J_{1/2}(x) = \sqrt{\frac{2}{\pi x}}\sin(x), \quad J_{-1/2}(x) = \sqrt{\frac{2}{\pi x}}\cos(x),$$

results obtained by direct reference to the infinite series for these Bessel functions. Putting $\nu = \frac{1}{2}$ into equation (16.30), we get

$$\frac{1}{x}J_{1/2}(x) = J_{3/2}(x) + J_{-1/2}(x).$$

Then

$$J_{3/2}(x) = \frac{1}{x}J_{1/2}(x) - J_{-1/2}(x)$$

$$= \frac{1}{x}\sqrt{\frac{2}{\pi x}}\sin(x) - \sqrt{\frac{2}{\pi x}}\cos(x)$$

$$= \sqrt{\frac{2}{\pi x}}\left(\frac{1}{x}\sin(x) - \cos(x)\right).$$

Then, upon putting $\nu = \frac{3}{2}$ into equation (16.30), we get

$$\frac{3}{x}J_{3/2}(x) = J_{5/2}(x) + J_{1/2}(x).$$

Then

$$J_{5/2}(x) = -J_{1/2}(x) + \frac{3}{x}J_{3/2}(x)$$

$$= -\sqrt{\frac{2}{\pi x}}\sin(x) + \frac{3}{x}\sqrt{\frac{2}{\pi x}}\left(\frac{1}{x}\sin(x) - \cos(x)\right)$$

$$= \sqrt{\frac{2}{\pi x}}\left[-\sin(x) + \frac{3}{x^2}\sin(x) - \frac{3}{x}\cos(x)\right].$$

This process can be continued indefinitely. The point is that this is a better way to generate Bessel functions $J_{n+1/2}(x)$ than by referring to the infinite series each time. ∎

16.2.9 Zeros of $J_\nu(x)$

We have seen in some of the applications that we sometimes need to know where $J_\nu(x) = 0$. Such points are the zeros of $J_\nu(x)$. We will show that $J_\nu(x)$ has infinitely many simple positive zeros, and also obtain estimates for their locations.

As a starting point, recall from equation (16.12) that $y = J_\nu(kx)$ is a solution of

$$x^2 y'' + y' + \left(k^2 x^2 - \nu^2\right) y = 0.$$

Let $k > 1$. Now put $u(x) = \sqrt{kx} J_\nu(kx)$. Substitute this into Bessel's equation to get

$$u''(x) + \left(k^2 - \frac{\nu^2 - \frac{1}{4}}{x^2}\right) u(x) = 0. \tag{16.31}$$

Our intuition is that, as x increases, the term $\left(\nu^2 - 1/4\right)/x^2$ exerts less influence on this equation for u, which begins to look more like $u'' + k^2 u = 0$, with sine and cosine solutions. This suggests that, for large x, $J_\nu(kx)$ is approximated by a trigonometric function, divided by $\sqrt{kx}$. Since such a function has infinitely many positive zeros, so must $J_\nu(kx)$.

In order to exploit this intuition, consider the equation

$$v''(x) + v(x) = 0. \tag{16.32}$$

This has solution $v(x) = \sin(x - \alpha)$, with α any positive number. Multiply equation (16.31) by v and equation (16.32) by u and subtract to get

$$uv'' - vu'' = \left(k^2 - \frac{\nu^2 - \frac{1}{4}}{x^2}\right) uv - uv.$$

Write this equation as

$$(uv' - vu')' = \left(k^2 - 1 - \frac{\nu^2 - \frac{1}{4}}{x^2}\right) uv.$$

Now compute

$$\int_\alpha^{\alpha + \pi} (uv' - vu')' dx$$

$$= u(\alpha + \pi)v'(\alpha + \pi) - u(\alpha)v'(\alpha) - v(\alpha + \pi)u'(\alpha + \pi) + v(\alpha)u'(\alpha)$$

$$= -u(\alpha + \pi) - u(\alpha)$$

$$= \int_\alpha^{\alpha + \pi} \left(k^2 - 1 - \frac{\nu^2 - \frac{1}{4}}{x^2}\right) u(x)v(x) dx.$$

Apply the mean value theorem for integrals to the last integral. There is some number τ between α and $\alpha + \pi$ such that

$$-u(\alpha + \pi) - u(\alpha) = u(\tau) \int_\alpha^{\alpha + \pi} \left(k^2 - 1 - \frac{\nu^2 - \frac{1}{4}}{x^2}\right) \sin(x - \alpha) dx.$$

Now $\sin(x - \alpha) > 0$ for $\alpha < x < \alpha + \pi$. Further, we can choose α large enough (depending on ν and k) that

$$k^2 - 1 - \frac{\nu^2 - \frac{1}{4}}{x^2} > 0$$

for $\alpha \leq x \leq \alpha + \pi$. Therefore the integral on the right in the last equation is positive. Then $u(\alpha + \pi)$, $u(\alpha)$, and $u(\tau)$ cannot all be of the same sign. Since u is continuous, u must have a zero somewhere between α and $\alpha + \pi$. Since $u(x) = \sqrt{kx}J_\nu(kx)$, this proves that $J_\nu(kx)$ has at least one zero between α and $\alpha + \pi$.

In general, if α is any sufficiently large number and $k > 1$, then $J_\nu(x)$ has a zero between α and $\alpha + k\pi$.

We can now state a general result on positive zeros of Bessel functions of the first kind.

THEOREM 16.17   Zeros of $J_\nu(x)$

Let $k > 1$ and let ν be a real number. Then, for α sufficiently large, there is a zero of $J_\nu(x)$ between $\alpha + kn\pi$ and $\alpha + k(n+1)\pi$ for $n = 0, 1, 2, \ldots$. Further, each zero is simple.

Proof   The argument given prior to the theorem shows that, for any number sufficiently large (depending on ν and the selected $k > 1$), there is a zero of $J_\nu(x)$ in the interval from that number to that number plus $k\pi$. Thus there is a zero between α and $\alpha + k\pi$, and then between $(\alpha + k\pi)$ and $(\alpha + (k+1)\pi)$, and so on.

Further, each zero is simple. For if a zero β has multiplicity greater than 1, then $J_\nu(\beta) = J_\nu'(\beta) = 0$. But then $J_\nu(x)$ is a solution of the initial value problem

$$x^2 y'' + y' + \left(k^2 x^2 - \nu^2\right) y = 0; \quad y(\beta) = y'(\beta) = 0.$$

Since the solution of this problem is unique, and the zero function is a solution, this would imply that $J_\nu(x) = 0$ for $x > 0$, a contradiction. Thus each zero is simple. ∎

The theorem implies that we can order the positive zeros of $J_\nu(x)$ in an increasing sequence

$$j_1 < j_2 < j_3 < \ldots,$$

so that $\lim_{n\to\infty} j_n = \infty$.

It can be shown that for $\nu > -1$, $J_\nu(x)$ has no complex zeros.

We will show that J_ν has no positive zero in common with $J_{\nu+1}$ or $J_{\nu-1}$. However, we claim that both $J_{\nu-1}$ and $J_{\nu+1}$ have at least one zero between any pair of positive zeros of J_ν. This is the interlacing lemma stated as Theorem 16.18 below, and it means that the graphs of these three functions weave about each other, as can be seen in Figure 16.12 for $J_7(x)$, $J_8(x)$ and $J_9(x)$. First we need the following.

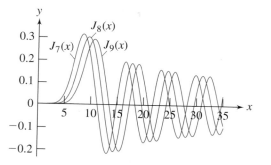

FIGURE 16.12   *Interlacing of $J_7(x)$, $J_8(x)$, and $J_9(x)$.*

LEMMA 16.1

Let ν be a real number. Then, except possibly for $x = 0$, J_ν has no zero in common with either $J_{\nu-1}$ or with $J_{\nu+1}$. ∎

Proof   Recall from the proof of Theorem 16.16 that

$$J_\nu'(x) + \frac{\nu}{x} J_\nu(x) = J_{\nu-1}(x).$$

If $\beta \neq 0$ and $J_\nu(\beta) = J_{\nu-1}(\beta) = 0$, then $J_\nu'(\beta) = 0$ also. But then β would be a zero of multiplicity at least two for J_ν, a contradiction.

A similar use of the relation

$$J_\nu'(x) - \frac{\nu}{x} J_\nu(x) = J_{\nu+1}(x)$$

shows that J_ν also cannot share a nonzero zero with $J_{\nu+1}$. ∎

THEOREM 16.18   *Interlacing Lemma*

Let ν be any real number. Let a and b be distinct positive zeros of J_ν. Then $J_{\nu-1}$ and $J_{\nu+1}$ each have at least one zero between a and b.

Proof   Let $f(x) = x^\nu J_\nu(x)$. Then $f(a) = f(b) = 0$. Because f is differentiable at all points between a and b, by Rolle's theorem, there is some c between a and b at which $f'(c) = 0$. But

$$f'(x) = \frac{d}{dx}(x^\nu J_\nu(x)) = x^\nu J_{\nu-1}(x),$$

so $f'(c) = 0$ implies that $J_{\nu-1}(c) = 0$.

Similar reasoning, applied to $g(x) = x^{-\nu} J_\nu(x)$, and using the recursion relation

$$\frac{d}{dx}(x^{-\nu} J_\nu(x)) = -x^{-\nu} J_{\nu+1}(x),$$

shows that $J_{\nu+1}$ has a zero between a and b. ∎

The following table gives the first five positive zeros of $J_\nu(x)$ for $\nu = 0, 1, 2, 3, 4$. The numbers here are rounded at the third decimal place. The interlacing property of successive indexed Bessel functions can be seen by looking down the columns. For example, the second positive zero of $J_2(x)$ falls between the second positive zeros of $J_1(x)$ and $J_3(x)$.

	j_1	j_2	j_3	j_4	j_5
$J_0(x)$	2.405	5.520	8.654	11.792	14.931
$J_1(x)$	3.832	7.016	10.173	13.323	16.470
$J_2(x)$	5.135	8.417	11.620	14.796	17.960
$J_3(x)$	6.379	9.760	13.017	16.224	19.410
$J_4(x)$	7.586	11.064	14.373	17.616	20.827

16.2.10   Fourier–Bessel Expansions

Taking a cue from the Legendre polynomials, we might suspect that Bessel functions are orthogonal on some interval. They are not.

However, let ν be any positive number. We know that J_ν has infinitely many positive zeros, which we can arrange in an ascending sequence

$$j_1 < j_2 < j_3 < \cdots.$$

For each such j_n, we can consider the function $\sqrt{x}J_\nu(j_n x)$ for $0 \le x \le 1$ (so $j_n x$ varies from 0 to j_n). We claim that these functions are orthogonal on $[0, 1]$, in the sense that the integral of the product of any two of these functions over $[0, 1]$, is zero.

THEOREM 16.19   *Orthogonality*

Let $\nu \ge 0$. Then the functions $\sqrt{x}J_\nu(j_n x)$, for $n = 1, 2, 3, \ldots$, are orthogonal on $[0, 1]$ in the sense that

$$\int_0^1 xJ_\nu(j_n x)J_\nu(j_m x)dx = 0 \quad \text{if} \quad n \ne m. \ \blacksquare$$

This is in the same spirit as the orthogonality of the Legendre polynomials on $[-1, 1]$, and orthogonality of the functions

$$1, \cos(x), \cos(2x), \ldots, \sin(x), \sin(2x), \ldots$$

on $[-\pi, \pi]$.

Proof   Again invoking equation (16.12), $u(x) = J_\nu(j_n x)$ satisfies

$$x^2 u'' + xu' + (j_n^2 x^2 - \nu^2)u = 0.$$

And $v(x) = J_\nu(j_m x)$ satisfies

$$x^2 v'' + xv' + (j_m^2 x^2 - \nu^2)v = 0.$$

Multiply the first equation by v and the second by u, and subtract the resulting equations to obtain

$$x^2 u'' v + xu' v + (j_n^2 x^2 - \nu^2)uv - x^2 v'' u - xv' u - (j_m^2 x^2 - \nu^2)uv = 0.$$

This equation can be written

$$x^2(u'' v - uv'') + x(u' v - uv') = (j_m^2 - j_n^2)x^2 uv.$$

Divide by x:

$$x(u'' v - uv'') + (u' v - uv') = (j_m^2 - j_n^2)xuv.$$

Write this equation as

$$[x(u' v - uv')]' = (j_m^2 - j_n^2)xuv.$$

Then

$$\int_0^1 [x(u' v - uv')]' dx = [x(u' v - uv')]_0^1$$

$$= J_\nu'(j_n)J_\nu(j_m) - J_\nu(j_n)J_\nu'(j_m) = 0$$

$$= (j_m^2 - j_n^2) \int_0^1 xJ_\nu(j_n x)J_\nu(j_m x)dx.$$

Since $j_n \ne j_m$, this proves the orthogonality of these functions on $[0, 1]$. $\blacksquare$

As usual, whenever we have an orthogonality relationship, we are led to attempt Fourier-type expansions. Let f be defined on $[0, 1]$. How should we choose the coefficients to have an expansion

$$f(x) = \sum_{n=1}^\infty a_n J_\nu(j_n x)?$$

Using a now familiar strategy, multiply this equation by $xJ_\nu(j_k x)$ and integrate to get

$$\int_0^1 xf(x)J_\nu(j_k x)dx = \sum_{n=1}^\infty a_n \int_0^1 xJ_\nu(j_n x)J_\nu(j_k x)dx = a_k \int_0^1 xJ_\nu^2(j_k x)dx.$$

The infinite series of integrals has collapsed to a single term because of the orthogonality. Then

$$a_k = \frac{\int_0^1 xf(x)J_\nu(j_k x)dx}{\int_0^1 xJ_\nu^2(j_k x)dx}.$$

We call these numbers the *Fourier–Bessel coefficients* of f. When these numbers are used in the series, we call $\sum_{n=1}^\infty a_n J_\nu(j_n x)$ the *Fourier–Bessel expansion*, or *Fourier–Bessel series*, of f in terms of the functions $\sqrt{x}J_\nu(j_n x)$.

Sometimes a different point of view if adopted. It is common to say that the functions $J_\nu(j_n x)$ are *orthogonal on* $[0, 1]$ *with respect to the weight function* $\rho(x) = x$. This simply means that the integral of the product of any two of these functions, and also multiplied by $\rho(x)$, is zero over the interval $[0, 1]$:

$$\int_0^1 \rho(x)J_\nu(j_n x)J_\nu(j_m x)dx = 0 \quad \text{if} \quad n \neq m.$$

This is the same integral we had before for orthogonality, but places the integral in the context of the weight function $\rho(x)$, a viewpoint we will see shortly with Sturm–Liouville theory. Putting $\rho(x) = x$ in this integral has the same effect as putting a factor $\sqrt{x}$ with each $J_\nu(j_n x)$.

As with Fourier and Fourier–Legendre expansions, the fact that we can compute the coefficients and write the series does not mean that it is related to the function in any particular way. The following convergence theorem deals with this issue.

THEOREM 16.20   *Convergence of Fourier–Bessel Series*

Let f be piecewise smooth on $[0, 1]$. Then, for $0 < x < 1$,

$$\sum_{n=1}^\infty a_n J_\nu(j_n x) = \frac{1}{2}(f(x+) + f(x-)),$$

where a_n is the nth Fourier–Bessel coefficient of f. ∎

We will give an example of a Fourier–Bessel expansion after we learn more about the coefficients.

16.2.11   Fourier–Bessel Coefficients

The integral $\int_0^1 xJ_\nu^2(j_k x)dx$ occurs in the denominator of the expression for the Fourier–Bessel coefficients of any function, so it is useful to have an evaluation of this integral.

THEOREM 16.21

If $\nu \geq 0$, then

$$\int_0^1 xJ_\nu^2(j_k x)dx = \frac{1}{2}J_{\nu+1}^2(j_k). \ ∎$$

Notice the importance here of the fact that J_ν and $J_{\nu+1}$ cannot have a positive zero in common. Knowing that $J_\nu(j_k) = 0$ implies that $J_{\nu+1}(j_k) \neq 0$.

Proof From the preceding discussion,

$$x^2 u'' + xu' + (j_k^2 x^2 - \nu^2)u = 0,$$

where $u(x) = J_\nu(j_k x)$. Multiply this equation by $2u'(x)$ to get

$$2x^2 u' u'' + 2x(u')^2 + 2(j_k^2 x^2 - \nu^2)uu' = 0.$$

We can write this equation as

$$[x^2(u')^2 + (j_k^2 x^2 - \nu^2)u^2]' - 2j_k^2 xu^2 = 0.$$

Now integrate, keeping in mind that $u(1) = 0$:

$$0 = \int_0^1 [x^2(u')^2 + (j_k^2 x^2 - \nu^2)u^2]' dx - 2j_k^2 \int_0^1 xu^2 dx$$

$$= [x^2(u')^2 + (j_k^2 x^2 - \nu^2)u^2]_0^1 - 2j_k^2 \int_0^1 xu^2 dx$$

$$= (u'(1))^2 - 2j_k^2 \int_0^1 xu^2 dx$$

$$= j_k^2 [J_k'(j_k)] - 2j_k^2 \int_0^1 x[J_\nu(j_k x)]^2 dx.$$

Then

$$\int_0^1 xJ_\nu^2(j_k x)dx = \frac{1}{2}[J_\nu'(j_k)]^2.$$

Now in general

$$J_\nu'(x) - \frac{\nu}{x}J_\nu(x) = -J_{\nu+1}(x).$$

Then

$$J_\nu'(j_k) - \frac{\nu}{j_k}J_\nu(j_k) = -J_{\nu+1}(j_k)$$

so

$$J_\nu'(j_k) = -J_{\nu+1}(j_k).$$

Therefore

$$\int_0^1 xJ_\nu^2(j_k x)dx = \frac{1}{2}[J_{\nu+1}(j_k)]^2. \blacksquare$$

In view of this conclusion, the Fourier–Bessel coefficient of f is

$$a_n = \frac{2}{[J_{\nu+1}(j_n)]^2} \int_0^1 xf(x)J_\nu(j_n x)dx.$$

Fourier–Bessel series will occur later when we solve the heat equation for certain kinds of regions. We will then be faced with the task of expanding the initial temperature function in a Fourier–Bessel series. We will also see a Fourier–Bessel expansion when we solve for the normal modes of vibration in a circular membrane.

Generally Fourier–Bessel coefficients are difficult to compute because Bessel functions are difficult to evaluate at particular points, and even their zeros must be approximated. However, with modern computing power we can often make approximations to whatever degree of accuracy is needed.

EXAMPLE 16.5

Let $f(x) = x(1-x)$ for $0 \leq x \leq 1$. Since f is continuous with a continuous derivative, its Fourier–Bessel series will converge to $f(x)$ on $(0, 1)$:

$$x(1-x) = \sum_{n=1}^{\infty} a_n J_1(j_n x) \quad \text{for} \quad 0 < x < 1,$$

where

$$a_n = \frac{2}{[J_2(j_n)]^2} \int_0^1 x^2(1-x)J_1(j_n x)dx.$$

We will compute a_1 through a_4, using eight decimal places in the first four zeros of $J_1(x)$:

$$j_1 = 3.83170597, \ j_2 = 7.01558667, \ j_3 = 10.17346814, \ j_4 = 13.32369194.$$

With the understanding that these integrations are approximations, compute

$$a_1 = \frac{2}{[J_2(3.83170597)]^2} \int_0^1 x^2(1-x)J_1(3.83170597x)dx$$

$$= 12.32930609 \int_0^1 x^2(1-x)J_1(3.83170597x)dx$$

$$= 0.45221702,$$

$$a_2 = \frac{2}{[J_2(7.01558667)]^2} \int_0^1 x^2(1-x)J_1(7.01558667x)dx$$

$$= 22.20508362 \int_0^1 x^2(1-x)J_1(7.01558667x)dx$$

$$= -0.03151859,$$

$$a_3 = \frac{2}{[J_2(10.17346814)]^2} \int_0^1 x^2(1-x)J_1(10.17346814x)dx$$

$$= 32.07568554 \int_0^1 x^2(1-x)J_1(10.17346814x)dx$$

$$= 0.03201789,$$

and

$$a_4 = \frac{2}{[J_2(13.32369194)]^2} \int_0^1 x^2(1-x)J_1(13.32369194x)dx$$

$$= 41.94557796 \int_0^1 x^2(1-x)J_1(13.32369194x)dx$$

$$= -0.00768864.$$

Then, for $0 < x < 1$,

$$x(1-x) \approx 0.45221702 J_1(3.83170597x) - 0.03151859 J_1(7.01558667x)$$

$$+ 0.03201794 J_1(10.17346814x) - 0.00768864 J_1(13.32369194x).$$

Figure 16.13 shows a graph of $x(1-x)$ and a graph of this four term sum of Bessel functions on $[0, 1]$. The graph is drawn on $[-1, \frac{3}{2}]$ to emphasize that, outside of $[0, 1]$, there is no claim

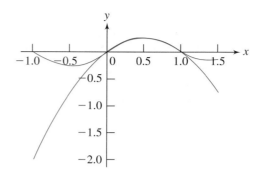

FIGURE 16.13 *Approximation of $x(1-x)$ on $[0, 1]$ by a Fourier–Bessel series.*

that $x(1-x)$ is approximated by the Fourier–Bessel series, and indeed the graphs diverge away from each other outside of $[0, 1]$. Accuracy on $[0, 1]$ can be improved by computing more terms in the series. ■

SECTION 16.2   PROBLEMS

1. Show that $x^a J_\nu(bx^c)$ is a solution of

$$y'' - \left(\frac{2a-1}{x}\right)y' + \left(b^2 c^2 x^{2c-2} + \frac{a^2 - \nu^2 c^2}{x^2}\right)y = 0.$$

In each of Problems 2 through 9, write the general solution of the differential equation in terms of functions $x^a J_\nu(bx^c)$ and $x^a J_{-\nu}(bx^c)$.

2. $y'' + \dfrac{1}{3x}y' + \left(1 + \dfrac{7}{144x^2}\right)y = 0$

3. $y'' + \dfrac{1}{x}y' + \left(4x^2 - \dfrac{4}{9x^2}\right)y = 0$

4. $y'' - \dfrac{5}{x}y' + \left(64x^6 + \dfrac{5}{x^2}\right)y = 0$

5. $y'' + \dfrac{3}{x}y' + \left(16x^2 - \dfrac{5}{4x^2}\right)y = 0$

6. $y'' - \dfrac{3}{x}y' + 9x^4 y = 0$

7. $y'' - \dfrac{7}{x}y' + \left(36x^4 + \dfrac{175}{16x^2}\right)y = 0$

8. $y'' + \dfrac{1}{x}y' - \dfrac{1}{16x^2}y = 0$

9. $y'' + \dfrac{5}{x}y' + \left(81x^4 + \dfrac{7}{4x^2}\right)y = 0$

10. Use the change of variables $by = \dfrac{1}{u}\dfrac{du}{dx}$ to transform the differential equation

$$\frac{dy}{dx} + by^2 = cx^m$$

into the differential equation

$$\frac{d^2u}{dx^2} - bcx^m u = 0.$$

Use the result of problem 1 to find the general solution of this differential equation in terms of Bessel functions, and use this solution to solve the original differential equation. Assume that b is a positive constant.

In each of Problems 11 through 16, use the given change of variables to transform the differential equation into one whose general solution can be written in terms of Bessel functions. Use this to write the general solution of the original differential equation.

11. $4x^2 y'' + 4xy' + (x-9)y = 0; z = \sqrt{x}$

12. $4x^2 y'' + 4xy' + (9x^3 - 36)y = 0; z = x^{3/2}$

13. $9x^2 y'' + 9xy' + (4x^{2/3} - 16)y = 0; z = 2x^{1/3}$

14. $9x^2 y'' - 27xy' + (9x^2 + 35)y = 0; u = y/x^2$

15. $36x^2 y'' - 12xy' + (36x^2 + 7)y = 0; u = x^{-2/3}y$

16. $4x^2 y'' + 8xy' + (4x^2 - 35)y = 0; u = y\sqrt{x}$

17. Show that $y(x) = \sqrt{x}J_{1/3}(2kx^{3/2}3)$ is a solution of $y'' + k^2 xy = 0$.

In each of Problems 18 through 22, write the general solution of the differential equation in terms of functions $x^a J_\nu(bx^c)$ and $x^a Y_\nu(bx^c)$.

18. $y'' - \dfrac{3}{x} y' + \left(4 - \dfrac{5}{x^2}\right) y = 0$

19. $y'' - \dfrac{1}{x} y' + \left(1 - \dfrac{3}{x^2}\right) y = 0$

20. $y'' - \dfrac{5}{x} y' + \left(1 - \dfrac{7}{x^2}\right) y = 0$

21. $y'' - \dfrac{3}{x} y' + \left(\dfrac{1}{4x} + \dfrac{3}{x^2}\right) y = 0$

22. $y'' - \dfrac{1}{x} y' + \left(16x^2 - \dfrac{15}{x^2}\right) y = 0$

23. Show that

$$J_{5/2}(x) = \sqrt{\dfrac{2}{\pi x}} \left[\left(\dfrac{3}{x^2} - 1\right) \sin(x) - \dfrac{3}{x} \cos(x)\right].$$

24. Show that

$$J_{-5/2}(x) = \sqrt{\dfrac{2}{\pi x}} \left[\left(\dfrac{3}{x^2} - 1\right) \cos(x) + \dfrac{3}{x} \sin(x)\right].$$

25. Let α be a positive zero of $J_0(x)$. Show that $\int_0^1 J_1(\alpha x) dx = 1/\alpha$.

26. Let $u(x) = J_0(\alpha x)$ and $v(x) = J_0(\beta x)$.

(a) Show that $xu'' + u' + \alpha^2 xu = 0$. Derive a similar differential equation for v.

(b) Multiply the differential equation for u by v, and the differential equation for v by u and subtract to show that

$$[x(u'v - v'u)]' = (\beta^2 - \alpha^2) xuv.$$

(c) Show from part (b) that

$$(\beta^2 - \alpha^2) \int xJ_0(\alpha x) J_0(\beta x) dx$$

$$= x\left[\alpha J_0'(\alpha x) J_0(\beta x) - \beta J_0'(\beta x) J_0(\alpha x)\right].$$

This is one of a set of formulas called *Lommel's integrals.*

27. Show that $[xI_0'(x)]' = xI_0(x)$.

28. In each of (a) through (d), find (approximately) the first five terms in the Fourier–Bessel expansion $\sum_{n=1}^{\infty} a_n J_1(j_n x)$ of $f(x)$, which is defined for $0 \le x \le 1$. Compare the graph of this function with the graph of the sum of the first five terms in the series.

(a) $f(x) = x$

(b) $f(x) = e^{-x}$

(c) $f(x) = xe^{-x}$

(d) $f(x) = x^2 e^{-x}$

29. Carry out the program of Problem 28, except now use an expansion $\sum_{n=1}^{\infty} a_n J_2(j_n x)$.

16.3   Sturm–Liouville Theory and Eigenfunction Expansions

16.3.1   The Sturm–Liouville Problem

We have now seen essentially the same scenario played out three times:

differential equation $\implies$ solutions that are orthogonal on $[a, b]$

$\implies$ expansions of arbitrary functions in series of these solutions

$\implies$ convergence theorem for the expansion.

First we had Fourier (trigonometric) series, then Legendre polynomials and Fourier–Legendre series, and then Bessel functions and Fourier–Bessel expansions.

It stretches the imagination to think that the similarities in the convergence theorems for these expansions are mere coincidence. We will now develop a general theory into which these convergence theorems fit naturally. This will also expand our arsenal of tools in preparation for solving partial differential equations.

Consider the differential equation

$$y'' + R(x)y' + (Q(x) + \lambda P(x))y = 0. \tag{16.33}$$

Given an interval (a, b) on which the coefficients are continuous, we seek values of λ for which this equation has nontrivial solutions. As we will see, in some cases there will be boundary conditions solutions must satisfy (conditions specified at a and b), and sometimes not.

First put the differential equation into a convenient standard form. Multiply equation (16.33) by

$$r(x) = e^{\int R(x)dx}$$

to get

$$y'' e^{\int R(x)dx} + R(x) y' e^{\int R(x)dx} + (Q(x) + \lambda P(x)) e^{\int R(x)dx} y = 0.$$

Since $r(x) \neq 0$, this equation has the same solutions as equation (16.33). Now recognize that the last equation can be written

$$(ry')' + (q + \lambda p)y = 0. \qquad (16.34)$$

Equation (16.34) is called the *Sturm–Liouville differential equation*, or the *Sturm–Liouville form of equation* (16.33). We will assume that p, q and r and r' are continuous on $[a, b]$, or at least on (a, b), and $p(x) > 0$ and $r(x) > 0$ on (a, b).

EXAMPLE 16.6

Legendre's differential equation is

$$(1 - x^2)y'' - 2xy' + \lambda y = 0.$$

We can immediately write this in Sturm–Liouville form as

$$((1 - x^2)y')' + \lambda y = 0,$$

for $-1 \leq x \leq 1$. Corresponding to the values $\lambda = n(n + 1)$, with $n = 0, 1, 2, \ldots$, the Legendre polynomials are solutions. As we saw in Section 16.1, there are also nonpolynomial solutions corresponding to other choices for λ. However, these nonpolynomial solutions are not bounded on $[-1, 1]$. ∎

EXAMPLE 16.7

Equation (16.12), with $a = 0$, $c = 1$ and $b = \sqrt{\lambda}$, can be written

$$(xy')' + \left(\lambda x - \frac{\nu^2}{x} \right) y = 0.$$

This is the Sturm–Liouville form of Bessel's equation. For $\lambda > 0$, this equation has solutions in terms of the Bessel functions of order ν of the first and second kinds, $J_\nu(\sqrt{\lambda}x)$ and $Y_\nu(\sqrt{\lambda}x)$. ∎

We will now distinguish three kinds of Sturm–Liouville problems.

The Regular Sturm–Liouville Problem   We want numbers λ for which there are nontrivial solutions of

$$(ry')' + (q + \lambda p)y = 0$$

on an interval $[a, b]$. These solutions must satisfy *regular boundary conditions*, which have the form

$$A_1 y(a) + A_2 y'(a) = 0, \; B_1 y(b) + B_2 y'(b) = 0.$$

A_1 and A_2 are given constants, not both zero, and similarly for B_1 and B_2.

The Periodic Sturm–Liouville Problem   Now suppose $r(a) = r(b)$. We seek numbers λ and corresponding nontrivial solutions of the Sturm–Liouville equation on $[a, b]$, satisfying the *periodic boundary conditions*

$$y(a) = y(b), \quad y'(a) = y'(b).$$

The Singular Sturm–Liouville Problem   We look for numbers λ and corresponding nontrivial solutions of the Sturm–Liouville equation on (a, b), subject to one of the following three kinds of boundary conditions:

    Type 1. $r(a) = 0$ and there is no boundary condition at a, while at b the boundary condition is

$$B_1 y(b) + B_2 y(b) = 0,$$

where B_1 and B_2 are not both zero.

    Type 2. $r(b) = 0$ and there is no boundary condition at b, while at a the condition is

$$A_1 y(a) + A_2 y'(a) = 0,$$

with A_1 and A_2 not both zero.

    Type 3. $r(a) = r(b) = 0$, and no boundary condition is specified at a or b. In this case we want solutions that are bounded functions on $[a, b]$.

Each of these problems is a *boundary value problem*, specifying certain conditions at the endpoints of an interval, as contrasted with an initial value problem, which specifies information about the function and its derivative at a point (in the second order case). Boundary value problems usually do not have unique solutions. Indeed, it is exactly this lack of uniqueness that can be exploited to solve many important problems.

In each of these problems, a number λ for which the Sturm–Liouville differential equation has a nontrivial solution is called an *eigenvalue* of the problem. A corresponding nontrivial solution is called an *eigenfunction associated with this eigenvalue*. The zero function cannot be an eigenfunction. However, any nonzero constant multiple of an eigenfunction associated with a particular eigenvalue, is also an eigenfunction for this eigenvalue. In mathematical models of problems in physics and engineering, eigenvalues usually have some physical significance. For example, in studying wave motion the eigenvalues are fundamental frequencies of vibration of the system.

We will consider examples of these kinds of problems. The first will be important in analyzing problems involving heat conduction and wave propagation.

EXAMPLE 16.8   A Regular Problem

Consider the regular problem

$$y'' + \lambda y = 0; \quad y(0) = y(L) = 0$$

on an interval $[0, L]$. We will find the eigenvalues and eigenfunctions by considering cases on λ. Since we will show later that a Sturm–Liouville problem cannot have a complex eigenvalue, there are three cases.

Case 1 $\lambda = 0$.
Then $y(x) = cx + d$ for some constants c and d. Now $y(0) = d = 0$, and $y(L) = cL = 0$ requires that $c = 0$. This means that $y(x) = cx + d$ must be the trivial solution. In the absence of a nontrivial solution, $\lambda = 0$ is not an eigenvalue of this problem.

Case 2 λ is negative, say $\lambda = -k^2$ for $k > 0$.

Now $y'' - k^2 y = 0$ has general solution

$$y(x) = c_1 e^{kx} + c_2 e^{-kx}.$$

Since

$$y(0) = c_1 + c_2 = 0$$

then $c_2 = -c_1$, so $y = 2c_1 \sinh(kx)$. But then

$$y(L) = 2c_1 \sinh(kL) = 0.$$

Since $kL > 0$, $\sinh(kL) > 0$, so $c_1 = 0$. This case also leads to the trivial solution, so this Sturm–Liouville problem has no negative eigenvalue.

Case 3 λ is positive, say $\lambda = k^2$.

The general solution of $y'' + k^2 y = 0$ is

$$y(x) = c_1 \cos(kx) + c_2 \sin(kx).$$

Now

$$y(0) = c_1 = 0,$$

so $y(x) = c_2 \sin(kx)$. Finally, we need

$$y(L) = c_2 \sin(kL) = 0.$$

To avoid the trivial solution, we need $c_2 \neq 0$. Then we must choose k so that $\sin(kL) = 0$, which means that kL must be a positive integer multiple of π, say $kL = n\pi$. Then

$$\lambda_n = \frac{n^2 \pi^2}{L^2} \quad \text{for} \quad n = 1, 2, 3, \ldots.$$

Each of these numbers is an eigenvalue of this Sturm–Liouville problem. Corresponding to each n, the eigenfunctions are

$$y_n(x) = c \sin\left(\frac{n\pi x}{L}\right),$$

in which c can be any nonzero real number. ∎

EXAMPLE 16.9 A Periodic Sturm–Liouville Problem

Consider the problem

$$y'' + \lambda y = 0; \quad y(-L) = y(L), \, y'(-L) = y'(L)$$

on an interval $[-L, L]$. Comparing this differential equation to equation (16.34), we have $r(x) = 1$, so $r(-L) = r(L)$, as required for a periodic Sturm–Liouville problem. Consider cases on λ.

Case 1 $\lambda = 0$.

Then $y = cx + d$. Now

$$y(-L) = -cL + d = y(L) = cL + d$$

implies that $c = 0$. The constant function $y = d$ satisfies both boundary conditions. Thus $\lambda = 0$ is an eigenvalue with nonzero constant eigenfunctions.

Case 2 $\lambda < 0$, say $\lambda = -k^2$.

Now

$$y(x) = c_1 e^{kx} + c_2 e^{-kx}.$$

Since $y(-L) = y(L)$, then

$$c_1 e^{-kL} + c_2 e^{kL} = c_1 e^{kL} + c_2 e^{-kL}. \tag{16.35}$$

And $y'(-L) = y'(L)$ gives us (after dividing out the common factor k)

$$c_1 e^{-kL} - c_2 e^{kL} = c_1 e^{kL} - c_2 e^{-kL}. \tag{16.36}$$

Rewrite equation (16.35) as

$$c_1(e^{-kL} - e^{kL}) = c_2(e^{-kL} - e^{kL}).$$

This implies that $c_1 = c_2$. Then equation (16.36) becomes

$$c_1(e^{-kL} - e^{kL}) = c_1(e^{kL} - e^{-kL})$$

But this implies that $c_1 = -c_1$, hence $c_1 = 0$. The solution is therefore trivial, hence this problem has no negative eigenvalue.

Case 3 λ is positive, say $\lambda = k^2$.
Now

$$y(x) = c_1 \cos(kx) + c_2 \sin(kx).$$

Now

$$y(-L) = c_1 \cos(kL) - c_2 \sin(kL) = y(L) = c_1 \cos(kL) + c_2 \sin(kL).$$

But this implies that

$$2c_2 \sin(kL) = 0.$$

Next,

$$y'(-L) = kc_1 \sin(kL) + kc_2 \cos(kL)$$
$$= y'(L) = -kc_1 \sin(kL) + kc_2 \cos(kL).$$

Then

$$kc_1 \sin(kL) = 0.$$

If $\sin(kL) \neq 0$, then $c_1 = c_2 = 0$, leaving the trivial solution. Thus suppose $\sin(kL) = 0$. This requires that $kL = n\pi$ for some positive integer n. Therefore the numbers

$$\lambda_n = \frac{n^2 \pi^2}{L^2}$$

are eigenvalues for $n = 1, 2, \ldots$, with corresponding eigenfunctions

$$y_n(x) = c_1 \cos\left(\frac{n\pi x}{L}\right) + c_2 \sin\left(\frac{n\pi x}{L}\right),$$

with c_1 and c_2 not both zero.

We can combine Cases 1 and 3 by allowing $n = 0$, so the eigenvalue $\lambda = 0$ has corresponding nonzero constant eigenfunctions. ∎

EXAMPLE 16.10   Bessel Functions as Eigenfunctions of a Singular Problem

Consider Bessel's equation of order ν,

$$(xy')' + \left(\lambda x - \frac{\nu^2}{x}\right) y = 0,$$

on the interval $(0, R)$. Here ν is any given nonnegative real number, and $R > 0$. In the context of the Sturm–Liouville differential equation, $r(x) = x$, and $r(0) = 0$, so there is no boundary condition at 0. Let the boundary condition at R be

$$y(R) = 0.$$

We know that, if $\lambda > 0$, then the general solution of Bessel's equation is

$$y(x) = c_1 J_\nu(\sqrt{\lambda}x) + c_2 Y_\nu(\sqrt{\lambda}x).$$

To have a solution that is bounded as $x \to 0+$, we must choose $c_2 = 0$. This leaves solutions of the form $y = c_1 J_\nu(\sqrt{\lambda}x)$. To satisfy the boundary condition at $x = R$, we must have

$$y(R) = c_1 J_\nu(\sqrt{\lambda}R) = 0.$$

We need $c_1 \neq 0$ to avoid the trivial solution, so we must choose λ so that $J_\nu(\sqrt{\lambda}R) = 0$. If $j_1, j_2, \ldots$ are the positive zeros of $J_\nu(x)$, then $\sqrt{\lambda}R$ can be chosen as any j_n. This yields an infinite sequence of eigenvalues

$$\lambda_n = \frac{j_n^2}{R^2},$$

with corresponding eigenfunctions

$$cJ_\nu\left(\frac{j_n x}{R}\right),$$

with c constant but nonzero.

This is an example of a type 1 singular Sturm–Liouville problem. ■

EXAMPLE 16.11   Legendre Polynomials as Eigenfunctions of a Singular Problem

Consider Legendre's differential equation

$$((1 - x^2)y')' + \lambda y = 0.$$

In the setting of Sturm–Liouville theory, $r(x) = 1 - x^2$. On the interval $[-1, 1]$, we have $r(-1) = r(1) = 0$, so there are no boundary conditions and this is a singular Sturm–Liouville problem of type 3. We want bounded solutions on this interval, so choose $\lambda = n(n + 1)$, with $n = 0, 1, 2, \ldots$. These are the eigenvalues of this problem. Corresponding eigenfunctions are nonzero constant multiples of the Legendre polynomials $P_n(x)$. ■

Finally, here is an example with more complicated boundary conditions.

EXAMPLE 16.12

Consider the regular problem

$$y'' + \lambda y = 0; \quad y(0) = 0, 3y(1) + y'(1) = 0.$$

This problem is defined on $[0, 1]$. To find the eigenvalues and eigenfunctions, consider cases on λ.

Case 1 $\lambda = 0$.
Now $y(x) = cx + d$, and $y(0) = d = 0$. Then $y = cx$. But from the second boundary condition,

$$3y(1) + y'(1) = 3c + c = 0$$

forces $c = 0$, so this case has only the trivial solution. This means that 0 is not an eigenvalue of this problem.

Case 2 $\lambda < 0$.
Write $\lambda = -k^2$ with $k > 0$, so $y'' - k^2 y = 0$, with general solution

$$y(x) = c_1 e^{kx} + c_2 e^{-kx}.$$

Now $y(0) = 0 = c_1 + c_2$, so $c_2 = -c_1$ and $y(x) = c_1 \sinh(kx)$. Next,

$$3y(1) + y'(1) = 0 = 3c_1 \sinh(k) + c_1 k \cosh(k).$$

But for $k > 0$, $\sinh(k)$ and $k \cosh(k)$ are positive, so this equation forces $c_1 = 0$ and again we obtain only the trivial solution. This problem has no negative eigenvalue.

Case 3 $\lambda > 0$, say $\lambda = k^2$
Now $y'' + k^2 y = 0$, with general solution

$$y(x) = c_1 \cos(kx) + c_2 \sin(kx).$$

Then $y(0) = c_1 = 0$, so $y(x) = c_2 \sin(kx)$. The second boundary condition gives us

$$0 = 3c_2 \sin(k) + kc_2 \cos(k).$$

We need $c_2 \neq 0$ to avoid the trivial solution, so look for k so that

$$3 \sin(k) + k \cos(k) = 0.$$

This means that

$$\tan(k) = -\frac{k}{3}.$$

This equation cannot be solved algebraically. However, Figure 16.14 shows graphs of $y = \tan(k)$ and $y = -k/3$ on the same set of axes. These graphs intersect infinitely often in the half plane

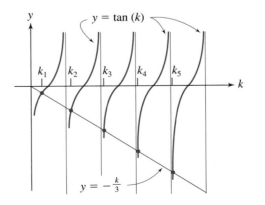

FIGURE 16.14

$k > 0$. Let the k coordinates of these points of intersection be $k_1, k_2, \ldots$ The numbers $\lambda_n = -k_n^2$ are the eigenvalues of this problem, with corresponding eigenfunctions $c \sin(k_n x)$ for $c \neq 0$. ∎

16.3.2 The Sturm–Liouville Theorem

With these examples as background, here is the fundamental theorem of Sturm–Liouville theory.

THEOREM 16.22

1. Each regular and each periodic Sturm–Liouville problem has an infinite number of distinct real eigenvalues. If these are labeled $\lambda_1, \lambda_2 \cdots$ so that $\lambda_n < \lambda_{n+1}$, then $\lim_{n \to \infty} \lambda_n = \infty$.

2. If λ_n and λ_m are distinct eigenvalues of any of the three kinds of Sturm–Liouville problems defined on an interval (a, b), and φ_n and φ_m are corresponding eigenfunctions, then

$$\int_a^b p(x)\varphi_n(x)\varphi_m(x)dx = 0.$$

3. All eigenvalues of a Sturm–Liouville problem are real numbers.

4. For a regular Sturm–Liouville problem, any two eigenfunctions corresponding to a single eigenvalue are constant multiples of each other. ∎

Conclusion (1) assures us of the existence of eigenvalues, at least for regular and periodic problems. A singular problem may also have an infinite sequence of eigenvalues, as we saw in Example 16.10 with Bessel functions. Conclusion (1) also asserts that the eigenvalues "spread out", so that, if arranged in increasing order, they increase without bound. For example, numbers $1 - 1/n$ could not be eigenvalues of a Sturm–Liouville problem, since these numbers approach 1 as $n \to \infty$.

In (2), denote $f \cdot g = \int_a^b p(x)f(x)g(x)dx$. This dot product for functions has many of the properties we have seen for the dot product of vectors. In particular, for functions f, g and h that are integrable on $[a, b]$,

$$f \cdot g = g \cdot f,$$

$$f \cdot (g + h) = f \cdot g + f \cdot h,$$

$$(\alpha f) \cdot g = \alpha(f \cdot g)$$

for any real number α, and

$$f \cdot f \geq 0.$$

The last property relies on the assumption made for the Sturm–Liouville equation that $p(x) > 0$ on (a, b). If f is also continuous on $[a, b]$, then $f \cdot f = 0$ only if f is the zero function, since in this case $\int_a^b p(x)f(x)^2 dx = 0$ can be true only if $f(x) = 0$ for $a \leq x \leq b$.

This analogy between vectors and functions is useful in visualizing certain processes and concepts, and now is an appropriate time to formalize the terminology.

DEFINITION 16.1

Let p be continuous on $[a, b]$ and $p(x) > 0$ for $a < x < b$.

1. If f and g are integrable on $[a, b]$, then the dot product of f with g, with respect to the weight function p, is given by

$$f \cdot g = \int_a^b p(x)f(x)g(x)dx.$$

2. f and g are orthogonal on $[a, b]$, with respect to the weight function p, if $f \cdot g = 0$.

The definition of orthogonality is motivated by the fact that two vectors $\mathbf{F}$ and $\mathbf{G}$ in 3-space are orthogonal exactly when $\mathbf{F} \cdot \mathbf{G} = 0$.

Conclusion (2) may now be stated: eigenfunctions associated with distinct eigenvalues are orthogonal on $[a, b]$, with weight function $p(x)$. The weight function p is the coefficient of λ in the Sturm–Liouville equation.

As we have seen explicitly for Fourier (trigonometric) series, Fourier–Legendre series and Fourier–Bessel series, this orthogonality of eigenfunctions is the key to expansions of functions in series of eigenfunctions of a Sturm–Liouville problem. This will become a significant issue when we solve certain partial differential equations modeling wave and radiation phenomena.

Conclusion (3) states that a Sturm–Liouville problem can have no complex eigenvalue. This is consistent with the fact that eigenvalues for certain problems have physical significance, such as measuring modes of vibration of a system.

Finally, conclusion (4) applies only to regular Sturm–Liouville problems. For example, the periodic Sturm–Liouville problem of Example 16.9 has eigenfunctions $\cos(n\pi x/L)$ and $\sin(n\pi x/L)$ associated with the single eigenvalue $n^2\pi^2/L^2$, and these functions are certainly not constant multiples of each other.

We will prove parts of the Sturm–Liouville theorem.

Proof A proof of (1) requires some delicate analysis that we will not pursue.

For (2), we will essentially reproduce arguments made previously for Legendre polynomials and Bessel functions. Begin with the fact that

$$(r\varphi_n')' + (q + \lambda_n p)\varphi_n = 0$$

and

$$(r\varphi_m')' + (q + \lambda_m p)\varphi_m = 0.$$

Multiply the first equation by φ_m and the second by φ_n and subtract to get

$$(r\varphi_n')'\varphi_m - (r\varphi_m')'\varphi_n = (\lambda_m - \lambda_n)p\varphi_n\varphi_m.$$

Then

$$\int_a^b \left[(r(x)\varphi_n'(x))'\varphi_m(x) - (r(x)\varphi_m'(x))'\varphi_n(x) \right] dx = (\lambda_m - \lambda_n) \int_a^b p(x)\varphi_n(x)\varphi_m(x)dx.$$

Since $\lambda_n \neq \lambda_m$, conclusion (2) will be proved if we can show that the left side of the last equation is zero. Integrate by parts:

$$\int_a^b (r(x)\varphi_n'(x))'\varphi_m(x)\,dx - \int_a^b (r(x)\varphi_m'(x))'\varphi_n(x)\,dx$$

$$= [\varphi_m(x)r(x)\varphi_n'(x)]_a^b - \int_a^b r(x)\varphi_n'(x)\varphi_m'(x)\,dx$$

$$\quad - [\varphi_n(x)r(x)\varphi_m'(x)]_a^b + \int_a^b r(x)\varphi_n'(x)\varphi_m'(x)\,dx$$

$$= r(b)\varphi_m(b)\varphi_n'(b) - r(a)\varphi_m(a)\varphi_n'(a)$$

$$\quad - r(b)\varphi_n(b)\varphi_m'(b) + r(a)\varphi_n(a)\varphi_m'(a)$$

$$= r(b)\left[\varphi_m(b)\varphi_n'(b) - \varphi_n(b)\varphi_m'(b)\right] - r(a)\left[\varphi_m(a)\varphi_n'(a) - \varphi_n(a)\varphi_m'(a)\right]. \tag{16.37}$$

To prove that this quantity is zero, use the boundary conditions that are in effect. Suppose first that we have a regular problem, with boundary conditions

$$A_1 y(a) + A_2 y'(a) = 0, \quad B_1 y(b) + B_2 y'(b) = 0.$$

Applying the boundary condition at a to φ_n and φ_m, we have

$$A_1\varphi_n(a) + A_2\varphi_n'(a) = 0$$

and

$$A_1\varphi_m(a) + A_2\varphi_m'(a) = 0.$$

Since A_1 and A_2 are assumed to be not both zero in the regular problem, then the system of algebraic equations

$$\varphi_n(a)X + \varphi_n'(a)Y = 0,$$

$$\varphi_m(a)X + \varphi_m'(a)Y = 0$$

has a nontrivial solution (namely $X = A_1$, $Y = A_2$). This requires that the determinant of the coefficients vanish:

$$\begin{vmatrix} \varphi_n(a) & \varphi_n'(a) \\ \varphi_m(a) & \varphi_m'(a) \end{vmatrix} = \varphi_n(a)\varphi_m'(a) - \varphi_m(a)\varphi_n'(a) = 0.$$

Using the boundary condition at b, we obtain

$$\varphi_n(b)\varphi_m'(b) - \varphi_m(b)\varphi_n'(b) = 0.$$

Therefore the right side of equation (16.37) is zero, proving the orthogonality relationship in the case of a regular Sturm–Liouville problem. The conclusion is proved similarly for the other kinds of Sturm–Liouville problems, by applying the relevant boundary conditions in equation (16.37).

To prove conclusion (3), suppose that a Sturm–Liouville problem has a complex eigenvalue $\lambda = \alpha + i\beta$. Let $\varphi(x) = u(x) + iv(x)$ be a corresponding eigenfunction. Now

$$(r\varphi')' + (q + \lambda p)\varphi = 0.$$

Take the complex conjugate of this equation, noting that $\varphi'(x) = u'(x) + iv'(x)$ and

$$\overline{\varphi'(x)} = u'(x) - iv'(x) = \left(\overline{\varphi(x)}\right)'.$$

Since $r(x)$, $p(x)$ and $q(x)$ are real-valued, these quantities are their own conjugates, and we get

$$(r\overline{\varphi}')' + (q + \overline{\lambda}p)\overline{\varphi} = 0.$$

This means that $\overline{\lambda}$ is also an eigenvalue, with eigenfunction $\overline{\varphi}$. Now, if $\beta \neq 0$, then λ and $\overline{\lambda}$ are distinct eigenvalues, hence

$$\int_a^b p(x)\varphi(x)\overline{\varphi(x)}dx = 0.$$

But then

$$\int_a^b p(x)[u(x)^2 + v(x)^2]dx = 0.$$

But, for a Sturm–Liouville problem, it is assumed that $p(x) > 0$ for $a < x < b$. Therefore $u(x)^2 + v(x)^2 = 0$, so

$$u(x) = v(x) = 0$$

on $[a, b]$ and $\varphi(x)$ is the trivial solution. This contradicts φ being an eigenfunction. We conclude that $\beta = 0$, so λ is real.

Finally, to prove (4), suppose λ is an eigenvalue of a regular Sturm–Liouville problem, and φ and ψ are both eigenfunctions associated with λ. Use the boundary condition at a, and reason as in part of the proof of (2), to show that

$$\varphi(a)\psi'(a) - \psi(a)\varphi'(a) = 0.$$

But then the Wronskian of φ and ψ vanishes at a, so φ and ψ are linearly dependent and one is a constant multiple of the other. ∎

We now have the machinery needed for general eigenfunction expansions.

16.3.3 Eigenfunction Expansions

In solving partial differential equations, we will often encounter the need to expand a function in a series of solutions of an associated ordinary differential equation—a Sturm–Liouville problem. Fourier series, Fourier–Legendre series, and Fourier–Bessel series are examples of such expansions. The function to be expanded will have some special significance in the problem. It might, for example, be an initial temperature function, or the initial displacement or velocity of a wave.

To create a unified setting in which such series expansions can be understood, consider an analogy with vectors in 3-space. Given a vector $\mathbf{F}$, we can always find real numbers a, b and c so that

$$\mathbf{F} = a\mathbf{i} + b\mathbf{j} + c\mathbf{k}.$$

Although the constants are easy to find, we will pursue a formal process in order to identify a pattern. First,

$$\mathbf{F} \cdot \mathbf{i} = a\mathbf{i} \cdot \mathbf{i} + b\mathbf{j} \cdot \mathbf{i} + c\mathbf{k} \cdot \mathbf{i} = a,$$

because

$$\mathbf{i} \cdot \mathbf{i} = 1 \quad \text{and} \quad \mathbf{j} \cdot \mathbf{i} = \mathbf{k} \cdot \mathbf{i} = 0.$$

Similarly,

$$b = \mathbf{F} \cdot \mathbf{j} \quad \text{and} \quad c = \mathbf{F} \cdot \mathbf{k}.$$

The orthogonality of **i**, **j** and **k** provides a convenient mechanism for determining the coefficients in the expansion by means of the dot product.

More generally, suppose **U**, **V** and **W** are any three nonzero vectors in 3-space that are mutually orthogonal, so

$$\mathbf{U} \cdot \mathbf{V} = \mathbf{U} \cdot \mathbf{W} = \mathbf{V} \cdot \mathbf{W} = 0.$$

These vectors need not be unit vectors, and do not have to be aligned along the axes. However, because of their orthogonality, we can also easily write **F** in terms of these three vectors. Indeed, if

$$\mathbf{F} = \alpha \mathbf{U} + \beta \mathbf{V} + \gamma \mathbf{W}$$

then

$$\mathbf{F} \cdot \mathbf{U} = \alpha \mathbf{U} \cdot \mathbf{U} + \beta \mathbf{V} \cdot \mathbf{U} + \gamma \mathbf{W} \cdot \mathbf{U} = \alpha \mathbf{U} \cdot \mathbf{U},$$

so

$$\alpha = \frac{\mathbf{F} \cdot \mathbf{U}}{\mathbf{U} \cdot \mathbf{U}}.$$

Similarly,

$$\beta = \frac{\mathbf{F} \cdot \mathbf{V}}{\mathbf{V} \cdot \mathbf{V}} \quad \text{and} \quad \gamma = \frac{\mathbf{F} \cdot \mathbf{W}}{\mathbf{W} \cdot \mathbf{W}}. \tag{16.38}$$

Again, we have a simple dot product formula for the coefficients.

The idea of expressing a vector as a sum of constants times mutually orthogonal vectors, with formulas for the coefficients, extends to writing functions in series of eigenfunctions of Sturm–Liouville problems, with a formula similar to equation (16.38) for the coefficients. We have seen three such instances already, which we will briefly review in the context of the Sturm–Liouville theorem.

Fourier Series   The Sturm–Liouville problem is

$$y'' + \lambda y = 0; \quad y(-L) = y(L) = 0$$

(a periodic problem) with eigenvalues $n^2 \pi^2 / L^2$ for $n = 0, 1, 2, \ldots$ and eigenfunctions

$$1, \cos(\pi x/L), \cos(2\pi x/L), \ldots, \sin(\pi x/L), \sin(2\pi x/L), \ldots.$$

Here $p(x) = 1$ and the dot product to be used is

$$f \cdot g = \int_{-L}^{L} f(x)g(x)\,dx.$$

If f is piecewise smooth on $[-L, L]$, then for $-L < x < L$,

$$\frac{1}{2}(f(x+) + f(x-)) = \frac{1}{2}a_0 + \sum_{n=1}^{\infty} a_n \cos\left(\frac{n\pi x}{L}\right) + b_n \sin\left(\frac{n\pi x}{L}\right),$$

where

$$a_n = \frac{\int_{-L}^{L} f(x)\cos(n\pi x/L)\,dx}{\int_{-L}^{L} \cos^2(n\pi x/L)\,dx} = \frac{f(x) \cdot \cos(n\pi x/L)}{\cos(n\pi x/L) \cdot \cos(n\pi x/L)} \quad \text{for } n = 0, 1, 2, \ldots$$

and

$$b_n = \frac{\int_{-L}^{L} f(x)\sin(n\pi x/L)\,dx}{\int_{-L}^{L} \sin^2(n\pi x/L)\,dx} = \frac{f(x) \cdot \sin(n\pi x/L)}{\sin(n\pi x/L) \cdot \sin(n\pi x/L)} \quad \text{for } n = 1, 2, \ldots.$$

Fourier–Legendre Series   The Sturm–Liouville problem is

$$((1-x^2)y')' + \lambda y = 0,$$

with no boundary conditions on $[-1, 1]$ because $r(x) = 1 - x^2$ vanishes at these endpoints. However, we seek bounded solutions. Eigenvalues are $n(n+1)$ with corresponding eigenfunctions the Legendre polynomials $P_0(x), P_1(x), \ldots$. Since $p(x) = 1$, use the dot product

$$f \cdot g = \int_{-1}^{1} f(x)g(x)dx.$$

If f is piecewise smooth on $[-1, 1]$, then for $-1 < x < 1$,

$$\frac{1}{2}(f(x+) + f(x-)) = \sum_{n=0}^{\infty} c_n P_n(x)$$

where

$$c_n = \frac{\int_{-1}^{1} f(x)P_n(x)dx}{\int_{-1}^{1} P_n^2(x)dx} = \frac{f \cdot P_n}{P_n \cdot P_n}.$$

Fourier–Bessel Series   Consider the Sturm–Liouville problem

$$(xy')' + \left(\lambda x - \frac{\nu^2}{x}\right)y = 0$$

with boundary condition $y(1) = 0$ on $(0, 1)$. Eigenvalues are $\lambda = j_n^2$ for $n = 1, 2, \ldots$, where $j_1, j_2 \ldots$ are the positive zeros of $J_\nu(x)$, and eigenfunctions are $J_\nu(j_n x)$. In this Sturm–Liouville problem, $p(x) = x$ and the dot product is

$$f \cdot g = \int_0^1 x f(x)g(x)dx.$$

If f is piecewise smooth on $[0, 1]$, then for $0 < x < 1$ we can write the series

$$\frac{1}{2}(f(x+) + f(x-)) = \sum_{n=1}^{\infty} c_n J_\nu(j_n x),$$

where

$$c_n = \frac{\int_0^1 x f(x) J_\nu(j_n x)dx}{\int_0^1 x J_\nu^2(j_n x)dx} = \frac{f(x) \cdot J_\nu(j_n x)}{J_\nu(j_n x) \cdot J_\nu(j_n x)},$$

again fitting the template we have seen in the other kinds of expansions.

These expansions are all special cases of a general theory of expansions in series of eigenfunctions of Sturm–Liouville problems.

THEOREM 16.23   *Convergence of Eigenfunction Expansions*

Let $\lambda_1, \lambda_2, \ldots$ be the eigenvalues of a Sturm–Liouville differential equation

$$(ry')' + (q + \lambda p)y = 0$$

on $[a, b]$, with one of the sets of boundary conditions specified previously. Let $\varphi_1, \varphi_2, \ldots$ be corresponding eigenfunctions, and define the dot product

$$f \cdot g = \int_a^b p(x)f(x)g(x)dx.$$

Let f be piecewise smooth on $[a, b]$. Then, for $a < x < b$,

$$\frac{1}{2}(f(x+) + f(x-)) = \sum_{n=1}^{\infty} c_n \varphi_n(x),$$

where

$$c_n = \frac{f \cdot \varphi_n}{\varphi_n \cdot \varphi_n}. \quad \blacksquare$$

We call the numbers

$$\frac{f \cdot \varphi_n}{\varphi_n \cdot \varphi_n} \tag{16.39}$$

the *Fourier coefficients of f with respect to the eigenfunctions of this Sturm–Liouville problem*. With this choice of coefficients, $\sum_{n=1}^{\infty} c_n \varphi_n(x)$ is the *eigenfunction expansion of f* with respect to these eigenfunctions.

If the differential equation generating the eigenvalues and eigenfunctions has a special name (such as Legendre's equation, or Bessel's equation), then the eigenfunction expansion is usually called the Fourier - $\cdots$ series, for example, Fourier–Legendre series and Fourier–Bessel series.

EXAMPLE 16.13

Consider the Sturm–Liouville problem

$$y'' + \lambda y = 0; \quad y'(0) = y'(\pi/2) = 0.$$

We find in a routine way that the eigenvalues of this problem are $\lambda = 4n^2$ for $n = 0, 1, 2, \ldots$. Corresponding to $\lambda = 0$, we can choose $\varphi_0(x) = 1$ as an eigenfunction. Corresponding to $\lambda = 4n^2$, $\varphi_n(x) = \cos(2nx)$ is an eigenfunction. This gives us the set of eigenfunctions

$$\varphi_0(x) = 1, \quad \varphi_1(x) = \cos(2x), \quad \varphi_2(x) = \cos(4x), \ldots.$$

Because the coefficient of λ in the differential equation is $p(x) = 1$, and the interval is $[0, \pi/2]$, the dot product for this problem is

$$f \cdot g = \int_0^{\pi/2} f(x)g(x)dx.$$

We will write the eigenfunction expansion of $f(x) = x^2(1 - x)$ for $0 \le x \le \pi/2$. Since f and f' are continuous, this expansion will converge to $x^2(1 - x)$ for $0 < x < \pi/2$. The coefficients in this expansion are

$$c_0 = \frac{f \cdot 1}{1 \cdot 1} = \frac{\int_0^{\pi/2} x^2(1-x)dx}{\int_0^{\pi/2} dx} = \frac{-\frac{1}{64}\pi^4 + \frac{1}{24}\pi^3}{\pi/2} = \pi^2\left(\frac{1}{12} - \frac{\pi}{32}\right).$$

and, for $n = 1, 2, \ldots$,

$$c_n = \frac{f \cdot \cos(2nx)}{\cos(2nx) \cdot \cos(2nx)}$$

$$= \frac{\int_0^{\pi/2} x^2(1-x)\cos(2nx)dx}{\int_0^{\pi/2} \cos^2(2nx)dx}$$

$$= -\frac{1}{4\pi n^4}\left(-4\pi n^2(-1)^n + 3\pi^2 n^2(-1)^n - 6(-1)^n + 6\right).$$

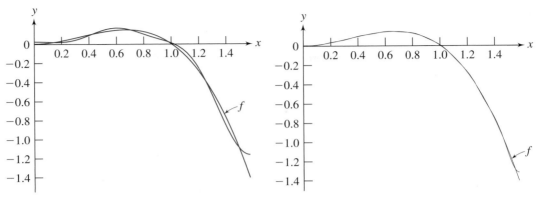

FIGURE 16.15(a) *Fifth partial sum in Example 16.13.*

FIGURE 16.15(b) *Fifteenth partial sum.*

Therefore, for $0 < x < \pi/2$,

$$x^2(1-x) = \pi^2 \left(\frac{1}{12} - \frac{\pi}{32} \right)$$

$$-\frac{1}{4\pi} \sum_{n=1}^{\infty} \frac{1}{n^4} \left(-4\pi n^2 (-1)^n + 3\pi^2 n^2 (-1)^n - 6(-1)^n + 6 \right) \cos(2nx).$$

Figure 16.15 (a) shows the fifth partial sum of this series, compared with f, and Figure 16.15 (b) shows the fifteenth partial sum of this expansion. Clearly this eigenfunction expansion is converging quite rapidly to $x^2(1-x)$ on this interval. ▪

16.3.4 Approximation in the Mean and Bessel's Inequality

In this and the next two sections we will discuss some additional properties of Fourier coefficients, as well as some subtleties in the convergence of Fourier series. For this discussion, let $\varphi_1, \varphi_2, \ldots$ be normalized eigenfunctions of a Sturm–Liouville problem on $[a, b]$. *Normalized* means that each eigenfunction φ_n has been multiplied by a positive constant so that $\varphi_n \cdot \varphi_n = 1$. This can always be done because a nonzero constant multiple of an eigenfunction is again an eigenfunction. We now have

$$\varphi_n \cdot \varphi_m = \int_a^b p(x)\varphi_n(x)\varphi_m(x)\,dx = \begin{cases} 1 & \text{if } n = m \\ 0 & \text{if } n \neq m \end{cases}.$$

For these normalized eigenfunctions, the nth Fourier coefficient is

$$c_n = \frac{f \cdot \varphi_n}{\varphi_n \cdot \varphi_n} = f \cdot \varphi_n. \tag{16.40}$$

We will now define one measure of how well a linear combination $\sum_{n=1}^{N} k_n \varphi_n$ approximates a given function f.

DEFINITION 16.2 *Best Mean Approximation*

Let N be a positive integer and let f be a function that is integrable on $[a, b]$. A linear combination

$$\sum_{n=1}^{N} k_n \varphi_n(x)$$

of $\varphi_1, \varphi_2, \ldots, \varphi_N$ is the *best approximation in the mean to f on $[a, b]$* if the coefficients $k_1, \ldots, k_N$ minimize the quantity

$$I_N(f) = \int_a^b p(x) \left(f(x) - \sum_{n=1}^{N} k_n \varphi_n(x) \right)^2 dx.$$

$I_N(f)$ is the dot product of $f(x) - \sum_{n=1}^{N} k_n \varphi_n(x)$ with itself (with weight function p). For vectors in R^3, the dot product of a vector $\mathbf{V} = a\mathbf{i} + b\mathbf{j} + c\mathbf{k}$ with itself is the square of its length:

$$\mathbf{V} \cdot \mathbf{V} = a^2 + b^2 + c^2 = (\text{length of } \mathbf{V})^2.$$

This suggests that we define a length for functions by

$$g \cdot g = \int_a^b p(x) g(x)^2 dx = (\text{length of } g)^2.$$

Now $I_N(f)$ has the geometric interpretation of being the (square of the) length of $f(x) - \sum_{n=1}^{N} k_n \varphi_n(x)$. The smaller this length is, the better the linear combination $\sum_{n=1}^{N} k_n \varphi_n(x)$ approximates $f(x)$ on $[a, b]$. This approximation is an average over the entire interval, as opposed to looking at the approximation at a particular point, hence the term "approximation in the mean". We want to choose the $k_n's$ to make $I_N(f)$ the best possible mean approximation to f on $[a, b]$, which means we want to make the length of $f(x) - \sum_{n=1}^{N} k_n \varphi_n(x)$ as small as possible.

To determine how to choose the $k_n's$, write

$$0 \le I_N(f) = \int_a^b p(x) \left(f(x)^2 - 2 \sum_{n=1}^{N} f(x) \varphi_n(x) + \left(\sum_{n=1}^{N} k_n \varphi_n(x) \right)^2 \right) dx$$

$$= \int_a^b p(x) f(x)^2 dx - 2 \sum_{n=1}^{N} k_n \int_a^b p(x) f(x) \varphi_n(x) dx$$

$$+ \sum_{n=1}^{N} \sum_{m=1}^{N} k_n k_m \int_a^b p(x) \varphi_n(x) \varphi_m(x) dx$$

$$= f \cdot f - 2 \sum_{n=1}^{N} k_n f \cdot \varphi_n + \sum_{n=1}^{N} \sum_{m=1}^{N} k_n k_m \varphi_n \cdot \varphi_m$$

$$= f \cdot f - 2 \sum_{n=1}^{N} k_n f \cdot \varphi_n + \sum_{n=1}^{N} k_n^2 \varphi_n \cdot \varphi_n$$

$$= f \cdot f - 2 \sum_{n=1}^{N} k_n f \cdot \varphi_n + \sum_{n=1}^{N} k_n^2,$$

since $\varphi_n \cdot \varphi_n = 1$ for this normalized set of eigenfunctions. Now let $c_n = f \cdot \varphi_n$, the nth Fourier coefficient of f for this set of normalized eigenfunctions. Complete the square by writing the last inequality as

$$0 \leq f \cdot f - 2\sum_{n=1}^{N} k_n c_n + \sum_{n=1}^{N} k_n^2 - \sum_{n=1}^{N} c_n^2 + \sum_{n=1}^{N} c_n^2$$

$$= f \cdot f + \sum_{n=1}^{N} (c_n - k_n)^2 - \sum_{n=1}^{N} c_n^2. \tag{16.41}$$

In this formulation, it is obvious that the right side achieves its minimum when each $k_n = c_n$. We have proved the following.

THEOREM 16.24

Let f be integrable on $[a, b]$, and N a positive integer. Then, the linear combination $\sum_{n=1}^{N} k_n \varphi_n$ that is the best approximation in the mean to f on $[a, b]$ is obtained by putting

$$k_n = f \cdot \varphi_n$$

for $n = 1, 2, \ldots$. ∎

Thus, for any given N, the Nth partial sum $\sum_{n=1}^{N} (f \cdot \varphi_n)\varphi_n$ of the Fourier series $\sum_{n=1}^{\infty} (f \cdot \varphi_n)\varphi_n$ of f, is the best approximation in the mean to f by a linear combination of $\varphi_1, \varphi_2, \ldots, \varphi_N$.

The argument leading to the theorem has another important consequence. Put $k_n = c_n = f \cdot \varphi_n$ in equality (16.41) to obtain

$$0 \leq f \cdot f - \sum_{n=1}^{N} (f \cdot \varphi_n)^2,$$

or

$$\sum_{n=1}^{N} (f \cdot \varphi_n)^2 \leq f \cdot f.$$

Since N can be any positive integer, the series of squares of the Fourier coefficients of f converges, and the sum of this series cannot exceed the dot product of f with itself. This is Bessel's inequality, and was proved in Section 14.5 (Theorem 14.7) for Fourier trigonometric series.

THEOREM 16.25 *Bessel's Inequality*

Let f be integrable on $[a, b]$. Then the series of squares of the Fourier coefficients of f with respect to the normalized eigenfunctions $\varphi_1, \varphi_2, \ldots$ converges. Further,

$$\sum_{n=1}^{\infty} (f \cdot \varphi_n)^2 \leq f \cdot f. ∎$$

Under some circumstances, the inequality can be replaced by an equality. This leads us to consider the concept of convergence in the mean.

16.3.5   Convergence in the Mean and Parseval's Theorem

Continuing from the preceding subsection, $\varphi_1, \varphi_2, \ldots$ are assumed to be the normalized eigenfunctions of a Sturm–Liouville problem on $[a, b]$. If f is continuous on $[a, b]$ with a piecewise continuous derivative, then for $a < x < b$,

$$f(x) = \sum_{n=1}^{\infty} (f \cdot \varphi_n) \varphi_n(x).$$

This convergence is called pointwise convergence, because it deals with convergence of the Fourier series individually at each x in (a, b). Under some conditions, this series may also converge uniformly.

In addition to these two kinds of convergence, convergence in the mean is often used in the context of eigenfunction expansions.

DEFINITION 16.3   *Convergence in the Mean*

Let f be integrable on $[a, b]$. The Fourier series $\sum_{n=1}^{\infty} (f \cdot \varphi_n) \varphi_n$ of f, with respect to the normalized eigenfunctions $\varphi_1, \varphi_2, \ldots$, is said to converge to f in the mean on $[a, b]$ if

$$\lim_{N \to \infty} \int_a^b p(x) \left(f(x) - \sum_{n=1}^{N} (f \cdot \varphi_n) \varphi_n \right)^2 dx = 0.$$

Convergence in the mean of a Fourier series of f, to f, occurs when the length of $f(x) - \sum_{n=1}^{N} (f \cdot \varphi_n) \varphi_n(x)$ approaches zero as N approaches infinity. This will certainly happen if the Fourier series converges to f, because then $f(x) = \sum_{n=1}^{\infty} (f \cdot \varphi_n) \varphi_n(x)$, and we know that this holds if f is continuous with a piecewise continuous derivative.

For the remainder of this section, let $C'[a, b]$ be the set of functions that are continuous on $[a, b]$, with piecewise continuous derivatives on (a, b).

THEOREM 16.26

---

1. If $f(x) = \sum_{n=1}^{\infty} (f \cdot \varphi_n) \varphi_n(x)$ for $a < x < b$, then $\sum_{n=1}^{\infty} (f \cdot \varphi_n) \varphi_n$ also converges in the mean to f on $[a, b]$.

2. If f is in $C'[a, b]$, then $\sum_{n=1}^{\infty} (f \cdot \varphi_n) \varphi_n$ converges in the mean to f on $[a, b]$. ∎

The converse of (1) is false. It is possible for the length of $f(x) - \sum_{n=1}^{N} (f \cdot \varphi_n) \varphi_n(x)$ to have limit zero as $N \to \infty$, but for the Fourier series not to converge to $f(x)$ on the interval. This is because the integral in the definition of mean convergence is an averaging process and does not focus on the behavior of the Fourier series at any particular point.

We will show that convergence in the mean for functions in $C'[a, b]$ is equivalent to being able to turn Bessel's inequality into an equality for all functions in this class.

THEOREM 16.27

$\sum_{n=1}^{\infty} (f \cdot \varphi_n)\varphi_n$ converges in the mean to f for every f in $C'[a, b]$ if and only if

$$\sum_{n=1}^{\infty} (f \cdot \varphi_n)^2 = f \cdot f$$

for every f in $C'[a, b]$.

Proof From the calculation done in proving Theorem 16.24, with $k_n = f \cdot \varphi_n$,

$$0 \le I_N(f) = \int_a^b p(x) \left(f(x) - \sum_{n=1}^{N} (f \cdot \varphi_n)\varphi_n \right)^2 dx = f \cdot f - \sum_{n=1}^{N} (f \cdot \varphi_n)^2.$$

Therefore

$$\lim_{N \to \infty} \int_a^b p(x) \left(f(x) - \sum_{n=1}^{N} (f \cdot \varphi_n)\varphi_n \right)^2 dx = 0$$

if and only if

$$f \cdot f - \sum_{n=1}^{\infty} (f \cdot \varphi_n)^2 = 0. \ \blacksquare$$

Replacing the inequality with an equality in Bessel's inequality yields the Parseval relationship. We can now state a condition under which this holds.

COROLLARY 16.1 *Parseval's Theorem*

If f is in $C'[a, b]$, then

$$\sum_{n=1}^{\infty} (f \cdot \varphi_n)^2 = f \cdot f. \ \blacksquare$$

This follows immediately from the last two theorems. We know by Theorem 16.26(2) that, if f is in $C'[a, b]$, then the Fourier series of f converges to f in the mean. Then, by Theorem 16.27, $\sum_{n=1}^{\infty} (f \cdot \varphi_n)^2 = f \cdot f$. With more effort, the Parseval equation can be proved under much weaker conditions on f.

16.3.6 Completeness of the Eigenfunctions

Completeness is a concept that is perhaps most easily understood in terms of vectors.

In 3-space, the vector $\mathbf{k}$ cannot be written as a linear combination $\alpha\mathbf{i} + \beta\mathbf{j}$, even though $\mathbf{i}$ and $\mathbf{j}$ are orthogonal. The reason for this is that there is another direction in 3-space that is orthogonal to the plane of $\mathbf{i}$ and $\mathbf{j}$, and $\mathbf{i}$ and $\mathbf{j}$ carry no information about the component a vector may have in this third direction. The vectors $\mathbf{i}$ and $\mathbf{j}$ are incomplete in R^3. By contrast, there is no nonzero vector that is orthogonal to each of $\mathbf{i}, \mathbf{j}$ and $\mathbf{k}$, so we say that these vectors are complete in R^3. Any 3-vector can be written as a linear combination of $\mathbf{i}, \mathbf{j}$ and $\mathbf{k}$.

Now consider the normalized eigenfunctions $\varphi_1, \varphi_2, \ldots$. Think of each φ_j as defining a different direction, or axis, in the space of functions under consideration, which we take to be $C'[a, b]$. We say that these eigenfunctions are *complete* in $C'[a, b]$ if the only function in $C'[a, b]$ that is orthogonal to every eigenfunction is the zero function. If, however, there is a nontrivial function f in $C'[a, b]$ that is orthogonal to every eigenfunction, then we say that the eigenfunctions are *incomplete*. In this case there is another axis, or direction, in $C'[a, b]$ that is not determined by all of the eigenfunctions. A function having a component in this other direction could not possibly be represented in a series of the incomplete eigenfunctions.

We claim that the eigenfunctions are complete in the space of continuous functions with piecewise continuous derivatives on (a, b).

THEOREM 16.28

The normalized eigenfunctions $\varphi_1, \varphi_2, \ldots$ are complete in $C'[a, b]$. ■

Proof   Suppose the eigenfunctions are not complete. Then there is some nontrivial function f in $C'[a, b]$ that is orthogonal to each φ_n. But because f is orthogonal to each φ_n, each $(f, \varphi_n) = 0$, so

$$f(x) = \sum_{n=1}^{\infty} (f \cdot \varphi_n)\varphi_n(x) = 0 \quad \text{for} \quad a < x < b.$$

This contradiction proves the theorem. ■

EXAMPLE 16.14

The normalized eigenfunctions of the Sturm–Liouville problem

$$y'' + \lambda y = 0; \quad y'(0) = y'(\pi/2) = 0$$

are

$$\sqrt{\frac{2}{\pi}}, \quad \frac{2}{\sqrt{\pi}}\cos(2x), \quad \frac{2}{\sqrt{\pi}}\cos(4x), \quad \frac{2}{\sqrt{\pi}}\cos(6x), \ldots.$$

The constants were chosen to normalize the eigenfunctions, since

$$\varphi_n \cdot \varphi_n = \int_0^{\pi/2} \varphi_n^2 \, dx = \int_0^{\pi/2} \frac{4}{\pi}\cos^2(2nx) \, dx = 1.$$

This set E of eigenfunctions is complete in $C'[0, \pi/2]$. This means that, except for $f(x) \equiv 0$, there is no f in $C'[a, b]$ that is orthogonal to each eigenfunction.

Observe the effect if one eigenfunction is removed. For example, the set E_1 of eigenfunctions

$$\sqrt{\frac{2}{\pi}}, \quad \frac{2}{\sqrt{\pi}}\cos(4x), \quad \frac{2}{\sqrt{\pi}}\cos(6x), \ldots,$$

is formed by removing $f(x) = \frac{2}{\sqrt{\pi}}\cos(2x)$ from E. Now $\cos(2x)$ has no expansion in terms of E_1, even though $\cos(2x)$ is continuous with a continuous derivative on $(0, \pi/2)$. Indeed, if

$$\cos(2x) = \sqrt{\frac{2}{\pi}}c_0 + \sum_{n=2}^{\infty} c_n \frac{2}{\sqrt{\pi}}\cos(2nx),$$

then

$$c_0 = \sqrt{\frac{2}{\pi}} \cdot \cos(2x) = 0$$

and, for $n = 2, 3, \ldots,$

$$c_n = \cos(2x) \cdot \frac{2}{\sqrt{\pi}} \cos(2nx) = 0,$$

implying that $\cos(2x) = 0$ for $0 < x < \pi/2$. This is an absurdity. The deleted set of eigenfunctions E_1, with one function removed from E, is not complete in $C'[0, \pi/2]$. ∎

SECTION 16.3   PROBLEMS

In each of Problems 1 through 12, classify the Sturm–Liouville problem as regular, periodic or singular; state the relevant interval; find the eigenvalues; and, corresponding to each eigenvalue, find an eigenfunction. In some cases eigenvalues may be implicitly defined by an equation.

1. $y'' + \lambda y = 0; y(0) = 0, y'(L) = 0$

2. $y'' + \lambda y = 0; y'(0) = 0, y'(L) = 0$

3. $y'' + \lambda y = 0; y'(0) = y(4) = 0$

4. $y'' + \lambda y = 0; y(0) = y(\pi), y'(0) = y'(\pi)$

5. $y'' + \lambda y = 0; y(-3\pi) = y(3\pi), y'(-3\pi) = y'(3\pi)$

6. $y'' + \lambda y = 0; y(0) = 0, y(\pi) + 2y'(\pi) = 0$

7. $y'' + \lambda y = 0; y(0) - 2y'(0) = 0, y'(1) = 0$

8. $y'' + 2y' + (1 + \lambda)y = 0; y(0) = y(1) = 0$

9. $(e^{2x}y')' + \lambda e^{2x}y = 0; y(0) = y(\pi) = 0$

10. $(e^{-6x}y')' + (1 + \lambda)e^{-6x}y = 0; y(0) = y(8) = 0$

11. $(x^3 y')' + \lambda xy = 0; y(1) = y(e^3) = 0$

12. $(x^{-1}y')' + (4 + \lambda)x^{-3}y = 0; y(1) = y(e^4) = 0$

In each of Problems 13 through 18, find the eigenfunction expansion of the given function in the eigenfunctions of the Sturm–Liouville problem. In each case, determine what the eigenfunction expansion converges to on the interval, and graph the function and the sum of first N terms of the eigenfunction expansion on the same set of axes for the given interval. (In Problem 13, do the graph for $L = 1$)

13. $f(x) = 1 - x$ for $0 \le x \le L$
$y'' + \lambda y = 0; y(0) = y(L) = 0; N = 40$

14. $f(x) = |x|$ for $0 \le x \le \pi$
$y'' + \lambda y = 0; y(0) = y'(\pi) = 0; N = 30$

15. $f(x) = \begin{cases} -1 & \text{for } 0 \le x \le 2 \\ 1 & \text{for } 2 < x \le 4 \end{cases}$

$y'' + \lambda y = 0; y'(0) = y(4) = 0; N = 40$

16. $f(x) = \sin(2x)$ for $0 \le x \le \pi$
$y'' + \lambda y = 0; y'(0) = y'(\pi) = 0; N = 30$

17. $f(x) = x^2$ for $-3\pi \le x \le 3\pi$
$y'' + \lambda y = 0; y(-3\pi) = y(3\pi), y'(-3\pi) = y'(3\pi);$
$N = 10$

18. $f(x) = \begin{cases} 0 & \text{for } 0 \le x \le 1/2 \\ 1 & \text{for } 1/2 < x \le 1 \end{cases}$

$y'' + 2y' + (1 + \lambda)y = 0; y(0) = y(1) = 0; N = 30$

19. Write Bessel's inequality for the function $f(x) = x(4 - x)$ for the eigenfunctions of the Sturm–Liouville problem of Problem 3.

20. Write Bessel's inequality for the function $f(x) = e^{-x}$ for the eigenfunctions of the Sturm–Liouville problem of Problem 6.

16.4   Wavelets

16.4.1   The Idea Behind Wavelets

Recent years have seen an explosion in both the mathematical development of wavelets, and their applications, which include signal analysis, data compression, filtering, and electromagnetics. Our purpose here is to introduce enough of the ideas behind wavelets to enable the student to pursue more thorough treatments.

Think of a function defined on the real line as a signal. If the signal contains one fundamental frequency ω_0, then f is a periodic function with period $2\pi/\omega_0$ and the Fourier series of $f(t)$ is one tool for analyzing the signal's frequency content. The amplitude spectrum of f consists of a plot of points $(n\omega_0, c_n/2)$, in which

$$c_n = \sqrt{a_n^2 + b_n^2},$$

with a_n and b_n the Fourier coefficients of f. Under certain conditions on f, this enables us to represent the signal as a trigonometric series displaying the natural frequencies:

$$f(t) = \frac{1}{2}a_0 + \sum_{n=1}^{\infty} a_n \cos(n\omega_0 t) + b_n \sin(n\omega_0 t).$$

Often we model the signal by taking a partial sum of the Fourier series:

$$f(t) \approx \frac{1}{2}a_0 + \sum_{n=1}^{N} a_n \cos(n\omega_0 t) + b_n \sin(n\omega_0 t).$$

Although this process has proved useful in many instances, the Fourier trigonometric representation is not always the best device for analyzing signals. First, we may be interested in a signal that is not periodic. More generally, we may have a signal that is defined over the entire real line with no periodicity, and we require only that its energy be finite. This means that $\int_{-\infty}^{\infty} (f(t))^2 dt$ is finite, or, if $f(t)$ is complex valued, that $\int_{-\infty}^{\infty} |f(t)|^2 dt$ is finite. This integral is the energy content of the signal, and functions having finite energy are said to be *square integrable*. In general, Fourier expansions are not the best tool for the analysis of such functions.

There are other disadvantages to Fourier trigonometric series. For a given f, we may have to choose N very large to model $f(t)$ by a partial sum of a Fourier series. Finally, if we are interested on focusing on the behavior of $f(t)$ in some finite time interval, or near some particular time, we cannot isolate those terms in the Fourier expansion that describe this behavior, but instead have to take the entire Fourier series, or its entire partial sum if we are modeling the signal.

To illustrate, consider the signal shown in Figure 16.16. Explicitly,

$$f(t) = \begin{cases} 1 & \text{for } 0 \leq t < \dfrac{1}{4} \\[2mm] -\dfrac{1}{5} & \text{for } \dfrac{1}{4} \leq t < \dfrac{3}{8} \\[2mm] \dfrac{11}{5} & \text{for } \dfrac{3}{8} \leq t < \dfrac{1}{2} \\[2mm] 1 & \text{for } \dfrac{1}{2} \leq t < \dfrac{3}{4} \\[2mm] -3 & \text{for } \dfrac{3}{4} \leq t < 1 \\[2mm] -\dfrac{4}{5} & \text{for } 1 \leq t < \dfrac{5}{4} \\[2mm] \dfrac{14}{5} & \text{for } \dfrac{5}{4} \leq t < \dfrac{11}{8} \\[2mm] \dfrac{4}{5} & \text{for } \dfrac{11}{8} \leq t < \dfrac{3}{2} \\[2mm] 0 & \text{for } t \geq \dfrac{3}{2} \quad \text{and for } t < 0 \end{cases}$$

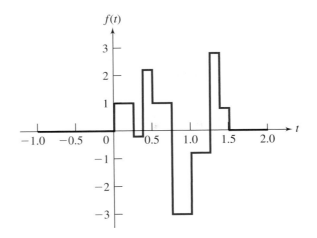

FIGURE 16.16   *The signal* $f(t)$.

The Fourier series of f on $\left[-\frac{3}{2}, \frac{3}{2}\right]$ is

$$\frac{1}{12} + \sum_{n=1}^{\infty} a_n \cos\left(\frac{2n\pi x}{3}\right) + b_n \sin\left(\frac{2n\pi x}{3}\right),$$

where

$$a_n = -\frac{1}{5n\pi}\left[-6\sin\left(\frac{n\pi}{6}\right) + 12\sin\left(\frac{n\pi}{4}\right) - 6\sin\left(\frac{n\pi}{3}\right) - 20\sin\left(\frac{n\pi}{2}\right)\right.$$
$$\left. + 11\sin\left(\frac{2n\pi}{3}\right) + 18\sin\left(\frac{5n\pi}{6}\right) - 10\sin\left(\frac{11n\pi}{12}\right)\right]$$

and

$$b_n = \frac{1}{5n\pi}\left[-6\cos\left(\frac{n\pi}{6}\right) + 5 + 12\cos\left(\frac{n\pi}{4}\right) - 6\cos\left(\frac{n\pi}{3}\right) - 20\cos\left(\frac{n\pi}{2}\right)\right.$$
$$\left. + 11\cos\left(\frac{2n\pi}{3}\right) + 18\cos\left(\frac{5n\pi}{6}\right) - 10\cos\left(\frac{11n\pi}{12}\right) - 4\cos(n\pi)\right].$$

This series converges very slowly to the function. Indeed, Figure 16.17(a) shows the 80th partial sum of this series, and Figure 16.17(b) the 100th partial sum. Even with this number of terms, this partial sum does not model the signal very well. In addition, if we were interested in focusing on just part of the signal, there is no way of distinguishing certain terms of the Fourier series as carrying the most information about this part of the signal. Put another way, Fourier series do not localize information.

These considerations suggest that we seek other sets of complete orthogonal functions in which square integrable functions might be expanded, and which overcome some of the difficulties just cited for Fourier trigonometric series. This is a primary motivation for wavelets. We will begin our discussion of wavelets by developing one important wavelet in detail, then use this construction to suggest some of the ideas behind wavelets in general.

16.4.2   The Haar Wavelets

We will construct an example that is important both historically and for present-day applications. The Haar wavelets were the first to be found (about 1910), and serve as a model of one approach to the development of other wavelets.

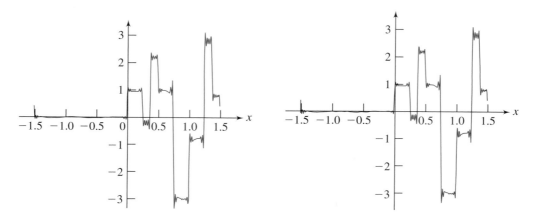

FIGURE 16.17(a) *Eightieth partial sum of the Fourier series of the signal.*

FIGURE 16.17(b) *One-hundredth partial sum of the Fourier series of the signal.*

Let $L^2(R)$ denote the set of all real valued functions that are defined on the entire real line, and are square integrable. $L^2(R)$ has the structure of a vector space, since linear combinations $\alpha_1 f_1 + \alpha_2 f_2 + \cdots + \alpha_n f_n$ of square integrable functions are square integrable. The dot product we will use for functions in $L^2(R)$ is

$$f \cdot g = \int_{-\infty}^{\infty} f(t)g(t)\,dt.$$

Now consider the characteristic function of an interval I (or of any set of numbers on the real line). This function is denoted χ_I, and has the value 1 for t in I, and zero for t not in I. That is,

$$\chi_I(t) = \begin{cases} 1 & \text{if } t \text{ is in } I \\ 0 & \text{if } t \text{ is not in } I \end{cases}.$$

In particular, we will use the characteristic function of the half-open unit interval:

$$\chi_{[0,1)}(t) = \begin{cases} 1 & \text{for } 0 \le t < 1 \\ 0 & \text{if } t < 0 \text{ or if } t \ge 1 \end{cases}.$$

A graph of $\chi_{[0,1)}$ is shown in Figure 16.18.

We want to introduce new functions by both scaling and translation, with the objective of producing a complete orthonormal set of functions in $L^2(R)$. Recall that the graph of $f(t-k)$

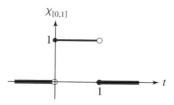

FIGURE 16.18 $\chi_{[0,1]}$

is the graph of $f(t)$ translated k units to the right if k is positive, and $|k|$ units to the left if k is negative. For example, Figure 16.19(a) shows a graph of

$$f(t) = \begin{cases} t\sin(t) & \text{for } 0 \le t \le 15 \\ 0 & \text{for } t < 0 \text{ and for } t > 15 \end{cases}.$$

Figure 16.19(b) is a graph of $f(t+5)$ (graph of $f(t)$ shifted five units to the left), and Figure 16.19(c) is a graph of $f(t-5)$ (shift the graph of $f(t)$ five units to the right). In addition, $f(kt)$ is a scaling of the graph of f. $f(kt)$ compresses (if $k > 1$) or stretches (if $0 < k < 1$) the graph of $f(t)$ for $a \le t \le b$ onto the interval $[a/k, b/k]$. For example, Figure 16.20(a) shows a graph of

$$f(t) = \begin{cases} t\sin(\pi t) & \text{for } -2 \le t \le 3 \\ 0 & \text{for } t < -2 \text{ and for } t > 0 \end{cases}.$$

Figure 16.20(b) shows a graph of $f(3t)$, compressing the graph of Figure 16.20(a) to the right and left, and Figure 16.20(c) shows a graph of $f(t/3)$, stretching out the graph of Figure 16.20(a).

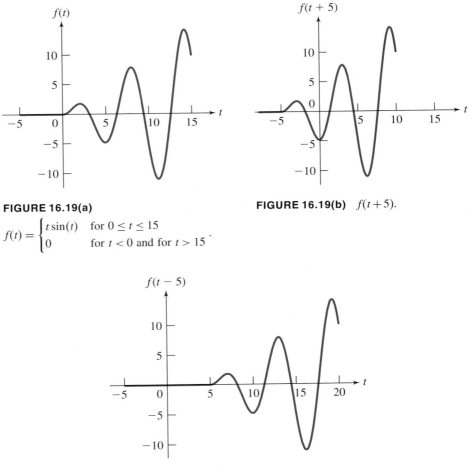

FIGURE 16.19(a)

$$f(t) = \begin{cases} t\sin(t) & \text{for } 0 \le t \le 15 \\ 0 & \text{for } t < 0 \text{ and for } t > 15 \end{cases}.$$

FIGURE 16.19(b) $f(t+5)$.

FIGURE 16.19(c) $f(t-5)$.

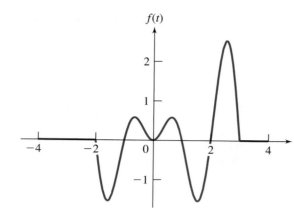

FIGURE 16.20(a)

$$f(t) = \begin{cases} t\sin(\pi t) & \text{for } -2 \leq t \leq 3 \\ 0 & \text{for } t < -2 \text{ and for } t > 0 \end{cases}.$$

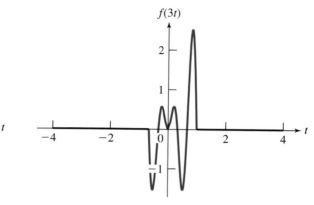

FIGURE 16.20(b) $f(3t)$.

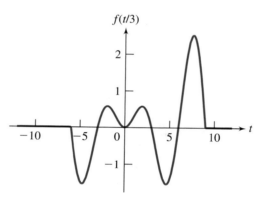

FIGURE 16.20(c) $f(t/3)$.

Let $\varphi(t) = \chi_{[0,1)}(t)$, and define

$$\psi(t) = \varphi(2t) - \varphi(2t-1) = \begin{cases} 1 & \text{for } 0 \leq t < \dfrac{1}{2} \\ -1 & \text{for } \dfrac{1}{2} \leq t < 1 \\ 0 & \text{for } t < 0 \text{ and for } t \geq 1 \end{cases}.$$

A graph of ψ is shown in Figure 16.21.

Next, consider translations $\psi(t-n)$, in which n is any integer. This is the function

$$\psi(t-n) = \varphi(2(t-n)) - \varphi(2(t-n)-1)$$

$$= \varphi(2t-2n) - \varphi(2t-2n-1)$$

$$= \begin{cases} 1 & \text{for } n \leq t < n + \dfrac{1}{2} \\ -1 & \text{for } n + \dfrac{1}{2} \leq t < n+1 \\ 0 & \text{for } t < n \text{ and for } t \geq n+1 \end{cases}.$$

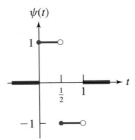

FIGURE 16.21
$\psi(t) = \varphi(2t) - \varphi(2t-1)$,
with $\varphi(t) = \chi_{[0,1]}$.

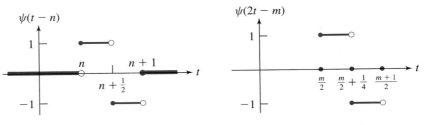

FIGURE 16.22
$\psi(t-n) = \varphi(2(t-n)) - \varphi(2(t-n)-1)$.

FIGURE 16.23 $\psi(2t-m) =$
$\varphi(2(2t-m)) - \varphi(2(2t-m)-1)$.

A graph of $\psi(t-n)$ is shown in Figure 16.22.

Now combine a translation with a scaling. Consider the function

$$\psi(2t-m) = \varphi(2(2t-m)) - \varphi(2(2t-m)-1)$$

$$= \varphi(4t-2m) - \varphi(4t-2m-1)$$

$$= \begin{cases} 1 & \text{for } \dfrac{m}{2} \le t < \left(\dfrac{m}{2}\right) + 1/4 \\ -1 & \text{for } \left(\dfrac{m}{2}\right) + 1/4 \le t < \dfrac{(m+1)}{2} \\ 0 & \text{for } t < \dfrac{m}{2} \text{ and for } t \ge \dfrac{(m+1)}{2} \end{cases},$$

in which m is any integer. A graph of this function is shown in Figure 16.23.

Before proceeding, we will observe that these translated and scaled functions are orthogonal in $L^2(R)$.

LEMMA 16.2

1. For distinct integers n and m,

$$\psi(t-n) \cdot \psi(t-m) = 0$$

and

$$\psi(2t-n) \cdot \psi(2t-m) = 0.$$

2. For any integers n and m,

$$\psi(t-n) \cdot \psi(2t-m) = 0.$$

Proof   If $n \neq m$, then the intervals $[n, n+1)$ on which $\psi(t-n)$ takes on its nonzero values, and $[m, m+1)$ on which $\psi(t-m)$ assumes its nonzero values, are disjoint. Then $\psi(t-n)\psi(t-m) = 0$ for all t and

$$\psi(t-n) \cdot \psi(t-m) = \int_{-\infty}^{\infty} \psi(t-n)\psi(t-m)dt = 0.$$

Similarly, for $n \neq m$, the intervals $[n/2, (n+1)/2)$ and $[m/2, (m+1)/2)$ on which $\psi(2t-n)$ and $\psi(2t-m)$, respectively, take on their nonzero values, are disjoint, so $\psi(2t-n) \cdot \psi(2t-m) = 0$.

For (2), let n and m be any integers. If the intervals on which $\psi(t-n)$ and $\psi(2t-m)$ have nonzero values are disjoint, then these functions are orthogonal. There are two cases in which these intervals are not disjoint.

Case 1 $n = m/2$.

In this case

$$\psi(t-n)\psi(2t-m) = \begin{cases} 1 & \text{for } n \le t < n + \dfrac{1}{4} \\ -1 & \text{for } n + \dfrac{1}{4} \le t < n + \dfrac{1}{2} \\ 0 & \text{for } t < n \text{ and for } t \ge n + \dfrac{1}{2} \end{cases}.$$

Then

$$\psi(t-n) \cdot \psi(2t-m) = \int_{n}^{n+1/4} dt - \int_{n+1/4}^{n+1/2} dt = 0.$$

Case 2 $n + 1/2 = m/2$.

Now

$$\psi(t-n)\psi(2t-m) = \begin{cases} -1 & \text{for } n + \dfrac{1}{2} \le t < n + \dfrac{3}{4} \\ 1 & \text{for } n + \dfrac{3}{4} \le t < n + 1 \\ 0 & \text{for } t < n + \dfrac{1}{2} \text{ and for } t \ge n + \dfrac{3}{4} \end{cases}$$

so

$$\psi(t-n) \cdot \psi(2t-m) = -\int_{n+1/2}^{n+3/4} dt + \int_{n+3/4}^{n+1} dt = 0. \quad \blacksquare$$

However, while the functions $\psi(t-n)$ and $\psi(2t-m)$ are orthogonal in $L^2(R)$, they do not form a complete set as n and m vary over the integers. We leave it for the student to produce nontrivial (that is, nonzero at least on some interval) square integrable functions that are orthogonal to all of these translated and scaled functions.

The idea now is to extend this set of functions by using scaling factors 2^m for integer m, to obtain functions that take on nonzero constant values on intervals that can be made shorter (positive m) or longer (negative m). Let

$$\sigma_{m,n}(t) = \psi(2^m t - n).$$

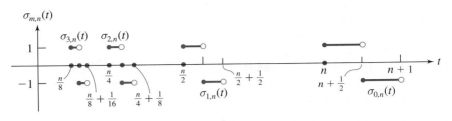

FIGURE 16.24 $\sigma_{m,n}(t)$ *for* $m = 0, 1, 2, 3$.

for each integer m and each integer n. Then

$$\sigma_{m,n}(t) = \varphi(2^{m+1}t - 2n) - \varphi(2^{m+1}t - 2n - 1)$$

$$= \begin{cases} 1 & \text{for } \dfrac{n}{2^m} \le t < \dfrac{n}{2^m} + \dfrac{1}{2^{m+1}} \\[2mm] -1 & \text{for } \dfrac{n}{2^m} + \dfrac{1}{2^{m+1}} \le t < \dfrac{n}{2^m} + \dfrac{1}{2^m} \\[2mm] 0 & \text{for } t < \dfrac{n}{2^m} \text{ and for } t \ge \dfrac{n}{2^m} + \dfrac{1}{2^m} \end{cases}.$$

Figure 16.24 shows graphs of $\sigma_{0,n}(t)$, $\sigma_{1,n}(t)$, $\sigma_{2,n}(t)$, and $\sigma_{3,n}(t)$ on the same set of axes, for comparison. Note that n determines how far out the t axis the graph occurs, while m controls the size of the interval over which the function is nonzero (shorter for m increasing and positive, longer for $|m|$ increasing but m negative). In the drawing n is a positive integer, but n can also be chosen negative, in which case the graphs are to the left of the vertical axis.

We claim that these functions form an orthogonal set in $L^2(R)$.

THEOREM 16.29

If n, m, n' and m' are integers, and $(m, n) \ne (m', n')$, then

$$\sigma_{m,n} \cdot \sigma_{m',n'} = 0. \ \blacksquare$$

A proof of this is left to the student.

One last detail before we get to the main point. The $\sigma'_{m,n}$s are orthogonal, but they are not orthonormal. This is easily fixed. Divide each of these functions by its length, as defined by the dot product in $L^2(R)$. Compute

$$\left(\text{length of } \sigma_{m,n}\right)^2 = \sigma_{m,n} \cdot \sigma_{m,n} = \int_{n/2^m}^{n/2^m+1/2^m} \sigma_{m,n}^2(t)\,dt = \int_{n/2^m}^{n/2^m+1/2^m} dt = \frac{1}{2^m}.$$

This suggests that we define the functions

$$\psi_{m,n}(t) = 2^{m/2}\sigma_{m,n}(t) = 2^{m/2}\left[\varphi(2^{m+1}t - 2n) - \varphi(2^{m+1}t - 2n - 1)\right]$$

$$= \begin{cases} 2^{m/2} & \text{for } \dfrac{n}{2^m} \le t < \dfrac{n}{2^m} + \dfrac{1}{2^{m+1}} \\[2mm] -2^{m/2} & \text{for } \dfrac{n}{2^m} + \dfrac{1}{2^{m+1}} \le t < \dfrac{n}{2^m} + \dfrac{1}{2^m} \\[2mm] 0 & \text{for } t < \dfrac{n}{2^m} \text{ and for } t \ge \dfrac{n}{2^m} + \dfrac{1}{2^m} \end{cases}.$$

The functions $\psi_{m,n}$ form an orthonormal set in $L^2(R)$. These functions are the *Haar wavelets*. In the construction, φ is called the *scaling function*, and $\psi(t) = \varphi(2t) - \varphi(2t - 1)$ is the *mother wavelet*. Graphs of these wavelets are similar to the graphs of Figure 16.24, but the segment at height 1 in Figure 16.24 is now at height $2^{m/2}$, and the segment at height -1 in Figure 16.24 is now at height $-2^{m/2}$.

The Haar wavelets are complete in $L^2(R)$. The idea behind this can be envisioned as follows. If f is square integrable, then $f(t)$ can be approximated as accurately as we like by a function g having compact support ($g(t) = 0$ outside some closed interval), and having constant values on half-open intervals of the form $[n/2^m, (n+1)/2^m)$, with n and m integers. Such intervals are of length $1/2^m$, which can be made longer or shorter by choice of the integer m. In turn, g can be approximated as closely as we like by a sum of constants times Haar wavelets, which are defined on such intervals, with the error in the approximation tending to zero as the number of terms in the sum is taken larger.

16.4.3 A Wavelet Expansion

Suppose f is a square integrable function. We can attempt an expansion of f in a series of the Haar wavelets, which form a complete orthonormal set in $L^2(R)$. Such an expansion has the appearance

$$f(t) = \sum_{m=-\infty}^{\infty} \sum_{n=-\infty}^{\infty} c_{mn} \psi_{m,n}(t).$$

The equality in this expression is taken to mean that the series on the right converges in the mean to $f(t)$. This means that

$$\lim_{M \to \infty} \int_{-\infty}^{\infty} \left(f(t) - \sum_{m=-\infty}^{M} \sum_{n=-\infty}^{\infty} c_{mn} \psi_{m,n}(t) \right)^2 dt = 0.$$

The coefficients c_{mn} can be found in the usual way by using the orthonormality of the Haar wavelets:

$$f \cdot \psi_{m_0,n_0} = \sum_{m=-\infty}^{\infty} \sum_{n=-\infty}^{\infty} c_{mn} \psi_{m,n} \cdot \psi_{m_0,n_0} = c_{m_0 n_0}.$$

We will complete the example begun in Section 16.5.1, in which f is the signal whose graph is shown in Figure 16.16. As we saw in Figures 16.17(a) and (b), we would have to use a very large number of terms to model this signal with the partial sum of its Fourier expansion on $[-\frac{3}{2}, \frac{3}{2}]$. However, if we calculate the coefficients in the Haar expansion, we find that

$$f(t) = \psi_{00}(t) + \sqrt{2}\psi_{1,1}(t) - 0.6\psi_{2,1}(t) - 0.4\sqrt{2}\psi_{1,2}(t) + \psi_{2,5}(t).$$

For some purposes we want Fourier trigonometric expansions, but for this signal the Haar wavelets provide a very efficient expansion.

16.4.4 Multiresolution Analysis with Haar Wavelets

The term multiresolution analysis refers to a sequence of closed subspaces of $L^2(R)$ that are related to the scaling used in defining a set of wavelets. We will discuss what this means in the context of the Haar wavelets.

Because $L^2(R)$ has the structure of a vector space, the following three conditions hold.

1. Linear combinations $\sum_{j=1}^{N} c_j f_j$ of functions in $L^2(R)$ are also in $L^2(R)$.

2. The zero function, $\theta(t) = 0$ for all t, is in $L^2(R)$, and serves as the zero vector of $L^2(R)$. For any function f in $L^2(R)$, $f + \theta = f$.

3. If f is in $L^2(R)$, $-f$, defined by $(-f)(t) = -f(t)$, is also in $L^2(R)$.

A set S of square integrable functions is said to be a subspace of $L^2(R)$ if S has at least one function in it, and, whenever f and g are in S, then $f - g$ is in S. For example, the set of all constant multiples of $\chi_{[0,1]}$ forms a subspace of $L^2(R)$.

A subspace S is closed if convergent sequences of functions in S have their limit functions in S. For example, the subspace of all continuous square integrable functions is not closed, because a limit (in the sense of mean convergence) of continuous functions need not be continuous.

If a subspace S is not closed, we can form the "smallest" subspace of $L^2(R)$ containing all the functions in S, together with all the limits of convergent sequences of functions in S. This subspace, which may be all of $L^2(R)$, is called the *closure* of S, and is denoted $\overline{S}$. $\overline{S}$ is closed, because by its formation it has all the limits of convergent sequences of functions that are in this space.

We will now show how the Haar wavelets generate a sequence of closed subspaces of $L^2(R)$, which can be indexed by the integers so that each is contained in the next one in the list. The spaces are generated by different scalings of the scaling function φ, and may be thought of as associated with different degrees of resolution of the signal.

To begin defining these spaces, let S_0 consist of all linear combinations of the translated scaling function. These translated scaling functions have the form $\varphi(t - n)$ for integer n, and a typical function in S_0 has the form

$$\sum_{j=1}^{N} c_j \varphi(t - n_j),$$

where N is a positive integer, the $c_j's$ are real numbers and each n_j is an integer. Now let V_0 be the closure of S_0:

$$V_0 = \overline{S_0}.$$

Next, let S_m be the space of all linear combinations of the functions $\varphi(2^m t - n)$, where n varies over the integers and m is a fixed integer in defining S_m. Let

$$V_m = \overline{S_m}.$$

From the scaling property of the scaling function,

$$\varphi(t) = \varphi(2t) + \varphi(2t - 1),$$

we find that $f(t)$ is in V_m exactly when $f(2t)$ is in V_{m+1}, and each V_m is contained within V_{m+1} (written $V_m \subset V_{m+1}$). Thus the closed subspaces V_m, with integer m, form an ascending chain:

$$\cdots \subset V_{-2} \subset V_{-1} \subset V_0 \subset V_1 \subset V_2 \subset \cdots$$

This chain has two additional properties of importance. First, there is no nontrivial function contained in every V_m. We say that the intersection of all the closed subspaces V_m consists of just the zero function. And, finally, the ascending chain ends in $L^2(R)$. This means that every function in $L^2(R)$ has a series expansion in terms of the Haar functions, a fact to which we have already alluded.

The spaces V_m are said to form a *multiresolution analysis* of $L^2(R)$. This multiresolution analysis is generated by the scaling function φ.

16.4.5   General Construction of Wavelets and Multiresolution Analysis

The Haar wavelets have been known for nearly a century, together with the chain of subspaces that form a multiresolution analysis of $L^2(R)$. However, it remained unknown for some time whether this construction could be duplicated, resulting in multiresolution analyses starting from different scaling functions. To this end, we will use the hindsight of the Haar construction to make a definition of a scaling function and the associated multiresolution analysis.

DEFINITION 16.4 *Scaling Function and Associated Multiresolution Analysis*

Let φ be in $L^2(R)$. Then φ is a scaling function with multiresolution analysis $\{V_m\}$ if

$$\cdots \subset V_{-2} \subset V_{-1} \subset V_0 \subset V_1 \subset V_2 \subset \cdots$$

is an ascending chain of closed subspaces of $L^2(R)$ satisfying the conditions:

1. The translated functions $\varphi(t-n)$, for integer n, are orthonormal, and every function in V_0 is a linear combination of functions of this form.
2. There is no nontrivial function that belongs to every V_m. (That is, the $V_m's$ have trivial intersection.)
3. $f(t)$ is in V_m exactly when $f(2t)$ is in V_{m+1}.
4. Every function in $L^2(R)$ can be expanded in a series of functions from the $V_m's$.

V_0 is a subspace of V_1, which contains functions orthogonal to every function in V_0. The subspace of V_1 containing all of these functions is called the *orthogonal complement* of V_0 in V_1. To draw an analogy from vectors in R^3, the constant multiples of $\mathbf{k}$ form a subspace of R^3 that is the orthogonal complement of the plane defined by $\mathbf{i}$ and $\mathbf{j}$. Every vector in this orthogonal complement is orthogonal to each linear combination $a\mathbf{i} + b\mathbf{j}$.

Now use the scaling function to produce a mother wavelet ψ, having the property that every function in this orthogonal complement of V_0 in V_1 is a linear combination of translates $\psi(t-n)$. If there is such a mother wavelet, then we can form the family of wavelets

$$\psi_{mn} = 2^{m/2}\psi(2^m t - n)$$

for integers m and n.

16.4.6 Shannon Wavelets

The Haar wavelets form a prototype for wavelets and multiresolution analysis, partly because they were the first, and partly because they are relatively easy to work with and visualize. The reason it took many years before other examples of scaling function/wavelet/multiresolution analysis were found is that this involves some fairly heavy analysis. However, there are other relatively simple examples. One consists of the Shannon wavelets. For these, begin with the Fourier transform of a potential scaling function. Let

$$\hat{\varphi}(\omega) = \chi_{[-\pi,\pi)}.$$

Taking the inverse Fourier transform, we obtain

$$\varphi(t) = \frac{\sin(\pi t)}{\pi t}.$$

This function occurs in the Shannon reconstruction theorem, which was proved in Section 15.4.7 for functions of bandwidth $\leq L$. In the case that $L = \pi$, the theorem states that a signal f whose

Fourier transform $\hat{f}(\omega)$ vanishes outside the interval $[-\pi, \pi]$ (that is, f has bandwidth $\leq \pi$), can be reconstructed by sampling its values on the integers. Specifically,

$$f(t) = \sum_{n=-\infty}^{\infty} f(n) \frac{\sin(\pi(t-n))}{\pi(t-n)} = \sum_{n=-\infty}^{\infty} f(n)\varphi(t-n).$$

The space V_0 in this context consists of functions in $L^2(R)$ of bandwidth not exceeding π.

By scaling (let $g(t) = f(2t)$) we can consider the space V_1 of functions of bandwidth not exceeding 2π, and so on, forming a multiresolution analysis. Thus φ is a scaling function. We now need a mother wavelet ψ that is orthogonal to each $\varphi(t-n)$, for integer n. By an argument we will not carry out (but whose conclusions can be verified in straightforward fashion), we obtain a suitable ψ from φ in this case by setting

$$\psi(t) = \varphi\left(t - \frac{1}{2}\right) - 2\varphi(2t - 1) = \frac{\sin(2\pi t) - \cos(\pi t)}{\pi(t - \frac{1}{2})}..$$

The frequency content of this function is obtained from its Fourier transform,

$$\hat{\psi}(\omega) = -e^{-i\omega/2}\chi_A(\omega),$$

where A consists of all ω in $[-2\pi, -\pi)$, together with all ω in $(\pi, 2\pi]$. That is, on each of these intervals, $\hat{\psi}(\omega) = -e^{-i\omega/2}$, and for ω outside of these intervals, $\hat{\psi}(\omega) = 0$. Figure 16.25 shows a graph of the mother wavelet ψ, and Figure 16.26 a graph of its amplitude spectrum. This gives the frequency content of ψ.

The Shannon wavelets are the functions

$$\psi_{mn}(t) = 2^{m/2}\psi(2^m t - n)$$

$$= \frac{2^{m/2}}{\pi(t - \frac{1}{2})}\left(\sin(2\pi(2^m t - n)) - \cos(\pi(2^m t - n))\right).$$

We leave it for the student to explore properties of these wavelets. Graphs of $\psi_{10}(t)$ and $\psi_{21}(t)$ are given in Figures 16.27(a) and (b).

There are many other families of wavelets, including Meyer wavelets, Daubechies wavelets and Stömberg wavelets. These require a good deal more preliminary work for their definitions. Different wavelets are constructed for specific purposes, and they have applications in such areas as signal analysis, data compression and solution of integral equations. For an application

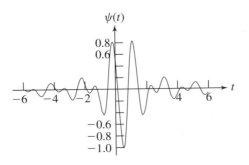

FIGURE 16.25 *Shannon mother wavelet*

$$\psi(t) = \frac{\sin(2\pi t) - \cos(\pi t)}{\pi\left(t - \frac{1}{2}\right)}.$$

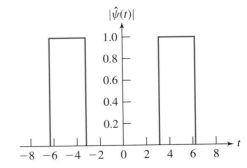

FIGURE 16.26 *Amplitude spectrum of the Shannon mother wavelet.*

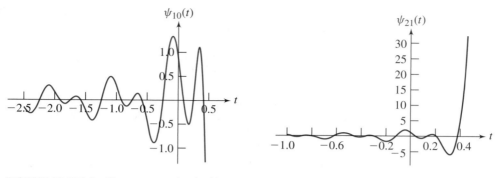

FIGURE 16.27(a) *Shannon wavelet $\psi_{10}(t)$.*

FIGURE 16.27(b) *Shannon wavelet $\psi_{21}(t)$.*

to the problem of using color patterns in the iris of the eye as a means of identification, see the article *Iris Recognition*, by John Daugman, appearing in American Scientist, July–August, 2001, pages 326–333.

SECTION 16.4   *PROBLEMS*

1. Show that $\sigma_{m,n}(t) \cdot \sigma_{m',n'}(t) = 0$ if $(m, n) \neq (m', n')$.

2. On the same set of axes, graph $\sigma_{1,1}(t)$ and $\sigma_{1,2}(t)$. Explain from the graph why these two functions are orthogonal.

3. On the same set of axes, graph $\sigma_{1,3}(t)$ and $\sigma_{-2,1}(t)$. Explain from the graph why these two functions are orthogonal.

4. On the same set of axes, graph $\sigma_{2,1}(t)$ and $\sigma_{1,1}(t)$. Explain from the graph why these two functions are orthogonal.

5. Graph $\psi(2t - 3)$.

6. Graph $\psi(2t + 6)$.

7. Let $f(t) = 4\sigma_{-3,-2}(t) + 6\sigma_{-1,1}(t)$. Write the Fourier series of $f(t)$ on $[-5, 5]$. Graph the fiftieth partial sum of this series on the same set of axes with a graph of $f(t)$.

8. Let $f(t) = -3\sigma_{2,-2}(t) + 4\sigma_{2,0}(t) + 7\sigma_{1,-1}(t)$. Write the Fourier series of $f(t)$ on $[-4, 4]$. Graph the fiftieth partial sum of this series on the same set of axes with a graph of $f(t)$.

9. Let $f(t) = 3\sigma_{-4,-1}(t) + 8\sigma_{-2,1}(t)$. Write the Fourier series of $f(t)$ on $[-6, 6]$. Graph the fiftieth partial sum of this series on the same set of axes with a graph of $f(t)$.

10. Let $f(t) = \sigma_{-2,-2}(t) + 4\sigma_{1,3}(t) + 2\sigma_{1,-2}(t)$. Write the Fourier series of $f(t)$ on $[-7, 7]$. Graph the fiftieth partial sum of this series on the same set of axes with a graph of $f(t)$.

$$\mu\rho\,\frac{\partial u}{\partial t} = K\left(\frac{\partial^2 u}{\partial x^2} + \frac{\partial^2 u}{\partial y^2} + \frac{\partial^2 u}{\partial z^2}\right) + \nabla K \cdot$$

$$\mu\rho\,\frac{\partial u}{\partial t} = K\left(\frac{\partial^2 u}{\partial x^2} + \frac{\partial^2 u}{\partial y^2} + \frac{\partial^2 u}{\partial z^2}\right) +$$

PART 6

$$\frac{\partial u}{\partial x}(0,t) = \frac{\partial u}{\partial x}$$

$$\frac{\partial u}{\partial t} =$$

$$\frac{\partial u}{\partial x}(0,t) =$$

$$u(x,0) =$$

$$X'' + \lambda X = 0, \quad T' + \lambda a^2$$

$$\frac{\partial u}{\partial t} = a^2 \frac{\partial^2 u}{\partial x^2}$$

Partial Differential Equations

$$a^2 \frac{\partial^2 u}{\partial x^2}$$

$$\frac{\partial u}{\partial x}(L,t)$$

A differential equation in which partial derivatives occur is called a *partial differential equation*. Mathematical models of physical phenomena involving more than one independent variable often include partial differential equations. They also arise in such diverse areas as epidemiology (for example, multivariable predator/prey models of AIDS), traffic flow studies and the analysis of economies.

We will be primarily concerned in this part with three broadly defined kinds of phenomena: wave motion, radiation or conduction of energy, and potential theory. Models of these phenomena involve partial differential equations called, respectively, the wave equation, the heat equation, and the potential equation, or Laplace's equation. We will consider each of these in turn, deriving solutions under a variety of boundary and initial conditions describing different settings.

The solution of partial differential equations requires a broad array of mathematical tools, including Fourier series, integrals and transforms, special functions and eigenfunction expansions. These were covered in Part 5, and can be referred to as needed.

CHAPTER 17

The Wave Equation

17.1   The Wave Equation and Initial and Boundary Conditions

Vibrations in a membrane or drum head, or oscillations induced in a guitar or violin string, are governed by a partial differential equation called the wave equation. We will derive this equation in a simple setting.

Consider an elastic string stretched between two pegs, as on a guitar. We want to describe the motion of the string if it is given a small displacement and released to vibrate in a plane.

Place the string along the x axis from 0 to L and assume that it vibrates in the x, y plane. We want a function $y(x, t)$ such that, at any time $t > 0$, the graph of the function $y = y(x, t)$ of x, is the shape of the string at that time. Thus $y(x, t)$ allows us to take a snapshot of the string at any time, showing it as a curve in the plane. For this reason $y(x, t)$ is called the *position function* for the string. Figure 17.1 shows a typical configuration.

To begin with a simple case, neglect damping forces such as air resistance and the weight of the string and assume that the tension $\mathbf{T}(x, t)$ in the string always acts tangentially to the string, and that individual particles of the string move only vertically. Also assume that the mass ρ per unit length is constant.

Now consider a typical segment of string between x and $x + \Delta x$ and apply Newton's second law of motion to write

> net force on this segment due to the tension $=$ acceleration of the center of mass
> of the segment times its mass.

This is a vector equation. For Δx small, the vertical component of this equation (Figure 17.2) gives us approximately

$$T(x + \Delta x, t) \sin(\theta + \Delta \theta) - T(x, t) \sin(\theta) = \rho \Delta x \frac{\partial^2 y}{\partial t^2}(\overline{x}, t),$$

781

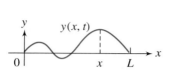

FIGURE 17.1 *String profile
at time t.*

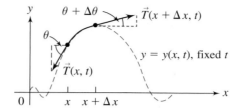

FIGURE 17.2

where $\bar{x}$ is the center of mass of the segment and $T(x, t) = \|\mathbf{T}(x, t)\| = $ magnitude of $\mathbf{T}$. Then

$$\frac{T(x + \Delta x, t)\sin(\theta + \Delta\theta) - T(x, t)\sin(\theta)}{\Delta x} = \rho\frac{\partial^2 y}{\partial t^2}(\bar{x}, t).$$

Now $v(x, t) = T(x, t)\sin(\theta)$ is the vertical component of the tension, so the last equation becomes

$$\frac{v(x + \Delta x, t) - v(x, t)}{\Delta x} = \rho\frac{\partial^2 y}{\partial t^2}(\bar{x}, t).$$

In the limit as $\Delta x \to 0$, we also have $\bar{x} \to x$ and the last equation becomes

$$\frac{\partial v}{\partial x} = \rho\frac{\partial^2 y}{\partial t^2}. \tag{17.1}$$

The horizontal component of the tension is $h(x, t) = T(x, t)\cos(\theta)$, so

$$v(x, t) = h(x, t)\tan(\theta) = h(x, t)\frac{\partial y}{\partial x}.$$

Substitute this into equation (17.1) to get

$$\frac{\partial}{\partial x}\left(h\frac{\partial y}{\partial x}\right) = \rho\frac{\partial^2 y}{\partial t^2}(x, t). \tag{17.2}$$

To compute the left side of this equation, use the fact that the horizontal component of the tension of the segment is zero, so

$$h(x + \Delta x, t) - h(x, t) = 0.$$

Thus h is independent of x and equation (17.2) can be written

$$h\frac{\partial^2 y}{\partial x^2} = \rho\frac{\partial^2 y}{\partial t^2}.$$

Letting $c^2 = \rho/h$, this equation is often written

$$\frac{\partial^2 y}{\partial x^2} = c^2\frac{\partial^2 y}{\partial t^2}.$$

This is the *one-dimensional (1-space dimension) wave equation*. If we use subscript notation for partial derivatives, in which

$$y_x = \frac{\partial y}{\partial x} \quad \text{and} \quad y_t = \frac{\partial y}{\partial t}$$

then the wave equation is

$$y_{tt} = c^2 y_{xx}.$$

This spectacular photo, taken by Ensign John Gay from the U.S.S. Constellation, shows a shock wave cloud forming over the tail of a U.S. Navy F/A-18 Hornet as it breaks the sound barrier. Current theory is that sound density waves generated by the plane accumulate in a cone at the plane's tail, and a drop in air pressure causes moist air to condense into water droplets there. Shock waves are not yet fully understood, and their mathematical modeling uses advanced techniques from the theory of partial differential equations.

In order to model the string's motion, we need more than just the wave equation. We must also incorporate information about constraints on the ends of the string, and about the initial velocity and position of the string, which will obviously influence the motion.

If the ends of the string are fixed, then

$$y(0, t) = y(L, t) = 0 \quad \text{for } t \geq 0.$$

These are the *boundary conditions*.

The *initial conditions* specify the initial (at time zero) position

$$y(x, 0) = f(x) \quad \text{for } 0 \leq x \leq L$$

and the initial velocity

$$\frac{\partial y}{\partial t}(x, 0) = g(x) \quad \text{for } 0 < x < L,$$

in which f and g are given functions satisfying certain compatibility conditions. For example, if the string is fixed at its ends, then the initial position function must reflect this by satisfying

$$f(0) = f(L) = 0.$$

If the initial velocity is zero (the string is released from rest), then $g(x) = 0$.

The wave equation, together with the boundary and initial conditions, constitute a *boundary value problem* for the position function $y(x, t)$ of the string. These constitute enough information to uniquely determine the solution $y(x, t)$.

If there is an external force of magnitude F units of force per unit length acting on the string in the vertical direction, then this derivation can be modified to obtain

$$\frac{\partial^2 y}{\partial x^2} = c^2 \frac{\partial^2 y}{\partial t^2} + \frac{1}{\rho} F.$$

Again, the boundary value problem consists of this wave equation and the boundary and initial conditions.

In 2-space dimensions the wave equation is

$$\frac{\partial^2 z}{\partial t^2} = c^2 \left(\frac{\partial^2 z}{\partial x^2} + \frac{\partial^2 z}{\partial y^2} \right). \tag{17.3}$$

This equation governs vertical displacements $z(x, y, t)$ of a membrane covering a specified region of the plane (for example, vibrations of a drum surface).

Again, boundary and initial conditions must be given to determine a unique solution. Typically, the frame is fixed on a boundary (the rim of the drum surface), so we would have no displacement of points on the boundary:

$$z(x, y, t) = 0 \quad \text{for } (x, y) \text{ on the boundary of the region and } t > 0.$$

Further, the initial displacement and initial velocity must be given. These initial conditions have the form

$$z(x, y, 0) = f(x, y), \quad \frac{\partial z}{\partial t}(x, y, 0) = g(x, y)$$

with f and g given.

We will have occasion to use the two dimensional wave equation (17.3) expressed in polar coordinates, so we will derive this equation. Let

$$x = r\cos(\theta), \quad y = r\sin(\theta).$$

Then

$$r = \sqrt{x^2 + y^2} \quad \text{and} \quad \theta = \tan^{-1}(y/x).$$

Let

$$z(x, y) = z(r\cos(\theta), r\sin(\theta)) = u(r, \theta).$$

Compute

$$\frac{\partial z}{\partial x} = \frac{\partial u}{\partial r}\frac{\partial r}{\partial x} + \frac{\partial u}{\partial \theta}\frac{\partial \theta}{\partial x}$$

$$= \frac{x}{\sqrt{x^2 + y^2}}\frac{\partial u}{\partial r} - \frac{y}{x^2 + y^2}\frac{\partial u}{\partial \theta}$$

$$= \frac{x}{r}\frac{\partial u}{\partial r} - \frac{y}{r^2}\frac{\partial u}{\partial \theta}.$$

Then

$$\frac{\partial^2 z}{\partial x^2} = \frac{\partial u}{\partial r} \frac{\partial}{\partial x}\left(\frac{y}{r}\right) - \frac{\partial u}{\partial \theta} \frac{\partial}{\partial x}\left(\frac{y}{r^2}\right) + \frac{x}{r} \frac{\partial}{\partial x}\left(\frac{\partial u}{\partial r}\right) - \frac{y}{r^2} \frac{\partial}{\partial x}\left(\frac{\partial u}{\partial \theta}\right)$$

$$= \frac{y^2}{r^3}\frac{\partial u}{\partial r} + \frac{2xy}{r^4}\frac{\partial u}{\partial \theta} + \frac{x^2}{r^2}\frac{\partial^2 u}{\partial r^2} - \frac{2xy}{r^3}\frac{\partial^2 u}{\partial r \partial \theta} + \frac{y^2}{r^4}\frac{\partial^2 u}{\partial \theta^2}.$$

By a similar calculation, we get

$$\frac{\partial z}{\partial y} = \frac{y}{r}\frac{\partial u}{\partial r} + \frac{x}{r^2}\frac{\partial u}{\partial \theta}$$

and

$$\frac{\partial^2 z}{\partial y^2} = \frac{x^2}{r^3}\frac{\partial u}{\partial r} - \frac{2xy}{r^4}\frac{\partial u}{\partial \theta} + \frac{y^2}{r^2}\frac{\partial^2 u}{\partial r^2} + \frac{2xy}{r^3}\frac{\partial^2 u}{\partial r \partial \theta} + \frac{x^2}{r^4}\frac{\partial^2 u}{\partial \theta^2}.$$

Then

$$\frac{\partial^2 z}{\partial x^2} + \frac{\partial^2 z}{\partial y^2} = \frac{\partial^2 u}{\partial r^2} + \frac{1}{r}\frac{\partial u}{\partial r} + \frac{1}{r^2}\frac{\partial^2 u}{\partial \theta^2}.$$

Therefore, in polar coordinates, the two-dimensional wave equation (17.3) is

$$\frac{\partial^2 u}{\partial t^2} = c^2\left(\frac{\partial^2 u}{\partial r^2} + \frac{1}{r}\frac{\partial u}{\partial r} + \frac{1}{r^2}\frac{\partial^2 u}{\partial \theta^2}\right), \tag{17.4}$$

in which $u(r, \theta, t)$ is the vertical displacement of the membrane from the x, y plane at point (r, θ) and time t.

For the rest of this chapter we will solve boundary value problems involving wave motion in a variety of settings, making use of several techniques.

SECTION 17.1   PROBLEMS

1. Let $y(x, t) = \sin(n\pi x/L)\cos(n\pi ct/L)$. Show that y satisfies the one-dimensional wave equation for any positive integer n.

2. Show that $z(x, y, t) = \sin(nx)\cos(my)\cos\left(\sqrt{n^2 + m^2}\,ct\right)$ satisfies the two-dimensional wave equation for any positive integers n and m.

3. Let f be any twice-differentiable function of one variable. Show that

$$y(x, t) = \frac{1}{2}[f(x + ct) + f(x - ct)]$$

satisfies the one-dimensional wave equation.

4. Show that $y(x, t) = \sin(x)\cos(ct) + \dfrac{1}{c}\cos(x)\sin(ct)$ satisfies the one-dimensional wave equation, together with the boundary conditions

$$y(0, t) = y(2\pi, t) = \frac{1}{c}\sin(ct) \quad \text{for } t > 0$$

and the initial conditions

$$y(x, 0) = \sin(x), \frac{\partial y}{\partial t}(x, 0) = \cos(x) \quad \text{for } 0 < x < \pi.$$

5. Formulate a boundary value problem (partial differential equation, boundary and initial conditions) for vibrations of a rectangular membrane occupying a region $0 \le x \le a$, $0 \le y \le b$ if the initial position is the graph of $z = f(x, y)$ and the initial velocity (at time zero) is $g(x, y)$. The membrane is fastened to a stiff frame along the rectangular boundary of the region.

6. Formulate a boundary value problem for the motion of an elastic string of length L, fastened at both ends and released from rest with an initial position given by $f(x)$. The string vibrates in the x, y plane. Its motion is opposed by air resistance, which has a force at each point of magnitude proportional to the square of the velocity at that point.

17.2   Fourier Series Solutions of the Wave Equation

We will begin with problems involving wave motion on a bounded interval. First we will consider the problem when there is an initial displacement, but no initial velocity (string released from rest). Following this we will allow an initial velocity but no initial displacement (string given an initial blow, but from its horizontal stretched position). Then we will show how to combine these to allow for both an initial velocity and initial displacement.

17.2.1   Vibrating String with Zero Initial Velocity

Consider an elastic string of length L, fastened at its ends on the x axis at $x = 0$ and $x = L$. The string is displaced, then released from rest to vibrate in the x, y plane. We want to find the displacement function $y(x, t)$, whose graph is a curve in the x, y plane showing the shape of the string at time t. If we took a snapshot of the string at time t, we would see this curve.

The boundary value problem for the displacement function is

$$\frac{\partial^2 y}{\partial t^2} = c^2 \frac{\partial^2 y}{\partial x^2} \quad \text{for } 0 < x < L, t > 0,$$

$$y(0, t) = y(L, t) = 0 \quad \text{for } t \geq 0,$$

$$y(x, 0) = f(x) \quad \text{for } 0 \leq x \leq L,$$

$$\frac{\partial y}{\partial t}(x, 0) = 0 \quad \text{for } 0 \leq x \leq L.$$

The graph of $f(x)$ is the position of the string before release.

The *Fourier method*, or *separation of variables*, consists of attempting a solution of the form $y(x, t) = X(x)T(t)$. Substitute this into the wave equation to obtain

$$XT'' = c^2 X'' T,$$

where $T' = dT/dt$ and $X' = dX/dx$. Then

$$\frac{X''}{X} = \frac{T''}{c^2 T}.$$

The left side of this equation depends only on x, and the right only on t. Because x and t are independent, we can choose any t_0 we like and fix the right side of this equation at the constant value $T''(t_0)/c^2 T(t_0)$, while varying x on the left side. Therefore X''/X must be constant for all x in $(0, L)$. But then $T''/c^2 T$ must equal the same constant for all $t > 0$. Denote this constant $-\lambda$. (The negative sign is customary and convenient, but we would arrive at the same final solution if we used just λ). λ is called the *separation constant*, and we now have

$$\frac{X''}{X} = \frac{T''}{c^2 T} = -\lambda.$$

Then

$$X'' + \lambda X = 0 \quad \text{and} \quad T'' + \lambda c^2 T = 0.$$

The wave equation has separated into two ordinary differential equations.

Now consider the boundary conditions. First,

$$y(0, t) = X(0)T(t) = 0$$

for $t \geq 0$. If $T(t) = 0$ for all $t \geq 0$, then $y(x, t) = 0$ for $0 \leq x \leq L$ and $t \geq 0$. This is indeed the solution if $f(x) = 0$, since in the absence of initial velocity or a driving force, and with zero displacement, the string remains stationary for all time. However, if $T(t) \neq 0$ for any time, then this boundary condition can be satisfied only if

$$X(0) = 0.$$

Similarly,

$$y(L, t) = X(L)T(t) = 0$$

for $t \geq 0$ requires that

$$X(L) = 0.$$

We now have a boundary-value problem for X:

$$X'' + \lambda X = 0; \quad X(0) = X(L) = 0.$$

The values of λ for which this problem has nontrivial solutions are the *eigenvalues* of this problem, and the corresponding nontrivial solutions for X are the *eigenfunctions*. We solved this regular Sturm–Liouville problem in Example 16.8, obtaining the eigenvalues

$$\lambda_n = \frac{n^2 \pi^2}{L^2}.$$

The eigenfunctions are nonzero constant multiples of

$$X_n(x) = \sin\left(\frac{n\pi x}{L}\right).$$

for $n = 1, 2, \ldots$. At this point we therefore have infinitely many possibilities for the separation constant and for $X(x)$.

Now turn to $T(t)$. Since the string is released from rest,

$$\frac{\partial y}{\partial t}(x, 0) = X(x)T'(0) = 0.$$

This requires that $T'(0) = 0$. The problem to be solved for T is therefore

$$T'' + \lambda c^2 T = 0; \quad T'(0) = 0.$$

However, we now know that λ can take on only values of the form $n^2 \pi^2 / L^2$, so this problem is really

$$T'' + \frac{n^2 \pi^2 c^2}{L^2} T = 0; \quad T'(0) = 0.$$

The differential equation for T has general solution

$$T(t) = a \cos\left(\frac{n\pi ct}{L}\right) + b \sin\left(\frac{n\pi ct}{L}\right)$$

Now

$$T'(0) = \frac{n\pi c}{L} b = 0,$$

so $b = 0$. We therefore have solutions for $T(t)$ of the form

$$T_n(t) = c_n \cos\left(\frac{n\pi ct}{L}\right)$$

for each positive integer n, with the constants c_n as yet undetermined.

We now have, for $n = 1, 2, \ldots$, functions

$$y_n(x, t) = c_n \sin\left(\frac{n\pi x}{L}\right) \cos\left(\frac{n\pi ct}{L}\right). \tag{17.5}$$

Each of these functions satisfies both boundary conditions and the initial condition $y_t(x, 0) = 0$. We need to satisfy the condition $y(x, 0) = f(x)$.

It may be possible to choose some n so that $y_n(x, t)$ is the solution for some choice of c_n. For example, suppose the initial displacement is

$$f(x) = 14 \sin\left(\frac{3\pi x}{L}\right).$$

Now choose $n = 3$ and $c_3 = 14$ to obtain the solution

$$y(x, t) = 14 \sin\left(\frac{3\pi x}{L}\right) \cos\left(\frac{3\pi ct}{L}\right).$$

This function satisfies the wave equation, the conditions $y(0) = y(L) = 0$, the initial condition $y(x, 0) = 14 \sin(3\pi x/L)$, and the zero initial velocity condition

$$\frac{\partial y}{\partial t}(x, 0) = 0.$$

However, depending on the initial displacement function, we may not be able to get by simply by picking a particular n and c_n in equation (17.5). For example, if we initially pick the string up in the middle and have initial displacement function

$$f(x) = \begin{cases} x & \text{for } 0 \le x \le L/2 \\ L - x & \text{for } L/2 < x \le L \end{cases}, \tag{17.6}$$

(as in Figure 17.3), then we can never satisfy $y(x, 0) = f(x)$ with one of the $y_n's$. Even if we try a finite linear combination

$$y(x, t) = \sum_{n=1}^{N} y_n(x, t)$$

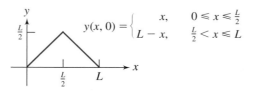

FIGURE 17.3

we cannot choose $c_1, \ldots, c_N$ to satisfy $y(x, 0) = f(x)$ for this function, since $f(x)$ cannot be written as a finite sum of sine functions.

We are therefore led to attempt an infinite superposition

$$y(x, t) = \sum_{n=1}^{\infty} c_n \sin\left(\frac{n\pi x}{L}\right) \cos\left(\frac{n\pi ct}{L}\right).$$

We must choose the $c_n's$ to satisfy

$$y(x, 0) = \sum_{n=1}^{\infty} c_n \sin\left(\frac{n\pi x}{L}\right).$$

We can do this! The series on the right is the Fourier sine expansion of $f(x)$ on $[0, L]$. Thus choose the Fourier sine coefficients

$$c_n = \frac{2}{L} \int_0^L f(\xi) \sin\left(\frac{n\pi\xi}{L}\right) d\xi.$$

With this choice, we obtain the solution

$$y(x, t) = \frac{2}{L} \sum_{n=1}^{\infty} \left(\int_0^L f(\xi) \sin\left(\frac{n\pi\xi}{L}\right) d\xi \right) \sin\left(\frac{n\pi x}{L}\right) \cos\left(\frac{n\pi ct}{L}\right). \qquad (17.7)$$

This strategy will work for any initial displacement function f which is continuous with a piecewise continuous derivative on $[0, L]$, and satisfies $f(0) = f(L) = 0$. These conditions ensure that the Fourier sine series of $f(x)$ on $[0, L]$ converges to $f(x)$ for $0 \leq x \leq L$.

In specific instances, where $f(x)$ is given, we can of course explicitly compute the coefficients in this solution. For example, if $L = \pi$ and the initial position function is $f(x) = x\cos(5x/2)$ on $[0, \pi]$, then the nth coefficient in the solution (17.7) is

$$c_n = \frac{2}{\pi} \int_0^\pi \xi\cos(5\xi/2) \sin\left(\frac{n\pi\xi}{L}\right) d\xi$$

$$= \frac{8}{\pi} \frac{n(-1)^{n+1}}{(5+2n)^2(5-2n)^2}.$$

The solution for this initial displacement function, and zero initial velocity, is

$$y(x, t) = \frac{8}{\pi} \sum_{n=1}^{\infty} \frac{n(-1)^{n+1}}{(5+2n)^2(5-2n)^2} \sin(nx) \cos(nct). \qquad (17.8)$$

Figure 17.4(a) shows graphs of this function (profiles of the string) at times $t = 0$, 0.2, 0.4, 0.7, 0.9 and 1.3 seconds. Figure 17.4(b) shows profiles at times $t = 1.2$, 1.9, 3, 3.5, 4.2 and 4.7. And Figure 17.4(c) shows the graphs at times $t = 5.1$, 5.6, 5.9, 6.4, 7 and 8, 3. These snapshots are made in groupings on the same set of axes to convey some sense of the motion with time.

The solution we have derived by separation of variables can be put into the context of Sturm–Liouville theory (Section 16.3). The problem for X, namely

$$X'' + \lambda X = 0; \quad X(0) = X(L) = 0,$$

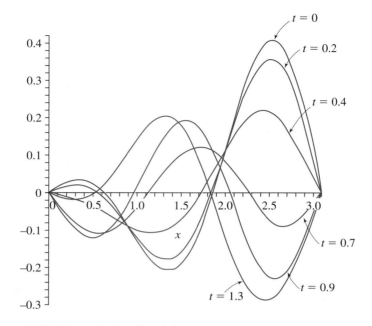

FIGURE 17.4(a) *Profiles of the solution at times* $t = 0, 0.2, 0.4, 0.7, 0.9,$ *and* $1.3.$

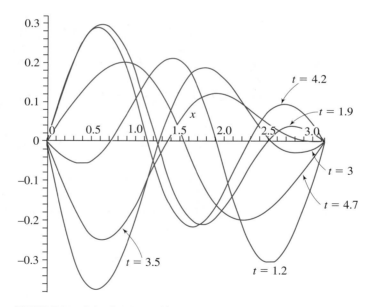

FIGURE 17.4(b) *String profiles at times* $t = 1.2, 1.9, 3, 3.5, 4.2,$ *and* $4.7.$

is a regular Sturm–Liouville problem, and we found its eigenvalues and corresponding eigenfunctions. The final step in the solution was to expand the initial position function in a series of the eigenfunctions. For this problem this series is the Fourier sine expansion of $f(x)$ on $[0, L]$.

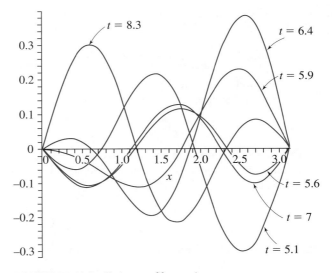

FIGURE 17.4(c) *String profiles at times*
$t = 5.1, 5.6, 5.9, 6.4, 7,$ *and* 8.3.

17.2.2   Vibrating String with Given Initial Velocity and Zero Initial Displacement

Now consider the case that the string is released from its horizontal position (zero initial displacement), but with an initial velocity given at x by $g(x)$. The boundary value problem for the displacement function is

$$\frac{\partial^2 y}{\partial t^2} = c^2 \frac{\partial^2 y}{\partial x^2} \quad \text{for } 0 < x < L, t > 0,$$

$$y(0, t) = y(L, t) = 0 \quad \text{for } t \geq 0,$$

$$y(x, 0) = 0 \quad \text{for } 0 \leq x \leq L,$$

$$\frac{\partial y}{\partial t}(x, 0) = g(x) \quad \text{for } 0 \leq x \leq L.$$

We begin as before with separation of variables. Put $y(x, t) = X(x)T(t)$. Since the partial differential equation and boundary conditions are the same as before, we again obtain

$$X'' + \lambda X = 0; \quad X(0) = X(L) = 0,$$

with eigenvalues

$$\lambda_n = \frac{n^2 \pi^2}{L^2}$$

and eigenfunctions constant multiples of

$$X_n(x) = \sin\left(\frac{n \pi x}{L}\right).$$

Now, however, the problem for T is different and we have

$$y(x, 0) = 0 = X(x)T(0),$$

so $T(0) = 0$. The problem for T is

$$T'' + \frac{n^2 \pi^2 c^2}{L^2} T = 0; \quad T(0) = 0.$$

(In the case of zero initial velocity we had $T'(0) = 0$). The general solution of the differential equation for T is

$$T(t) = a\cos\left(\frac{n\pi ct}{L}\right) + b\sin\left(\frac{n\pi ct}{L}\right).$$

Since $T(0) = a = 0$, solutions for $T(t)$ are constant multiples of $\sin(n\pi ct/L)$. Thus, for $n = 1, 2, \ldots$, we have functions

$$y_n(x, t) = c_n \sin\left(\frac{n\pi x}{L}\right) \sin\left(\frac{n\pi ct}{L}\right).$$

Each of these functions satisfies the wave equation, the boundary conditions and the zero initial displacement condition. To satisfy the initial velocity condition $y_t(x, 0) = g(x)$, we generally must attempt a superposition

$$y(x, t) = \sum_{n=1}^{\infty} c_n \sin\left(\frac{n\pi x}{L}\right) \sin\left(\frac{n\pi ct}{L}\right).$$

Assuming that we can differentiate this series term by term, then

$$\frac{\partial y}{\partial t}(x, 0) = \sum_{n=1}^{\infty} c_n \frac{n\pi c}{L} \sin\left(\frac{n\pi x}{L}\right) = g(x).$$

This is the Fourier sine expansion of $g(x)$ on $[0, L]$. Choose the *entire coefficient* of $\sin(n\pi x/L)$ to be the Fourier sine coefficient of $g(x)$ on $[0, L]$:

$$c_n \frac{n\pi c}{L} = \frac{2}{L} \int_0^L g(\xi) \sin\left(\frac{n\pi \xi}{L}\right) d\xi,$$

or

$$c_n = \frac{2}{n\pi c} \int_0^L g(\xi) \sin\left(\frac{n\pi \xi}{L}\right) d\xi.$$

The solution is

$$y(x, t) = \frac{2}{\pi c} \sum_{n=1}^{\infty} \frac{1}{n} \left(\int_0^L g(\xi) \sin\left(\frac{n\pi \xi}{L}\right) d\xi\right) \sin\left(\frac{n\pi x}{L}\right) \sin\left(\frac{n\pi ct}{L}\right). \tag{17.9}$$

For example, suppose the string is released from its horizontal position with an initial velocity given by $g(x) = x(1 + \cos(\pi x/L))$. Compute

$$\int_0^L g(\xi) \sin\left(\frac{n\pi \xi}{L}\right) d\xi = \int_0^L \xi\left(1 + \cos\left(\frac{\pi \xi}{L}\right)\right) \sin\left(\frac{n\pi \xi}{L}\right) d\xi$$

$$= \begin{cases} \frac{L^2(-1)^n}{n\pi(n^2-1)} & \text{if } n \neq 1 \\ \frac{3L^2}{4\pi} & \text{if } n = 1 \end{cases}.$$

The solution corresponding to this initial velocity function is

$$y(x, t) = \frac{2}{\pi c}\left(\frac{3L^2}{4\pi}\right) \sin\left(\frac{\pi x}{L}\right) \sin\left(\frac{\pi ct}{L}\right) + \frac{2}{\pi c} \sum_{n=2}^{\infty} \frac{L^2(-1)^n}{n^2\pi(n^2-1)} \sin\left(\frac{n\pi x}{L}\right) \sin\left(\frac{n\pi ct}{L}\right) \tag{17.10}$$

If we let $c = 1$ and $L = \pi$, the solution 17.10 becomes

$$y(x, t) = \frac{3}{2}\sin(x)\sin(t) + \sum_{n=2}^{\infty} \frac{2(-1)^n}{n^2(n^2-1)} \sin(nx)\sin(nt).$$

Figure 17.5 shows graphs of this solution (positions of the string) at times $t = 0.4, 1.2, 1.7, 2.6, 3.5$ and 4.3.

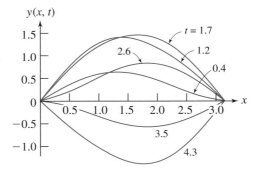

FIGURE 17.5 *String profiles at times* $t = 0.4$,
1.2, 1.7, 2.6, 3.5, and 4.3.

17.2.3   Vibrating String with Initial Displacement and Velocity

Consider the motion of the string with both initial displacement $f(x)$ and initial displacement $g(x)$.

Formulate two separate problems, the first with initial displacement $f(x)$ and zero initial velocity, and the second with zero initial displacement and initial velocity $g(x)$. We know how to solve both of these. Let $y_1(x, t)$ be the solution of the first problem, and $y_2(x, t)$ the solution of the second. Now let

$$y(x, t) = y_1(x, t) + y_2(x, t).$$

Then y satisfies the wave equation and the boundary conditions. Further,

$$y(x, 0) = y_1(x, 0) + y_2(x, 0) = f(x) + 0 = f(x)$$

and

$$\frac{\partial y}{\partial t}(x, 0) = \frac{\partial y_1}{\partial t}(x, 0) + \frac{\partial y_2}{\partial t}(x, 0) = 0 + g(x) = g(x).$$

Thus $y(x, t)$ is the solution in this case of nonzero initial displacement and velocity functions.

For example, let the initial displacement function be

$$f(x) = \begin{cases} x & \text{for } 0 \le x \le L/2 \\ L - x & \text{for } L/2 < x \le L \end{cases},$$

and the initial velocity

$$g(x) = x\left(1 + \cos\left(\frac{\pi x}{L}\right)\right).$$

The solution for the displacement function is the sum of the solution $y_1(x, t)$ for just displacement $f(x)$, with zero initial velocity, and the solution $y_2(x, t)$ with zero initial displacement and initial velocity $g(x)$. For $y_1(x, t)$, use the solution (17.7). First evaluate

$$\frac{2}{L}\left(\int_0^L f(\xi) \sin\left(\frac{n\pi\xi}{L}\right) d\xi\right)$$

$$= \frac{2}{L}\int_0^{L/2} \xi \sin\left(\frac{n\pi\xi}{L}\right) d\xi + \frac{2}{L}\int_{L/2}^L (L - \xi) \sin\left(\frac{n\pi\xi}{L}\right) d\xi$$

$$= \frac{4L}{n^2\pi^2} \sin(n\pi/2).$$

Therefore

$$y_1(x, t) = \sum_{n=1}^{\infty} \frac{4L}{n^2 \pi^2} \sin(n\pi/2) \sin\left(\frac{n\pi x}{L}\right) \cos\left(\frac{n\pi ct}{L}\right).$$

We have already solved for $y_2(x, t)$, obtaining

$$y_2(x, t) = \frac{2}{\pi c}\left(\frac{3L^2}{4\pi}\right) \sin\left(\frac{\pi x}{L}\right) \sin\left(\frac{\pi ct}{L}\right)$$

$$+ \frac{2}{\pi c} \sum_{n=2}^{\infty} \frac{L^2(-1)^n}{n^2 \pi(n^2 - 1)} \sin\left(\frac{n\pi x}{L}\right) \sin\left(\frac{n\pi ct}{L}\right).$$

The solution with the given initial position and initial velocity is $y(x, t) = y_1(x, t) + y_2(x, t)$. If we let $L = \pi$ and $c = 1$, this solution is

$$y(x, t) = \sum_{n=1}^{\infty} \frac{4}{n^2 \pi} \sin(n\pi/2) \sin(nx) \cos(nt)$$

$$+ \left(\frac{3}{2}\right) \sin(x) \sin(t)$$

$$+ \sum_{n=2}^{\infty} \frac{2(-1)^n}{n^2(n^2 - 1)} \sin(nx) \sin(nt).$$

Graphs of this string profile are shown in Figure 17.6 for times $t = 0.125, 0.46, 0.93, 1.9, 2.5, 3.4$ and 5.2.

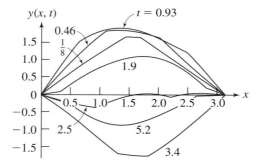

FIGURE 17.6 *Snapshot of the string at times* $t = \frac{1}{8}, 0.46, 0.93, 1.9, 2.5, 3.4,$ *and* 5.2.

17.2.4 Verification of Solutions

In the solutions we have obtained thus far we have had to use an infinite series

$$y(x, t) = \sum_{n=1}^{\infty} y_n(x, t)$$

and determine the coefficients in the $y_n's$ by using a Fourier expansion. The question now is whether this infinite sum is indeed a solution of the boundary value problem.

To be specific, consider the problem with initial position function $f(x)$ and zero initial velocity. We derived the proposed solution

$$y(x, t) = \sum_{n=1}^{\infty} c_n \sin\left(\frac{n\pi x}{L}\right) \cos\left(\frac{n\pi ct}{L}\right), \tag{17.11}$$

in which

$$c_n = \frac{2}{L} \int_0^L f(\xi) \sin\left(\frac{n\pi\xi}{L}\right) d\xi.$$

Certainly $y(0, t) = y(L, t) = 0$, because every term in the series for $y(x, t)$ vanishes at $x = 0$ and at $x = L$. Further, under reasonable conditions on f, the Fourier sine series of $f(x)$ converges to $f(x)$ on $[0, L]$, so $y(x, 0) = f(x)$,

It is not obvious, however, that $y(x, t)$ satisfies the wave equation, even though each term in the series certainly does. The reason for this uncertainty is that we cannot justify term by term differentiation of the proposed series solution.

We will now demonstrate a remarkable fact, which has other ramifications as well. We will show that the series in equation (17.11) can be summed in closed form. To do this, first write

$$\sin\left(\frac{n\pi x}{L}\right)\cos\left(\frac{n\pi ct}{L}\right) = \frac{1}{2}\left[\sin\left(\frac{n\pi(x+ct)}{L}\right) + \sin\left(\frac{n\pi(x-ct)}{L}\right)\right].$$

Then equation (17.11) becomes

$$y(x, t) = \frac{1}{2}\left\{\sum_{n=1}^{\infty} c_n \sin\left(\frac{n\pi(x+ct)}{L}\right) + \sum_{n=1}^{\infty} c_n \sin\left(\frac{n\pi(x-ct)}{L}\right)\right\}. \tag{17.12}$$

If the Fourier sine series for $f(x)$ converges to $f(x)$ on $[0, L]$, as might normally be expected of a function that can be a displacement function for a string, then

$$f(x) = \sum_{n=1}^{\infty} c_n \sin\left(\frac{n\pi x}{L}\right)$$

for $0 \le x \le L$, and equation (17.12) becomes

$$y(x, t) = \frac{1}{2}[f(x+ct) + f(x-ct)].$$

If f is twice differentiable, we can use the chain rule to verify directly that $y(x, t)$ given by this expression satisfies the wave equation, wherever $f(x+ct)$ and $f(x-ct)$ are defined.

This raises a difficulty, however, since $f(x)$ is defined only for $0 \le x \le L$. But t can be any nonnegative number, so the numbers $x+ct$ and $x-ct$ can vary over the entire real line. How then can we evaluate $f(x+ct)$ and $f(x-ct)$?

This difficulty can be overcome in two steps. First, extend f to an odd function f_o defined on $[-L, L]$ by setting

$$f_o(x) = \begin{cases} f(x) & \text{for } 0 \le x \le L \\ -f(-x) & \text{for } -L < x < 0 \end{cases}.$$

Notice that $f_o(0) = f_o(L) = f_o(-L) = 0$ because the ends of the string are fixed.

Now extend f_o to a periodic function F of period $2L$ by replicating the graph of f_o on successive intervals $[L, 3L], [3L, 5L], \ldots, [-3L, -L], [-5L, -3L], \ldots$. Figure 17.7(a) displays the odd extension of f defined on $[0, L]$ to f_o defined on $[-L, L]$, and Figure 17.7(b) shows the periodic extension of f_o to the real line.

We now have

$$y(x, t) = \frac{1}{2}[F(x+ct) + F(x-ct)] \tag{17.13}$$

for $0 \le x \le L$ and $t > 0$. Assuming that f is twice differentiable, and that the joins at the ends of intervals where f has been extended to produce F are sufficiently smooth, then F is also twice differentiable, and the chain rule can be used to directly verify that $y(x, t)$ satisfies the

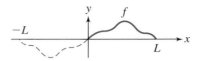

FIGURE 17.7(a)   *Odd extension of*
f to $[-L, L]$.

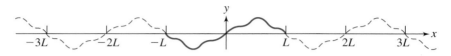

FIGURE 17.7(b)   *Periodic extension F of f_o to the real line.*

wave equation. This is an elegant expression for the solution in terms of the initial displacement function and the number c, which depends on the material from which the string is made. It is reasonable that the motion should be determined by these quantities.

In practice, there will often be finitely many points in $[0, L]$ at which f is not differentiable. For example, $f(x)$ as given by equation (17.6) is not differentiable at $L/2$. In such a case $y(x, t)$ given by equation (17.13) is the solution in a restricted sense, as there are isolated points at which it does not satisfy all the conditions of the boundary value problem.

Equation (17.13) has an appealing physical interpretation. If we think of $F(x)$ as a wave, then $F(x + ct)$ is this wave translated ct units to the left, and $F(x - ct)$ is the wave translated ct units to the right. The motion of the string (in this case with zero initial velocity) is a sum of two waves, one moving to the right with velocity c, the other to the left with velocity c, and both waves are determined by the initial displacement function. We will say more about this when we discuss d'Alembert's solution for the motion of an infinitely long string.

17.2.5   Transformation of Boundary Value Problems Involving the Wave Equation

There are boundary value problems involving the wave equation for which separation of variables does not lead to the solution. This can occur because of the form of wave equation (for example, there may be an external forcing term), or because of the form of the boundary conditions. Here is an example of such a problem and a strategy for overcoming the difficulty.

Consider the boundary value problem

$$\frac{\partial^2 y}{\partial t^2} = \frac{\partial^2 y}{\partial x^2} + Ax \quad \text{for } 0 < x < L, t > 0.$$

$$y(0, t) = y(L, t) = 0 \quad \text{for } t \geq 0,$$

$$y(x, 0) = 0, \frac{\partial y}{\partial t}(x, 0) = 1 \quad \text{for } 0 < x < L.$$

A is a positive constant. The term Ax in the wave equation represents an external force which at x has magnitude Ax. We have let $c = 1$ in this problem.

If we put $y(x, t) = X(x)T(t)$ into the partial differential equation, we get

$$XT'' = X''T + Ax,$$

and there is no way to separate the t dependency on one side of the equation, and the x dependent terms on the other.

We will transform this problem into one for which separation of variables works. Let

$$y(x, t) = Y(x, t) + \psi(x).$$

The idea is to choose ψ to reduce the given problem to one we have already solved. Substitute $y(x, t)$ into the partial differential equation to get

$$\frac{\partial^2 Y}{\partial t^2} = \frac{\partial^2 Y}{\partial x^2} + \psi''(x) + Ax.$$

This will be simplified if we choose ψ so that

$$\psi''(x) + Ax = 0.$$

There are many such choices. By integrating twice, we get

$$\psi(x) = -A\frac{x^3}{6} + Cx + D,$$

with C and D constants we can still choose any way we like. Now look at the boundary conditions. First,

$$y(0, t) = Y(0, t) + \psi(0) = 0.$$

This will be just $y(0, t) = Y(0, t)$ if we choose

$$\psi(0) = D = 0.$$

Next,

$$y(L, t) = Y(L, t) + \psi(L) = Y(L, t) - A\frac{L^3}{6} + CL = 0.$$

This will reduce to $y(0, t) = Y(L, t)$ if we choose C so that

$$\psi(L) = -A\frac{L^3}{6} + CL = 0$$

or

$$C = \frac{1}{6}AL^2.$$

This means that

$$\psi(x) = -\frac{1}{6}Ax^3 + \frac{1}{6}AL^2x = \frac{1}{6}Ax\left(L^2 - x^2\right).$$

With this choice of ψ,

$$Y(0, t) = Y(L, t) = 0.$$

Now relate the initial conditions for y to initial condition for Y. First,

$$Y(x, 0) = y(x, 0) - \psi(x) = -\psi(x) = \frac{1}{6}Ax(x^2 - L^2).$$

And

$$\frac{\partial Y}{\partial t}(x, 0) = \frac{\partial y}{\partial t}(x, 0) = 1.$$

We now have a boundary value problem for $Y(x, t)$:

$$\frac{\partial^2 Y}{\partial t^2} = \frac{\partial^2 Y}{\partial x^2} \quad \text{for } 0 < x < L, t > 0,$$

$$Y(0, t) = 0, Y(L, t) = 0 \quad \text{for } t > 0,$$

$$Y(x, 0) = \frac{1}{6} Ax(x^2 - L^2), \frac{\partial Y}{\partial t}(x, 0) = 1 \quad \text{for } 0 < x < L.$$

Using equations 17.7 and 17.9, we immediately write the solution

$$Y(x, t) = \frac{2}{L} \sum_{n=1}^{\infty} \left(\int_0^L \frac{1}{6} A\xi(\xi^2 - L^2) \sin\left(\frac{n\pi\xi}{L}\right) d\xi \right) \sin\left(\frac{n\pi x}{L}\right) \cos\left(\frac{n\pi t}{L}\right)$$

$$+ \frac{2}{\pi} \sum_{n=1}^{\infty} \frac{1}{n} \left(\int_0^L \sin\left(\frac{n\pi\xi}{L}\right) d\xi \right) \sin\left(\frac{n\pi x}{L}\right) \sin\left(\frac{n\pi t}{L}\right)$$

$$= \frac{2AL^3}{\pi^3} \sum_{n=1}^{\infty} \frac{(-1)^n}{n^3} \sin\left(\frac{n\pi x}{L}\right) \cos\left(\frac{n\pi t}{L}\right)$$

$$+ \frac{2L}{\pi^2} \sum_{n=1}^{\infty} \frac{1 - (-1)^n}{n^2} \sin\left(\frac{n\pi x}{L}\right) \sin\left(\frac{n\pi t}{L}\right).$$

The solution of the original problem is

$$y(x, t) = Y(x, t) + \frac{1}{6} Ax \left(L^2 - x^2\right).$$

Figure 17.8(a) shows graphs of the string's position at times $t = 0.03, 0.2, 0.5, 0.9, 1.4$ and 2.2, with $c = 1$ and $L = \pi$. Figure 17.8(b) shows this string at times $t = 2.8, 3.7, 4.4, 4.8, 5.3, 6.1$ and 6.7. These use $L = \pi$ and $c = 1$.

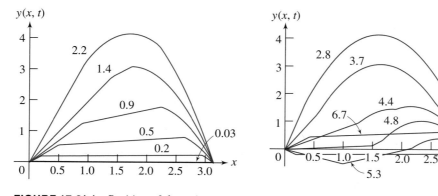

FIGURE 17.8(a) *Position of the string at times $t = 0.03, 0.2, 0.5, 0.9, 1.4,$ and 2.2.*

FIGURE 17.8(b) *Position at times $t = 2.8$, 3.7, 4.4, 4.8, 5.3, 6.1, and 6.7.*

17.2.6 Effects of Initial Conditions and Constants on the Motion

Using separation of variables, we have obtained series solutions of problems involving the vibrating string on a bounded interval. It is interesting to examine the effects that constants occuring in the problem have on the solution. We begin with an example investigating the effect of the constant c in the motion of the string.

EXAMPLE 17.1

Consider again the problem of the wave equation with zero initial displacement and initial velocity given by

$$g(x) = x\left(1 + \cos\left(\frac{\pi x}{L}\right)\right).$$

The solution previously obtained, with $L = \pi$, is

$$y(x, t) = \frac{3}{2c}\sin(x)\sin(ct) + \sum_{n=2}^{\infty}\frac{2(-1)^n}{n^2 c}\frac{1}{n^2 - 1}\sin(nx)\sin(nct).$$

Figure 17.5 shows graphs of the string's position at various times, with $c = 1$. Now we want to focus on how c influences the motion. Figure 17.9(a) shows the string profile at time $t = 5.3$, with $c = 1.05$. Figures 17.9(b) and (c) show the profile at the same time, with with $c = 1.1$ and 1.2, respectively. These graphs are placed on the same set of axes for comparison in Figure 17.9(d). The student is invited to select other times and graph the solution for different values of c. ■

Next, consider a problem in which the initial data of the problem depends on a parameter.

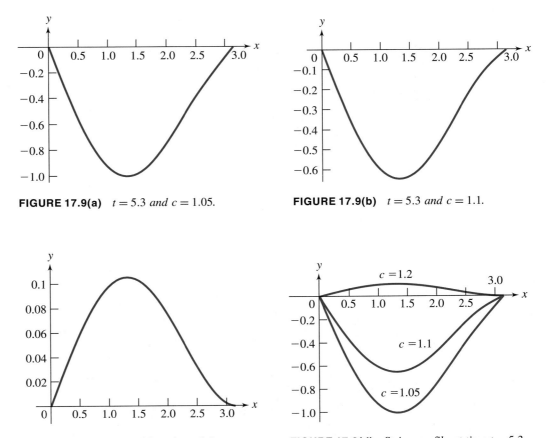

FIGURE 17.9(a) *t = 5.3 and c = 1.05.*

FIGURE 17.9(b) *t = 5.3 and c = 1.1.*

FIGURE 17.9(c) *t = 5.3 and c = 1.2.*

FIGURE 17.9(d) *String profile at time t = 5.3 with c having values 1.05, 1.1, and 1.2.*

EXAMPLE 17.2

Consider the problem

$$\frac{\partial^2 y}{\partial t^2} = 1.44\frac{\partial^2 y}{\partial x^2} \quad \text{for } 0 < x < \pi, t > 0,$$

$$y(0, t) = y(\pi, t) = 0 \quad \text{for } t \geq 0,$$

$$y(x, 0) = 0, \frac{\partial y}{\partial t}(x, 0) = \sin(\epsilon x) \quad \text{for } 0 < x < \pi,$$

in which ϵ is a positive number that is not an integer. It is routine to write the solution

$$y(x, t) = \frac{5}{3\pi} \sum_{n=1}^{\infty} \frac{\sin(\pi\epsilon)(-1)^{n+1}}{n^2 - \epsilon^2} \sin(nx) \sin(1.2nt).$$

Now compare graphs of this solution at various times, with different choices of ϵ. Figure 17.10(a) shows the string profile at $t = 0.5$ for ϵ equal to 0.7, 0.9, 1.5, 4.7 and 9.3. Figure 17.10(b) shows the graphs for these values of ϵ at $t = 1.1$, and Figure 17.10(c) shows the graphs at $t = 2.8$. We can also follow the motion of the string at different times for the same value of ϵ. Figure 17.11(a) shows the string profiles for $\epsilon = 0.7$ at times $t = 0.5$, 1.1 and 2.8. Figures 17.11(b), (c), (d) and (e) each show the string profile for a given ϵ and for these three times. ∎

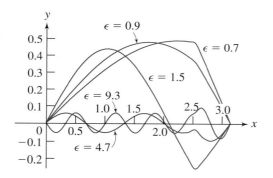

FIGURE 17.10(a)   *String profiles at $t = 0.5$ for ϵ equal to 0.7, 0.9, 1.5, 4.7, and 9.3.*

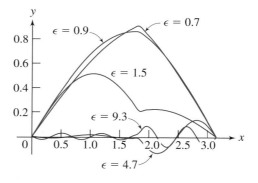

FIGURE 17.10(b)   *String profiles at $t = 1.1$.*

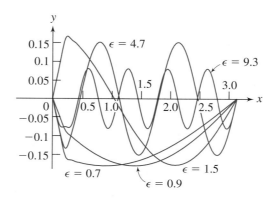

FIGURE 17.10(c)   *String profiles at $t = 2.8$.*

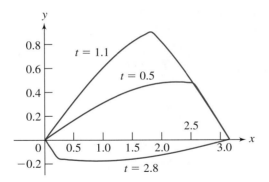

FIGURE 17.11(a)   *Graphs of the string with* $\epsilon = 0.7$ *for times* $t = 0.5, 1.1,$ *and* $2.8.$

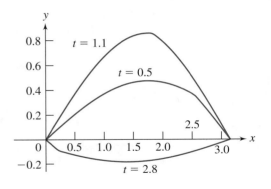

FIGURE 17.11(b) $\epsilon = 0.9.$

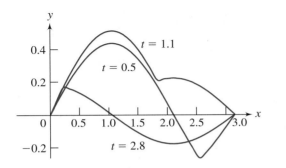

FIGURE 17.11(c) $\epsilon = 1.5.$

FIGURE 17.11(d) $\epsilon = 4.7.$

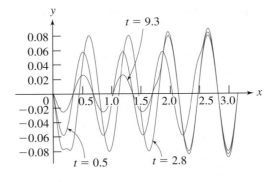

FIGURE 17.11(e) $\epsilon = 9.3.$

In some of the exercises we will ask the student to employ a graphics package to exhibit string profiles at different times and under different conditions.

17.2.7   Numerical Solution of the Wave Equation

We will describe a numerical method for approximating solutions of the wave equation on an interval. The underlying idea is useful in approximating solutions of the heat equation as well, and involves difference approximations of the derivative. To understand this idea, begin with a function f of a single variable which is differentiable at x_0. Approximate

$$f'(x_0) \approx \frac{f(x_0 + h) - f(x_0)}{h}$$

and also

$$f'(x_0) \approx \frac{f(x_0 - h) - f(x_0)}{-h}$$

with the approximation improving as h is chosen closer to zero. If $h > 0$, these are, respectively, the *forward* and *backward difference approximations* of $f'(x_0)$. If we average these we get

$$f'(x_0) \approx \frac{f(x_0 + h) - f(x_0 - h)}{2h}.$$

This is the *centered difference approximation of $f'(x_0)$.*

If f is twice differentiable at x_0, then

$$f''(x_0) \approx \frac{f'(x_0 + h) - f'(x_0 - h)}{2h}$$

$$\approx \frac{1}{2h} \left(\frac{f(x_0 + 2h) - f(x_0)}{2h} - \frac{f(x_0) - f(x_0 - 2h)}{2h} \right)$$

$$= \frac{f(x_0 + 2h) - 2f(x_0) + f(x_0 - 2h)}{4h^2}.$$

Replacing $2h$ by h, we can write

$$f''(x_0) \approx \frac{f(x_0 + h) - 2f(x_0) + f(x_0 - h)}{h^2}.$$

This is the *centered difference approximation of the second derivative.*

Applying these ideas to $y(x, t)$, we can take increments Δx in x and Δt in t and write centered difference approximations of second partial derivatives:

$$\frac{\partial^2 y}{\partial x^2}(x, t) \approx \frac{y(x + \Delta x, t) - 2y(x, t) + y(x - \Delta x, t)}{(\Delta x)^2}$$

and

$$\frac{\partial^2 y}{\partial t^2}(x, t) \approx \frac{y(x, t + \Delta t) - 2y(x, t) + y(x, t - \Delta t)}{(\Delta t)^2}.$$

We will use these to write numerical approximations of the solution to the problem:

$$\frac{\partial^2 y}{\partial t^2} = c^2 \frac{\partial^2 y}{\partial x^2} \quad \text{for } 0 < x < L, t > 0,$$

$$y(0, t) = y(L, t) = 0 \quad \text{for } t \geq 0,$$

$$y(x, 0) = f(x) \quad \text{for } 0 \leq x \leq L,$$

$$\frac{\partial y}{\partial t}(x, 0) = g(x) \quad \text{for } 0 \leq x \leq L.$$

The $x, t-$ region of interest is the strip $0 \leq x \leq L, t \geq 0$. Choose a positive integer N and let $\Delta x = L/N$. Partition $[0, L]$ by points $x_j = j\Delta x$, so

$$0 < \frac{L}{N} < \frac{2L}{N} < \cdots < \frac{(N-1)L}{N} < \frac{NL}{N} = L.$$

Also choose an increment Δt in time and let $t_k = k\Delta t$ for $k = 0, 1, 2, \ldots$. In this way form a grid of points (x_j, t_k), called *lattice points*, over the $x, t-$ strip, as shown in Figure 17.12.

It is convenient to write

$$y_{j,k} = y(x_j, t_k) = y(j\Delta x, k\Delta t).$$

Now replace the partial derivatives in the wave equation with centered difference approximations to get

$$\frac{y_{j,k+1} - 2y_{j,k} + y_{j,k-1}}{(\Delta t)^2} = c^2 \frac{y_{j+1,k} - 2y_{j,k} + y_{j-1,k}}{(\Delta x)^2}$$

at (x_j, y_k). Solve this for $y_{j,k+1}$ to get

$$y_{j,k+1} = \left(\frac{c\Delta t}{\Delta x}\right)^2 \left(y_{j+1,k} - 2y_{j,k} + y_{j-1,k}\right) + 2y_{j,k} - y_{j,k-1}. \tag{17.14}$$

Figure 17.13 shows why this equation is useful. The horizontal lines $t = t_k$ divide the $x, t-$ strip into horizontal time layers Δt units apart. Compute approximate values $y_{j,k}$ at the lattice points (x_j, t_k). The points (x_j, t_{k+1}), (x_{j-1}, t_k), (x_j, t_k), (x_{j+1}, t_k) and (x_j, t_{k-1}) appear as a diamond configuration, with the middle three points at the t_k level, the last point at the t_{k-1} level, and the first at the highest, t_{k+1} level. If we know the (approximate) value of $y(x, t)$ at each of the last four points (in levels t_k and t_{k-1}), then we know all the terms on the right of equation (17.14), hence we know the (approximate) value $y_{j,k+1}$ at the t_{k+1} level. We can work our way up such five point configurations, always solving for the value of $y(x, t)$ at the highest level, from previously derived values at the two next lower levels.

This process fails at the edges of the $x, t-$ region because we cannot form this five point diamond configuration there. However, the initial and boundary information of the problem give information about $y(x, t)$ at the edges. In particular:

$y(x, 0) = f(x)$ at each point on the bottom side ($t = 0$) of the strip, and
$y(0, t) = y(L, t) = 0$ on the left and right sides of the strip.
Thus,

$$y(0, t_k) = y(L, t_k) = 0,$$

or equivalently,

$$y_{0,k} = y_{L,k} = 0 \quad \text{for } k = 0, 1, 2, \ldots.$$

And

$$y(x_j, 0) = y_{j,0} = f(j\Delta x) \quad \text{for } j = 1, \ldots, N - 1.$$

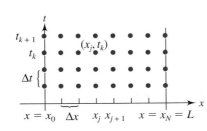

FIGURE 17.12 *Lattice of points at which approximations are made.*

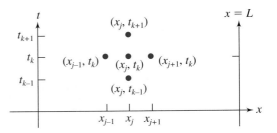

FIGURE 17.13 *For the wave equation, approximation of $y(x_j, t_{k+1})$ from preceding approximations, three at level t_k and one at level t_{k-1}.*

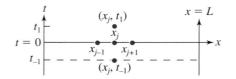

FIGURE 17.14 *A t_{-1} layer must be created to implement the scheme of Figure 17.13 at the t_1 layer.*

We have not yet used the initial condition on the velocity. Use the backward difference approximation of the first derivative to write

$$\frac{\partial y}{\partial t}(x_j, 0) \approx \frac{y(x_j, -\Delta t) - y(x_j, 0)}{-\Delta t}$$

$$= \frac{y_{j,-1} - y_{j,0}}{-\Delta t} = g(x_j) = g(j\Delta x), \ .j = 1, \dots, N-1. \tag{17.15}$$

Notice that this equation contains a $y_{j,-1}$ term. This is at the layer below the bottom edge ($t = 0$) of the $x, t-$ strip. There is really no such layer in a natural sense, but we create it artificially using this backward difference approximation in order to use the initial information $(\partial y/\partial t)(x, 0) = g(x)$ for $0 \le x \le L$. Solve equation (17.15) for $y_{j,-1}$ to get

$$y_{j,-1} = y_{j,0} - g(j\Delta x)\Delta t,$$

enabling us to determine the appropriate values to fill in on this lowest layer, in terms of known values on level zero and the initial velocity function. This provides the diamond configuration of Figure 17.14 when $k = 0$.

The strategy now is to begin by filling in the $y(x, t)$ values at the grid points at levels $k = -1$ and $k = 0$. Then work up the layers, using equation (17.14) to fill in approximate values of $y(x, t)$ at successively higher layers. With today's computing power, this can be done for a very large number of grid points.

One fine point – the number $(c\Delta t/\Delta x)^2$ has a bearing on the stability of the method. If this number is less than $1/2$, the method is stable and produces approximations that improve as Δx and Δt are chosen smaller (keeping $(c\Delta t/\Delta x)^2 < 1/2$). If $(c\Delta t/\Delta x)^2 \ge 1/2$, the numerical approximations can be unstable, yielding unreliable results.

EXAMPLE 17.3

Consider the problem

$$\frac{\partial^2 y}{\partial t^2} = \frac{\partial^2 y}{\partial x^2} \quad \text{for } 0 < x < 1, t > 0$$

$$y(0, t) = y(1, t) = 0$$

$$y(x, 0) = x\cos(\pi x/2), \frac{\partial y}{\partial t}(x, 0) = \begin{cases} 1 & \text{for } 0 \le x \le 1/2 \\ 0 & \text{for } 1/2 < x \le 1 \end{cases}.$$

The exact solution is

$$y(x, t) = \frac{16}{\pi^2} \sum_{n=1}^{\infty} \left(\frac{(-1)^n}{(4n^2 - 1)^2} \right) \sin(n\pi x) \cos(n\pi t)$$

$$+ \frac{2}{\pi} \sum_{n=1}^{\infty} \frac{1}{n} \left(\frac{\cos(n\pi/2) - 1}{n\pi} \right) \sin(n\pi x) \sin(n\pi t)$$

We will choose $N = 10$, so $\Delta x = 0.1$. Let $\Delta t = 0.025$. Then $(c\Delta t/\Delta x)^2 = (0.025/0.1)^2 = 0.0625 < 1/2$. The equations for the approximations are

$$y_{j,k+1} = (0.0625)\left(y_{j+1,k} - 2y_{j,k} + y_{j-1,k}\right) + 2y_{j,k} - y_{j,k-1} \quad \text{for } j = 1, \ldots, 9, \, k = 0, 1, 2, \ldots,$$

$$\tag{17.16}$$

$$y_{j,0} = f(0.1j) \quad \text{for } j = 1, \ldots, 9,$$

and

$$y_{j,-1} = y_{j,0} - g(j\Delta x)\Delta t = f(0.1j) - 0.025g(0.1j) \quad \text{for } j = 1, \ldots, 9.$$

Note that we take j from 1 through $N - 1 = 9$ because $j = 0$ corresponds to the left side of the $x, t-$ strip, and $j = N = 10$ refers to the right side of this strip, and information is given on these sides: $y(0, t) = y(1, t) = 0$.

First, compute the values $y_{j,-1}$ on the lowest horizontal level:

$$y_{1,-1} = 0.07377, y_{2,-1} = 0.16521, y_{3,-1} = 0.24230$$

$$y_{4,-1} = 0.29861, y_{5,-1} = 0.32855, y_{6,-1} = 0.35267, y_{7,-1} = 0.31779,$$

$$y_{8,-1} = 0.24721, y_{9,-1} = 0.14079.$$

Next, compute the approximate values $y_{j,0}$:

$$y_{1,0} = 0.09877, y_{2,0} = 0.19021, y_{3,0} = 0.26730,$$

$$y_{4,0} = 0.32361, y_{5,0} = 0.35355, y_{6,0} = 0.35267, y_{7,0} = 0.31779,$$

$$y_{8,0} = 0.24721, y_{9,0} = 0.14079.$$

Now systematically move up the $t-$ axis, one level at a time. For $t = 0.025$, put $k = 0$ in equation (17.16), we have

$$y_{j,1} = (0.0625)\left(y_{j+1,0} - 2y_{j,0} + y_{j-1,0}\right) + 2y_{j,0} - y_{j,-1} \quad \text{for } j = 1, \ldots, 9.$$

The computed values are:

$$y_{1,1} = 0.12331, y_{2,1} = 0.21431, y_{3,1} = 0.291$$

$$y_{4,1} = 0.34696, y_{5,1} = 0.37662, y_{6,1} = 0.35055,$$

$$y_{7,1} = 0.31556, y_{8,1} = 0.24160, y_{9,1} = 0.13864.$$

Next get the approximate values on the $k = 2$ layer ($t = 2(0.025) = 0.05$) by putting $k = 1$ in equation (17.16) and using

$$y_{j,2} = (0.0625)\left(y_{j+1,2} - 2y_{j,2} + y_{j-1,2}\right) + 2y_{j,2} - y_{j,1}$$

for $j = 1, \ldots, 9$. In this way, we can form approximations at lattice points as high as we want in the $x, t-$ strip. ■

SECTION 17.2 PROBLEMS

In each of Problems 1 through 8, solve the boundary value problem using separation of variables. Graph some of the partial sums of the series solution, for selected values of the time.

1. $\dfrac{\partial^2 y}{\partial t^2} = c^2 \dfrac{\partial^2 y}{\partial x^2}$ for $0 < x < 2, t > 0$,

$y(0, t) = y(2, t) = 0$ for $t \geq 0$,

$y(x, 0) = 0, \dfrac{\partial y}{\partial t}(x, 0) = g(x)$ for $0 \leq x \leq 2$,

where $g(x) = \begin{cases} 2x & \text{for } 0 \leq x \leq 1 \\ 0 & \text{for } 1 < x < 2 \end{cases}$

2. $\dfrac{\partial^2 y}{\partial t^2} = 9 \dfrac{\partial^2 y}{\partial x^2}$ for $0 < x < 4, t > 0$,

$y(0, t) = y(4, t) = 0$ for $t \geq 0$,

$y(x, 0) = 2 \sin(\pi x), \dfrac{\partial y}{\partial t}(x, 0) = 0$ for $0 \leq x \leq 4$

3. $\dfrac{\partial^2 y}{\partial t^2} = 4 \dfrac{\partial^2 y}{\partial x^2}$ for $0 < x < 3, t > 0$,

$y(0, t) = y(3, t) = 0$ for $t \geq 0$,

$y(x, 0) = 0, \dfrac{\partial y}{\partial t}(x, 0) = x(3 - x)$ for $0 \leq x \leq 3$

4. $\dfrac{\partial^2 y}{\partial t^2} = 9 \dfrac{\partial^2 y}{\partial x^2}$ for $0 < x < \pi, t > 0$,

$y(0, t) = y(\pi, t) = 0$ for $t \geq 0$,

$y(x, 0) = \sin(x), \dfrac{\partial y}{\partial t}(x, 0) = 1$ for $0 \leq x \leq \pi$

5. $\dfrac{\partial^2 y}{\partial t^2} = 8 \dfrac{\partial^2 y}{\partial x^2}$ for $0 < x < 2\pi, t > 0$,

$y(0, t) = y(2\pi, t) = 0$ for $t \geq 0$,

$y(x, 0) = f(x), \dfrac{\partial y}{\partial t}(x, 0) = 0$ for $0 \leq x \leq 2\pi$,

where

$f(x) = \begin{cases} 3x & \text{for } 0 \leq x \leq \pi \\ 6\pi - 3x & \text{for } \pi < x \leq 2\pi \end{cases}$

6. $\dfrac{\partial^2 y}{\partial t^2} = 4 \dfrac{\partial^2 y}{\partial x^2}$ for $0 < x < 5, t > 0$,

$y(0, t) = y(5, t) = 0$ for $t \geq 0$,

$y(x, 0) = 0, \dfrac{\partial y}{\partial t}(x, 0) = g(x)$ for $0 \leq x \leq 4$,

where

$g(x) = \begin{cases} 0 & \text{for } 0 \leq x < 4 \\ 5 - x & \text{for } 4 \leq x \leq 5 \end{cases}$

7. $\dfrac{\partial^2 y}{\partial t^2} = 9 \dfrac{\partial^2 y}{\partial x^2}$ for $0 < x < 2, t > 0$,

$y(0, t) = y(2, t) = 0$ for $t \geq 0$,

$y(x, 0) = x(x - 2), \dfrac{\partial y}{\partial t}(x, 0) = g(x)$ for $0 \leq x \leq 2$,

where

$g(x) = \begin{cases} 0 & \text{for } 0 \leq x < 1/2 \quad \text{and} \quad \text{for } 1 < x \leq 2 \\ 3 & \text{for } 1/2 \leq x \leq 1 \end{cases}$

8. $\dfrac{\partial^2 y}{\partial t^2} = 25 \dfrac{\partial^2 y}{\partial x^2}$ for $0 < x < \pi, t > 0$,

$y(0, t) = y(\pi, t) = 0$ for $t \geq 0$,

$y(x, 0) = \sin(2x), \dfrac{\partial y}{\partial t}(x, 0) = \pi - x$ for $0 \leq x \leq \pi$

9. Solve the boundary value problem

$\dfrac{\partial^2 y}{\partial t^2} = 3 \dfrac{\partial^2 y}{\partial x^2} + 2x$ for $0 < x < 2, t > 0$,

$y(0, t) = y(2, t) = 0$ for $t \geq 0$,

$y(x, 0) = 0, \dfrac{\partial y}{\partial t}(x, 0) = 0$ for $0 \leq x \leq 2$.

Graph some partial sums of the series solution.
Hint: Upon putting $y(x, t) = X(x)T(t)$, we find that the variables do not separate. Put $Y(x, t) = y(x, t) + h(x)$ and choose h to obtain a boundary value problem that can be solved by Fourier series.

10. Solve

$\dfrac{\partial^2 y}{\partial t^2} = 9 \dfrac{\partial^2 y}{\partial x^2} + x^2$ for $0 < x < 4, t > 0$,

$y(0, t) = y(4, t) = 0$ for $t \geq 0$,

$y(x, 0) = 0, \dfrac{\partial y}{\partial t}(x, 0) = 0$ for $0 \leq x \leq 4$.

Graph some partial sums of the solution for values of t.

11. Solve

$$\frac{\partial^2 y}{\partial t^2} = \frac{\partial^2 y}{\partial x^2} - \cos(x) \quad \text{for } 0 < x < 2\pi, t > 0,$$

$$y(0, t) = y(2\pi, t) = 0 \quad \text{for } t \geq 0,$$

$$y(x, 0) = 0, \frac{\partial y}{\partial t}(x, 0) = 0 \quad \text{for } 0 \leq x \leq 2\pi.$$

Graph some partial sums of the solution for selected values of the time.

12. Transverse vibrations in a homogeneous rod of length π are modeled by the partial differential equation

$$a^2 \frac{\partial^4 u}{\partial x^4} + \frac{\partial^2 u}{\partial t^2} = 0 \quad \text{for } 0 < x < \pi, t > 0.$$

Here $u(x, t)$ is the displacement at time t of the cross-section through x perpendicular to the x axis, and $a^2 = EI/\rho A$, where E is Young's modulus, I is the moment of inertia of a cross-section perpendicular to the x axis, ρ is the constant density, and A the cross-sectional area, assumed constant.

(a) Let $u(x, t) = X(x)T(t)$ to separate the variables.

(b) Solve for values of the separation constant and for X and T in the case of free ends:

$$\frac{\partial^2 u}{\partial x^2}(0, t) = \frac{\partial^2 u}{\partial x^2}(\pi, t) = \frac{\partial^3 u}{\partial x^3}(0, t) = \frac{\partial^3 u}{\partial x^3}(\pi, t) = 0$$

for $t > 0$.

(c) Solve for values of the separation constant and for X and T in the case of supported ends:

$$u(0, t) = u(\pi, t) = \frac{\partial^2 u}{\partial x^2}(0, t) = \frac{\partial^2 u}{\partial x^2}(\pi, t) = 0$$

for $t > 0$.

13. Solve the *telegraph equation*

$$\frac{\partial^2 u}{\partial t^2} + A\frac{\partial u}{\partial t} + Bu = c^2 \frac{\partial^2 u}{\partial x^2} \quad \text{for } 0 < x < L, t > 0.$$

Here A and B are positive constants. The boundary conditions are

$$u(0, t) = u(L, t) = 0 \quad \text{for } t \geq 0.$$

The initial conditions are

$$u(x, 0) = f(x), \frac{\partial u}{\partial t}(x, 0) = 0 \quad \text{for } 0 \leq x \leq L.$$

Assume that $A^2 L^2 < 4(BL^2 + c^2\pi^2)$.

14. Consider the boundary value problem

$$\frac{\partial^2 y}{\partial t^2} = 9\frac{\partial^2 y}{\partial x^2} + 5x^3 \quad \text{for } 0 < x < 4, t > 0,$$

$$y(0, t) = y(4, t) = 0 \quad \text{for } t \geq 0$$

$$y(x, 0) = \cos(\pi x), \frac{\partial y}{\partial t}(x, 0) = 0 \quad \text{for } 0 \leq x \leq 4.$$

(a) Write a series solution.

(b) Find a series solution when the term $5x^3$ is removed from the wave equation.

(c) In order to gauge the effect of the forcing term on the motion, graph the 40th partial sum of the solution for (a) and (b) on the same set of axes at time $t = 0.4$ seconds. Repeat this procedure successively for times $t = 0.8$, 1.4, 2, 2.5, 3 and 4 seconds.

15. Consider the boundary value problem

$$\frac{\partial^2 y}{\partial t^2} = 9\frac{\partial^2 y}{\partial x^2} + \cos(\pi x) \quad \text{for } 0 < x < 4, t > 0,$$

$$y(0, t) = y(4, t) = 0 \quad \text{for } t \geq 0$$

$$y(x, 0) = x(4 - x), \frac{\partial y}{\partial t}(x, 0) = 0 \quad \text{for } 0 \leq x \leq 4.$$

(a) Write a series solution.

(b) Find a series solution when the term $\cos(\pi x)$ is removed from the wave equation.

(c) In order to gauge the effect of the forcing term on the motion, graph the 40th partial sum of the solution for (a) and (b) on the same set of axes at time $t = 0.6$ seconds. Repeat this procedure successively for times $t = 1$, 1.4, 2, 3, 5 and 7 seconds.

16. Consider the boundary value problem

$$\frac{\partial^2 y}{\partial t^2} = 9\frac{\partial^2 y}{\partial x^2} - e^{-x} \quad \text{for } 0 < x < 4, t > 0,$$

$$y(0, t) = y(4, t) = 0 \quad \text{for } t \geq 0$$

$$y(x, 0) = \sin(\pi x), \frac{\partial y}{\partial t}(x, 0) = 0 \quad \text{for } 0 \leq x \leq 4.$$

(a) Write a series solution.

(b) Find a series solution when the term e^{-x} is removed from the wave equation.

(c) In order to gauge the effect of the forcing term on the motion, graph the 40th partial sum of the solution for (a) and (b) on the same set of axes at time $t = 0.6$ seconds. Repeat this procedure successively for times $t = 1$, 1.4, 2, 3, 5 and 7 seconds.

17. Consider the problem

$$\frac{\partial^2 y}{\partial t^2} = \frac{\partial^2 y}{\partial x^2} \quad \text{for } 0 < x < 1, t > 0,$$

$$y(0, t) = y(1, t) = 0 \quad \text{for } t \geq 0,$$

$$y(x, 0) = f(x) \quad \text{for } 0 \leq x \leq 1,$$

$$\frac{\partial y}{\partial t}(x, 0) = 0 \quad \text{for } 0 \leq x \leq 1,$$

where

$$f(x) = \begin{cases} x & \text{for } 0 \leq x \leq 1/2 \\ 1 - x & \text{for } 1/2 \leq x \leq 1. \end{cases}$$

Use $\Delta x = 0.1$ and $\Delta t = 0.025$ to compute approximate values of $y(x, t)$ at lattice points in the $x, t-$strip $0 \leq x \leq 1$, $t \geq 0$. Carry out the computations for five $t-$ layers (that is, for $t = 0$ through $t = 5(0.025) = 0.125$.

18. Consider the problem

$$\frac{\partial^2 y}{\partial t^2} = \frac{\partial^2 y}{\partial x^2} \quad \text{for } 0 < x < 2, t > 0,$$

$$y(0, t) = y(2, t) = 0 \quad \text{for } t \geq 0,$$

$$y(x, 0) = 0 \quad \text{for } 0 \leq x \leq 2,$$

$$\frac{\partial y}{\partial t}(x, 0) = 1 \quad \text{for } 0 \leq x \leq 2.$$

Use $\Delta x = 0.1$ and $\Delta t = 0.025$ and compute approximate values of $y(x, t)$, going up five layers from $t = 0$ through $t = 0.125$.

19. Consider the problem

$$\frac{\partial^2 y}{\partial t^2} = \frac{\partial^2 y}{\partial x^2} \quad \text{for } 0 < x < 2, t > 0,$$

$$y(0, t) = y(2, t) = 0 \quad \text{for } t \geq 0,$$

$$y(x, 0) = \sin(\pi x) \quad \text{for } 0 \leq x \leq 2,$$

$$\frac{\partial y}{\partial t}(x, 0) = 1 \quad \text{for } 0 \leq x \leq 2.$$

Use $\Delta x = 0.1$ and $\Delta t = 0.025$. Compute approximate values of $y(x, t)$, going up five layers from $t = 0$ through $t = 0.125$.

20. Consider the problem

$$\frac{\partial^2 y}{\partial t^2} = \frac{\partial^2 y}{\partial x^2} \quad \text{for } 0 < x < 1, t > 0,$$

$$y(0, t) = y(1, t) = 0 \quad \text{for } t \geq 0,$$

$$y(x, 0) = x(1 - x)^2 \quad \text{for } 0 \leq x \leq 1,$$

$$\frac{\partial y}{\partial t}(x, 0) = x^2 \quad \text{for } 0 \leq x \leq 1.$$

Use $\Delta x = 0.2$ and $\Delta t = 0.025$. Compute approximate values of $y(x, t)$, going up five layers from $t = 0$ through $t = 0.125$.

21. Consider the problem

$$\frac{\partial^2 y}{\partial t^2} = \frac{\partial^2 y}{\partial x^2} \quad \text{for } 0 < x < 1, t > 0,$$

$$y(0, t) = y(1, t) = 0 \quad \text{for } t \geq 0,$$

$$y(x, 0) = 0 \quad \text{for } 0 \leq x \leq 1,$$

$$\frac{\partial y}{\partial t}(x, 0) = \cos(\pi x) \quad \text{for } 0 \leq x \leq 1.$$

Use $\Delta x = 0.1$ and $\Delta t = 0.025$. Compute approximate values of $y(x, t)$, going up five layers from $t = 0$ through $t = 0.125$.

17.3   Wave Motion Along Infinite and Semi-Infinite Strings

17.3.1   Wave Motion Along an Infinite String

If long distances are involved (such as with sound waves in the ocean used to monitor temperature changes), wave motion is sometimes modeled by an infinite string, in which case there are no boundary conditions. As with the finite string, we will consider separately the cases of zero initial velocity and zero initial displacement.

Zero Initial Velocity   Consider the initial value problem

$$\frac{\partial^2 y}{\partial t^2} = c^2 \frac{\partial^2 y}{\partial x^2} \quad \text{for } -\infty < x < \infty, t > 0$$

$$y(x, 0) = f(x), \frac{\partial y}{\partial t}(x, 0) = 0 \quad \text{for } \infty < x < \infty.$$

There are no boundary conditions, but we will impose the condition that the solution be a bounded function.

To separate the variables, let $y(x, t) = X(x)T(x)$ and obtain, as before,

$$X'' + \lambda X = 0, \quad T'' + \lambda c^2 T = 0.$$

Consider cases on λ.

Case 1 $\lambda = 0$.
Now $X(x) = ax + b$. This is a bounded solution if $a = 0$. Thus $\lambda = 0$ is an eigenvalue, with nonzero constant eigenfunctions.

Case 2 $\lambda < 0$.
Write $\lambda = -\omega^2$ with $\omega > 0$. Then $X'' - \omega^2 X = 0$, with general solution

$$X(x) = ae^{\omega x} + be^{-\omega x}.$$

But $e^{\omega x}$ is unbounded on $(0, \infty)$, so we must choose $a = 0$. And $e^{-\omega x}$ is unbounded on $(-\infty, 0)$, so we must choose $b = 0$, leaving only the zero solution. This problem has no negative eigenvalue.

Case 3 $\lambda > 0$, say $\lambda = \omega^2$ with $\omega > 0$.
Now $X'' + \omega^2 X = 0$, with general solution

$$X_\omega(x) = a\cos(\omega x) + b\sin(\omega x).$$

These functions are bounded for all $\omega > 0$. Thus every positive number $\lambda = \omega^2$ is an eigenvalue, with corresponding eigenfunction $a\cos(\omega x) + b\sin(\omega x)$ for a and b not both zero.

We can include Case 1 in Case 3, since $a\cos(\omega x) + b\sin(\omega x) = \text{constant}$ if $\omega = 0$.

Now consider the equation for T, which we can now write as $T'' + c^2\omega^2 T = 0$ for $\omega \geq 0$. This has general solution

$$T(t) = a\cos(\omega ct) + b\sin(\omega ct).$$

Now

$$\frac{\partial y}{\partial t}(x, 0) = X(t)T'(0) = X(t)\omega cb = 0,$$

so $b = 0$. Thus solutions for T are constant multiples of

$$T_\omega(t) = \cos(\omega ct).$$

For any $\omega \geq 0$, we now have a function

$$y_\omega(x, t) = X_\omega(x)T_\omega(t) = [a_\omega \cos(\omega x) + b_\omega \sin(\omega x)]\cos(\omega ct)$$

which satisfies the wave equation and the condition

$$\frac{\partial y}{\partial t}(x, 0) = 0.$$

We need to satisfy the condition $y(x, 0) = f(x)$. For the similar problem on $[0, L]$, we had a function $y_n(x, t)$ for each positive integer n, and we attempted a superposition $\sum_{n=1}^{\infty} y_n(x, t)$. Now the eigenvalues fill out the entire nonnegative real line, so replace $\sum_{n=1}^{\infty}$ with $\int_0^{\infty} \cdots d\omega$ in forming the superposition:

$$y(x, t) = \int_0^{\infty} y_\omega(x, t)d\omega = \int_0^{\infty} [a_\omega \cos(\omega x) + b_\omega \sin(\omega x)]\cos(\omega ct)d\omega. \tag{17.17}$$

The initial displacement condition requires that

$$y(x, 0) = \int_0^\infty [a_\omega \cos(\omega x) + b_\omega \sin(\omega x)] \, d\omega = f(x).$$

The integral on the left is the Fourier integral representation of $f(x)$ for $-\infty < x < \infty$. Thus choose the constants as the Fourier integral coefficients:

$$a_\omega = \frac{1}{\pi} \int_{-\infty}^\infty f(\xi) \cos(\omega \xi) \, d\xi$$

and

$$b_\omega = \frac{1}{\pi} \int_{-\infty}^\infty f(\xi) \sin(\omega \xi) \, d\xi.$$

With this choice of the coefficients, and certain conditions on f (see the convergence theorem for Fourier integrals in Section 15.1), equation (17.17) is the solution of the problem.

EXAMPLE 17.4

Consider the problem

$$\frac{\partial^2 y}{\partial t^2} = c^2 \frac{\partial^2 y}{\partial x^2} \quad \text{for } -\infty < x < \infty, t > 0$$

$$y(x, 0) = e^{-|x|}, \frac{\partial y}{\partial t}(x, 0) = 0 \quad \text{for } \infty < x < \infty.$$

A graph of the initial position of the string is given in Figure 17.15.
    To use equation (17.17), compute the Fourier integral coefficients:

$$a_\omega = \frac{1}{\pi} \int_{-\infty}^\infty e^{-|\xi|} \cos(\omega \xi) \, d\xi = \frac{2}{\pi(1 + \omega^2)}$$

and

$$b_\omega = \frac{1}{\pi} \int_{-\infty}^\infty e^{-|\xi|} \sin(\omega \xi) \, d\xi = 0.$$

(For b_ω we need not actually carry out the integration because the integrand is an odd function). The solution is

$$y(x, t) = \frac{2}{\pi} \int_0^\infty \frac{1}{1 + \omega^2} \cos(\omega x) \cos(\omega c t) \, d\omega. \quad \blacksquare$$

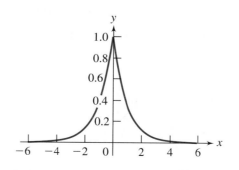

FIGURE 17.15   *Graph of $y = e^{-|x|}$.*

The solution (17.17) may be written in more compact form as follows. Insert the integral formulas for the coefficients:

$$y(x, t) = \int_0^\infty [a_\omega \cos(\omega x) + b_\omega \sin(\omega x)] \cos(\omega c t) d\omega$$

$$= \frac{1}{\pi} \int_0^\infty \left[\left(\int_{-\infty}^\infty f(\xi) \cos(\omega \xi) d\xi \right) \cos(\omega x) \right.$$

$$\left. + \left(\int_{-\infty}^\infty f(\xi) \sin(\omega \xi) d\xi \right) \sin(\omega x) \right] \cos(\omega c t) d\omega$$

$$= \frac{1}{\pi} \int_{-\infty}^\infty \int_0^\infty [\cos(\omega \xi) \cos(\omega x) + \sin(\omega \xi) \sin(\omega x)] f(\xi) \cos(\omega c t) d\omega d\xi$$

$$= \frac{1}{\pi} \int_{-\infty}^\infty \int_0^\infty \cos(\omega(\xi - x)) f(\xi) \cos(\omega c t) d\omega d\xi. \tag{17.18}$$

Zero Initial Displacement   Suppose now the string is released from the horizontal position (zero initial displacement), with initial velocity $g(x)$. The initial value problem for the displacement function is

$$\frac{\partial^2 y}{\partial t^2} = c^2 \frac{\partial^2 y}{\partial x^2} \quad \text{for } -\infty < x < \infty, t > 0$$

$$y(x, 0) = 0, \frac{\partial y}{\partial t}(x, 0) = g(x) \quad \text{for } \infty < x < \infty.$$

Let $y(x, t) = X(x)T(t)$ and proceed exactly as in the case of initial displacement $f(x)$ and zero initial velocity, obtaining eigenvalues $\lambda = \omega^2$ for $\omega \geq 0$ and eigenfunctions

$$X_\omega(x) = a_\omega \cos(\omega x) + b_\omega \sin(\omega x).$$

Turning to T, we obtain, again as before,

$$T(t) = a \cos(\omega c t) + b \sin(\omega c t).$$

However, this problem differs from the preceding one in the initial condition on $T(t)$. Now we have

$$y(x, 0) = X(x)T(0) = 0,$$

so $T(0) = 0$ and hence $a = 0$. Thus in this, for each $\omega \geq 0$, $T(t)$ is a constant multiple of $\sin(\omega c t)$. This gives us functions

$$y_\omega(x, t) = [a_\omega \cos(\omega x) + b_\omega \sin(\omega x)] \sin(\omega c t).$$

Now use the superposition

$$y(x, t) = \int_0^\infty [a_\omega \cos(\omega x) + b_\omega \sin(\omega x)] \sin(\omega c t) d\omega \tag{17.19}$$

in order to satisfy the initial condition. Compute

$$\frac{\partial y}{\partial t} = \int_0^\infty [a_\omega \cos(\omega x) + b_\omega \sin(\omega x)] \omega c \cos(\omega c t) d\omega.$$

We need

$$\frac{\partial y}{\partial t}(x,0) = \int_0^\infty [\omega c a_\omega \cos(\omega x) + \omega c b_\omega \sin(\omega x)] d\omega = g(x).$$

This is a Fourier integral expansion of the initial velocity function. With conditions on g (such as are given in the convergence theorem for Fourier integrals), choose

$$\omega c a_\omega = \frac{1}{\pi} \int_{-\infty}^\infty g(\xi) \cos(\omega \xi) d\xi$$

and

$$\omega c b_\omega = \frac{1}{\pi} \int_{-\infty}^\infty g(\xi) \sin(\omega \xi) d\xi.$$

Then

$$a_\omega = \frac{1}{\pi c \omega} \int_{-\infty}^\infty g(\xi) \cos(\omega \xi) d\xi \quad \text{and} \quad b_\omega = \frac{1}{\pi c \omega} \int_{-\infty}^\infty g(\xi) \sin(\omega \xi) d\xi.$$

With these coefficients, equation (17.19) is the solution of the problem.

EXAMPLE 17.5

Suppose the initial displacement is zero and the initial velocity is given by

$$g(x) = \begin{cases} e^x & \text{for } 0 \le x \le 1 \\ 0 & \text{for } x < 0 \text{ and for } x > 1 \end{cases}.$$

A graph of this function is shown in Figure 17.16. To use equation (17.19) to write the displacement function, compute the coefficients:

$$a_\omega = \frac{1}{\pi c \omega} \int_{-\infty}^\infty g(\xi) \cos(\omega \xi) d\xi = \frac{1}{\pi c \omega} \int_0^1 e^\xi \cos(\omega \xi) d\xi$$

$$= \frac{1}{\pi c \omega} \frac{e \cos(\omega) + e\omega \sin(\omega) - 1}{1 + \omega^2}$$

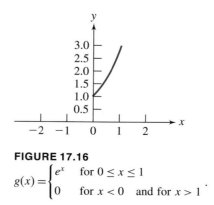

FIGURE 17.16

$$g(x) = \begin{cases} e^x & \text{for } 0 \le x \le 1 \\ 0 & \text{for } x < 0 \quad \text{and for } x > 1 \end{cases}.$$

and

$$b_\omega = \frac{1}{\pi c \omega} \int_{-\infty}^{\infty} g(\xi) \sin(\omega \xi) d\xi = \frac{1}{\pi c \omega} \int_0^1 e^\xi \sin(\omega \xi) d\xi$$

$$= -\frac{1}{\pi c \omega} \frac{e\omega \cos(\omega) - e\sin(\omega) - \omega}{1 + \omega^2}$$

The solution is

$$y(x, t) = \int_0^\infty \left(\frac{1}{\pi c \omega} \frac{e\cos(\omega) + e\omega \sin(\omega) - 1}{1 + \omega^2} \right) \cos(\omega x) \sin(\omega c t) d\omega$$

$$- \int_0^\infty \left(\frac{1}{\pi c \omega} \frac{e\omega \cos(\omega) - e\sin(\omega) - \omega}{1 + \omega^2} \right) \sin(\omega x) \sin(\omega c t) d\omega. \ \blacksquare$$

As in the case of wave motion on $[0, L]$, the solution of a problem with nonzero initial velocity and displacement can be obtained as the sum of the solutions of two problems, in one of which there is no initial displacement, and in the other, zero initial velocity.

17.3.2 Wave Motion Along a Semi-Infinite String

We will now consider the problem of wave motion along a string fastened at the origin and stretched along the nonnegative x axis. Unlike the case of the string along the entire line, there is now one boundary condition, at $x = 0$. The problem is

$$\frac{\partial^2 y}{\partial t^2} = c^2 \frac{\partial^2 y}{\partial x^2} \quad \text{for } 0 < x < \infty, t > 0,$$

$$y(0, t) = 0 \quad \text{for } t \geq 0,$$

$$y(x, 0) = f(x), \frac{\partial y}{\partial t}(x, 0) = g(x) \quad \text{for } 0 < x < \infty.$$

Again, we want a bounded solution.

Let $y(x, t) = X(x)T(t)$ and obtain

$$X'' + \lambda X = 0, \ T'' + \lambda c^2 T = 0.$$

In this problem we have a boundary condition:

$$y(0, t) = X(0)T(t) = 0,$$

implying that $X(0) = 0$. Begin by looking for the eigenvalues λ and corresponding eigenfunctions. Consider cases on λ.

Case 1 $\lambda = 0$.
Now $X(x) = ax + b$. Since $X(0) = b = 0$, then $X(x) = ax$. This is unbounded on $[0, \infty)$ unless $a = 0$, so $\lambda = 0$ yields no bounded nontrivial solution for X, and 0 is not an eigenvalue.

Case 2 λ is negative.
Now write $\lambda = -\omega^2$ to obtain $X'' - \omega^2 X = 0$. This has general solution

$$X(x) = ae^{\omega x} + be^{-\omega x}.$$

Now

$$X(0) = a + b = 0$$

implies that $b = -a$, so $X(x) = 2a \sinh(\omega x)$. This is unbounded for $x > 0$ unless $a = 0$, so this problem has no negative eigenvalue.

Case 3 λ is positive.
Now write $\lambda = \omega^2$ and obtain

$$X(x) = a\cos(\omega x) + b\sin(\omega x).$$

Since $X(0) = a = 0$, only the sine terms remain. Thus every positive number is an eigenvalue, with corresponding eigenfunctions nonzero constant multiples of $\sin(\omega x)$.

Now the problem for T is $T'' + c^2\omega^2 T = 0$, with general solution

$$T(t) = a\cos(\omega c t) + b\sin(\omega c t).$$

At this point we must isolate the problem into one with zero initial displacement or zero initial velocity. Suppose, to be specific, that $g(x) = 0$. Then $T'(0) = 0$, so $b = 0$ and $T(t)$ must be a constant multiple of $\cos(\omega c t)$. We therefore have functions

$$y_\omega(x, t) = c_\omega \sin(\omega x)\cos(\omega c t)$$

for each $\omega > 0$. Define the superposition

$$y(x, t) = \int_0^\infty c_\omega \sin(\omega x)\cos(\omega c t)\,d\omega.$$

Each such function satisfies the wave equation and the boundary condition, as well as $y_t(x, 0) = 0$ for $x > 0$. To satisfy the condition on initial displacement, we must choose the coefficients so that

$$y(x, 0) = \int_0^\infty c_\omega \sin(\omega x)\,d\omega = f(x).$$

This is the Fourier integral expansion of $f(x)$ on $[0, \infty)$, so choose

$$c_\omega = \frac{2}{\pi}\int_0^\infty f(\xi)\sin(\omega\xi)\,d\xi.$$

The solution of the problem is

$$y(x, t) = \frac{2}{\pi}\int_0^\infty \left(\int_0^\infty f(\xi)\sin(\omega\xi)\,d\xi\right)\sin(\omega x)\cos(\omega c t)\,d\omega.$$

If the problem has zero initial displacement, but initial velocity $g(x)$, then a similar analysis leads to the solution

$$y(x, t) = \int_0^\infty c_\omega \sin(\omega x)\sin(\omega c t)\,d\omega,$$

where

$$c_\omega = \frac{2}{\pi c\omega}\int_0^\infty g(\xi)\sin(\omega\xi)\,d\xi.$$

EXAMPLE 17.6

Consider wave motion along the half-line governed by the problem:

$$\frac{\partial^2 y}{\partial t^2} = 16\frac{\partial^2 y}{\partial x^2}\quad\text{for } x > 0, t > 0,$$

$$y(0, t) = 0\quad\text{for } t \geq 0,$$

$$\frac{\partial y}{\partial t}(x, 0) = 0,\, y(x, 0) = \begin{cases} \sin(\pi x) & \text{for } 0 \leq x \leq 4 \\ 0 & \text{for } x > 4. \end{cases}$$

Here $c = 4$. To write the solution, we need only compute the coefficients

$$c_\omega = \frac{2}{\pi} \int_0^\infty f(\xi) \sin(\omega\xi)d\xi$$

$$= \frac{2}{\pi} \int_0^4 \sin(\pi\xi) \sin(\omega\xi)d\xi = 8\sin(\omega)\cos(\omega)\frac{2\cos^2(\omega) - 1}{\omega^2 - \pi^2}.$$

The solution is

$$y(x, t) = \int_0^\infty 8\sin(\omega)\cos(\omega)\frac{2\cos^2(\omega) - 1}{\omega^2 - \pi^2}\sin(\omega x)\cos(4\omega t)d\omega. \ \blacksquare$$

17.3.3 Fourier Transform Solution of Problems on Unbounded Domains

It is useful to have a variety of tools and methods available to solve boundary value problems. To this end, we will revisit problems of wave motion on the line and half line and approach the solution through the use of a Fourier transform.

First, here is brief description of what is involved in using a transform.

1. The range of values for the variable in which the transform will be performed is one determining factor in choosing a transform. Another is how the information given in the boundary value problem fits into the operational formula for the transform. For example, the operational formula for the Fourier sine transform is

$$\mathfrak{F}_S[f''(x)](\omega) = -\omega^2 \hat{f}_S(\omega) + \omega f(0),$$

so we must be given information about $f(0)$ in the problem to make use of this transform.

2. If the transform is performed with respect to a variable α of the boundary value problem, we obtain a differential equation involving the other variable(s). This differential equation must be solved subject to other information given in the problem. This solution gives the transform of the solution of the original boundary value problem.

3. Once we have the transform of the solution of the boundary value problem, we must invert it to obtain the solution of the boundary value problem itself.

Finally, the Fourier transform of a real-valued function is often complex-valued. If the solution is real-valued, then the real part of the expression obtained using the Fourier transform is the solution. However, because expressions such as $e^{-i\omega x}$ are often easier to manipulate than $\cos(\omega x)$ and $\sin(\omega x)$, we often retain the entire complex expression as the "solution", extracting the real part when we need numerical values, graphs, or other information.

For reference, we will summarize (without conditions on the functions) some facts about the Fourier transform and the Fourier sine and cosine transforms.

Fourier Transform

$$\mathfrak{F}[f](\omega) = \hat{f}(\omega) = \int_{-\infty}^\infty f(x)e^{-i\omega x}dx$$

$$f(x) = \frac{1}{2\pi} \int_{-\infty}^\infty \hat{f}(\omega)e^{i\omega x}d\omega$$

$$\mathfrak{F}[f''](\omega) = -\omega^2 \hat{f}(\omega)$$

Fourier Cosine Transform

$$\mathfrak{F}_C[f](\omega) = \hat{f}_C(\omega) = \int_0^\infty f(x)\cos(\omega x)dx$$

$$f(x) = \frac{2}{\pi}\int_0^\infty \hat{f}_C(\omega)\cos(\omega x)d\omega$$

$$\mathfrak{F}_C[f''](\omega) = -\omega^2 \hat{f}_C(\omega) - f'(0)$$

Fourier Sine Transform

$$\mathfrak{F}_S[f](\omega) = \hat{f}_S(\omega) = \int_0^\infty f(x)\sin(\omega x)dx$$

$$f(x) = \frac{2}{\pi}\int_0^\infty \hat{f}_S(\omega)\sin(\omega x)d\omega$$

$$\mathfrak{F}_S[f''](\omega) = -\omega^2 \hat{f}_S(\omega) + \omega f(0)$$

Fourier Transform Solution of the Wave Equation on the Line   Consider again the problem

$$\frac{\partial^2 y}{\partial t^2} = c^2 \frac{\partial^2 y}{\partial x^2} \quad \text{for } -\infty < x < \infty, t > 0$$

$$y(x, 0) = f(x), \frac{\partial y}{\partial t}(x, 0) = 0 \quad \text{for } -\infty < x < \infty.$$

Because x varies over the entire line, we can try the Fourier transform in the x variable. To do this, transform $y(x, t)$ as a function of x, leaving t as a parameter. First apply $\mathfrak{F}$ to the wave equation:

$$\mathfrak{F}\left[\frac{\partial^2 y}{\partial t^2}\right](\omega) = c^2 \mathfrak{F}\left[\frac{\partial^2 y}{\partial x^2}\right](\omega).$$

Because we are transforming in x, leaving t alone, we have

$$\mathfrak{F}\left[\frac{\partial^2 y}{\partial t^2}\right](\omega) = \int_{-\infty}^\infty \frac{\partial^2 y}{\partial t^2}(x, t)e^{-i\omega x}dx = \frac{\partial^2}{\partial t^2}\int_{-\infty}^\infty y(x, t)e^{-i\omega x}dx = \frac{\partial^2}{\partial t^2}\hat{y}(\omega, t),$$

where $\hat{y}(\omega, t)$ is the Fourier transform, with respect to x, of $y(x, t)$. The partial derivative with respect to t passes through the integral with respect to x because x and t are independent.

For the Fourier transform, in x, of $\partial^2 y/\partial x^2$, use the operational formula:

$$\mathfrak{F}\left[\frac{\partial^2 y}{\partial x^2}\right](\omega) = -\omega^2 \hat{y}(\omega, t).$$

The transformed wave equation is therefore

$$\frac{\partial^2}{\partial t^2}\hat{y}(\omega, t) = -c^2 \omega^2 \hat{y}(\omega, t),$$

or

$$\frac{\partial^2}{\partial t^2}\hat{y}(\omega, t) + c^2 \omega^2 \hat{y}(\omega, t) = 0.$$

Think of this as an ordinary differential equation for $\hat{y}(\omega, t)$ in t, with ω carried along as a parameter. The general solution has the form

$$\hat{y}(\omega, t) = a_\omega \cos(\omega c t) + b_\omega \sin(\omega c t).$$

We obtain the coefficients by transforming the initial data. First,

$$\hat{y}(\omega, 0) = a_\omega = \mathfrak{F}[y(x,0)](\omega) = \mathfrak{F}[f](\omega) = \hat{f}(\omega),$$

the transform of the initial position function. Next

$$\omega c b_\omega = \frac{\partial \hat{y}}{\partial t}(\omega, 0) = \mathfrak{F}\left[\frac{\partial y}{\partial t}(x, 0)\right](\omega) = \mathfrak{F}[0](\omega) = 0$$

because the initial velocity is zero. Therefore $b_\omega = 0$ and

$$\hat{y}(\omega, t) = \hat{f}(\omega)\cos(\omega ct).$$

We now know the transform of the solution $y(x, t)$. Invert this to find $y(x, t)$:

$$y(x, t) = \frac{1}{2\pi}\int_{-\infty}^{\infty} \hat{f}(\omega)\cos(\omega ct)e^{i\omega x}\,d\omega. \tag{17.20}$$

This is an integral formula for the solution, since $\hat{f}(\omega)$ is presumably known to us because we were given f. Since $e^{i\omega x}$ is complex-valued, we must actually take the real part of this integral to obtain $y(x, t)$. However, the integral is often left in the form of equation (17.20) with the understanding that $y(x, t)$ is the real part.

We will show that the solutions of this problem obtained by Fourier transform and Fourier integral are the same. Write the solution just obtained by transform as

$$y_{tr}(x, t) = \frac{1}{2\pi}\int_{-\infty}^{\infty} \hat{f}(\omega)\cos(\omega ct)e^{i\omega x}\,d\omega$$

$$= \frac{1}{2\pi}\int_{-\infty}^{\infty}\left(\int_{-\infty}^{\infty} f(\xi)e^{-i\omega\xi}\,d\xi\right)\cos(\omega ct)e^{i\omega x}\,d\omega$$

$$= \frac{1}{2\pi}\int_{-\infty}^{\infty}\int_{-\infty}^{\infty} e^{-i\omega(\xi - x)}\cos(\omega ct)f(\xi)\,d\omega\,d\xi$$

$$= \frac{1}{2\pi}\int_{-\infty}^{\infty}\int_{-\infty}^{\infty}[\cos(\omega(\xi - x)) - i\sin(\omega(\xi - x))]\cos(\omega ct)f(\xi)\,d\omega\,d\xi.$$

Since the displacement function is real-valued, we must take the real part of this integral, obtaining

$$y(x, t) = \frac{1}{2\pi}\int_{-\infty}^{\infty}\int_{-\infty}^{\infty}\cos(\omega(\xi - x))\cos(\omega ct)f(\xi)\,d\omega\,d\xi.$$

Finally, this integrand is an even function of ω, so

$$\frac{1}{2\pi}\int_{-\infty}^{\infty}\cdots d\omega = 2\frac{1}{2\pi}\int_{0}^{\infty}\cdots d\omega = \frac{1}{\pi}\int_{0}^{\infty}\cdots d\omega,$$

yielding

$$y(x, t) = \frac{1}{\pi}\int_{-\infty}^{\infty}\int_{0}^{\infty}\cos(\omega(\xi - x))\cos(\omega ct)f(\xi)\,d\omega\,d\xi$$

This agrees with the solution (17.18) obtained by Fourier integral.

EXAMPLE 17.7

Solve for the displacement function on the real line if the initial velocity is zero and the initial displacement function is given by

$$f(x) = \begin{cases} \cos(x) & \text{for } -\pi/2 \leq x \leq \pi/2 \\ 0 & \text{for } |x| > \pi/2 \end{cases}.$$

To use the solution (17.20) we must compute

$$\hat{f}(\omega) = \int_{-\infty}^{\infty} f(\xi)e^{-i\omega\xi}d\xi = \int_{-\pi/2}^{\pi/2} \cos(\xi)e^{-i\omega\xi}d\xi$$

$$= \begin{cases} 2\frac{\cos\left(\frac{\pi\omega}{2}\right)}{1-\omega^2} & \text{for } \omega \neq 1 \\ \frac{\pi}{2} & \text{for } \omega = 1 \end{cases}.$$

$\hat{f}(\omega)$ is continuous, since

$$\lim_{\omega \to 1} \frac{2\cos(\pi\omega/2)}{1-\omega^2} = \frac{\pi}{2}.$$

The solution can be written

$$y(x, t) = \frac{1}{\pi} \int_{-\infty}^{\infty} \frac{\cos(\pi\omega/2)}{1-\omega^2} \cos(\omega ct)e^{i\omega x}d\omega,$$

with the understanding that $y(x, t)$ is the real part of the integral on the right. If we explicitly take this real part, then

$$y(x, t) = \frac{1}{\pi} \int_{-\infty}^{\infty} \frac{\cos(\pi\omega/2)}{1-\omega^2} \cos(\omega x)\cos(\omega ct)d\omega. \quad \blacksquare$$

EXAMPLE 17.8

In some instances a clever use of the Fourier transform can yield a closed form solution. Consider the problem

$$\frac{\partial^2 y}{\partial t^2} = 9\frac{\partial^2 y}{\partial x^2} \quad \text{for } -\infty < x < \infty, t \geq 0,$$

$$y(x, 0) = 4e^{-5|x|} \quad \text{for } -\infty < x < \infty,$$

$$\frac{\partial y}{\partial t}(x, 0) = 0.$$

Take the transform of the differential equation, obtaining as in the discussion

$$\frac{\partial^2 \hat{y}}{\partial t^2}(\omega, t) = -9\omega^2 \hat{y}(\omega, t),$$

with general solution

$$\hat{y}(\omega, t) = a_\omega \cos(3\omega t) + b_\omega \sin(3\omega t).$$

Now use the initial conditions. Using the initial position function we have

$$\hat{y}(\omega, 0) = a_\omega = \mathfrak{F}[y(x, 0)](\omega) = \mathfrak{F}\left[4e^{-5|x|}\right](\omega) = \frac{40}{25+\omega^2}.$$

Next, using the initial velocity, write

$$\frac{\partial \hat{y}}{\partial t}(\omega, 0) = 3\omega b_\omega = \mathfrak{F}\left[\frac{\partial y}{\partial t}(x, 0)\right](\omega) = 0,$$

so $b_\omega = 0$. Then

$$\hat{y}(\omega, t) = \frac{40}{15 + \omega^2}\cos(3\omega t).$$

We can now write the solution in integral form as

$$y(x, t) = \mathfrak{F}^{-1}[\hat{y}(\omega, t)](x) = \frac{1}{2\pi}\int_{-\infty}^{\infty}\frac{40}{25 + \omega^2}\cos(3\omega t)e^{i\omega x}\,d\omega.$$

However, in this case we can explicitly invert $\hat{y}(\omega, t)$, using some facts about the Fourier transform. Begin by using the convolution theorem to write

$$y(x, t) = \mathfrak{F}^{-1}\left[\frac{40}{25 + \omega^2}\cos(3\omega t)\right]$$

$$= \mathfrak{F}^{-1}\left[\frac{40}{25 + \omega^2}\right] * \mathfrak{F}^{-1}[\cos(3\omega t)]$$

$$= 4e^{-5|x|} * \mathfrak{F}^{-1}[\cos(3\omega t)]. \tag{17.21}$$

We need to compute the inverse Fourier transform of $\cos(3\omega t)$. Here ω is the variable of the transformed function, with t carried along as a parameter. The variable of the inverse transform will be x. Combine the fact that $\mathfrak{F}[\delta(t)](\omega) = 1$ from Section 15.4.5, with the modulation theorem (Theorem 15.6 in Section 15.3) to get

$$\mathfrak{F}[\cos(\omega_0 x) = \pi[\delta(\omega + \omega_0) + \delta(\omega - \omega_0)],$$

in which δ is the Dirac delta function. By the symmetry theorem (Theorem 15.5 of Section 15.3),

$$\mathfrak{F}[\pi[\delta(\omega + \omega_0) + \delta(\omega - \omega_0)]] = 2\pi\cos(\omega_0\omega).$$

Therefore

$$\mathfrak{F}^{-1}[\cos(\omega_0\omega)](x) = \frac{1}{2}[\delta(x + \omega_0) + \delta(x - \omega_0)].$$

Now put $\omega_0 = 3t$ to get

$$\mathfrak{F}^{-1}[\cos(3\omega t)](x) = \frac{1}{2}[\delta(x + 3t) + \delta(x - 3t)].$$

Therefore equation 17.21 gives

$$y(x, t) = 4e^{-5|x|} * \frac{1}{2}\pi[\delta(x + 3t) + \delta(x - 3t)]$$

$$= 2\left(e^{-5|x|} * \delta(x + 3t) + e^{-5|x|} * \delta(x - 3t)\right)$$

$$= 2\int_{-\infty}^{\infty}e^{-5|x - \xi|}\delta(\xi + 3t)\,d\xi + 2\int_{-\infty}^{\infty}e^{-5|x - \xi|}\delta(\xi - 3t)\,d\xi$$

$$= 2e^{-5|x + 3t|} + 2e^{-5|x - 3t|},$$

in which the last line was obtained by using the filtering property of the Delta function (Theorem 15.13 of Section 15.4.5). This closed form of the solution and is easily verified directly. ∎

Transform Solution of the Wave Equation on a Half-Line   We will use a transform to solve a wave problem on a half-line, with the left end fixed at $x = 0$. This time we will take the case of zero initial displacement, but a nonzero initial velocity:

$$\frac{\partial^2 y}{\partial t^2} = c^2 \frac{\partial^2 y}{\partial x^2} \quad \text{for } 0 < x < \infty, t > 0,$$

$$y(0, t) = 0 \quad \text{for } t \geq 0,$$

$$y(x, 0) = 0, \quad \frac{\partial y}{\partial t}(x, 0) = g(x) \quad \text{for } 0 < x < \infty.$$

Now the Fourier transform is inappropriate because both x and t range only over the nonnegative real numbers. We can try the Fourier sine or cosine transform in x. The operational formula for the sine transform requires the value of the solution at $x = 0$, while the formula for the cosine transform uses the value of the derivative at the origin. Since we are given the condition $y(0, t) = 0$ (fixed left end of the string), we are led to try the sine transform. Let $\hat{y}_S(\omega, t)$ be the sine transform of $y(x, t)$ in the $x-$ variable. Take the sine transform of the wave equation. The partial derivatives with respect to t pass through the transform, and we use the operational formula for the transform of the second derivative with respect to x:

$$\frac{\partial^2 \hat{y}_S}{\partial t^2} = c^2 \mathfrak{F}_S \left[\frac{\partial^2 y}{\partial x^2} \right] = -c^2 \omega^2 \hat{y}_S(\omega, t) + \omega c^2 y(0, t) = -c^2 \omega^2 \hat{y}_S(\omega, t).$$

Then

$$\hat{y}_S(\omega, t) = a_\omega \cos(\omega c t) + b_\omega \sin(\omega c t).$$

Now

$$a_\omega = \hat{y}_S(\omega, 0) = \mathfrak{F}_S[y(x, 0)](\omega) = \mathfrak{F}_S[0](\omega) = 0,$$

and

$$\frac{\partial \hat{y}_S}{\partial t}(\omega, 0) = \omega c b_\omega = \hat{g}_S(\omega),$$

so

$$b_\omega = \frac{1}{\omega c} \hat{g}_S(\omega).$$

Therefore

$$\hat{y}(\omega, t) = \frac{1}{\omega c} \hat{g}_S(\omega) \sin(\omega c t).$$

This is the sine transform of the solution. The solution is obtained by inverting:

$$y(x, t) = \mathfrak{F}_S^{-1} \left[\frac{1}{\omega c} \hat{g}_S(\omega) \sin(\omega c t) \right](x) = \frac{2}{\pi} \int_0^\infty \frac{1}{\omega c} \hat{g}_S(\omega) \sin(\omega x) \sin(\omega c t) d\omega.$$

EXAMPLE 17.9

Consider the following problem on a half-line

$$\frac{\partial^2 y}{\partial t^2} = 25 \frac{\partial^2 y}{\partial x^2} \quad \text{for } x > 0, t > 0,$$

$$y(0, t) = 0 \quad \text{for } t \geq 0,$$

$$y(x, 0) = 0, \quad \frac{\partial y}{\partial t}(x, 0) = g(x) \quad \text{for } 0 < x < \infty,$$

where

$$g(x) = \begin{cases} 9 - x^2 & \text{for } 0 \leq x \leq 3 \\ 0 & \text{for } x > 3. \end{cases}$$

If we use the Fourier sine transform, then the solution is

$$y(x, t) = \frac{2}{\pi} \int_0^\infty \frac{1}{5\omega} \hat{g}_S(\omega) \sin(\omega x) \sin(5\omega t) d\omega.$$

All that is left to do is compute

$$\hat{g}_S(\omega) = \int_0^\infty g(\xi) \sin(\omega x) dx$$

$$= \int_0^3 (9 - x^2) \sin(\omega x) dx$$

$$= \frac{-8\cos^3(\omega) + 6\cos(\omega) - 24\omega \sin(\omega)\cos^2(\omega) + 6\omega \sin(\omega) + 9\omega^2 + 2}{\omega^3},$$

yielding an integral expression for the solution. ∎

SECTION 17.3   PROBLEMS

In each of Problems 1 through 6, consider the wave equation $\frac{\partial^2 y}{\partial t^2} = c^2 \frac{\partial^2 y}{\partial x^2}$ on the line, for the given value of c and the given initial conditions $y(x, 0) = f(x)$ and $\frac{\partial y}{\partial t}(x, 0) = g(x)$. Solve the problem using the Fourier integral and then again using the Fourier transform.

1. $c = 12, f(x) = e^{-5|x|}, g(x) = 0$

2. $c = 8, f(x) = \begin{cases} 8 - x & \text{for } 0 \leq x \leq 8 \\ 0 & \text{for } x < 0 \quad \text{and} \quad \text{for } x > 0 \end{cases}$

$g(x) = 0$

3. $c = 4, f(x) = 0, g(x) = \begin{cases} \sin(x) & \text{for } -\pi \leq x \leq \pi \\ 0 & \text{for } |x| > \pi \end{cases}$

4. $c = 1, f(x) = \begin{cases} 2 - |x| & \text{for } -2 \leq x \leq 2 \\ 0 & \text{for } |x| > 2 \end{cases}$

$g(x) = 0$

5. $c = 3, f(x) = 0, g(x) = \begin{cases} e^{-2x} & \text{for } x \geq 1 \\ 0 & \text{for } x < 1 \end{cases}$

6. $c = 2, f(x) = 0,$

$$g(x) = \begin{cases} 1 & \text{for } 0 \leq x \leq 2 \\ -1 & \text{for } -2 \leq x < 0 \\ 0 & \text{for } x > 2 \quad \text{and} \quad \text{for } x < -2 \end{cases}$$

In each of Problems 7 through 11, consider the wave equation $\frac{\partial^2 y}{\partial t^2} = c^2 \frac{\partial^2 y}{\partial x^2}$ on the half-line, with $y(x, 0) = 0$ for $x > 0$, and for the given value of c and the given boundary initial conditions $y(x, 0) = f(x)$ and $\frac{\partial y}{\partial t}(x, 0) = g(x)$ for $x \geq 0$. Solve the problem using separation of variables (the Fourier sine integral) and then again using the Fourier sine transform.

7. $c = 3$, $f(x) = \begin{cases} x(1-x) & \text{for } 0 \le x \le 1 \\ 0 & \text{for } x > 1 \end{cases}$

$g(x) = 0$

8. $c = 3$, $f(x) = 0$, $g(x) = \begin{cases} 0 & \text{for } 0 \le x < 4 \\ 2 & \text{for } 4 \le x \le 11 \\ 0 & \text{for } x > 11 \end{cases}$

9. $c = 2$, $f(x) = 0$,

$g(x) = \begin{cases} \cos(x) & \text{for } \pi/2 \le x \le 5\pi/2 \\ 0 & \text{for } 0 \le x < \pi/2 \text{ and for } x > 5\pi/2 \end{cases}$

10. $c = 6$, $f(x) = -2e^{-x}$, $g(x) = 0$

11. $c = 14$, $f(x) = 0$, $g(x) = \begin{cases} x^2(3-x) & \text{for } 0 \le x \le 3 \\ 0 & \text{for } x > 3 \end{cases}$

Sometimes the Laplace transform is effective in solving boundary value problems involving the wave equation. Use the Laplace transform to solve the following.

12. $\dfrac{\partial^2 y}{\partial t^2} = c^2 \dfrac{\partial^2 y}{\partial x^2}$ for $x > 0$, $t > 0$

$y(0, t) = \begin{cases} \sin(2\pi t) & \text{for } 0 \le t \le 1 \\ 0 & \text{for } t > 0 \end{cases}$

$y(x, 0) = \dfrac{\partial y}{\partial t}(x, 0) = 0$

for $x > 0$

13. Solve

$\dfrac{\partial^2 y}{\partial t^2} = c^2 \dfrac{\partial^2 y}{\partial x^2}$ for $x > 0$, $t > 0$

$y(0, t) = t$ for $t > 0$

$y(x, 0) = 0$, $\dfrac{\partial y}{\partial t}(x, 0) = A$ for $x > 0$

17.4   Characteristics and d'Alembert's Solution

This section will involve repeated chain rule differentiations, which are efficiently written using subscript notation for partial derivatives. For example, $\frac{\partial u}{\partial t} = u_t$, $\frac{\partial u}{\partial x} = u_x$, $\frac{\partial^2 u}{\partial t^2} = u_{tt}$, and so on. Our objective is to examine a different perspective on the problem

$$u_{tt} = c^2 u_{xx} \quad \text{for } -\infty < x < \infty, t > 0,$$

$$u(x, 0) = f(x), u_t(x, 0) = g(x) \quad \text{for } -\infty < x < \infty.$$

Here we are using $u(x, t)$ as the position function because we will be changing variables from the (x, y) plane to a (ξ, η) plane, and we do not want to confuse the solution function with coordinates of points.

This boundary value problem, which we have solved using the Fourier integral and again using the Fourier transform, is referred to as the *Cauchy problem for the wave equation.* We will write a solution that dates to the eighteenth century. The lines

$$x - ct = k_1, \quad x + ct = k_2,$$

with k_1 and k_2 any real constants, are called *characteristics* of the wave equation. These form two families of lines, one consisting of parallel lines with slope $1/c$, the other of parallel lines with slope $-1/c$. Figure 17.17 shows some of these characteristics. We will see that these lines are closely related to the wave motion. However, our first use of them will be to write an explicit solution of the wave equation in terms of the initial data.

Define a change of coordinates

$$\xi = x - ct, \quad \eta = x + ct.$$

This transformation is invertible, since

$$x = \frac{1}{2}(\xi + \eta), \quad t = \frac{1}{2c}(-\xi + \eta).$$

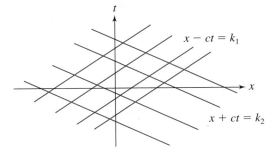

FIGURE 17.17 *Characteristics of the wave equation.*

Define

$$U(\xi, \eta) = u(x(\xi, \eta), y(\xi, \eta)).$$

Now compute derivatives:

$$u_x = U_\xi \xi_x + U_\eta \eta_x = U_\xi + U_\eta,$$

$$u_{xx} = U_{\xi\xi}\xi_x + U_{\xi\eta}\eta_x + U_{\eta\xi}\xi_x + U_{\eta\eta}\eta_x$$

$$= U_{\xi\xi} + 2U_{\xi\eta} + U_{\eta\eta}$$

$$u_t = U_\xi(-c) + U_\eta(c)$$

and

$$u_{tt} = -c[U_{\xi\xi}(-c) + U_{\xi\eta}(c)] + c[U_{\eta\xi}(-c) + U_{\eta\eta}(c)] = c^2 U_{\xi\xi} - 2c^2 U_{\xi\eta} + c^2 U_{\eta\eta}.$$

Then

$$u_{tt} - c^2 u_{xx} = 4c^2 U_{\xi\eta}.$$

In the new coordinates, the wave equation is

$$U_{\xi\eta} = 0.$$

This is called the *canonical form of the wave equation*, and it is an easy equation to solve. First write it as

$$(U_\eta)_\xi = 0.$$

This means that U_η is independent of ξ, say

$$U_\eta = h(\eta).$$

Integrate to get

$$U(\xi, \eta) = \int h(\eta)d\eta + F(\xi),$$

in which $F(\xi)$ is the "constant" of integration of the partial derivative with respect to η. Now $\int h(\eta)d\eta$ is just another function of η which we will write as $G(\eta)$. Thus

$$U(\xi, \eta) = F(\xi) + G(\eta),$$

where F and G must be twice continuously differentiable functions of one variable, but are otherwise arbitrary. We have shown that the solution of $u_{tt} = c^2 u_{xx}$ has the form

$$u(x, t) = F(x - ct) + G(x + ct). \tag{17.22}$$

Equation (17.22) is called *d'Alembert's solution* of the wave equation, after the French mathematician Jean le Rond d'Alembert (1717–1783). Every solution of $u_{tt} = c^2 u_{xx}$ must have this form.

Now we will show how to choose F and G to satisfy the initial conditions. First,

$$u(x, 0) = F(x) + G(x) = f(x) \tag{17.23}$$

and

$$u_t(x, 0) = -cF'(x) + cG'(x) = g(x). \tag{17.24}$$

Integrate equation (17.24) and rearrange terms to obtain

$$-F(x) + G(x) = \frac{1}{c} \int_0^x g(\xi) d\xi - F(0) + G(0).$$

Add this equation to equation (17.23) to get

$$2G(x) = f(x) + \frac{1}{c} \int_0^x g(\xi) d\xi - F(0) + G(0).$$

Therefore

$$G(x) = \frac{1}{2} f(x) + \frac{1}{2c} \int_0^x g(\xi) d\xi - \frac{1}{2} F(0) + \frac{1}{2} G(0). \tag{17.25}$$

But then, from equation (17.23),

$$F(x) = f(x) - G(x) = \frac{1}{2} f(x) - \frac{1}{2c} \int_0^x g(\xi) d\xi + \frac{1}{2} F(0) - \frac{1}{2} G(0). \tag{17.26}$$

Finally, use equations (17.25) and (17.26) to write the solution as

$$u(x, t) = F(x - ct) + G(x + ct)$$

$$= \frac{1}{2} f(x - ct) - \frac{1}{2c} \int_0^{x-ct} g(\xi) d\xi + \frac{1}{2} F(0) - \frac{1}{2} G(0)$$

$$+ \frac{1}{2} f(x + ct) + \frac{1}{2c} \int_0^{x+ct} g(\xi) d\xi - \frac{1}{2} F(0) + \frac{1}{2} G(0),$$

or, after cancellations,

$$u(x, t) = \frac{1}{2} \left(f(x - ct) + f(x + ct) \right) + \frac{1}{2c} \int_{x-ct}^{x+ct} g(\xi) d\xi. \tag{17.27}$$

Equation (17.27) is *d'Alembert's formula* for the solution of the Cauchy problem for the wave equation on the entire line. It is an explicit formula for the solution of the Cauchy problem, in terms of the given initial position and velocity functions.

EXAMPLE 17.10

We will solve the boundary value problem

$$u_{tt} = 4u_{xx} \quad \text{for } -\infty < x < \infty, t > 0,$$

$$u(x, 0) = e^{-|x|}, u_t(x, 0) = \cos(4x) \quad \text{for } -\infty < x < \infty.$$

By d'Alembert's formula, we immediately have

$$u(x,t) = \frac{1}{2}\left(e^{-|x-2t|} + e^{-|x+2t|}\right) + \frac{1}{4}\int_{x-2t}^{x+2t}\cos(4\xi)\,d\xi$$

$$= \frac{1}{2}\left(e^{-|x-2t|} + e^{-|x+2t|}\right) + \frac{1}{16}\left(\sin(4(x+2t)) - \sin(4(x-2t))\right)$$

$$= \frac{1}{2}\left(e^{-|x-2t|} + e^{-|x+2t|}\right) + \frac{1}{8}\sin(4x)\cos(8t). \quad\blacksquare$$

17.4.1 A Nonhomogeneous Wave Equation

Using the characteristics, we will write an expression for the solution of the nonhomogeneous problem:

$$u_{tt} = c^2 u_{xx} + F(x,t) \quad \text{for } -\infty < x < \infty, t > 0,$$

$$u(x,0) = f(x), u_t(x,0) = g(x) \quad \text{for } -\infty < x < \infty.$$

This problem is called nonhomogeneous because of the term $F(x,t)$, which we assume to be continuous for all real x and $t \geq 0$. $F(x,t)$ can be thought of as an external driving or damping force acting on the string.

Suppose we want the solution at (x_0, t_0). Recall that the characteristics of the wave equation are straight lines in the x, t plane. There are exactly two characteristics through this point, and these are the lines

$$x - ct = x_0 - ct_0 \quad \text{and} \quad x + ct = x_0 + ct_0.$$

Segments of these characteristics, together with the interval $[x_0 - ct_0, x_0 + ct_0]$, form a *characteristic triangle* Δ, shown in Figure 17.18. Label the sides of Δ as L, M and I. Since Δ is a region in the x, t plane, we can compute the double integral of $-F(x,t)$ over Δ:

$$-\iint_\Delta F(x,t)\,dA = \iint_\Delta (c^2 u_{xx} - u_{tt})\,dA = \iint_\Delta \left(\frac{\partial}{\partial x}(c^2 u_x) - \frac{\partial}{\partial t}(u_t)\right)dA.$$

Apply Green's theorem to the last integral, with x and t as the independent variables instead of x and y. This converts the double integral to a line integral around the boundary C of Δ. This piecewise smooth curve, which consists of three line segments, is oriented counterclockwise.

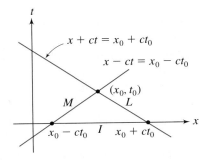

FIGURE 17.18 *Characteristic triangle.*

We obtain by Green's theorem,

$$-\iint_\Delta F(x,t)\,dA = \oint_C u_t\,dx + c^2 u_x\,dt.$$

Now evaluate the line integral on the right by evaluating it on each segment of C in turn.
On I, $t = 0$, so $dt = 0$, and x varies from $x_0 - ct_0$ to $x_0 + ct_0$, so

$$\int_I u_t\,dx + c^2 u_x\,dt = \int_{x_0 - ct_0}^{x_0 + ct_0} u_t(x,0)\,dx = \int_{x_0 - ct_0}^{x_0 + ct_0} g(\xi)\,d\xi.$$

On L, $x + ct = x_0 + ct_0$, so $dx = -c\,dt$ and

$$\int_L u_t\,dx + c^2 u_x\,dt = \int_L u_t(-c)\,dt + c^2 u_x\left(-\frac{1}{c}\right)dx = -c\int_L du$$

$$= -c\left[u(x_0, t_0) - u(x_0 + ct_0, 0)\right].$$

Finally, on M, $x - ct = x_0 - ct_0$, so $dx = c\,dt$ and

$$\int_M u_t\,dx + c^2 u_x\,dt = \int_L u_t(c)\,dt + c^2 u_x\left(\frac{1}{c}\right)dx = c\int_M du$$

$$= c\left[u(x_0 - ct_0, 0) - u(x_0, t_0)\right].$$

M has initial point (x_0, t_0) and terminal point $(x_0 - ct_0, 0)$ because of the counterclockwise orientation on the boundary of Δ.
Upon summing these line integrals, we obtain

$$-\iint_\Delta F(x,t)\,dA = \int_{x_0 - ct_0}^{x_0 + ct_0} g(\xi)\,d\xi$$

$$- c\left[u(x_0, t_0) - u(x_0 + ct_0, 0)\right] + c\left[u(x_0 - ct_0, 0) - u(x_0, t_0)\right].$$

Then

$$-\iint_\Delta F(x,t)\,dA = \int_{x_0 - ct_0}^{x_0 + ct_0} g(\xi)\,d\xi - 2cu(x_0, t_0) + cu(x_0 + ct_0, 0) + cu(x_0 - ct_0, 0).$$

$$= \int_{x_0 - ct_0}^{x_0 + ct_0} g(\xi)\,d\xi - 2u(x_0, t_0) + c\left[f(x_0 + ct_0) + f(x_0 - ct_0)\right].$$

Solve this equation for $u(x_0, t_0)$ to obtain

$$u(x_0, t_0) = \frac{1}{2}\left[f(x_0 - ct_0) + f(x_0 + ct_0)\right] + \frac{1}{2c}\int_{x_0 - ct_0}^{x_0 + ct_0} g(\xi)\,d\xi + \frac{1}{2c}\iint_\Delta F(x,t)\,dA.$$

We have used the subscript 0 on (x_0, t_0) to focus attention on the point at which we are evaluating the solution. However, this can be any point with x_0 real and $t_0 > 0$. Thus the solution at an arbitrary point (x, t) is

$$u(x, t) = \frac{1}{2}\left[f(x - ct) + f(x + ct)\right] + \frac{1}{2c}\int_{x - ct}^{x + ct} g(\xi)\,d\xi + \frac{1}{2c}\iint_\Delta F(\xi, \eta)\,d\xi\,d\eta.$$

The solution at (x, t) of the problem with the forcing term $F(x, t)$ is therefore d'Alembert's solution for the homogeneous problem (no forcing term), plus $(1/2c)$ times the double integral of the forcing term over the characteristic triangle having (x, t) as a vertex.

EXAMPLE 17.11

Consider the problem

$$u_{tt} = 25u_{xx} + x^2t^2 \quad \text{for} \ -\infty < x < \infty, t > 0,$$

$$u(x, 0) = x\cos(x), u_t(x, 0) = e^{-x} \quad \text{for} \ -\infty < x < \infty.$$

The solution at any point x and time t has the form

$$u(x, t) = \frac{1}{2}[(x - 5t)\cos(x - 5t) + (x + 5t)\cos(x + 5t)] + \frac{1}{10}\int_{x-5t}^{x+5t} e^{-\xi}d\xi$$

$$+ \frac{1}{10}\iint_\Delta \xi^2\eta^2 d\xi d\eta.$$

All we have to do is evaluate the integrals. First,

$$\frac{1}{10}\int_{x-5t}^{x+5t} e^{-\xi}d\xi = -\frac{1}{10}e^{-x-5t} + \frac{1}{10}e^{-x+5t}.$$

For the double integral of the forcing term, proceed from Figure 17.19:

$$\frac{1}{10}\iint_\Delta \xi^2\eta^2 d\xi d\eta = \frac{1}{10}\int_0^t \int_{x-5t+5\eta}^{x+5t-5\eta} \xi^2\eta^2 d\xi d\eta$$

$$= \frac{1}{12}t^4x^2 + \frac{5}{36}t^6.$$

The solution is

$$u(x, t) = \frac{1}{2}[(x - 5t)\cos(x - 5t) + (x + 5t)\cos(x + 5t)]$$

$$- \frac{1}{10}e^{-x-5t} + \frac{1}{10}e^{-x+5t} + \frac{1}{12}t^4x^2 + \frac{5}{36}t^6. \ \blacksquare$$

In the last example, $u(x, t)$ gives the position function of the string, at any given time t. The graph of $u(x, t)$ in the x, t plane is not a snapshot of the string at any time. Rather, a picture of the string at time t is the graph of points $(x, u(x, t))$, with t fixed at the time of interest. Figure 17.20(a) shows a segment of the string at time $t = 0.3$, both for the forced and unforced motion. Figure 17.20(b) shows a segment of the string for $t = 0.6$, again both for unforced and forced motion.

This method of characteristics can also be used to solve boundary value problems involving the wave equation on a bounded interval $[0, L]$. However, this is a good deal more involved than the solution on the entire line, so we will leave this to a more advanced treatment of partial differential equations.

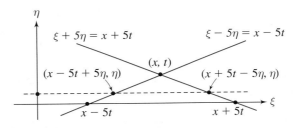

FIGURE 17.19

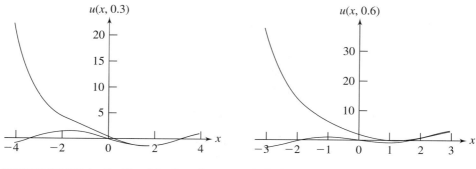

FIGURE 17.20(a) *Profile of the forced and unforced string at $t = 0.3$.*

FIGURE 17.20(b) $t = 0.6$.

17.4.2   Forward and Backward Waves

Continuing with the boundary value problem for the wave equation on the entire real line, we can write d'Alembert's formula (17.27) for the solution as

$$u(x, t) = \frac{1}{2}\left(f(x - ct) - \frac{1}{c} \int_0^{x-ct} g(\xi)d\xi \right)$$

$$+ \frac{1}{2}\left(f(x + ct) + \frac{1}{c} \int_0^{x+ct} g(\xi)d\xi \right)$$

$$= \varphi(x - ct) + \beta(x + ct),$$

where

$$\varphi(x) = \frac{1}{2}f(x) - \frac{1}{2c} \int_0^x g(\xi)d\xi$$

and

$$\beta(x) = \frac{1}{2}f(x) + \frac{1}{2c} \int_0^x g(\xi)d\xi.$$

We call $\varphi(x - ct)$ a forward (or right) wave, and $\beta(x + ct)$ a backward (or left) wave. The graph of $\varphi(x - ct)$ is the graph of $\varphi(x)$ translated ct units to the right. We may therefore think of $\varphi(x - ct)$ as the graph of $\varphi(x)$ moving to the right with velocity c. The graph of $\beta(x + ct)$ is the graph of $\beta(x)$ translated ct units to the left. Thus $\beta(x + ct)$ is the graph of $\beta(x)$ moving to the left with velocity c. The string profile at time t, given by the graph of $y = u(x, t)$ as a function of x, is the sum of these forward and backward waves at time t.

As an example of this process, consider the boundary value problem in which $c = 1$,

$$f(x) = \begin{cases} 4 - x^2 & \text{for } -2 \le x \le 2 \\ 0 & \text{for } |x| > 2 \end{cases}$$

and $g(x) = 0$. This initial position function is shown in Figure 17.21(a). The solution is a sum of a forward and a backward wave:

$$u(x, t) = \varphi(x + ct) + \beta(x - ct) = \frac{1}{2}f(x + t) + \frac{1}{2}f(x - t).$$

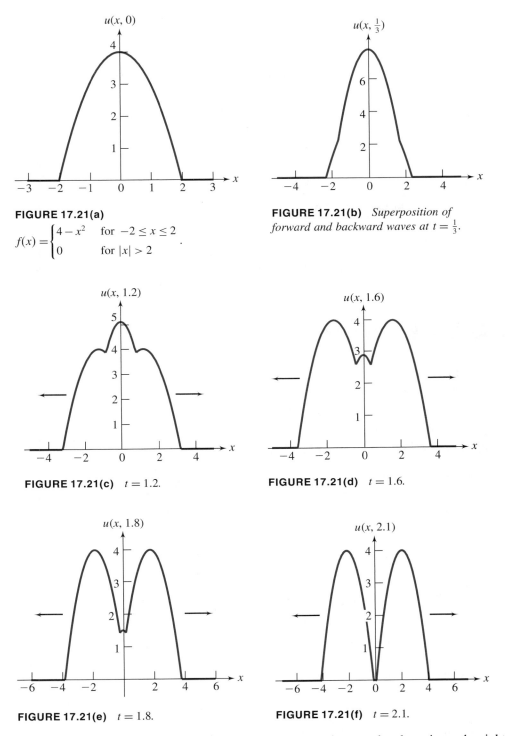

FIGURE 17.21(a)

$$f(x) = \begin{cases} 4 - x^2 & \text{for } -2 \le x \le 2 \\ 0 & \text{for } |x| > 2 \end{cases}.$$

FIGURE 17.21(b) *Superposition of forward and backward waves at $t = \frac{1}{3}$.*

FIGURE 17.21(c) $t = 1.2$.

FIGURE 17.21(d) $t = 1.6$.

FIGURE 17.21(e) $t = 1.8$.

FIGURE 17.21(f) $t = 2.1$.

At any time t, the motion consists of the initial position function translated t units to the right, superimposed on the initial position function translated t units to the left. We see the motion as the initial position function (Figure 17.21(a)) moving simultaneously right and left. Because $f(x)$ vanishes outside of $[-2, 2]$, these forward and backward waves actually separate and

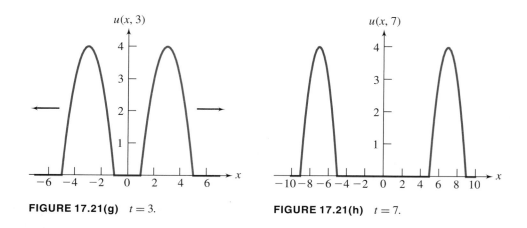

FIGURE 17.21(g) $t = 3$.   **FIGURE 17.21(h)** $t = 7$.

become disjoint, one continuing to move to the right, and the other to the left on the real line. This process is shown in Figures 17.21(b) through (h).

SECTION 17.4   PROBLEMS

In each of Problems 1 through 6, determine the characteristics of the wave equation for the problem

$$u_{tt} = c^2 u_{xx} \quad \text{for } -\infty < x < \infty, t > 0,$$
$$u(x, 0) = f(x), u_t(x, 0) = g(x) \quad \text{for } -\infty < x < \infty$$

for the given value of c, and write the d'Alembert solution.

1. $c = 1$, $f(x) = x^2$, $g(x) = -x$
2. $c = 4$, $f(x) = x^2 - 2x$, $g(x) = \cos(x)$
3. $c = 7$, $f(x) = \cos(\pi x)$, $g(x) = 1 - x^2$
4. $c = 5$, $f(x) = \sin(2x)$, $g(x) = x^3$
5. $c = 14$, $f(x) = e^x$, $g(x) = x$
6. $c = 12$, $f(x) = -5x + x^2$, $g(x) = 3$

In each of Problems 7 through 12, solve the problem

$$u_{tt} = c^2 u_{xx} + F(x, t) \quad \text{for } -\infty < x < \infty, t > 0,$$
$$u(x, 0) = f(x), u_t(x, 0) = g(x) \quad \text{for } -\infty < x < \infty$$

for the given c, $f(x)$ and $g(x)$.

7. $c = 4$, $f(x) = x$, $g(x) = e^{-x}$, $F(x, t) = x + t$
8. $c = 2$, $f(x) = \sin(x)$, $g(x) = 2x$, $F(x, t) = 2xt$
9. $c = 8$, $f(x) = x^2 - x$, $g(x) = \cos(2x)$, $F(x, t) = xt^2$
10. $c = 4$, $f(x) = x^2$, $g(x) = xe^{-x}$, $F(x, t) = x \sin(t)$
11. $c = 3$, $f(x) = \cosh(x)$, $g(x) = 1$, $F(x, t) = 3xt^3$
12. $c = 7$, $f(x) = 1 + x$, $g(x) = \sin(x)$, $F(x, t) = x - \cos(t)$

In each of Problems 13 through 18, write the solution of the problem

$$u_{tt} = u_{xx} \quad \text{for } -\infty < x < \infty, t > 0,$$
$$u(x, 0) = f(x), u_t(x, 0) = 0 \quad \text{for } -\infty < x < \infty.$$

as a sum of a forward and backward wave. Graph the initial position function and then graph the solution at selected times, showing the solution as a superposition of forward and backward waves moving in opposite directions along the real line.

13. $f(x) = \begin{cases} \sin(2x) & \text{for } -\pi \le x \le \pi \\ 0 & \text{for } |x| > \pi \end{cases}$

14. $f(x) = \begin{cases} 1 - |x| & \text{for } -1 \le x \le 1 \\ 0 & \text{for } |x| > 1 \end{cases}$

15. $f(x) = \begin{cases} \cos(x) & \text{for } -\pi/2 \le x \le \pi/2 \\ 0 & \text{for } |x| > \pi/2 \end{cases}$

16. $f(x) = \begin{cases} 1 - x^2 & \text{for } |x| \le 1 \\ 0 & \text{for } |x| > 1 \end{cases}$

17. $f(x) = \begin{cases} x^2 - x - 2 & \text{for } -1 \le x \le 2 \\ 0 & \text{for } x < -1 \quad \text{and} \quad \text{for } x > 2 \end{cases}$

18. $f(x) = \begin{cases} x^3 - x^2 - 4x + 4 & \text{for } -2 \le x \le 2 \\ 0 & \text{for } |x| > 2 \end{cases}$

17.5   Normal Modes of Vibration of a Circular Elastic Membrane

We will analyze the motion of a membrane (such as a drumhead) fastened onto a circular frame and set in motion with given initial position and velocity. Let the rest position of the membrane be in the x, y plane with the origin at the center, and let the membrane have radius R. Using polar coordinates, the particle of membrane at (r, θ) is assumed to vibrate vertical to the x, y plane, and its displacement from the rest position at time t is $z(r, \theta, t)$.

Equation (17.4) gives the wave equation for this displacement function:

$$\frac{\partial^2 z}{\partial t^2} = c^2 \left(\frac{\partial^2 z}{\partial r^2} + \frac{1}{r} \frac{\partial z}{\partial r} + \frac{1}{r^2} \frac{\partial^2 z}{\partial \theta^2} \right).$$

We will assume for the moment that the motion of the membrane is symmetric about the origin, in which case z depends only on r and t. Now the wave equation is

$$\frac{\partial^2 z}{\partial t^2} = c^2 \left(\frac{\partial^2 z}{\partial r^2} + \frac{1}{r} \frac{\partial z}{\partial r} \right).$$

Let the initial displacement be given by $z(r, 0) = f(r)$, and let the initial velocity be

$$\frac{\partial z}{\partial t}(r, 0) = g(r).$$

Attempt a solution

$$z(r, t) = F(r)T(\theta).$$

We obtain, after a routine calculation,

$$T'' + \lambda T = 0 \quad \text{and} \quad F'' + \frac{1}{r}F' + \frac{\lambda}{c^2}F = 0.$$

If $\lambda > 0$, say $\lambda = \omega^2$, the equation for F is a zero order Bessel equation, with general solution

$$F(r) = aJ_0 \left(\frac{\omega}{c}r \right) + bY_0 \left(\frac{\omega}{c}r \right).$$

Since $Y_0(\omega r/c) \to -\infty$ as $r \to 0$ (the center of the membrane), choose $b = 0$. Now the equation for T is

$$T'' + \omega^2 T = 0,$$

with general solution

$$T(t) = d\cos(\omega t) + k\sin(\omega t).$$

We have, for each $\omega > 0$, a function

$$z_\omega(r, t) = a_\omega J_0 \left(\frac{\omega}{c}r \right) \cos(\omega t) + b_\omega J_0 \left(\frac{\omega}{c}r \right) \sin(\omega t).$$

Since the membrane is fixed on a circular frame,

$$z_\omega(R, t) = a_\omega J_0 \left(\frac{\omega}{c}R \right) \cos(\omega t) + b_\omega J_0 \left(\frac{\omega}{c}R \right) \sin(\omega t) = 0$$

for $t > 0$. This condition is satisfied if $J_0(\omega R/c) = 0$. Let $j_1, j_2, \ldots$ be the positive zeros of J_0, with

$$j_1 < j_2 < \cdots,$$

and choose

$$\frac{\omega R}{c} = j_n$$

or

$$\omega_n = \frac{j_n c}{R}$$

for $n = 1, 2, \ldots$. This yields the eigenvalues of this problem:

$$\lambda_n = \omega_n^2 = \frac{j_n^2 c^2}{R^2}.$$

We now have

$$z_n(r, t) = a_n J_0\left(\frac{j_n r}{R}\right)\cos\left(\frac{j_n ct}{R}\right) + b_n J_0\left(\frac{j_n r}{R}\right)\sin\left(\frac{j_n ct}{R}\right).$$

All of these functions satisfy the boundary condition $z(R, t) = 0$. To satisfy the initial conditions, attempt a superposition

$$z(r, t) = \sum_{n=1}^{\infty}\left[a_n J_0\left(\frac{j_n r}{R}\right)\cos\left(\frac{j_n ct}{R}\right) + b_n J_0\left(\frac{j_n r}{R}\right)\sin\left(\frac{j_n ct}{R}\right)\right]. \tag{17.28}$$

Now

$$z(r, 0) = f(r) = \sum_{n=1}^{\infty} a_n J_0\left(\frac{j_n r}{R}\right),$$

a Fourier-Bessel expansion of $f(r)$. Let $s = r/R$ to convert this series to

$$f(Rs) = \sum_{n=1}^{\infty} a_n J_0(j_n s),$$

in which s varies from 0 to 1. We know from Section 16.3.3 that the coefficients in this expansion are given by

$$a_n = \frac{2}{[J_1(j_n)]^2}\int_0^1 sf(Rs)J_0(j_n s)\,ds$$

for $n = 1, 2, \ldots$.

Next we must solve for the $b_n's$. Compute

$$\frac{\partial z}{\partial t}(r, 0) = g(r) = \sum_{n=1}^{\infty} b_n\frac{j_n c}{R}J_0\left(\frac{j_n r}{R}\right).$$

This is a Fourier–Bessel expansion of $g(r)$. Again referring to Section 16.3.3, we must choose

$$b_n\frac{j_n c}{R} = \frac{2}{[J_1(j_n)]^2}\int_0^1 sg(Rs)J_0(j_n s)\,ds,$$

or

$$b_n = \frac{2R}{c j_n[J_1(j_n)]^2}\int_0^1 sg(Rs)J_0(j_n s)\,ds$$

for $n = 1, 2, \ldots$. With these coefficients, equation (17.28) is the solution for the position function of the membrane.

The numbers $\omega_n = j_n c/R$ are the frequencies of normal modes of vibration, which have periods $2\pi/\omega_n = 2\pi R/j_n c$. The normal modes of vibration are the functions $z_n(r, t)$. Often these functions are written in phase angle form as

$$z_n(r, t) = A_n J_0\left(\frac{j_n r}{R}\right) \cos(\omega_n t + \delta_n)$$

in which A_n and δ_n are constants.

The first normal mode is

$$z_1(r, t) = A_1 J_0\left(\frac{j_1 r}{R}\right) \cos(\omega_1 t + \delta_1).$$

As r varies from 0 to R, $j_1 r/R$ varies from 0 to j_1. At any time t, a radial section through the membrane takes the shape of the graph of $J_0(x)$ for $0 \le x \le j_1$ (Figure 17.22(a)).

The second normal mode is

$$z_2(r, t) = A_2 J_0\left(\frac{j_2 r}{R}\right) \cos(\omega_2 t + \delta_2).$$

Now as r varies from 0 to R, $j_2 r/R$ varies from 0 to j_2, passing through j_1 along the way. Since $J_0(j_2 r/R) = 0$ when $j_2 r/R = j_1$, this mode has a nodal circle (fixed in the motion) at radius

$$r = \frac{j_1 R}{j_2}.$$

A section through the membrane takes the shape of the graph of $J_0(x)$ for $0 \le x \le j_2$ (Figure 17.22(b)).

Similarly, the third normal mode is

$$z_3(r, t) = A_3 J_0\left(\frac{j_3 r}{R}\right) \cos(\omega_3 t + \delta_3),$$

and this mode had two nodes, one at $r = j_1 R/j_3$ and the second at $r = j_2 R/j_3$. Now a radial section has the shape of the graph of $J_0(x)$ for $0 \le x \le j_3$ (Figure 17.22(c)).

In general, the nth normal mode has $N - 1$ nodes (fixed circles in the motion of the membrane), occurring at $j_1 R/j_n, \ldots, j_{n-1} R/j_n$.

In the next section we will revisit this problem, this time retaining the θ dependence of the displacement function. This will lead us to a solution involving a double Fourier sine series.

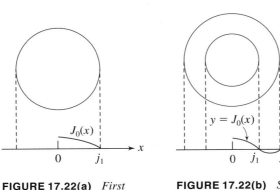

FIGURE 17.22(a) *First normal mode.*

FIGURE 17.22(b) *Second normal mode.*

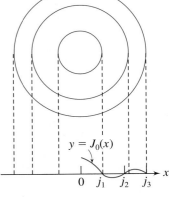

FIGURE 17.22(c) *Third normal mode.*

1. Let $c = R = 1$, $f(r) = 1 - r$ and $g(r) = 0$. Using material from Section 16.2 (Bessel functions), approximate the coefficients a_1 through a_5 in the solution given by equation 17.28 and graph the fifth partial sum of the solution for a selection of different times. Write the (approximate) normal modes $z_n(r, t) = A_n J_0(j_n r) \cos(\omega_n t + \delta_n)$ for $n = 1, \dots 5$.

2. Repeat Problem 1, except now use $f(r) = 1 - r^2$ and $g(r) = 0$.

3. Repeat Problem 1, but now use $f(r) = \sin(\pi r)$ and $g(r) = 0$.

17.6   Vibrations of a Circular Elastic Membrane, Revisited

We will continue from the last section with vibrations of an elastic membrane fixed on a circular frame. Now, however, retain the θ-dependence of the displacement function and consider the entire wave equation

$$\frac{\partial^2 z}{\partial t^2} = c^2 \left(\frac{\partial^2 z}{\partial r^2} + \frac{1}{r} \frac{\partial z}{\partial r} + \frac{1}{r^2} \frac{\partial^2 z}{\partial \theta^2} \right)$$

for $0 \le r < R$, $-\pi \le \theta \le \pi$, $t > 0$. We will use the initial conditions

$$z(r, \theta, 0) = f(r, \theta), \quad \frac{\partial z}{\partial t}(r, \theta, 0) = 0,$$

so the membrane is released from rest with the given initial displacement.

In cylindrical coordinates θ can be replaced by $\theta + 2n\pi$ for any integer n, so we will also impose the *periodicity conditions*

$$z(r, -\pi, t) = z(r, \pi, t) \quad \text{and} \quad \frac{\partial z}{\partial \theta}(r, -\pi, t) = \frac{\partial z}{\partial \theta}(r, \pi, t)$$

for $0 \le r < R$ and $t > 0$.

Put $z(r, \theta, t) = F(r)\Theta(\theta)T(r)$ in the wave equation to get

$$\frac{T''}{c^2 T} = \frac{F'' + (1/r)F'}{F} + \frac{1}{r^2} \frac{\Theta''}{\Theta} = -\lambda$$

for some constant λ since the left side depends only on t, and the right side only on r and θ. Then

$$T'' + \lambda c^2 T = 0$$

and

$$\frac{r^2 F'' + rF'}{F} + \lambda r^2 = -\frac{\Theta''}{\Theta}.$$

Because the left side depends only on r and the right side only on θ, and these are independent, for some constant μ,

$$\frac{r^2 F'' + rF'}{F} + \lambda r^2 = -\frac{\Theta''}{\Theta} = \mu.$$

Then

$$\Theta'' + \mu\Theta = 0$$

and

$$r^2 F'' + rF' + (\lambda r^2 - \mu)F = 0.$$

In solving these differential equations for $T(t)$, $F(r)$ and $\Theta(\theta)$, we have the following boundary conditions. First, by periodicity,

$$\Theta(-\pi) = \Theta(\pi) \quad \text{and} \quad \Theta'(-\pi) = \Theta'(\pi).$$

Next, because the membrane is fixed on the circular frame,

$$F(R) = 0.$$

Finally, because the initial velocity of the membrane is zero,

$$T'(0) = 0.$$

The problem for $\Theta(\theta)$ is a periodic Sturm–Liouville problem which was solved in Section 16.3.1 (Example 16.9). The eigenvalues are

$$\mu_n = n^2 \quad \text{for } n = 0, 1, 2, \ldots,$$

and eigenfunctions are

$$\Theta_n(\theta) = a_n \cos(n\theta) + b_n \sin(n\theta).$$

With $\mu = n^2$, the problem for F is

$$r^2 F''(r) + rF'(r) + (\lambda r^2 - n^2)F(r) = 0; \quad F(R) = 0.$$

We have seen (Section 15.2.2) that this differential equation has general solution

$$F(r) = aJ_n(\sqrt{\lambda}r) + bY_n(\sqrt{\lambda}r),$$

in terms of Bessel functions of order n of the first and second kinds. Because $Y_n(\sqrt{\lambda}r)$ is unbounded as $r \to 0+$, choose $b = 0$ to have a bounded solution. This leaves $F(r) = aJ_n(\sqrt{\lambda}r)$. To find admissable values of λ, we need

$$F(R) = aJ_n(\sqrt{\lambda}R) = 0.$$

We want to satisfy this with a nonzero to avoid a trivial solution. Thus $\sqrt{\lambda}R$ must be one of the positive zeros of J_n. Let these positive zeros be

$$j_{n1} < j_{n2} < \cdots,$$

doubly indexed because this derivation depends on the choice of $\mu = n^2$. Then

$$\lambda_{nk} = \frac{j_{nk}^2}{R^2},$$

with j_{nk} the kth positive zero of $J_n(x)$. The λ_{nk}s are the eigenvalues. Corresponding eigenfunctions are nonzero multiples of

$$J_n\left(\frac{j_{nk}}{R}r\right) \quad \text{for } n = 0, 1, 2, \ldots \quad \text{and} \quad k = 1, 2, \ldots.$$

With these values of λ, the problem for T is

$$T'' + c^2 \left(\frac{j_{nk}}{R}\right)^2 T = 0; \quad T'(0) = 0$$

with solutions constant multiples of

$$T_{nk}(t) = \cos\left(\frac{j_{nk}}{R}ct.\right)$$

We can now form functions

$$z_{nk}(r, \theta, t) = [a_{nk}\cos(n\theta) + b_{nk}\sin(n\theta)]J_n\left(\frac{j_{nk}}{R}r\right)\cos\left(\frac{j_{nk}}{R}ct\right)$$

for $n = 0, 1, 2, \ldots$ and $k = 1, 2, \ldots$. Each of these functions satisfies the wave equation and the boundary conditions, together with the condition of zero initial velocity. To satisfy the condition that the initial position is given by f, write a superposition

$$z(r, \theta, t) = \sum_{n=0}^{\infty}\sum_{k=1}^{\infty}[a_{nk}\cos(n\theta) + b_{nk}\sin(n\theta)]J_n\left(\frac{j_{nk}}{R}r\right)\cos\left(\frac{j_{nk}}{R}ct\right). \tag{17.29}$$

Now we need

$$z(r, \theta, 0) = f(r, \theta)) = \sum_{n=0}^{\infty}\sum_{k=1}^{\infty}[a_{nk}\cos(n\theta) + b_{nk}\sin(n\theta)]J_n\left(\frac{j_{nk}}{R}r\right).$$

To see how to choose these coefficients, first write this equation in the form

$$f(r, \theta) = \sum_{k=1}^{\infty}a_{0k}J_0\left(\frac{j_{0k}}{R}r\right)$$

$$+ \sum_{n=1}^{\infty}\left(\left[\sum_{k=1}^{\infty}a_{nk}J_n\left(\frac{j_{nk}}{R}r\right)\right]\cos(n\theta) + \left[\sum_{k=1}^{\infty}b_{nk}J_n\left(\frac{j_{nk}}{R}r\right)\right]\sin(n\theta)\right).$$

For a given r, think of $f(r, \theta)$ as a function of θ. The last equation is the Fourier series expansion, on $[-\pi, \pi]$, of this function of θ. Since we know the coefficients in the Fourier expansion of a function of θ, we can immediately write

$$\sum_{k=1}^{\infty}a_{0k}J_0\left(\frac{j_{0k}}{R}r\right) = \frac{1}{2\pi}\int_{-\pi}^{\pi}f(r, \theta)d\theta = \alpha_0(r),$$

and, for $n = 1, 2, \ldots$,

$$\sum_{k=1}^{\infty}a_{nk}J_n\left(\frac{j_{nk}}{R}r\right) = \frac{1}{\pi}\int_{-\pi}^{\pi}f(r, \theta)\cos(n\theta)d\theta = \alpha_n(r)$$

and

$$\sum_{k=1}^{\infty}b_{nk}J_n\left(\frac{j_{nk}}{R}r\right) = \frac{1}{\pi}\int_{-\pi}^{\pi}f(r, \theta)\sin(n\theta)d\theta = \beta_n(r)$$

Now recognize that, for each $n = 0, 1, 2, \ldots$, the last three equations are expansions of functions of r in series of Bessel functions, with sets of coefficients, respectively, a_{0k}, a_{nk} and b_{nk}. From Section 16.3.3, we know the coefficients in these expansions:

$$a_{0k} = \frac{2}{[J_1(j_{0k})]^2}\int_0^1 \xi\alpha_0(R\xi)J_0(j_{0k}\xi)d\xi \quad \text{for } k = 1, 2, \ldots,$$

and, for $n = 1, 2, \ldots$,

$$a_{nk} = \frac{2}{[J_{n+1}(j_{nk})]^2}\int_0^1 \xi\alpha_n(R\xi)J_n(j_{nk}\xi)d\xi \quad \text{for } k = 1, 2, \ldots,$$

and

$$b_{nk} = \frac{2}{[J_{n+1}(j_{nk})]^2} \int_0^1 \xi \beta_n(R\xi) J_n(j_{nk}\xi) d\xi \quad \text{for } k = 1, 2, \ldots.$$

The idea in calculating the coefficients is to first perform the integrations with respect to θ to obtain the functions $\alpha_0(r)$, $\alpha_n(r)$ and $\beta_n(r)$, written as Fourier-Bessel series. We then obtain the coefficients in these series, which are the a'_{nk}s and the b'_{nk}s, by evaluating the integrals for the coefficients in this type of eigenfunction expansion. In practice, these integrals must be approximated because the zeros of the Bessel functions of order n can only be approximated.

SECTION 17.6   PROBLEMS

1. Approximate the vertical deflection of the center of a circular membrane of radius 2 for any time $t > 0$ by computing the first three nonzero terms of the solution for the case $c = 2$ and the initial displacement is $f(r, \theta) = (4 - r^2) \sin^2(\theta)$, with $g(r, \theta) = \theta$.

2. Use the solution given in the section to prove the plausible fact that the center of the membrane remains undeflected for all time if the initial displacement is an odd function of θ (that is, $f(r, -\theta) = -f(r, \theta)$). *Hint*: The only integer order Bessel function that is different from zero at $r = 0$ is J_0.

17.7   Vibrations of a Rectangular Membrane

Consider an elastic membrane stretched across a rectangular frame, to which it is fixed. Suppose the frame and the rectangle it encloses occupy the region of the x, y plane defined by $0 \le x \le L$, $0 \le y \le K$. The membrane is given an initial displacement and released with a given initial velocity. We want to determine the vertical displacement function $z(x, y, t)$. At any time t, the graph of $z = z(x, y, t)$ for $0 < x < L$, $0 < y < K$ is a snapshot of the membrane's position at that time. If we had a film of this function evolving over time, we would have a motion picture of the membrane.

The boundary value problem for z is

$$\frac{\partial^2 z}{\partial t^2} = a^2 \left(\frac{\partial^2 z}{\partial x^2} + \frac{\partial^2 z}{\partial y^2} \right) \quad \text{for } 0 < x < L, 0 < y < K, t > 0,$$

$$z(x, 0, t) = z(x, K, t) = 0 \quad \text{for } 0 < x < L, t > 0,$$

$$z(0, y, t) = y(L, y, t) = 0 \quad \text{for } 0 < y < K, t > 0,$$

$$z(x, y, 0) = f(x, y) \quad \text{for } 0 < x < L, 0 < y < K,$$

$$\frac{\partial z}{\partial t}(x, y, 0) = g(x, y) \quad \text{for } 0 < x < L, 0 < y < K.$$

We will solve this problem for the case of zero initial velocity, $g(x, y) = 0$.

Attempt a separation of variables, $z(x, y, t) = X(x)Y(y)T(t)$. We get

$$XYT'' = a^2[X''YT + XY''T],$$

or

$$\frac{T''}{a^2 T} - \frac{Y''}{Y} = \frac{X''}{X}.$$

We are unable to isolate three variables on different sides of an equation. However, we can argue that the left side is a function of just y and t, and the right side just of x, and these three variables are independent. Therefore, for some constant λ,

$$\frac{T''}{a^2 T} - \frac{Y''}{Y} = \frac{X''}{X} = -\lambda.$$

Now we have

$$X'' + \lambda X = 0 \quad \text{and} \quad \frac{T''}{a^2 T} + \lambda = \frac{Y''}{Y}.$$

In the last equation, the left side depends only on t and the right side only on y, so for some constant μ,

$$\frac{T''}{a^2 T} + \lambda = \frac{Y''}{Y} = -\mu.$$

Then

$$Y'' + \mu Y = 0 \quad \text{and} \quad T'' + a^2(\lambda + \mu)T = 0.$$

The variables have been separated, at the cost of introducing two separation constants. Now use the boundary conditions:

$$z(0, y, t) = X(0)Y(y)T(t) = 0 \text{ implies that } X(0) = 0.$$

Similarly,

$$X(L) = 0, \ Y(0) = 0 \quad \text{and} \quad Y(K) = 0.$$

The two problems for X and Y are

$$X'' + \lambda X = 0; \quad X(0) = X(L) = 0$$

and

$$Y'' + \mu Y = 0; \quad Y(0) = Y(K) = 0.$$

These have solutions:

$$\lambda_n = \frac{n^2 \pi^2}{L^2}, \quad X_n(x) = \sin\left(\frac{n\pi x}{L}\right)$$

and

$$\mu_m = \frac{m^2 \pi^2}{K^2}, \quad Y_m(y) = \sin\left(\frac{m\pi y}{K}\right),$$

with n and m varying independently over the positive integers. The problem for T now becomes

$$T'' + a^2 \left(\frac{n^2 \pi^2}{L^2} + \frac{m^2 \pi^2}{L^2}\right)T = 0$$

Further, because of the assumption of zero initial velocity,

$$\frac{\partial z}{\partial t}(x, y, 0) = X(x)Y(y)T'(0) = 0,$$

so $T'(0) = 0$. Then T must be a constant multiple of

$$\cos\left(\sqrt{\frac{n^2}{L^2} + \frac{m^2}{K^2}} \, \pi a t\right).$$

For each positive integer n and m, we now have a function

$$z_{nm}(x, y, t) = a_{nm} \sin\left(\frac{n\pi x}{L}\right) \sin\left(\frac{m\pi y}{K}\right) \cos\left(\sqrt{\frac{n^2}{L^2} + \frac{m^2}{K^2}} \, \pi a t\right)$$

that satisfies all of the conditions of the problem, except possibly the initial condition $z(x, y, 0) = f(x, y)$. For this, use a superposition

$$z(x, y, t) = \sum_{n=1}^{\infty} \sum_{m=1}^{\infty} a_{nm} \sin\left(\frac{n\pi x}{L}\right) \sin\left(\frac{m\pi y}{K}\right) \cos\left(\sqrt{\frac{n^2}{L^2} + \frac{m^2}{K^2}} \, \pi a t\right).$$

We must choose the constants to satisfy

$$z(x, y, 0) = f(x, y) = \sum_{n=1}^{\infty} \sum_{m=1}^{\infty} a_{nm} \sin\left(\frac{n\pi x}{L}\right) \sin\left(\frac{m\pi y}{K}\right).$$

We can do this by exploiting a trick we used when introducing Fourier series. Pick a positive integer m_0 and multiply both sides of this equation by $\sin(m_0 \pi y / K)$ to get

$$f(x, y) \sin\left(\frac{m_0 \pi y}{K}\right) = \sum_{n=1}^{\infty} \sum_{m=1}^{\infty} a_{nm} \sin\left(\frac{n\pi x}{L}\right) \sin\left(\frac{m\pi y}{K}\right) \sin\left(\frac{m_0 \pi y}{K}\right).$$

Now integrate from 0 to K in the $y-$ variable, leaving terms in x alone. We get

$$\int_0^K f(x, y) \sin\left(\frac{m_0 \pi y}{K}\right) dy = \sum_{n=1}^{\infty} \sum_{m=1}^{\infty} a_{nm} \sin\left(\frac{n\pi x}{L}\right) \int_0^K \sin\left(\frac{m\pi y}{K}\right) \sin\left(\frac{m_0 \pi y}{K}\right) dy.$$

By orthogonality of these sine functions on $[0, K]$, all of the integrals are zero except for the term $m = m_0$. The series in m therefore collapses to a single term, with

$$\int_0^K \sin^2\left(\frac{m_0 \pi y}{K}\right) dy = \frac{K}{2}$$

when $m = m_0$. So far we have

$$\int_0^K f(x, y) \sin\left(\frac{m_0 \pi y}{K}\right) dy = \sum_{n=1}^{\infty} \frac{K}{2} a_{nm_0} \sin\left(\frac{n\pi x}{L}\right).$$

The left side of this equation is a function of x. Pick any positive integer n_0 and multiply this equation by $\sin(n_0 \pi x / L)$:

$$\int_0^K f(x, y) \sin\left(\frac{n_0 \pi x}{L}\right) \sin\left(\frac{m_0 \pi y}{K}\right) dy = \sum_{n=1}^{\infty} \frac{K}{2} a_{nm_0} \sin\left(\frac{n\pi x}{L}\right) \sin\left(\frac{n_0 \pi x}{L}\right).$$

Integrate, this time in the x-variable:

$$\int_0^L \int_0^K f(x, y) \sin\left(\frac{n_0 \pi x}{L}\right) \sin\left(\frac{m_0 \pi y}{K}\right) dy dx$$

$$= \sum_{n=1}^{\infty} \frac{K}{2} a_{nm_0} \int_0^L \sin\left(\frac{n\pi x}{L}\right) \sin\left(\frac{n_0 \pi x}{L}\right) dx.$$

All the integrals on the right are zero except when $n = n_0$, and this integral is $L/2$. The last equation becomes

$$\int_0^L \int_0^K f(x, y) \sin\left(\frac{n_0 \pi x}{L}\right) \sin\left(\frac{m_0 \pi y}{K}\right) dy dx = \frac{K}{2} \frac{L}{2} a_{n_0 m_0}.$$

Dropping the zero subscripts, which were just for ease in keeping track of which integers were fixed, we now have

$$a_{nm} = \frac{4}{LK} \int_0^L \int_0^K f(x, y) \sin\left(\frac{n\pi x}{L}\right) \sin\left(\frac{m\pi y}{K}\right) dy dx.$$

With this choice of the coefficients, we have the solution for the displacement function.

EXAMPLE 17.12

Suppose the initial displacement is given by

$$z(x, y, 0) = x(L - x)y(K - y),$$

and the initial velocity is zero. The coefficients in the double Fourier expansion are

$$a_{nm} = \frac{4}{LK} \int_0^L \int_0^K x(L-x)y(K-y) \sin\left(\frac{n\pi x}{L}\right) \sin\left(\frac{m\pi y}{K}\right) dy dx$$

$$= \frac{4}{LK} \left(\int_0^L x(L-x) \sin\left(\frac{n\pi x}{L}\right) dx \right) \left(\int_0^K y(K-y) \sin\left(\frac{m\pi y}{K}\right) dy \right)$$

$$= \frac{16L^2 K^2}{(nm\pi^2)^3} [(-1)^n - 1][(-1)^m - 1].$$

The solution for the displacement function in this case is

$$z(x, y, t) = \sum_{n=1}^\infty \sum_{m=1}^\infty \left[\frac{16L^2 K^2}{(nm\pi^2)^3} [(-1)^n - 1][(-1)^m - 1] \sin\left(\frac{n\pi x}{L}\right) \sin\left(\frac{m\pi y}{K}\right) \cos\left(\sqrt{\frac{n^2}{L^2} + \frac{m^2}{K^2}} \pi a t\right) \right]. \quad \blacksquare$$

SECTION 17.7 PROBLEMS

1. Solve

$$\frac{\partial^2 z}{\partial t^2} = \frac{\partial^2 z}{\partial x^2} + \frac{\partial^2 z}{\partial y^2} \quad \text{for } 0 < x < 2\pi,$$
$$0 < y < 2\pi, t > 0,$$

$z(x, 0, t) = z(x, 2\pi, t) = 0 \quad \text{for } 0 < x < 2\pi, t > 0,$

$z(0, y, t) = z(2\pi, y, t) = 0 \quad \text{for } 0 < y < 2\pi, t > 0,$

$z(x, y, 0) = x^2 \sin(y) \quad \text{for } 0 < x < 2\pi, 0 < y < 2\pi,$

$\frac{\partial z}{\partial t}(x, y, 0) = 0 \quad \text{for } 0 < x < 2\pi, 0 < y < 2\pi.$

2. Solve

$$\frac{\partial^2 z}{\partial t^2} = 9\left(\frac{\partial^2 z}{\partial x^2} + \frac{\partial^2 z}{\partial y^2}\right) \quad \text{for } 0 < x < \pi,$$
$$0 < y < \pi, t > 0,$$

$z(x, 0, t) = z(x, \pi, t) = 0 \quad \text{for } 0 < x < \pi, t > 0,$

$z(0, y, t) = z(\pi, y, t) = 0 \quad \text{for } 0 < y < \pi, t > 0,$

$z(x, y, 0) = \sin(x)\cos(y) \quad \text{for } 0 < x < \pi, 0 < y < \pi,$

$\frac{\partial z}{\partial t}(x, y, 0) = xy \quad \text{for } 0 < x < \pi, 0 < y < \pi.$

3. Solve

$$\frac{\partial^2 z}{\partial t^2} = 4\left(\frac{\partial^2 z}{\partial x^2} + \frac{\partial^2 z}{\partial y^2}\right) \quad \text{for } 0 < x < 2\pi,$$
$$0 < y < 2\pi, t > 0,$$

$z(x, 0, t) = z(x, 2\pi, t) = 0 \quad \text{for } 0 < x < 2\pi, t > 0,$

$z(0, y, t) = z(2\pi, y, t) = 0 \quad \text{for } 0 < y < 2\pi, t > 0,$

$z(x, y, 0) = 0 \quad \text{for } 0 < x < 2\pi, 0 < y < 2\pi,$

$\frac{\partial z}{\partial t}(x, y, 0) = 1 \quad \text{for } 0 < x < 2\pi, 0 < y < 2\pi.$

CHAPTER 18

The Heat Equation

Heat and radiation phenomena are often modeled by a partial differential equation called the heat equation. We derived a three-dimensional version of the heat equation, using Gauss's divergence theorem. We will now examine the heat equation more closely and solve it under a variety of conditions, following a program that parallels the one just carried out for the wave equation.

18.1   The Heat Equation and Initial and Boundary Conditions

Let $u(x, y, z, t)$ be the temperature at time t and location (x, y, z) in a region of space. In Section 13.7.2, we showed that u satisfies the partial differential equation

$$\mu\rho\frac{\partial u}{\partial t} = K\left(\frac{\partial^2 u}{\partial x^2} + \frac{\partial^2 u}{\partial y^2} + \frac{\partial^2 u}{\partial z^2}\right) + \nabla K \cdot \nabla u,$$

in which $K(x, y, z)$ is the thermal conductivity of the medium, $\mu(x, y, z)$ is the specific heat and $\rho(x, y, z)$ is the density. The term $\nabla K \cdot \nabla u$ is the dot product of the gradients of K and u. This is the heat equation in three space variables and the time.

If the thermal conductivity of the medium is constant, then ∇K is the zero vector and the term $\nabla K \cdot \nabla u = 0$. Now the three-dimensional heat equation is

$$\mu\rho\frac{\partial u}{\partial t} = K\left(\frac{\partial^2 u}{\partial x^2} + \frac{\partial^2 u}{\partial y^2} + \frac{\partial^2 u}{\partial z^2}\right).$$

The 1-dimensional heat equation is

$$\frac{\partial u}{\partial t} = \frac{K}{\mu\rho}\frac{\partial^2 u}{\partial x^2}.$$

This equation often applies, for example, to heat conduction in a thin bar whose length is much larger than its other dimensions. To get some feeling for what is involved in the one-dimensional heat equation, we will give a separate derivation of it from basic principles.

841

Consider a straight, thin bar of constant density ρ and constant cross-sectional area A, placed along the x axis from 0 to L. Assume that the sides of the bar are insulated and do not allow heat loss, and that the temperature on the cross section of the bar perpendicular to the x axis at x is a function $u(x, t)$ of x and t only. Let the specific heat μ and the thermal conductivity K be constant.

Consider a typical segment of the bar between $x = \alpha$ and $x = \beta$, as in Figure 18.1. By the definition of specific heat, the rate at which heat energy accumulates in this segment is

$$\int_{\alpha}^{\beta} \mu \rho A \frac{\partial u}{\partial t} \, dx.$$

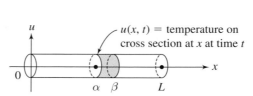

FIGURE 18.1

By Newton's law of cooling, heat energy flows within this segment from the warmer to the cooler end at a rate equal to K times the negative of the temperature gradient (difference in temperature at the ends of the segment). Therefore, the net rate at which heat energy enters this segment of the bar at time t is

$$KA\frac{\partial u}{\partial x}(\beta, t) - KA\frac{\partial u}{\partial x}(\alpha, t).$$

Assume that no energy is produced within the segment. Such production could occur, for example, if there is radiation or a heat source such as a chemical reaction. These would also change the mass of the segment with time. In the absence of these effects, the rate at which heat energy accumulates within the segment must balance the rate at which it enters the segment. Therefore

$$\int_{\alpha}^{\beta} \mu \rho A \frac{\partial u}{\partial t} \, dx = KA\left(\frac{\partial u}{\partial x}(\beta, t) - \frac{\partial u}{\partial x}(\alpha, t)\right) = KA \int_{\alpha}^{\beta} \frac{\partial^2 u}{\partial x^2} \, dx,$$

so

$$\int_{\alpha}^{\beta} \left(\mu \rho \frac{\partial u}{\partial t} - K\frac{\partial^2 u}{\partial x^2}\right) dx = 0.$$

This equation must be true for every α and β with $0 \leq \alpha < \beta \leq L$. If the term in parentheses in this integral were nonzero at any x_0 and t_0, then by continuity we could choose an interval (α, β) about x_0 throughout which this term would be strictly positive or strictly negative. But then this integral of a positive or negative function over (α, β) would be, respectively, positive or negative, a contradiction. We conclude that

$$\mu \rho \frac{\partial u}{\partial t} - K\frac{\partial^2 u}{\partial x^2} = 0$$

for $0 < x < L$ and for $t > 0$. This is the 1-dimensional heat equation.

Often this partial differential equation is written

$$\frac{\partial u}{\partial t} = k\frac{\partial^2 u}{\partial x^2},$$

where $k = K/\mu \rho$ is a positive constant depending on the material of the bar. The number k is called the *diffusivity* of the bar.

This equation certainly does not determine the temperature function $u(x, t)$ uniquely. For example, if $u(x, t)$ is one solution, so is $u(x, t) + c$ for any real number c. For uniqueness of the solution, which we expect in models of physical phenomena, we need *boundary conditions* specifying information at the ends of the bar at all times, and *initial conditions*, giving the temperature throughout the bar at some time usually designated as time zero. The heat equation, together with certain initial and boundary conditions, uniquely determine the temperature distribution throughout the bar at all later times.

For example, we might have the boundary value problem

$$\frac{\partial u}{\partial t} = k\frac{\partial^2 u}{\partial x^2} \quad \text{for } 0 < x < L, t > 0,$$

$$u(0, t) = T_1, u(L, t) = T_2 \quad \text{for } t \geq 0,$$

$$u(x, 0) = f(x) \quad \text{for } 0 \leq x \leq L.$$

This problem models the temperature distribution in a bar of length L, whose left end is kept at constant temperature T_1 and right end at constant temperature T_2, and whose initial temperature in the cross section at x is $f(x)$. The conditions at the ends of the bar are the boundary conditions, and the temperature at time zero is the initial condition.

As a second example, consider the boundary value problem

$$\frac{\partial u}{\partial t} = k\frac{\partial^2 u}{\partial x^2} \quad \text{for } 0 < x < L, t > 0,$$

$$\frac{\partial u}{\partial x}(0, t) = \frac{\partial u}{\partial x}(L, t) = 0 \quad \text{for } t \geq 0,$$

$$u(x, 0) = f(x) \quad \text{for } 0 \leq x \leq L.$$

This problem models the temperature distribution in a bar having no heat loss across its ends. The boundary conditions given in this problem are called *insulation conditions*.

Still other kinds of boundary conditions can be specified. For example, we might have a combination of fixed temperature and insulation conditions. If the left end is kept at constant temperature T and the right end is insulated, then

$$u(0, t) = T \quad \text{and} \quad \frac{\partial u}{\partial x}(L, t) = 0.$$

Or we might have free radiation (convection), in which the bar loses heat by radiation from its ends into the surrounding medium, which is assumed to be maintained at constant temperature T. Now the model consists of the heat equation, the initial temperature function, and the boundary conditions

$$\frac{\partial u}{\partial x}(0, t) = A[u(0, t) - T], \quad \frac{\partial u}{\partial x}(L, t) = -A[u(L, t) - T]$$

for $t \geq 0$. Here A is a positive constant. Notice that if the bar is kept hotter than the surrounding medium, then the heat flow, as measured by $\partial u/\partial x$, must be positive at the left end and negative at the right end.

Boundary conditions

$$u(0, t) = T_1, \quad \frac{\partial u}{\partial x}(L, t) = -A[u(L, t) - T_2]$$

are used if the left end is kept at the constant temperature T_1 while the right end radiates heat energy into a medium of constant temperature T_2.

In 2-space dimensions, with constant thermal conductivity, the heat equation is

$$\frac{\partial u}{\partial t} = k\left(\frac{\partial^2 u}{\partial x^2} + \frac{\partial^2 u}{\partial y^2}\right),$$

while in 3-space dimensions it is

$$\frac{\partial u}{\partial t} = k\left(\frac{\partial^2 u}{\partial x^2} + \frac{\partial^2 u}{\partial y^2} + \frac{\partial^2 u}{\partial z^2}\right).$$

SECTION 18.1   PROBLEMS

1. Formulate a boundary value problem modeling heat conduction in a thin bar of length L, if the left end is kept at temperature zero and the right end is insulated. The initial temperature in the cross section at x is $f(x)$.

2. Formulate a boundary value problem modeling heat conduction in a thin bar of length L, if the left end is kept at temperature $\alpha(t)$ and the right end at temperature $\beta(t)$. The initial temperature in the cross section at x is $f(x)$.

3. Formulate a boundary value for the temperature function in a thin bar of length L if the left end is kept insulated and the right end at temperature $\beta(t)$. The initial temperature in the cross section at x is $f(x)$.

18.2   Fourier Series Solutions of the Heat Equation

In this section we will solve several boundary value problems modeling heat conduction on a bounded interval. For this setting we will use separation of variables and Fourier series.

18.2.1   Ends of the Bar Kept at Temperature Zero

Suppose we want the temperature distribution $u(x, t)$ in a thin, homogeneous (constant density) bar of length L, given that the initial temperature in the bar at time zero in the cross section at x perpendicular to the x axis is $f(x)$. The ends of the bar are maintained at temperature zero for all time.

The boundary value problem modeling this temperature distribution is

$$\frac{\partial u}{\partial t} = k\frac{\partial^2 u}{\partial x^2} \quad \text{for } 0 < x < L, t > 0,$$

$$u(0, t) = u(L, t) = 0 \quad \text{for } t \geq 0,$$

$$u(x, 0) = f(x) \quad \text{for } 0 \leq x \leq L.$$

We will use separation of variables. Substitute $u(x, t) = X(x)T(t)$ into the heat equation to get

$$XT' = kX''T$$

or

$$\frac{T'}{kT} = \frac{X''}{X}.$$

The left side depends only on time, and the right side only on position, and these variables are independent. Therefore for some constant λ,

$$\frac{T'}{kT} = \frac{X''}{X} = -\lambda.$$

Now

$$u(0, t) = X(0)T(t) = 0.$$

If $T(t) = 0$ for all t, then the temperature function has the constant value zero, which occurs if the initial temperature $f(x) = 0$ for $0 \le x \le L$. Otherwise $T(t)$ cannot be identically zero, so we must have $X(0) = 0$. Similarly, $u(L, t) = X(L)T(t) = 0$ implies that $X(L) = 0$. The problem for X is therefore

$$X'' + \lambda X = 0; \quad X(0) = X(L) = 0.$$

We seek values of λ (the eigenvalues) for which this problem for X has nontrivial solutions (the eigenfunctions).

This problem for X is exactly the same one encountered for the space-dependent function in separating variables in the wave equation. There we found that the eigenvalues are

$$\lambda_n = \frac{n^2 \pi^2}{L^2}$$

for $n = 1, 2, \ldots$, and corresponding eigenfunctions are nonzero constant multiples of

$$X_n(x) = \sin\left(\frac{n\pi x}{L}\right).$$

The problem for T becomes

$$T' + \frac{n^2 \pi^2 k}{L^2} T = 0,$$

which has general solution

$$T_n(t) = c_n e^{-n^2 \pi^2 kt / L^2}.$$

For $n = 1, 2, \cdots$, we now have functions

$$u_n(x, t) = c_n \sin\left(\frac{n\pi x}{L}\right) e^{-n^2 \pi^2 kt / L^2}$$

which satisfy the heat equation on $[0, L]$ and the boundary conditions $u(0, t) = u(L, t) = 0$. There remains to find a solution satisfying the initial condition. We can choose n and c_n so that

$$u_n(x, 0) = c_n \sin\left(\frac{n\pi x}{L}\right) = f(x)$$

only if the given initial temperature function is a multiple of this sine function. This need not be the case. In general, we must attempt to construct a solution using the superposition

$$u(x, t) = \sum_{n=1}^{\infty} c_n \sin\left(\frac{n\pi x}{L}\right) e^{-n^2 \pi^2 kt / L^2}.$$

Now we need

$$u(x, 0) = \sum_{n=1}^{\infty} c_n \sin\left(\frac{n\pi x}{L}\right) = f(x),$$

which we recognize as the Fourier sine expansion of $f(x)$ on $[0, L]$. Thus choose

$$c_n = \frac{2}{L} \int_0^L f(\xi) \sin\left(\frac{n\pi\xi}{L}\right) d\xi.$$

With this choice of the coefficients, we have the solution for the temperature distribution function:

$$u(x, t) = \frac{2}{L} \sum_{n=1}^{\infty} \left(\int_0^L f(\xi) \sin\left(\frac{n\pi\xi}{L}\right) d\xi \right) \sin\left(\frac{n\pi x}{L}\right) e^{-n^2\pi^2 kt/L^2}. \tag{18.1}$$

EXAMPLE 18.1

Suppose the initial temperature function is constant A for $0 < x < L$, while the temperature at the ends is maintained at zero. To write the solution for the temperature distribution function, we need to compute

$$c_n = \frac{2}{L} \int_0^L A \sin\left(\frac{n\pi\xi}{L}\right) d\xi = \frac{2A}{n\pi}[1 - \cos(n\pi)] = \frac{2A}{n\pi}[1 - (-1)^n].$$

The solution (18.1) is

$$u(x, t) = \frac{2A}{\pi} \sum_{n=1}^{\infty} \frac{1 - (-1)^n}{n} \sin\left(\frac{n\pi x}{L}\right) e^{-n^2\pi^2 kt/L^2}.$$

Since $1 - (-1)^n$ is zero if n is even, and equals 2 if n is odd, we need only sum over the odd integers and can write

$$u(x, t) = \frac{4A}{\pi} \sum_{n=1}^{\infty} \frac{1}{2n - 1} \sin\left(\frac{(2n - 1)\pi x}{L}\right) e^{-(2n-1)^2\pi^2 kt/L^2}. \quad \blacksquare$$

Verification of the Solution   The function given by equation (18.1) clearly satisfies the boundary and initial conditions of the problem. Each term vanishes at $x = 0$ and at $x = L$, and the coefficients were chosen so that $u(x, 0) = f(x)$. If we could differentiate this series term-by-term, it would also be easy to show that $u(x, t)$ satisfies the heat equation, since each term does.

When we were faced with this problem with the wave equation, we used a trigonometric identity to sum the series. Here, because of the rapidly decaying exponential function in $u(x, t)$, we can easily prove that the series converges uniformly. Choose any $t_0 > 0$. Then, for $t \geq t_0$,

$$\left| \frac{1}{2n - 1} \sin\left(\frac{(2n - 1)\pi x}{L}\right) e^{-(2n-1)^2\pi^2 kt/L^2} \right| \leq \frac{1}{2n - 1} e^{-(2n-1)^2\pi^2 kt_0/L^2}.$$

Because the series

$$\sum_{n=1}^{\infty} \frac{1}{2n - 1} e^{-(2n-1)^2\pi^2 kt_0/L^2}$$

converges, the series for $u(x, t)$ converges uniformly for $0 \leq x \leq L$ and $t \geq t_0$, by a theorem of Weierstrass often referred to as the M–test.

By a similar argument, we can show that the series obtained by differentiating $u(x, t)$ term-by-term, once with respect to t, or twice with respect to x, also converge uniformly. We can therefore differentiate this series term by term, once with respect to t, and twice with respect to x. Since each term in the series satisfies the heat equation, so does $u(x, t)$, verifying the solution (18.1).

We will now consider the problem of heat conduction in a bar with insulated ends.

18.2.2   Temperature in a Bar with Insulated Ends

Consider heat conduction in a bar with insulated ends, hence no energy loss across the ends. If the initial temperature is $f(x)$, the temperature function is modeled by the boundary value problem

$$\frac{\partial u}{\partial t} = k \frac{\partial^2 u}{\partial x^2} \quad \text{for } 0 < x < L, t > 0,$$

$$\frac{\partial u}{\partial x}(0, t) = \frac{\partial u}{\partial x}(L, t) = 0 \quad \text{for } t > 0,$$

$$u(x, 0) = f(x) \quad \text{for } 0 \leq x \leq L.$$

Attempt a separation of variables by putting $u(x, t) = X(x)T(t)$. We obtain, as in the preceding subsection,

$$X'' + \lambda X = 0, T' + \lambda k T = 0.$$

Now

$$\frac{\partial u}{\partial x}(0, t) = X'(0)T(t) = 0$$

implies (except in the trivial case of zero temperature) that $X'(0) = 0$. Similarly,

$$\frac{\partial u}{\partial x}(L, t) = X'(L)T(t) = 0$$

implies that $X'(L) = 0$. The problem for $X(x)$ is therefore

$$X'' + \lambda X = 0; \quad X'(0) = X'(L) = 0.$$

The eigenvalues are

$$\lambda_n = \frac{n^2 \pi^2}{L^2}$$

for $n = 0, 1, 2, \ldots$, with eigenfunctions nonzero constant multiples of

$$X_n(x) = \cos\left(\frac{n \pi x}{L}\right).$$

The equation for T is now

$$T' + \frac{n^2 \pi^2 k}{L^2} T = 0.$$

When $n = 0$ we get

$$T_0(t) = \text{ constant}.$$

For $n = 1, 2, \ldots$,

$$T_n(t) = c_n e^{-n^2 \pi^2 k t / L^2}.$$

We now have functions

$$u_n(x, t) = c_n \cos\left(\frac{n \pi x}{L}\right) e^{-n^2 \pi^2 k t / L^2}$$

for $n = 0, 1, 2, \ldots$, each of which satisfies the heat equation and the insulation boundary conditions. To satisfy the initial condition we must generally use a superposition

$$u(x, t) = \frac{1}{2} c_0 + \sum_{n=1}^{\infty} c_n \cos\left(\frac{n \pi x}{L}\right) e^{-n^2 \pi^2 k t / L^2}.$$

Here we wrote the constant term ($n = 0$) as $c_0/2$ in anticipation of a Fourier cosine expansion. Indeed, we need

$$u(x, 0) = f(x) = \frac{1}{2}c_0 + \sum_{n=1}^{\infty} c_n \cos\left(\frac{n\pi x}{L}\right), \tag{18.2}$$

the Fourier cosine expansion of $f(x)$ on $[0, L]$. (This is also the expansion of the initial temperature function in the eigenfunctions of this problem.) We therefore choose

$$c_n = \frac{2}{L} \int_0^L f(\xi) \cos\left(\frac{n\pi\xi}{L}\right) d\xi.$$

With this choice of coefficients, equation (18.2) gives the solution of this boundary value problem.

EXAMPLE 18.2

Suppose the left half of the bar is initially at temperature A, and the right half is kept at temperature zero. Thus

$$f(x) = \begin{cases} A & \text{for } 0 \le x \le L/2 \\ 0 & \text{for } L/2 < x \le L \end{cases}.$$

Then

$$c_0 = \frac{2}{L} \int_0^{L/2} A \, d\xi = A$$

and, for $n = 1, 2, \ldots,$

$$c_n = \frac{2}{L} \int_0^{L/2} A \cos\left(\frac{n\pi\xi}{L}\right) d\xi = \frac{2A}{n\pi} \sin(n\pi/2).$$

The solution for this temperature function is

$$u(x, t) = \frac{1}{2}A + \frac{2A}{\pi} \sum_{n=1}^{\infty} \sin\left(\frac{n\pi}{2}\right) \cos\left(\frac{n\pi x}{L}\right) e^{-n^2\pi^2 kt/L^2}.$$

Now $\sin(n\pi/2)$ is zero if n is even. Further, if $n = 2k - 1$ is odd, then $\sin(n\pi/2) = (-1)^{k+1}$. The solution may therefore be written

$$u(x, t) = \frac{1}{2}A + \frac{2A}{\pi} \sum_{n=1}^{\infty} \frac{(-1)^{n+1}}{2n-1} \cos\left(\frac{(2n-1)\pi x}{L}\right) e^{-(2n-1)^2\pi^2 kt/L^2}. \blacksquare$$

18.2.3 Temperature Distribution in a Bar with Radiating End

Consider a thin homogeneous bar of length L, with the left end maintained at zero temperature, while the right end radiates energy into the surrounding medium, which is kept at temperature zero. If the initial temperature in the bar's cross section at x is $f(x)$, then the temperature distribution is modeled by the boundary value problem

$$\frac{\partial u}{\partial t} = k\frac{\partial^2 u}{\partial x^2} \quad \text{for } 0 < x < L, t > 0,$$

$$u(0, t) = 0, \frac{\partial u}{\partial x}(L, t) = -Au(L, t) \quad \text{for } t > 0,$$

$$u(x, 0) = f(x) \quad \text{for } 0 \le x \le L.$$

The boundary condition at L assumes that heat energy radiates from this end at a rate proportional to the temperature at that end of the bar. A is a positive constant called the *transfer coefficient*.

Let $u(x, t) = X(x)T(t)$ and obtain

$$X'' + \lambda X = 0, T' + \lambda kT = 0.$$

Since $u(0, t) = X(0)T(t) = 0$, then

$$X(0) = 0.$$

The condition at the right end of the bar implies that

$$X'(L) = -AX(L)T(t),$$

hence

$$X'(L) + AX(L) = 0.$$

The problem for X is therefore

$$X'' + \lambda X = 0, \quad X(0) = 0, \quad X'(L) + AX(L) = 0.$$

This is a regular Sturm–Liouville problem which we solved in Example 16.12 for the case $A = 3$ and $L = 1$, with $y(x)$ in place of $X(x)$. We will find the eigenvalues and eigenvalues in this more general setting by following that analysis. Consider cases on λ.

Case 1 $\lambda = 0$.
Then $X(x) = cx + d$. Since $X(0) = d = 0$, then $X(x) = cx$. But then

$$X'(L) = c = -AX(L) = -AcL$$

implies that $c(1 + AL) = 0$. But $1 + AL > 0$, so $c = 0$ and this case has only the trivial solution. Hence 0 is not an eigenvalue of this problem.

Case 2 $\lambda < 0$.
Write $\lambda = -\alpha^2$ with $\alpha > 0$. Then $X'' - \alpha^2 X = 0$, with general solution

$$X(x) = ce^{\alpha x} + de^{-\alpha x}.$$

Now

$$X(0) = c + d = 0$$

so $d = -c$. Then $X(x) = 2c \sinh(\alpha x)$. Next,

$$X'(L) = 2\alpha c \cosh(\alpha L) = -AX(L) = -2Ac \sinh(\alpha L).$$

Now $\alpha L > 0$, so $2\alpha c \cosh(\alpha L) > 0$ and $-2Ac \sinh(\alpha L) < 0$, so this equation is impossible unless $c = 0$. This case therefore yields only the trivial solution for X, so this problem has no negative eigenvalue.

Case 3 $\lambda > 0$.

Now write $\lambda = \alpha^2$ with $\alpha > 0$. Now $X'' + \alpha^2 X = 0$, so

$$X(x) = c\cos(\alpha x) + d\sin(\alpha x).$$

Then

$$X(0) = c = 0$$

so $X(x) = d\sin(\alpha x)$. Next,

$$X'(L) = d\alpha\cos(\alpha L) = -AX(L) = -Ad\sin(\alpha L).$$

Then $d = 0$ or

$$\tan(\alpha L) = -\frac{\alpha}{A}.$$

We can therefore have a nontrivial solution for X if α is chosen to satisfy this equation. Let $z = \alpha L$ to write this condition as

$$\tan(z) = -\frac{1}{AL}z.$$

Figure 18.2 shows graphs of $y = \tan(z)$ and $y = -z/AL$ in the z, y plane (with z as the horizontal axis). These graphs have infinitely many points of intersection to the right of the vertical axis. Let the z coordinates of these points of intersection be $z_1, z_2, \ldots$, written in increasing order. Since $\alpha = z/L$, then

$$\lambda_n = \alpha_n^2 = \frac{z_n^2}{L^2}$$

are the eigenvalues of this problem, for $n = 1, 2, \ldots$. Eigenfunctions are nonzero constant multiples of $\sin(\alpha_n x)$, or $\sin(z_n x/L)$.

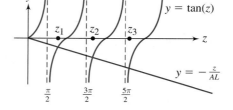

FIGURE 18.2   *Eigenvalues of the problem for a bar with a radiating end.*

The eigenvalues here are obtained as solutions of a transcendental equation which we cannot solve exactly. Nevertheless, from Figure 18.2 it is clear that there is an infinite number of positive eigenvalues, and these can be approximated as closely as we like by numerical techniques.

Now the equation for T is

$$T' + \frac{z_n^2 k}{L^2}T = 0$$

with general solution

$$T_n(t) = c_n e^{-z_n^2 kt/L^2}.$$

For each positive integer n, let

$$u_n(x, t) = X_n(x)T_n(t) = c_n \sin\left(\frac{z_n x}{L}\right) e^{-z_n^2 kt/L^2}.$$

Each of these functions satisfies the heat equation and the boundary conditions. To satisfy the initial condition, we must generally employ a superposition

$$u(x, t) = \sum_{n=1}^{\infty} c_n \sin\left(\frac{z_n x}{L}\right) e^{-z_n^2 kt/L^2}$$

and choose the $c_n's$ so that

$$u(x, 0) = \sum_{n=1}^{\infty} c_n \sin\left(\frac{z_n x}{L}\right) = f(x).$$

This is not a Fourier sine series. It is, however, an expansion of the initial temperature function in eigenfunctions of the Sturm-Liouville problem for X. From Section 16.3.3, choose

$$c_n = \frac{\int_0^L f(\xi) \sin(z_n \xi/L)d\xi}{\int_0^L \sin^2(z_n \xi/L)d\xi}.$$

The solution is

$$u(x, t) = \sum_{n=1}^{\infty} \left(\frac{\int_0^L f(\xi) \sin(z_n \xi/L)d\xi}{\int_0^L \sin^2(z_n \xi/L)d\xi}\right) \sin\left(\frac{z_n x}{L}\right) e^{-z_n^2 kt/L^2}.$$

If we want to compute numerical values of the temperature at different points and times, we must make approximations. As an example, suppose $A = L = 1$ and $f(x) = 1$ for $0 < x < 1$. Use Newton's method to solve $\tan(z) = -z$ approximately to obtain

$$z_1 \approx 2.0288, \quad z_2 \approx 4.9132, \quad z_3 = 7.9787, \quad z_4 \approx 11.0855.$$

Using these values, perform numerical integrations to obtain

$$c_1 \approx 1.9207, \quad c_2 \approx 2.6593, \quad c_3 \approx 4.1457, \quad c_4 \approx 5.6329.$$

Using just the first four terms, we have the approximation

$$u(x, t) \approx 1.9027 \sin(2.0288x)e^{-4.1160kt} + 2.6593 \sin(4.9132x)e^{-24.1395kt}$$

$$+ 4.1457 \sin(7.9787x)e^{-63.6597kt} + 5.6329 \sin(11.0855x)e^{-122.8883kt}.$$

Depending on the magnitude of a, these exponentials may be decaying so fast that these first few terms would suffice for some applications.

18.2.4   Transformations of Boundary Value Problems Involving the Heat Equation

Depending on the partial differential equation and the boundary conditions, it may be impossible to separate the variables in a boundary value problem involving the heat equation. Here is an example of a strategy that works for some problems.

Heat Conduction in a Bar With Ends at Different Temperatures   Consider a thin, homogeneous bar extending from $x = 0$ to $x = L$. The left end is maintained at constant temperature T_1, and the right end at constant temperature T_2. The initial temperature throughout the bar in the cross section at x is $f(x)$.

The boundary value problem modeling this setting is

$$\frac{\partial u}{\partial t} = k \frac{\partial^2 u}{\partial x^2} \quad \text{for } 0 < x < L, t > 0,$$

$$u(0, t) = T_1, u(L, t) = T_2 \quad \text{for } t > 0,$$

$$u(x, 0) = f(x) \quad \text{for } 0 \le x \le L.$$

We assume that T_1 and T_2 are not both zero.

Attempt a separation of variables by putting $u(x, t) = X(x)T(t)$ into the heat equation to obtain

$$X'' + \lambda X = 0, \quad T' + \lambda k T = 0.$$

The variables have been separated. However, we must satisfy

$$u(0, t) = X(0)T(t) = T_1.$$

If $T_1 = 0$, this equation is satisfied by making $X(0) = 0$. If, however, $T_1 \ne 0$, then $T(t) = T_1/X(0) = $ constant. Similarly, $u(L, t) = X(L)T(t) = T_2$, so $T(t) = T_2/X(L) = $ constant. These conditions are impossible to satisfy except in trivial cases (such as $f(x) = 0$ and $T_1 = T_2 = 0$).

We will perturb the temperature distribution function with the idea of obtaining a more tractable problem for the perturbed function. Set

$$u(x, t) = U(x, t) + \psi(x).$$

Substitute this into the heat equation to get

$$\frac{\partial U}{\partial t} = k \left(\frac{\partial^2 U}{\partial x^2} + \psi''(x) \right).$$

This is the standard heat equation if we choose ψ so that

$$\psi''(x) = 0.$$

This means that ψ must have the form

$$\psi(x) = cx + d.$$

Now

$$u(0, t) = T_1 = U(0, t) + \psi(0)$$

becomes the more friendly condition $U(0, t) = 0$ if $\psi(0) = T_1$. Thus choose

$$d = T_1.$$

So far $\psi(x) = cx + T_1$. Next,

$$u(L, t) = T_2 = U(L, t) + \psi(L)$$

becomes $U(L, t) = 0$ if $\psi(L) = cL + T_1 = T_2$, so choose

$$c = \frac{1}{L}(T_2 - T_1).$$

Thus let

$$\psi(x) = \frac{1}{L}(T_2 - T_1)x + T_1.$$

Finally,

$$u(x, 0) = f(x) = U(x, 0) + \psi(x)$$

becomes the following initial condition for U:

$$U(x, 0) = f(x) - \psi(x).$$

We now have a boundary value problem for U:

$$\frac{\partial U}{\partial t} = k\frac{\partial^2 U}{\partial x^2},$$

$$U(0, t) = U(L, t) = 0,$$

$$U(x, 0) = f(x) - \frac{1}{L}(T_2 - T_1)x - T_1.$$

We know the solution of this problem (equation 18.1), and can immediately write

$$U(x, t) = \frac{2}{L}\sum_{n=1}^{\infty}\left(\int_0^L \left[f(\xi) - \frac{1}{L}(T_2 - T_1)x - T_1\right]\sin\left(\frac{n\pi\xi}{L}\right)d\xi\right)\sin\left(\frac{n\pi x}{L}\right)e^{-n^2\pi^2 kt/L^2}.$$

Once we obtain $U(x, t)$, the solution of the original problem is

$$u(x, t) = U(x, t) + \frac{1}{L}(T_2 - T_1)x + T_1.$$

Physically we may regard this solution as a decomposition of the temperature distribution into a transient part and a steady-state part. The transient part is $U(x, t)$, which decays to zero as t increases. The other term, $\psi(x)$, equals $\lim_{t\to\infty} u(x, t)$ and is the steady-state part. This part is independent of the time, representing the limiting value which the temperature approaches in the long-term.

Such decompositions are seen in many physical systems. For example, in a typical electrical circuit the current can be written as a transient part, which decays to zero as time increases, and a steady-state part, which is the limit of the current function as $t \to \infty$.

EXAMPLE 18.3

Suppose, in the above discussion, $T_1 = 1$, $T_2 = 2$ and $f(x) = \frac{3}{2}$ for $0 < x < L$. Compute

$$\int_0^L \left(f(\xi) - \frac{1}{L}(T_2 - T_1)\xi - T_1\right)\sin\left(\frac{n\pi\xi}{L}\right)d\xi = \int_0^L\left(\frac{1}{2} - \frac{1}{L}\xi\right)\sin\left(\frac{n\pi\xi}{L}\right)d\xi$$

$$= \frac{1}{2}L\frac{1 + (-1)^n}{n\pi}.$$

The solution in this case is

$$u(x, t) = \sum_{n=1}^{\infty}\left(\frac{1 + (-1)^n}{n\pi}\right)\sin\left(\frac{n\pi x}{L}\right)e^{-n^2\pi^2 kt/L^2} + \frac{1}{L}x + 1. \quad \blacksquare$$

18.2.5   A Nonhomogeneous Heat Equation

In this section we will consider a nonhomogeneous heat conduction problem on a finite interval:

$$\frac{\partial u}{\partial t} = k\frac{\partial^2 u}{\partial x^2} + F(x, t) \quad \text{for } 0 < x < L, t > 0,$$

$$u(0, t) = u(L, t) = 0 \quad \text{for } t \geq 0,$$

$$u(x, 0) = f(x) \quad \text{for } 0 \leq x \leq L.$$

The term $F(x, t)$ could, for example, account for a heat source within the medium. It is easy to check that separation of variables does not work for this heat equation. To develop another approach, go back to the simple case that $F(x, t) = 0$. In this event we found a solution

$$u(x, t) = \sum_{n=1}^{\infty} b_n \sin\left(\frac{n\pi x}{L}\right) e^{-n^2\pi^2 kt/L^2},$$

in which b_n is the nth coefficient in the Fourier sine expansion of $f(x)$ on $[0, L]$. Taking a cue from this, we will attempt a solution of the current problem of the form

$$u(x, t) = \sum_{n=1}^{\infty} T_n(t) \sin\left(\frac{n\pi x}{L}\right). \tag{18.3}$$

The problem is to determine each $T_n(t)$. The strategy for doing this is to derive a differential equation for $T_n(t)$.

If t is fixed, then the left side of equation (18.3) is just a function of x, and the right side is its Fourier sine expansion on $[0, L]$. We know the coefficients in this expansion, so

$$T_n(t) = \frac{2}{L}\int_0^L u(\xi, t) \sin\left(\frac{n\pi\xi}{L}\right) d\xi. \tag{18.4}$$

Now assume that, for any choice of $t \geq 0$, $F(x, t)$, thought of as a function of x, can also be expanded in a Fourier sine series on $[0, L]$:

$$F(x, t) = \sum_{n=1}^{\infty} B_n(t) \sin\left(\frac{n\pi x}{L}\right), \tag{18.5}$$

where

$$B_n(t) = \frac{2}{L}\int_0^L F(\xi, t) \sin\left(\frac{n\pi\xi}{L}\right) d\xi. \tag{18.6}$$

This coefficient may of course depend on t.

Differentiate equation (18.4) to get

$$T_n'(t) = \frac{2}{L}\int_0^L \frac{\partial u}{\partial t}(\xi, t) \sin\left(\frac{n\pi\xi}{L}\right) d\xi. \tag{18.7}$$

Substitute for $\partial u/\partial t$ from the heat equation to get

$$T_n'(t) = \frac{2k}{L}\int_0^L \frac{\partial^2 u}{\partial x^2}(\xi, t) \sin\left(\frac{n\pi\xi}{L}\right) d\xi + \frac{2}{L}\int_0^L F(\xi, t) \sin\left(\frac{n\pi\xi}{L}\right) d\xi.$$

In view of equation (18.5), this equation becomes

$$T_n'(t) = \frac{2k}{L}\int_0^L \frac{\partial^2 u}{\partial x^2}(\xi, t) \sin\left(\frac{n\pi\xi}{L}\right) d\xi + B_n(t). \tag{18.8}$$

Now apply integration by parts twice to the integral on the right side of equation (18.8), at the end making use of the boundary conditions and of equation (18.4):

$$\int_0^L \frac{\partial^2 u}{\partial x^2}(\xi, t) \sin\left(\frac{n\pi\xi}{L}\right) d\xi = \left[\frac{\partial u}{\partial x}(\xi, t) \sin\left(\frac{n\pi\xi}{L}\right)\right]_0^L - \int_0^L \frac{n\pi}{L} \frac{\partial u}{\partial x}(\xi, t) \cos\left(\frac{n\pi\xi}{L}\right) d\xi$$

$$= -\frac{n\pi}{L} \int_0^L \frac{\partial u}{\partial x}(\xi, t) \cos\left(\frac{n\pi\xi}{L}\right) d\xi$$

$$= -\frac{n\pi}{L}\left[u(\xi, t) \cos\left(\frac{n\pi\xi}{L}\right)\right]_0^L + \frac{n\pi}{L}\int_0^L -\frac{n\pi}{L}u(\xi, t) \sin\left(\frac{n\pi\xi}{L}\right) d\xi$$

$$= -\frac{n^2\pi^2}{L^2} \int_0^L u(\xi, t) \sin\left(\frac{n\pi\xi}{L}\right) d\xi$$

$$= -\frac{n^2\pi^2}{L^2}\frac{L}{2}T_n(t) = -\frac{n^2\pi^2}{2L}T_n(t).$$

Substitute this into equation (18.8) to get

$$T_n'(t) = -\frac{n^2\pi^2 k}{L^2}T_n(t) + B_n(t).$$

For $n = 1, 2, \ldots$, we now have a first order ordinary differential equation for $T_n(t)$:

$$T_n'(t) + \frac{n^2\pi^2 k}{L^2}T_n(t) = B_n(t).$$

Next, use equation (18.4) to get the condition

$$T_n(0) = \frac{2}{L}\int_0^L u(\xi, 0) \sin\left(\frac{n\pi\xi}{L}\right) d\xi = \frac{2}{L}\int_0^L f(\xi) \sin\left(\frac{n\pi\xi}{L}\right) d\xi = b_n,$$

the nth coefficient in the Fourier sine expansion of $f(x)$ on $[0, L]$. Solve the differential equation for $T_n(t)$ subject to this condition to get

$$T_n(t) = \int_0^t e^{-n^2\pi^2 k(t-\tau)/L^2} B_n(\tau) d\tau + b_n e^{-n^2\pi^2 kt/L^2}.$$

Finally, substitute this into equation (18.3) to obtain the solution

$$u(x, t) = \sum_{n=1}^{\infty}\left(\int_0^t e^{-n^2\pi^2 k(t-\tau)/L^2} B_n(\tau) d\tau\right) \sin\left(\frac{n\pi x}{L}\right)$$

$$+ \frac{2}{L}\sum_{n=1}^{\infty}\left(\int_0^L f(\xi) \sin\left(\frac{n\pi\xi}{L}\right) d\xi\right) \sin\left(\frac{n\pi x}{L}\right) e^{-n^2\pi^2 kt/L^2}. \tag{18.9}$$

Notice that the last term is the solution of the problem if the term $F(x, t)$ is missing, while the first term is the effect of the source term on the solution.

EXAMPLE 18.4

Solve the problem

$$\frac{\partial u}{\partial t} = 4\frac{\partial^2 u}{\partial x^2} + xt \quad \text{for } 0 < x < \pi, t > 0,$$

$$u(0, t) = u(\pi, t) = 0 \quad \text{for } t \geq 0,$$

$$u(x, 0) = f(x) = \begin{cases} 20 & \text{for } 0 \leq x \leq \frac{\pi}{4} \\ 0 & \text{for } \frac{\pi}{4} < x \leq \pi \end{cases}.$$

Since we have a formula for the solution, we need only carry out the required integrations. First compute

$$B_n(t) = \frac{2}{\pi}\int_0^\pi \xi t \sin(n\xi)\, d\xi = 2\frac{(-1)^{n+1}}{n}t.$$

Now we can evaluate

$$\int_0^t e^{-4n^2(t-\tau)}B_n(\tau)d\tau = \int_0^t 2\frac{(-1)^{n+1}}{n}\tau e^{-4n^2(t-\tau)}d\tau$$

$$= \frac{1}{8}(-1)^{n+1}\frac{-1+4n^2t+e^{-4n^2t}}{n^5}.$$

Finally, we need

$$b_n = \frac{2}{\pi}\int_0^\pi f(\xi)\sin(n\xi)\, d\xi = \frac{40}{\pi}\int_0^{\pi/4}\sin(n\xi)d\xi = \frac{40}{\pi}\frac{1-\cos(n\pi/4)}{n}.$$

We can now write the solution

$$u(x, t) = \sum_{n=1}^\infty \left(\frac{1}{8}(-1)^{n+1}\frac{-1+4n^2t+e^{-4n^2t}}{n^5}\right)\sin(nx)$$

$$+ \sum_{n=1}^\infty \frac{40}{\pi}\frac{1-\cos(n\pi/4)}{n}\sin(nx)e^{-4n^2t}.$$

The second term on the right is the solution of the problem with the term xt deleted in the heat equation. Denote this "non-source" solution as

$$u_0(x, t) = \sum_{n=1}^\infty \frac{40}{\pi}\frac{1-\cos(n\pi/4)}{n}\sin(nx)e^{-4n^2t}.$$

The solution with the source term is

$$u(x, t) = u_0(x, t) + \sum_{n=1}^\infty \left(\frac{1}{8}(-1)^{n+1}\frac{-1+4n^2t+e^{-4n^2t}}{n^5}\right)\sin(nx).$$

To gauge the effect on the solution of the term xt in the heat equation, Figures 18.3(a) through (d) show graphs of $u(x, t)$ and $u_0(x, t)$ at times $t = 0.3, 0.8, 1.2$ and 1.32. Both solutions decay to zero quite rapidly as time increases. This is shown in Figures 18.4, which shows the evolution of $u_0(x, t)$ over these times, and Figure 18.5, which follows $u(x, t)$. The effect of the xt term is to retard this decay. Other terms $F(x, t)$ would of course have different effects. ∎

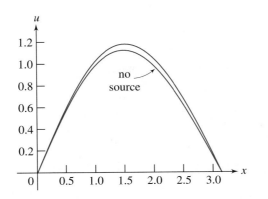

FIGURE 18.3(a) *Comparison of solutions with and without a source term for* $t = 0.3$.

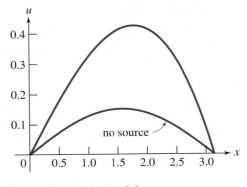

FIGURE 18.3(b) $t = 0.8$.

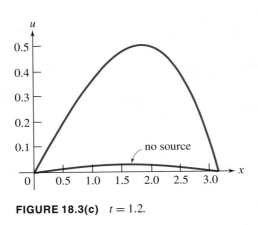

FIGURE 18.3(c) $t = 1.2$.

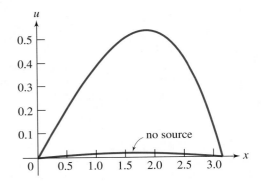

FIGURE 18.3(d) $t = 1.32$.

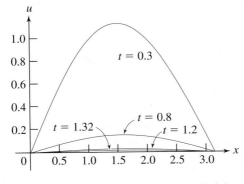

FIGURE 18.4 $u_0(x, t)$ *at times* $t = 0.3, 0.8,$ 1.2, *and* 1.32.

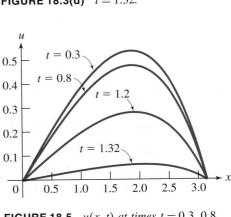

FIGURE 18.5 $u(x, t)$ *at times* $t = 0.3, 0.8,$ 1.2, *and* 1.32.

18.2.6   Effects of Boundary Conditions and Constants on Heat Conduction

We have solved several problems involving heat conduction in a thin homogeneous bar of finite length. As we did with wave motion on an interval, computing power enables us to examine the effects of various constants or terms appearing in these problems, on the behavior of the solutions.

EXAMPLE 18.5

Consider a thin bar of length π, whose initial temperature is given by $f(x) = x^2 \cos(x/2)$. The ends of the bar are assumed to be maintained at zero temperature. The temperature function satisfies

$$\frac{\partial u}{\partial t} = k\frac{\partial^2 u}{\partial x^2} \quad \text{for } 0 < x < \pi, t > 0,$$

$$u(0, t) = u(\pi, t) = 0 \quad \text{for } t > 0,$$

$$u(x, 0) = x^2 \cos(x/2) \quad \text{for } 0 \le x \le \pi.$$

The solution is

$$u(x, t) = \frac{2}{\pi}\sum_{n=1}^{\infty}\left(\int_0^\pi \xi^2 \cos(\xi/2)\sin(n\xi)\,d\xi\right)\sin(nx)\,e^{-n^2 kt}$$

$$= \frac{4}{\pi}\sum_{n=1}^{\infty}\left(\frac{16\pi n\,(-1)^n - 64\pi n^3\,(-1)^n - 48n - 64n^3}{64n^6 - 48n^4 + 12n^2 - 1}\right)\sin(nx)\,e^{-n^2 kt}.$$

We can examine the effects of the diffusivity constant k on this solution by drawing graphs of $y = u(x, t)$ for various times, with different choices of this constant. Figure 18.6(a) shows the temperature distributions at time $t = 0.2$, for k taking the values 0.3, 0.6, 1.1 and 2.7. Figure 18.6(b) shows the temperature distributions at time $t = 1.2$ for these values of k. ■

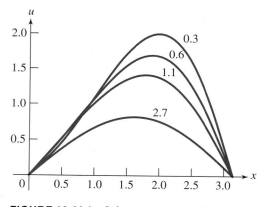

FIGURE 18.6(a) *Solution at time* $t = 0.2$ *with* $k = 0.3, 0.6, 1.1,$ *and* 2.7.

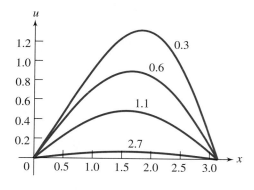

FIGURE 18.6(b) *Solution at time* $t = 1.2$ *with* $k = 0.3, 0.6, 1.1,$ *and* 2.7.

EXAMPLE 18.6

What difference does it make in the temperature distribution whether the ends are insulated or kept at temperature zero? Consider an initial temperature function $f(x) = x^2(\pi - x)$, with a bar of length π. Let the diffusivity be $k = \frac{1}{4}$. The solution if the ends are kept at temperature zero is

$$u_1(x, t) = \sum_{n=1}^{\infty}\left(\frac{8(-1)^{n+1} - 4}{n^3}\right)\sin(nx)\,e^{-n^2 t/4}$$

The solution if the ends are insulated is

$$u_2(x, t) = \frac{1}{12}\pi^3 + \sum_{n=1}^{\infty} \left(\frac{n^2\pi^2(-1)^{n+1} + 6(-1)^n - 6}{n^4} \right) \cos(nx)e^{-n^2 t/4}.$$

Figures 18.7(a) through (d) compare these two solutions for different values of the time. Figure 18.8(a) shows the evolution of the solution with zero end temperatures at different times, and Figure 18.8(b) shows this evolution for the solution with insulated ends. ■

18.2.7 Numerical Approximation of Solutions

Consider the standard heat conduction problem

$$\frac{\partial u}{\partial t} = k\frac{\partial^2 u}{\partial x^2} \quad \text{for } 0 < x < L, t > 0,$$

$$u(0, t) = u(L, t) = 0 \quad \text{for } t \geq 0,$$

$$u(x, 0) = f(x) \quad \text{for } 0 \leq x \leq L.$$

One strategy for computing a numerical approximation of the solution is to begin by forming a grid over the $x, t-$ strip $0 \leq x \leq L, t \geq 0$, as we did with the wave equation on a bounded interval.

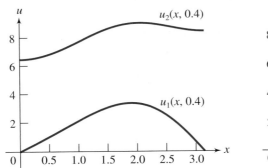

FIGURE 18.7(a) *Comparison of the solution with insulated ends, with the solution having ends kept at zero temperature, at time t=0.4.*

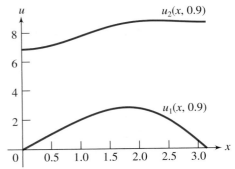

FIGURE 18.7(b) $t = 0.9.$

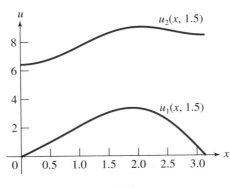

FIGURE 18.7(c) $t = 1.5.$

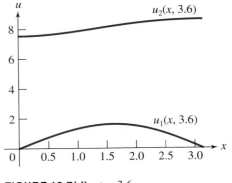

FIGURE 18.7(d) $t = 3.6.$

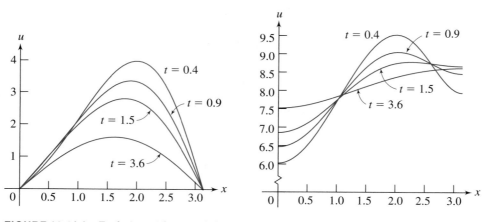

FIGURE 18.8(a) *Evolution with time of the solution with ends kept at zero temperature.*

FIGURE 18.8(b) *Evolution of the solution with insulated ends.*

Choose $\Delta x = L/N$, where N is a positive integer, and let $x_j = j\Delta x$ for $j = 0, 1, \ldots, N$. Also choose Δt positive. This defines lattice points $(x_j, t_k) = (j\Delta x, k\Delta t)$. Denote $u(j\Delta x, k\Delta t) = u_{i,j}$.

Use centered difference approximations to the derivatives to replace the heat equation with:

$$\frac{u_{j,k+1} - u_{j,k}}{\Delta t} = k \frac{u_{j+1,k} - 2u_{j,k} + u_{j-1,k}}{(\Delta x)^2}.$$

In the heat equation, the partial derivative in t is first order, so this equation uses the approximation to $\partial u/\partial t$ on the left. Solve this equation for $u_{j,k+1}$:

$$u_{j,k+1} = \frac{k\Delta t}{(\Delta x)^2}(u_{j+1,k} - 2u_{j,k} + u_{j-1,k}) + u_{j,k}.$$

This enables us to approximate solution values at lattice points on the $k+1^{st}$ horizontal level, from information at the next lower level, where approximations have already been made (Figure 18.9).

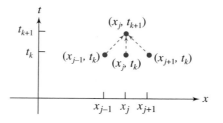

FIGURE 18.9 *Approximation of $u(x_j, t_{k+1})$ is based on approximate values at three points in the t_k layer.*

Since we are moving up the layers of lattice points, filling in approximations at each layer from the layer below, there must be a starting layer at which we already have information. Data for a starting layer is provided by the initial and boundary conditions:

$$u_{0,k} = u_{N,k} = 0$$

(values at lattice points on the left and right sides of the strip), and

$$u_{j,0} = f(x_j) = f(j\Delta x).$$

These values are indicated in Figure 18.10.

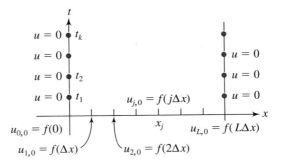

FIGURE 18.10 *Boundary data give exact values of*
$u(x, t)$ at lattice points on the boundary of the strip.

The quantity $k(\Delta t)/(\Delta x)^2$ should be less than $1/2$ to ensure stability of the method.

EXAMPLE 18.7

Consider the problem

$$\frac{\partial u}{\partial t} = \frac{\partial^2 u}{\partial x^2} \quad \text{for } 0 < x < 1, t > 0,$$

$$u(0, t) = u(1, t) = 0,$$

$$u(x, 0) = x(1 - x) \quad \text{for } 0 < x < 1.$$

This has exact solution

$$u(x, t) = \frac{8}{\pi^3} \sum_{n=1}^{\infty} \frac{1}{(2n - 1)^3} \sin((2n - 1)\pi x)e^{-(2n-1)^2\pi^2 t}.$$

To make numerical approximations, we will choose $\Delta x = 0.1$ ($N = 10$) and $\Delta t = 0.0025$. In this example, $k = 1$ so $k(\Delta t)/(\Delta x)^2 = 1/4 < 1/2$. We know that

$$u_{0,k} = u_{10,k} = 0.$$

Further

$$u_{j,0} = f(j\Delta x) = j(0.1)(1 - j(0.1)).$$

This initiates the approximation. These values are filled in at the lowest ($t = 0$) level lattice points in Figure 18.11.

To move from one horizontal layer to the next one up (according to the idea of Figure 18.9), use

$$u_{j,k+1} = 0.25(u_{j+1,k} - 2u_{j,k} + u_{j-1,k}) + u_{j,k}.$$

From here go on to the $k = 1$ ($t = 0.0025$) level, obtaining the values shown in Figure 18.12. Figure 18.13 shows the next level, $k = 2$, or $t = 0.005$. And Figure 18.14 shows the $k = 3$, or $t = 0.0075$, level. Proceeding in this way, we can fill in approximate values at lattice points on any vertical level in the lattice. ■

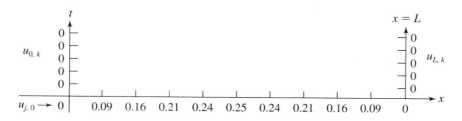

FIGURE 18.11 *Values of $u_{j,0}$, $u_{0,k}$ and $u_{1,k}$ are known at lattice boundary points.*

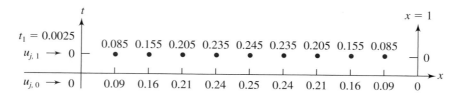

FIGURE 18.12 *Approximate values at the $t_1 = 0.0025$ level computed from known values at the $t_0 = 0$ level.*

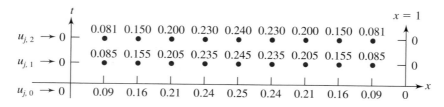

FIGURE 18.13 *Approximate values at the $t_2 = 0.005$ level computed from approximate values at the $t_1 = 0.0025$ level.*

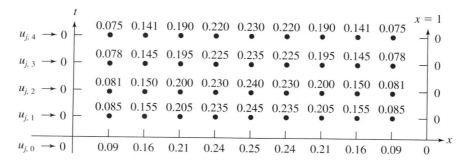

FIGURE 18.14 *Approximate values of the solution $u(x, t)$ at successive t-levels.*

In each of Problems 1 through 7, write a solution of the boundary value problem. Graph the twentieth partial sum of the temperature distribution function on the same set of axes for different values of the time.

1.
$$\frac{\partial u}{\partial t} = k \frac{\partial^2 u}{\partial x^2} \quad \text{for } 0 < x < L, t > 0$$
$$u(0, t) = u(L, t) = 0 \quad \text{for } t \geq 0$$
$$u(x, 0) = x(L - x) \quad \text{for } 0 \leq x \leq L$$

2.
$$\frac{\partial u}{\partial t} = 4 \frac{\partial^2 u}{\partial x^2} \quad \text{for } 0 < x < L, t > 0$$
$$u(0, t) = u(L, t) = 0 \quad \text{for } t \geq 0$$
$$u(x, 0) = x^2(L - x) \quad \text{for } 0 \leq x \leq L$$

3.
$$\frac{\partial u}{\partial t} = 3 \frac{\partial^2 u}{\partial x^2} \quad \text{for } 0 < x < L, t > 0$$
$$u(0, t) = u(L, t) = 0 \quad \text{for } t \geq 0$$
$$u(x, 0) = L[1 - \cos(2\pi x/L)] \quad \text{for } 0 \leq x \leq L$$

4.
$$\frac{\partial u}{\partial t} = \frac{\partial^2 u}{\partial x^2} \quad \text{for } 0 < x < \pi, t > 0$$
$$\frac{\partial u}{\partial x}(0, t) = \frac{\partial u}{\partial x}(\pi, t) = 0 \quad \text{for } t \geq 0$$
$$u(x, 0) = \sin(x) \quad \text{for } 0 \leq x \leq \pi$$

5.
$$\frac{\partial u}{\partial t} = 4 \frac{\partial^2 u}{\partial x^2} \quad \text{for } 0 < x < 2\pi, t > 0$$
$$\frac{\partial u}{\partial x}(0, t) = \frac{\partial u}{\partial x}(2\pi, t) = 0 \quad \text{for } t \geq 0$$
$$u(x, 0) = x(2\pi - x) \quad \text{for } 0 \leq x \leq 2\pi$$

6.
$$\frac{\partial u}{\partial t} = 4 \frac{\partial^2 u}{\partial x^2} \quad \text{for } 0 < x < 3, t > 0$$
$$\frac{\partial u}{\partial x}(0, t) = \frac{\partial u}{\partial x}(3, t) = 0 \quad \text{for } t \geq 0$$
$$u(x, 0) = x^2 \quad \text{for } 0 \leq x \leq 3$$

7.
$$\frac{\partial u}{\partial t} = 2 \frac{\partial^2 u}{\partial x^2} \quad \text{for } 0 < x < 6, t > 0$$
$$\frac{\partial u}{\partial x}(0, t) = \frac{\partial u}{\partial x}(6, t) = 0 \quad \text{for } t \geq 0$$
$$u(x, 0) = e^{-x} \quad \text{for } 0 \leq x \leq 6$$

8. A thin, homogeneous bar of length L has insulated ends and initial temperature B, a positive constant. Find the temperature distribution in the bar.

9. A thin, homogeneous bar of length L has initial temperature equal to a constant B, and the right end $(x = L)$ is insulated, while the left end is kept at a zero temperature. Find the temperature distribution in the bar.

10. A thin, homogeneous bar of thermal diffusivity 9 and length 2 cm and insulated sides has its left end maintained at temperature zero, while its right end is perfectly insulated. The bar has an initial temperature $f(x) = x^2$ for $0 \leq x \leq 2$. Determine the temperature distribution in the bar. What is $\lim_{t \to \infty} u(x, t)$?

11. Show that the partial differential equation
$$\frac{\partial u}{\partial t} = k \left(\frac{\partial^2 u}{\partial x^2} + A \frac{\partial u}{\partial x} + Bu \right)$$
can be transformed into a standard heat equation by choosing α and β appropriately and letting $u(x, t) = e^{\alpha x + \beta t} v(x, t)$.

12. Use the idea of Problem 11 to solve:
$$\frac{\partial u}{\partial t} = \left(\frac{\partial^2 u}{\partial x^2} + 4 \frac{\partial u}{\partial x} + 2u \right) \quad \text{for } 0 < x < \pi, t > 0$$
$$u(0, t) = u(\pi, t) = 0 \quad \text{for } t \geq 0$$
$$u(x, 0) = x(\pi - x) \quad \text{for } 0 \leq x \leq \pi.$$

13. Use the idea of Problem 11 to solve:
$$\frac{\partial u}{\partial t} = \left(\frac{\partial^2 u}{\partial x^2} + 6 \frac{\partial u}{\partial x} \right) \quad \text{for } 0 < x < 4, t > 0$$
$$u(0, t) = u(4, t) = 0 \quad \text{for } t \geq 0$$
$$u(x, 0) = 1 \quad \text{for } 0 \leq x \leq 4.$$

Graph the twentieth partial sum of the solution for a selection of times.

14. Use the idea of Problem 11 to solve
$$\frac{\partial u}{\partial t} = \left(\frac{\partial^2 u}{\partial x^2} - 6 \frac{\partial u}{\partial x} \right) \quad \text{for } 0 < x < \pi, t > 0$$
$$u(0, t) = u(\pi, t) = 0 \quad \text{for } t \geq 0$$
$$u(x, 0) = x^2(\pi - x) \quad \text{for } 0 \leq x \leq \pi.$$

Graph the twentieth partial sum of the solution for selected times.

15. Solve

$$\frac{\partial u}{\partial t} = 16\frac{\partial^2 u}{\partial x^2} \quad \text{for } 0 < x < 1, t > 0$$

$$u(0, t) = 2, u(1, t) = 5 \quad \text{for } t \geq 0$$

$$u(x, 0) = x^2 \quad \text{for } 0 \leq x \leq 1.$$

Graph the twentieth partial sum of the solution for selected times.

16. Solve

$$\frac{\partial u}{\partial t} = k\frac{\partial^2 u}{\partial x^2} \quad \text{for } 0 < x < L, t > 0$$

$$u(0, t) = T, u(L, t) = 0 \quad \text{for } t \geq 0$$

$$u(x, 0) = x(L - x) \quad \text{for } 0 \leq x \leq L.$$

17. Solve

$$\frac{\partial u}{\partial t} = 4\frac{\partial^2 u}{\partial x^2} - Au \quad \text{for } 0 < x < 9, t > 0$$

$$u(0, t) = u(9, t) = 0 \quad \text{for } t \geq 0$$

$$u(x, 0) = 0 \quad \text{for } 0 \leq x \leq 9.$$

Here A is a positive constant.

Choose $A = \frac{1}{4}$ and graph the twentieth partial sum of the solution for a selection of times, using the same set of axes. Repeat this for the values $A = \frac{1}{2}$, $A = 1$ and $A = 3$. This gives some sense of the effect of the $-Au$ term in the heat equation on the behavior of the temperature distribution.

18.

$$\frac{\partial u}{\partial t} = 9\frac{\partial^2 u}{\partial x^2} \quad \text{for } 0 < x < L, t > 0$$

$$u(0, t) = T, u(L, t) = 0 \quad \text{for } t \geq 0$$

$$u(x, 0) = 0 \quad \text{for } 0 \leq x \leq 2\pi.$$

In each of Problems 19 through 23, solve the problem

$$\frac{\partial u}{\partial t} = k\frac{\partial^2 u}{\partial x^2} + F(x, t) \quad \text{for } 0 < x < L, t > 0,$$

$$u(0, t) = u(L, t) = 0 \quad \text{for } t \geq 0,$$

$$u(x, 0) = f(x) \quad \text{for } 0 \leq x \leq L$$

for the given F, k, L and f. In each, choose a value of the time and, on the same set of axes, graph the twentieth partial sum of the solution of the given problem, together with the twentieth partial sum of the solution of the problem with the source term $F(x, t)$ removed. Repeat this for other times. This yields some sense of the significance of $F(x, t)$ on the behavior of the temperature distribution.

19. $k = 4$, $F(x, t) = t$, $f(x) = x(\pi - x)$, $L = \pi$

20. $k = 1$, $F(x, t) = x\sin(t)$, $f(x) = 1$, $L = 4$

21. $k = 1$, $F(x, t) = t\cos(x)$, $f(x) = x^2(5 - x)$, $L = 5$

22. $k = 4$, $F(x, t) = \begin{cases} K & \text{for } 0 \leq x \leq 1 \\ 0 & \text{for } 1 < x \leq 2 \end{cases}$

$f(x) = \sin(\pi x/2)$, $L = 2$

23. $k = 16$, $F(x, t) = xt$, $f(x) = K$, $L = 3$

24. Devise a definition of continuous dependence of the solution on the initial data for the problem

$$\frac{\partial y}{\partial t} = k\frac{\partial^2 y}{\partial x^2} \quad \text{for } 0 < x < L, t > 0$$

$$u(0, t) = u(L, t) = 0 \quad \text{for } t > 0$$

$$u(x, 0) = f(x) \quad \text{for } 0 < x < L.$$

Prove that this problem depends continuously on the initial data.

25. Find approximate solution values for the problem

$$\frac{\partial u}{\partial t} = \frac{\partial^2 u}{\partial x^2} \quad \text{for } 0 < x < 1, t > 0,$$

$$u(0, t) = u(1, t) = 0 \quad \text{for } t \geq 0,$$

$$u(x, 0) = x^2(1 - x) \quad \text{for } 0 \leq x \leq 1.$$

Use $\Delta x = 0.1$ and $\Delta t = 0.0025$. Carry out calculations for the first four horizontal layers, including the $t = 0$ layer.

26. Find approximate solution values for the problem

$$\frac{\partial u}{\partial t} = \frac{\partial^2 u}{\partial x^2} \quad \text{for } 0 < x < 2, t > 0,$$

$$u(0, t) = u(1, t) = 0 \quad \text{for } t \geq 0,$$

$$u(x, 0) = \sin(\pi x/2) \quad \text{for } 0 \leq x \leq 2.$$

Use $\Delta x = 0.2$ and $\Delta t = 0.0025$. Carry out calculations for the first four horizontal layers, including the $t = 0$ layer.

27. Find approximate solution values for the problem

$$\frac{\partial u}{\partial t} = \frac{\partial^2 u}{\partial x^2} \quad \text{for } 0 < x < 1, t > 0,$$

$$u(0, t) = u(1, t) = 0 \quad \text{for } t \geq 0,$$

$$u(x, 0) = x\cos(\pi x/2) \quad \text{for } 0 \leq x \leq 1.$$

Use $\Delta x = 0.1$ and $\Delta t = 0.0025$. Carry out calculations for the first four horizontal layers, including the $t = 0$ layer.

18.3 Heat Conduction in Infinite Media

We will now consider problems involving the heat equation with the space variable extending over the entire real line or half-line.

18.3.1 Heat Conduction in an Infinite Bar

For a setting in which the length of the medium is very much greater than the other dimensions, it is sometimes suitable to model heat conduction by imagining the space variable free to vary over the entire real line. Consider the problem

$$\frac{\partial u}{\partial t} = k\frac{\partial^2 u}{\partial x^2} \quad \text{for } -\infty < x < \infty, t > 0,$$

$$u(x, 0) = f(x) \quad \text{for } -\infty < x < \infty.$$

There are no boundary conditions, so we impose the physically realistic condition that solutions should be bounded.

Separate the variables by putting $u(x, t) = X(x)T(t)$ to obtain

$$X'' + \lambda X = 0, \quad T' + \lambda k T = 0.$$

The problem for X is the same as that encountered with the wave equation on the line, and the same analysis yields eigenvalues $\lambda = \omega^2$ for $\omega \geq 0$ and eigenfunctions of the form $a_\omega \cos(\omega x) + b_\omega \sin(\omega x)$.

The problem for T is $T' + \omega^2 kT = 0$, with general solution $de^{-\omega^2 kt}$. This is bounded for $t \geq 0$.

We now have, for $\omega \geq 0$, functions

$$u_\omega(x, t) = [a_\omega \cos(\omega x) + b_\omega \sin(\omega x)] e^{-\omega^2 kt}$$

that satisfy the heat equation and are bounded on the real line. To satisfy the initial condition, attempt a superposition of these functions over all $\omega \geq 0$, which takes the form of an integral:

$$u(x, t) = \int_0^\infty [a_\omega \cos(\omega x) + b_\omega \sin(\omega x)] e^{-\omega^2 kt} d\omega. \tag{18.10}$$

We need

$$u(x, 0) = \int_0^\infty [a_\omega \cos(\omega x) + b_\omega \sin(\omega x)] d\omega = f(x).$$

This is the Fourier integral of $f(x)$ on the real line, leading us to choose the coefficients

$$a_\omega = \frac{1}{\pi} \int_{-\infty}^\infty f(\xi) \cos(\omega \xi) d\xi$$

and

$$b_\omega = \frac{1}{\pi} \int_{-\infty}^\infty f(\xi) \sin(\omega \xi) d\xi.$$

EXAMPLE 18.8

Suppose the initial temperature function is $f(x) = e^{-|x|}$. Compute the coefficients

$$a_\omega = \frac{1}{\pi} \int_{-\infty}^\infty e^{-|\xi|} \cos(\omega \xi) d\xi = \frac{2}{\pi} \frac{1}{1 + \omega^2}$$

and

$$b_\omega = \frac{1}{\pi} \int_{-\infty}^{\infty} e^{-|\xi|} \sin(\omega\xi) d\xi = 0.$$

The solution for this initial temperature distribution is

$$u(x, t) = \frac{2}{\pi} \int_0^{\infty} \frac{1}{1+\omega^2} \cos(\omega x) e^{-\omega^2 kt} d\omega. \quad \blacksquare$$

The integral (18.10) for the solution is sometimes written in more compact form, reminiscent of the calculation in Section 17.3.1 for Fourier integral solutions of the wave equation on the entire line. Substitute the integrals for the coefficients into the integral for the solution to write

$$u(x, t) = \int_0^{\infty} \left[\frac{1}{\pi} \int_{-\infty}^{\infty} f(\xi) \cos(\omega\xi) d\xi \cos(\omega x) \right.$$

$$\left. + \frac{1}{\pi} \int_{-\infty}^{\infty} f(\xi) \sin(\omega\xi) d\xi \sin(\omega x) \right] e^{-\omega^2 kt} d\omega$$

$$= \frac{1}{\pi} \int_0^{\infty} \int_{-\infty}^{\infty} [\cos(\omega\xi) \cos(\omega x) + \sin(\omega\xi) \sin(\omega x)] f(\xi) d\xi e^{-\omega^2 kt} d\omega$$

$$= \frac{1}{\pi} \int_0^{\infty} \int_{-\infty}^{\infty} \cos(\omega(\xi - x)) f(\xi) e^{-\omega^2 kt} d\xi d\omega.$$

A Single Integral Expression for the Solution on the Real Line   Consider again the problem

$$\frac{\partial u}{\partial t} = k \frac{\partial^2 u}{\partial x^2} \quad \text{for } -\infty < x < \infty, t > 0,$$

$$u(x, 0) = f(x) \quad \text{for } -\infty < x < \infty.$$

We have solved this problem to obtain the double integral expression

$$u(x, t) = \frac{1}{\pi} \int_0^{\infty} \int_{-\infty}^{\infty} \cos(\omega(\xi - x)) f(\xi) e^{-\omega^2 kt} d\xi d\omega.$$

Since the integrand is an even function in ω, then $\int_0^{\infty} \cdots d\omega = \frac{1}{2} \int_{-\infty}^{\infty} \cdots d\omega$ and this solution can also be written

$$u(x, t) = \frac{1}{2\pi} \int_{-\infty}^{\infty} \int_{-\infty}^{\infty} \cos(\omega(\xi - x)) f(\xi) e^{-\omega^2 kt} d\xi d\omega.$$

We will show how this solution can be put in terms of a single integral. We need the following.

LEMMA 18.1

For real α and β, with $\beta \neq 0$,

$$\int_{-\infty}^{\infty} e^{-\zeta^2} \cos\left(\frac{\alpha\zeta}{\beta}\right) d\zeta = \sqrt{\pi} e^{-\alpha^2/4\beta^2}. \quad \blacksquare$$

Proof   Let

$$F(x) = \int_0^{\infty} e^{-\zeta^2} \cos(x\zeta) d\zeta.$$

One can show that this integral converges for all x, as does the integral obtained by interchanging d/dx and $\int_0^\infty \cdots d\zeta$. We can therefore compute

$$F'(x) = \int_0^\infty -e^{-\zeta^2} \zeta \sin(x\zeta) d\zeta.$$

Integrate by parts to get

$$F'(x) = -\frac{x}{2} F(x).$$

Then

$$\frac{F'(x)}{F(x)} = -\frac{x}{2}$$

and an integration yields

$$\ln|F(x)| = -\frac{1}{4}x^2 + c.$$

Then

$$F(x) = Ae^{-x^2 4}.$$

To evaluate the constant A, use the fact that

$$F(0) = A = \int_0^\infty e^{-\zeta^2} d\zeta = \frac{\sqrt{\pi}}{2},$$

a result found in many integral tables. Therefore

$$\int_0^\infty e^{-\zeta^2} \cos(x\zeta) d\zeta = \frac{\sqrt{\pi}}{2} e^{-x^2/4}.$$

Finally, let $x = \alpha/\beta$ and use the fact that the integrand is even with respect to ζ to obtain

$$\int_{-\infty}^\infty e^{-\zeta^2} \cos\left(\frac{\alpha\zeta}{\beta}\right) d\zeta = 2 \int_0^\infty e^{-\zeta^2} \cos\left(\frac{\alpha\zeta}{\beta}\right) d\zeta = \sqrt{\pi} e^{-\alpha^2/4\beta^2}. \ \blacksquare$$

Now let

$$\zeta = \sqrt{kt}\,\omega, \ \alpha = x - \xi \ \text{and} \ \beta = \sqrt{kt}.$$

Then

$$\frac{\alpha\zeta}{\beta} = \omega(x - \xi)$$

and

$$\int_{-\infty}^\infty e^{-\zeta^2} \cos\left(\frac{\alpha\zeta}{\beta}\right) d\zeta = \int_{-\infty}^\infty e^{-\omega^2 kt} \cos(\omega(x-\xi)) \sqrt{kt}\, d\omega = \sqrt{\pi} e^{-(x-\xi)^2/4kt}.$$

Then

$$\int_{-\infty}^\infty e^{-\omega^2 kt} \cos(\omega(x-\xi)) d\omega = \frac{\sqrt{\pi}}{\sqrt{kt}} e^{-(x-\xi)^2/4kt}.$$

The solution of the heat conduction on the real line is therefore

$$u(x, t) = \frac{1}{2\pi} \int_{-\infty}^\infty \int_{-\infty}^\infty f(\xi) \cos(\omega(\xi - x)) e^{-\omega^2 kt} d\xi d\omega$$

$$= \frac{1}{2\pi} \int_{-\infty}^\infty \frac{\sqrt{\pi}}{\sqrt{kt}} e^{-(x-\xi)^2/4kt} f(\xi) d\xi.$$

After some manipulation, this solution is

$$u(x, t) = \frac{1}{2\sqrt{\pi k t}} \int_{-\infty}^{\infty} e^{-(x-\xi)^2/4kt} f(\xi) d\xi.$$

This is simpler than the previously stated solution in the sense of containing only one integral.

18.3.2   Heat Conduction in a Semi-Infinite Bar

If we consider heat conduction in a bar extending from 0 to infinity, then there is a boundary condition at the left end. If the temperature is maintained at zero at this end, then the problem is

$$\frac{\partial u}{\partial t} = k \frac{\partial^2 u}{\partial x^2} \quad \text{for } 0 < x < \infty, t > 0,$$

$$u(0, t) = 0 \quad \text{for } t \geq 0,$$

$$u(x, 0) = f(x) \quad \text{for } 0 < x < \infty.$$

Letting $u(x, t) = X(x)T(t)$, the problems for X and T are

$$X'' + \lambda X = 0, \ T' + \lambda k T = 0.$$

If we proceed as we did for the real line, we obtain $\lambda = \omega^2$ for $\omega \geq 0$, and functions

$$X_\omega(x) = a_\omega \cos(\omega x) + b_\omega \sin(\omega x).$$

Now, however, we also have the condition

$$u(0, t) = X(0)T(t) = 0,$$

implying that

$$X(0) = 0.$$

Thus we must choose each $a_\omega = 0$, leaving $X_\omega(x) = b_\omega \sin(\omega x)$. Solutions for T have the form of constants times $e^{-\omega^2 kt}$, so for each $\omega > 0$ we have functions

$$u_\omega(x, t) = b_\omega \sin(\omega x)e^{-\omega^2 kt}.$$

Each of these functions satisfies the heat equation and the boundary condition $u(0, t) = 0$. To satisfy the initial condition, write a superposition

$$u(x, t) = \int_0^\infty b_\omega \sin(\omega x)e^{-\omega^2 kt} d\omega. \qquad (18.11)$$

Now the initial condition requires that

$$u(x, 0) = \int_0^\infty b_\omega \sin(\omega x) d\omega,$$

so choose the $b'_\omega s$ as the coefficients in the Fourier sine integral of $f(x)$ on $[0, \infty)$:

$$b_\omega = \frac{2}{\pi} \int_0^\infty f(\xi) \sin(\omega \xi) d\xi.$$

With this choice of coefficients, the function given by equation (18.11) is the solution of the problem.

EXAMPLE 18.9

Suppose the initial temperature function is given by

$$f(x) = \begin{cases} \pi - x & \text{for } 0 \le x \le \pi \\ 0 & \text{for } x > \pi \end{cases}.$$

The coefficients in the solution (18.11) are

$$b_\omega = \frac{2}{\pi} \int_0^\pi (\pi - \xi) \sin(\omega \xi) d\xi = \frac{2}{\pi} \frac{\pi\omega - \sin(\pi\omega)}{\omega^2}.$$

The solution for this initial temperature function is

$$u(x, t) = \frac{2}{\pi} \int_0^\infty \left(\frac{\pi\omega - \sin(\pi\omega)}{\omega^2} \right) \sin(\omega x) e^{-\omega^2 kt} d\omega. \blacksquare$$

18.3.3 Integral Transform Methods for the Heat Equation in an Infinite Medium

As we did with the wave equation on an unbounded domain, we will illustrate the use of Fourier transforms in problems involving the heat equation.

Heat Conduction on the Line Consider again the problem

$$\frac{\partial u}{\partial t} = k\frac{\partial^2 u}{\partial x^2} \quad \text{for } -\infty < x < \infty, t > 0,$$

$$u(x, 0) = f(x) \quad \text{for } -\infty < x < \infty,$$

which we have solved by separation of variables. Since x varies over the real line, we can attempt to use the Fourier transform in the x variable. Take the transform of the heat equation to get

$$\mathfrak{F}\left[\frac{\partial u}{\partial t}\right] = k\mathfrak{F}\left[\frac{\partial^2 u}{\partial x^2}\right].$$

Because x and t are independent, the transform passes through the partial derivative with respect to t:

$$\mathfrak{F}\left[\frac{\partial u}{\partial t}\right](\omega) = \int_{-\infty}^\infty \frac{\partial u(\xi, t)}{\partial t} e^{-i\omega\xi} d\xi = \frac{\partial}{\partial t} \int_{-\infty}^\infty u(\xi, t) e^{-i\omega\xi} d\xi = \frac{\partial}{\partial t} \hat{u}(\omega, t).$$

For the transform, in the $x-$ variable, of the second partial derivative of u with respect to x, use the operational formula:

$$\mathfrak{F}\left[\frac{\partial^2 u}{\partial x^2}\right](\omega) = -\omega^2 \hat{u}(\omega, t).$$

The transform of the heat equation is therefore

$$\frac{\partial}{\partial t} \hat{u}(\omega, t) + k\omega^2 \hat{u}(\omega, t) = 0,$$

with general solution

$$\hat{u}(\omega, t) = a_\omega e^{-\omega^2 kt}.$$

To determine the coeffocient a_ω, take the transform of the initial condition to get

$$\hat{u}(\omega, 0) = \hat{f}(\omega) = a_\omega.$$

Therefore

$$\hat{u}(\omega, t) = \hat{f}(\omega)e^{-\omega^2 kt}.$$

This is the Fourier transform of the solution of the problem. To retrieve the solution, apply the inverse Fourier transform:

$$u(x, t) = \mathfrak{F}^{-1}\left[\hat{f}(\omega)e^{-\omega^2 kt}\right](x) = \frac{1}{2\pi}\int_{-\infty}^{\infty}\hat{f}(\omega)e^{-\omega^2 kt}e^{i\omega x}\,d\omega.$$

Of course, the real part of this expression is $u(x, t)$. To see that this solution agrees with that obtained by separation of variables, insert the integral for $\hat{f}(\omega)$ to obtain

$$\frac{1}{2\pi}\int_{-\infty}^{\infty}\hat{f}(\omega)e^{-\omega^2 kt}e^{i\omega x}\,d\omega = \frac{1}{2\pi}\int_{-\infty}^{\infty}\left(\int_{-\infty}^{\infty}f(\xi)e^{-i\omega\xi}\,d\xi\right)e^{i\omega x}e^{-\omega^2 kt}\,d\omega$$

$$= \frac{1}{2\pi}\int_{-\infty}^{\infty}\int_{-\infty}^{\infty}f(\xi)e^{-i\omega(\xi-x)}e^{-\omega^2 kt}\,d\xi d\omega$$

$$= \frac{1}{2\pi}\int_{-\infty}^{\infty}\int_{-\infty}^{\infty}f(\xi)\cos(\omega(\xi - x))e^{-\omega^2 kt}\,d\xi d\omega$$

$$- \frac{i}{2\pi}\int_{-\infty}^{\infty}\int_{-\infty}^{\infty}f(\xi)\sin(\omega(\xi - x))e^{-\omega^2 kt}\,d\xi d\omega.$$

Taking the real part of this expression, we have

$$u(x, t) = \frac{1}{2\pi}\int_{-\infty}^{\infty}\int_{-\infty}^{\infty}f(\xi)\cos(\omega(\xi - x))e^{-\omega^2 kt}\,d\xi d\omega,$$

the solution obtained by separation of variables.

Heat Conduction on the Half-Line   Consider again the problem

$$\frac{\partial u}{\partial t} = k\frac{\partial^2 u}{\partial x^2} \quad \text{for } 0 < x < \infty, t > 0,$$

$$u(0, t) = 0 \quad \text{for } t \geq 0,$$

$$u(x, 0) = f(x) \quad \text{for } -\infty < x < \infty,$$

which we have solved by separation of variables. To illustrate the transform technique, we will solve this problem again using the Fourier sine transform. Take the sine transform of the heat equation with respect to x, using the operational formula for the transform of the $\partial^2 u/\partial x^2$ term, to get

$$\frac{\partial}{\partial t}\hat{u}_S(\omega, t) = -\omega^2 k\hat{u}_S(\omega, t) + \omega k u(0, t).$$

Since $u(0, t) = 0$, this is

$$\frac{\partial}{\partial t}\hat{u}_S(\omega, t) = -\omega^2 k\hat{u}_S(\omega, t),$$

with general solution

$$\hat{u}_S(\omega, t) = b_\omega e^{-\omega^2 kt}.$$

Now $u(x, 0) = f(x)$, so

$$\hat{u}_S(\omega, 0) = \hat{f}_S(\omega) = b_\omega$$

and therefore

$$\hat{u}_S(\omega, t) = \hat{f}_S(\omega)e^{-\omega^2 kt}.$$

This is the sine transform of the solution. For the solution, apply the inverse Fourier sine transform to obtain

$$u(x, t) = \frac{2}{\pi}\int_0^\infty \hat{f}_S(\omega)e^{-\omega^2 kt}\sin(\omega x)\,d\omega.$$

We leave it for the student to insert the integral expression for $\hat{f}_S(\omega)$ and show that this solution agrees with that obtained by separation of variables.

Laplace Transform Solution of a Boundary Value Problem We have illustrated the use of the Fourier transform and Fourier sine transform in solving heat conduction problems. Here is an example in which the Laplace transform is the natural transform to use.

Consider the problem on a half-line:

$$\frac{\partial u}{\partial t} = k\frac{\partial^2 u}{\partial x^2} \quad \text{for } x > 0, t > 0,$$

$$u(x, 0) = A \quad \text{for } x > 0,$$

$$u(0, t) = \begin{cases} B & \text{for } 0 \leq t \leq t_0 \\ 0 & \text{for } t > t_0 \end{cases},$$

in which A, B and t_0 are positive constants. This specifies a problem with nonzero constant initial temperature and a discontinuous temperature distribution at the left end of the bar.

We can write the boundary condition more neatly in terms of the Heaviside function H defined in Section 3.3.2:

$$u(0, t) = B[1 - H(t - t_0)].$$

Because of the discontinuity in $u(0, t)$, we think of trying a Laplace transform in t. Denote

$$\mathcal{L}[u(x, t)](s) = U(x, s),$$

with s the variable of the transformed function, and x carried along as a parameter. Take the Laplace transform of the heat equation:

$$\mathcal{L}\left[\frac{\partial u}{\partial t}\right] = k\mathcal{L}\left[\frac{\partial^2 u}{\partial x^2}\right].$$

For the transform of $\partial u/\partial t$, the derivative of the transformed variable, use the operational formula for the Laplace transform:

$$\mathcal{L}\left[\frac{\partial u}{\partial t}\right](s) = sU(x, s) - u(x, 0) = sU(x, s) - A.$$

The transform passes through $\partial^2 u/\partial x^2$ because x and t are independent:

$$\mathfrak{L}\left[\frac{\partial^2 u}{\partial x^2}\right](s) = \int_0^\infty e^{-st}\frac{\partial^2 u}{\partial x^2}(x, t)\,dt = \frac{\partial^2}{\partial x^2}\int_0^\infty e^{-st}u(x, t)\,dt = \frac{\partial^2 U(x, s)}{\partial x^2}.$$

Transforming the heat equation therefore yields

$$sU(x, s) - A = k\frac{\partial^2 U(x, s)}{\partial x^2}.$$

Write this equation as

$$\frac{\partial^2 U(x, s)}{\partial x^2} - \frac{s}{k}U(x, s) = -\frac{A}{k},$$

a differential equation in x, for each $s > 0$. The general solution of this equation is

$$U(x, s) = a_s e^{\sqrt{s/k}\,x} + b_s e^{-\sqrt{s/k}\,x} + \frac{A}{s}.$$

The notation reflects the fact that the coefficients will in general depend on s. Now, to have a bounded solution we need $a_s = 0$, since $e^{\sqrt{s/k}\,x} \to \infty$ as $s \to \infty$. Therefore

$$U(x, s) = b_s e^{-\sqrt{s/k}\,x} + \frac{A}{s}. \tag{18.12}$$

To obtain b_s, take the Laplace transform of $u(0, t) = B[1 - H(t - t_0)]$ to get

$$U(0, s) = B\mathfrak{L}[1](s) - B\mathfrak{L}[H(t - t_0)](s) = B\frac{1}{s} - B\frac{1}{s}e^{-t_0 s}.$$

Then

$$U(0, s) = B\frac{1}{s} - B\frac{1}{s}e^{-t_0 s} = b_s + \frac{A}{s},$$

so

$$b_s = \frac{B - A}{s} - \frac{B}{s}e^{-t_0 s}.$$

Put this into equation (18.12) to get

$$U(x, s) = \left[\frac{B - A}{s} - \frac{B}{s}e^{-t_0 s}\right]e^{-\sqrt{s/k}\,x} + \frac{A}{s}.$$

The solution is now obtained by using the inverse Laplace transform:

$$u(x, t) = \mathfrak{L}^{-1}[U(x, s)].$$

This inverse can be calculated using standard tables and makes use of the error function and complementary error function, which see frequent use in statistics. These functions are defined by

$$\operatorname{erf}(x) = \frac{2}{\sqrt{\pi}}\int_0^x e^{-\xi^2}\,d\xi$$

and

$$\operatorname{erfc}(x) = \frac{2}{\sqrt{\pi}}\int_x^\infty e^{-\xi^2}\,d\xi = 1 - \operatorname{erf}(x).$$

We obtain

$$
u(x, t) = \left(A \operatorname{erf}\left(\frac{x}{2\sqrt{kt}}\right) + B \operatorname{erfc}\left(\frac{x}{2\sqrt{kt}}\right) \right) (1 - H(t - t_0))
$$

$$
+ \left(A \operatorname{erf}\left(\frac{x}{2\sqrt{kt}}\right) + B \operatorname{erfc}\left(\frac{x}{2\sqrt{kt}}\right) - B \operatorname{erfc}\left(\frac{x}{2\sqrt{k(t - t_0)}}\right) \right) H(t - t_0).
$$

SECTION 18.3   PROBLEMS

In each of Problems 1 through 4, consider the problem

$$
\frac{\partial u}{\partial t} = k\frac{\partial^2 u}{\partial x^2} \quad \text{for } -\infty < x < \infty, t > 0
$$
$$
u(x, 0) = f(x) \quad \text{for } -\infty < x < \infty.
$$

Obtain a solution first by separation of variables (Fourier integral), and then again by Fourier transform.

1. $f(x) = e^{-4|x|}$

2. $f(x) = \begin{cases} \sin(x) & \text{for } |x| \leq \pi \\ 0 & \text{for } |x| > \pi \end{cases}$

3. $f(x) = \begin{cases} x & \text{for } 0 \leq x \leq 4 \\ 0 & \text{for } x < 0 \text{ and for } x > 4 \end{cases}$

4. $f(x) = \begin{cases} e^{-x} & \text{for } -1 \leq x \leq 1 \\ 0 & \text{for } |x| > 1 \end{cases}$

In each of Problems 5 through 8, solve the problem

$$
\frac{\partial u}{\partial t} = k\frac{\partial^2 u}{\partial x^2} \quad \text{for } 0 < x < \infty, t > 0,
$$

$$
u(0, t) = 0 \quad \text{for } t \geq 0,
$$

$$
u(x, 0) = f(x) \quad \text{for } 0 < x < \infty.
$$

5. $f(x) = e^{-\alpha x}$, with α any positive constant.

6. $f(x) = xe^{-\alpha x}$, with $\alpha > 0$.

7. $f(x) = \begin{cases} 1 & \text{for } 0 \leq x \leq h \\ 0 & \text{for } x > h \end{cases}$
with h any positive number.

8. $f(x) = \begin{cases} x & \text{for } 0 \leq x \leq 2 \\ 0 & \text{for } x > 2 \end{cases}$

In each of Problems 9 and 10, use a Fourier transform on the half-line to obtain a solution.

9.
$$
\frac{\partial u}{\partial t} = \frac{\partial^2 u}{\partial x^2} - tu \quad \text{for } x > 0, t > 0
$$
$$
u(x, 0) = xe^{-x} \quad \text{for } x > 0
$$
$$
u(0, t) = 0 \quad \text{for } t > 0
$$

10.
$$
\frac{\partial u}{\partial t} = \frac{\partial^2 u}{\partial x^2} - u \quad \text{for } x > 0, t > 0
$$
$$
u(x, 0) = 0 \quad \text{for } x > 0
$$
$$
\frac{\partial u}{\partial x}(0, t) = f(t) \quad \text{for } t > 0
$$

In each of Problems 11 and 12, use the Laplace transform to obtain a solution.

11.
$$
\frac{\partial u}{\partial t} = k\frac{\partial^2 u}{\partial x^2} \quad \text{for } x > 0, t > 0,
$$
$$
u(0, t) = t^2 \quad \text{for } t > 0,
$$
$$
u(x, 0) = 0 \quad \text{for } x > 0
$$

12.
$$
\frac{\partial u}{\partial t} = k\frac{\partial^2 u}{\partial x^2} \quad \text{for } x > 0, t > 0,
$$
$$
u(0, t) = 0 \quad \text{for } t > 0,
$$
$$
u(x, 0) = e^{-x} \quad \text{for } x > 0
$$

18.4   Heat Conduction in an Infinite Cylinder

We will consider the problem of determining the temperature distribution function in a solid, infinitely long, homogeneous cylinder of radius R. Let the axis of the cylinder be along the z

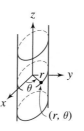

FIGURE 18.15

axis in x, y, z space (Figure 18.15). If $u(x, y, z, t)$ is the temperature function, then u satisfies the 3-dimensional heat equation

$$\frac{\partial u}{\partial t} = k\left(\frac{\partial^2 u}{\partial x^2} + \frac{\partial^2 u}{\partial y^2} + \frac{\partial^2 u}{\partial z^2}\right).$$

It is convenient to use cylindrical coordinates, which consist of polar coordinates in the plane together with the usual z coordinate, as in the diagram. With $x = r\cos(\theta)$ and $y = r\sin(\theta)$, let

$$u(x, y, z, t) = U(r, \theta, z, t).$$

We saw in Section 17.1 that

$$\frac{\partial^2 u}{\partial x^2} + \frac{\partial^2 u}{\partial y^2} = \frac{\partial^2 U}{\partial r^2} + \frac{1}{r}\frac{\partial U}{\partial r} + \frac{1}{r^2}\frac{\partial^2 U}{\partial \theta^2}.$$

Thus, in cylindrical coordinates, with $U(r, \theta, z, t)$ the temperature in the cylinder at point (r, θ, z), and time t, U satisfies:

$$\frac{\partial U}{\partial t} = k\left(\frac{\partial^2 U}{\partial r^2} + \frac{1}{r}\frac{\partial U}{\partial r} + \frac{1}{r^2}\frac{\partial^2 U}{\partial \theta^2} + \frac{\partial^2 U}{\partial z^2}\right).$$

This is a formidable equation to engage at this point, so we will assume that the temperature at any point in the cylinder depends only on the time t and the horizontal distance r from the z axis. This symmetry assumption means that $\partial U/\partial \theta = \partial U/\partial z = 0$, and the heat equation becomes

$$\frac{\partial U}{\partial t} = k\left(\frac{\partial^2 U}{\partial r^2} + \frac{1}{r}\frac{\partial U}{\partial r}\right) \quad \text{for } 0 \leq r < R, t > 0.$$

In this case we will write $U(r, t)$ instead of $U(r, \theta, z, t)$.

The boundary condition is

$$U(R, t) = 0 \quad \text{for } t > 0.$$

This means that the outer surface of the cylinder is kept at zero temperature.

The initial condition is

$$U(r, 0) = f(r) \quad \text{for } 0 \leq r < R.$$

Separate the variables in the heat equation by putting $U(r, t) = F(r)T(t)$. We obtain

$$F(r)T'(t) = k\left(F''(r)T(t) + \frac{1}{r}F'(r)T(t)\right).$$

Because r and t are independent variables, this yields

$$\frac{T'}{kT} = \frac{F'' + (1/r)F'}{F} = -\lambda,$$

in which λ is the separation constant. Then

$$T' + \lambda k T = 0 \text{ and } F'' + \frac{1}{r}F' + \lambda F = 0.$$

Further, $U(R, t) = F(R)T(t) = 0$ for $t > 0$, so we have the boundary condition

$$F(R) = 0.$$

The problem for F is a singular Sturm-Liouville problem (see Section 16.3.1) on $[0, R]$, with only one boundary condition. We impose the condition that the solution must be bounded. Consider cases on λ.

Case 1 $\lambda = 0$.
Now

$$F'' + \frac{1}{r}F' = 0.$$

To solve this, put $w = F'(r)$ to get

$$w'(r) + \frac{1}{r}w(r) = 0,$$

or

$$rw' + w = (rw)' = 0.$$

This has general solution

$$rw(r) = c,$$

so

$$w(r) = \frac{c}{r} = F'(r).$$

Then

$$F(r) = c\ln(r) + d.$$

Now $\ln(r) \to -\infty$ as $r \to 0+$ (center of the cylinder), so choose $c = 0$ to have a bounded solution. This means that $F(r) = $ constant for $\lambda = 0$. The equation for T in this case is $T' = 0$, with $T = $ constant also. In this event $U(r, t) = $ constant. Since $U(R, t) = 0$, this constant must be zero. In fact, $U(r, t) = 0$ is the solution in the case that $f(r) = 0$. If the temperature on the surface is maintained at zero, and the temperature throughout the cylinder is initially zero, then the temperature distribution remains zero at all later times, in the absence of heat sources.

Case 2 $\lambda < 0$.
Write $\lambda = -\omega^2$ with $\omega > 0$. Now $T' - k\omega^2 T = 0$ has general solution

$$T(t) = ce^{\omega^2 kt},$$

which is unbounded unless $c = 0$, leading again to $u(r, t) = 0$. This case leads only to the trivial solution.

Case 3 $\lambda > 0$, say $\lambda = \omega^2$.
Now $T' + k\omega^2 T = 0$ has solutions that are constant multiples of $e^{-\omega^2 kt}$, and these are bounded for $t > 0$. The equation for F is

$$F''(r) + \frac{1}{r}F'(r) + \omega^2 F(r) = 0,$$

or

$$r^2 F''(r) + r F'(r) + \omega^2 r^2 F(r) = 0.$$

In this form we recognize Bessel's equation of order zero, with general solution

$$F(r) = c J_0(\omega r) + d Y_0(\omega r).$$

J_0 is Bessel's function of the first kind order zero, and Y_0 is Bessel's function of the second kind of order zero (see Section 16.2.3). Since $Y_0(\omega r) \to -\infty$ as $r \to 0+$, we must have $d = 0$. However, $J_0(\omega r)$ is bounded on $[0, R]$, so $F(r)$ is a constant multiple of $J_0(\omega r)$.

The condition $F(R) = 0$ now requires that this constant be zero (in which case we get the trivial solution), or that ω be chosen so that

$$J_0(\omega R) = 0.$$

This can be done. Recall that $J_0(x)$ has infinitely many positive zeros, which we arrange as

$$0 < j_1 < j_2 < \cdots.$$

We can therefore have $J_0(\omega R) = 0$ if ωR is any one of these numbers. Thus choose

$$\omega_n = \frac{j_n}{R}.$$

The numbers

$$\lambda_n = \omega_n^2 = \frac{j_n^2}{R^2}$$

are the eigenvalues of this problem, and the eigenfunctions are nonzero constant multiples of $J_0(j_n r / R)$.

We now have, for each positive integer n, a function

$$U_n(r, t) = a_n J_0\left(\frac{j_n r}{R}\right) e^{-j_n^2 k t / R^2}.$$

To satisfy the initial condition $U(r, 0) = f(r)$ we must generally use a superposition

$$U(r, t) = \sum_{n=1}^{\infty} a_n J_0\left(\frac{j_n r}{R}\right) e^{-j_n^2 k t / R^2}.$$

We now must choose the coefficients so that

$$U(r, 0) = \sum_{n=1}^{\infty} a_n J_0\left(\frac{j_n r}{R}\right) = f(r).$$

This is an eigenfunction expansion of $f(r)$ in terms of the eigenfunctions of the singular Sturm-Liouville problem for $F(r)$. We know from Section 16.3.3 how to find the coefficients. Let $\xi = r/R$. Then

$$f(R\xi) = \sum_{n=1}^{\infty} a_n J_0(j_n \xi),$$

and

$$a_n = \frac{2}{[J_1(j_n)]^2} \int_0^1 \xi f(R\xi) J_0(j_n \xi) \, d\xi.$$

The solution of the problem is

$$U(r, t) = \sum_{n=1}^{\infty} \left(\frac{2}{[J_1(j_n)]^2} \int_0^1 \xi f(R\xi) J_0(j_n \xi) \, d\xi \right) J_0\left(\frac{j_n r}{R}\right) e^{-j_n^2 k t / R^2}.$$

1. Suppose the cylinder has radius $R = 1$, and, in polar coordinates, initial temperature $U(r, 0) = f(r) = r$ for $0 \le r < 1$. Assume that $U(1, t) = 0$ for $t > 0$. Approximate the integral in the solution and write the first five terms in the series solution for $U(r, t)$, with $k = 1$. (The first five zeros of $J_0(x)$ are given in Section 16.2). Graph this sum of five terms for different values of t.

2. Suppose the cylinder has radius $R = 3$, and, in polar coordinates, initial temperature $U(r, 0) = f(r) = e^r$ for $0 \le r < 3$. Assume that $U(3, t) = 0$ for $t > 0$. Approximate the integral in the solution and write the first five terms in the series solution for $U(r, t)$, with $k = 16$. Graph this sum of five terms for different values of t.

3. Suppose the cylinder has radius $R = 3$, and, in polar coordinates, initial temperature $U(r, 0) = f(r) = 9 - r^2$ for $0 \le r < 3$. Assume that $U(3, t) = 0$ for $t > 0$.

Approximate the integral in the solution and write the first five terms in the series solution for $U(r, t)$, with $a = \dfrac{1}{2}$. Graph this sum of five terms for different values of t.

4. Determine the temperature distribution in a homogeneous circular cylinder of radius R with insulated top and bottom caps under the assumption that the temperature is independent of both the radial angle and height. Assume that heat is radiating from the lateral surface into the surrounding medium, which has temperature zero, with transfer coefficient A. The initial temperature is $U(r, 0) = f(r)$. *Hint*: It will be necessary to know that an equation of the form $kJ_0'(x) + AJ_0(x) = 0$ has infinitely many positive solutions. This can be proved, but assume it here. Solutions of this equation yield the eigenvalues for this problem.

18.5   Heat Conduction in a Rectangular Plate

Consider the temperature distribution $u(x, y, t)$ in a flat, square homogeneous plate covering the region $0 \le x \le 1$, $0 \le y \le 1$ in the plane. The sides are kept at temperature zero and the interior temperature at time zero at (x, y) is given by

$$f(x, y) = x(1 - x^2)y(1 - y).$$

The problem for u is

$$\frac{\partial u}{\partial t} = k\left(\frac{\partial^2 u}{\partial x^2} + \frac{\partial^2 u}{\partial y^2}\right) \quad \text{for } 0 \le x \le 1, 0 \le y \le 1, t > 0,$$

$$u(x, 0, t) = u(x, 1, t) = 0 \quad \text{for } 0 < x < 1, t > 0$$

$$u(0, y, t) = u(1, y, t) = 0 \quad \text{for } 0 < y < 1, t > 0,$$

$$u(x, y, 0) = x(1 - x^2)y(1 - y).$$

Let $u(x, y, t) = X(x)Y(y)T(t)$ and obtain

$$X'' + \lambda X = 0, \quad Y'' + \mu Y = 0, \quad T' + (\lambda + \mu)kT = 0,$$

where λ and μ are the separation constants. The boundary conditions imply in the usual way that

$$X(0) = X(1) = 0, \quad Y(0) = Y(1) = 0.$$

The eigenvalues and eigenfunctions are

$$\lambda_n = n^2\pi^2, \quad X_n(x) = \sin(n\pi x),$$

for $n = 1, 2, \ldots$ and

$$\mu_m = m^2\pi^2, \quad Y_m(y) = \sin(m\pi y)$$

for $m = 1, 2, \ldots$. The problem for T is now

$$T' + (n^2 + m^2)\pi^2 kT = 0,$$

with general solution

$$T_{nm}(t) = c_{nm}e^{-(n^2+m^2)\pi^2 kt}.$$

For each positive integer n and each positive integer m, we now have functions

$$u_{nm}(x, y, t) = c_{nm}\sin(n\pi x)\sin(m\pi y)e^{-(n^2+m^2)\pi^2 kt}$$

which satisfy the heat equation and the boundary conditions. To satisfy the initial condition, let

$$u(x, y, t) = \sum_{n=1}^{\infty}\sum_{m=1}^{\infty} c_{nm}\sin(n\pi x)\sin(m\pi y)e^{-(n^2+m^2)\pi^2 kt}.$$

We must choose the coefficients so that

$$u(x, y, 0) = x(1-x^2)y(1-y) = \sum_{n=1}^{\infty}\sum_{m=1}^{\infty} c_{nm}\sin(n\pi x)\sin(m\pi y).$$

We find (as in Section 17.7) that

$$c_{nm} = 4\int_0^1\int_0^1 x(1-x^2)y(1-y)\sin(n\pi x)\sin(m\pi y)dxdy$$

$$= 4\left(\int_0^1 x(1-x^2)\sin(n\pi x)dx\right)\left(\int_0^1 y(1-y)\sin(m\pi y)dy\right)$$

$$= 48\left(\frac{(-1)^n}{n^3\pi^3}\right)\left(\frac{(-1)^n-1}{m^3\pi^3}\right).$$

The solution is

$$u(x, y, z) =$$

$$\frac{48}{\pi^6}\sum_{n=1}^{\infty}\sum_{m=1}^{\infty}\left(\frac{(-1)^n}{n^3}\right)\left(\frac{(-1)^n-1}{m^3}\right)\sin(n\pi x)\sin(m\pi y)e^{-(n^2+m^2)\pi^2 kt}.$$

SECTION 18.5 PROBLEMS

1. Taking a cue from the problem just solved, write a double series solution for the following more general problem:

$$\frac{\partial u}{\partial t} = k\left(\frac{\partial^2 u}{\partial x^2} + \frac{\partial^2 u}{\partial y^2}\right) \quad \text{for } 0 \le x \le L,$$

$$0 \le y \le K, t > 0,$$

$$u(x, 0, t) = u(x, K, t) = 0 \quad \text{for } 0 < x < L, t > 0$$

$$u(0, y, t) = u(L, y, t) = 0 \quad \text{for } 0 < y < K, t > 0,$$

$$u(x, y, 0) = f(x, y).$$

2. Write the solution for Problem 1 in the case that $k = 4$, $L = 2$, $K = 3$ and $f(x, y) = x^2(L - x)\sin(y)(K - y)$.

3. Write the solution for Problem 1 in the case that $k = 1$, $L = \pi$, $K = \pi$, and $f(x, y) = \sin(x)y\cos(y/2)$.

CHAPTER 19

The Potential Equation

19.1   Harmonic Functions and the Dirichlet Problem

The partial differential equation

$$\frac{\partial^2 u}{\partial x^2} + \frac{\partial^2 u}{\partial y^2} = 0$$

is called *Laplace's equation* in two dimensions. In 3-dimensions this equation is

$$\frac{\partial^2 u}{\partial x^2} + \frac{\partial^2 u}{\partial y^2} + \frac{\partial^2 u}{\partial z^2} = 0.$$

The Laplacian ∇^2 (read "del squared") is defined in 2-dimensions by

$$\nabla^2 u = \frac{\partial^2 u}{\partial x^2} + \frac{\partial^2 u}{\partial y^2}$$

and in three dimensions by

$$\nabla^2 u = \frac{\partial^2 u}{\partial x^2} + \frac{\partial^2 u}{\partial y^2} + \frac{\partial^2 u}{\partial z^2}.$$

In this notation, Laplace's equation is $\nabla^2 u = 0$.

    A function satisfying Laplace's equation in a certain region is said to be *harmonic* on that region. For example,

$$x^2 - y^2$$

and

$$2xy$$

are both harmonic over the entire plane.

Laplace's equation is encountered in problems involving potentials, such as potentials for force fields in mechanics, or electromagnetic or gravitational fields. Laplace's equation is also known as the *steady-state heat equation*. The heat equation in 2- or 3-space dimensions is

$$\frac{\partial u}{\partial t} = k\nabla^2 u.$$

In the steady-state case (the limit as $t \to \infty$) the solution becomes independent of t, so $\partial u/\partial t = 0$ and the heat equation becomes Laplace's equation.

In problems involving Laplace's equation there are no initial conditions. However, we often encounter the problem of solving

$$\nabla^2 u(x, y) = 0$$

for (x, y) in some region D of the plane, subject to the condition that

$$u(x, y) = f(x, y),$$

for (x, y) on the boundary of D. This boundary is denoted ∂D. Here f is a function having given values on ∂D, which is often a curve, or made up of several curves (Figure 19.1). The problem of determining a harmonic function having given boundary values is called a *Dirichlet problem*, and f is called the *boundary data* of the problem. There are versions of this problem in higher dimensions, but we will be concerned primarily with dimension 2.

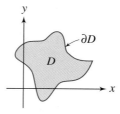

FIGURE 19.1
*Typical boundary ∂D
of a region D.*

The difficulty of a Dirichlet problem is usually dependent on how complicated the region D is. In general, we have a better chance of solving a Dirichlet problem for a region that possesses some type of symmetry, such as a disk or rectangle. We will begin by solving the Dirichlet problem for some familiar regions in the plane.

SECTION 19.1   PROBLEMS

1. Let f and g be harmonic on a set D of points in the plane. Show that $f + g$ is harmonic, as well as αf for any real number α.

2. Show that the following functions are harmonic on the entire plane:

   (a) $x^3 - 3xy^2$

   (b) $3x^2y - y^3$

   (c) $x^4 - 6x^2y^2 + y^4$

   (d) $4x^3y - 4xy^3$

   (e) $\sin(x)\cosh(y)$

   (f) $\cos(x)\sinh(y)$

   (g) $e^{-x}\cos(y)$

3. Show that $\ln(x^2 + y^2)$ is harmonic on the plane with the origin removed.

4. Show that $r^n \cos(n\theta)$ and $r^n \sin(n\theta)$, in polar coordinates, are harmonic on the plane, for any positive integer n. *Hint*: Look up Laplace's equation in polar coordinates.

5. Show that, for any positive integer n, $r^{-n} \cos(n\theta)$ and $r^{-n} \sin(n\theta)$ are harmonic on the plane with the origin removed.

19.2 Dirichlet Problem for a Rectangle

Let R be a solid rectangle, consisting of points (x, y) with $0 \le x \le L$, $0 \le y \le K$. We want to find a function that is harmonic at points interior to R, and takes on prescribed values on the four sides of R, which form the boundary ∂R of R.

This kind of problem can be solved by separation of variables if the boundary data is nonzero on only one side of the rectangle. We will illustrate this kind of problem, and then outline a strategy to follow if the boundary data is nonzero on more than one side.

EXAMPLE 19.1

Consider the Dirichlet problem

$$\nabla^2 u(x, y) = 0 \quad \text{for } 0 < x < L, 0 < y < K,$$

$$u(x, 0) = 0 \quad \text{for } 0 \le x \le L,$$

$$u(0, y) = u(L, y) = 0 \quad \text{for } 0 \le y \le K,$$

$$u(x, K) = (L - x) \sin(x) \quad \text{for } 0 \le x \le L.$$

Figure 19.2 shows the region and the boundary data.

Let $u(x, y) = X(x)Y(y)$ and substitute into Laplace's equation to obtain

$$\frac{X''}{X} = -\frac{Y''}{Y} = -\lambda.$$

Then

$$X'' + \lambda X = 0 \quad \text{and} \quad Y'' - \lambda Y = 0.$$

From the boundary conditions,

$$u(x, 0) = X(x)Y(0) = 0$$

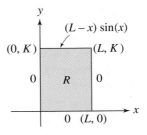

FIGURE 19.2 *Boundary data given on boundary sides of the rectangle.*

so $Y(0) = 0$. Similarly,

$$X(0) = X(L) = 0.$$

The problem for $X(x)$ is a familiar one, with eigenvalues $\lambda_n = n^2\pi^2/L^2$ and eigenfunctions that are nonzero constant multiples of $\sin(n\pi x/L)$.

The problem for Y is now

$$Y'' - \frac{n^2\pi^2}{L^2}Y = 0; \quad Y(0) = 0.$$

Solutions of this problem are constant multiples of $\sinh(n\pi y/L)$.

For each positive integer $n = 1, 2, \ldots$, we now have functions

$$u_n(x, y) = b_n \sin\left(\frac{n\pi x}{L}\right)\sinh\left(\frac{n\pi y}{L}\right)$$

which are harmonic on the rectangle, and satisfy the zero boundary conditions on the top, bottom and left sides of the rectangle. To satisfy the boundary condition on the side $y = K$, we must use a superposition

$$u(x, y) = \sum_{n=1}^{\infty} b_n \sin\left(\frac{n\pi x}{L}\right)\sinh\left(\frac{n\pi y}{L}\right).$$

Choose the coefficients so that

$$u(x, K) = \sum_{n=1}^{\infty} b_n \sin\left(\frac{n\pi x}{L}\right)\sinh\left(\frac{n\pi K}{L}\right) = (L - x)\sin(x).$$

This is a Fourier sine expansion of $(L - x)\sin(x)$ on $[0, L]$, so we must choose the entire coefficient to be the sine coefficient:

$$b_n \sinh\left(\frac{n\pi K}{L}\right) = \frac{2}{L}\int_0^L (L - \xi)\sin(\xi)\sin\left(\frac{n\pi\xi}{L}\right)d\xi$$

$$= 4L^2\frac{n\pi[1 - (-1)^n\cos(L)]}{L^4 - 2L^2n^2\pi^2 + n^4\pi^4}.$$

Then

$$b_n = \frac{4L^2}{\sinh(n\pi k/L)}\frac{n\pi[1 - (-1)^n\cos(L)]}{(L^2 - n^2\pi^2)^2}.$$

The solution is

$$u(x, y) = \sum_{n=1}^{\infty}\frac{4L^2}{\sinh(n\pi k/L)}\frac{n\pi[1 - (-1)^n\cos(L)]}{(L^2 - n^2\pi^2)^2}\sin\left(\frac{n\pi x}{L}\right)\sinh\left(\frac{n\pi y}{L}\right). \blacksquare$$

If nonzero boundary data is prescribed on all four sides of R, define four Dirichlet problems, in each of which the boundary data is nonzero on only one side. This process is outlined in Figure 19.3. Each of these problems can be solved by separation of variables. If $u_j(x, y)$ is the solution of the jth problem, then

$$u(x, y) = \sum_{j=1}^{4} u_j(x, y)$$

is the solution of the original problem. This sum will satisfy the original boundary data because each $u_j(x, y)$ satisfies the nonzero data on one side and is zero on the other three.

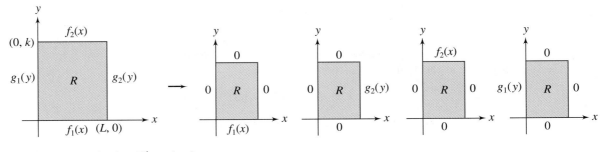

FIGURE 19.3 $u(x, y) = \sum_{j=1}^{4} u_j(x, y)$.

SECTION 19.2   PROBLEMS

In each of Problems 1 through 5, solve the Dirichlet problem for the rectangle, with the given boundary conditions.

1. $u(0, y) = u(1, y) = 0$ for $0 \le y \le \pi$, $u(x, \pi) = 0$ and $u(x, 0) = \sin(\pi x)$ for $0 \le x \le 1$

2. $u(0, y) = y(2 - y)$, $u(3, y) = 0$ for $0 \le y \le 2$, $u(x, 0) = u(x, 2) = 0$ for $0 \le x \le 3$

3. $u(0, y) = u(1, y) = 0$ for $0 \le y \le 4$, $u(x, 0) = 0$, $u(x, 4) = x \cos(\pi x/2)$ for $0 \le x \le 1$

4. $u(0, y) = \sin(y)$, $u(\pi, y) = 0$ for $0 \le y \le \pi$, $u(x, 0) = x(\pi - x)$, $u(x, \pi) = 0$ for $0 \le x \le \pi$

5. $u(0, y) = 0$, $u(2, y) = \sin(y)$ for $0 \le y \le \pi$, $u(x, 0) = 0$, $u(x, \pi) = x \sin(\pi x)$ for $0 \le x \le 2$

6. Apply separation of variables to solve the following mixed boundary value problem (mixed means that some boundary conditions are given on the function, and others on its partial derivatives).

$$\nabla^2 u(x, y) = 0 \quad \text{for } 0 < x < a, 0 < y < b$$

$$u(x, 0) = \frac{\partial u}{\partial y}(x, b) = 0 \quad \text{for } 0 \le x \le a$$

$$u(0, y) = 0, u(a, y) = g(y) \quad \text{for } 0 \le y \le b.$$

7. Apply separation of variables to solve the following mixed boundary value problem:

$$\nabla^2 u(x, y) = 0 \quad \text{for } 0 < x < a, 0 < y < b$$

$$u(x, 0) = 0, u(x, b) = f(x) \quad \text{for } 0 \le x \le a$$

$$u(0, y) = \frac{\partial u}{\partial x}(a, y) = 0 \quad \text{for } 0 \le y \le b.$$

8. Solve for the steady-state temperature distribution in a thin flat plate covering the rectangle $0 \le x \le a$, $0 \le y \le b$ if the temperature on the vertical sides and bottom side are kept at zero, and the temperature along the top side is $f(x) = x(x - a)^2$.

9. Solve for the steady-state temperature distribution in a thin flat plate covering the rectangle $0 \le x \le 4$, $0 \le y \le 1$ if the temperature on the horizontal sides is zero, while on the left side it is $f(y) = \sin(\pi y)$ and on the right side it is $f(y) = y(1 - y)$.

19.3   Dirichlet Problem for a Disk

We will solve the Dirichlet problem for a disk of radius R centered about the origin. In polar coordinates, the problem is

$$\nabla^2 u(r, \theta) = 0 \quad \text{for } 0 \le r < R, -\pi \le \theta \le \pi,$$

$$u(R, \theta) = f(\theta) \quad \text{for } -\pi \le \theta \le \pi.$$

Laplace's equation in polar coordinates is

$$\frac{\partial^2 u}{\partial r^2} + \frac{1}{r}\frac{\partial u}{\partial r} + \frac{1}{r^2}\frac{\partial^2 u}{\partial \theta^2} = 0.$$

It is easy to check that the functions

$$1, r^n \cos(n\theta), \quad \text{and} \quad r^n \sin(n\theta)$$

are all harmonic on the entire plane. Thus attempt a solution

$$u(r, \theta) = \frac{1}{2}a_0 + \sum_{n=1}^{\infty} a_n r^n \cos(n\theta) + b_n r^n \sin(n\theta).$$

To satisfy the boundary condition, we need to choose the coefficients so that

$$u(R, \theta) = f(\theta) = \frac{1}{2}a_0 + \sum_{n=1}^{\infty} a_n R^n \cos(n\theta) + b_n R^n \sin(n\theta).$$

But this is just the Fourier expansion of $f(\theta)$ on $[-\pi, \pi]$, leading us to choose

$$a_0 = \frac{1}{\pi}\int_{-\pi}^{\pi} f(\xi)d\xi,$$

$$a_n R^n = \frac{1}{\pi}\int_{-\pi}^{\pi} f(\xi)\cos(n\xi)d\xi,$$

and

$$b_n R^n = \frac{1}{\pi}\int_{-\pi}^{\pi} f(\xi)\sin(n\xi)d\xi.$$

Then

$$a_n = \frac{1}{\pi R^n}\int_{-\pi}^{\pi} f(\xi)\cos(n\xi)d\xi$$

and

$$b_n = \frac{1}{\pi R^n}\int_{-\pi}^{\pi} f(\xi)\cos(n\xi)d\xi.$$

The solution is

$$u(r, \theta) = \frac{1}{2\pi}\int_{-\pi}^{\pi} f(\xi)d\xi$$
$$+ \frac{1}{\pi}\sum_{n=1}^{\infty}\left(\frac{r}{R}\right)^n\left(\int_{-\pi}^{\pi} f(\xi)\cos(n\xi)d\xi\cos(n\theta) + \int_{-\pi}^{\pi} f(\xi)\sin(n\xi)d\xi\sin(n\theta)\right).$$

This can also be written

$$u(r, \theta) = \frac{1}{2\pi}\int_{-\pi}^{\pi} f(\xi)d\xi + \frac{1}{\pi}\sum_{n=1}^{\infty}\left(\frac{r}{R}\right)^n\int_{-\pi}^{\pi} f(\xi)\cos(n(\xi - \theta))d\xi,$$

or

$$u(r, \theta) = \frac{1}{2\pi}\int_{-\pi}^{\pi}\left[1 + 2\sum_{n=1}^{\infty}\left(\frac{r}{R}\right)^n\cos(n(\xi - \theta))\right]f(\xi)d\xi.$$

EXAMPLE 19.2

Solve the Dirichlet problem

$$\nabla^2 u(r, \theta) = 0 \quad \text{for } 0 \le r < 4, -\pi \le \theta \le \pi,$$

$$u(4, \theta) = f(\theta) = \theta^2 \quad \text{for } -\pi \le \theta \le \pi.$$

The solution is

$$u(r, \theta) = \frac{1}{2\pi} \int_{-\pi}^{\pi} \xi^2 d\xi + \frac{1}{\pi} \sum_{n=1}^{\infty} \left(\frac{r}{4}\right)^n \int_{-\pi}^{\pi} \xi^2 \cos(n(\xi - \theta)) d\xi$$

$$= \frac{1}{3}\pi^2 + \sum_{n=1}^{\infty} \frac{4(-1)^n}{n^2} \left(\frac{r}{4}\right)^n \cos(n\theta). \quad \blacksquare$$

EXAMPLE 19.3

Solve the Dirichlet problem

$$\nabla^2 u(x, y) = 0 \quad \text{for } x^2 + y^2 < 9,$$

$$u(x, y) = x^2 y^2 \quad \text{for } x^2 + y^2 = 9.$$

Convert the problem to polar coordinates, using $x = r\cos(\theta)$ and $y = r\sin(\theta)$. Let

$$u(x, y) = u(r\cos(\theta), r\sin(\theta)) = U(r, \theta).$$

The condition on the boundary, where $r = 3$, becomes

$$U(3, \theta) = 9\cos^2(\theta)9\sin^2(\theta) = 81\cos^2(\theta)\sin^2(\theta) = f(\theta).$$

The solution is

$$U(r, \theta) = \frac{1}{2\pi} \int_{-\pi}^{\pi} 81\sin^2(\xi)\cos^2(\xi)d\xi$$

$$+ \frac{1}{\pi} \sum_{n=1}^{\infty} \left(\frac{r}{3}\right)^n \left[\int_{-\pi}^{\pi} 81\cos^2(\xi)\sin^2(\xi)\cos(n\xi)d\xi \cos(n\theta)\right.$$

$$\left. + \int_{-\pi}^{\pi} 81\cos^2(\xi)\sin^2(\xi)\sin(n\xi)d\xi \sin(n\theta)\right].$$

Now

$$\int_{-\pi}^{\pi} 81\sin^2(\xi)\cos^2(\xi)d\xi = \frac{81}{4}\pi,$$

$$\int_{-\pi}^{\pi} 81\cos^2(\xi)\sin^2(\xi)\cos(n\xi)d\xi = \begin{cases} 0 & \text{if } n \ne 4 \\ -81\pi/8 & \text{for } n = 4 \end{cases},$$

and

$$\int_{-\pi}^{\pi} 81\cos^2(\xi)\sin^2(\xi)\sin(n\xi)d\xi = 0.$$

Therefore

$$U(r, \theta) = \frac{1}{2\pi}\frac{81\pi}{4} - \frac{1}{\pi}\frac{81\pi}{8}\left(\frac{r}{3}\right)^4 \cos(4\theta) = \frac{81}{8} - \frac{1}{8}r^4\cos(4\theta).$$

To convert this solution back to rectangular coordinates, use the fact that

$$\cos(4\theta) = 8\cos^4\theta - 8\cos^2\theta + 1.$$

Then

$$U(r, \theta) = \frac{81}{8} - \frac{1}{8}\left(8r^4\cos^4(\theta) - 8r^2r^2\cos^2(\theta) + r^4\right)$$

$$= \frac{81}{8} - \frac{1}{8}\left(8x^4 - 8(x^2 + y^2)x^2 + (x^2 + y^2)^2\right) = u(x, y). \blacksquare$$

SECTION 19.3   PROBLEMS

In each of Problems 1 through 8, find a series solution for the Dirichlet problem for a disk of the given radius, with the given boundary data (in polar coordinates).

1. $R = 3, f(\theta) = 1$

2. $R = 3, f(\theta) = 8\cos(4\theta)$

3. $R = 2, f(\theta) = \theta^2 - \theta$

4. $R = 5, f(\theta) = \theta\cos(\theta)$

5. $R = 4, f(\theta) = e^{-\theta}$

6. $R = 1, f(\theta) = \sin^2(\theta)$

7. $R = 8, f(\theta) = 1 - \theta^3$

8. $R = 4, f(\theta) = \theta e^{2\theta}$

By converting to polar coordinates, write a solution for each of the following Dirichlet problems.

9. $\nabla^2 u(x, y) = 0$ for $x^2 + y^2 < 16$
$u(x, y) = x^2$ for $x^2 + y^2 = 16$

10. $\nabla^2 u(x, y) = 0$ for $x^2 + y^2 < 9$
$u(x, y) = x - y$ for $x^2 + y^2 = 9$

11. $\nabla^2 u(x, y) = 0$ for $x^2 + y^2 < 4$
$u(x, y) = x^2 - y^2$ for $x^2 + y^2 = 4$

12. $\nabla^2 u(x, y) = 0$ for $x^2 + y^2 < 25$
$u(x, y) = xy$ for $x^2 + y^2 = 25$

19.4   Poisson's Integral Formula for the Disk

We have a series formula for the solution of the Dirichlet problem for a disk. In this section we will derive an integral formula for this solution. The problem for a disk of radius 1, in polar coordinates, is

$$\nabla^2 u(r, \theta) = 0 \quad \text{for } 0 \leq r < 1, -\pi \leq \theta \leq \pi,$$

$$u(1, \theta) = f(\theta) \quad \text{for } -\pi \leq \theta \leq \pi.$$

The series solution from the preceding section, with $R = 1$, is

$$u(r, \theta) = \frac{1}{2\pi}\int_{-\pi}^{\pi}\left[1 + 2\sum_{n=1}^{\infty}r^n\cos(n(\xi - \theta))\right]f(\xi)d\xi. \tag{19.1}$$

The quantity

$$\frac{1}{2\pi}\left[1 + 2\sum_{n=1}^{\infty}r^n\cos(n\zeta)\right]$$

is called the *Poisson kernel*, and is denoted $P(r, \zeta)$. In terms of the Poisson kernel, the solution is

$$u(r, \theta) = \int_{-\pi}^{\pi} P(r, \xi - \theta) f(\xi) d\xi.$$

We will now obtain a closed form for the Poisson kernel, yielding an integral formula for the solution. Let $z = re^{i\zeta}$. By Euler's formula,

$$z^n = r^n e^{in\zeta} = r^n \cos(n\zeta) + ir^n \sin(n\zeta),$$

so $r^n \cos(n\zeta)$, which appears in the Poisson kernel, is the real part of z^n, denoted $\text{Re}(z^n)$. Then

$$1 + 2\sum_{n=1}^{\infty} r^n \cos(n\zeta) = \text{Re}\left(1 + 2\sum_{n=1}^{\infty} z^n\right).$$

But $|z| = r < 1$ in the unit disk, so the geometric series $\sum_{n=1}^{\infty} z^n$ converges. Further,

$$\sum_{n=1}^{\infty} z^n = \frac{z}{1-z}.$$

Then

$$1 + 2\sum_{n=1}^{\infty} r^n \cos(n\zeta) = \text{Re}\left(1 + 2\sum_{n=1}^{\infty} z^n\right)$$

$$= \text{Re}\left(1 + 2\frac{z}{1-z}\right) = \text{Re}\left(\frac{1+z}{1-z}\right) = \text{Re}\left(\frac{1 + re^{i\zeta}}{1 - re^{i\zeta}}\right).$$

The rest is just computation to help us extract this real part:

$$\frac{1 + re^{i\zeta}}{1 - re^{i\zeta}} = \left(\frac{1 + re^{i\zeta}}{1 - re^{i\zeta}}\right)\left(\frac{1 - re^{-i\zeta}}{1 - re^{-i\zeta}}\right)$$

$$= \frac{1 - r^2 + r\left(e^{i\zeta} - e^{-i\zeta}\right)}{1 + r^2 - r\left(e^{i\zeta} + e^{-i\zeta}\right)} = \frac{1 - r^2 + 2ir\sin(\zeta)}{1 + r^2 - 2r\cos(\zeta)}.$$

Therefore

$$1 + 2\sum_{n=1}^{\infty} r^n \cos(n\zeta) = \text{Re}\left(1 + 2\sum_{n=1}^{\infty} z^n\right) = \frac{1 - r^2}{1 + r^2 - 2r\cos(\zeta)},$$

hence the solution given by equation (19.1) is

$$u(r, \theta) = \frac{1}{2\pi} \int_{-\pi}^{\pi} \frac{1 - r^2}{1 + r^2 - 2r\cos(\xi - \theta)} f(\xi) d\xi.$$

This is *Poisson's integral formula* for the solution of the Dirichlet problem for the unit disk. For a disk of radius R, a simple change of variables yields the solution

$$u(r, \theta) = \frac{1}{2\pi} \int_{-\pi}^{\pi} \frac{R^2 - r^2}{R^2 + r^2 - 2Rr\cos(\xi - \theta)} f(\xi) d\xi. \tag{19.2}$$

This integral, for the disk of radius R, is also known as *Poisson's formula*.

EXAMPLE 19.4

Revisit the problem

$$\nabla^2 u(r, \theta) = 0 \quad \text{for } 0 \le r < 4, \, -\pi \le \theta \le \pi,$$

$$u(4, \theta) = f(\theta) = \theta^2 \quad \text{for } -\pi \le \theta \le \pi,$$

which was solved by Fourier series in the preceding section. The Poisson integral formula for the solution is

$$u(r, \theta) = \frac{1}{2\pi} \int_{-\pi}^{\pi} \frac{16 - r^2}{16 + r^2 - 8r\cos(\xi - \theta)} \xi^2 \, d\xi$$

$$= \frac{16 - r^2}{2\pi} \int_{-\pi}^{\pi} \frac{\xi^2}{16 + r^2 - 8r\cos(\xi - \theta)} \, d\xi.$$

This integral cannot be evaluated in closed form, but is often more suitable for numerical approximations than the infinite series solution. ■

SECTION 19.4   PROBLEMS

In each of Problems 1 through 4, write an integral formula for the solution of the Dirichlet problem for a disk of radius R about the origin, with the given data function on the boundary. Use the integral solution to approximate the value of $u(r, \theta)$ at the given points.

1. $R = 1$, $f(\theta) = \theta$; $(1/2, \pi)$, $(3/4, \pi/3)$, $(0.2, \pi/4)$

2. $R = 4$, $f(\theta) = \sin(4\theta)$; $(1, \pi/6)$, $(3, 7\pi/2)$, $(1, \pi/4)$, $(2.5, \pi/12)$

3. $R = 15$, $f(\theta) = \theta^3 - \theta$; $(4, \pi)$, $(12, 3\pi/2)$, $(8, \pi/4)$, $(7, 0)$

4. $R = 6$, $f(\theta) = e^{-\theta}$; $(5.5, 3\pi/5)$, $(4, 2\pi/7)$, $(1, \pi)$, $(4, 9\pi/4)$

5. Dirichlet's integral formula can sometimes be used to evaluate quite general integrals. As an example, let n be a positive integer and let $u(r, \theta) = r^n \sin(n\theta)$ for $0 \le r < R$, $0 \le \theta \le 2\pi$. We know that u is harmonic on the entire plane. We may therefore think of u as the solution of the Dirichlet problem on the disk $r \le R$

satisfying $u(R, \theta) = f(\theta) = R^n \sin(n\theta)$. Use the Poisson integral formula of equation (19.2) (knowing in this case the solution) to write

$$r^n \sin(n\theta) = \frac{1}{2\pi} \int_0^{2\pi} \frac{R^2 - r^2}{r^2 - 2rR\cos(\theta - \xi) + R^2}$$

$$\times R^n \sin(n\xi) d\xi.$$

Now evaluate $u(R/2, \pi/2)$ to derive the integral formula

$$\int_0^{2\pi} \frac{\sin(n\xi)}{5 - 4\sin(\xi)} d\xi = \frac{\pi}{3(2^{n-1})} \sin(n\pi/2).$$

6. In Problem 5, evaluate $u(R/2, \pi)$. What integral is obtained?

7. Use the strategy outlined in Problem 5, but now use $u(r, \theta) = r^n \cos(n\theta)$. Obtain integrals by evaluating $u(R/2, \pi/2)$ and $u(R/2, \pi)$.

8. What integral formula is obtained by setting $u(r, \theta) = 1$ in Poisson's integral formula?

19.5   Dirichlet Problems in Unbounded Regions

We will consider the Dirichlet problem for some regions that are unbounded in the sense of containing points arbitrarily far from the origin. For such problems, the Fourier integral, Fourier transform, or Fourier sine or cosine transform may be a good means to a solution.

19.5.1   Dirichlet Problem for the Upper Half Plane

Consider the problem

$$\nabla^2 u(x, y) = 0 \quad \text{for } -\infty < x < \infty, y > 0,$$

$$u(x, 0) = f(x) \quad \text{for } -\infty < x < \infty.$$

We want a function that is harmonic on the upper half plane, and takes on given values along the x-axis. Let $u(x, y) = X(x)Y(y)$ and separate the variables in Laplace's equation to obtain

$$X'' + \lambda X = 0, \quad Y'' - \lambda Y = 0.$$

We want a bounded solution. Consider cases on λ.

Case 1 $\lambda = 0$.
Now $X(x) = ax + b$, and we obtain a bounded solution by choosing $a = 0$. Thus 0 is an eigenvalue of this problem, with constant eigenfunctions.

Case 2 $\lambda = -\omega^2 < 0$.
Now $X(x) = ae^{\omega x} + be^{-\omega x}$. But $e^{\omega x} \to \infty$ as $x \to \infty$, so we must choose $a = 0$. And $e^{-\omega x} \to \infty$ as $x \to -\infty$, so we must let $b = 0$ also, leaving the trivial solution. This problem has no negative eigenvalue.

Case 3 $\lambda = \omega^2 > 0$.
Now $X(x) = a\cos(\omega x) + b\sin(\omega x)$, a bounded function for any constants a and b.

The equation for Y now becomes $Y'' - \omega^2 Y = 0$, with general solution $Y(y) = ae^{\omega y} + be^{-\omega y}$. Since $y > 0$ and $\omega > 0$, $e^{\omega y} \to \infty$ as $y \to \infty$, so we need $a = 0$. However, $e^{-\omega y}$ is bounded for $y > 0$, so $Y(y) = be^{-\omega y}$.

For each $\omega \geq 0$, we now have a function

$$u_\omega(x, y) = [a_\omega \cos(\omega x) + b_\omega \sin(\omega x)]e^{-\omega y}$$

that satisfies Laplace's equation. Attempt a solution of the problem with the superposition

$$u(x, y) = \int_0^\infty [a_\omega \cos(\omega x) + b_\omega \sin(\omega x)]e^{-\omega y} d\omega.$$

To satisfy the boundary condition, choose the coefficients so that

$$u(x, 0) = f(x) = \int_0^\infty [a_\omega \cos(\omega x) + b_\omega \sin(\omega x)] d\omega.$$

This is the Fourier integral expansion of $f(x)$, so

$$a_\omega = \frac{1}{\pi} \int_{-\infty}^\infty f(\xi) \cos(\omega \xi) d\xi$$

and

$$b_\omega = \frac{1}{\pi} \int_{-\infty}^\infty f(\xi) \sin(\omega \xi) d\xi.$$

With these coefficients, we have the solution, which can be written in a compact form, involving only one integral, as follows. Write

$$u(x, y) = \frac{1}{\pi} \int_0^\infty \left[\left(\int_{-\infty}^\infty f(\xi) \cos(\omega\xi)d\xi \right) \cos(\omega x) \right.$$

$$\left. + \left(\int_{-\infty}^\infty f(\xi) \sin(\omega\xi)d\xi \right) \sin(\omega x) \right] e^{-\omega y} d\omega$$

$$= \frac{1}{\pi} \int_0^\infty \int_{-\infty}^\infty [\cos(\omega\xi) \cos(\omega x) + \sin(\omega\xi) \sin(\omega x)] f(\xi) e^{-\omega y} d\xi d\omega$$

$$= \frac{1}{\pi} \int_{-\infty}^\infty \left[\int_0^\infty \cos(\omega(\xi - x)) e^{-\omega y} d\omega \right] f(\xi) d\xi.$$

The inner integral can be evaluated explicitly:

$$\int_0^\infty \cos(\omega(\xi - x)) e^{-\omega y} d\omega = \left[\frac{e^{-\omega y}}{y^2 + (\xi - x)^2} [-y\cos(\omega(\xi - x)) + (\xi - x) \sin(\omega(\xi - x))] \right]_0^\infty$$

$$= \frac{y}{y^2 + (\xi - x)^2}.$$

Therefore the solution of the Dirichlet problem for the upper half plane is

$$u(x, y) = \frac{y}{\pi} \int_{-\infty}^\infty \frac{f(\xi)}{y^2 + (\xi - x)^2} d\xi. \tag{19.3}$$

To illustrate the technique, we will solve this problem again using the Fourier transform.

Solution Using the Fourier Transform   Apply the Fourier transform in the x variable, to Laplace's equation. Now $\partial/\partial y$ passes through the transform, and we can use the operational rule to take the transform of the derivative with respect to x. We get

$$\mathfrak{F}\left(\frac{\partial^2 u}{\partial y^2} \right) + \mathfrak{F}\left(\frac{\partial^2 u}{\partial x^2} \right) = \frac{\partial^2 \hat{u}}{\partial y^2}(\omega, y) - \omega^2 \hat{u}(\omega, y) = 0.$$

The general solution of this differential equation in the y variable is

$$\hat{u}(\omega, y) = a_\omega e^{\omega y} + b_\omega e^{-\omega y}.$$

Keep in mind that here ω varies over the real line (unlike in the solution by Fourier integral, whee ω designated a variable of integration over the half-line). Because $e^{\omega y} \to \infty$ as $y \to \infty$, we must have $a_\omega = 0$ for positive ω. But $e^{-\omega y} \to \infty$ as $y \to \infty$ if $\omega < 0$, so $b_\omega = 0$ for negative ω. Thus,

$$\hat{u}(\omega, y) = \begin{cases} b_\omega e^{-\omega y} & \text{if } \omega \geq 0 \\ a_\omega e^{\omega y} & \text{if } \omega < 0 \end{cases}.$$

We can consolidate this notation by writing

$$\hat{u}(\omega, y) = c_\omega e^{-|\omega|y}.$$

To solve for c_ω, use the fact that $u(x, 0) = f(x)$ to get

$$\hat{u}(\omega, 0) = \hat{f}(\omega) = c_\omega.$$

The Fourier transform of the solution is

$$\hat{u}(\omega, y) = \hat{f}(\omega) e^{-|\omega|y}.$$

To obtain $u(x, y)$, apply the inverse Fourier transform to this function:

$$u(x, y) = \mathfrak{F}^{-1}\left[\hat{f}(\omega)e^{-|\omega|y}\right](x)$$

$$= \frac{1}{2\pi}\int_{-\infty}^{\infty}\hat{f}(\omega)e^{-|\omega|y}e^{i\omega x}\,d\omega$$

$$= \frac{1}{2\pi}\int_{-\infty}^{\infty}\left(\int_{-\infty}^{\infty}f(\xi)e^{-i\omega\xi}\,d\xi\right)e^{-|\omega|y}e^{i\omega x}\,d\omega$$

$$= \frac{1}{2\pi}\int_{-\infty}^{\infty}\left(\int_{-\infty}^{\infty}e^{-|\omega|y}e^{-i\omega(\xi-x)}\,d\omega\right)f(\xi)\,d\xi.$$

Now

$$e^{-i\omega(\xi-x)} = \cos(\omega(\xi-x)) - i\sin(\omega(\xi-x))$$

and a routine integration gives

$$\int_{-\infty}^{\infty}e^{-|\omega|y}e^{-i\omega(\xi-x)}\,d\omega = \frac{2y}{y^2+(\xi-x)^2}.$$

The solution by Fourier transform is

$$u(x, y) = \frac{y}{\pi}\int_{-\infty}^{\infty}\frac{f(\xi)}{y^2+(\xi-x)^2}\,d\xi,$$

in agreement with the solution obtained by using separation of variables.

19.5.2 Dirichlet Problem for the Right Quarter Plane

Sometimes we can use the solution of one problem to produce a solution of another problem. We will illustrate this with the Dirichlet problem for the right quarter plane:

$$\nabla^2 u(x, y) = 0 \quad \text{for } x > 0, y > 0,$$

$$u(x, 0) = f(x) \quad \text{for } x \geq 0,$$

$$u(0, y) = 0 \quad \text{for } y \geq 0.$$

The boundary of the right quarter plane consists of the nonnegative x axis, together with the nonnegative y axis, and information about the function sought must be given on both segments. In this case we are prescribing zero values on the vertical part, and given values $f(x)$ on the horizontal part of the boundary.

We could solve this problem be separation of variables. However, if we fold the upper half plane across the vertical axis, we obtain the right quarter-plane, suggesting that we explore the possibility of using the solution for the upper half-plane to obtain the solution for the right quarter plane. To do this, let

$$g(x) = \begin{cases} f(x) & \text{for } x \geq 0 \\ \text{anything} & \text{for } x < 0 \end{cases}.$$

By "anything," we mean that for the moment we do not care what values are given $g(x)$ for $x < 0$, but reserve the right to assign these values later.

The Dirichlet problem

$$\nabla^2 u(x, y) = 0 \quad \text{for } -\infty < x < \infty, y > 0,$$

$$u(x, 0) = g(x) \quad \text{for } -\infty < x < \infty$$

for the upper half-plane has the solution

$$u_{hp}(x, y) = \frac{y}{\pi} \int_{-\infty}^{\infty} \frac{g(\xi)}{y^2 + (\xi - x)^2} d\xi.$$

Write this as

$$u_{hp}(x, y) = \frac{y}{\pi} \left[\int_{-\infty}^{0} \frac{g(\xi)}{y^2 + (\xi - x)^2} d\xi + \int_{0}^{\infty} \frac{g(\xi)}{y^2 + (\xi - x)^2} d\xi \right].$$

Change variables in the left-most integral by letting $w = -\xi$. This integral becomes

$$\int_{-\infty}^{0} \frac{g(\xi)}{y^2 + (\xi - x)^2} d\xi = \int_{\infty}^{0} \frac{g(-w)}{y^2 + (w + x)^2} (-1) dw.$$

Now replace the integration variable by ξ again to write

$$u_{hp}(x, y) = \frac{y}{\pi} \left[\int_{\infty}^{0} \frac{g(-\xi)}{y^2 + (\xi + x)^2} (-1) d\xi + \int_{0}^{\infty} \frac{g(\xi)}{y^2 + (\xi - x)^2} d\xi \right]$$

$$= \frac{y}{\pi} \int_{0}^{\infty} \left(\frac{g(-\xi)}{y^2 + (\xi + x)^2} + \frac{f(\xi)}{y^2 + (\xi - x)^2} \right) d\xi,$$

where in the last integral we have used the fact that $g(\xi) = f(\xi)$ if $\xi \geq 0$. Now fill in the "anything" in the definition of g. Observe that the last integral will vanish on the positive y axis, at points $(0, y)$, if $f(\xi) + g(-\xi) = 0$ for $\xi \geq 0$. This will occur if $g(-\xi) = -f(\xi)$. That is, make g the odd extension of f to the entire real line, obtaining

$$u_{hp}(x, y) = \frac{y}{\pi} \int_{0}^{\infty} \left(\frac{1}{y^2 + (\xi - x)^2} - \frac{1}{y^2 + (\xi + x)^2} \right) f(\xi) d\xi.$$

This is the solution of this particular Dirichlet problem for the upper half-plane. But this function is also harmonic on the right quarter-plane, vanishes when $x = 0$, and equals $f(x)$ if $x \geq 0$ and $y = 0$. Therefore $u_{hp}(x, y)$ is also the solution of this Dirichlet problem for the right quarter-plane.

EXAMPLE 19.5

Consider the problem

$$\nabla^2 u = 0 \quad \text{for } x > 0, y > 0,$$

$$u(0, y) = 0 \quad \text{for } y > 0,$$

$$u(x, 0) = xe^{-x} \quad \text{for } x > 0.$$

The solution is

$$u(x, y) = \frac{y}{\pi} \int_{0}^{\infty} \left(\frac{1}{y^2 + (\xi - x)^2} - \frac{1}{y^2 + (\xi + x)^2} \right) \xi e^{-\xi} d\xi. \quad \blacksquare$$

EXAMPLE 19.6

We will solve the problem

$$\nabla^2 u = 0 \quad \text{for } x > 0, y > 0,$$

$$u(0, y) = 0 \quad \text{for } y > 0,$$

$$u(x, 0) = 1 \quad \text{for } x > 0.$$

The solution is

$$u(x, y) = \frac{y}{\pi} \int_0^\infty \frac{1}{y^2 + (\xi - x)^2} \, d\xi - \frac{y}{\pi} \int_0^\infty \frac{1}{y^2 + (\xi + x)^2} \, d\xi.$$

These integrals can be evaluated in closed form. For the first,

$$\frac{y}{\pi} \int_0^\infty \frac{1}{y^2 + (\xi - x)^2} \, d\xi = \frac{y}{\pi} \int_0^\infty \frac{1}{y^2 \left[1 + \left(\frac{\xi - x}{y} \right)^2 \right]} \, d\xi$$

$$= \frac{y}{\pi} \frac{1}{y} \left(\frac{\pi}{2} - \arctan \left(-\frac{x}{y} \right) \right) = \frac{1}{2} + \frac{1}{\pi} \arctan \left(\frac{x}{y} \right).$$

By a similar calculation,

$$\frac{y}{\pi} \int_0^\infty \frac{1}{y^2 + (\xi + x)^2} \, d\xi = \frac{1}{2} - \frac{1}{\pi} \arctan \left(\frac{x}{y} \right).$$

Then

$$u(x, y) = \frac{2}{\pi} \arctan \left(\frac{x}{y} \right).$$

This function is harmonic on the right quarter plane and $u(0, y) = 0$ for $y > 0$. Further, if $x > 0$,

$$\lim_{y \to 0+} \frac{2}{\pi} \arctan \left(\frac{x}{y} \right) = \frac{2}{\pi} \frac{\pi}{2} = 1,$$

as required. ■

19.5.3   An Electrostatic Potential Problem

Consider the problem

$$\nabla^2 u(x, y) = -h \quad \text{for } 0 < x < \pi, \, y > 0,$$

$$u(0, y) = 0, \, u(\pi, y) = 1 \quad \text{for } y > 0,$$

$$u(x, 0) = 0 \quad \text{for } 0 < x < \pi.$$

This is a Dirichlet problem if $h = 0$, but we will assume that h is a positive constant. This problem models the electrostatic potential in the strip consisting of all (x, y) with $0 < x < \pi$ and $y > 0$, assuming a uniform distribution of charge having density $h/4\pi$ throughout this region. The partial differential equation $\nabla^2 u = -h$ is called *Poisson's equation*. The boundary of the strip consists of the half-lines $x = 0$ and $x = \pi$ with $y \geq 0$, and the segment on the x axis with $0 \leq x \leq \pi$. The strip and its boundary are shown in Figure 19.4.

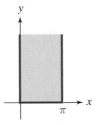

FIGURE 19.4
Strip $0 \leq x \leq \pi$,
$y \geq 0$.

Consider the possibilities for approaching this problem. Since $y > 0$, we might consider a Fourier sine or cosine transform in y. The difficulty here is that, in transforming Poisson's equation, we would have to take the transform of $-h$, and a constant does not have a sine or cosine transform. For example, if we try to compute the Fourier sine transform, we must evaluate

$$\int_0^\infty -h\sin(\omega x)\,dx,$$

and this integral diverges.

Since x varies from 0 to π, we might try a finite Fourier sine or cosine transform in x. If we try the finite Fourier cosine transform, then the operational formula requires that we have information about the derivative of the function at the origin, and we have no such information. However, the finite sine transform's operational formula requires information about the function at the ends of the interval, and this is given in the boundary conditions for $y > 0$. We will therefore attempt a solution using this transform. Denote the finite Fourier sine transform in the x variable as

$$\mathfrak{S}[u(x, y)] = \tilde{u}_S(n, y).$$

Now apply the transform with respect to x to Poisson's equation:

$$\mathfrak{S}\left[\frac{\partial^2 u}{\partial x^2}\right] + \mathfrak{S}\left[\frac{\partial^2 u}{\partial y^2}\right] = \mathfrak{S}[-h].$$

By the operational formula,

$$\mathfrak{S}\left[\frac{\partial^2 u}{\partial x^2}\right] = -n^2\tilde{u}_S(n, y) - n(-1)^n u(\pi, y) + nu(0, y).$$

Because x and y are independent,

$$\mathfrak{S}\left[\frac{\partial^2 u}{\partial y^2}\right] = \int_0^\pi \frac{\partial^2 u}{\partial y^2}(x, y)\sin(nx)\,dx = \frac{\partial^2}{\partial y^2}\int_0^\pi u(x, y)\sin(nx)\,dx = \frac{\partial^2}{\partial y^2}\tilde{u}_S(n, y).$$

Finally,

$$\mathfrak{S}[-h] = \int_0^\pi -h\sin(nx)\,dx = -\frac{h}{n}[1 - (-1)^n].$$

Therefore Poisson's equation transforms to

$$-n^2\tilde{u}_S(n, y) - n(-1)^n u(\pi, y) + nu(0, y) + \frac{\partial^2}{\partial y^2}\tilde{u}_S(n, y) = -\frac{h}{n}[1 - (-1)^n].$$

Now $u(\pi, y) = 1$ and $u(0, y) = 0$, so this equation can be written as

$$\frac{\partial^2}{\partial y^2}\tilde{u}_S(n, y) - n^2\tilde{u}_S(n, y) = n(-1)^n - \frac{h}{n}[1 - (-1)^n].$$

For $n = 1, 2, \ldots$, this equation has general solution

$$\tilde{u}_S(n, y) = a_n e^{ny} + b_n e^{-ny} + \frac{(-1)^{n+1}}{n} + \frac{h}{n^3}[1 - (-1)^n].$$

For this function to remain bounded for $y > 0$, choose $a_n = 0$ for $n = 1, 2, \ldots$ Then

$$\tilde{u}_S(n, y) = b_n e^{-ny} + \frac{(-1)^{n+1}}{n} + \frac{h}{n^3}[1 - (-1)^n].$$

To solve for b_n, take the transform of the condition $u(x, 0) = 0$ to get

$$0 = \tilde{u}_S(n, 0) = b_s + \frac{(-1)^{n+1}}{n} + \frac{h}{n^3}[1 - (-1)^n].$$

Then

$$b_n = \frac{(-1)^n}{n} - \frac{h}{n^3}[1 - (-1)^n].$$

We therefore have

$$\tilde{u}_S(n, y) = \left[\frac{(-1)^n}{n} - \frac{h}{n^3}[1 - (-1)^n] \right] e^{-ny} + \frac{(-1)^{n+1}}{n} + \frac{h}{n^3}[1 - (-1)^n]$$

$$= \left[\frac{(-1)^n}{n} - \frac{h}{n}[1 - (-1)^n] \right] (e^{-ny} - 1).$$

By the inversion formula, these are the coefficients in the Fourier sine series (in x) of the solution so the solution is

$$u(x, y) = \frac{2}{\pi} \sum_{n=1}^{\infty} \left[\frac{(-1)^n}{n} - \frac{h}{n}[1 - (-1)^n] \right] (e^{-ny} - 1) \sin(nx).$$

SECTION 19.5   PROBLEMS

1. Write an integral solution for the Dirichlet problem for the upper half plane if the boundary data is

$$f(x) = \begin{cases} -1 & \text{for } -4 \le x < 0 \\ 1 & \text{for } 0 \le x \le 4 \\ 0 & \text{for } |x| > 4. \end{cases}$$

2. Write an integral solution for the Dirichlet problem for the upper half plane if the boundary data is $f(x) = e^{-|x|}$.

3. Write an integral solution for the Dirichlet problem for the right quarter plane if

$$u(x, 0) = e^{-x} \cos(x) \quad \text{for } x > 0$$

and

$$u(0, y) = 0 \quad \text{for } y > 0.$$

4. Write an integral solution for the Dirichlet problem for the right quarter plane if

$$u(x, 0) = 0 \quad \text{for } x > 0$$

and

$$u(0, y) = g(y) \quad \text{for } y > 0.$$

Derive a solution first using separation of variables, and then by using an appropriate Fourier transform

5. Write an integral solution for the Dirichlet problem for the right quarter-plane if

$$u(x, 0) = f(x) \quad \text{for } x > 0$$

and

$$u(0, y) = g(y) \quad \text{for } y > 0.$$

6. Write an integral solution for the Dirichlet problem for the lower half-plane $y < 0$.

7. Solve the electrostatic potential problem for the strip $0 < x < \pi$, $y > 0$ with the boundary data

$$u(0, y) = 0, u(\pi, y) = 0 \quad \text{for } y > 0$$

$$u(x, 0) = B \sin(x) \quad \text{for } 0 < x < \pi.$$

Here B is a positive constant.

8. Solve the Dirichlet problem for the strip $-\infty < x < \infty$, $0 < y < 1$ if

$$u(x, 0) = 0 \quad \text{for } x < 0$$

and

$$u(x, 0) = e^{-\alpha x} \quad \text{for } x > 0,$$

with α a positive number.

9. Solve the Dirichlet problem for the strip $0 < x < \pi$, $y > 0$ if

$$u(0, y) = 0 \quad \text{and} \quad u(\pi, y) = 2 \quad \text{for } y > 0$$

and

$$u(x, 0) = -4 \quad \text{for } 0 < x < \pi.$$

10. Solve the following problem in which data on the boundary is a mixture of values of the function and values of a partial derivative of the function:

$$\nabla^2 u = 0 \quad \text{for } 0 < x < \pi, 0 < y < 2,$$

$$u(0, y) = 0$$

and

$$u(\pi, y) = 4 \quad \text{for } 0 < y < 2$$

and

$$\frac{\partial u}{\partial y}(x, 0) = u(x, 2) = 0 \quad \text{for } 0 < x < \pi.$$

11. Find the steady-state temperature distribution in a thin, homogeneous flat plate extending over the right quarter plane $x \geq 0$, $y \geq 0$ if the temperature at y on

the vertical side is e^{-y} and the temperature on the horizontal side is zero.

12. Solve for the steady-state temperature distribution in a homogeneous infinite flat plate covering the half-plane $x \geq 0$ if the temperature on the boundary $x = 0$ is $f(y)$, where

$$f(y) = \begin{cases} 1 & \text{for } |y| \leq 1 \\ 0 & \text{for } |y| > 1. \end{cases}$$

13. Solve for the steady-state temperature distribution in an infinite, homogeneous flat plate covering the half-plane $y \geq 0$ if the temperature on the boundary $y = 0$ is zero for $x < 4$, constant A for $4 \leq x \leq 8$, and zero for $x > 8$.

14. Write a general expression for the stead-state temperature distribution in an infinite, homogeneous flat plate covering the strip $0 \leq y \leq 1$, $x \geq 0$ if the temperatures on the left boundary and on the bottom side are zero, and the temperature on the top part of the boundary is $f(x)$.

19.6 A Dirichlet Problem for a Cube

We will illustrate a Dirichlet problem in 3-space. Consider:

$$\nabla^2 u(x, y, z) = 0 \quad \text{for } 0 < x < A, 0 < y < B, 0 < z < C,$$

$$u(x, y, 0) = u(x, y, C) = 0,$$

$$u(0, y, z) = u(A, y, z) = 0,$$

$$u(x, 0, z) = 0, u(x, B, z) = f(x, z).$$

We want a function that is harmonic on the cube (which may have sides of unequal length), and zero on five sides, but with prescribed values $f(x, z)$ on the sixth side.

Let $u(x, y, z) = X(x)Y(y)Z(z)$ to obtain

$$\frac{X''}{X} = -\frac{Y''}{Y} - \frac{Z''}{Z} = -\lambda,$$

and then, after a second separation,

$$\frac{Z''}{Z} = \lambda - \frac{Y''}{Y} = -\mu.$$

Then

$$X'' + \lambda X = 0, Z'' + \mu Z = 0, \quad \text{and} \quad Y'' - (\lambda + \mu)Y = 0.$$

From the boundary conditions,

$$X(0) = X(A) = 0,$$

$$Z(0) = Z(C) = 0,$$

and

$$Y(0) = 0.$$

The problems for X and Z are familiar ones, and we obtain eigenvalues and eigenfunctions:

$$\lambda_n = \frac{n^2 \pi^2}{A^2}, \quad X_n(x) = \sin\left(\frac{n\pi x}{A}\right)$$

and

$$\mu_m = \frac{m^2 \pi^2}{C^2}; \quad Z_m(z) = \sin\left(\frac{m\pi z}{C}\right),$$

with n and m independently varying over the positive integers.

The differential equation for $Y(y)$ becomes

$$Y'' - \left(\frac{n^2 \pi^2}{A^2} + \frac{m^2 \pi^2}{C^2}\right) Y = 0; \quad Y(0) = 0.$$

This has solutions that are constant multiples of $\sinh(\beta_{nm} y)$, where

$$\beta_{nm} = \sqrt{\frac{n^2 \pi^2}{A^2} + \frac{m^2 \pi^2}{C^2}}.$$

For each positive integer n and m, we now have a function

$$u_{nm}(x, y, z) = c_{nm} \sin\left(\frac{n\pi x}{A}\right) \sin\left(\frac{m\pi z}{C}\right) \sinh(\beta_{nm} y),$$

which satisfies Laplace's equation and the zero boundary conditions given on five of the faces of the cube. To satisfy the condition on the sixth face, we generally must use a superposition

$$u(x, y, z) = \sum_{n=1}^{\infty} \sum_{m=1}^{\infty} c_{nm} \sin\left(\frac{n\pi x}{A}\right) \sin\left(\frac{m\pi z}{C}\right) \sinh(\beta_{nm} y).$$

Now we must choose the coefficients so that

$$u(x, B, z) = f(x, z) = \sum_{n=1}^{\infty} \sum_{m=1}^{\infty} c_{nm} \sin\left(\frac{n\pi x}{A}\right) \sin\left(\frac{m\pi z}{C}\right) \sinh(\beta_{nm} B).$$

We have encountered this kind of double Fourier sine expansion previously, in treating vibrations of a fixed-frame rectangular elastic membrane. From that experience, we can write

$$c_{nm} = \frac{4}{AC \sinh(\beta_{nm} B)} \int_0^A \int_0^C f(\xi, \zeta) \sin\left(\frac{n\pi \xi}{A}\right) \sin\left(\frac{m\pi \zeta}{C}\right) d\zeta d\xi.$$

As usual, if nonzero data is prescribed on more than one face, then we split the Dirichlet problem into a sum of problems, on each of which there is nonzero data on only one face.

1. Solve

$$\nabla^2 u(x, y, z) = 0 \quad \text{for } 0 < x < 1, 0 < y < 1, 0 < z < 1,$$

$$u(x, y, 0) = u(x, 1, z) = 0,$$

$$u(0, y, z) = u(1, y, z) = 0,$$

$$u(x, 0, z) = 0, u(x, y, 1) = xy.$$

2. Solve

$$\nabla^2 u(x, y, z) = 0 \quad \text{for } 0 < x < 2\pi, 0 < y < 2\pi, 0 < z < 1,$$

$$u(x, y, 0) = u(x, y, 1) = 0,$$

$$u(0, y, z) = 0,$$

$$u(x, 0, z) = 0, u(x, 2\pi, z) = 0,$$

$$u(2\pi, y, z) = z$$

3. $\nabla^2 u(x, y, z) = 0$ for $0 < x < 1, 0 < y < 2\pi, 0 < z < \pi$,

$$u(x, y, 0) = 0, u(x, y, \pi) = x(\pi - x)y(\pi - y),$$

$$u(0, y, z) = u(1, y, z) = 0,$$

$$u(x, 0, z) = u(x, y, 0) = 0,$$

$$u(x, y, \pi) = 1, u(x, 2\pi, z) = 2.$$

4. $\nabla^2 u(x, y, z) = 0$ for $0 < x < 1, 0 < y < 2, 0 < z < \pi$,

$$u(x, y, 0) = x^2(1 - x)y(2 - y), u(x, y, \pi) = 0,$$

$$u(0, y, z) = 0, u(1, y, z) = \sin(\pi y)\sin(z),$$

$$u(x, 0, z) = u(x, 2, z) = 0.$$

19.7   The Steady-State Heat Equation for a Solid Sphere

Consider a solid sphere of radius R, centered at the origin. We want to solve for the steady-state temperature distribution, given the temperature at all times on the surface.

In the steady-state case, $\partial u / \partial t = 0$ and the heat equation is Laplace's equation $\nabla^2 u = 0$. We will use spherical coordinates (ρ, θ, φ), in which ρ is the distance from the origin to (x, y, z), θ is the polar angle between the positive x axis and the projection onto the x, y plane of the line from the origin to (x, y, z), and φ is the angle of declination from the positive z axis to this line (Figure 19.5). We will also assume symmetry about the z axis, so u is a function of ρ and φ only. Then $\partial u / \partial \theta = 0$, and Laplace's equation becomes

$$\nabla^2 u(\rho, \varphi) = \frac{\partial^2 u}{\partial \rho^2} + \frac{2}{\rho}\frac{\partial u}{\partial \rho} + \frac{1}{\rho^2}\frac{\partial^2 u}{\partial \varphi^2} + \frac{\cot(\varphi)}{\rho^2}\frac{\partial u}{\partial \varphi} = 0.$$

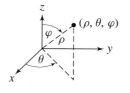

FIGURE 19.5
Spherical coordinates.

The temperature on the surface is

$$u(R, \varphi) = f(\varphi).$$

To separate variables in the differential equation, let $u(\rho, \varphi) = X(\rho)\Phi(\varphi)$ to obtain

$$X''\Phi + \frac{2}{\rho}X'\Phi + \frac{1}{\rho^2}X\Phi'' + \frac{\cot(\varphi)}{\rho^2}X\Phi' = 0.$$

Then

$$\frac{\Phi''}{\Phi} + \cot(\varphi)\frac{\Phi'}{\Phi} = -\rho^2\frac{X''}{X} - 2\rho\frac{X'}{X} = -\lambda.$$

Then

$$\rho^2 X'' + 2\rho X' - \lambda X = 0 \quad \text{and} \quad \Phi'' + \cot(\varphi)\Phi' + \lambda\Phi = 0.$$

The differential equation for Φ can be written

$$\frac{1}{\sin(\varphi)}[\Phi' \sin(\varphi)]' + \lambda\Phi = 0. \tag{19.4}$$

Change variables by putting

$$x = \cos(\varphi).$$

Then $\varphi = \arccos(x)$. Let

$$G(x) = \Phi(\arccos(x)).$$

Since $0 \le \varphi \le \pi$, then $-1 \le x \le 1$. Compute

$$\Phi'(\varphi)\sin(\varphi) = \sin(\varphi)\frac{d\Phi}{dx}\frac{dx}{d\varphi}$$

$$= \sin(\varphi)G'(x)[-\sin(\varphi)]$$

$$= -\sin^2(\varphi)G'(x) = -[1 - \cos^2(\varphi)]G'(x)$$

$$= -(1 - x^2)G'(x).$$

Then

$$\frac{d}{d\varphi}[\Phi'(\varphi)\sin(\varphi)] = -\frac{d}{d\varphi}[(1 - x^2)G'(x)]$$

$$= -\frac{d}{dx}[(1 - x^2)G'(x)]\frac{dx}{d\varphi}$$

$$= -\frac{d}{dx}[(1 - x^2)G'(x)](-\sin(\varphi)).$$

Then

$$\frac{1}{\sin(\varphi)}\frac{d}{d\varphi}[\Phi'(\varphi)\sin(\varphi)] = \frac{d}{dx}[(1 - x^2)G'(x)],$$

and equation (19.4) transforms to

$$[(1 - x^2)G'(x)]' + \lambda G(x) = 0.$$

This is Legendre's differential equation (Section 16.1). For bounded solutions, choose $\lambda = n(n+1)$ for $n = 0, 1, 2, \ldots$. These are the eigenvalues of this problem. The eigenfunctions are nonzero constant multiples of the Legendre polynomials $P_n(x)$.

For $n = 0, 1, 2, \ldots$, we now have a solution of the differential equation for Φ:

$$\Phi_n(\varphi) = G(\cos(\varphi)) = P_n(\cos(\varphi)).$$

Now that we know the admissible values for λ, the differential equation for X becomes

$$\rho^2 X'' + 2\rho X' - n(n+1)X = 0.$$

This is a second order Euler differential equation, with general solution

$$X(\rho) = a\rho^n + b\rho^{-n-1}.$$

We must choose $b = 0$ to have a bounded solution at the center of the sphere, because $\rho^{-n-1} \to \infty$ as $\rho \to 0+$. Thus

$$X_n(\rho) = a_n \rho^n.$$

For each nonnegative integer n, we now have a function

$$u_n(\rho, \varphi) = a_n \rho^n P_n(\cos(\varphi))$$

that satisfies Laplace's equation. To satisfy the boundary condition, write a superposition of these functions:

$$u(\rho, \varphi) = \sum_{n=0}^{\infty} a_n \rho^n P_n(\cos(\varphi)).$$

We must choose the coefficients to satisfy

$$u(R, \varphi) = \sum_{n=0}^{\infty} a_n R^n P_n(\cos(\varphi)) = f(\varphi).$$

To put this into the setting of Fourier-Legendre expansions, let $\varphi = \arccos(x)$ to write

$$\sum_{n=0}^{\infty} a_n R^n P_n(x) = f(\arccos(x)).$$

This is a Fourier-Legendre series for the known function $f(\arccos(x))$. From Section 16.1.5, the coefficients are

$$a_n R^n = \frac{2n+1}{2} \int_{-1}^{1} f(\arccos(x)) P_n(x) dx,$$

or

$$a_n = \frac{2n+1}{2R^n} \int_{-1}^{1} f(\arccos(x)) P_n(x) dx.$$

The steady-state temperature distribution is

$$u(\rho, \varphi) = \sum_{n=0}^{\infty} \frac{2n+1}{2} \left(\int_{-1}^{1} f(\arccos(x)) P_n(x) dx \right) \left(\frac{\rho}{R} \right)^n P_n(\cos(\varphi)).$$

EXAMPLE 19.7

Consider this solution in a specific case, with $f(\varphi) = \varphi$. Now

$$u(\rho, \varphi) = \sum_{n=0}^{\infty} \frac{2n+1}{2} \left(\int_{-1}^{1} \arccos(x) P_n(x) dx \right) \left(\frac{\rho}{R} \right)^n P_n(\cos(\varphi)).$$

We will approximate some of these coefficients by approximating the integrals. From Section 16.1, the first six Legendre polynomials are

$$P_0(x) = 1, P_1(x) = x, \quad P_2(x) = \frac{1}{2}(3x^2 - 1)$$

$$P_3(x) = \frac{1}{2}(5x^3 - 3x), \quad P_4(x) = \frac{1}{8}(35x^4 - 30x^2 + 3),$$

$$P_5(x) = \frac{1}{8}(63x^5 - 70x^3 + 15x).$$

Approximate:

$$\int_{-1}^{1} \arccos(x)\,dx \approx \pi, \int_{-1}^{1} x\arccos(x)\,dx \approx -.785\,4,$$

$$\int_{-1}^{1} \frac{1}{2}(3x^2 - 1)\arccos(x)\,dx = 0,$$

$$\int_{-1}^{1} \frac{1}{2}(5x^3 - 3x)\arccos(x)\,dx \approx -4.908\,7 \times 10^{-2}$$

$$\int_{-1}^{1} \frac{1}{8}(35x^4 - 30x^2 + 3)\arccos(x)\,dx = 0,$$

and

$$\int_{-1}^{1} \frac{1}{8}(63x^5 - 70x^3 + 15x)\arccos(x)\,dx \approx -1.227\,2 \times 10^{-2}.$$

Taking the first six terms of the series as an approximation to the solution, we obtain

$$u(\rho, \varphi) \approx \frac{1}{2}\pi - \frac{3}{2}(.7854)\frac{\rho}{R}\cos(\varphi) - \frac{7}{2}(.049087)\frac{1}{2}\left(\frac{\rho}{R}\right)^3 \left(5\cos^3(\varphi) - 3\cos(\varphi)\right)$$

$$- \frac{11}{2}(.012272)\left(\frac{\rho}{R}\right)^3 \frac{1}{8}\left(63\cos^5(\varphi) - 70\cos^3(\varphi) + 15\cos(\varphi)\right).$$

Some of these terms can be combined, but we have written them all out initially to indicate how they arise. ■

We will return to the Dirichlet problem again when we treat complex analysis. There we will be in a position to exploit conformal mappings. The idea will be to map the region of interest in a certain way to the unit disk. Since we can solve the Dirichlet problem for the disk (that is, we know a formula for the solution), this maps the original problem to a problem we can solve. We then attempt to invert the map to transform the solution for the disk back into the solution for the original region.

We will conclude this chapter with a brief discussion of the Neumann problem.

SECTION 19.7   PROBLEMS

1. Write a solution for the steady-state temperature distribution in the sphere if the initial data is given by $f(\varphi) = A\varphi^2$, in which A is a positive constant. Carry out an approximation integration to obtain the coefficients, and write (approximately) the first six terms of the series solution.

2. Carry out the program of Problem 1 for the initial data function $f(\varphi) = \sin(\varphi)$ for $0 \leq \varphi \leq \pi$.

3. Carry out the program of Problem 1 for the initial data function $f(\varphi) = \varphi^3$.

4. Carry out the program of Problem 1 for the initial data function $f(\varphi = 2 - \varphi^2$.

5. Solve for the steady-state temperature distribution in a hollowed sphere, given in spherical coordinates by $R_1 \leq \rho \leq R_2$. The inner surface $\rho = R_1$ is kept at constant temperature T_1, while the outer surface $\rho = R_2$ is kept at temperature zero. Assume that the temperature distribution is a function of ρ and φ only.

6. Approximate the solution of Problem 5 by writing the first six terms of the series solution, carrying out any required integrations by a numerical method.

7. Solve for the steady-state temperature distribution in a solid closed hemisphere, which in spherical coordi-

nates is given by $0 \leq \rho \leq R, 0 \leq \theta \leq 2\pi, 0 \leq \varphi \leq \pi/2$. The base disk is kept at temperature zero and the hemispherical surface is kept at constant temperature A. Assume that the distribution is independent of θ.

8. Redo Problem 7, except now the base is insulated instead of being kept at temperature zero.

9. Redo Problem 7 for the case that the temperature on the hemispherical surface is $u(R, \varphi) = f(\varphi)$, not necessarily constant.

19.8   The Neumann Problem

A Neumann problem in the plane consists of finding a function that is harmonic on a given region D, and whose normal derivative on the boundary of the region is given. This problem has the form

$$\nabla^2 u(x, y) = 0 \quad \text{for } (x, y) \text{ in } D,$$

$$\frac{\partial u}{\partial n}(x, y) = g(x, y) \quad \text{for } (x, y) \text{ in } \partial D,$$

where, as usual, ∂D denotes the boundary of D. This boundary is often a piecewise smooth curve in the plane (but not necessarily a closed curve). The normal derivative is defined by

$$\frac{\partial u}{\partial n} = \nabla u \cdot \mathbf{n},$$

the dot product of the gradient of u with the unit outer normal to the curve (Figure 19.6). If this normal is $\mathbf{n} = n_1 \mathbf{i} + n_2 \mathbf{j}$, then $\partial u / \partial n$ is

$$\frac{\partial u}{\partial n} = n_1 \frac{\partial u}{\partial x} + n_2 \frac{\partial u}{\partial y}.$$

We will use the following.

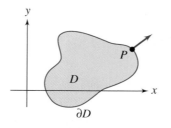

FIGURE 19.6   *Outer normal* $\mathbf{n}$ *at a point on* ∂D.

LEMMA 19.1 *Green's First Identity*

Let D be a bounded region in the plane, whose boundary ∂D is a closed, piecewise smooth curve. Let k and h be continuous with continuous first and second partial derivatives on D and its boundary. Then

$$\oint_{\partial D} k \frac{\partial h}{\partial n} ds = \iint_D (k\nabla^2 h + \nabla k \cdot \nabla h) dA. \quad \blacksquare$$

In this line integral, ds denotes integration with respect to arc length along the curve bounding D. A 3-dimensional version was proved in Section 13.8.4 using Gauss's divergence theorem. Here is a proof for this version in the plane.

Proof   By Green's theorem write

$$\oint_{\partial D} k \frac{\partial h}{\partial n} ds = \oint_{\partial D} (k\nabla h) \cdot \mathbf{n} ds = \iint_D div(k\nabla h) dA.$$

Now,

$$div(k\nabla h) = div \left(k\frac{\partial h}{\partial x}\mathbf{i} + k\frac{\partial h}{\partial y}\mathbf{j} \right)$$

$$= \frac{\partial}{\partial x} \left(k\frac{\partial h}{\partial x} \right) + \frac{\partial}{\partial y} \left(k\frac{\partial h}{\partial y} \right)$$

$$= k \left(\frac{\partial^2 h}{\partial x^2} + \frac{\partial^2 h}{\partial y^2} \right) + \frac{\partial k}{\partial x}\frac{\partial h}{\partial x} + \frac{\partial k}{\partial y}\frac{\partial h}{\partial y}$$

$$= k\nabla^2 h + \nabla k \cdot \nabla h. \quad \blacksquare$$

Use this result as follows. If $k = 1$ and $h = u$, a harmonic function on D, then the double integral is zero because its integrand vanishes, and the line integral is just the line integral of the normal derivative of u over the boundary of the region. But on ∂D, $\partial u/\partial n = g$, a given function. We conclude that

$$\oint_{\partial D} \frac{\partial u}{\partial n} ds = \oint_{\partial D} g ds = 0.$$

This means that a necessary condition for a Neumann problem to have a solution is for the integral of the given normal derivative about the boundary of the region to be zero. This conclusion can be extended to the case that ∂D is not a closed curve. For example, the boundary of the upper half plane is the horizontal axis, which is not a closed curve.

EXAMPLE 19.8

Solve the Neumann problem for a square:

$$\nabla^2 u(x, y) = 0 \quad \text{for } 0 \le x \le 1, 0 \le y \le 1,$$

subject to

$$\frac{\partial u}{\partial n} = 0$$

on the left side and top and bottom sides, while

$$\frac{\partial u}{\partial n}(1, y) = y^2 \quad \text{for } 0 \le y \le 1.$$

Since

$$\oint_{\partial D} \frac{\partial u}{\partial n} ds = \int_0^1 y^2 dy = \frac{1}{3} \neq 0,$$

this problem has no solution. ■

Existence can also be a question for a Dirichlet problem. However, for a Dirichlet problem, if the function given on the boundary is well-behaved (for example, continuous), and the region is "simple" (such as a disk, rectangle, half-planes and the like), then the Dirichlet problem has a solution. For Neumann problems, even for simple regions and apparently well-behaved data given for the normal derivative, there may be no solution if the integral of the data function about the boundary is not zero.

We will now solve two Neumann problem to illustrate what is involved.

19.8.1   A Neumann Problem for a Rectangle

Consider the problem

$$\nabla^2 u(x, y) = 0 \quad \text{for } 0 < x < a, 0 < y < b,$$

$$\frac{\partial u}{\partial y}(x, 0) = \frac{\partial u}{\partial y}(x, b) = 0 \quad \text{for } 0 \leq x \leq a,$$

$$\frac{\partial u}{\partial x}(0, y) = 0 \quad \text{for } 0 \leq y \leq b,$$

$$\frac{\partial u}{\partial x}(a, y) = g(y) \quad \text{for } 0 \leq y \leq b.$$

For the rectangle, the normal derivative is $\partial u / \partial x$ on the vertical sides, and $\partial u / \partial y$ on the horizontal sides. As a necessary (but not sufficient) condition for existence of a solution, we require that

$$\int_0^b g(y) dy = 0.$$

This example will clarify why there can be no solution without this condition.

Let $u(x, y) = X(x)Y(y)$ and obtain

$$X'' + \lambda X = 0, \ Y'' - \lambda Y = 0.$$

Now

$$\frac{\partial u}{\partial y}(x, 0) = X(x)Y'(0) = 0$$

implies that $Y'(0) = 0$. Similarly,

$$\frac{\partial u}{\partial y}(x, b) = X(x)Y'(b) = 0$$

implies that $Y'(b) = 0$. The problem for Y is

$$Y'' - \lambda Y = 0; \ Y'(0) = Y'(b) = 0.$$

This familiar Sturm–Liouville has eigenvalues and eigenfunctions

$$\lambda_n = -\frac{n^2 \pi^2}{b^2} \quad \text{and} \quad Y_n(y) = \cos\left(\frac{n \pi y}{b}\right)$$

for $n = 0, 1, 2, \ldots$.

Now the problem for X is

$$X'' - \frac{n^2\pi^2}{b^2}X = 0.$$

Further,

$$\frac{\partial u}{\partial x}(0, y) = X'(0)Y(y) = 0$$

implies that $X'(0) = 0$.

For $n = 0$, the differential equation for X is just $X'' = 0$, so $X(x) = cx + d$. Then $X'(0) = c = 0$, so $X(x) = $ constant in this case.

If n is a positive integer, then the differential equation for X has general solution

$$X(x) = ce^{n\pi x/b} + de^{-n\pi x/b}.$$

Now

$$X'(0) = \frac{n\pi}{b}c - \frac{n\pi}{b}d = 0$$

implies that $c = d$. This gives us

$$X_n(x) = \cosh\left(\frac{n\pi x}{b}\right).$$

We now have functions

$$u_0(x, y) = \text{ constant}$$

and, for each positive integer n,

$$u_n(x, y) = c_n \cosh\left(\frac{n\pi x}{b}\right) \cos\left(\frac{n\pi y}{b}\right).$$

To satisfy the last boundary condition (on the right side of the rectangle), use a superposition

$$u(x, y) = c_0 + \sum_{n=1}^{\infty} c_n \cosh\left(\frac{n\pi x}{b}\right) \cos\left(\frac{n\pi y}{b}\right).$$

We need

$$\frac{\partial u}{\partial x}(a, y) = g(y) = \sum_{n=1}^{\infty} \frac{n\pi}{b}c_n \sinh\left(\frac{n\pi a}{b}\right) \cos\left(\frac{n\pi y}{b}\right),$$

a Fourier cosine expansion of $g(y)$ on $[0, b]$. Notice that the constant term in this expansion of $g(y)$ is zero. This constant term is

$$\frac{1}{b}\int_0^b g(y)\,dy,$$

which we have assumed to be zero. If this integral were not zero, then the cosine expansion of $g(y)$ would have a nonzero constant term, contradicting the fact that that it does not. In this event this Neumann problem would have no solution.

For the other coefficients in this cosine series, we have

$$\frac{n\pi}{b}c_n \sinh\left(\frac{n\pi a}{b}\right) = \frac{2}{b}\int_0^b g(\xi)\cos\left(\frac{n\pi\xi}{b}\right)d\xi,$$

so

$$c_n = \frac{2}{n\pi\sinh(n\pi a/b)}\int_0^b g(\xi)\cos\left(\frac{n\pi\xi}{b}\right)d\xi.$$

With this choice of coefficients, the solution of this Neumann problem is

$$u(x, y) = c_0 + \sum_{n=1}^{\infty} c_n \cosh\left(\frac{n\pi x}{b}\right) \cos\left(\frac{n\pi y}{b}\right).$$

The number c_0 is undetermined and remains arbitrary. This is because Neumann problems do not have unique solutions. If u is any solution of a Neumann problem, so is $u + c$ for any constant c, because the boundary condition is on the normal derivative and c vanishes in this differentiation.

19.8.2   A Neumann Problem for a Disk

We will solve the Neumann problem for a disk of radius R centered about the origin. In polar coordinates, the problem is

$$\nabla^2 u(r, \theta) = 0 \quad \text{for } 0 \leq r < R, -\pi \leq \theta \leq \pi,$$

$$\frac{\partial u}{\partial r}(R, \theta) = f(\theta) \quad \text{for } -\pi \leq \theta \leq \pi.$$

The normal derivative here is $\partial/\partial r$, since the line from the origin to a point on this circle is in the direction of the outer normal vector to the circle at that point.

A necessary condition for existence of a solution is that

$$\int_{-\pi}^{\pi} f(\theta) d\theta = 0,$$

and we assume that f satisfies this condition.

As we did with the Dirichlet problem for a disk, attempt a solution

$$u(r, \theta) = \frac{1}{2}a_0 + \sum_{n=1}^{\infty} a_n r^n \cos(n\theta) + b_n r^n \sin(n\theta).$$

We need

$$\frac{\partial u}{\partial r}(R, \theta) = f(\theta) = \sum_{n=1}^{\infty} n a_n R^{n-1} \cos(n\theta) + n b_n R^{n-1} \sin(n\theta).$$

This is a Fourier expansion of $f(\theta)$ on $[-\pi, \pi]$. The constant term in this expansion is

$$\frac{1}{\pi} \int_{-\pi}^{\pi} f(\theta) d\theta,$$

and this must be zero because this Fourier series for $(\partial u/\partial r)(R, \theta)$ has a zero constant term. The assumption that this integral is zero is therefore consistent with this boundary condition.

For the other coefficients, we need

$$n a_n R^{n-1} a_n = \frac{1}{\pi} \int_{-\pi}^{\pi} f(\xi) \cos(n\xi) d\xi$$

and

$$n a_n R^{n-1} b_n = \frac{1}{\pi} \int_{-\pi}^{\pi} f(\xi) \sin(n\xi) d\xi.$$

Thus choose

$$a_n = \frac{1}{n\pi R^{n-1}} \int_{-\pi}^{\pi} f(\xi) \cos(n\xi) d\xi$$

and

$$b_n = \frac{1}{n\pi R^{n-1}} \int_{-\pi}^{\pi} f(\xi)\sin(n\xi)d\xi.$$

Upon inserting these coefficients, the solution is

$$u(r,\theta) = \frac{1}{2}a_0 + \frac{R}{\pi}\sum_{n=1}^{\infty}\frac{1}{n}\left(\frac{r}{R}\right)^n \int_{-\pi}^{\pi}[\cos(n\xi)\cos(n\theta) + \sin(n\xi)\sin(n\theta)]f(\xi)d\xi.$$

We can also write this solution as

$$u(r,\theta) = \frac{1}{2}a_0 + \frac{R}{\pi}\sum_{n=1}^{\infty}\frac{1}{n}\left(\frac{r}{R}\right)^n \int_{-\pi}^{\pi}\cos(n(\xi-\theta))f(\xi)d\xi.$$

The term $a_0/2$ is an arbitrary constant. The factor of $1/2$ in this arbitrary constant is just customary.

EXAMPLE 19.9

Solve the Neumann problem

$$\nabla^2 u(x,y) = 0 \quad \text{for } x^2 + y^2 < 1,$$

$$\frac{\partial u}{\partial n}(x,y) = xy^2 \quad \text{for } x^2 + y^2 = 1.$$

Switch to polar coordinates, letting $u(r\cos(\theta), r\sin(\theta)) = U(r,\theta)$. Then

$$\nabla^2 U(r,\theta) = 0 \quad \text{for } 0 \le r < 1, -\pi \le \theta \le \pi,$$

$$\frac{\partial U}{\partial r}(1,\theta) = \cos(\theta)\sin^2(\theta).$$

First, compute

$$\int_{-\pi}^{\pi}\cos(\theta)\sin^2(\theta)d\theta = 0,$$

so it is worthwhile to try to solve this problem. Write the solution

$$U(r,\theta) = \frac{1}{2}a_0 + \frac{1}{\pi}\sum_{n=1}^{\infty}\frac{1}{n}(r)^n \int_{-\pi}^{\pi}\cos(n(\xi-\theta))\cos(\xi)\sin^2(\xi)d\xi.$$

Evaluate

$$\int_{-\pi}^{\pi}\cos(n(\xi-\theta))\cos(\xi)\sin^2(\xi)d\xi = \begin{cases} 0 & \text{for } n = 2,4,5,6,\ldots \\ \frac{\pi\cos(\theta)}{4} & \text{if } n = 1 \\ -\pi\cos^3(\theta) + \frac{3\pi\cos(\theta)}{4} & \text{if } n = 3 \end{cases}.$$

The solution is therefore

$$U(r,\theta) = \frac{1}{2}a_0 + \frac{1}{4}r\cos(\theta) + \frac{1}{3}r^3\left(-\cos^3(\theta) + \frac{3}{4}\cos(\theta)\right)$$

$$= \frac{1}{2}a_0 + \frac{1}{4}r\cos(\theta) - \frac{1}{3}r^3\cos^3(\theta) + \frac{1}{4}r^3\cos(\theta).$$

To obtain the solution in rectangular coordinates, use $x = r\cos(\theta)$ and $r^2 = x^2 + y^2$ to write

$$u(x,y) = \frac{1}{2}a_0 + \frac{1}{4}x - \frac{1}{3}x^3 + \frac{1}{4}x(x^2 + y^2). \quad \blacksquare$$

Again, the solution has an arbitrary constant, which is written with a factor of $\frac{1}{2}$ simply because we started with a Fourier series and the constant is often called $a_0/2$.

19.8.3 A Neumann Problem for the Upper Half Plane

As an illustration of a Neumann problem for an unbounded domain, consider:

$$\nabla^2 u(x, y) = 0 \quad \text{for } -\infty < x < \infty, y > 0,$$

$$\frac{\partial u}{\partial y}(x, 0) = f(x) \quad \text{for } -\infty < x < \infty.$$

The boundary of the region is the real axis, and $\partial/\partial y$ is the derivative normal to this line.

We require that $\int_{-\infty}^{\infty} f(x)dx = 0$ as a necessary condition for a solution to exist.

There is an elegant device for reducing this problem to one we have already solved. Let $v = \partial u/\partial y$. Then

$$\nabla^2 v = \frac{\partial^2}{\partial x^2}\left(\frac{\partial u}{\partial y}\right) + \frac{\partial^2}{\partial y^2}\left(\frac{\partial u}{\partial y}\right) = \frac{\partial}{\partial y}\left(\frac{\partial^2 u}{\partial x^2} + \frac{\partial^2 u}{\partial y^2}\right) = 0,$$

so v is harmonic wherever u is. Further

$$v(x, 0) = \frac{\partial u}{\partial y}(x, 0) = f(x) \quad \text{for } -\infty < x < \infty.$$

Therefore v is the solution of a Dirichlet problem for the upper half plane. But we know the solution of this problem:

$$v(x, y) = \frac{y}{\pi} \int_{-\infty}^{\infty} \frac{f(\xi)}{y^2 + (\xi - x)^2} d\xi.$$

Now recover u from v by integrating. To within an arbitrary constant,

$$u(x, y) = \int \frac{\partial u}{\partial y} dy = \int \frac{y}{\pi} \int_{-\infty}^{\infty} \frac{f(\xi)}{y^2 + (\xi - x)^2} d\xi dy$$

$$= \frac{1}{\pi} \int_{-\infty}^{\infty} \left(\int \frac{y}{y^2 + (\xi - x)^2} dy\right) f(\xi) d\xi$$

$$= \frac{1}{2\pi} \int_{-\infty}^{\infty} \ln(y^2 + (\xi - x)^2) f(\xi) d\xi + c,$$

in which c is an arbitrary constant. This gives the solution of the Neumann problem for the upper half-plane.

SECTION 19.8   PROBLEMS

1. Solve

$$\nabla^2 u(x, y) = 0 \quad \text{for } 0 < x < 1, 0 < y < 1,$$

$$\frac{\partial u}{\partial y}(x, 0) = 4\cos(\pi x), \frac{\partial u}{\partial y}(x, 1) = 0 \quad \text{for } 0 \le x \le 1,$$

$$\frac{\partial u}{\partial x}(0, y) = \frac{\partial u}{\partial x}(1, y) = 0 \quad \text{for } 0 \le y \le 1.$$

2. Solve

$$\nabla^2 u(x, y) = 0 \quad \text{for } 0 < x < 1, 0 < y < \pi,$$

$$\frac{\partial u}{\partial y}(x, 0) = \frac{\partial u}{\partial y}(x, \pi) = 0 \quad \text{for } 0 \le x \le 1,$$

$$\frac{\partial u}{\partial x}(0, y) = y - \frac{\pi}{2} \quad \text{for } 0 \le y \le \pi,$$

$$\frac{\partial u}{\partial x}(\pi, y) = \cos(y) \quad \text{for } 0 \le y \le \pi.$$

3. Solve

$$\nabla^2 u(x, y) = 0 \quad \text{for } 0 < x < \pi, 0 < y < \pi,$$

$$\frac{\partial u}{\partial y}(x, 0) = \cos(3x),$$

$$\frac{\partial u}{\partial y}(x, \pi) = 6x - 3\pi \quad \text{for } 0 \le x \le \pi,$$

$$\frac{\partial u}{\partial x}(0, y) = \frac{\partial u}{\partial x}(\pi, y) = 0 \quad \text{for } 0 \le y \le \pi.$$

4. Use separation of variables to solve the mixed boundary value problem

$$\nabla^2 u(x, y) = 0 \quad \text{for } 0 < x < \pi, 0 < y < \pi,$$

$$u(x, 0) = f(x), u(x, \pi) = 0 \quad \text{for } 0 \le x \le \pi,$$

$$\frac{\partial u}{\partial x}(0, y) = \frac{\partial u}{\partial x}(\pi, y) = 0 \quad \text{for } 0 \le y \le \pi.$$

Does this problem have a unique solution?

5. Attempt a separation of variables to solve

$$\nabla^2 u(x, y) = 0 \quad \text{for } 0 < x < 1, 0 < y < 1,$$

$$u(x, 0) = u(x, 1) = 0 \quad \text{for } 0 \le x \le 1,$$

$$\frac{\partial u}{\partial x}(0, y) = 3y^2 - 2y,$$

$$\frac{\partial u}{\partial x}(1, y) = 0 \quad \text{for } 0 \le y \le 1.$$

6. Write a series solution for

$$\nabla^2 u(r, \theta) = 0 \quad \text{for } 0 \le r < R, -\pi \le \theta \le \pi,$$

$$\frac{\partial u}{\partial r}(R, \theta) = \sin(3\theta) \quad \text{for } -\pi \le \theta \le \pi.$$

7. Write a solution for

$$\nabla^2 u(r, \theta) = 0 \quad \text{for } 0 \le r < R, -\pi \le \theta \le \pi,$$

$$\frac{\partial u}{\partial r}(R, \theta) = \cos(2\theta) \quad \text{for } -\pi \le \theta \le \pi.$$

8. Solve the following Neumann problem for the upper half plane:

$$\nabla^2 u(x, y) = 0 \quad \text{for } -\infty < x < \infty, y > 0,$$

$$\frac{\partial u}{\partial y}(x, 0) = xe^{-|x|} \quad \text{for } -\infty < x < \infty.$$

9. Solve the following Neumann problem for the upper half plane:

$$\nabla^2 u(x, y) = 0 \quad \text{for } -\infty < x < \infty, y > 0,$$

$$\frac{\partial u}{\partial y}(x, 0) = e^{-|x|} \sin(x) \quad \text{for } -\infty < x < \infty.$$

10. Solve the following Neumann problem for the lower half plane:

$$\nabla^2 u(x, y) = 0 \quad \text{for } -\infty < x < \infty, y < 0,$$

$$\frac{\partial u}{\partial y}(x, 0) = f(x) \quad \text{for } -\infty < x < \infty.$$

11. Solve the following Neumann problem for the right quarter plane:

$$\nabla^2 u(x, y) = 0 \quad \text{for } x > 0, y > 0,$$

$$\frac{\partial u}{\partial x}(0, y) = 0 \quad \text{for } y \ge 0,$$

$$\frac{\partial u}{\partial y}(x, 0) = f(x) \quad \text{for } 0 \le x < \infty.$$

12. Solve the following mixed problem:

$$\nabla^2 u(x, y) = 0 \quad \text{for } x > 0, y > 0,$$

$$u(0, y) = 0 \quad \text{for } y \ge 0,$$

$$\frac{\partial u}{\partial y}(x, 0) = f(x) \quad \text{for } 0 \le x < \infty.$$

$$\lim_{h\to 0}\frac{f(z+h)-f(z)}{h} = \lim_{h\to 0}\frac{(z+h)-f(z)}{h} = \lim_{h\to 0}\frac{f(z+h)-f(z)}{h} = \lim_{h\to 0}\frac{\overline{z+h}-\overline{z}}{h}$$

$$= \lim_{h\to 0}\frac{\overline{z+h}-\overline{z}}{h}$$

$$= \lim_{h\to 0}\frac{\overline{z}+\overline{h}-\overline{z}}{h} = \lim_{h\to 0}\frac{\overline{h}}{h}.$$

PART 7

Complex Analysis

This part is devoted to the calculus of functions that act on complex numbers and produce complex numbers. Such functions are called complex functions, and we are interested in their derivatives and integrals. These have not only a rich theory, but applications that are sometimes surprising.

We will begin with the algebra and geometry of the complex number system.

CHAPTER 20

Geometry and Arithmetic of Complex Numbers

20.1   Complex Numbers

A *complex number* is a symbol of the form $x + iy$, or $x + yi$, in which x and y are real numbers and $i^2 = -1$. Arithmetic of complex numbers is defined by

$$\text{equality: } a + ib = c + id \text{ exactly when } a = c \text{ and } b = d,$$

$$\text{addition: } (a + ib) + (c + id) = (a + c) + i(b + d),$$

and

$$\text{multiplication: } (a + ib)(c + id) = ac - bd + i(ad + bc).$$

In multiplying complex numbers, we proceed exactly as we would with first order polynomials $a + bx$ and $c + dx$, but with i in place of x:

$$(a + bi)(c + di) = ac + adi + bci + bdi^2$$

$$= ac - bd + (ad + bc)i$$

because $i^2 = -1$. For example,

$$(6 - 4i)(8 + 13i) = (6)(8) - (-4)(13) + i[(6)(13) + (-4)(8)] = 100 + 46i.$$

The real number a is called the real part of $a + bi$, and is denoted $\text{Re}(a + bi)$. The real number b is the imaginary part, denoted $\text{Im}(a + bi)$. For example,

$$\text{Re}(-23 + 7i) = -23 \quad \text{and} \quad \text{Im}(-23 + 7i) = 7.$$

Both the real and imaginary part of any complex number are real numbers.

We may think of the complex number system as an extension of the real number system in the sense that every real number a is a complex number $a + 0i$. This extension of the reals to the complex numbers has profound consequences, both for algebra and analysis. For example, the polynomial equation $x^2 + 1 = 0$ has no real solution, but it has two complex solutions, i and $-i$. More generally, the fundamental theorem of algebra states that every polynomial of positive degree n, having complex coefficients (some or all of which may be real), has exactly n roots in the complex numbers, counting repeated roots. This means that we need never extend beyond the complex numbers to find roots of polynomials having complex coefficients, as we have to extend beyond the reals to find the roots of a simple polynomial such as $x^2 + 1$.

Complex addition obeys many of the same rules of arithmetic as real numbers. Specifically, for any complex numbers z, w and u,

$z + w = w + z$ (commutativity of addition)

$zw = wz$ (commutativity of multiplication)

$z + (w + u) = (z + w) + u$ (associativity of addition)

$z(wu) = (zw)u$ (associativity of multiplication)

$z(w + u) = zw + zu$ (distributivity)

$z + 0 = 0 + z$

$z \cdot 1 = 1 \cdot z$.

20.1.1 The Complex Plane

Complex numbers admit two natural geometric intepretations.

First, we may identify the complex number $a + bi$ with the point (a, b) in the plane, as in Figure 20.1. In this interpretation each real number a, or $a + 0i$, is identified with the point $(a, 0)$ on the horizontal axis, which is therefore called the *real axis*. A number $0 + bi$, or just bi, is called a *pure imaginary number*, and is associated with the point $(0, b)$ on the vertical axis. This axis is called the *imaginary axis*. Because of this correspondence between complex numbers and points in the plane, we often refer to the x, y plane as the *complex plane*.

When complex numbers were first noticed (in solving polynomial equations), mathematicians were suspicious of them, and even the great eighteenth-century Swiss mathematician Leonhard Euler, who used them in calculations with unparalleled proficiency, did not recognize them as "legitimate" numbers. It was the nineteenth century German mathematician Carl Friedrich Gauss who fully appreciated their geometric significance, and used his standing in the scientific community to promote their legitimacy to other mathematicians and natural philosophers.

The second geometric interpretation of complex numbers is in terms of vectors. The complex number $z = a + bi$, or the point (a, b), may be thought of as a vector $a\mathbf{i} + b\mathbf{j}$ in the plane, which may in turn be represented as an arrow from the origin to (a, b) as in Figure 20.2. The first component of this vector is $\text{Re}(z)$ and the second component is $\text{Im}(z)$. In this interpretation the definition of addition of complex numbers is equivalent to the parallelogram law for vector addition, since we add two vectors by adding their respective components (Figure 20.3).

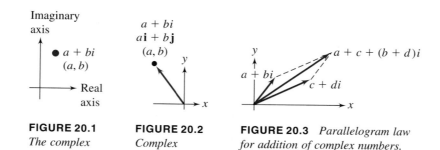

FIGURE 20.1 *The complex plane.*

FIGURE 20.2 *Complex numbers as vectors in a plane.*

FIGURE 20.3 *Parallelogram law for addition of complex numbers.*

20.1.2 Magnitude and Conjugate

DEFINITION 20.1 *Magnitude*

The magnitude of $a + bi$ is denoted $|a + bi|$, and is defined by

$$|a + bi| = \sqrt{a^2 + b^2}.$$

Of course, the magnitude of zero is zero. As Figure 20.4 suggests, if $z = a + ib$ is a nonzero complex number, then $|z|$ is the distance from the origin to the point (a, b). Alternatively, $|z|$ is the length of the vector $a\mathbf{i} + b\mathbf{j}$ representing z.

For example,

$$|2 - 5i| = \sqrt{4 + 25} = \sqrt{29}.$$

The magnitude of a complex number is also called its *modulus*.

DEFINITION 20.2 *Conjugate*

The complex conjugate (or just conjugate) of $a + bi$ is the number denoted $\overline{a + bi}$, and defined by

$$\overline{a + bi} = a - bi.$$

We get the conjugate of z by changing the sign of the imaginary part of z. For example,

$$\overline{3 - 8i} = 3 + 8i, \quad \overline{i} = -i \text{ and } \overline{-25} = -25.$$

This operation does not change the real part of z. We have

$$\text{Re}\left(\overline{a + ib}\right) = a = \text{Re}(a + ib)$$

and

$$\text{Im}(\overline{a + ib}) = -b = -\text{Im}(a + ib).$$

The operation of taking the conjugate can be interpreted as a reflection across the real axis, because the point $(a, -b)$ associated with $a - ib$ is the reflection across the horizontal axis of the point (a, b) associated with $a + ib$ (Figure 20.5).

Here are some computational rules for magnitude and conjugate.

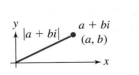

FIGURE 20.4
Magnitude of a complex number.

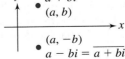

FIGURE 20.5
Conjugate of a complex number.

THEOREM 20.1

Let z and w be complex numbers. Then

1. $\bar{\bar{z}} = z$.
2. $\overline{z+w} = \bar{z} + \bar{w}$.
3. $\overline{zw} = (\bar{z})(\bar{w})$.
4. $|z| = |\bar{z}|$.
5. $|zw| = |z|\,|w|$.
6. $\mathrm{Re}(z) = \frac{1}{2}(z + \bar{z})$ and $\mathrm{Im}(z) = \frac{1}{2i}(z - \bar{z})$.
7. $|z| \geq 0$, and $|z| = 0$ if and only if $z = 0$.
8. $z\bar{z} = |z|^2$.

Proof   Conclusion (1) states that taking the conjugate of a conjugate returns the original number. This is geometrically evident, since a reflection of (x, y) to $(x, -y)$, followed by a reflection of $(x, -y)$ to (x, y), returns to the original point. For an analytical argument, write

$$\overline{\overline{a+ib}} = \overline{a - ib} = a + ib.$$

For conclusion (5), let $z = a + ib$ and $w = c + id$. Then

$$|zw| = |(ac - bd) + i(ad + bc)|$$

$$= \sqrt{(ac - bd)^2 + (ad + bc)^2}$$

$$= \sqrt{a^2c^2 + b^2d^2 - 2acbd + a^2d^2 + b^2c^2 + 2adbc}$$

$$= \sqrt{a^2c^2 + a^2d^2 + b^2c^2 + b^2d^2}$$

$$= \sqrt{a^2 + b^2}\sqrt{c^2 + d^2} = |z|\,|w|.$$

A much neater proof of (5) will be available when we know about the polar form of a complex number.

The other parts of the theorem are left to the student. ∎

20.1.3   Complex Division

Suppose we want to form the quotient z/w, where $w \neq 0$. This quotient is the complex number u such that $wu = z$. This is not very helpful in actually finding u, however. Here is a computationally effective way of performing complex division. Let $z = a + ib$ and $w = c + id$ and write

$$\frac{a+ib}{c+id} = \frac{a+ib}{c+id}\frac{c-id}{c-id} = \frac{ac + bd + i(bc - ad)}{c^2 + d^2}.$$

By multiplying and dividing the original fraction by the conjugate of the denominator, we obtain an expression in which the real and imaginary parts of the quotient are apparent. The reason for this is that the denominator is $w\bar{w}$, which is the real number $|w|^2$.

For example,

$$\frac{2-7i}{8+3i} = \frac{2-7i}{8+3i}\frac{8-3i}{8-3i} = \frac{-5 - 62i}{64 + 9} = -\frac{5}{73} - \frac{62}{73}i,$$

so the real part of this quotient is $-5/73$ and the imaginary part is $-62/73$.

20.1.4   Inequalities

There are several inequalities we will have occasion to use.

THEOREM 20.2

Let z and w be complex numbers. Then

1. $|\text{Re}(z)| \leq |z|$ and $|\text{Im}(z)| \leq |z|$.
2. $|z + w| \leq |z| + |w|$.
3. $||z| - |w|| \leq |z - w|$.

Proof   If $z = a + ib$, then

$$|\text{Re}(z)| = |a| \leq \sqrt{a^2 + b^2} = |z|$$

and

$$|\text{Im}(z)| = |b| \leq \sqrt{a^2 + b^2} = |z|.$$

Conclusion (2), which is called the triangle inequality, was proved for vectors. Here is a separate proof in the context of complex numbers:

$$0 \leq |z + w|^2 = (z + w)(\overline{z + w}) = (z + w)(\overline{z} + \overline{w}) = z\overline{z} + z\overline{w} + w\overline{z} + w\overline{w}$$

$$= |z|^2 + z\overline{w} + \overline{z\overline{w}} + |w|^2 = |z|^2 + 2\text{Re}(z\overline{w}) + |w|^2 \leq |z|^2 + 2|z\overline{w}| + |w|^2$$

$$= |z|^2 + 2|z||\overline{w}| + |w|^2 = |z|^2 + 2|z||w| + |w|^2 = (|z| + |w|)^2.$$

In summary,

$$0 \leq |z + w|^2 \leq (|z| + |w|)^2.$$

Upon taking the square root of these nonnegative quantities, we obtain the triangle inequality.

For (3), use the triangle inequality to write

$$|z| = |(z + w) - w| \leq |z + w| + |w|,$$

hence

$$|z| - |w| \leq |z + w|.$$

By interchanging z and w,

$$|w| - |z| \leq |z + w|.$$

Therefore

$$-|z + w| \leq |z| - |w| \leq |z + w|,$$

so

$$||z| - |w|| \leq |z + w|. \quad \blacksquare$$

20.1.5   Argument and Polar Form of a Complex Number

Let $z = a + ib$ be a nonzero complex number. Then (a, b) is a point other than the origin in the plane. Let this point have polar coordinates (r, θ). As is standard with polar coordinates, the polar angle θ of (a, b) is not uniquely determined. If we walk out the real axis r units to the right from the origin, and rotate this segment θ_0 radians until the segment ends at (a, b), as in Figure 20.6, then the polar angle θ for (a, b) is any number $\theta_0 + 2n\pi$, in which n is any integer. A positive choice for n corresponds to rotating the segment from 0 to r an initial θ_0 radians to reach (a, b), and then continuing counterclockwise an additional n full circles, which again lands us on (a, b). A negative choice for n corresponds to rotating the segment from 0 to r an initial θ_0 radians, and then going around an additional n circles clockwise, again ending at (a, b). Thus, by convention, we think of counterclockwise rotations as having positive orientation in the plane, and clockwise rotations as having negative orientation.

To illustrate, consider $z = 1 + i$. The point $(1, 1)$ has polar coordinates $(\sqrt{2}, \pi/4)$, since $1 + i$ is $\sqrt{2}$ units from the origin, and the segment from the origin to $1 + i$ makes an angle $\pi/4$ radians with the positive real axis (Figure 20.7). All of the polar coordinates of $(1, 1)$ have the form

$$(\sqrt{2}, \pi/4 + 2n\pi),$$

in which n can be any integer.

If nonzero z has polar coordinates (r, θ), then $r = |z|$. The angle θ (which we will always express in radians) is called an *argument* of z. Any nonzero number has infinitely many arguments, and they differ from each other by integer multiples of 2π. The arguments of $1 + i$ are $\pi/4 + 2n\pi$, for n any integer.

Now recall Euler's formula

$$e^{i\theta} = \cos(\theta) + i\sin(\theta).$$

If θ is any argument of $z = a + ib$, then (a, b) has polar coordinates (r, θ), so $a = r\cos(\theta)$ and $b = r\sin(\theta)$. Combining this fact with Euler's formula, we have

$$z = a + ib = r\cos(\theta) + ir\sin(\theta) = re^{i\theta}.$$

This exponential form for z is called the *polar form* of z. Any argument of z can be used in this polar form, because any two arguments θ_0 and θ_1 differ by some integer multiple of 2π. If, say $\theta_1 = \theta_0 + 2k\pi$, then

$$re^{i\theta_1} = r[\cos(\theta_0 + 2k\pi) + i\sin(\theta_0 + 2k\pi)]$$

$$= r[\cos(\theta_0) + i\sin(\theta_0)] = re^{i\theta_0}.$$

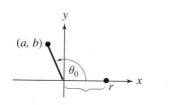

FIGURE 20.6   *(a, b) has polar coordinates $(r, \theta_0 + 2n\pi)$, n any integer.*

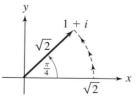

FIGURE 20.7   *Polar coordinates of $1 + i$ are $(\sqrt{2}, \pi/4 + 2n\pi)$, n any integer.*

EXAMPLE 20.1

We will find the polar form of $-1+4i$. First, $r = |-1+4i| = \sqrt{17}$. Now consider Figure 20.8. θ is an argument of $-1+4i$, and α will be handy in determining θ. From the diagram, $\tan(\alpha) = 4$, so

$$\theta = \pi - \alpha = \pi - \tan^{-1}(4).$$

We can therefore write the polar form

$$-1+4i = \sqrt{17}e^{i(\pi - \tan^{-1}(4))}. \quad \blacksquare$$

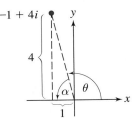

FIGURE 20.8
$\pi - \tan^{-1}(4)$ *is an*
argument of $-1+4i$.

EXAMPLE 20.2

We will find the polar form of $3+3i$. As indicated in Figure 20.9, $\pi/4$ is an argument of $3+3i$. The polar form is

$$3+3i = \sqrt{18}e^{i\pi/4}. \quad \blacksquare$$

FIGURE 20.9
$\pi/4$ *is an*
argument of
$3+3i$.

For any real θ,

$$\left|e^{i\theta}\right| = \cos^2(\theta) + \sin^2(\theta) = 1.$$

This means that, in writing the polar form $z = re^{i\theta}$, the magnitude of z is wholly contained in the factor r, while $e^{i\theta}$, which has magnitude 1, contributes all the information about the direction of (nonzero) z from the origin.

Because of the properties of the exponential function, some computations with complex numbers are simplified if polar forms are used. To illustrate, suppose we want to prove that $|zw| = |z|\,|w|$, something we did before by algebraic manipulation. Put $z = re^{i\theta}$ and $w = \rho e^{i\xi}$ to immediately get

$$|zw| = \left|r\rho e^{i\theta}e^{i\xi}\right| = r\rho\left|e^{i(\theta+\xi)}\right| = r\rho = |z|\,|w|.$$

The fact that $e^{i(\theta+\xi)} = e^{i\theta}e^{i\xi}$ also means that the argument of a product is the sum of the arguments of the factors, to within an integer multiple of 2π. Put more carefully, if θ_0 is any argument of z, and θ_1 is any argument of w, and Θ is any argument of zw, then for some integer n,

$$\Theta = \theta_0 + \theta_1 + 2n\pi.$$

Multiplying two complex numbers has the effect of adding their arguments, to within integer multiples of 2π.

EXAMPLE 20.3

Let $z = i$ and $w = 2 - 2i$. One argument of z is $\theta_0 = \pi/2$, and one argument of w is $\theta_1 = 7\pi/4$ (Figure 20.10). Now

$$zw = i(2 - 2i) = 2 + 2i,$$

and one argument of $2 + 2i$ is $\Theta = \pi/4$. With this choice of arguments,

$$\theta_0 + \theta_1 = \frac{\pi}{2} + \frac{7\pi}{4} = \frac{9\pi}{4} = \Theta + 2\pi.$$

If we had chosen $\theta_0 = \pi/2$ and $\theta_1 = -\pi/4$, then we would get

$$\theta_0 + \theta_1 = \frac{\pi}{2} - \frac{\pi}{4} = \frac{\pi}{4} = \Theta. \; \blacksquare$$

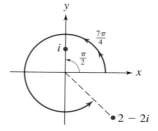

FIGURE 20.10 $\pi/2$ *is an argument of i, and $7\pi/4$ an argument of $2 - 2i$.*

20.1.6   Ordering

Given any two distinct real numbers a and b, exactly one of $a < b$ or $b < a$ must be true. The real numbers are said to be ordered. We will show that there is no ordering of complex numbers.

To understand why this is true, we must investigate the idea behind the ordering of the reals. The ordering of the real numbers is actually a partitioning of the nonzero real numbers into two mutually exclusive sets, N and P, with the following properties:

1. If x is a nonzero real number, then x is in P or $-x$ is in P, but not both.

2. If x and y are in P, then $x + y$ and xy are in P.

Think of P as the set of positive numbers, and N as the set of negative numbers. The existence of such a partition of the nonzero reals satisfing conditions (1) and (2) is the reason why we can order the reals. An ordering is established by defining $x < y$ if and only if $y - x$ is in P. For example, $2 < 5$ because $5 - 2 = 3$ is positive.

Does there exist a partition of the nonzero complex numbers into two sets, P and N, having properties (1) and (2)? If so, we can order the complex numbers.

Suppose such a partition exists. Then either i is in P, or $-i$ is in P, but not both. If i is in P, then $i^2 = -1$ is in P by (2), so $(-1)(i) = -i$ is in P. But this violates condition (1). If $-i$ is in P, then $(-i)(-i) = i^2 = -1$ is in P, so $(-1)(-i) = i$ is in P, again violating (1).

This shows that no such partition exists, and the complex numbers cannot be ordered. Whenever we write $z < w$, we are assuming that z and w are real numbers.

SECTION 20.1 **PROBLEMS**

In each of Problems 1 through 10, carry out the indicated calculation.

1. $(3 - 4i)(6 + 2i)$

2. $i(6 - 2i) + |1 + i|$

3. $\dfrac{2 + i}{4 - 7i}$

4. $\dfrac{(2 + i) - (3 - 4i)}{(5 - i)(3 + i)}$

5. $(17 - 6i)(\overline{-4 - 12i})$

6. $\left| \dfrac{3i}{-4 + 8i} \right|$

7. $i^3 - 4i^2 + 2$

8. $(3 + i)^3$

9. $\left(\dfrac{-6 + 2i}{1 - 8i} \right)^2$

10. $(-3 - 8i)(2i)(4 - i)$

11. Prove that, for any positive integer n,
$$i^{4n} = 1, \; i^{4n+1} = i, \; i^{4n+2} = -1, \; \text{and} \; i^{4n+3} = -i.$$

12. Let $z = a + ib$. Determine $\text{Re}(z^2)$ and $\text{Im}(z^2)$.

13. Let $z = a + ib$. Determine $\text{Re}(z^2 - iz + 1)$ and $\text{Im}(z^2 - iz + 1)$.

14. Prove that $z^2 = \bar{z}^2$ if and only if z is either real or pure imaginary.

15. Let z, w and u be complex numbers. Prove that, when represented as points in the plane, these numbers form the vertices of an equilateral triangle if and only if
$$z^2 + w^2 + u^2 = zw + zu + wu.$$

16. Prove that $\text{Re}(iz) = -\text{Im}(z)$ and $\text{Im}(iz) = \text{Re}(z)$.

In each of Problems 17 through 22, determine $\arg(z)$. The answer should include all arguments of the number.

17. $3i$

18. $-2 + 2i$

19. $-3 + 2i$

20. $8 + i$

21. -4

22. $3 - 4i$

In each of Problems 23 through 28, write the complex number in polar form.

23. $-2 + 2i$

24. $-7i$

25. $5 - 2i$

26. $-4 - i$

27. $8 + i$

28. $-12 + 3i$

29. Let z and w be complex numbers such that $\bar{z}w \neq 1$, but such that either z or w has magnitude 1. Prove that
$$\left| \frac{z - w}{1 - \bar{z}w} \right| = 1.$$

Hint: In problems involving magnitude, it is often useful to recall Theorem 20.1(8). To apply this result, square both sides of the proposed equality.

30. Prove that, for any complex numbers z and w,
$$|z + w|^2 + |z - w|^2 = 2 \left(|z|^2 + |w|^2 \right).$$

Hint: Keep Theorem 20.1(8) in mind.

20.2 Loci and Sets of Points in the Complex Plane

Sometimes complex notation is very efficient in specifying loci of points in the plane. In this section we will illustrate this, and also discuss the complex representation of certain sets that occur frequently in discussions of complex integrals and derivatives.

20.2.1   Distance

If $z = a + ib$ is any complex number, $|z| = \sqrt{a^2 + b^2}$ is the distance from the origin to z (point (a, b)) in the complex plane.

If $w = c + id$ is also a complex number, then

$$|z - w| = |(a - c) + i(b - d)|$$
$$= \sqrt{(a - c)^2 + (b - d)^2}$$

is the distance between z and w in the complex plane (Figure 20.11). This is the standard formula from geometry for the distance between points (a, b) and (c, d).

20.2.2   Circles and Disks

If a is a complex number and r is a positive (hence real) number, the equation

$$|z - a| = r$$

is satisfied by exactly those z whose distance from a is r. The locus of points satisfying this condition is the circle of radius r about a (Figure 20.12). This is the way we specify circles in the complex plane, and we often refer to "the circle $|z - a| = r$."

If $a = 0$, then any point on the circle $|z| = r$ has polar form

$$z = re^{i\theta},$$

where θ is the angle from the positive real axis to the line from the origin through z (Figure 20.13). As θ varies from 0 to 2π, the point $z = re^{i\theta}$ moves once counterclockwise around this circle, starting at $z = r$ on the positive real axis when $\theta = 0$, reaching ri when $\theta = \pi/2$, $-r$ when $\theta = \pi$, $-ri$ when $\theta = 3\pi/2$, and returning to r when $\theta = 2\pi$.

If $a \neq 0$, then the center of the circle $|z - a| = r$ is a instead of the origin. Now a point on the circle has the form

$$z = a + re^{i\theta},$$

which is simply a polar coordinate system translated to have a as its origin (Figure 20.14). As θ varies from 0 to 2π, this point moves once counterclockwise about this circle. For example, the equation $|z - 3 + 7i| = 4$ defines the circle of radius 4 about the point $(3, -7)$ in the plane. The complex number $3 - 7i$ is the center of the circle. A typical point on the circle has the form $z = 3 - 7i + 4e^{i\theta}$ (Figure 20.15).

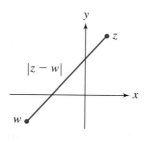

FIGURE 20.11 $|z - w|$ *is the distance between z and w.*

FIGURE 20.12
The circle of radius r about a.

FIGURE 20.13
The circle of radius r about the origin.

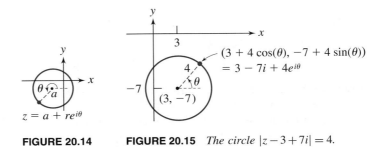

FIGURE 20.14   **FIGURE 20.15**   *The circle* $|z - 3 + 7i| = 4$.

An inequality $|z - a| < r$ specifies all points within the disk of radius r about a. Such a set is called an *open disk*. Open here means that points on the circumference of the circle bounding this disk are not in this set. A point on this circle would satisfy $|z - a| = r$, not $|z - a| < r$. We often indicate in a drawing that a disk is open by drawing a dashed boundary circle (Figure 20.16). For example, $|z - i| < 8$ specifies the points within the open disk of radius 8 about i.

A *closed disk* of radius r and center a consists of all points on or within the circle of radius a about r. This set is specified by the weak inequality $|z - a| \leq r$. In a drawing of such a set, we often draw a solid circle as boundary to indicate that these points are included in the closed disk (Figure 20.17).

20.2.3   The Equation $|z - a| = |z - b|$

Let w_1 and w_2 be distinct complex numbers. An equation

$$|z - w_1| = |z - w_2|$$

can be verbalized as "the distance between z and w_1 must equal the distance between z and w_2." As Figure 20.18 suggests, this requires that z be on the perpendicular bisector of the line segment connecting w_1 and w_2. The equation $|z - w_1| = |z - w_2|$ may therefore be considered the equation of this line.

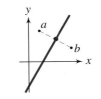

FIGURE 20.16
$|z - a| < r$, *the open disk of radius r about a.*

FIGURE 20.17
$|z - a| \leq r$, *the closed disk of radius r about a.*

FIGURE 20.18
$|z - a| = |z - b|$ *is satisfied by all z on the perpendicular bisector of the segment $\overline{ab}$.*

EXAMPLE 20.4

The equation

$$|z + 6i| = |z - 1 + 3i|$$

is satisfied by all points on the perpendicular bisector of the segment between $-6i$ and $1 - 3i$. This is the segment connecting $(0, -6)$ and $(1, -3)$, as shown in Figure 20.19.

We can obtain the "standard" equation of this line as follows. First write

$$|z + 6i|^2 = |z - 1 + 3i|^2,$$

or

$$(z + 6i)(\overline{z} - 6i) = (z - 1 + 3i)(\overline{z} - 1 - 3i).$$

This eliminates the absolute value signs. Carry out the multiplications to obtain

$$z\overline{z} + 6i(\overline{z} - z) + 36 = z\overline{z} - z - 3iz - \overline{z} + 1 + 3i + 3i\overline{z} - 3i + 9.$$

Let $z = x + iy$. Then $\overline{z} - z = (x - iy) - (x + iy) = -2iy$ and $-\overline{z} - z = -2x$, so the last equation becomes

$$6i(-2iy) + 36 = -2x + 3i(-2iy) + 10,$$

or

$$12y = -2x + 6y - 26.$$

This is the line

$$y = -\frac{1}{3}(x + 13). \blacksquare$$

Now consider the inequality

$$|z + 6i| < |z - 1 + 3i|.$$

We already know that the equation $|z + 6i| = |z - 1 + 3i|$ describes a line separating the plane into two sets, having this line as boundary (Figure 20.19). The given inequality holds for points in one of these sets, on one side or the other of this line. Clearly z is closer to $-6i$ than to $1 - 3i$ if z is below the boundary line. Thus the inequality specifies all z below this line, the shaded region in Figure 20.20. The boundary line itself is drawn dashed because points on this line do not belong to this region.

The weak inequality $|z + 6i| \le |z - 1 + 3i|$ specifies all points in the shaded region of Figure 20.21, together with all points on the boundary line itself.

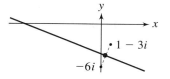

FIGURE 20.19 *The locus of the equation $|z + 6i| = |z - 1 + 3i|$.*

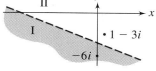

FIGURE 20.20 *Region I consists of points satisfying $|z + 6i| < |z - 1 + 3i|$.*

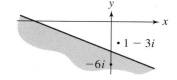

FIGURE 20.21 *The region given by $|z + 6i| \le |z - 1 + 3i|$.*

20.2.4 Other Loci

When a geometric argument is not apparent, we try to determine a locus by substituting $z = x + iy$ into the given equation or inequality.

EXAMPLE 20.5

Consider the equation

$$|z|^2 + 3\text{Re}(z^2) = 4.$$

If $z = x + iy$, this equation becomes

$$x^2 + y^2 + 3(x^2 - y^2) = 4,$$

or

$$4x^2 - 2y^2 = 4.$$

The graph of this equation is the hyperbola of Figure 20.22. A complex number satisfies the given equation if and only if its representation as a point in the plane lies on this hyperbola. ∎

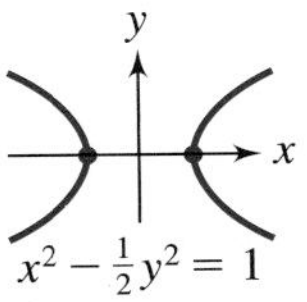

$$x^2 - \tfrac{1}{2}y^2 = 1$$

FIGURE 20.22
Locus
of points z with
$|z|^2 + 3\,\text{Re}(z^2) = 4.$

20.2.5 Interior Points, Boundary Points, and Open and Closed Sets

In the development of the calculus of complex functions, certain kinds of sets and points will be important. For this section let S be a set of complex numbers. A number is an interior point of S if it is in a sense completely surrounded by points of S.

DEFINITION 20.3   *Interior Point*

A complex number z_0 is an interior point of S if there is an open disk about z_0 containing only points of S.

This means that, for some positive r, all points satisfying $|z - z_0| < r$ are in S. Clearly this forces z_0 to be in S as well.

DEFINITION 20.4   Open Set

S is open if every point of S is an interior point.

EXAMPLE 20.6

Let K be the open disk $|z - a| < r$ (Figure 20.23). Every point of K is an interior point because about any point in K we can draw a disk of small enough radius to contain only points in K. Thus K is an open set, justifying the terminology "open disk" used previously for a disk that does not include any points on its bounding circle. ■

EXAMPLE 20.7

Let L consist of all points satisfying $|z - a| \leq r$. Now L contains points that are not interior points, specifically those on the circle $|z - a| = r$. Any open disk drawn about such a point will contain points outside of the disk L (Figure 20.24). This set is not an open set. ■

EXAMPLE 20.8

Let V consist of all $z = x + iy$ with $x > 0$. This is the right half plane, not including the imaginary axis that forms the boundary between the left and right half planes. As suggested by Figure 20.25, every point of V is an interior point, because about any point $z_0 = x_0 + iy_0$ with $x_0 > 0$, we can draw a small enough disk that all points it encloses will also have positive real parts. Since every point of V is an interior point, V is an open set. ■

EXAMPLE 20.9

Let M consist of all $z = x + iy$ with $x \geq 0$. Every point in M with positive real part is an interior point, just as in the preceding example. But not every point of M is interior. A point $z = iy$ on the imaginary axis is in M, but cannot be enclosed in a disk that contains only points

FIGURE 20.23
An open disk is an open set (all points are interior points).

FIGURE 20.24
Points on $|z - a| = r$ are not interior points of $|z - a| \leq r$.

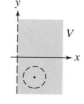

FIGURE 20.25
Half plane $\mathrm{Re}(z) > 0$ (an open set).

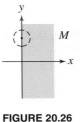

FIGURE 20.26
Half plane
$Re(z) \geq 0$ *(not an open set).*

in M, having nonnegative real part (Figure 20.26). Since M contains points that are not interior points, M is not open. ▪

EXAMPLE 20.10

Let W consist of all points on the real axis. Then no point of W is an interior point. Any disk, no matter how small the radius, drawn about a point on the real axis will contain points not on this axis, hence not in W. No point of W is an interior point of W. ▪

Returning again to the general discussion. boundary points of a set S are complex numbers that are in some sense on the "edge" of S.

DEFINITION 20.5 Boundary Point

A point z_0 is a boundary point of S if every open disk about z_0 contains at least one point in S and at least one point not in S.

A boundary point itself may or may not be in S. Because the definitions of interior point and boundary point are exclusive, no point can be an interior point and a boundary point of the same set. The set of all boundary points of S is called the *boundary* of S, and is denoted ∂S.

EXAMPLE 20.11

The sets K and L of Examples 20.6 and 20.7 have the same boundary, namely the points on the circle $|z - a| = r$. K does not contain any of its boundary points, while L contains them all. ▪

EXAMPLE 20.12

The set V of Example 20.8 has all the points on the imaginary axis as its boundary points. This set does not contain any of its boundary points. By contrast, M of Example 20.9 has the same boundary points as V, namely all points on the imaginary axis, but M contains all of these boundary points.

EXAMPLE 20.13

For the real line (W in Example 20.10), every point of W is a boundary point. If we draw any open disk about a real number x, this disk contains a point of W, namely x, and many points not in W. There are no other boundary points of W. ▇

EXAMPLE 20.14

Let E consist of all complex numbers $z = x + iy$ with $y > 0$, together with the point $-23i$ (Figure 20.27). Then $-23i$ is a boundary point of E, because every disk about $-23i$ certainly contains points not in E, but also contains a point of E, namely $-23i$ itself. Every real number (horizontal axis) is also a boundary point of E. ▇

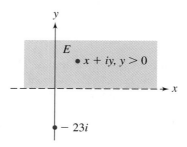

FIGURE 20.27 $-23i$ *is a boundary point of E.*

A careful reading of the definition shows that every point of a set is either an interior point or a boundary point.

THEOREM 20.3

Let S be a set of complex numbers and let z be in S. Then z is either a boundary point of S or an interior point of S. ▇

Proof Suppose z is in S, but is not an interior point. If D is any open disk about z, then D cannot contain only points of S, and so must contain at least one point not in S. But D also contains a point of S, namely z itself. Thus z must be a boundary point of S. ▇

We emphasize, however, that a set may have boundary points that are not in the set, as occurs in some of the above examples.

We also observe that an open set cannot contain any of its boundary points.

THEOREM 20.4

Let S be a set of complex numbers. If S is open, then S can contain no boundary point. ▇

Proof Suppose z is in S and S is open. Then some open disk D about z contains only points of S. But then this disk does not contain any points not in S, so z cannot be a boundary point of S. ▇

DEFINITION 20.6   Closed Set

A set of complex numbers is closed if it contains all of its boundary points.

For example, the closed disk $|z - z_0| \leq r$ is a closed set. The boundary points are all the points on the circle $|z - z_0| = r$, and these are all in the set. The set M of Example 20.9 is closed. Its boundary points are all the points on the imaginary axis, and these all belong to the set. The set W of Example 20.10 is closed, since every point in the set is a boundary point, and the set has no other boundary points.

The terms closed and open are not mutually exclusive, and one is not the opposite of the other. A set may be both closed and open, or closed and not open, or open and not closed, or neither open nor closed. For example, the set $\mathfrak{C}$ of all complex number is open (every point is interior), and closed (every point is a boundary point, and $\mathfrak{C}$ contains them all). A closed disk is closed but not open, and an open disk is open and not closed. The following example gives a set that is neither open nor closed.

EXAMPLE 20.15

Let T consist of all points $z = x + iy$ with $-1 \leq x \leq 1$ and $y > 0$. This is the infinite strip shown in Figure 20.28. The boundary points are all points $-1 + iy$ with $y \geq 0$, all points $1 + iy$ with $y \geq 0$, and all points x with $-1 \leq x \leq 1$. Some of these points are in T, for example, the boundary points $-1 + iy$ with $y > 0$. This means that T cannot be open. But some of these boundary points are not in T, for example, the points x with $-1 \leq x \leq 1$. Thus T is not closed. ■

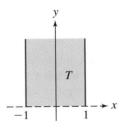

FIGURE 20.28 *The strip consisting of all $z = x + iy$ with $-1 \leq x \leq 1$, $y > 0$.*

20.2.6   Limit Points

A number z_0 is a *limit point* of S if there are points of S arbitrarily close to z_0, but different from z_0.

DEFINITION 20.7   *Limit Point*

A complex number z_0 is a limit point of a set S if every open disk about z_0 contains at least one point of S different from z_0.

Limit point differs from boundary point in requiring that every open disk about the point contain something from S *other than the point itself*. In Example 20.14, $-23i$ is a boundary point of W, but not a limit point of W, because there are open disks about $-23i$ that contain no other point of W.

EXAMPLE 20.16

For the set V of Example 20.8, every point on the vertical axis is a limit point. Given any such point $z_0 = iy_0$, every disk about z_0 contains points of V other than iy_0. Thus z_0 is both a boundary point and a limit point. This example shows that a limit point of a set need not belong to the set. This set has many other limit points. For example, every number $x + iy$ with $x > 0$ is a limit point that also belongs to V. ∎

EXAMPLE 20.17

Let Q consist of the numbers i/n for $n = 1, 2, \ldots$. Every open disk about 0, no matter how small the radius, contains points i/n in Q if we choose n large enough. Therefore 0 is a limit point of Q. In this example, 0 is also a boundary point of Q (its only boundary point). ∎

EXAMPLE 20.18

Let N consist of all in, with n an integer. Then N has no limit points. An open disk of radius $1/2$ about in can have only one point in common with N, namely in itself. ∎

As these examples show, a limit point of a set may or may not be in the set. We claim that closed sets are exactly those that contain all of their limit points, with the understanding that a set contains all of its limit points in a vacuous sense if it has no limit points.

THEOREM 20.5

Let S be a set of complex numbers. Then S is closed if and only if S contains all of its limit points. ∎

Proof   Suppose first that S is closed and let w be a limit point of S. We will show that w is in S. Suppose w is not in S. We know that any disk $|z - w| < r$ must contain a point z_r of S other than w. But then this disk contains a point in S (namely z_r) and a point not in S (namely w itself). Therefore w is a boundary point of S. But S is closed, and so contains all of its boundary points, in particular w. This contradiction shows that w must be in S, hence S contains all of its limit points.

Converely, suppose, if w is a limit point of S, then w is in S. We want to show that S is closed. To do this, we will show that S contains its boundary points. Let b be a boundary point of S. Suppose b is not in S. If $|z - b| < r$ is an open disk about b, then this disk contains a point of S, because b is a boundary point. But this point is not b, because we have assumed that b is not in S. Then every open disk about b contains a point of S other than b, hence b is a limit point of S. But we have supposed that every limit point of S is in S, so b is in S. This contradiction proves that S contains all of its boundary points, hence S is closed. ∎

Here are some additional examples of limit points.

EXAMPLE 20.19

Let X consist of all numbers $2 - i/n$, with $n = 1, 2, \ldots$. Then 2 is a limit point (and boundary point) of X. There are no other limit points of X. ∎

EXAMPLE 20.20

Let Q consist of all complex numbers $a + ib$ with a and b rational numbers. Then every complex number is both a limit point and a boundary point of Q. Some limit points of Q are in Q (if a and b are rational), and some are not (if a or b is irrational). ∎

EXAMPLE 20.21

Let P consist of all complex numbers $x + iy$ with $-1 \le y < 1$. Then each point of P is a limit point, and the points $x + i$ are also limit points of P that do not belong to P. ∎

EXAMPLE 20.22

Let D be the open disk $|z - z_0| < r$. Every point in D is a limit point. However, the points on the boundary circle $|z - z_0| = r$, which do not belong to D, are also limit points, as well as boundary points, of D. ∎

20.2.7 Complex Sequences

The notion of complex sequence is a straightforward adaptation from the concept of real sequence.

DEFINITION 20.8 *Sequence*

A complex sequence $\{z_n\}$ is an assignment of a complex number z_n to each positive integer n.

The number z_n is the nth term of the sequence. For example, $\{i^n\}$ has n^{th} term i^n.

We often indicate a sequence by listing the first few terms, including enough terms so that the pattern becomes clear and one can predict what z_n is for any n. For example, we might write $\{i^n\}$ as

$$i, i^2, i^3, \ldots, i^n, \ldots.$$

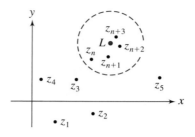

FIGURE 20.29 *Convergence of $\{z_n\}$ to L.*

Convergence of complex sequences is also modeled after convergence of real sequences.

DEFINITION 20.9 *Convergence*

The complex sequence $\{z_n\}$ converges to the number L if, given any positive number ϵ, there is a positive number N such that

$$|z_n - L| < \epsilon \text{ if } n \geq N.$$

This means that we can make each term z_n as close as we like to L by choosing n at least as large as some number N. Put another way, given any open disk D about z_0, we can find some term of the sequence so that all terms beyond this one in the list (that is, for large enough index) lie in D (Figure 20.29). This is the same idea as that behind convergence of real sequences, except on the real line open intervals replace open disks. When $\{z_n\}$ converges to L, we write $z_n \to L$, or $\lim_{n\to\infty} z_n = L$.

If a sequence does not converge to any number, then we say that the sequence *diverges*.

EXAMPLE 20.23

The sequence $\{i^n\}$ diverges. This is the sequence

$$i, -1, -i, 1, i, -1, -i, 1, \ldots$$

and there is no point in the sequence beyond which all the terms approach one specific number arbitrarily closely. For example, if we take the disk $|z - i| < \frac{1}{2}$, then the first term of the sequence, and every fourth term after this, is in this disk, but no other term is in this disk. ∎

EXAMPLE 20.24

The sequence $\{1 + i/n\}$ converges to 1. This follows from the definition since, if $\epsilon > 0$, then

$$\left|(1 + \frac{i}{n}) - 1\right| = \left|\frac{i}{n}\right| = \frac{1}{n} < \epsilon$$

if n is chosen larger than $1/\epsilon$. Given $\epsilon > 0$, we can choose $N = 1/\epsilon$ in the definition of convergence. ∎

Convergence of a complex sequence can always be reduced to an issue of convergence of two real sequences.

THEOREM 20.6

Let $z_n = x_n + iy_n$ and $L = a + ib$. Then $z_n \to L$ if and only if $x_n \to a$ and $y_n \to b$. ■

For example, let $z_n = (1 + 1/n)^n + ((n+2)/n)i$. We know that

$$\lim_{n \to \infty} \left(1 + \frac{1}{n}\right)^n = e$$

and

$$\lim_{n \to \infty} \frac{n+2}{n} = 1.$$

Then

$$\lim_{n \to \infty} z_n = e + i.$$

Proof Suppose first that $z_n \to a + bi$. Let $\epsilon > 0$. For some N, $|z_n - L| < \epsilon$ if $n \geq N$. Then, by Theorem 20.2(1), for $n \geq N$,

$$|x_n - a| = |\text{Re}(z_n - L)| \leq |z_n - L| < \epsilon,$$

so $x_n \to a$. Similarly, if $n \geq N$,

$$|y_n - b| = |\text{Im}(z_n - L)| \leq |z_n - L| < \epsilon,$$

so $y_n \to b$.

Conversely, suppose $x_n \to a$ and $y_n \to b$. Let $\epsilon > 0$. For some N_1,

$$|x_n - a| < \frac{\epsilon}{2} \text{ if } n \geq N_1.$$

For some N_2,

$$|y_n - b| < \frac{\epsilon}{2} \text{ if } n \geq N_2.$$

Then, for $n \geq N_1 + N_2$,

$$|z_n - L| = |(x_n - a) + i(y_n - b)|$$

$$\leq |x_n - a| + |y_n - b| < \frac{\epsilon}{2} + \frac{\epsilon}{2} = \epsilon,$$

proving that $z_n \to L$. ■

The notion of convergence of a complex sequence is intimately tied to the concept of a limit point of a set.

THEOREM 20.7

Let K be a set of complex numbers and let w be a complex number. Then w is a limit point of K if and only if there is a sequence $\{k_n\}$ of points in K, with each $k_n \neq w$, that converges to w. ■

This is the rationale for the term *limit point*. A number w can be a limit point of a set only if w is the limit of a sequence of points in the set, all different from w. This holds whether or not w itself is in the set.

For example, consider the open unit disk $|z| < 1$. We know that i is a limit point of this disk, because any open disk about i contains points of the unit disk different from i. But we can also find a sequence of points in the unit disk converging to i, for example, $z_n = (1 - 1/n)i$.

Proof   Suppose first that w is a limit point of K. Then, for each positive integer n, the open disk of radius $1/n$ about w must contain a point of K different from w. Choose such a point and call it k_n. Then each $k_n \neq w$, k_n is in K, and $|k_n - w| < 1/n$. Since $1/n \to 0$ as $n \to \infty$, then $\{k_n\}$ converges to w.

Conversely, suppose there is a sequence of points k_n in K, all different from w, and converging to w. Let D be any open disk about w , say of radius ϵ. Because $k_n \to w$, D must contain all k_n for n larger than some number N. But then D contains points of K different from w, and hence w is a limit point of K. ∎

20.2.8   Subsequences

A subsequence of a sequence is formed by picking out certain terms to form a new sequence.

DEFINITION 20.10   *Subsequence*
_____

A sequence $\{w_j\}$ is a subsequence of $\{z_n\}$ if there are positive integers

$$n_1 < n_2 < \cdots$$

such that

$$w_j = z_{n_j}.$$

The subsequence is therefore formed from $\{z_n\}$ by listing the terms of this sequence,

$$z_1, z_2, z_3, \ldots$$

and then choosing, in order from left to right, some of the $z'_j s$ to form a new sequence. A subsequence is a sequence in its own right, but consists of selected terms of an initially given sequence.

EXAMPLE 20.25
_____

Let $z_n = i^n$. We can define many subsequences of $\{z_n\}$, but here is one. Let

$$w_j = z_{4j}$$

for $j = 1, 2, \ldots$. Then each $w_j = z_{4j} = i^{4j} = 1$, and every term of this subsequence equals 1. Here $n_j = 4j$ in the definition. ∎

If a sequence converges, then every subsequence of it converges to the same limit. To see this, suppose $z_n \to L$. Let D be an open disk about L. Then "eventually" (that is, for large enough n), every z_n is in D. If $\{w_j\}$ is a subsequence, then each $w_j = z_{n_j}$, so eventually all of these terms will also be in D and the subsequence also converges to L.

However, a subsequence of a divergent sequence may diverge, or it may converge, as Example 20.25 shows. The sequence $\{i^n\}$ diverges, but we were able to choose a subsequence having every term equal to 1, and this subsequence converges to 1.

It is also possible for a divergent sequence to have no convergent subsequence. For example, let $z_n = ni$. This sequence diverges, and we cannot choose a subsequence that converges. Now matter what subsequence is chosen, its terms will simply increase without bound the further out we go in the subsequence.

In this example, the sequence $\{ni\}$ is unbounded, hence divergent, and any subsequence is also unbounded and divergent. We get a more interesting result with bounded sequences.

DEFINITION 20.11   *Bounded Sequence*

$\{z_n\}$ is a bounded sequence if for some number M, $|z_n| \leq M$ for $n = 1, 2, \ldots$.

Alternatively, a sequence is bounded if there is some disk that contains all of its terms. We claim that every bounded sequence, convergent or not, has a convergent subsequence.

THEOREM 20.8

Let $\{z_n\}$ be a bounded sequence. Then $\{z_n\}$ has a convergent subsequence. ■

This result has important consequences, for example, in treating the Cauchy integral theorem. Assuming the corresponding result for bounded real sequences, the conclusion for bounded complex sequences follows from Theorem 20.6.

Proof   Let $z_n = x_n + iy_n$ form a bounded sequence. Then $\{x_n\}$ is a bounded real sequence, and so has a subsequence $\{x_{n_j}\}$ that converges to some real number a. But then $\{y_{n_j}\}$ is also a bounded real sequence, and so has a convergent subsequence $\{y_{n_{jk}}\}$ that converges to some real number b. Using these indices, form the subsequence $\{x_{n_{jk}}\}$ of $\{x_{n_j}\}$. This subsequence also converges to a. Then $\{x_{n_{jk}} + iy_{n_{jk}}\}$ is a subsequence of $\{z_n\}$ that converges to $a + ib$.

20.2.9   Compactness and the Bolzano-Weierstrass Theorem

DEFINITION 20.12   *Bounded Set*

A set K of complex numbers is bounded if, for some number M, $|z| \leq M$ for all z in K.

A bounded set is therefore one whose points cannot be arbitrarily far from the origin. Certainly any finite set is bounded, as is any open or closed disk. The set of points in, for integer n, is not bounded.

The concepts of closed set and bounded set are independent. However, when combined, they characterize sets that have properties that are important in the analysis of complex functions. Such sets are called *compact*.

DEFINITION 20.13 *Compact Set*

A set K of complex number is compact if it is closed and bounded.

Any closed disk is compact, while an open disk is not (it is not closed). The set of points *in* for integer n is not compact because it is not bounded (even though it is closed). Any finite set is compact.

We will now show that any infinite compact set must contain at least one limit point. This is a remarkable result, since closed sets need not contain (or even have) any limit points, and bounded sets need not have limit points.

THEOREM 20.9 *Bolzano–Weierstrass*

Let K be an infinite compact set of complex numbers. Then K contains a limit point. ■

Proof Since K is closed, any limit point of K must be in K. We will therefore concentrate on showing that there is a limit point of K.

Choose any number z_1 in K. Because K is infinite, we can choose a second number z_2 in K, distinct from z_1. Next choose some z_3 in K distinct from z_1 and z_2, and continue this process. In this way generate an infinite sequence $\{z_n\}$ of distinct points in K. Because K is a bounded set, this sequence is bounded. Therefore $\{z_n\}$ contains a subsequence $\{z_{n_j}\}$ that converges to some number L. Because each term of this sequence is distinct from all the others, we can choose the subsequence so that no z_{n_j} equals L. By Theorem 20.7, L is a limit point of K. ■

We are now ready to begin the calculus of complex functions.

SECTION 20.2   **PROBLEMS**

In each of Problems 1 through 11, determine the set of all z satisfying the given equation or inequality. In some cases it may be convenient to specify the set by a clearly labeled diagram.

1. $|z - 8 + 4i| = 9$

2. $|z| = |z - i|$

3. $|z|^2 + \text{Im}(z) = 16$

4. $|z - i| + |z| = 9$

5. $|z| + \text{Re}(z) = 0$

6. $z + \bar{z}^2 = 4$

7. $\text{Im}(z - i) = \text{Re}(z + 1)$

8. $|z| = \text{Im}(z - i)$

9. $|z + 1 + 6i| = |z - 3 + i|$

10. $|z - 4i| \leq |z + 1|$

11. $|z + 2 + i| > |z - 1|$

In each of Problems 12 through 19, a set of points (complex numbers) is given. Determine whether the set is open, closed, open and closed, or neither open nor closed. Determine all limit points of the set, all boundary points, the boundary of the set, and its closure. Also determine whether the set is compact.

12. S is the set of all z with $|z| > 2$.

13. K is the set of all z satisfying $|z - 1| \leq |z + 4i|$.

14. T is the set of all z with $4 \leq |z + i| \leq 8$.

15. M consists of all z with $\text{Im}(z) < 7$.

16. R is the set of all complex numbers $1/m + (1/n)i$, in which m and n may be any positive integers.

17. U is the set of all z such that $1 < \text{Re}(z) \leq 3$.

18. V is the set of all z such that $2 < \text{Re}(z) \leq 3$ and $-1 < \text{Im}(z) < 1$.

19. W consists of all z such that $\text{Re}(z) > (In(z))^2$.

20. Suppose S is a finite set of complex numbers, say consisting of numbers $z_1, z_2, \ldots, z_n$.

(a) Show that S has no limit point.

(b) Show that every z_j is a boundary point of S.

(c) Show that S is closed.

In each of Problems 21 through 27, find the limit of the sequence, or state that the sequence diverges.

21. $\left\{ 1 + \dfrac{2in}{n+1} \right\}$

22. $\left\{ i^{2n} \right\}$

23. $\left\{ \dfrac{1+2n^2}{n^2} - \dfrac{n-1}{n}i \right\}$

24. $\left\{ e^{n\pi i/3} \right\}$

25. $\left\{ -(i^{4n}) \right\}$

26. $\left\{ \sin(n)i \right\}$

27. $\left\{ \dfrac{1+3n^2i}{2n^2-n} \right\}$

28. Consider the sequence $\{ e^{n\pi i/3} \}$ of Problem 24. Find two different convergent subsequences of this sequence.

29. Find two convergent subsequences of the sequence $\{ i^{2n} \}$ of Problem 22.

CHAPTER 21

Complex Functions

21.1 Limits, Continuity, and Derivatives

A *complex function* is a function that is defined for complex numbers in some set S, and takes on complex values. If $\mathfrak{C}$ denotes the set of complex numbers, and f is such a function, then we write $f : S \to \mathfrak{C}$. This simply means that $f(z)$ is a complex number for each z in S. The set S is called the *domain* of f. For example, let S consist of all z with $|z| < 1$ and define $f(z) = z^2$ for z in S. Then $f : S \to \mathfrak{C}$ and f is a complex function.

Often we define a function by some explicit expression in z, for example

$$f(z) = \frac{z+i}{z^2+4}.$$

In the absence of specifying a domain S, we agree to allow all z for which the expression for $f(z)$ is defined. This function is therefore defined for all complex z except $2i$ and $-2i$.

21.1.1 Limits

The notion of limit for a complex function is modeled after that for real-valued functions, with disks replacing intervals.

DEFINITION 21.1 *Limit*

Let $f : S \to \mathfrak{C}$ be a complex function and let z_0 be a limit point of S. Let L be a complex number. Then

$$\lim_{z \to z_0} f(z) = L$$

---

if and only if, given $\epsilon > 0$, there exists a positive number δ such that

$$|f(z) - L| < \epsilon$$

for all z in S such that

$$0 < |z - z_0| < \delta.$$

When $\lim_{z \to z_0} f(z) = L$, we call L the limit of $f(z)$ as z approaches z_0.

Thus, $\lim_{z \to z_0} f(z) = L$ if function values $f(z)$ can be made to lie arbitrarily close (within ϵ) to L by choosing z in S (so $f(z)$ is defined) and close enough (within δ) to z_0, but not actually equal to z_0. The condition $0 < |z - z_0| < \delta$ excludes z_0 itself from consideration. We are only interested in the behavior of $f(z)$ at other points close to z_0.

Put another way, given an open disk D_ϵ of radius ϵ about L, we must be able to find an open disk D_δ of radius δ about z_0, so that every point in D_δ, except z_0 itself, that is also in S, is sent by the function into D_ϵ. This is illustrated in Figure 21.1.

While it is not required in this definition that $f(z_0)$ be defined, we do require that there be points arbitrarily close to z_0 at which $f(z)$ is defined. This is assured by making z_0 a limit point of S, and is the reason for making this a requirement in the definition. It makes no sense to speak of a limit of $f(z)$, as z approaches z_0, if $f(z)$ is not defined as z nears z_0.

Even if $f(z_0)$ is defined, there is no requirement in this limit that $f(z_0) = L$.

EXAMPLE 21.1

Let

$$f(z) = \begin{cases} z^2 & \text{for } z \neq i \\ 0 & \text{for } z = i \end{cases}.$$

Then $\lim_{z \to i} f(z) = -1$, but the limit does not equal $f(0)$. Indeed, even if $f(0)$ were not defined, we would still have $\lim_{z \to i} f(z) = -1$. ∎

Often we write

$$f(z) \to L \quad \text{as} \quad z \to z_0$$

when $\lim_{z \to z_0} f(z) = L$.

Many limit theorems from real calculus hold for complex functions as well. Suppose $\lim_{z \to z_0} f(z) = L$ and $\lim_{z \to z_0} g(z) = K$. Then

$$\lim_{z \to z_0} [f(z) + g(z)] = L + K,$$

$$\lim_{z \to z_0} [f(z) - g(z)] = L - K,$$

$$\lim_{z \to z_0} cf(z) = cL \text{ for any number } c,$$

$$\lim_{z \to z_0} [f(z)g(z)] = LK,$$

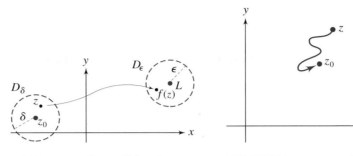

FIGURE 21.1 $\lim_{z \to a} f(z) = L$.

FIGURE 21.2 *z approaches z_0 along any path in defining* $\lim_{z \to z_0} f(z)$.

and, if $K \neq 0$,

$$\lim_{z \to z_0} \frac{f(z)}{g(z)} = \frac{L}{K}.$$

One significant difference between limits of complex functions and limits of real functions is the way the variable can approach the point. For a real function g, $\lim_{x \to a} g(x)$ involves the behavior of $g(x)$ as x approaches a from either side. On the line there are only two ways x can approach a. But $\lim_{z \to z_0} f(z) = L$ involves the behavior of $f(z)$ as z approaches z_0 in the complex plane (or in a specified set S of allowable values) and this may involve z approaching z_0 from any direction (Figure 21.2). The numbers $f(z)$ must approach L along every path of approach of z to z_0 in S. If along a single path of approach of z to z_0, $f(z)$ does not approach L, then $f(z)$ does not have limit L there. This makes $\lim_{z \to z_0} f(z) = L$ in the complex plane a stronger statement than its real counterpart, requiring more of $f(z)$ for z near z_0 than is required of real functions. We will exploit this fact later to derive facts about complex functions.

21.1.2 Continuity

DEFINITION 21.2
_____

A complex function $f : S \to \mathfrak{C}$ is continuous at a number z_0 in S if and only if

$$\lim_{z \to z_0} f(z) = f(z_0).$$

We say that f is continuous on a set K if f is continuous at each point of K. In particular, if f is continuous at all z for which $f(z)$ is defined, then f is a continuous function.

Many familiar functions are continuous. Any polynomial is continuous for all z, and any rational function (quotient of polynomials) is continuous wherever its denominator is nonzero. When we have complex versions of the trigonometric and exponential functions, we will see that they are also continuous.

If f is continuous at z_0, so is $|f|$. We should expect this. If, as z is chosen closer to z_0, $f(z)$ becomes closer to $f(z_0)$, then it is reasonable that $|f(z)|$ approaches $|f(z_0)|$. More rigorously,

$$0 \leq ||f(z)| - |f(z_0)|| \leq |f(z) - f(z_0)| \to 0$$

if $\lim_{z \to z_0} f(z) = f(z_0)$.

If $\{z_n\}$ is a sequence of complex numbers and each $f(z_n)$ is defined, then $\{f(z_n)\}$ is also a complex sequence. For example, if $f(z) = 2z^2$ and $z_n = 1/n$, then $f(z_n) = 2/n^2$. We claim that $\{f(z_n)\}$ converges if $\{z_n\}$ does, when f is continuous. Another way of saying this is that continuity preserves convergence of sequences.

THEOREM 21.1

Let $f: S \to \mathbb{C}$ be continuous, and let $\{z_n\}$ be a sequence of complex numbers in S. If $\{z_n\}$ converges to a number w in S, then $\{f(z_n)\}$ converges to $f(w)$. ∎

Here is the idea behind the theorem. Since f is continuous at w, then $\lim_{z \to w} f(z) = f(w)$. This means that $f(z)$ must approach $f(w)$ along any path of approach of z to w in S. But, if $z_n \to w$, we can think of the $z_n's$ as determining a path of approach of the variable z to w. Then $f(z)$ must approach $f(w)$ along this path, and hence $f(z_n) \to f(w)$.

A converse of Theorem 21.1 can also be proved. If $f(z_n) \to f(w)$ for *every* sequence $\{z_n\}$ of points of S converging to w, then f is continuous at w.

We will now develop a significant property of continuous functions. First, define a complex function (continuous or not) to be bounded if the numbers $f(z)$ do not become arbitrarily large in magnitude.

DEFINITION 21.3   Bounded Function

Let $f: S \to \mathbb{C}$. Then f is a bounded function if there is a positive number M such that

$$|f(z)| \leq M$$

for all z in S.

Alternatively, f is bounded if there is a disk about the origin containing all the numbers $f(z)$ for z in S.

A continuous function need not be bounded (look at $f(z) = 1/z$ for $z \neq 0$). We claim, however, that a continuous function defined on a compact set is bounded. This is analogous to the result that a real function that is continuous on a closed interval is bounded. On the real line, closed intervals are compact sets.

THEOREM 21.2

Let $f: S \to \mathbb{C}$. Suppose S is compact and f is continuous on S. Then f is bounded. ∎

Proof Suppose f is not bounded. Then, if n is a positive integer, the disk of radius n about the origin cannot contain all $f(z)$ for z in S. This means that there is some z_n in S such that $|f(z_n)| > n$.

Now $\{z_n\}$ is a sequence of points in the bounded set S, hence has a convergent subsequence $\{z_{n_j}\}$. Let this subsequence converge to w. Then w is a limit point of S, and S is closed, so w is in S also.

Because f is continuous, $f(z_{n_j}) \to f(w)$. Then, for some N , we can make each $f(z_{n_j})$ lie in the open disk of radius 1 about $f(w)$ by choosing $n_j \geq N$. But this contradicts the fact that each $\left| f(z_{n_j}) \right| > n_j$. Therefore f must be a bounded function. ∎

We can improve on this theorem as follows. Under the conditions of the preceding theorem, $|f(z)|$, which is real-valued, actually assumes a maximum and a minimum on S.

THEOREM 21.3

Let $f: S \to \mathfrak{C}$ be continuous, and suppose S is compact. Then there are numbers z_1 and z_2 in S such that, for all z in S,

$$|f(z_1)| \leq |f(z)| \leq |f(z_2)|. \quad \blacksquare$$

21.1.3 The Derivative of a Complex Function

DEFINITION 21.4 *Derivative*

Let $f: S \to \mathfrak{C}$, and suppose S is an open set. Let z_0 be in S. Then f is differentiable at z_0 if, for some complex number L,

$$\lim_{h \to 0} \frac{f(z_0 + h) - f(z_0)}{h} = L.$$

In this event we call L the derivative of f at z_0 and denote it $f'(z_0)$.

If f is differentiable at each point of a set, then we say that f is differentiable on this set.

The reason for having S open in this definition is to be sure that there is some open disk about z_0 throughout which $f(z)$ is defined. When the complex number h is small enough in magnitude, then $z_0 + h$ is in this disk and $f(z_0 + h)$ is defined. This allows h to approach zero from any direction in the limit defining the derivative. This will have important ramifications shortly in the Cauchy–Riemann equations.

EXAMPLE 21.2

Let $f(z) = z^2$ for all complex z. Then

$$f'(z) = \lim_{h \to 0} \frac{(z + h)^2 - z^2}{h} = \lim_{h \to 0} (2z + h) = 2z$$

for all z. $\blacksquare$

For familiar functions such as polynomials, the usual rules for taking derivatives apply. For example, if n is a positive integer, and $f(z) = z^n$, then $f'(z) = nz^{n-1}$. When we develop the complex sine function $f(z) = \sin(z)$, we will see that $f'(z) = \cos(z)$. Other familiar derivative formulas are:

$$(f + g)'(z) = f'(z) + g'(z),$$
$$(f - g)'(z) = f'(z) - g'(z),$$
$$(cf)'(z) = cf'(z),$$
$$(fg)'(z) = f(z)g'(z) + f'(z)g(z),$$

and

$$\left(\frac{f}{g}\right)'(z) = \frac{g(z)f'(z) - f(z)g'(z)}{[g(z)]^2} \quad \text{if } g(z) \neq 0.$$

These conclusions assume that the derivatives involved exist. There is also a complex version of the chain rule. Recall that the composition of two functions is defined by

$$(f \circ g)(z) = f(g(z)).$$

The chain rule for differentiating a composition is

$$(f \circ g)'(z) = f'(g(z))g'(z),$$

assuming that g is differentiable at z and f is differentiable at $g(z)$.

Often $f'(z)$ is denoted using the Leibniz notation

$$\frac{df}{dz}.$$

In this notation, the chain rule is

$$\frac{d}{dz}(f(g(z))) = \frac{df}{dw}\frac{dw}{dz},$$

where $w = g(z)$.

Not all functions are differentiable.

EXAMPLE 21.3

Let $f(z) = \bar{z}$. We will show that f is not differentiable at any point. To see why this is true, compute

$$\frac{f(z+h) - f(z)}{h} = \frac{\overline{z+h} - \bar{z}}{h} = \frac{\bar{h}}{h}.$$

We want the limit of this quotient as $h \to 0$. But this limit is in the complex plane, and the complex number h must be allowed to approach zero along any path. If h approaches zero along the real axis, then h is real, $\bar{h} = h$ and $\bar{h}/h = 1 \to 1$. But if h approaches zero along the imaginary axis, then $h = ik$ for k real, and

$$\frac{\bar{h}}{h} = \frac{-ik}{ik} = -1 \to -1$$

as $k \to 0$. The quotient $\bar{h}/h$ approaches different numbers as h approaches zero along different paths. This means that

$$\lim_{h \to 0} \frac{\bar{h}}{h}$$

does not exist, so f has no derivative at any point. ∎

As with real functions, a complex function is continuous wherever it is differentiable.

THEOREM 21.4

Let f be differentiable at z_0. Then f is continuous at z_0. ∎

Proof   We know that

$$\lim_{h \to 0} \left(\frac{f(z_0 + h) - f(z_0)}{h} - f'(z_0) \right) = 0.$$

Let

$$\epsilon(h) = \frac{f(z_0 + h) - f(z_0)}{h} - f'(z_0).$$

Then $\lim_{h \to 0} \epsilon(h) = 0$. Further,

$$f(z_0 + h) - f(z_0) = hf'(z_0) + h\epsilon(h).$$

Since the right side has limit zero as $h \to 0$, then

$$\lim_{h \to 0} [f(z_0 + h) - f(z_0)] = 0.$$

This is the same as

$$\lim_{h \to 0} f(z_0 + h) = f(z_0),$$

and this in turn implies that $\lim_{z \to z_0} f(z) = f(z_0)$. Therefore f is continuous at z_0. ∎

21.1.4   The Cauchy–Riemann Equations

We will derive a set of partial differential equations that must be satisfied by the real and imaginary parts of a differentiable complex function. These equations also play a role in potential theory and in treatments of the Dirichlet problem.

Let f be a complex function. If $z = x + iy$, we can always write

$$f(z) = f(x + iy) = u(x, y) + iv(x, y),$$

in which u and v are real-valued functions of the two real variables x and y. Then

$$u(x, y) = \text{Re}[f(z)] \quad \text{and} \quad v(x, y) = \text{Im}[f(z)].$$

EXAMPLE 21.4

Let $f(z) = 1/z$ for $z \neq 0$. Then

$$f(x + iy) = \frac{1}{x + iy} = \frac{1}{x + iy} \frac{x - iy}{x - iy} = \frac{x}{x^2 + y^2} - i\frac{y}{x^2 + y^2}.$$

For this function

$$u(x, y) = \frac{x}{x^2 + y^2} \quad \text{and} \quad v(x, y) = -\frac{y}{x^2 + y^2}. \quad ∎$$

We will now derive a relationship between partial derivatives of u and v, at any point where f is differentiable.

THEOREM 21.5   *Cauchy–Riemann Equations*

Let $f : S \to \mathbb{C}$, with S an open set. Write $f = u + iv$. Suppose $z = x + iy$ is a point of S and $f'(z)$ exists. Then, at (x, y),

$$\frac{\partial u}{\partial x} = \frac{\partial v}{\partial y} \quad \text{and} \quad \frac{\partial v}{\partial x} = -\frac{\partial u}{\partial y}.$$

Proof Begin with

$$f'(z) = \lim_{h \to 0} \frac{f(z+h) - f(z)}{h}.$$

We know that this limit exists, hence must have the same value, $f'(z)$, however h approaches zero. Consider two paths of approach of h to the origin.

First, let $h \to 0$ along the real axis (Figure 21.3). Now h is real, and $z + h = x + h + iy$. Then

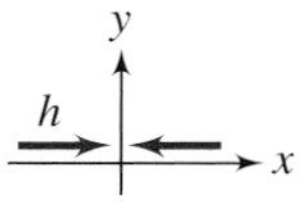

FIGURE 21.3

$$f'(z) = \lim_{h \to 0} \frac{u(x+h, y) + iv(x+h, y) - u(x, y) - iv(x, y)}{h}$$

$$= \lim_{h \to 0} \left(\frac{u(x+h, y) - u(x, y)}{h} + i\frac{v(x+h, y) - v(x, y)}{h} \right)$$

$$= \frac{\partial u}{\partial x} + i\frac{\partial v}{\partial x}.$$

Next, take the limit along the imaginary axis (Figure 21.4). Put $h = ik$ with k real, so $h \to 0$ as $k \to 0$. Now $z = x + i(y+k)$ and

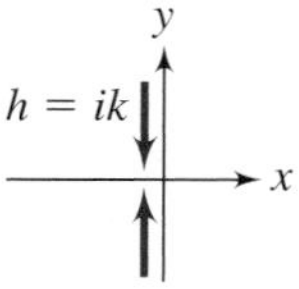

FIGURE 21.4

$$f'(z) = \lim_{k \to 0} \frac{u(x, y+k) + iv(x, y+k) - u(x, y) - iv(x, y)}{ik}$$

$$= \lim_{k \to 0} \left(\frac{1}{i}\frac{u(x, y+k) - u(x, y)}{k} + \frac{v(x, y+k) - v(x, y)}{k} \right)$$

$$= -i\frac{\partial u}{\partial y} + \frac{\partial v}{\partial y},$$

in which we have used the fact that $1/i = -i$.

We now have two expressions for $f'(z)$, so they must be equal:

$$\frac{\partial u}{\partial x} + i\frac{\partial v}{\partial x} = -i\frac{\partial u}{\partial y} + \frac{\partial v}{\partial y}.$$

Setting the real part of the left side equal to the real part of the right, and then the imaginary part of the left side to the imaginary part of the right, yields the Cauchy–Riemann equations. ∎

One extra dividend of this proof is that we have also derived formulas for $f'(z)$ in terms of the real and imaginary parts of $f(z)$. For example, if $f(z) = z^3$, then

$$f(z) = f(x+iy) = (x+iy)^3 = x^3 - 3xy^2 + i(3x^2y - y^3).$$

Then

$$u(x, y) = x^3 - 3xy^2 \quad \text{and} \quad v(x, y) = 3x^2y - y^3,$$

so

$$f'(z) = \frac{\partial u}{\partial x} + i\frac{\partial v}{\partial x} = (3x^2 - 3y^2) + i(6xy).$$

This automatically displays the real and imaginary parts of $f'(z)$. Of course, for this simple function it is just as easy to write directly

$$f'(z) = 3z^2 = 3(x+iy)^2 = 3(x^2 - y^2) + 6xyi.$$

The Cauchy–Riemann equations constitute a necessary condition for f to be differentiable at a point. If they are not satisfied, then $f'(z)$ does not exist at this point.

EXAMPLE 21.5

Let $f(z) = \bar{z}$. Then $f(z) = x - iy$ and $u(x, y) = x$, $v(x, y) = -y$. Now

$$\frac{\partial u}{\partial x} = 1 \neq \frac{\partial v}{\partial y},$$

so the Cauchy–Riemann equations do not hold for f, at any point, and therefore f is not differentiable at any point. ∎

EXAMPLE 21.6

Let $f(z) = z \operatorname{Re}(z)$. Then

$$f(x + iy) = (x + iy)x = x^2 + ixy,$$

so $u(x, y) = x^2$ and $v(x, y) = xy$. Now

$$\frac{\partial u}{\partial x} = 2x, \quad \frac{\partial v}{\partial y} = x$$

and

$$\frac{\partial u}{\partial y} = 0, \quad \frac{\partial v}{\partial x} = y.$$

The Cauchy–Riemann equations do not hold at any point except $z = 0$. This means that f is not differentiable at z if $z \neq 0$, but may have a derivative at 0. In fact, this function is differentiable at 0, since

$$f'(0) = \lim_{h \to 0} \frac{f(h) - f(0)}{h} = \lim_{h \to 0} \operatorname{Re}(h) = 0. \ \blacksquare$$

While the Cauchy–Riemann equations are necessary for differentiability, they are not sufficient. If the Cauchy–Riemann equations hold at a point z, then f may or may not be differentiable at z. In the preceding example, the Cauchy–Riemann equations held at the origin, and $f'(0)$ existed. Here is an example in which the Cauchy–Riemann equations are satisfied at the origin, but f has no derivative there.

EXAMPLE 21.7

Let

$$f(z) = \begin{cases} z^5 / |z|^4 & \text{for } z \neq 0 \\ 0 & \text{for } z = 0 \end{cases}.$$

We will show that the Cauchy–Riemann equations are satisfied at $z = 0$, but that f is not differentiable at 0. First do some algebra to obtain

$$u(x, y) = \frac{5xy^4 - 10x^3y^2 + x^5}{(x^2 + y^2)^2} \quad \text{if } (x, y) \neq (0, 0),$$

$$v(x, y) = \frac{y^5 - 10x^2y^3 + 5x^4y}{(x^2 + y^2)^2} \quad \text{if } (x, y) \neq (0, 0),$$

and

$$u(0, 0) = v(0, 0) = 0.$$

Compute the partial derivatives at the origin:

$$\frac{\partial u}{\partial x}(0, 0) = \lim_{h \to 0} \frac{u(h, 0) - u(0, 0)}{h} = \lim_{h \to 0} \frac{h^5}{hh^4} = 1;$$

$$\frac{\partial u}{\partial y}(0, 0) = \lim_{h \to 0} \frac{u(0, h) - u(0, 0)}{h} = \lim_{h \to 0} 0 = 0;$$

$$\frac{\partial v}{\partial x}(0, 0) = \lim_{h \to 0} \frac{v(h, 0) - v(0, 0)}{h} = \lim_{h \to 0} 0 = 0;$$

and

$$\frac{\partial v}{\partial y}(0, 0) = \lim_{h \to 0} \frac{v(0, h) - v(0, 0)}{h} = \lim_{h \to 0} \frac{h^5}{hh^4} = 1.$$

Therefore the Cauchy–Riemann equations are satisfied at the origin. However, f is not differentiable at 0. Consider

$$\frac{f(0 + h) - f(0)}{h} = \frac{h^5}{h\,|h|^4} = \frac{h^5}{h(h\overline{h})^2} = \frac{h^2}{(\overline{h})^2} = \left(\frac{h}{\overline{h}} \right)^2.$$

We claim that $(h/\overline{h})^2$ has no limit as $h \to 0$. This is easily seen by converting to polar form. If $h = re^{i\theta}$, then $\overline{h} = re^{-i\theta}$, and

$$\left(\frac{h}{\overline{h}} \right)^2 = \frac{r^2 e^{2i\theta}}{r^2 e^{-2i\theta}} = e^{4i\theta}.$$

On the line making an angle θ with the positive real axis (Figure 21.5), the difference quotient

$$\frac{f(0 + h) - f(0)}{h}$$

has the constant value $e^{4i\theta}$, and so approaches this number as $h \to 0$. The difference quotient therefore approaches different values along different paths, and so has no limit as $h \to 0$. ∎

    This example means that some condition(s) must be added to the Cauchy–Riemann equations to guarantee existence of a derivative at a point. The following theorem gives sufficient conditions for differentiability.

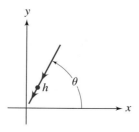

FIGURE 21.5

THEOREM 21.6

Let $f : S \to \mathbb{C}$ be a complex function, with S an open set. Let $f = u + iv$. Suppose u, v and their first partial derivatives are continuous on S. Suppose also that u and v satisfy the Cauchy–Riemann equations on S. Then f is differentiable at each point of S. ∎

In real calculus, a function whose derivative is zero throughout an interval must be constant on that interval. Here is the complex analogue of this result, together with another result we will need later.

THEOREM 21.7

Let f be differentiable on an open disk D. Let $f = u + iv$, and suppose u and v satisfy the Cauchy–Riemann equations, and are continuous with continuous first partial derivatives in D. Then,

1. If $f'(z) = 0$ for all z in D, then $f(z)$ is constant on D.
2. If $|f(z)|$ is constant in D, so is $f(z)$.

Proof To prove (1), recall from the proof of Theorem 21.5 that, for z in D,

$$f'(z) = 0 = \frac{\partial u}{\partial x} + i \frac{\partial v}{\partial x}.$$

But then $\partial u / \partial x$ and $\partial v / \partial x$ are zero throughout D. By the Cauchy–Riemann equations, $\partial u / \partial y$ and $\partial v / \partial y$ are also zero at each point of D. Then $u(x, y)$ and $v(x, y)$ are constant on D, hence so is $f(z)$.

For (2), suppose $|f(z)| = k$ for all z in D. Then

$$|f(z)|^2 = u(x, y)^2 + v(x, y)^2 = k^2 \tag{21.1}$$

for (x, y) in D. If $k = 0$, then $|f(z)| = 0$ for all z in D, hence $f(z) = 0$ on D. If $k \neq 0$, differentiate equation (21.1) with respect to x to get

$$u \frac{\partial u}{\partial x} + v \frac{\partial v}{\partial x} = 0 \tag{21.2}$$

Differentiate equation (21.1) with respect to y to get

$$u \frac{\partial u}{\partial y} + v \frac{\partial v}{\partial y} = 0. \tag{21.3}$$

Using the Cauchy–Riemann equations, equations (21.2) and (21.3) can be written

$$u \frac{\partial u}{\partial x} - v \frac{\partial u}{\partial y} = 0 \tag{21.4}$$

and

$$u \frac{\partial u}{\partial y} + v \frac{\partial u}{\partial x} = 0. \tag{21.5}$$

Multiply equation (21.4) by u and equation (21.5) by v and add the resulting equations to get

$$(u^2 + v^2) \frac{\partial u}{\partial x} = k^2 \frac{\partial u}{\partial x} = 0.$$

Therefore

$$\frac{\partial u}{\partial x} = 0$$

for all (x, y) in D. By the Cauchy–Riemann equations,

$$\frac{\partial v}{\partial y} = 0$$

throughout D. Now a similar manipulation shows that

$$\frac{\partial u}{\partial y} = \frac{\partial v}{\partial x} = 0$$

on D. Therefore $u(x, y)$ and $v(x, y)$ are constant on D, so $f(z)$ is constant also. ∎

SECTION 21.1 PROBLEMS

In each of Problems 1 through 12, find u and v so that $f(z) = u(x, y) + iv(x, y)$, determine all points (if any) at which the Cauchy–Riemann equations are satisfied, and determine all points at which the function is differentiable. Familiar facts about continuity of real-valued functions of two variables may be assumed.

1. $f(z) = z - i$

2. $f(z) = z^2 - iz$

3. $f(z) = |z|$

4. $f(z) = \dfrac{2z + 1}{z}$

5. $f(z) = i|z|^2$

6. $f(z) = z + \text{Im}(z)$

7. $f(z) = \dfrac{z}{\text{Re}(z)}$

8. $f(z) = z^3 - 8z + 2$

9. $f(z) = \bar{z}^2$

10. $f(z) = iz + |z|$

11. $f(z) = -4z + \dfrac{1}{z}$

12. $f(z) = \dfrac{z - i}{z + i}$

21.2 Power Series

We now know some facts about continuity and differentiability. However, the only complex functions we have at this point are polynomials and rational functions. A complex polynomial is a function

$$p(z) = a_0 + a_1 z + a_2 z^2 + \cdots + a_n z^n,$$

in which the $a_j's$ are complex numbers, and a rational function is a quotient of polynomials,

$$R(z) = \frac{a_0 + a_1 z + \cdots + a_n z^n}{b_0 + b_1 z + \cdots + b_m z^m}.$$

Polynomials are differentiable for all z, and a rational function is differentiable for all z at which the denominator does not vanish.

The vehicle for expanding our catalog of functions, obtaining exponential and trigonometric functions, logarithms, power functions and others, is the power series. We will precede a development of complex power series with some facts about series of constants.

21.2.1 Series of Complex Numbers

We will assume standard results about series of real numbers. Consider a complex series $\sum_{n=1}^{\infty} c_n$, with each c_n a complex number. The Nth *partial sum* of this series is the finite sum $\sum_{n=1}^{N} c_n$. The sequence $\left\{\sum_{n=1}^{N} c_n\right\}$ is the *sequence of partial sums* of this series, and the series converges if and only if this sequence of partial sums converges.

If $c_n = a_n + ib_n$, then

$$\sum_{n=1}^{N} c_n = \sum_{n=1}^{N} a_n + i \sum_{n=1}^{N} b_n,$$

so $\left\{\sum_{n=1}^{N} c_n\right\}$ converges if and only if the real partial sums $\sum_{n=1}^{N} a_n$ and $\sum_{n=1}^{N} b_n$ converge as $N \to \infty$. Further, if $\sum_{n=1}^{\infty} a_n = A$ and $\sum_{n=1}^{\infty} b_n = B$, then

$$\sum_{n=1}^{\infty} c_n = A + iB.$$

We can therefore study any series of complex constants by considering two series of real constants, for which tests are available (ratio test, root test, integral test, comparison test and others).

As with real series, if $\sum_{n=1}^{\infty} c_n$ converges, then necessarily $\lim_{n \to \infty} c_n = 0$.

In some instances we can not only show that a series converges, but we can find its sum. The geometric series is an important illustration of this which we will use often.

EXAMPLE 21.8

Consider the series $\sum_{n=1}^{\infty} z^n$, with z a given complex number. A series which adds successive powers of a single number is called a *geometric series*. We can sum this series as follows. Let

$$S_N = \sum_{n=1}^{N} z^n = z + z^2 + z^3 + \cdots + z^{N-1} + z^N.$$

Then

$$z S_N = z^2 + z^3 + \cdots + z^N + z^{N+1},$$

If we subtract these finite sums, most terms cancel and we are left with

$$S_N - z S_N = (1-z) S_N = z - z^{N+1}.$$

Then, for $z \neq 1$,

$$S_N = \frac{z}{1-z} - \frac{1}{1-z} z^{N+1}.$$

If $|z| < 1$, then $|z|^{N+1} \to 0$ as $N \to \infty$, hence $z^{N+1} \to 0$ also and in this case the geometric series converges:

$$\sum_{n=1}^{\infty} z^n = \lim_{N \to \infty} S_N = \frac{z}{1-z}.$$

If $|z| \geq 1$, the geometric series diverges. ∎

Sometimes we have a geometric series with first term equal to 1. This is the series

$$\sum_{n=0}^{\infty} z^n = 1 + \sum_{n=1}^{\infty} z^n = 1 + \frac{z}{1-z} = \frac{1}{1-z} \quad \text{if } |z| < 1.$$

The series $\sum_{n=1}^{\infty} c_n$ is said to *converge absolutely* if the real series $\sum_{n=1}^{\infty} |c_n|$ converges.

THEOREM 21.8

If $\sum_{n=1}^{\infty} c_n$ converges absolutely, then this series converges. ∎

Proof   Let $c_n = a_n + ib_n$. Suppose $\sum_{n=1}^{\infty} |c_n|$ converges. Since $0 \le |a_n| \le |c_n|$, then by comparison, $\sum_{n=1}^{\infty} a_n$ converges. Similarly, $0 \le |b_n| \le |c_n|$, so $\sum_{n=1}^{\infty} b_n$ converges. Then $\sum_{n=1}^{\infty} a_n + ib_n = \sum_{n=1}^{\infty} c_n$ converges. ∎

EXAMPLE 21.9

Consider the series

$$\sum_{n=1}^{\infty} (-1)^n \frac{2-i}{(1+i)^n}.$$

Compute

$$\left| (-1)^n \frac{2-i}{(1+i)^n} \right| = \frac{\sqrt{5}}{(\sqrt{2})^n}.$$

Now the real series $\sum_{n=1}^{\infty} \sqrt{5}/(\sqrt{2})^n$ converges. This is $\sqrt{5}$ times the real geometric series $\sum_{n=1}^{\infty} 1/(\sqrt{2})^n$, which converges because $1/\sqrt{2} < 1$. Therefore the given complex series converges absolutely, hence converges.

The point to Theorem 21.8 is that $\sum_{n=1}^{\infty} |c_n|$ is a real series, and we have methods to test real series for convergence or divergence. We can therefore (in the case of absolute convergence) test a complex series for convergence by testing a real series. This approach is not all-inclusive, however, because a series may converge, but not converge absolutely. Such a series is said to *converge conditionally*. For example, the series

$$\sum_{n=1}^{\infty} \frac{(-1)^n}{n}$$

is well known to converge, but the series of absolute values of its terms is the divergent harmonic series $\sum_{n=1}^{\infty} (1/n)$.

With this background on complex series, we can take up power series.

21.2.2   Power Series

DEFINITION 21.5   *Power Series*

A power series is a series of the form

$$\sum_{n=0}^{\infty} c_n (z - z_0)^n,$$

in which z_0 and each c_n is a given complex number.

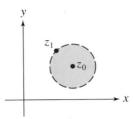

FIGURE 21.6
Convergence at $z_1 \neq z_0$ implies convergence on $|z - z_0| < r = |z_1 - z_0|$.

The summation in a power series begins at $n = 0$ to allow for a constant term:

$$\sum_{n=0}^{\infty} c_n(z - z_0)^n = c_0 + c_1(z - z_0) + c_2(z - z_0)^2 + \cdots.$$

The number z_0 is the *center* of the series, and the numbers c_n are its *coefficients*.

Given a power series, we want to know for what values of z, if any, it converges. Certainly any power series converges at its center $z = z_0$, because then the series is just c_0. The following theorem provides the key to determining if there are other values of z for which it converges. It says that, if we find a point $z_1 \neq z_0$ where the power series converges, then the series must converge absolutely at least for all points closer to z_0 than z_1. This gives (absolute) convergence at least at points interior to the disk of Figure 21.6.

THEOREM 21.9

Suppose $\sum_{n=0}^{\infty} c_n(z - z_0)^n$ converges for some z_1 different from z_0. Then the power series converges absolutely for all z satisfying

$$|z - z_0| < |z_1 - z_0|.$$

Proof Suppose $\sum_{n=0}^{\infty} c_n(z_1 - z_0)^n$ converges. Then $\lim_{n \to \infty} c_n(z_1 - z_0)^n = 0$. Then, for some N,

$$|c_n(z_1 - z_0)^n| < 1 \quad \text{if } n \geq N.$$

Then, for $n \geq N$,

$$|c_n(z - z_0)^n| = |c_n| \left| \frac{(z - z_0)^n}{(z_1 - z_0)^n} \right| |(z_1 - z_0)^n| \leq \left| \frac{(z - z_0)^n}{(z_1 - z_0)^n} \right| = \left| \frac{z - z_0}{z_1 - z_0} \right|^n.$$

But if $|z - z_0| < |z_1 - z_0|$, then

$$\left| \frac{z - z_0}{z_1 - z_0} \right| < 1$$

and then the geometric series

$$\sum_{n=1}^{\infty} \left| \frac{z - z_0}{z_1 - z_0} \right|^n$$

converges. By comparison (since these are series of real numbers),

$$\sum_{n=N}^{\infty} |c_n(z - z_0)^n|$$

converges. But then

$$\sum_{n=0}^{\infty} |c_n(z - z_0)^n|$$

converges, so $\sum_{n=0}^{\infty} c_n(z - z_0)^n$ converges absolutely, as we wanted to prove. ∎

Apply this conclusion as follows. Imagine standing at z_0 in the complex plane. Looking out in all directions, we may see no other points at which the power series converges. In this event, the series converges only for $z = z_0$. This is an uninteresting power series.

A second possibility is that we see only points at which the power series converges. Now the power series converges for all z.

The third possibility is that we see some points at which the series converges, and some at which it diverges. Let R be the distance from z_0 to the nearest point, say ζ, at which the power series diverges. The distance R is critical in the following sense.

If z is further from z_0 than ζ, then the power series must diverge at z. For if it converged, then it would converge at all points closer to z_0 than z, and hence would converge at ζ by Theorem 21.9.

If z is closer to z_0 than ζ, then the power series must converge at z, since ζ is the point closest to z_0 at which the series diverges.

This means that, in this third case, the power series

converges for all z with $|z - z_0| < R$,

and

diverges for all z with $|z - z_0| > R$.

The number R is called the *radius of convergence* of the power series, and the open disk $|z - z_0| < R$ is called the *open disk of convergence*. The series converges inside this disk, and diverges outside the closed disk $|z - z_0| \leq R$. At points on the boundary of this disk, $|z - z_0| = R$, the series might converge or diverge.

If the power series converges only for $z = z_0$, we let the radius of convergence be $R = 0$. In this case we do not speak of an open disk of convergence.

If the power series converges for all z, let $R = \infty$. Now the open disk of convergence is the entire complex plane. In this case it is convenient to denote the disk of convergence as $|z - z_0| < \infty$.

Sometimes the radius of convergence can be calculated for a power series by using the ratio test.

EXAMPLE 21.10

Consider the power series

$$\sum_{n=0}^{\infty} (-1)^n \frac{2^n}{n+1} (z - 1 + 2i)^{2n}.$$

The center is $z_0 = 1 - 2i$. We want the radius of convergence of this series.

Consider the magnitude of the ratio of successive terms of this series:

$$\left| \frac{(-1)^{n+1} \frac{2^{n+1}}{n+2} (z-1+2i)^{2n+2}}{(-1)^n \frac{2^n}{n+1} (z-1+2i)^{2n}} \right| = \frac{2(n+1)}{n+2} |z-1+2i|^2$$

$$\rightarrow 2|z-1+2i|^2 \quad \text{as } n \rightarrow \infty.$$

From the ratio test for real series, the power series will converge absolutely if this limit is less than 1, and diverge if this limit is greater than 1. Thus, the power series converges absolutely if

$$2|z-1+2i|^2 < 1,$$

or

$$|z-1+2i| < \frac{1}{\sqrt{2}}.$$

And the series diverges if

$$2|z-1+2i|^2 > 1,$$

or

$$|z-1+2i| > \frac{1}{\sqrt{2}}.$$

The radius of convergence is $1/\sqrt{2}$ and the open disk of convergence is $|z-1+2i| < 1/\sqrt{2}$ (Figure 21.7). ■

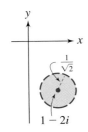

FIGURE 21.7

Suppose now that a power series has a positive or infinite radius of convergence. For each z in the open disk of convergence, let

$$f(z) = \sum_{n=1}^{\infty} c_n (z-z_0)^n.$$

This defines a function f over this disk. We want to explore the properties of this function, in particular, whether it is differentiable. Answering this question requires the following technical lemma.

LEMMA 21.1

The power series $\sum_{n=0}^{\infty} c_n (z-z_0)^n$ and $\sum_{n=1}^{\infty} n c_n (z-z_0)^{n-1}$ have the same radius of convergence. ■

The lemma states that term by term differentiation of a power series does not change the radius of convergence. This means that, within the open disk of convergence, a power series defines a differentiable function whose derivative can be obtained by term by term differentiation.

THEOREM 21.10

Let $\sum_{n=0}^{\infty} c_n (z-z_0)^n$ have positive or infinite radius of convergence. For each z in the open disk of convergence, let

$$f(z) = \sum_{n=0}^{\infty} c_n (z-z_0)^n.$$

Then f is differentiable on this open disk, and

$$f'(z) = \sum_{n=1}^{\infty} nc_n(z-z_0)^{n-1}. \; \blacksquare$$

Using this theorem, we know how to differentiate a function defined by a power series. But there is more to Theorem 21.10 than this. The series $\sum_{n=1}^{\infty} nc_n(z-z_0)^{n-1}$ is a power series in its own right, having the same radius of convergence as the series $\sum_{n=0}^{\infty} c_n(z-z_0)^n$. We can therefore apply the theorem to this differentiated series and obtain

$$f''(z) = \sum_{n=2}^{\infty} n(n-1)c_n(z-z_0)^{n-2}$$

within the open disk of convergence. Further, we can continue to differentiate as many times as we like within this disk. If $f^{(k)}(z)$ denotes the kth derivative, then

$$f^{(3)}(z) = \sum_{n=3}^{\infty} n(n-1)(n-2)c_n z^{n-3},$$

and in general

$$f^{(k)}(z) = \sum_{n=k}^{\infty} n(n-1)(n-2)\cdots(n-k+1)c_n(z-z_0)^{n-k}.$$

If the kth derivative is evaluated at z_0, then all terms of the series for $f^{(k)}(z_0)$ having positive powers of $z-z_0$ vanish, leaving just the constant first term in this differentiated series. In this way, we get

$$f(z_0) = c_0,$$
$$f'(z_0) = c_1,$$
$$f''(z_0) = 2c_2,$$
$$f^{(3)}(z_0) = 3(2)c_3$$

and, in general,

$$f^{(k)}(z_0) = k(k-1)(k-2)\cdots(1)c_k.$$

We can solve these equations for the coefficients in terms of the function and its derivatives at z_0:

$$c_k = \frac{1}{k!}f^{(k)}(z_0) \quad \text{for } k = 0, 1, 2, \ldots, \tag{21.6}$$

where $k!$ is the product of the integers from 1 through k, $0! = 1$ by convention, and the zeroeth derivative $f^{(0)}(z)$ is just $f(z)$. This notation enables us to write one formula for the coefficients without considering the case $k = 0$ separately. The numbers given by equation (21.6) are the *Taylor coefficients* of f at z_0, and the power series

$$\sum_{n=0}^{\infty} \frac{1}{n!}f^{(n)}(z_0)(z-z_0)^n$$

is called the *Taylor series* for f at (or about) z_0.

We have shown that, if a function f is defined in a disk by a power series centered at z_0, then the coefficients in this power series must be the Taylor coefficients, and the power series must be the Taylor series of f about z_0.

We are now in a position to define some of the elementary complex functions, including exponential and trigonometric functions and power functions.

SECTION 21.2   PROBLEMS

In each of Problems 1 through 8, determine the radius of convergence and open disk of convergence of the power series.

1. $\sum_{n=0}^{\infty} \dfrac{n+1}{2^n}(z+3i)^n$

2. $\sum_{n=0}^{\infty}(-1)^n \dfrac{1}{(2n+1)^2}(z-i)^{2n}$

3. $\sum_{n=0}^{\infty} \dfrac{n^n}{(n+1)^n}(z-1+3i)^n$

4. $\sum_{n=0}^{\infty}\left(\dfrac{2i}{5+i}\right)^n(z+3-4i)^n$

5. $\sum_{n=0}^{\infty} \dfrac{i^n}{2^{n+1}}(z+8i)^n$

6. $\sum_{n=0}^{\infty} \dfrac{(1-i)^n}{n+2}(z-3)^n$

7. $\sum_{n=0}^{\infty} \dfrac{n^2}{2n+1}(z+6+2i)^n$

8. $\sum_{n=0}^{\infty} \dfrac{n^3}{4^n}(z+2i)^{3n}$

9. Is it possible for $\sum c_n(z-2i)^n$ to converge at 0 and diverge at i?

10. Is it possible for $\sum_{n=0}^{\infty} c_n(z-4+2i)^n$ to converge at i and diverge at $1+i$?

11. Consider $\sum_{n=0}^{\infty} c_n z^n$, where $c_n = 2$ if n is even and $c_n = 1$ if n is odd. Show that the radius of convergence of this power series is 1, but that this number cannot be computed using the ratio test. (This simply means that it is not always possible to use this test to determine the radius of convergence of a power series).

21.3   The Exponential and Trigonometric Functions

We want to define the complex exponential function e^z so that it agrees with the real exponential function when z is real. For all real x,

$$e^x = \sum_{n=0}^{\infty} \frac{1}{n!}x^n.$$

Replace x with z in this series to obtain the power series

$$\sum_{n=0}^{\infty} \frac{1}{n!}z^n.$$

Compute

$$\lim_{n\to\infty}\left|\frac{z^{n+1}/(n+1)!}{z^n/n!}\right| = \lim_{n\to\infty}\frac{1}{n+1}|z| = 0.$$

Because this limit is less than 1 for all z, this power series converges for all z, and we can make the following definition.

DEFINITION 21.6 **Exponential Function**

For complex z, define the complex exponential function e^z by

$$e^z = \sum_{n=0}^{\infty} \frac{1}{n!} z^n.$$

THEOREM 21.11

For every complex number, and every positive integer k, the kth derivative of e^z is

$$f^{(k)}(z) = e^z. \quad \blacksquare$$

Proof Compute

$$f'(z) = \sum_{n=1}^{\infty} \frac{1}{n!} nz^{n-1} = \sum_{n=1}^{\infty} \frac{1}{(n-1)!} z^{n-1} = \sum_{n=0}^{\infty} \frac{1}{n!} z^n = e^z.$$

Therefore $f'(z) = e^z$. Continued differentiation now gives $f^{(k)}(z) = e^z$ for any positive integer k. $\blacksquare$

We will list properties of the complex exponential function, many of which are familiar from the real case. Conclusion (8) gives the real and imaginary parts of e^z, enabling us to write $e^z = u(x, y) + iv(x, y)$. Conclusion (9) has perhaps the main surprise we find when we extend the real exponential function to the complex plane. The complex exponential function is periodic! This period does not manifest itself in the real case because it is pure imaginary.

THEOREM 21.12

1. $e^0 = 1$.
2. If g is differentiable at z, then so is $e^{g(z)}$, and

$$\frac{d}{dz} e^{g(z)} = g'(z) e^{g(z)}.$$

3. $e^{z+w} = e^z e^w$ for all complex z and w.
4. $e^z \neq 0$ for all z.
5. $e^{-z} = 1/e^z$.
6. If z is real, then e^z is real and $e^z > 0$.
7. (Euler's Formula) If y is real, then

$$e^{iy} = \cos(y) + i\sin(y).$$

8. If $z = x + iy$, then

$$e^z = e^x \cos(y) + ie^x \sin(y).$$

9. e^z is periodic with period $2n\pi i$ for any integer n.

Proof (1) is obvious and (2) follows from the chain rule for differentiation.

To prove (3), fix any complex number u and define $f(z) = e^z e^{u-z}$, for all complex z. Then

$$f'(z) = e^z e^{u-z} - e^z e^{u-z} = 0$$

for all z. By Theorem 21.7, on any open disk $D : |z| < R$, $f(z)$ is constant. For some number K, $f(z) = K$ for $|z| < R$. But then $f(0) = K = e^0 e^u = e^u$, so for all z in D,

$$e^z e^{u-z} = e^u.$$

Now let $u = z + w$ to get

$$e^z e^w = e^{z+w}.$$

Since R can be as large as we want, this holds for all complex z and w.

To prove (4), suppose $e^\alpha = 0$. Then

$$1 = e^0 = e^{\alpha - \alpha} = e^\alpha e^{-\alpha} = 0,$$

a contradiction.

For (5), argue as in (4) that

$$1 = e^0 = e^{z-z} = e^z e^{-z},$$

so

$$e^{-z} = 1/e^z.$$

To prove (7), write

$$e^{iy} = \sum_{n=0}^{\infty} \frac{1}{n!}(iy)^n = \sum_{n=0}^{\infty} \frac{1}{(2n)!}(iy)^{2n} + \sum_{n=0}^{\infty} \frac{1}{(2n+1)!}(iy)^{2n+1}$$

$$= \sum_{n=0}^{\infty} \frac{1}{(2n)!} i^{2n} y^{2n} + \sum_{n=0}^{\infty} \frac{1}{(2n+1)!} i^{2n+1} y^{2n+1}.$$

Now

$$i^{2n} = (i^2)^n = (-1)^n$$

and

$$i^{2n+1} = i(i^{2n}) = i(-1)^n,$$

so

$$e^{iy} = \sum_{n=0}^{\infty} \frac{(-1)^n}{(2n)!} y^{2n} + i \sum_{n=0}^{\infty} \frac{(-1)^n}{(2n+1)!} y^{2n+1} = \cos(y) + i\sin(y),$$

in which we have used the (real) Maclaurin expansions of $\cos(y)$ and $\sin(y)$ for real y.

For (8), use (7) to write

$$e^z = e^{x+iy} = e^x e^{iy} = e^x(\cos(y) + i\sin(y)).$$

Finally, for conclusion (9), for any integer n,

$$e^{z+2n\pi i} = e^{x+i(y+2n\pi)} = e^x\left(\cos(y+2n\pi) + i\sin(y+2n\pi)\right)$$

$$= e^x \cos(y) + ie^x \sin(y) = e^z.$$

Thus for any nonzero integer n, $2n\pi i$ is a period of e^z.

Conclusion (8) actually gives the polar form of e^z in terms of x and y. It implies that the magnitude of e^z is e^x, and that an argument of e^z is y. We may state these conclusions:

$$|e^z| = e^{\text{Re}(z)} = e^x$$

and

$$\arg(e^z) = \text{Im}(z) + 2n\pi = y + 2n\pi.$$

It is also easy to verify that

$$\overline{e^z} = e^{\bar{z}}.$$

To see this, write

$$\overline{e^z} = \overline{e^x(\cos(y) + i\sin(y))} = e^x(\cos(y) - i\sin(y)) = e^{x-iy} = e^{\bar{z}}.$$

For example,

$$\overline{e^{2+6i}} = e^{\overline{2+6i}} = e^{2-6i} = e^2(\cos(6) - i\sin(6)).$$

Conclusion (9) can be improved. Not only is $2n\pi i$ a period of e^z, but these numbers are the only periods. This is part (4) of the next theorem.

THEOREM 21.13

---

1. $e^z = 1$ if and only if $z = 2n\pi i$ for some integer n.
2. $e^z = -1$ if and only if $z = (2n+1)\pi i$ for some integer n.
3. $e^z = e^w$ if and only if $z - w = 2n\pi i$ for some integer n.
4. If p is a period of e^z, then $p = 2n\pi i$ for some integer n.

Contrast conclusion (2) of this theorem with conclusion (6) of the preceding theorem. If x is real, then e^x is a positive real number. However, the complex exponential function can assume negative values. Conclusion (2) of this theorem gives all values of z such that e^z assumes the value -1.

Proof For (1), suppose first that $e^z = 1$. Then

$$e^z = 1 = e^x\cos(y) + ie^x\sin(y).$$

Then

$$e^x\cos(y) = 1 \quad \text{and} \quad e^x\sin(y) = 0.$$

Now x is real, so $e^x > 0$ and the second equation requires that $\sin(y) = 0$. Since this is the real sine function, we know all of its zeros, and can conclude that $y = k\pi$ for integer k. Now we must have

$$e^x\cos(y) = e^x\cos(k\pi) = 1.$$

But $\cos(k\pi) = (-1)^k$ for integer k, so

$$e^x(-1)^k = 1.$$

For this to be satisfied, we first need $(-1)^k$ to be positive, hence k must be an even integer, say $k = 2n$. This leaves us with

$$e^x = 1$$

so $x = 0$. Therefore $z = x + iy = 2n\pi i$.

Conversely, suppose $z = 2n\pi i$ for some integer n. Then

$$e^z = \cos(2n\pi) + i\sin(2n\pi) = 1.$$

Conclusion (2) can be proved by an argument that closely parallels that just done for (1). For (3), if $z - w = 2n\pi i$, then

$$e^{z-w} = \frac{e^z}{e^w} = e^{2n\pi i} = 1,$$

so

$$e^z = e^w.$$

Conversely, suppose $e^z = e^w$. Then $e^{z-w} = 1$, so by (1), $z - w = 2n\pi i$ for some integer n. Finally, for (4), suppose p is a period of e^z. Then

$$e^{z+p} = e^z$$

for all z. But then

$$e^z e^p = e^z$$

so $e^p = 1$ and, by (1), $p = 2n\pi i$ for some integer n. ■

Using the properties we have derived for e^z, we can sometimes solve equations involving this function.

EXAMPLE 21.11

Find all z such that

$$e^z = 1 + 2i.$$

To do this, let $z = x + iy$, so

$$e^x \cos(y) + ie^x \sin(y) = 1 + 2i.$$

Then

$$e^x \cos(y) = 1$$

and

$$e^x \sin(y) = 2.$$

Add the squares of these equations to get

$$e^{2x}(\cos^2(y) + \sin^2(y)) = e^{2x} = 5.$$

Then

$$x = \frac{1}{2}\ln(5),$$

in which $\ln(5)$ is the real natural logarithm of 5. Next, divide:

$$\frac{e^x \sin(y)}{e^x \cos(y)} = \tan(y) = 2,$$

so $y = \tan^{-1}(2)$. One solution of the given equation is $z = \frac{1}{2}\ln(5) + i\tan^{-1}(2)$, or approximately $0.8047 + 1.1071i$. ■

We are now ready to extend the trigonometric functions from the real line to the complex plane. We want to define $\sin(z)$ and $\cos(z)$ for all complex z, so that these functions agree with the real sine and cosine functions when z is real. Following the method used to extend the exponential function from the real line to the complex plane, we begin with power series.

DEFINITION 21.7

For all complex z, let

$$\sin(z) = \sum_{n=0}^{\infty} \frac{(-1)^n}{(2n+1)!} z^{2n+1} \quad \text{and} \quad \cos(z) = \sum_{n=0}^{\infty} \frac{(-1)^n}{(2n)!} z^{2n}.$$

The definition presupposes that these series converge for all complex z, a fact that is easy to show.

From the power series, it is immediate that

$$\cos(-z) = \cos(z) \quad \text{and} \quad \sin(-z) = -\sin(z).$$

By differentiating the series term by term, we find that, for all z,

$$\frac{d}{dz} \sin(z) = \cos(z) \quad \text{and} \quad \frac{d}{dz} \cos(z) = -\sin(z).$$

Euler's formula states that, for real y, $e^{iy} = \cos(y) + i\sin(y)$. We will now extend this to the entire complex plane.

THEOREM 21.14

For every complex number z,

$$e^{iz} = \cos(z) + i\sin(z). \quad \blacksquare$$

The proof follows that of Theorem 21.12(7), with z in place of x.

We can express $\sin(z)$ and $\cos(z)$ in terms of the exponential function as follows. First, from Theorem 21.14,

$$e^{iz} = \cos(z) + i\sin(z)$$

and

$$e^{-iz} = \cos(z) - i\sin(z).$$

Solve these equations for $\sin(z)$ and $\cos(z)$ to obtain

$$\cos(z) = \frac{1}{2}\left(e^{iz} + e^{-iz}\right) \quad \text{and} \quad \sin(z) = \frac{1}{2i}\left(e^{iz} - e^{-iz}\right).$$

Formulas such as these reveal one of the benefits of extending these familiar functions to the complex plane. On the real line, there is no apparent connection between e^x, $\sin(x)$ and $\cos(x)$. These formulations are also convenient for carrying out many manipulations involving $\sin(z)$ and $\cos(z)$. For example, to derive the identity

$$\sin(2z) = 2\cos(z)\sin(z),$$

we have immediately that

$$2\sin(z)\cos(z) = 2\frac{1}{2}\left(e^{iz} + e^{-iz}\right)\frac{1}{2i}\left(e^{iz} - e^{-iz}\right)$$

$$= \frac{1}{2i}\left(e^{2iz} - e^{-2iz} + 1 - 1\right) = \frac{1}{2i}\left(e^{2iz} - e^{-2iz}\right) = \sin(2z).$$

Identities involving real trigonometric functions remain true in the complex case, and we will often use them without proof. For example,

$$\sin(z + w) = \sin(z)\cos(w) + \cos(z)\sin(w).$$

Not all properties of the real sine and cosine are passed along to their complex extensions. Recall that $|\cos(x)| \leq 1$ and $|\sin(x)| \leq 1$ for real x. Contrast this with the following.

THEOREM 21.15

$\cos(z)$ and $\sin(z)$ are unbounded in the complex plane. ∎

The proof consists of simply showing that both functions can be made arbitrarily large in magnitude by certain choices of z. Let $z = iy$ with y real. Then

$$\sin(z) = \sin(iy) = \frac{1}{2i}\left(e^{-y} - e^{y}\right)$$

so

$$|\sin(z)| = \frac{1}{2}\left|e^{y} - e^{-y}\right|,$$

and the right side can be made as large as we like by choosing y sufficiently large in magnitude. That is, as z moves away from the origin in either direction along the vertical axis, $|\sin(z)|$ increases in magnitude without bound. It is easy to check that $|\cos(z)|$ exhibits the same behavior.

It is often useful to know the real and imaginary parts of these functions.

THEOREM 21.16

Let $z = x + iy$. Then

$$\cos(z) = \cos(x)\cosh(y) - i\sin(x)\sinh(y)$$

and

$$\sin(z) = \sin(x)\cosh(y) + i\cos(x)\sinh(y). \quad ∎$$

These expressions are routine to derive starting from the exponential expressions for $\sin(z)$ and $\cos(z)$.

We will now show that the complex sine and cosine functions have exactly the same periods and zeros as their real counterparts.

THEOREM 21.17

1. $\sin(z) = 0$ if and only if $z = n\pi$ for some integer n.
2. $\cos(z) = 0$ if and only if $z = (2n + 1)\pi/2$ for some integer n.

3. $\sin(z)$ and $\cos(z)$ are periodic with periods $2n\pi$, for n any nonzero integer. Further, these are the only periods of these functions. ∎

Conclusion (3) means that

$$\cos(z + 2n\pi) = \cos(z) \quad \text{and} \quad \sin(z + 2n\pi) = \sin(z)$$

for all complex z and, conversely, if

$$\cos(z + p) = \cos(z) \quad \text{for all } z$$

then $p = 2n\pi$, and if

$$\sin(z + q) = \sin(z) \quad \text{for all } z$$

then $q = 2n\pi$. This guarantees that the sine and cosine functions do not pick up additional periods when extended to the complex plane, as occurs with the complex exponential function.

Proof   For (1), if n is an integer, then

$$\sin(n\pi) = \frac{1}{2i}\left(e^{n\pi i} - e^{-n\pi i}\right) = \frac{1}{2i}(1 - 1) = 0.$$

Thus every $z = n\pi$, with n an integer, is a zero of $\sin(z)$. To show that these are the only zeros, suppose $\sin(z) = 0$. Let $z = x + iy$. Then

$$\sin(x)\cosh(y) + i\cos(x)\sinh(y) = 0.$$

Then

$$\sin(x)\cosh(y) = 0 \quad \text{and} \quad \cos(x)\sinh(y) = 0.$$

Since $\cosh(y) > 0$ for all real y, then $\sin(x) = 0$, and for this real sine function, this means that $x = n\pi$ for some integer n. Then

$$\cos(x)\sinh(y) = \cos(n\pi)\sinh(y) = 0.$$

But $\cos(n\pi) = (-1)^n \neq 0$, so $\sinh(y) = 0$ and this forces $y = 0$. Thus $z = n\pi$.

(2) can be proved by an argument similar to that used for (1).

For (3), if n is an integer, then

$$\sin(z + 2n\pi) = \frac{1}{2i}\left(e^{i(z+2n\pi)} - e^{-i(z+2n\pi)}\right)$$

$$= \frac{1}{2i}\left(e^{iz}e^{2n\pi i} - e^{-iz}e^{-2n\pi i}\right) = \frac{1}{2i}\left(e^{iz} - e^{-iz}\right) = \sin(z),$$

so each even integer multiple of π is a period of $\sin(z)$. To show that there are no other periods, suppose p is a period of $\sin(z)$. Then

$$\sin(z + p) = \sin(z)$$

for all complex z. In particular, this must hold for $z = 0$, so $\sin(p) = 0$ and then by (1), $p = n\pi$ for integer n. But we can also put $z = i$ to have

$$\sin(i + n\pi) = \sin(i).$$

Then

$$e^{i(i+n\pi)} - e^{-i(i+n\pi)} = e^{-1} - e.$$

Therefore

$$e^{-1}\cos(n\pi) - e\cos(n\pi) = e^{-1} - e.$$

If n is even, then $\cos(n\pi) = 1$ and this equation is true. If n is odd, then $\cos(n\pi) = -1$ and this equation becomes

$$-e^{-1} + e = e^{-1} - e,$$

an impossibility. Therefore n is even, and the only periods of $\sin(z)$ are even integer multiples of π.

A similar argument establishes the same result for periods of $\cos(z)$. ∎

Here is an example in which facts about $\cos(z)$ are used to solve an equation.

EXAMPLE 21.12

Solve $\cos(z) = i$.
    Let $z = x + iy$, so

$$\cos(x)\cosh(y) - i\sin(x)\sinh(y) = i.$$

Then

$$\cos(x)\cosh(y) = 0 \quad \text{and} \quad \sin(x)\sinh(y) = -1.$$

Since $\cosh(y) > 0$ for all real y, the first equation implies that $\cos(x) = 0$, so

$$x = \frac{2n+1}{2}\pi,$$

in which (so far) n can be any integer. From the second equation,

$$\sin\left(\frac{2n+1}{2}\pi\right)\sinh(y) = -1.$$

Now $\sin((2n+1)\pi/2) = (-1)^n$, so

$$\sinh(y) = (-1)^{n+1},$$

with n any integer. Thus $y = \sinh^{-1}((-1)^{n+1})$. The solutions of $\cos(z) = i$ are therefore the complex numbers

$$\frac{2n+1}{2}\pi + i\sinh^{-1}(-1) \quad \text{for } n \text{ an even integer,}$$

and

$$\frac{2n+1}{2}\pi + i\sinh^{-1}(1) \quad \text{for } n \text{ an odd integer.}$$

A standard formula for the inverse hyperbolic sine function gives

$$\sinh^{-1}(\beta) = \ln\left(\beta + \sqrt{\beta^2 + 1}\right)$$

for β real. Therefore the solutions can be written

$$\frac{2n+1}{2}\pi + i\ln(-1 + \sqrt{2}) \quad \text{for } n \text{ an even integer,}$$

and

$$\frac{2n+1}{2}\pi + i\ln(1 + \sqrt{2}) \quad \text{for } n \text{ an even integer.} \quad ∎$$

The other trigonometric functions are defined by

$$\sec(z) = \frac{1}{\cos(z)}, \quad \csc(z) = \frac{1}{\sin(z)},$$

$$\tan(z) = \frac{\sin(z)}{\cos(z)}, \quad \cot(z) = \frac{\cos(z)}{\sin(z)},$$

in each case for all z for which the denominator does not vanish. Properties of these functions can be derived from properties of $\sin(z)$ and $\cos(z)$.

SECTION 21.3   PROBLEMS

In each of Problems 1 through 10, write the function value in the form $a + bi$.

1. e^i

2. $\sin(1 - 4i)$

3. $\cos(3 + 2i)$

4. $\tan(3i)$

5. e^{5+2i}

6. $\cot\left(1 - \dfrac{\pi i}{4}\right)$

7. $\sin^2(1 + i)$

8. $\cos(2 - i) - \sin(2 - i)$

9. $e^{\pi i/2}$

10. $\sin(e^i)$

11. Find $u(x, y)$ and $v(x, y)$ such that $e^{z^2} = u(x, y) + iv(x, y)$. Show that u and v satisfy the Cauchy-Riemann equations for all complex z.

12. Find $u(x, y)$ and $v(x, y)$ such that $e^{1/z} = u(x, y) + iv(x, y)$. Show that u and v satisfy the Cauchy-Riemann equations for all z except zero.

13. Find $u(x, y)$ and $v(x, y)$ such that $\tan(z) = u(x, y) + iv(x, y)$. Determine where these functions are defined, and show that they satisfy the Cauchy-Riemann equations for these points (x, y).

14. Find $u(x, y)$ and $v(x, y)$ such that $\sec(z) = u(x, y) + iv(x, y)$. Determine where these functions are defined and show that they satisfy the Cauchy-Riemann equations for all such points.

15. Prove that $\sin^2(z) + \cos^2(z) = 1$ for all complex z.

16. Let z and w be complex numbers.

   (a) Prove that $\sin(z + w) = \sin(z)\cos(w) + \cos(z)\sin(w)$.

   (b) Prove that $\cos(z + w) = \cos(z)\cos(w) - \sin(z)\sin(w)$.

17. Find all solutions of $e^z = 2i$.

18. Find all solutions of $\sin(z) = i$.

19. Find all solutions of $e^z = -2$.

21.4   The Complex Logarithm

In real calculus, the natural logarithm is the inverse of the exponential function: for $x > 0$,

$$y = \ln(x) \quad \text{if and only if } x = e^y.$$

In this way, the real natural logarithm can be thought of as the solution of the equation $x = e^y$ for y in terms of x.

   We can attempt this approach in seeking a definition of the complex logarithm. Given $z \neq 0$, we ask whether there are complex numbers w such that

$$e^w = z.$$

To answer this question, put z in polar form as $z = re^{i\theta}$. Let $w = u + iv$. Then

$$z = re^{i\theta} = e^w = e^u e^{iv}. \tag{21.7}$$

Since θ and v are real, $\left|e^{i\theta}\right| = \left|e^{iv}\right| = 1$ and equation (21.7) gives us $r = |z| = e^u$. Hence

$$u = \ln(r),$$

the real natural logarithm of the positive number r.

But now equation (21.7) implies that $e^{i\theta} = e^{iv}$, so by Theorem 2.13(3),

$$iv = i\theta + 2n\pi i$$

and therefore

$$v = \theta + 2n\pi,$$

in which n can be any integer.

In summary, given nonzero complex $z = re^{i\theta}$, there are infinitely many complex numbers w such that $e^w = z$, and these numbers are

$$w = \ln(r) + i\theta + 2n\pi i,$$

with n any integer. Since θ is any argument of z, and all arguments of z are contained in the expression $\theta + 2n\pi$ for n integer, then in terms of z,

$$w = \ln(|z|) + i\arg(z),$$

with the understanding that there are infinitely many different values for $\arg(z)$. Each of these numbers is called a *complex logarithm* of z.

Each nonzero complex number therefore has infinitely many logarithms. To emphasize this, we often write

$$\log(z) = \{\ln(|z| + i\arg(z)\}.$$

This is read, "the logarithm of z is the set of all numbers $\ln(|z|) + i\theta$, where θ varies over all arguments of z."

EXAMPLE 21.13

Let $z = 1 + i$. Then $z = \sqrt{2}e^{i(\pi/4 + 2n\pi)}$. Then

$$\log(z) = \left\{\ln(\sqrt{2}) + i\frac{\pi}{4} + 2n\pi i\right\}.$$

Some of the logarithms of $1 + i$ are

$$\ln(\sqrt{2}) + \frac{\pi}{4}i, \quad \ln(\sqrt{2}) + \frac{9\pi}{4}i, \quad \ln(\sqrt{2}) - \frac{7\pi}{4}i, \ldots. \ \blacksquare$$

EXAMPLE 21.14

Let $z = -3$. An argument of z is π, and in polar form $z = 3e^{i(\pi + 2n\pi)} = 3e^{(2n+1)\pi i}$. Then

$$\log(z) = \{\ln(3) + (2n+1)\pi i\}.$$

Some values of $\log(-3)$ are $\ln(3) + \pi i, \ln(3) + 3\pi i, \ln(3) + 5\pi i, \ldots, \ln(3) - \pi i, \ln(3) - 3\pi i,$ and so on. $\blacksquare$

The complex logarithm is not a function, because with each nonzero z it associates infinitely many different complex numbers. Nevertheless, $\log(z)$ exhibits some of the properties we are accustomed to with real logarithm functions, if properly understood.

THEOREM 21.18

Let $z \neq 0$. If w is any value of $\log(z)$, then $e^w = z$. ∎

This is the complex function equivalent of the fact that, in real calculus, $e^{\ln(x)} = x$. This is the condition we used to reason to a definition of $\log(z)$.

THEOREM 21.19

Let z and w be nonzero complex numbers. Then each value of $\log(zw)$ is a sum of values of $\log(z)$ and $\log(w)$.

Proof   Let $z = re^{i\theta}$ and $w = \rho e^{i\varphi}$. Then $zw = r\rho e^{i(\theta+\varphi)}$. If α is any value of $\log(zw)$, then for some integer N,

$$\alpha = \ln(\rho r) + i(\theta + \varphi + 2N\pi) = [\ln(r) + i\theta] + [\ln(\rho) + i(\varphi + 2N\pi)].$$

But $\ln(r) + i\theta$ is one value of $\log(z)$, and $\ln(\rho) + i(\varphi + 2N\pi)$ is one value of $\log(w)$, proving the theorem. ∎

Here is an example of the use of the logarithm to solve an equation involving the exponential function.

EXAMPLE 21.15

Solve for all z such that $e^z = 1 + 2i$.

In Example 21.11 we found one solution by separating the real and imaginary parts of e^z. Using the logarithm, we obtain all solutions as follows:

$$e^z = 1 + 2i$$

means that

$$z = \log(1 + 2i) = \ln(|1 + 2i|) + i\arg(1 + 2i) = \frac{1}{2}\ln(5) + i\left(\arctan(2) + 2n\pi\right),$$

in which n is any positive integer. ∎

Sometimes it is convenient to agree on a particular logarithm to use for nonzero complex numbers. This can be done by choosing an argument. For example, we could define, for $z \neq 0$,

$$Log(z) = \ln(|z|) + i\theta,$$

where $0 \leq \theta < 2\pi$. This assigns to the symbol $Log(z)$ that particular value of $\log(z)$ corresponding to the argument of z lying in $[0, 2\pi)$. For example,

$$Log(1 + i) = \ln(\sqrt{2}) + i\frac{\pi}{4}$$

and

$$Log(-3) = \ln(3) + i\pi.$$

If this is done, then care must be taken in doing computations. For example, in general $Log(zw) \neq Log(z) + Log(w)$.

PROBLEMS

In each of Problems 1 through 6, determine all values of $\log(z)$ and also the value of $Log(z)$ defined in the discussion.

1. $-4i$

2. $2 - 2i$

3. -5

4. $1 + 5i$

5. $-9 + 2i$

6. 5

7. Let z and w be nonzero complex numbers. Show that each value of $\log(z/w)$ is equal to a value of $\log(z)$ minus a value of $\log(w)$.

8. Give an example to show that in general $Log(zw) \neq Log(z) + Log(w)$ for all nonzero complex z and w.

21.5 Powers

We want to assign a meaning to the symbol z^w when w and z are complex numbers and $z \neq 0$. We will build this idea in steps. Throughout this section z is a nonzero complex number.

21.5.1 Integer Powers

Integer powers present no problem. Define $z^0 = 1$. If n is a positive integer, then $z^n = z \cdot z \cdots z$, a product of n factors of z. For example,

$$(1 + i)^4 = (1 + i)(1 + i)(1 + i)(1 + i) = -4.$$

If n is a negative integer, then $z^n = 1/z^{|n|}$. For example,

$$(1 + i)^{-4} = \frac{1}{(1 + i)^4} = -\frac{1}{4}.$$

21.5.2 $z^{1/n}$ for Positive Integer n

Let n be a positive integer. A number u such that $u^n = z$ is called an nth *root* of z, and is denoted $z^{1/n}$. Like the logarithm and argument, this is a symbol that denotes more than one number. In fact, we will see that every nonzero complex number has exactly n distinct n^{th} roots.

To determine these n^{th} roots of z, let $z = re^{i\theta}$, with $r = |z|$ and θ is any argument of z. Then

$$z = re^{i(\theta + 2k\pi)},$$

in which k can be any integer. Then

$$z^{1/n} = r^{1/n} e^{i(\theta + 2k\pi)/n}. \tag{21.8}$$

Here $r^{1/n}$ is the unique real n^{th} root of the positive number r. As k varies over the integers, the expression on the right side of equation (21.8) produces complex numbers whose n^{th} powers equal z. Let us see how many such numbers it produces.

For $k = 0, 1, \ldots, n-1$, we get n distinct n^{th} roots of z. They are

$$r^{1/n}e^{i\theta/n}, \; r^{1/n}e^{i(\theta+2\pi)/n}, \; r^{1/n}e^{i(\theta+4\pi)/n}, \ldots, r^{1/n}e^{i(\theta+2(n-1)\pi)/n}. \tag{21.9}$$

We claim that other choices of k simply reproduce one of these n^{th} roots. For example, if $k = n$, then equation (21.8) yields

$$r^{1/n}e^{i(\theta+2n\pi)/n} = r^{1/n}e^{i\theta/n}e^{2\pi i} = r^{1/n}e^{i\theta/n},$$

the first number in the list (21.9). If $k = n+1$, we get

$$r^{1/n}e^{i(\theta+2(n+1)\pi)/n} = r^{1/n}e^{i(\theta+2\pi)/n}e^{2\pi i} = r^{1/n}e^{i(\theta+2\pi)/n},$$

the second number in the list (21.9), and so on.

To sum up, for any positive integer n, the number of nth roots of any nonzero complex number z, is n. These n^{th} roots are

$$r^{1/n}e^{i(\theta+2k\pi)/n} \quad \text{for} \quad k = 0, 1, \ldots, n-1,$$

or

$$r^{1/n}\left(\cos\left(\frac{\theta+2k\pi}{n}\right) + i\sin\left(\frac{\theta+2k\pi}{n}\right)\right) \quad \text{for} \quad k = 0, 1, \ldots, n-1.$$

EXAMPLE 21.16

Find the fourth roots of $1 + i$.

Since one argument of $1 + i$ is $\pi/4$, and $|1 + i| = \sqrt{2}$, we have the polar form

$$1 + i = \sqrt{2}e^{i(\pi/4+2k\pi)}.$$

The fourth roots are

$$(\sqrt{2})^{1/4}e^{i(\pi/4+2k\pi)/4} \quad \text{for} \quad k = 0, 1, 2, 3.$$

These numbers are

$$2^{1/8}e^{\pi i/16}, \quad 2^{1/8}e^{i(\pi/4+2\pi)/4}, \quad 2^{1/8}e^{i(\pi/4+4\pi)/4}, \quad 2^{1/8}e^{i(\pi/4+6\pi)/4},$$

or

$$2^{1/8}\left(\cos\left(\frac{\pi}{16}\right) + i\sin\left(\frac{\pi}{16}\right)\right),$$

$$2^{1/8}\left(\cos\left(\frac{9\pi}{16}\right) + i\sin\left(\frac{9\pi}{16}\right)\right),$$

$$2^{1/8}\left(\cos\left(\frac{17\pi}{16}\right) + i\sin\left(\frac{17\pi}{16}\right)\right),$$

$$2^{1/8}\left(\cos\left(\frac{25\pi}{16}\right) + i\sin\left(\frac{25\pi}{16}\right)\right). \quad \blacksquare$$

EXAMPLE 21.17

The nth roots of 1 are called the nth *roots of unity*. These numbers have many uses, for example, in connection with the fast Fourier Transform. Since 1 has magnitude 1, and an argument of 1 is zero, the nth roots of unity are

$$e^{2k\pi i/n} \quad \text{for} \quad k = 0, 1, \ldots, n-1.$$

FIGURE 21.8

If we put $\omega = e^{2\pi i/n}$, then these n^{th} roots of unity are $1, \omega, \omega^2, \ldots, \omega^{n-1}$.

For example, the fifth roots of unity are

$$1, e^{2\pi i/5}, e^{4\pi i/5}, e^{6\pi i/5} \quad \text{and} \quad e^{8\pi i/5}.$$

These are

$$1, \cos\left(\frac{2\pi}{5}\right) + i\sin\left(\frac{2\pi}{5}\right), \cos\left(\frac{4\pi}{5}\right) + i\sin\left(\frac{4\pi}{5}\right),$$

$$\cos\left(\frac{6\pi}{5}\right) + i\sin\left(\frac{6\pi}{5}\right), \cos\left(\frac{8\pi}{5}\right) + i\sin\left(\frac{8\pi}{5}\right). \quad \blacksquare$$

If plotted as points in the plane, the nth roots of unity form vertices of a regular polygon with vertices on the unit circle $|z| = 1$, and having one vertex at $(1, 0)$. Figure 21.8 shows the fifth roots of unity displayed in this way.

If n is a negative integer, then

$$z^{1/n} = \frac{1}{z^{1/|n|}},$$

in the sense that the $|n|$ numbers represented by the symbol on the left are calculated by taking the $|n|$ numbers produced on the right. These are just the reciprocals of the $|n|^{th}$ roots of z.

21.5.3 Rational Powers

A rational number is a quotient of integers, say $r = m/n$. We may assume that n is positive and that m and n have no common factors. Write

$$z^r = z^{m/n} = (z^m)^{1/n},$$

the nth roots of z^m.

It is routine to check that we get the same numbers if we first take the nth roots of z, then raise each to power m. This is because

$$(z^m)^{1/n} = \left(r^m e^{im(\theta+2k\pi)}\right)^{1/n} = r^{m/n} e^{im(\theta+2k\pi)/n} = \left(r^{1/n} e^{i(\theta+2k\pi)/n}\right)^m = \left(z^{1/n}\right)^m.$$

EXAMPLE 21.18

We will find all values of $(2 - 2i)^{3/5}$.

First, $(2 - 2i)^3 = -16 - 16i$. Thus we want the fifth roots of $-16 - 16i$. Now $|-16 - 16i| = \sqrt{512}$, and $5\pi/4$ is an argument of $-16 - 16i$. Then

$$-16 - 16i = (512)^{1/2} e^{i(5\pi/4 + 2k\pi)}$$

and

$$(-16 - 16i)^{1/5} = (512)^{1/10} e^{i(5\pi/4 + 2k\pi)/5}.$$

Letting $k = 0, 1, 2, 3, 4$, we obtain the numbers

$$(512)^{1/10} e^{5\pi i/4}, \quad (512)^{1/10} e^{13\pi i/20}, \quad (512)^{1/10} e^{21\pi i/20}, \quad (512)^{1/10} e^{29\pi i/20}, \quad (512)^{1/10} e^{37\pi i/20}.$$

These are all values of $(2 - 2i)^{3/5}$. ∎

21.5.4 Powers z^w

Suppose $z \neq 0$, and let w be any complex number. We want to define the symbol z^w.

In the case of real powers, a^b is defined to be $b \ln(a)$. For example, $2^\pi = e^{\pi \ln(2)}$, and this is defined because $\ln(2)$ is defined. We will take the same approach to z^w, except now we must allow for the fact that $\log(z)$ denotes an infinite set of complex numbers. We therefore define z^w to be the set of all numbers $e^{w \log(z)}$.

If $w = m/n$, a rational number with common factors divided out, then $e^{w \log(z)}$ has n distinct values. If w is not a rational number, then z^w is an infinite set of complex numbers.

EXAMPLE 21.19

We will find all values of $(1 - i)^{1+i}$.

These numbers are obtained as $e^{(1+i) \log(1-i)}$. First, $|1 - i| = \sqrt{2}$ and $-\pi/4$ is an argument of $1 - i$ (we reach the point $(1, -1)$ by rotating $\pi/4$ radians clockwise from the positive real axis). Therefore, in polar form,

$$1 - i = \sqrt{2} e^{i(-\pi/4 + 2n\pi)}.$$

Thus all values of $\log(1 - i)$ are given by

$$\ln(\sqrt{2}) + i\left(-\frac{\pi}{4} + 2n\pi\right).$$

Every value of $(1 - i)^{1+i}$ is contained in the expression

$$e^{(1+i)[\ln(\sqrt{2}) + i(-\pi/4 + 2n\pi)]} = e^{\ln(\sqrt{2}) + \pi/4 - 2n\pi} e^{i(\ln(\sqrt{2}) - \pi/4 + 2n\pi)}$$

$$= \sqrt{2} e^{\pi/4 - 2n\pi} \left(\cos(\ln(\sqrt{2}) - \pi/4 + 2n\pi) + i \sin(\ln(\sqrt{2}) - \pi/4 + 2n\pi)\right)$$

$$= \sqrt{2} e^{\pi/4 - 2n\pi} \left(\cos(\ln(\sqrt{2}) - \pi/4) + i \sin(\ln(\sqrt{2}) - \pi/4)\right).$$

As n varies over all integer values, this expression gives all values of $(1 - i)^{1+i}$. ∎

SECTION 21.5 PROBLEMS

In each of Problems 1 through 14, determine all values of z^w.

1. i^{1+i}

2. $(1 + i)^{2i}$

3. i^i

4. $(1 + i)^{2-i}$

5. $(-1 + i)^{-3i}$

6. $(1 - i)^{1/3}$

7. $i^{1/4}$

8. $16^{1/4}$

9. $(-4)^{2-i}$

10. 6^{-2-3i}

11. $(-16)^{1/4}$

12. $\left(\dfrac{1+i}{1-i}\right)^{1/3}$

13. $1^{1/6}$

14. $(7i)^{3i}$

15. Let n be a positive integer, and let $u_1, \ldots, u_n$ be the nth roots of unity. Prove that $\sum_{j=1}^{n} u_j = 0$. *Hint*: Write each nth root of unity as a power of $e^{2\pi i/n}$.

16. Let n be a positive integer, and $\omega = e^{2\pi i/n}$. Evaluate $\sum_{j=0}^{n-1} (-1)^j \omega^j$.

CHAPTER 22

Complex Integration

We now know some important complex functions, as well as some facts about derivatives of complex functions. Next we want to develop an integral for complex functions.

Real functions are defined over sets of real numbers, and are usually integrated over intervals. Complex functions are defined over sets of points in the plane, and are integrated over curves. Before defining this integral, we will review some facts about curves. For reference, real line integrals are discussed in Chapter 13.

22.1 Curves in the Plane

A *curve* in the complex plane is a function $\Gamma\colon [a, b] \to \mathbb{C}$, defined on a real interval $[a, b]$ and having complex values. For each number t in $[a, b]$, $\Gamma(t)$ is a complex number, or point in the plane. The locus of such points is the *graph* of the curve. However, the curve is more than just a locus of points in the plane. Γ has a natural orientation, which is the direction the point $\Gamma(t)$ moves along the graph as t increases from a to b. In this sense, it is natural to refer to $\Gamma(a)$ as the *initial point* of the curve, and $\Gamma(b)$ as the *terminal point*.

If $\Gamma(t) = x(t) + iy(t)$, then the graph of Γ is the locus of points $(x(t), y(t))$ for $a \le t \le b$. The initial point of Γ is $(x(a), y(a))$ and the terminal point is $(x(b), y(b))$, and $(x(t), y(t))$ moves from the initial to the terminal point as t varies from a to b. The functions $x(t)$ and $y(t)$ are the *coordinate functions* of Γ.

EXAMPLE 22.1

Let $\Gamma(t) = 2t + t^2 i$ for $0 \le t \le 2$. Then

$$\Gamma(t) = x(t) + iy(t),$$

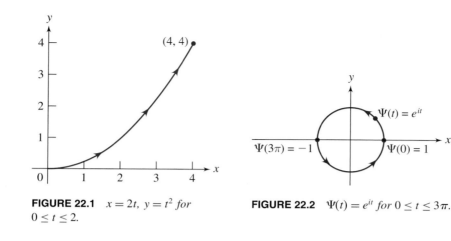

FIGURE 22.1 $x = 2t$, $y = t^2$ for $0 \le t \le 2$.

FIGURE 22.2 $\Psi(t) = e^{it}$ for $0 \le t \le 3\pi$.

where $x(t) = 2t$ and $y(t) = t^2$. The graph of this curve is the part of the parabola $y = (x/2)^2$, shown in Figure 22.1. As t varies from 0 to 2, the point $\Gamma(t) = (2t, t^2)$ moves along this graph from the initial point $\Gamma(0) = (0, 0)$ to the terminal point $\Gamma(2) = (4, 4)$. The arrow on the graph indicates this orientation. ∎

EXAMPLE 22.2

Let $\Psi(t) = e^{it}$ for $0 \le t \le 3\pi$. Then $\Psi(t) = \cos(t) + i\sin(t) = x(t) + iy(t)$, so

$$x(t) = \cos(t), \quad y(t) = \sin(t).$$

Since $x^2 + y^2 = 1$, every point on this curve is on the unit circle about the origin. However, the initial point of Ψ is $\Psi(0) = 1$ and the terminal point is $\Psi(3\pi) = e^{3\pi i} = -1$. This curve is not closed. If this were a racetrack, the race begins at 1 in Figure 22.2, and ends at -1. A circular racetrack does not mean that the starting and ending points of the race are the same. This is not apparent from the graph itself. Ψ is oriented counterclockwise, as the arrow indicates. ∎

EXAMPLE 22.3

Let $\Theta(t) = e^{it}$ for $0 \le t \le 4\pi$. This curve is closed, since $\Theta(0) = 1 = \Theta(4\pi)$. However, the point $(x(t), y(t))$ moves around the unit circle $x^2 + y^2 = 1$ twice as t varies from 0 to 4π. This is also not apparent from just the graph itself (Figure 22.3). ∎

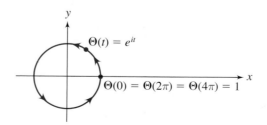

FIGURE 22.3 $\Theta(t) = e^{it}$ for $0 \le t \le 4\pi$.

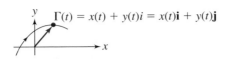

FIGURE 22.4 *Position vector of a curve.*

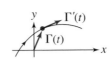

FIGURE 22.5 *Tangent vector to a curve.*

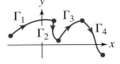
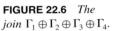

FIGURE 22.6 *The join $\Gamma_1 \oplus \Gamma_2 \oplus \Gamma_3 \oplus \Gamma_4$.*

A curve Γ is *simple* if $\Gamma(t_1) \neq \Gamma(t_2)$ whenever $t_1 \neq t_2$. This means that the same point is never repeated at different times. An exception is made for closed curves, which require that $\Gamma(a) = \Gamma(b)$. If this is the only point at which $\Gamma(t_1) = \Gamma(t_2)$ with $t_1 \neq t_2$, then we call Γ a *simple closed curve*. The curve Θ of Example 22.3 is closed, but not simple. If we define $\Lambda(t) = e^{it}$ for $0 \leq t \leq 2\pi$, then $(x(t), y(t))$ goes around the circle exactly once as t varies from 0 to 2π, and Λ is a simple closed curve.

A curve $\Gamma: [a, b] \rightarrow \mathfrak{C}$ is *continuous* if each of its coordinate functions is continuous on $[a, b]$. If $x(t)$ and $y(t)$ are differentiable on $[a, b]$ we call Γ a *differentiable curve*. If $x'(t)$ and $y'(t)$ are continuous, and do not both vanish for the same value of t, we call Γ a *smooth curve*. All the curves in the above examples are smooth.

In vector terms, we can write $\Gamma(t) = x(t)\mathbf{i} + y(t)\mathbf{j}$ (Figure 22.4). If Γ is differentiable, and $x'(t)$ and $y'(t)$ are not both zero, then $\Gamma'(t) = x'(t)\mathbf{i} + y'(t)\mathbf{j}$ is the tangent vector to the curve at the point $(x(t), y(t))$ (Figure 22.5). If Γ is smooth, then $x'(t)$ and $y'(t)$ are continuous, so this tangent vector is continuous. A smooth curve is therefore one having a continuous tangent. To illustrate, in Example 22.3, $\Theta(t) = \cos(t) + i\sin(t)$, so $\Theta'(t) = -\sin(t) + i\cos(t)$. We can leave this as it is, or write the tangent vector $\Theta'(t) = -\sin(t)\mathbf{i} + \cos(t)\mathbf{j}$, exploiting the natural correspondence between complex numbers and vectors in the plane.

Sometimes we form a curve Γ by joining several curves $\Gamma_1, \ldots, \Gamma_n$ in succession, with the understanding that the terminal point of Γ_{j-1} must be the same as the initial point of Γ_j for $j = 2, \ldots, n$ (Figure 22.6). Such a curve is called the *join* of $\Gamma_1, \ldots, \Gamma_n$ and is denoted

$$\Gamma = \Gamma_1 \oplus \Gamma_2 \oplus \cdots \oplus \Gamma_n.$$

The curves Γ_j are the *components* of this join. If each component of a join is smooth, then the join is *piecewise smooth*. It has a continuous tangent at each point, except perhaps at the seams where Γ_{j-1} is joined to Γ_j. If the seams join in a smooth fashion, a join can even have a tangent at each of these points and itself be smooth.

EXAMPLE 22.4

Let $\Gamma_1(t) = e^{it}$ for $0 \leq t \leq \pi$, and let $\Gamma_2(t) = -1 + ti$ for $0 \leq t \leq 3$. Then $\Gamma_1(\pi) = -1 = \Gamma_2(0)$, so the terminal point of Γ_1 is the initial point of Γ_2. Figure 22.7 shows a graph of $\Gamma_1 \oplus \Gamma_2$. This curve is piecewise smooth, being a join of two smooth curves. The join has a tangent at each point except -1, where the connection is made to form the join. ∎

We will define a kind of equivalence of curves. Suppose

$$\Gamma: [a, b] \rightarrow \mathfrak{C} \quad \text{and} \quad \Phi: [A, B] \rightarrow \mathfrak{C}$$

are two smooth curves. We call these curves *equivalent* if one can be obtained from the other by a change of variables defined by a differentiable, increasing function. This means that there is a function φ taking points of $[A, B]$ to $[a, b]$ such that

1. $\varphi'(t) > 0$ for $A < t < B$,
2. $\varphi(A) = a$ and $\varphi(B) = b$, and
3. $\Phi(p) = \Gamma(\varphi(p))$ for $A \le t \le B$.

If we think of $t = \varphi(p)$, then $\Gamma(t) = \Phi(p)$. The curves have the same initial and terminal points and the same graph and orientation, but $\Gamma(t)$ moves along the graph as t varies from a to b, while $\Phi(p)$ moves along the same graph in the same direction as p varies from A to B. Informally, two curves are equivalent if one is just a reparametrization of the other.

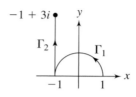

FIGURE 22.7 *The join of $\Gamma_1(t) = e^{it}$ for $0 \le t \le \pi$, with $\Gamma_2(t) = -1 + it$ for $0 \le t \le 3$.*

EXAMPLE 22.5

Let

$$\Gamma(t) = t^2 - 2ti \text{ for } 0 \le t \le 1,$$

and

$$\Phi(p) = \sin^2(p) - 2\sin(p)i \text{ for } 0 \le p \le \pi/2.$$

Both of these curves have the same graph (Figure 22.8), extending from initial point 0 to terminal point $1 - 2i$. Let

$$t = \varphi(p) = \sin(p) \text{ for } 0 \le p \le \pi/2.$$

Then φ is a differentiable, increasing function that takes $[0, \pi/2]$ onto $[0, 1]$. Further, for $0 \le p \le \pi/2$,

$$\Gamma(\sin(p)) = \sin^2(p) - 2\sin(p)i = \Phi(p).$$

These curves are therefore equivalent. ∎

Informally, we will often describe a curve geometrically and speak of a curve and its graph interchangeably. When this is done, it is important to keep track of the orientation along the curve, and whether or not the curve is closed.

For example, suppose Γ is the straight line from $1 + i$ to $3 + 3i$ (Figure 22.9). This gives the graph and its orientation, and from this we can find Γ. Since the graph is the segment of the straight line from $(1, 1)$ to $(3, 3)$, the coordinate functions are

$$x = t, y = t \text{ for } 1 \le t \le 3.$$

Then

$$\Gamma(t) = x(t) + y(t)i = (1 + i)t \text{ for } 1 \le t \le 3$$

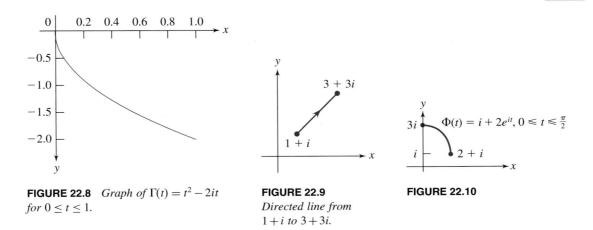

FIGURE 22.8 *Graph of* $\Gamma(t) = t^2 - 2it$ *for* $0 \le t \le 1$.

FIGURE 22.9 *Directed line from* $1 + i$ *to* $3 + 3i$.

FIGURE 22.10

is one representation of the curve that has been described. There are of course other, equivalent representations.

As another example, suppose Φ is the quarter-circle of radius 2 about i, from $2 + i$ to $3i$ (Figure 22.10). Again, we have given the graph and its orientation. Using polar coordinates centered at $i = (0, 1)$, we can write the coordinate functions

$$x(t) = 2\cos(t), \ y(t) = 1 + 2\sin(t) \ \text{ for } 0 \le t \le \pi/2.$$

As a function, this curve can be written

$$\Phi(t) = 2\cos(t) + 2i\sin(t) + i = i + 2e^{it} \ \text{ for } 0 \le t \le \pi/2.$$

Other, equivalent, representations can also be used.

Finally, we will often make statements such as "f is continuous on Γ," by which we mean that f is a complex function that is continuous at all points on the graph of Γ. And when we refer to "z on Γ," we mean a complex number z lying on the graph of Γ.

Curves are the objects over which we integrate complex functions. We will now define this integral.

SECTION 22.1 PROBLEMS

In each of Problems 1 through 10, graph the curve, determine its initial and terminal points, whether it is closed or not closed, whether or not it is simple, and the tangent to the curve at each point where the tangent exists. This tangent may be expressed as a vector or as a complex function.

1. $\Gamma(t) = 4 - 2i + 2e^{it}$ for $0 \le t \le \pi$

2. $\Gamma(t) = ie^{2it}$ for $0 \le t \le 2\pi$

3. $\Gamma(t) = t + t^2 i$ for $1 \le t \le 3$

4. $\Gamma(t) = 3\cos(t) + 5\sin(t)i$ for $0 \le t \le 2\pi$

5. $\Theta(t) = 3\cos(t) + 5\sin(t)i$ for $0 \le t \le 4\pi$

6. $\Lambda(t) = 4\sin(t) - 2\cos(t)i$ for $-\pi \le t \le \pi/2$

7. $\Psi(t) = t - t^2 i$ for $-2 \le t \le 4$

8. $\Phi(t) = (2t + 1) - \dfrac{1}{2}t^2 i$ for $-3 \le t \le -1$

9. $\Gamma(t) = \cos(t) - 2\sin(2t)i$ for $0 \le t \le 2$

10. $\Delta(t) = t^2 - t^4 i$ for $-1 \le t \le 1$

22.2   The Integral of a Complex Function

We will define the integral of a complex function in two stages, beginning with the special case that f is a complex function defined on an interval $[a, b]$ of real numbers. An example of such a function is $f(x) = x^2 + \sin(x)i$ for $0 \le x \le \pi$. It is natural to integrate such a function as

$$\int_0^\pi f(x)dx = \int_0^\pi x^2 dx + i \int_0^\pi \sin(x)dx = \frac{1}{3}\pi^3 + 2i.$$

This is the model we follow in general for such functions.

DEFINITION 22.1

Let $f : [a, b] \to \mathfrak{C}$ be a complex function. Let $f(x) = u(x) + iv(x)$ for $a \le x \le b$. Then

$$\int_a^b f(x)dx = \int_a^b u(x)dx + i \int_a^b v(x)dx.$$

Both of the integrals on the right are Riemann integrals of real-valued functions over $[a, b]$.

EXAMPLE 22.6

Let $f(x) = x - ix^2$ for $1 \le x \le 2$. Then

$$\int_1^2 f(x)dx = \int_1^2 x\, dx - i \int_1^2 x^2 dx = \frac{3}{2} - \frac{7}{3}i. \quad \blacksquare$$

EXAMPLE 22.7

Let $f(x) = \cos(2x) + i\sin(2x)$ for $0 \le x \le \pi/4$. Then

$$\int_0^{\pi/4} f(x)dx = \int_0^{\pi/4} \cos(2x)dx + i \int_0^{\pi/4} \sin(2x)dx = \frac{1}{2} + \frac{1}{2}i. \quad \blacksquare$$

In the last example, it is tempting to let $f(x) = e^{2ix}$ and adapt the fundamental theorem of calculus to complex functions to obtain

$$\int_0^{\pi/4} f(x)dx = \int_0^{\pi/4} e^{2ix}dx = \left[\frac{1}{2i}e^{2ix}\right]_0^{\pi/4} = \frac{1}{2i}\left(e^{\pi i/2} - 1\right)$$

$$= \frac{1}{2i}(\cos(\frac{\pi}{2}) + i\sin(\frac{\pi}{2}) - 1) = \frac{1}{2i}(-1 + i) = \frac{1}{2}(1 + i).$$

We will justify this calculation shortly.

We can now define the integral of a complex function over a curve in the plane.

DEFINITION 22.2

Let f be a complex function. Let $\Gamma: [a, b] \to \mathbb{C}$ be a smooth curve in the plane. Assume that f is continuous at all points on Γ. Then the integral of f over Γ is defined to be

$$\int_\Gamma f(z)\,dz = \int_a^b f(\Gamma(t))\Gamma'(t)\,dt.$$

Since $z = \Gamma(t)$ on the curve, this integral is often written

$$\int_\Gamma f(z)\,dz = \int_a^b f(z(t))z'(t)\,dt.$$

This formulation has the advantage of suggesting the way $\int_\Gamma f(z)\,dz$ is evaluated – replace z with $z(t)$ on the curve, let $dz = z'(t)\,dt$, and integrate over the interval $a \leq t \leq b$.

EXAMPLE 22.8

Evaluate $\int_\Gamma \bar{z}\,dz$ if $\Gamma(t) = e^{it}$ for $0 \leq t \leq \pi$.

The graph of Γ is the upper half of the unit circle, oriented counterclockwise from 1 to -1 (Figure 22.11). On Γ, $z(t) = e^{it}$ and $z'(t) = ie^{it}$. Further, $f(z(t)) = \overline{z(t)} = e^{-it}$ because t is real. Then

$$\int_\Gamma f(z)\,dz = \int_0^\pi e^{-it}ie^{it}\,dt = i\int_0^\pi dt = \pi i. \quad \blacksquare$$

EXAMPLE 22.9

Evaluate $\int_\Phi z^2\,dz$ if $\Phi(t) = t + it$ for $0 \leq t \leq 1$.

The graph of Φ is the straight line segment from the origin to $(1, 1)$, as shown in Figure 22.12. On the curve, $z(t) = (1 + i)t$. Since $f(z) = z^2$,

$$f(z(t)) = (z(t))^2 = (1 + i)^2 t^2 = 2it^2$$

and

$$z'(t) = 1 + i.$$

Then

$$\int_\Phi z^2\,dz = \int_0^1 2it^2(1 + i)\,dt = (-2 + 2i)\int_0^1 t^2\,dt = \frac{2}{3}(-1 + i). \quad \blacksquare$$

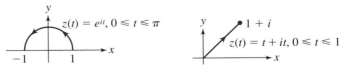

FIGURE 22.11   **FIGURE 22.12**

EXAMPLE 22.10

Evaluate $\int_\Gamma z\,\mathrm{Re}(z)\,dz$ if $\Gamma(t) = t - it^2$ for $0 \le t \le 2$.

Here $f(z) = z\,\mathrm{Re}(z)$, and on this curve, $z(t) = t - it^2$, so

$$f(z(t)) = z(t)\,\mathrm{Re}(z(t)) = (t - it^2)t = t^2 - it^3.$$

Further,

$$z'(t) = 1 - 2it,$$

so

$$\int_\Gamma z\,\mathrm{Re}(z)\,dz = \int_0^2 (t^2 - it^3)(1 - 2it)\,dt = \int_0^2 (t^2 - 3it^3 - 2t^4)\,dt$$

$$= \int_0^2 (t^2 - 2t^4)\,dt - 3i\int_0^2 t^3\,dt = -\frac{152}{15} - 12i. \ \blacksquare$$

We will show that the integrals of a function over equivalent curves are equal. This is important because we can parametrize a given curve infinitely many different ways, and this should not change the value of the integral of a given function over the curve.

THEOREM 22.1

Let Γ and Φ be equivalent curves and let f be continuous on their graph. Then

$$\int_\Gamma f(z)\,dz = \int_\Phi f(z)\,dz. \ \blacksquare$$

Proof Suppose $\Gamma : [a, b] \to \mathfrak{C}$ and $\Phi : [A, B] \to \mathfrak{C}$. Because these curves are equivalent, there is a continuous function φ with positive derivative on $[A, B]$ such that $\varphi(A) = a$ and $\varphi(B) = b$, and $\Phi(p) = \Gamma(\varphi(p))$ for $A \le p \le B$. By the chain rule,

$$\Phi'(p) = \Gamma'(\varphi(p))\varphi'(p).$$

Then

$$\int_\Phi f(z)\,dz = \int_A^B f(\Phi(p))\Phi'(p)\,dp = \int_A^B f(\Gamma(\varphi(p)))\Gamma'(\varphi(p))\varphi'(p)\,dp.$$

Let $s = \varphi(p)$. Then s varies from a to b as p varies from A to B. Continuing from the last equation, we have

$$\int_\Phi f(z)\,dz = \int_a^b f(\Gamma(s))\Gamma'(s)\,ds = \int_\Gamma f(z)\,dz. \ \blacksquare$$

Thus far we can integrate only over smooth curves. We can extend the definition to an integral over piecewise smooth curves by adding the integrals over the components of the join.

DEFINITION 22.3

Let $\Gamma = \Gamma_1 \oplus \Gamma_2 \oplus \cdots \oplus \Gamma_n$ be a join of smooth curves. Let f be continuous on each Γ_j. Then

$$\int_\Gamma f(z)\,dz = \sum_{j=1}^n \int_{\Gamma_j} f(z)\,dz.$$

EXAMPLE 22.11

Let $\Gamma_1(t) = 3e^{it}$ for $0 \le t \le \pi/2$, and let $\Gamma_2(t) = t^2 + 3i(t+1)$ for $0 \le t \le 1$. Γ_1 is the quarter circle of radius 3 about the origin, extending counterclockwise from 3 to $3i$, and Γ_2 is the part of the parabola $x = (y-3)^2/9$ from $3i$ to $1+6i$. Figure 22.13 shows a graph of $\Gamma = \Gamma_1 \oplus \Gamma_2$. We will evaluate $\int_\Gamma \text{Im}(z)\,dz$.

FIGURE 22.13

On Γ_1, write $z(t) = 3e^{it} = 3\cos(t) + 3i\sin(t)$. Then

$$\int_{\Gamma_1} \text{Im}(z)\,dz = \int_0^{\pi/2} \text{Im}(z(t))z'(t)\,dt = \int_0^{\pi/2} 3\sin(t)[-3\sin(t) + 3i\cos(t))\,dt$$

$$= -9\int_0^{\pi/2} \sin^2(t)\,dt + 9i\int_0^{\pi/2} \sin(t)\cos(t)\,dt = -\frac{9}{4}\pi + \frac{9}{2}i.$$

On Γ_2, $z(t) = t^2 + 3i(t+1)$ and $z'(t) = 2t + 3i$, so

$$\int_{\Gamma_2} \text{Im}(z)\,dz = \int_0^1 \text{Im}[t^2 + 3i(t+1)][2t + 3i]\,dt$$

$$= \int_0^1 3(t+1)(2t+3i)\,dt = \int_0^1 \left(6t^2 + 6t + 9it + 9i\right)dt$$

$$= \int_0^1 6t^2 + 6t)\,dt + 9i\int_0^1 (t+1)\,dt = 5 + \frac{27}{2}i.$$

Then

$$\int_\Gamma f(z)\,dz = -\frac{9}{4}\pi + \frac{9}{2}i + 5 + \frac{27}{2}i = 5 - \frac{9}{2}\pi + 18i. \quad\blacksquare$$

22.2.1 The Complex Integral in Terms of Real Integrals

It is possible to think of the integral of a complex function over a curve as a sum of line integrals of real-valued functions of two real variables over the curve. Let $f(z) = u(x, y) + iv(x, y)$ and, on the curve Γ, suppose $z(t) = x(t) + iy(t)$ for $a \le t \le b$. Now

$$f(z(t)) = u(x(t), y(t)) + iv(x(t), y(t))$$

and

$$z'(t) = x'(t) + iy'(t)$$

so

$$f(z(t))z'(t) = [u(x(t), y(t)) + iv(x(t), y(t))][x'(t) + iy'(t)]$$
$$= u(x(t), y(t))x'(t) - v(x(t), y(t))y'(t)$$
$$+ i[v(x(t), y(t))x'(t) + u(x(t), y(t))y'(t)].$$

Then

$$\int_\Gamma f(z)\,dz = \int_a^b [u(x(t), y(t))x'(t) - v(x(t), y(t))y'(t)]\,dt$$
$$+ i\int_a^b [v(x(t), y(t))x'(t) + u(x(t), y(t))y'(t)]\,dt.$$

In the notation of real line integrals,

$$\int_\Gamma f(z)\,dz = \int_\Gamma u\,dx - v\,dy + i\int_\Gamma v\,dx + u\,dy. \tag{22.1}$$

This formulation allows a perspective that is sometimes useful in developing properties of complex integrals.

EXAMPLE 22.12

Evaluate $\int_\Gamma iz^2\,dz$ if $\Gamma(t) = 4\cos(t) + i\sin(t)$ for $0 \le t \le \pi/2$. Figure 22.14 shows a graph of Γ, which is part of the ellipse

$$\frac{x^2}{16} + y^2 = 1.$$

To evaluate $\int_\Gamma iz^2\,dz$ in terms of real line integrals, first compute

$$f(z) = iz^2 = -2xy + i(x^2 - y^2) = u + iv,$$

where

$$u(x, y) = -2xy \quad \text{and} \quad v(x, y) = x^2 - y^2.$$

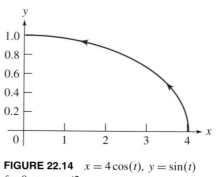

FIGURE 22.14 $x = 4\cos(t)$, $y = \sin(t)$
for $0 \le t \le \pi/2$.

On the curve, $x(t) = 4\cos(t)$ and $y(t) = \sin(t)$. Now equation (22.1) gives us

$$\int_{\Gamma} iz^2 \, dz = \int_0^{\pi/2} \left(-8\cos(t)\sin(t)\right)\left(-4\sin(t)\right)dt - \int_0^{\pi/2} \left(16\cos^2(t) - \sin^2(t)\right)\cos(t)dt$$

$$+ i\left[\int_0^{\pi/2} \left(16\cos^2(t) - \sin^2(t)\right)\left(-4\sin(t)\right)dt + \int_0^{\pi/2} \left(-8\cos(t)\sin(t)\right)\cos(t)dt\right]$$

$$= \frac{1}{3} - \frac{64}{3}i. \quad \blacksquare$$

We will have an easier way of evaluating simple line integrals such as $\int_{\Gamma} iz^2 \, dz$, when we have more properties of complex integrals.

22.2.2 Properties of Complex Integrals

We will develop some properties of $\int_{\Gamma} f(z) \, dz$.

THEOREM 22.2 *Linearity*

Let Γ be a piecewise smooth curve and let f and g be continuous on Γ. Let α and β be complex numbers. Then

$$\int_{\Gamma} (\alpha f(z) + \beta g(z)) \, dz = \alpha \int_{\Gamma} f(z) \, dz + \beta \int_{\Gamma} g(z) \, dz. \quad \blacksquare$$

This conclusion is certainly something we expect of anything called an integral. The result extends to arbitrary finite sums:

$$\int_{\Gamma} \sum_{j=1}^{n} \alpha_j f_j(z) \, dz = \sum_{j=1}^{n} \alpha_j \int_{\Gamma} f_j(z) \, dz.$$

Orientation plays a significant role in the complex integral, because it is an intrinsic part of the curve over which the integral is taken. Suppose $\Gamma : [a, b] \to \mathfrak{C}$ is a smooth curve, as typically shown in Figure 22.15. The arrow indicates orientation. We can reverse this orientation by defining the new curve

$$\Gamma_r(t) = \Gamma(a + b - t) \quad \text{for } a \le t \le b.$$

Γ_r is a smooth curve having the same graph as Γ. However,

$$\Gamma_r(a) = \Gamma(b) \quad \text{and} \quad \Gamma_r(b) = \Gamma(a).$$

Γ_r starts where Γ ends, and Γ_r ends where Γ begins. The orientation has been reversed. We claim that reversing orientation changes the sign of the integral.

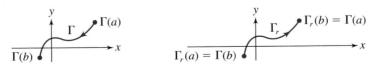

FIGURE 22.15 *Reversing orientation on a curve.*

THEOREM 22.3 **Reversal of Orientation**

Let $\Gamma : [a, b] \to C$ be a smooth curve. Let f be continuous on Γ. Then

$$\int_{\Gamma} f(z)\,dz = -\int_{\Gamma_r} f(z)\,dz. \quad \blacksquare$$

Proof Let $u = a + b - t$. By the chain rule,

$$\frac{d}{dt}\Gamma_r(t) = \frac{d}{dt}\Gamma(a+b-t) = \Gamma'(u)u'(t) = -\Gamma'(u) = -\Gamma'(a+b-t).$$

Then

$$\int_{\Gamma_r} f(z)\,dz = \int_a^b f(\Gamma_r(t))\Gamma_r'(t)\,dt = -\int_a^b f(\Gamma(a+b-t))\Gamma'(a+b-t)\,dt.$$

Now change variables by putting $s = a + b - t$. Then

$$\int_{\Gamma_r} f(z)\,dz = -\int_b^a f(\Gamma(s))\Gamma'(s)(-1)\,ds = -\int_a^b f(\Gamma(s))\Gamma'(s)\,ds = -\int_{\Gamma} f(z)\,dz. \quad \blacksquare$$

We need not actually define Γ_r to reverse orientation in specific integrals — just integrate from b to a instead of from a to b. This reverses the roles of the initial and terminal points and hence the orientation. Or we can integrate from a to b and take the negative of the result.

We will next state a complex version of the fundamental theorem of calculus. It states that, if f has a continuous antiderivative F, then the value of $\int_{\Gamma} f(z)\,dz$ is the value of F at the terminal point of Γ, minus the value of F at the initial point.

THEOREM 22.4

Let f be continuous on an open set G, and suppose $F'(z) = f(z)$ for z in G. Let $\Gamma : [a, b] \to G$ be a smooth curve in G. Then

$$\int_a^b f(z)\,dz = F(\Gamma(b)) - F(\Gamma(a)).$$

Proof With $\Gamma(t) = z(t) = x(t) + iy(t)$, and $F(z) = U(x, y) + iV(x, y)$,

$$\int_{\Gamma} f(z)\,dz = \int_a^b f(z(t))z'(t)\,dt = \int_a^b F'(z(t))z'(t)\,dt = \int_a^b \frac{d}{dt}F(z(t))\,dt.$$

$$= \int_a^b \frac{d}{dt}U(x(t), y(t))\,dt + i\int_a^b \frac{d}{dt}V(x(t), y(t))\,dt.$$

Now we can apply the fundamental theorem of calculus to the two real integrals on the right to obtain

$$\int_{\Gamma} f(z)\,dz = U(x(b), y(b)) + iV(x(b), y(b)) - [U(x(a), y(a)) + iV(x(a), y(a))]$$

$$= F(x(b), y(b)) - F(x(a), y(a)) = F(\Gamma(b)) - F(\Gamma(a)). \quad \blacksquare$$

EXAMPLE 22.13

We will compute $\int_{\Gamma}(z^2 + iz)\,dz$ if $\Gamma(t) = t^5 - t\cos(t)i$ for $0 \le t \le 1$.

This is an elementary but tedious calculation if done by computing $\int_0^1 f(z(t))z'(t)dt$. However, if we let G be the entire complex plane, then G is open, and $F(z) = z^3/3 + iz^2/2$ satisfies $F'(z) = f(z)$. The initial point of Γ is $\Gamma(0) = 0$ and the terminal point is $\Gamma(1) = 1 - \cos(1)i$. Therefore

$$\int_\Gamma (z^2 + iz)dz = F(\Gamma(1)) - F(\Gamma(0)) = F(1 - \cos(1)i) - F(0)$$

$$= \frac{1}{3}(1 - \cos(1)i)^3 + \frac{i}{2}(1 - \cos(1)i)^2 = (1 - \cos(1)i)^2 \left(\frac{1}{3}(1 - \cos(1)i) + \frac{1}{2}i \right). \blacksquare$$

One ramification of Theorem 22.4 is that, under the given conditions, the value of $\int_\Gamma f(z)dz$ depends only on the initial and terminal points of the curve. If Φ is also a smooth curve in G having the same initial point as Γ and the same terminal point as Γ, then

$$\int_\Gamma f(z)dz = \int_\Phi f(z)dz.$$

This is called *independence of path*, about which we will say more later.

Another consequence is that, if Γ is a closed curve in G, then the initial and terminal points coincide and

$$\int_\Gamma f(z)dz = 0.$$

We will consider this circumstance in more detail when we consider Cauchy's theorem.

The next result is used in bounding the magnitude of an integral, as we sometimes need to do in making estimates in equations or inequalities.

THEOREM 22.5

Let $\Gamma : [a, b] \to C$ be a smooth curve and let f be continuous on Γ. Then

$$\left| \int_\Gamma f(z)dz \right| \leq \int_a^b |f(z(t))| \, |z'(t)| \, dt.$$

If, in addition, there is a positive number M such that $|f(z)| \leq M$ for all z on Γ, then

$$\left| \int_\Gamma f(z)dz \right| \leq ML,$$

where L is the length of Γ.

Proof Write the complex number $\int_\Gamma f(z)dz$ in polar form:

$$\int_\Gamma f(z)dz = re^{i\theta}.$$

Then

$$r = e^{-i\theta} \int_\Gamma f(z)dz = e^{-i\theta} \int_a^b f(z(t))z'(t)dt.$$

Since r is real,

$$r = \text{Re}(r) = \text{Re}\left[e^{-i\theta} \int_a^b f(z(t))z'(t)dt \right] = \int_a^b \text{Re}\left[e^{-i\theta} f(z(t))z'(t) \right] dt.$$

Now for any complex number w, $\text{Re}(w) \leq |w|$. Therefore

$$\text{Re}\left[e^{-i\theta} f(z(t))z'(t) \right] \leq \left| e^{-i\theta} f(z(t))z'(t) \right| = |f(z(t))z'(t)|,$$

since $\left|e^{-i\theta}\right| = 1$ for θ real. Then

$$\left|\int_{\Gamma} f(z)dz\right| = r = \left|\int_a^b f(z(t))z'(t)dt\right| \le \int_a^b |f(z(t))z'(t)|\,dt = \int_a^b |f(z(t))|\,|z'(t)|\,dt,$$

as we wanted to show.

If now $|f(z)| \le M$ on Γ, then

$$\left|\int_{\Gamma} f(z)dz\right| \le \int_a^b |f(z(t))|\,|z'(t)|\,dt \le M\int_a^b |z'(t)|\,dt.$$

If $\Gamma(t) = x(t) + iy(t)$, then

$$|z'(t)| = |x'(t) + iy'(t)| = \sqrt{(x'(t))^2 + (y'(t))^2},$$

so

$$\left|\int_{\Gamma} f(z)dz\right| \le M\int_a^b \sqrt{(x'(t))^2 + (y'(t))^2}\,dt = ML.$$

EXAMPLE 22.14

We will obtain a bound on $\left|\int_{\Gamma} e^{\operatorname{Re}(z)}dz\right|$, where Γ is the circle of radius 2 about the origin, traversed once counterclockwise.

On Γ we can write $z(t) = 2\cos(t) + 2i\sin(t)$ for $0 \le t \le 2\pi$. Now

$$\left|e^{\operatorname{Re}(z(t))}\right| = e^{2\cos(t)} \le e^2$$

for $0 \le t \le 2\pi$. Since the length of Γ is 4π, then

$$\left|\int_{\Gamma} e^{\operatorname{Re}(z)}dz\right| \le 4\pi e^2. \ \blacksquare$$

This number bounds the magnitude of the integral. It is not claimed to be an approximation to the value of the integral to any degree of accuracy.

22.2.3 Integrals of Series of Functions

We often want to interchange an integral and a series. We would like conditions under which

$$\int_{\Gamma} \left(\sum_{n=1}^{\infty} f_n(z)dz\right) \overset{?}{=} \sum_{n=1}^{\infty} \int_{\Gamma} f_n(z)dz.$$

We will show that, if we can bound each $f_n(z)$, for z on the curve, by a positive constant M_n so that $\sum_{n=1}^{\infty} M_n$ converges, then we can interchange the summation and the integral and integrate the series term-by-term.

THEOREM 22.6   Term-by-Term Integration

Let Γ be a smooth curve and let f_n be continuous on Γ for $n = 1, 2, \ldots$. Suppose for each positive integer n there is a positive number M_n such that $\sum_{n=1}^{\infty} M_n$ converges and, for all z on Γ,

$$|f_n(z)| \le M_n.$$

Then $\sum_{n=1}^{\infty} f_n(z)$ converges absolutely for all z on Γ. Further, if we denote $\sum_{n=1}^{\infty} f_n(z) = g(z)$, then

$$\int_\Gamma g(z)\,dz = \sum_{n=1}^{\infty} \int_\Gamma f_n(z)\,dz. \quad \blacksquare$$

Proof For each z on Γ, the real series $\sum_{n=1}^{\infty} |f_n(z)|$ converges by comparison with the convergent series $\sum_{n=1}^{\infty} M_n$. Now let L be the length of Γ and consider the partial sum

$$F_N(z) = \sum_{n=1}^{N} f_n(z).$$

Each F_N is continuous on Γ and

$$\left| \int_\Gamma g(z)\,dz - \sum_{n=1}^{N} \int_\Gamma f_n(z)\,dz \right| = \left| \int_\Gamma [g(z)\,dz - F_N(z)]\,dz \right|$$

$$\leq L \left(\max_{z \text{ on } \Gamma} |g(z) - F_N(z)| \right).$$

Now for all z on Γ,

$$|g(z) - F_n(z)| = \left| \sum_{n=N+1}^{\infty} f_n(z) \right| \leq \left| \sum_{n=N+1}^{\infty} M_n \right|.$$

If ϵ is any positive number, we can choose N large enough that $\sum_{n=N+1}^{\infty} M_n < \epsilon/L$, because $\sum_{n=1}^{\infty} M_n$ converges. But then

$$\max_{z \text{ on } \Gamma} |g(z) - F_N(z)| < \frac{\epsilon}{L},$$

so

$$\left| \int_\Gamma g(z)\,dz - \sum_{n=1}^{N} \int_\Gamma f_n(z)\,dz \right| < L\frac{\epsilon}{L} = \epsilon$$

for N sufficiently large. This proves that

$$\lim_{N \to \infty} \sum_{n=1}^{N} \int_\Gamma f_n(z)\,dz = \int_\Gamma g(z)\,dz,$$

as we wanted to show. $\blacksquare$

Of course, the theorem applies to a power series within its circle of convergence, with $f_n(z) = c_n(z - z_0)^n$.

SECTION 22.2   PROBLEMS

In each of Problems 1 through 15, evaluate $\int_\Gamma f(z)\,dz$. All closed curves are oriented counterclockwise unless specific exception is made.

1. $f(z) = 1$; $\Gamma(t) = t^2 - it$ for $1 \leq t \leq 3$

2. $f(z) = z^2 - iz$; Γ is the quarter circle about the origin from 2 to $2i$

3. $f(z) = \text{Re}(z)$; Γ is the line segment from 1 to $2+i$

4. $f(z) = 1/z$; Γ is the part of the half-circle of radius 4 about the origin, from $4i$ to $-4i$

5. $f(z) = z - 1$; Γ is any piecewise smooth curve from $2i$ to $1 - 4i$

6. $f(z) = iz^2$; Γ is the line segment from $1 + 2i$ to $3 + i$

7. $f(z) = \sin(2z)$; Γ is the line segment from $-i$ to $-4i$

8. $f(z) = 1 + z^2$; Γ is the part of the circle of radius 3 about the origin from $-3i$ to $3i$

9. $f(z) = -i\cos(z)$; Γ is any piecewise smooth curve from 0 to $2 + i$

10. $f(z) = |z|^2$; Γ is the line segment from -4 to i

11. $f(z) = (z - i)^3$; $\Gamma(t) = t - it^2$ for $0 \le t \le 2$

12. $f(z) = e^{iz}$; Γ is any piecewise smooth curve from -2 to $-4 - i$

13. $f(z) = i\overline{z}$; Γ is the line segment from 0 to $-4 + 3i$

14. $f(z) = \operatorname{Im}(z)$; Γ is the circle of radius 1 about the origin

15. $f(z) = |z|^2$; Γ is the line segment from $-i$ to 1

16. Find a bound for $\left| \int_\Gamma \cos(z^2)\,dz \right|$, if Γ is the circle of radius 4 about the origin.

17. Find a bound for $\left| \int_\Gamma \dfrac{1}{1+z}\,dz \right|$, if Γ is the line segment from $2 + i$ to $4 + 2i$.

22.3   Cauchy's Theorem

Cauchy's theorem (or the Cauchy integral theorem) is considered the fundamental theorem of complex integration, and is named for the early nineteenth-century French mathematician and engineer Augustin-Louis Cauchy. He had the idea of the theorem, as well as many of its consequences, but was able to prove it only under what were later found to be unnecessarily restrictive conditions. Edouard Goursat proved the theorem as it is now usually stated, and for this reason it is sometimes called the Cauchy–Goursat theorem.

The statement of the theorem implicitly makes use of the Jordan curve theorem, discussed previously in Section 13.2 in connection with Green's theorem. It states that a continuous simple closed curve Γ in the plane separates the plane into two open sets. One of these sets is unbounded, and is called the *exterior* of Γ, and the other set is bounded and is called the *interior* of Γ. The (graph of the) curve itself does not belong to either of these sets, but forms the boundary for both. Figure 22.16 illustrates the theorem. Although this conclusion may seem obvious for closed curves we might routinely sketch, it is difficult to prove because of the generality of its statement.

Some terminology will make the statement of Cauchy's theorem more efficient.

DEFINITION 22.4   *Path*

A path is a simple, piecewise smooth curve.

     A path in a set S is a path whose graph lies in S.

Thus, a path is a join of smooth curves with no self-intersections.

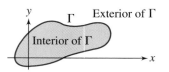

FIGURE 22.16   *Jordan curve theorem.*

DEFINITION 22.5   *Connected Set*

A set S of complex numbers is connected if, given any two points z and w in S, there is a path in S having z and w as end points.

S is connected if it is possible to get from any point of S to any other point by moving along some path lying completely in S. An open disk is connected, as is a closed disk, while the set consisting of the two open disks $|z| < 1$ and $|z - 10i| < 1$ is not (Figure 22.17), because we cannot get from 0 to $10i$ without going outside the set.

DEFINITION 22.6   *Domain*

An open, connected set of complex numbers is called a domain.

D is a domain if

1. about any z in D, there is some open disk containing only points of D, and
2. we can get from any point in D to any other point in D by a path in D.

For example, any open disk is a domain, as is the upper half plane consisting of all z with $\text{Im}(z) > 0$. A closed disk is not a domain (it is connected but not open), and a set consisting of two disjoint open disks is not a domain (it is open but not connected).

DEFINITION 22.7   *Simply Connected*

A set S of complex numbers is simply connected if every closed path in S encloses only points of S.

Every open disk is simply connected (Figure 22.18). If we draw a closed path in an open disk, this closed path will enclose only points in the open disk. The annulus of Figure 22.19, consisting of points between two concentric circles, is not simply connected, even though it is connected. We can draw a closed path contained in the annulus, but enclosing the inner boundary circle of the annulus. This curve encloses points not in the annulus, namely those enclosed by the inner boundary circle.

We are now ready to state one version of Cauchy's theorem.

THEOREM 22.7   *Cauchy's Theorem*

Let f be differentiable on a simply connected domain G. Let Γ be a closed path in G. Then

$$\int_\Gamma f(z)\,dz = 0. \quad \blacksquare$$

Often integrals around closed paths are denoted $\oint$. In this notation, the conclusion of the theorem reads $\oint_\Gamma f(z)\,dz = 0$. The oval on the integral sign is just a reminder that the path is closed, and does not alter the way we operate with the integral or the way it is evaluated.

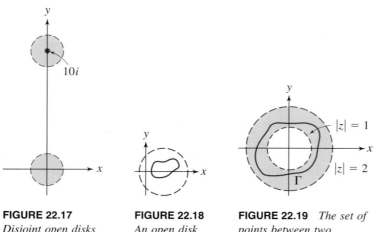

FIGURE 22.17
*Disjoint open disks
form a set that is
not connected.*

FIGURE 22.18
*An open disk
is simply
connected.*

FIGURE 22.19 *The set of
points between two
concentric circles is not
simply connected.*

Informally, Cauchy's theorem states that $\oint_\Gamma f(z)\,dz = 0$ if f is differentiable on the curve and on all points enclosed by the curve. As a convention, closed curves are understood to be oriented positively (counterclockwise), unless specific exception is made.

EXAMPLE 22.15

Evaluate $\oint_\Gamma e^{z^2}\,dz$, where Γ is any closed path in the plane.

Figure 22.20 shows a typical Γ. Here $f(z) = e^{z^2}$ is differentiable for all z, and the entire plane is a simply connected domain. Therefore

$$\oint_\Gamma e^{z^2}\,dz = 0. \quad \blacksquare$$

EXAMPLE 22.16

Evaluate

$$\oint_\Gamma \frac{2z+1}{z^2+3iz}\,dz,$$

where Γ is the circle $|z+3i| = 2$ of radius 2 and center $-3i$ (Figure 22.21).

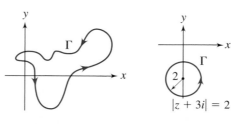

FIGURE 22.20 *A
simple closed path Γ.*

FIGURE 22.21

We can parametrize $\Gamma(t) = -3i + 2e^{it}$ for $0 \le t \le 2\pi$. $\Gamma(t)$ traverses the circle once counterclockwise as t varies from 0 to 2π.

First observe that $f(z)$ is differentiable except at points where the denominator vanishes, 0 and $-3i$. Use a partial fractions decomposition to write

$$f(z) = \frac{1}{3i}\frac{1}{z} + \left(\frac{6+i}{3}\right)\frac{1}{z+3i}.$$

Since $1/z$ is differentiable on and within the simply connected domain enclosed by Γ, by Cauchy's theorem,

$$\oint_\Gamma \frac{1}{3i}\frac{1}{z}dz = 0.$$

However, $1/(z+3i)$ is not differentiable in the simply connected domain enclosed by Γ, so Cauchy's theorem does not apply to an integral of this function. We will evaluate this integral directly by writing $z(t) = -3i + 2e^{it}$:

$$\oint_\Gamma \left(\frac{6+i}{3}\right)\frac{1}{z+3i}dz = \frac{6+i}{3}\int_0^{2\pi}\frac{1}{z(t)+3i}z'(t)dt$$

$$= \frac{6+i}{3}\int_0^{2\pi}\frac{1}{2e^{it}}2ie^{it}dt = \frac{6+i}{3}\int_0^{2\pi}idt = \frac{6+i}{3}(2\pi i).$$

Therefore

$$\oint_\Gamma \frac{2z+1}{z^2+3iz}dz = \frac{6+i}{3}(2\pi i) = \left(-\frac{2}{3}+4i\right)\pi. \quad \blacksquare$$

We will see more impressive ramifications of Cauchy's theorem shortly.

22.3.1 Proof of Cauchy's Theorem for a Special Case

If we add an additional hypothesis, Cauchy's theorem is easy to prove. Let $f(z) = u(x,y) + iv(x,y)$ and assume that u and v and their first partial derivatives are continuous on G. Now we obtain Cauchy's theorem immediately by applying Green's theorem and the Cauchy–Riemann equations to equation (22.1). If D consists of all points on and enclosed by Γ, then

$$\oint_\Gamma f(z)dz = \oint_\Gamma udx - vdy + i\oint_\Gamma vdx + udy$$

$$= \iint_D \left(\frac{\partial(-v)}{\partial x} - \frac{\partial u}{\partial y}\right)dA + i\iint_D \left(\frac{\partial u}{\partial x} - \frac{\partial v}{\partial y}\right)dA = 0,$$

because, by the Cauchy–Riemann equations,

$$\frac{\partial u}{\partial x} = \frac{\partial v}{\partial y} \quad \text{and} \quad \frac{\partial u}{\partial y} = -\frac{\partial v}{\partial x}.$$

This argument is good enough for many settings in which Cauchy's theorem is used. However, it is not an optimal argument because it makes the additional assumption about continuity of the partial derivatives of u and v. A rigorous proof of the theorem as stated involves topological subtleties we do not wish to engage here.

In the next section we will develop some important consequences of Cauchy's theorem.

SECTION 22.3 PROBLEMS

In each of Problems 1 through 12, evaluate the integral of the function over the given closed path. All paths are positively oriented (counterclockwise). In some cases Cauchy's theorem applies, and in some it does not.

1. $f(z) = \sin(3z)$; Γ is the circle $|z| = 4$

2. $f(z) = \dfrac{2z}{z-i}$; Γ is the circle $|z-i| = 3$

3. $f(z) = \dfrac{1}{(z-2i)^3}$; Γ is given by $|z-2i| = 2$

4. $f(z) = z^2 \sin(z)$; Γ is the square having vertices 0, 1, $1+i$ and i

5. $f(z) = \bar{z}$; Γ is the unit circle about the origin

6. $f(z) = 1/\bar{z}$; , Γ is the circle of radius 5 about the origin

7. $f(z) = ze^z$; Γ is the circle $|z-3i| = 8$

8. $f(z) = z^2 - 4z + i$; Γ is the rectangle with vertices 1, 8, $8+4i$ and $1+4i$

9. $f(z) = |z|^2$; Γ is the circle of radius 7 about the origin

10. $f(z) = \sin(1/z)$; Γ is the circle $|z-1+2i| = 1$

11. $f(z) = \text{Re}(z)$; Γ is given by $|z| = 2$

12. $f(z) = z^2 + \text{Im}(z)$; Γ is the square with vertices 0, $-2i$, $2-2i$ and 2

22.4 Consequences of Cauchy's Theorem

This section lays out some of the main results of complex integration, with profound implications for understanding the behavior and properties of complex functions, as well as for applications of the integral. As usual, all integrals over closed curves are taken with a counterclockwise orientation, unless otherwise noted.

22.4.1 Independence of Path

In Section 22.2.2 we mentioned independence of path, according to which, under certain conditions on f, the value of $\int_\Gamma f(z)\,dz$ depends only on the end points of the curve, and not on the particular curve chosen between those end points.

Independence of path can also be viewed from the perspective of Cauchy's theorem. Suppose f is differentiable on a simply connected domain G, and z_0 and z_1 are points of G. Let Γ_1 and Γ_2 be piecewise smooth curves in G having initial point z_0 and terminal point z_1 (Figure 22.22). If we reverse the orientation on Γ_2, we obtain the new curve, $-\Gamma_2$, going from z_1 to z_0. Further, the join of Γ_1 and $-\Gamma_2$ forms a closed curve Γ, having initial and terminal point z_0 (Figure 22.23). By Cauchy's theorem and Theorem 22.3,

$$\oint_\Gamma f(z)\,dz = 0 = \oint_{\Gamma_1 \oplus (-\Gamma_2)} f(z)\,dz = \oint_{\Gamma_1} f(z)\,dz - \oint_{\Gamma_2} f(z)\,dz,$$

implying that

$$\oint_{\Gamma_1} f(z)\,dz = \oint_{\Gamma_2} f(z)\,dz.$$

This means that the integral does not depend on the particular curve (in G) between z_0 and z_1, and is therefore independent of path.

This argument is not entirely rigorous, because $\Gamma_1 \oplus (-\Gamma_2)$ need not be a simple curve (Figure 22.24). In fact, Γ_1 and Γ_2 may cross each other any number of times as they progress from z_0 to z_1. Nevertheless, we wanted to point out the connection between Cauchy's theorem and the concept of independence of path of an integral which was discussed previously.

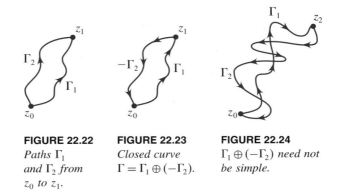

FIGURE 22.22
Paths Γ_1
and Γ_2 from
z_0 to z_1.

FIGURE 22.23
Closed curve
$\Gamma = \Gamma_1 \oplus (-\Gamma_2)$.

FIGURE 22.24
$\Gamma_1 \oplus (-\Gamma_2)$ need not
be simple.

If $\int_\Gamma f(z)\,dz$ is independent of path in G, and Γ is any path from z_0 to z_1, we sometimes write

$$\oint_\Gamma f(z)\,dz = \int_{z_0}^{z_1} f(z)\,dz.$$

The symbol on the right has the value of the line integral on the left, with Γ any path from z_0 to z_1 in G.

22.4.2 The Deformation Theorem

The deformation theorem enables us, under certain conditions, to replace one closed path of integration with another, perhaps more convenient one.

THEOREM 22.8 *Deformation Theorem*

Let Γ and γ be closed paths in the plane, with γ in the interior of Γ. Let f be differentiable on an open set containing both paths and all points between them. Then,

$$\int_\Gamma f(z)\,dz = \int_\gamma f(z)\,dz. \ \blacksquare$$

Figure 22.25 shows the setting of the theorem. We may think of deforming one curve, say γ, to the other. Imagine γ as made of rubber, and continuously deform it into the shape of Γ. In doing this, it is necessary that the intermediate stages of the deformation from γ to Γ only

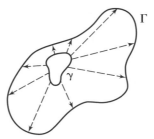

FIGURE 22.25 *Deforming*
γ continuously into Γ.

cross over points at which f is differentiable, hence the hypothesis about f being differentiable on some open set containing both paths and all points between them.

The theorem states that the integral of f has the same value over both paths when one can be deformed into the other, moving only over points at which the function is differentiable. This means that we can replace Γ with another path γ that may be more convenient to use in evaluating the integral. Consider the following example.

EXAMPLE 22.17

Evaluate

$$\oint_{\Gamma} \frac{1}{z-a}\,dz$$

over any closed path enclosing the given complex number a.

Figure 22.26 shows a typical such path. We cannot parametrize Γ because we do not know it specifically – it is simply any path enclosing a. Let γ be a circle of radius r about a, with r small enough that γ is enclosed by Γ (Figure 22.27). Now $f(z) = 1/(z-a)$ is differentiable at all points except a, hence on both curves and the region between them. By the deformation theorem,

$$\oint_{\Gamma} \frac{1}{z-a}\,dz = \oint_{\gamma} \frac{1}{z-a}\,dz.$$

But γ is easily parametrized: $\gamma(t) = a + re^{it}$ for $0 \le t \le 2\pi$. Then

$$\oint_{\gamma} \frac{1}{z-a}\,dz = \int_0^{2\pi} \frac{1}{re^{it}} ire^{it}\,dt = \int_0^{2\pi} i\,dt = 2\pi i.$$

Therefore

$$\oint_{\Gamma} \frac{1}{z-a}\,dz = 2\pi i.$$

The point is that, by means of the deformation theorem, we can evaluate this integral over any path enclosing a. Of course, if Γ does not enclose a, and a is not on Γ, then $1/(z-a)$ is differentiable on Γ and the set it encloses, so $\oint_{\Gamma}[1/(z-a)]dz = 0$ by Cauchy's theorem. ∎

The proof of the theorem employs a technique we will find useful in several settings.

Proof   Figure 22.28 shows graphs of typical paths Γ and γ. Insert lines L_1 and L_2 between Γ and γ (Figure 22.29) and use these to form two closed paths Φ and Ψ (shown separated for emphasis in Figure 22.30). One path, Φ, consists of parts of Γ and γ, together with L_1 and L_2, with orientation on each piece as shown in order to have positive orientation on Φ. The other path, Ψ, consists of the rest of Γ and γ, again with L_1 and L_2, with the orientation chosen on each piece so that Ψ has positive orientation. Figure 22.31 shows the paths more realistically,

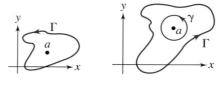

FIGURE 22.26   **FIGURE 22.27**

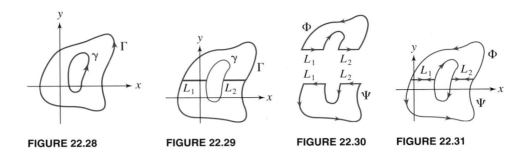

FIGURE 22.28   **FIGURE 22.29**   **FIGURE 22.30**   **FIGURE 22.31**

sharing the inserted segments L_1 and L_2. In Figure 22.31, Γ is oriented counterclockwise, but γ is clockwise, due to their orientations as parts of Φ and Ψ.

Because f is differentiable on both Φ and Ψ and the sets they enclose, Cauchy's theorem yields

$$\oint_{\Phi} f(z)\,dz = \oint_{\Psi} f(z)\,dz = 0.$$

Then

$$\oint_{\Phi} f(z)\,dz + \oint_{\Psi} f(z)\,dz = 0. \tag{22.2}$$

In this sum of integrals, each L_1 and L_2 is integrated over in one direction as part of Φ and the opposite direction as part of Ψ. The contributions from these segments therefore cancel in the sum (22.2). Next observe that, in adding these integrals, we obtain the integral over all of Γ, oriented counterclockwise, together with the integral over all of γ, oriented clockwise. In view of Theorem 22.3, equation (22.2) becomes

$$\oint_{\Phi} f(z)\,dz - \oint_{\gamma} f(z)\,dz = 0,$$

or

$$\oint_{\Phi} f(z)\,dz = \oint_{\gamma} f(z)\,dz,$$

in which the orientation on both Γ and γ in these integrals is positive (counterclockwise). This proves the theorem. ∎

22.4.3   Cauchy's Integral Formula

We will now state a remarkable result which gives an integral formula for the values of a differentiable function.

THEOREM 22.9   *Cauchy Integral Formula*

Let f be differentiable on an open set G. Let Γ be a closed path in G enclosing only points of G. Then, for any z_0 enclosed by Γ,

$$f(z_0) = \frac{1}{2\pi i} \oint_{\Gamma} \frac{f(z)}{z - z_0}\,dz. \quad ∎$$

We will see many uses for this theorem, but one is immediate. Write the formula as

$$\oint_{\Gamma} \frac{f(z)}{z - z_0}\,dz = 2\pi i f(z_0).$$

This gives, under the conditions of the theorem, an evaluation of the integral on the left as a constant multiple of the function value on the right.

EXAMPLE 22.18

Evaluate

$$\oint_\Gamma \frac{e^{z^2}}{z-i}\,dz$$

for any closed path that does not pass through i.

Let $f(z) = e^{z^2}$. Then f is differentiable for all z. There are two cases.

Case 1 Γ does not enclose i. Now $\oint_\Gamma \frac{e^{z^2}}{z-i}\,dz = 0$ by Cauchy's theorem, because $e^{z^2}/(z-2)$ is differentiable on and within Γ.

Case 2 Γ encloses i. By Cauchy's integral formula, with $z_0 = i$,

$$\oint_\Gamma \frac{e^{z^2}}{z-i}\,dz = 2\pi i f(i) = 2\pi i e^{-1}. \quad \blacksquare$$

EXAMPLE 22.19

Evaluate

$$\oint_\Gamma \frac{e^{2z}\sin(z^2)}{z-2}\,dz$$

over any path not passing through 2.

Let $f(z) = e^{2z}\sin(z^2)$. Then f is differentiable for all z. This leads to two cases.

Case 1 If Γ does not enclose 2, then $f(z)/(z-2)$ is differentiable on the curve and at all points it encloses. Now the integral is zero by Cauchy's theorem.

Case 2 If Γ encloses 2, then by the integral formula,

$$\oint_\Gamma \frac{e^{2z}\sin(z^2)}{z-2}\,dz = 2\pi i f(2) = 2\pi i e^4 \sin(4). \quad \blacksquare$$

Observe the distinction between the roles of $f(z)$ in Cauchy's theorem and in Cauchy's integral representation. Cauchy's theorem is concerned with $\oint_\Gamma f(z)\,dz$. The integral representation is concerned with integrals of the form $\oint_\Gamma [f(z)/(z-z_0)]\,dz$, with $f(z)$ given, but multiplied by a factor $1/(z-z_0)$ which is not defined at z_0. If Γ does not enclose z_0, then $f(z)/(z-z_0) = g(z)$ may be differentiable at z_0 and we can attempt to apply Cauchy's theorem to $\oint_\Gamma g(z)\,dz$. If z_0 is enclosed by Γ, then under the appropriate conditions, the integral formula gives $\oint_\Gamma g(z)\,dz$ in terms of $f(z_0)$.

Here is a proof of the integral representation.

Proof First use the deformation theorem to replace Γ with a circle γ of radius r about z_0, as in Figure 22.32. Then

$$\oint_\Gamma \frac{f(z)}{z-z_0}\,dz = \oint_\gamma \frac{f(z)}{z-z_0}\,dz = \oint_\gamma \frac{f(z) - f(z_0) + f(z_0)}{z-z_0}\,dz$$

$$= f(z_0)\oint_\gamma \frac{1}{z-z_0}\,dz + \oint_\gamma \frac{f(z) - f(z_0)}{z-z_0}\,dz,$$

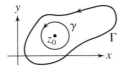

FIGURE 22.32

in which $f(z_0)$ could be brought outside the first integral because $f(z_0)$ is constant. By Example 22.17,

$$\oint_\gamma \frac{1}{z - z_0} dz = 2\pi i$$

because γ encloses z_0. Therefore

$$\oint_\Gamma \frac{f(z)}{z - z_0} dz = 2\pi i f(z_0) + \oint_\gamma \frac{f(z) - f(z_0)}{z - z_0} dz.$$

The integral representation is proved if we can show that the last integral is zero. Write $\gamma(t) = z_0 + re^{it}$ for $0 \le t \le 2\pi$. Then

$$\left| \oint_\gamma \frac{f(z) - f(z_0)}{z - z_0} dz \right| = \left| \int_0^{2\pi} \frac{f(z_0 + re^{it}) - f(z_0)}{re^{it}} ire^{it} dt \right|$$

$$= \left| \int_0^{2\pi} [f(z_0 + re^{it}) - f(z_0)] dt \right|$$

$$\le \int_0^{2\pi} \left| f(z_0 + re^{it}) - f(z_0) \right| dt$$

$$\le 2\pi \left(\max_{0 \le t \le 2\pi} \left| f(z_0 + re^{it}) - f(z_0) \right| \right).$$

By continuity of $f(z)$ at z_0, $f(z_0 + re^{it}) \to f(z_0)$ as $r \to 0$, so the term on the right in this inequality has limit zero as $r \to 0$. Therefore we can make

$$\left| \oint_\gamma \frac{f(z) - f(z_0)}{z - z_0} dz \right|$$

arbitrarily small by choosing r sufficiently small. But this integral is independent of r by the deformation theorem. Hence

$$\left| \oint_\gamma \frac{f(z) - f(z_0)}{z - z_0} dz \right| = 0,$$

so

$$\oint_\gamma \frac{f(z) - f(z_0)}{z - z_0} dz = 0$$

and the theorem is proved. ∎

The integral representation gives some idea of how strong the condition of differentiability is for complex functions. The integral

$$\oint_\Gamma \frac{f(z)}{z - z_0} dz$$

equals $2\pi i f(z_0)$, and so determines $f(z_0)$ at each z_0 enclosed by Γ. But the value of this integral depends only on the values of $f(z)$ on Γ. Thus, for a differentiable function, knowing function values on Γ determines the values of the function at all points enclosed by Γ. There is no analogous result for differentiable real functions. Knowing the values of a differentiable real function $\varphi(x)$ at the end points of an interval in general gives no information about values of this function throughout the interval.

22.4.4   Cauchy's Integral Formula for Higher Derivatives

We will now show that a complex function that is differentiable on an open set must have derivatives of all orders on this set. There is no result like this for real functions. A real function that is differentiable need not have a second derivative. And if it has a second derivative, it need not have a third, and so on.

Not only does a differentiable complex function have derivatives of all orders, we will show that the nth derivative of the function at a point is also given by an integral formula, very much in the spirit of Cauchy's integral formula.

THEOREM 22.10   *Cauchy's Integral Formula for Higher Derivatives*

Let f be differentiable on an open set G. Then f has derivatives of all orders at each point of G. Further, if Γ is a closed path in G enclosing only points of G, and z_0 is any point enclosed by Γ, then

$$f^{(n)}(z_0) = \frac{n!}{2\pi i} \oint_\Gamma \frac{f(z)}{(z - z_0)^{n+1}} \, dz. \ \blacksquare$$

The integral on the right is exactly what we would obtain by differentiating Cauchy's integral formula for $f(z_0)$, n times with respect to z_0, under the integral sign.

As with the integral formula, this conclusion is often used to evaluate integrals

---

EXAMPLE 22.20

Evaluate

$$\oint_\Gamma \frac{e^{z^3}}{(z - i)^3} \, dz$$

with Γ any path not passing through i.

If Γ does not enclose i then this integral is zero by Cauchy's theorem, since the only point at which $e^{z^3}/(z - i)^3$ fails to be differentiable is i. Thus suppose Γ encloses i. Because the factor $z - i$ occurs to the third power in the denominator, use $n = 2$ in the theorem, with $f(z) = e^{z^3}$, to get

$$\oint_\Gamma \frac{e^{z^3}}{(z - i)^3} \, dz = \frac{2\pi i}{2!} f^{(2)}(i) = \pi i f''(i).$$

Now

$$f'(z) = 3z^2 e^{z^3} \quad \text{and} \quad f''(z) = 6z e^{z^3} + 9z^4 e^{z^3},$$

so

$$\oint_\Gamma \frac{e^{z^3}}{(z - i)^3} \, dz = \pi i \left[6ie^{-i} + 9e^{-i} \right] = (-6 + 9i)\pi e^{-i}. \ \blacksquare$$

The theorem can be proved by induction on n, but we will not carry out the details.

22.4.5 Bounds on Derivatives and Liouville's Theorem

Cauchy's integral formula for higher derivatives can be used to obtain bounds on derivatives of all orders.

THEOREM 22.11

Let f be differentiable on an open set G. Let z_0 be a point of G and let the open disk of radius r about z_0 be in G. Suppose

$$|f(z)| \leq M$$

for z on the circle of radius r about z_0. Then, for any positive integer n,

$$\left| f^{(n)}(z_0) \right| \leq \frac{Mn!}{r^n}. \quad \blacksquare$$

Proof Let $\gamma(t) = z_0 + re^{it}$ for $0 \leq t \leq 2\pi$. Then $|f(z_0 + re^{it})| \leq M$ for $0 \leq t \leq 2\pi$. By Theorems 22.10 and 22.5,

$$\left| f^{(n)}(z_0) \right| = \frac{n!}{2\pi} \left| \oint_\gamma \frac{f(z)}{(z - z_0)^{n+1}} \, dz \right| = \frac{n!}{2\pi} \left| \int_0^{2\pi} \frac{f(z_0 + re^{it})}{r^{n+1} e^{i(n+1)t}} i re^{it} \, dt \right|$$

$$\leq \frac{n!}{2\pi} \int_0^{2\pi} \frac{|f(z_0 + re^{it})|}{r^n} \, dt \leq \frac{n!}{2\pi} (2\pi) M \frac{1}{r^n} = \frac{Mn!}{r^n}. \quad \blacksquare$$

As an application of this theorem, we will prove Liouville's theorem on bounded, differentiable functions.

THEOREM 22.12 *Liouville*

Let f be a bounded function that is differentiable for all z. Then f is a constant function. $\blacksquare$

Previously we noted that $\sin(z)$ is not a bounded function in the complex plane, as it is on the real line. This is consistent with Liouville's theorem. Since $\sin(z)$ is differentiable for all z, and is clearly not a constant function, it cannot be bounded.

Here is a proof of Liouville's theorem.

Proof Suppose $|f(z)| \leq M$ for all complex z. Choose any number z_0 and any $r > 0$. By Theorem 22.11, with $n = 1$,

$$|f'(z_0)| \leq \frac{M}{r}.$$

Since f is differentiable in the entire complex plane, r may be chosen as large as we like, so $|f'(z_0)|$ must be less than any positive number. We conclude that $|f'(z_0)| = 0$, hence $f'(z_0) = 0$. Since z_0 is any number, then $f(z) = $ constant. $\blacksquare$

Liouville's theorem can be used to give a simple proof of the fundamental theorem of algebra. This theorem states that any nonconstant complex polynomial $p(z) = a_0 + a_1 z + \cdots + a_n z^n$ has a complex root. That is, for some number ζ, $p(\zeta) = 0$. From this it can be further shown that, if $a_n \neq 0$, then $p(z)$ must have exactly n roots, counting each root k times in the list if its multiplicity is k. For example, $p(z) = z^2 - 6z + 9$ has exactly two roots, 3 and 3 (a root of multiplicity 2).

This fundamental theorem assumes only elementary terminology for its statement, and is usually included, in some form, in the high school mathematics curriculum. The leading nineteenth century mathematician Carl Friedrich Gauss considered the theorem so important that he devised many proofs (some say nearly twenty) over his lifetime. But even today rigorous proofs of the theorem require mathematical terms and devices far beyond those needed to state it.

To prove the theorem using Liouville's theorem, suppose $p(z)$ is a nonconstant complex polynomial and that $p(z) \neq 0$ for all z. Then $1/p(z)$ is differentiable for all z.

Let $p(z) = a_0 + a_1 z + \cdots + a_n z^n$ with $n \geq 1$ and $a_n \neq 0$. We will show that $|p(z)|$ is bounded for all z. Since

$$a_n z^n = p(z) - a_0 - a_1 z - \cdots - a_{n-1} z^{n-1},$$

then

$$|a_n| |z|^n \leq |p(z)| + |a_0| + |a_1| |z| + \cdots + |a_{n-1}| |z|^{n-1}.$$

Then, for $|z| \geq 1$,

$$|p(z)| \geq |a_n| |z|^n - \left(|a_0| + |a_1| |z| + \cdots + |a_{n-1}| |z|^{n-1} \right)$$

$$= |z|^{n-1} \left(|a_n| |z| - \frac{|a_0|}{|z|^{n-1}} - \frac{|a_1|}{|z|^{n-2}} - \cdots - \frac{|a_{n-1}|}{|z|^{n-n}} \right)$$

$$\geq |z|^{n-1} \left(|a_n| |z| - |a_0| - |a_1| - \cdots - |a_{n-1}| \right).$$

But then

$$\frac{1}{|p(z)|} \leq \frac{1}{|z|^{n-1} \left(|a_n| |z| - |a_0| - |a_1| - \cdots - |a_{n-1}| \right)} \to 0$$

as $|z| \to \infty$. Therefore $\lim_{n \to \infty} 1/|p(z)| = 0$. This implies that, for some positive number R,

$$\frac{1}{|p(z)|} < 1 \text{ if } |z| > R.$$

But the closed disk $|z| \leq R$ is compact, and $1/|p(z)|$ is continuous, so $1/|p(z)|$ is bounded on this disk by Theorem 21.1. Therefore, for some M,

$$\frac{1}{|p(z)|} \leq M \text{ for } |z| \leq R.$$

Now we have $1/|p(z)|$ bounded both inside and outside $|z| \leq 1$. Putting these bounds together,

$$\frac{1}{|p(z)|} \leq M + 1 \text{ for all } z,$$

both in $|z| \leq R$ and in $|z| \geq R$. This makes $1/p(z)$ a bounded function that is differentiable for all z. By Liouville's theorem, $1/p(z)$ must be constant, a contradiction. Therefore there must be some complex ζ such that $p(\zeta) = 0$, proving the fundamental theorem of algebra.

Complex analysis provides several proofs of this theorem. Later we will see one using a technique for evaluating real integrals of rational functions involving sines and cosines.

22.4.6 An Extended Deformation Theorem

The deformation theorem allows us to deform one closed path Γ of integration into another, γ, without changing the value of the line integral of a differentiable function f. A crucial condition for this process is that no stage of the deformation should pass over a point at which f fails to be differentiable. This means that f needs to be differentiable on both curves and the region between them. We will now extend this result to the case that Γ encloses any finite number of disjoint closed paths. As usual, unless explicitly stated otherwise, all closed paths are assumed to be oriented positively (counterclockwise).

THEOREM 22.13   Extended Deformation Theorem

Let Γ be a closed path. Let $\gamma_1, \ldots, \gamma_n$ be closed paths enclosed by Γ. Assume that no two of $\Gamma, \gamma_1, \ldots, \gamma_n$ intersect, and no point interior to any γ_j is interior to any other γ_k. Let f be differentiable on an open set containing Γ, each γ_j, and all points that are both interior to Γ and exterior to each γ_j. Then,

$$\oint_\Gamma f(z)\,dz = \sum_{j=1}^n \oint_{\gamma_j} f(z)\,dz. \quad\blacksquare$$

This is the deformation theorem in the case $n = 1$. Figure 22.33 shows a typical scenario covered by this theorem. With the curves as shown (and the differentiability assumption on f), the integral of f about Γ is the sum of the integrals of f about each of the closed curves $\gamma_1, \ldots, \gamma_n$.

We will outline a proof after an illustration of a typical use of the theorem.

EXAMPLE 22.21

Consider

$$\oint_\Gamma \frac{z}{(z+2)(z-4i)}\,dz,$$

where Γ is a closed path enclosing -2 and $4i$. We will evaluate this integral using the extended deformation theorem. Place a circle γ_1 about -2 and a circle γ_2 about $4i$, of sufficiently small radii that neither circle intersects the other or Γ and each is enclosed by Γ (Figure 22.34). Then

$$\oint_\Gamma \frac{z}{(z+2)(z-4i)}\,dz = \oint_{\gamma_1} \frac{z}{(z+2)(z-4i)}\,dz + \oint_{\gamma_2} \frac{z}{(z+2)(z-4i)}\,dz.$$

Use a partial fractions decomposition to write

$$\frac{z}{(z+2)(z-4i)} = \frac{\frac{1}{5} - \frac{2}{5}i}{z+2} + \frac{\frac{4}{5} + \frac{2}{5}i}{z-4i}.$$

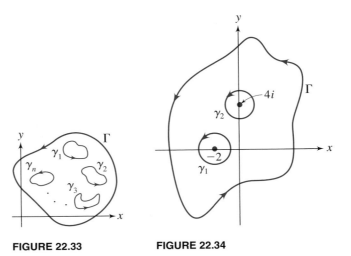

FIGURE 22.33   **FIGURE 22.34**

Then

$$\oint_{\Gamma} \frac{z}{(z+2)(z-4i)} dz = \left(\frac{1}{5} - \frac{2}{5}i\right) \oint_{\gamma_1} \frac{1}{z+2} dz + \left(\frac{4}{5} + \frac{2}{5}i\right) \oint_{\gamma_1} \frac{1}{z-4i} dz$$

$$+ \left(\frac{1}{5} - \frac{2}{5}i\right) \oint_{\gamma_2} \frac{1}{z+2} dz + \left(\frac{4}{5} + \frac{2}{5}i\right) \oint_{\gamma_2} \frac{1}{z-4i} dz.$$

On the right, the second and third integrals are zero by Cauchy's theorem (γ_1 does not enclose $4i$ and γ_2 does not enclose -2). The first and fourth integrals equal $2\pi i$ by Example 22.17. Therefore

$$\oint_{\Gamma} \frac{z}{(z+2)(z-4i)} dz = 2\pi i \left[\left(\frac{1}{5} - \frac{2}{5}i\right) + \left(\frac{4}{5} + \frac{2}{5}i\right)\right] = 2\pi i. \quad \blacksquare$$

A proof of the theorem can be modeled after the proof of the deformation theorem.

Proof   As suggested in Figure 22.35, draw line segments L_1 from Γ to γ_1, L_2 from γ_1 to $\gamma_2, \ldots, L_n$ from γ_{n-1} to γ_n and, finally, L_{n+1} from γ_n to Γ. Form the closed paths Φ and Δ shown separately in Figures 22.36 and 22.37, and as they actually appear in Figure 22.38. Then

$$\oint_{\Phi} f(z)dz + \oint_{\Delta} f(z)dz = 0,$$

both integrals being zero by Cauchy's theorem. (By the hypotheses of the theorem, f is differentiable on and inside both Φ and Δ).

In this sum of integrals over Φ and Δ, each line segment L_j is integrated over in both directions, hence the contributions of the integrals over these segments is zero. Further, in this sum we retrieve the integral of $f(z)$ over all of Γ, and all of each γ_j, with the orientation counterclockwise on Γ and clockwise on each γ_j (note the orientations in Figure 22.38).

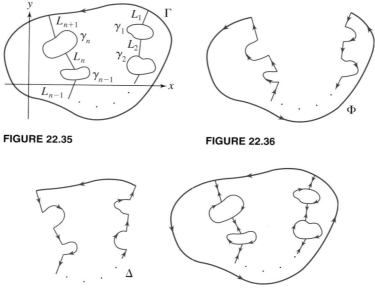

FIGURE 22.35   FIGURE 22.36

FIGURE 22.37   FIGURE 22.38

Reversing the orientations on the $\gamma'_j s$, so that all paths are oriented counterclockwise, the last sum becomes

$$\oint_\Gamma f(z)dz - \sum_{j=1}^n \oint_{\gamma_j} f(z)dz = 0,$$

yielding the conclusion of the theorem. ■

SECTION 22.4 PROBLEMS

In each of Problems 1 through 12, evaluate $\int f(z)dz$ for the given function and closed (positively oriented) path. These problems may involve Cauchy's theorem, Cauchy's integral formulas and/or the deformation theorems.

1. $f(z) = \dfrac{z^4}{z - 2i}$; Γ is any closed path enclosing $2i$

2. $f(z) = \dfrac{\sin(z^2)}{z - 5}$; Γ is any closed path enclosing 5

3. $f(z) = \dfrac{z^2 - 5z + i}{z - 1 + 2i}$; Γ is the circle $|z| = 3$

4. $f(z) = \dfrac{2z^3}{(z-2)^2}$; Γ is the rectangle having vertices $4 \pm i$ and $-4 \pm i$

5. $f(z) = \dfrac{ie^z}{(z-2+i)^2}$; Γ is the circle $|z-1| = 4$

6. $f(z) = \dfrac{\cos(z-i)}{(z+2i)^3}$; Γ is any closed path enclosing $-2i$

7. $f(z) = \dfrac{z\sin(3z)}{(z+4)^3}$; Γ is the circle $|z - 2i| = 9$

8. $f(z) = 2i\bar{z}|z|$; Γ is the line segment from 1 to $-i$

9. $f(z) = -\dfrac{(2+i)\sin(z^4)}{(z+4)^2}$; Γ is any closed path enclosing -4

10. $f(z) = (z-i)^2$; Γ is the semicircle of radius 1 about 0 from i to $-i$

11. $f(z) = \text{Re}(z+4)$; Γ is the line segment from $3 + i$ to $2 - 5i$

12. $f(z) = \dfrac{3z^2 \cosh(z)}{(z+2i)^2}$; Γ is the circle of radius 8 about 1

13. Evaluate

$$\int_0^{2\pi} e^{\cos(\theta)} \cos(\sin(\theta))d\theta.$$

Hint: Consider $\oint_\Gamma (e^z/z)dz$, with Γ the unit circle about the origin. Evaluate this integral once using Cauchy's integral formula, then again directly by using the coordinate functions for Γ.

14. Use the extended form of the deformation theorem to evaluate $\oint_\Gamma \dfrac{z-4i}{z^3 + 4z}dz$, where Γ is a closed path enclosing the origin, $2i$ and $-2i$.

CHAPTER 23

Series Representations of Functions

We will now develop two kinds of representations of a $f(z)$ in series of powers of $z - z_0$. The first series will contain only nonnegative integer powers, hence is a power series, and applies when f is differentiable at z_0. The second will contain negative integer powers of $z - z_0$ as well, and will be used when f is not differentiable at z_0.

23.1 Power Series Representations

We know that a power series that converges in an open disk, or perhaps the entire plane, defines a function that is infinitely differentiable within this disk or the plane. We will now go the other way and show that a function that is differentiable on an open disk is represented by a power series expansion about the center of this disk. This will have important applications, including information about zeros of functions, and the maximum value that can be taken by the modulus $|f(z)|$ of a differentiable function.

THEOREM 23.1 *Taylor Series*

Let f be differentiable on an open disk D about z_0. Then, for each z in D,

$$f(z) = \sum_{n=0}^{\infty} \frac{f^{(n)}(z_0)}{n!}(z - z_0)^n. \quad \blacksquare$$

The series on the right is the *Taylor series* of $f(z)$ about z_0, and the number $f^{(n)}(z_0)/n!$ is the nth *Taylor coefficient* of $f(z)$ at z_0. The theorem asserts that the Taylor series of $f(z)$ converges to $f(z)$, hence represents $f(z)$, within this disk.

FIGURE 23.1

Proof Let z be any point of D and R the radius of D. Choose a number r with $|z - z_0| < r < R$ and let γ be the circle of radius r about z_0 (Figure 23.1). By the Cauchy integral formula, using w for the variable of integration on γ,

$$f(z) = \frac{1}{2\pi i} \oint_\gamma \frac{f(w)}{w - z}\, dw.$$

Now

$$\frac{1}{w - z} = \frac{1}{w - z_0 - (z - z_0)} = \frac{1}{w - z_0} \frac{1}{1 - (z - z_0)/(w - z_0)}.$$

Since w is on γ, and z is enclosed by γ, then

$$\left| \frac{z - z_0}{w - z_0} \right| < 1$$

so we can use a convergent geometric series to write

$$\frac{1}{w - z} = \frac{1}{w - z_0} \sum_{n=0}^{\infty} \left(\frac{z - z_0}{w - z_0} \right)^n = \sum_{n=0}^{\infty} \frac{1}{(w - z_0)^{n+1}} (z - z_0)^n.$$

Then

$$\frac{f(w)}{w - z} = \sum_{n=0}^{\infty} \frac{f(w)}{(w - z_0)^{n+1}} (z - z_0)^n. \tag{23.1}$$

Since f is continuous on γ, for some M, $|f(w)| \le M$ for w on γ. Further, $|w - z_0| = r$, so

$$\left| \frac{f(w)}{(w - z_0)^{n+1}} (z - z_0)^n \right| \le M \frac{1}{r} \left(\frac{|z - z_0|}{r} \right)^n.$$

Designate

$$M \frac{1}{r} \left(\frac{|z - z_0|}{r} \right)^n = M_n.$$

Then $\sum_{n=0}^{\infty} M_n$ converges (this series is a constant times a convergent geometric series). By Theorem 22.6, the series in equation (23.1) can be integrated term-by-term to yield

$$f(z) = \frac{1}{2\pi i} \oint_\gamma \frac{f(w)}{w - z}\, dw = \frac{1}{2\pi i} \oint_\gamma \left(\sum_{n=0}^{\infty} \frac{f(w)}{(w - z_0)^{n+1}} (z - z_0)^n \right) dw$$

$$= \sum_{n=0}^{\infty} \left(\frac{1}{2\pi i} \oint_\gamma \frac{f(w)}{(w - z_0)^{n+1}}\, dw \right) (z - z_0)^n = \sum_{n=0}^{\infty} \frac{f^{(n)}(z_0)}{n!} (z - z_0)^n,$$

in which we used Cauchy's integral formula for the nth derivative to write the coefficient in the last series. This proves the theorem. ∎

A complex function is said to be *analytic* at z_0 if it has a power series expansion in some open disk about z_0. We have just proved that a function that is differentiable on an open disk about a point is analytic at that point.

We only compute the coefficients of a Taylor series by derivative or integral formulas when other means fail. When possible, we use known series and operations such as differentiation and integration to derive a series representation. This strategy makes use of the uniqueness of power series representations.

THEOREM 23.2

Suppose, in some disk $|z - z_0| < r$,

$$\sum_{n=0}^{\infty} c_n (z - z_0)^n = \sum_{n=0}^{\infty} d_n (z - z_0)^n.$$

Then, for $n = 0, 1, 2, \ldots, c_n = d_n$.

Proof   If we let $f(z)$ be the function defined in this disk by both power series, then

$$c_n = \frac{f^{(n)}(z_0)}{n!} = d_n. \;\blacksquare$$

This means that, no matter what method is used to find a power series for $f(z)$ about z_0, the end result is the Taylor series.

EXAMPLE 23.1

Find the Taylor expansion of e^z about i.

We know that, for all z,

$$e^z = \sum_{n=0}^{\infty} \frac{1}{n!} z^n.$$

For an expansion about i, the power series must be in terms of powers of $z - i$. Thus write

$$e^z = e^{z-i+i} = e^i e^{z-i} = \sum_{n=0}^{\infty} e^i \frac{1}{n!} (z - i)^n.$$

This series converges for all z. $\blacksquare$

In this example, it would have been just as easy to compute the Taylor coefficients directly:

$$c_n = \frac{f^{(n)}(i)}{n!} = \frac{e^i}{n!}.$$

EXAMPLE 23.2

Write the Maclaurin series for $\cos(z^3)$.

A Maclaurin expansion is a Taylor series about zero. For all z,

$$\cos(z) = \sum_{n=0}^{\infty} \frac{(-1)^n}{(2n)!} z^{2n}.$$

All we need to do is replace z with z^3:

$$\cos(z^3) = \sum_{n=0}^{\infty} \frac{(-1)^n}{(2n)!} (z^3)^{2n} = \sum_{n=0}^{\infty} \frac{(-1)^n}{(2n)!} z^{6n}.$$

Since this is an expansion about the origin, it is the expansion we seek. $\blacksquare$

EXAMPLE 23.3

Expand

$$\frac{2i}{4+iz}$$

in a Taylor series about $-3i$.

We want a series in powers of $z+3i$. Do some algebraic manipulation and then use a geometric series. In order to get $z+3i$ into the picture, write

$$\frac{2i}{4+iz} = \frac{2i}{4+i(z+3i)+3} = \frac{2i}{7+i(z+3i)} = \frac{2i}{7}\frac{1}{1+\frac{i}{7}(z+3i)}.$$

If $|t| < 1$, then

$$\frac{1}{1+t} = \frac{1}{1-(-t)} = \sum_{n=0}^{\infty}(-t)^n = \sum_{n=0}^{\infty}(-1)^n.$$

With $t = (z+3i)i/7$, we have

$$\frac{1}{1+\frac{i}{7}(z+3i)} = \sum_{n=0}^{\infty}(-1)^n\left(\frac{i}{7}(z+3i)\right)^n.$$

Therefore

$$\frac{2i}{4+iz} = \frac{2i}{7}\sum_{n=0}^{\infty}(-1)^n\left(\frac{i}{7}\right)^n(z+3i)^n = \sum_{n=0}^{\infty}\frac{2(-1)^ni^{n+1}}{7^{n+1}}(z+3i)^n.$$

Because this is a series expansion of the function about $-3i$, it is the Taylor series about $-3i$. This series converges for

$$\left|\frac{i}{7}(z+3i)\right| < 1,$$

or

$$|z+3i| < 7.$$

Thus z must be in the open disk of radius 7 about $-3i$. The radius of convergence of this series is 7. ■

From Section 21.2, we can differentiate a Taylor series term by term within its open disk of convergence. This is sometimes useful in deriving the Taylor expansion of a function.

EXAMPLE 23.4

Find the Taylor expansion of $f(z) = 1/(1-z)^3$ about the origin.

We could do this by algebraic manipulation, but it is easier to begin with the familiar geometric series

$$g(z) = \frac{1}{1-z} = \sum_{n=0}^{\infty}z^n \quad \text{for } |z| < 1.$$

Then

$$g'(z) = \frac{1}{(1-z)^2} = \sum_{n=1}^{\infty}nz^{n-1}$$

and

$$g''(z) = \frac{2}{(1-z)^3} = \sum_{n=2}^{\infty} n(n-1)z^{n-2} = \sum_{n=0}^{\infty} (n+1)(n+2)z^n$$

for $|z| < 1$. Then

$$f(z) = \sum_{n=0}^{\infty} \frac{1}{2}(n+1)(n+2)z^n \quad \text{for } |z| < 1. \ \blacksquare$$

When $f(z)$ is expanded in a power series about z_0, the radius of convergence of the series will be the distance from z_0 to the nearest point at which $f(z)$ is not differentiable. Think of a disk expanding uniformly from z_0, free to continue its expansion until it hits a point at which $f(z)$ is not differentiable.

For example, suppose $f(z) = 2i/(4+iz)$, and we want a Taylor expansion about $-3i$. The only point at which $f(z)$ is not defined is $4i$, so the radius of convergence of this series will be the distance between $-3i$ and $4i$, or 7. We obtained this result previously from the Taylor expansion $\sum_{n=0}^{\infty} (2(-1)^n i^{n+1}/7^{n+1})(z+3i)^n$ of $f(z)$.

EXAMPLE 23.5

We will find the radius of convergence of the Taylor series of $\csc(z)$ about $3 - 4i$.

Since $\csc(z) = 1/\sin(z)$, this function is differentiable except at $z = n\pi$, with n any integer. As Figure 23.2 illustrates, π is the nearest point to $3 - 4i$ at which $\csc(z)$ is not differentiable. The distance between π and $3 - 4i$ is

$$\sqrt{(\pi - 3)^2 + 16},$$

and this is the radius of convergence of the expansion of $\csc(z)$ about $3 - 4i$. $\blacksquare$

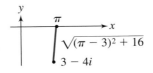

FIGURE 23.2

Existence of a power series expansion implies the existence of an antiderivative.

THEOREM 23.3

Let f be differentiable in an open disk D about z_0. Then there is a differentiable function F such that $F'(z) = f(z)$ for all z in D.

Proof We know that f has a power series expansion in D:

$$f(z) = \sum_{n=0}^{\infty} c_n(z - z_0)^n.$$

Let

$$F(z) = \sum_{n=0}^{\infty} \frac{1}{n+1} c_n(z - z_0)^{n+1}$$

for z in D. It is routine to check that this power series has radius of convergence at least as large as the radius of D, and that

$$F'(z) = f(z)$$

for z in D. ■

23.1.1 Isolated Zeros and the Identity Theorem

We will use the Taylor series representation of a differentiable function to derive important information about its zeros.

DEFINITION 23.1

A number ζ is a zero of f if $f(\zeta) = 0$.
   A zero ζ of f is isolated if there is an open disk about ζ containing no other zero of f.

For example, the zeros of $\sin(z)$ are $n\pi$, with n any integer. These zeros are all isolated. By contrast, let

$$f(z) = \begin{cases} \sin(1/z) & \text{if } z \neq 0 \\ 0 & \text{if } z = 0 \end{cases}.$$

The zeros of f are 0 and the numbers $1/n\pi$, with n any nonzero integer. However, 0 is not an isolated zero, since any open disk about zero contains other zeros, $1/n\pi$, for n sufficiently large.
   We will show that the behavior of the zeros in this example disqualifies f from being differentiable at 0.

THEOREM 23.4

Let f be differentiable on an open disk G and let ζ be a zero of f in G. Then either ζ is an isolated zero of f, or there is an open disk about ζ on which $f(z)$ is identically zero.

   This means that a differentiable function that is not identically zero on some disk can have only isolated zeros.

Proof   Write the power series expansion of $f(z)$ about ζ,

$$f(z) = \sum_{n=0}^{\infty} c_n (z - \zeta)^n,$$

in some open disk D centered at ζ. Now consider two cases.

Case 1 If each $c_n = 0$, then $f(z) = 0$ throughout D.

Case 2 Suppose, instead, that some coefficients in the power series are not zero. Let m be the smallest integer such that $c_m \neq 0$. Then $c_0 = c_1 = \cdots = c_{m-1} = 0$ and $c_m \neq 0$. For z in D,

$$f(z) = \sum_{n=m}^{\infty} c_n (z - \zeta)^n = \sum_{n=0}^{\infty} c_{n+m} (z - \zeta)^{n+m} = (z - \zeta)^m \sum_{n=0}^{\infty} c_{n+m} (z - \zeta)^n.$$

Now $\sum_{n=0}^{\infty} c_{n+m}(z-\zeta)^n$ is a power series, and so defines a differentiable function $g(z)$ for z in D. Further,

$$f(z) = (z-\zeta)^m g(z).$$

But $g(\zeta) = c_m \neq 0$, so there is some open disk K about ζ in which $g(z) \neq 0$. Therefore, for $z \neq \zeta$ in K, $f(z) \neq 0$ also, hence ζ is an isolated zero of f. ∎

This proof contained additional information about zeros that will be useful later. The number m in the proof is called the *order* of the zero ζ of $f(z)$. It is the smallest integer m such that the coefficient c_m in the expansion of $f(z)$ about ζ is nonzero. Now recall that $c_n = f^{(n)}(\zeta)/n!$. Thus $c_0 = c_1 = \cdots = c_{m-1} = 0$ implies that

$$f(\zeta) = f'(\zeta) = \cdots = f^{(m-1)}(\zeta) = 0,$$

while $c_m \neq 0$ implies that

$$f^{(m)}(\zeta) \neq 0.$$

In summary, an isolated zero ζ of f has order m if the function and its first $m-1$ derivatives vanish at ζ, but the mth derivative at ζ is nonzero. Put another way, the order of the zero ζ is the lowest order derivative of f that does not vanish at ζ.

We also derived the important fact that, if ζ is an isolated zero of order m of f, then we can write

$$f(z) = (z-\zeta)^m g(z),$$

where g is also differentiable in some disk about ζ, and $g(\zeta) \neq 0$.

EXAMPLE 23.6

Consider $f(z) = z^2 \cos(z)$. 0 is an isolated zero of this differentiable function. Compute

$$f'(z) = 2z \cos(z) - z^2 \sin(z)$$

and

$$f''(z) = 2\cos(z) - 4z\sin(z) + z^2 \cos(z).$$

Observe that $f(0) = f'(0) = 0$ while $f''(0) \neq 0$. Thus 0 is a zero of order 2 of f. In this case, we already have

$$f(z) = (z-0)^2 g(z)$$

with $g(0) \neq 0$, since we can choose $g(z) = \cos(z)$. ∎

EXAMPLE 23.7

We have to exercise some care in identifying the order of a zero. Consider $f(z) = z^2 \sin(z)$. 0 is an isolated zero of f. Compute

$$f'(z) = 2z\sin(z) + z^2 \cos(z),$$

$$f''(z) = 2\sin(z) + 4z\cos(z) - z^2 \sin(z),$$

$$f^{(3)}(z) = 2\cos(z) + 4\cos(z) - 4z\sin(z) - 2z\sin(z) - z^2 \cos(z)$$

$$= 6\cos(z) - 6z\sin(z) - z^2 \cos(z).$$

Then

$$f(0) = f'(0) = f''(0) = 0$$

while

$$f^{(3)}(0) \neq 0.$$

This means that 0 is a zero of order 3. We can write

$$f(z) = z^2 \sum_{n=0}^{\infty} \frac{(-1)^n}{(2n+1)!} z^{2n+1} = z^3 \sum_{n=0}^{\infty} \frac{(-1)^n}{(2n+1)!} z^{2n} = z^3 g(z),$$

where

$$g(z) = \sum_{n=0}^{\infty} \frac{(-1)^n}{(2n+1)!} z^{2n}$$

is differentiable (in this example, for all z) and $g(0) = 1 \neq 0$. ∎

As a result of Theorem 23.3, we can show that, if a differentiable complex function vanishes on a convergent sequence of points in a domain (open, connected set), then the function is *identically zero throughout the entire domain*. This is a very strong result, for which there is no analogue for real functions. For example, consider

$$h(x) = \begin{cases} 0 & \text{for } x \leq 0 \\ x^2 & \text{for } x > 0 \end{cases},$$

whose graph is shown in Figure 23.3 This function is differentiable for all real x, and is identically zero on half the line, but is not identically zero over the entire line. Another difference between differentiability for real and complex functions is evident in this example. While h is differentiable, it does not have a power series expansion about 0. By contrast, a complex function that is differentiable on an open set has a power series expansion about each point of the set.

THEOREM 23.5

Let f be differentiable on a domain G. Suppose $\{z_n\}$ is a sequence of distinct zeros of f in G, converging to a point of G. Then $f(z) = 0$ for all z in G.

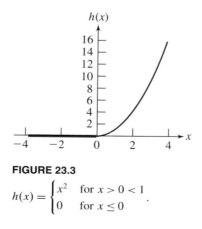

FIGURE 23.3

$$h(x) = \begin{cases} x^2 & \text{for } x > 0 < 1 \\ 0 & \text{for } x \leq 0 \end{cases}.$$

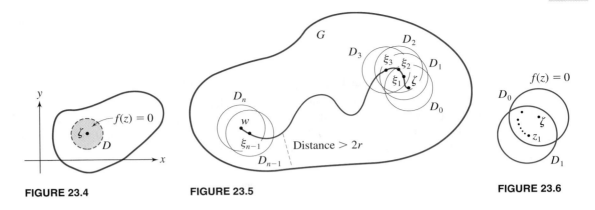

FIGURE 23.4   **FIGURE 23.5**   **FIGURE 23.6**

Proof Suppose $z_n \to \zeta$ in G. Since f is continuous, $f(z_n) \to f(\zeta)$. But each $f(z_n) = 0$, so $f(\zeta) = 0$ also, and ζ must also be a zero of f in G. This means that ζ is not an isolated zero, so by Theorem 23.3, there must be an open disk D about ζ, in which $f(z)$ is identically zero (Figure 23.4).

We want to prove that this forces $f(z) = 0$ for all z in G. To do this, let w be any point of G. We will show that $f(w) = 0$.

Since G is connected, there is a path Γ in G from ζ to w. Choose a number r such that every point of Γ is at a distance at least $2r$ from the boundary of G, and also choose r to be less than the radius of D. Now walk along Γ from ζ to w, along the way selecting points at distance less than r from each other. This yields points $\zeta = \xi_0, \xi_1, \ldots, \xi_n = w$ on Γ, as in Figure 23.5. Form an open disk D_j of radius r about each ξ_j. (By choice of r, none of these disks reaches the boundary of G). Each ξ_{j-1} is in D_{j-1}, D_j and D_{j+1} for $j = 1, \ldots, n-1$. Further, $\xi_0 = \zeta$ is in D_0 and D_1, and w is in D_{n-1} and D_n.

Since ξ_1 is in D_0 and D_1, there is a sequence of points in both D_0 and D_1 converging to ξ_1 (Figure 23.6). But $f(z)$ is identically zero on D_0, so $f(z)$ vanishes on this sequence. Since this sequence is also in D_1, $f(z) = 0$ for all z in D_1.

Now ξ_2 is in D_1 and D_2. Choose a sequence of points common to both of these disks, and converging to ξ_2. Since $f(z)$ is identically zero on D_1, then $f(z) = 0$ at each point of this sequence. But since this sequence is also in D_2, then $f(z)$ is identically zero on D_2.

Continuing in this way, walk along Γ from ζ to w. We find that $f(z)$ is identically zero on each of the disks along the way. Finally, $f(z)$ is zero on D_n. But w is in D_n, so $f(w) = 0$, and therefore $f(z) = 0$ for all z in G. ∎

This theorem leads immediately to the conclusion that two differentiable functions that agree on a convergent sequence in a domain must be the same function. This is called the *identity theorem.*

COROLLARY 23.1 *Identity Theorem*

Let f and g be differentiable on a domain G. Suppose $f(z)$ and $g(z)$ agree on a convergent sequence of distinct points of G. Then $f(z) = g(z)$ for all z in G. ∎

Proof Apply Theorem 23.4 to the differentiable function $f - g$. ∎

To get some idea of the power of this result, consider the problem of defining the complex sine function $\sin(z)$ so that it agrees with the real sine function when z is real. How many ways can this be done?

Put another way, is it possible to invent two distinct differentiable complex functions, f and g, defined for all z, such that, when z is real,

$$f(x) = g(x) = \sin(x)?$$

If this could be done, then we would have $f(z) = g(z)$ on a convergent sequence of complex numbers (chosen along the real line) in a domain (the entire plane), so necessarily $f = g$. There can be only one extension of a differentiable function from the real to the complex domain.

This is why, when we extend a real function (such as the exponential or trigonometric functions) to the complex plane, we can be assured that this extension is unique.

23.1.2 The Maximum Modulus Theorem

Suppose $f: S \to \mathbb{C}$, and S is a compact set. We know from Theorem 21.3 that $|f(z)|$ assumes a maximum value on S. This means that, for at least one ζ in S, $|f(z)| \leq |f(\zeta)|$ for all ζ in S. But this does not give any information about where in S the point ζ might be. We will now prove that any such ζ must lie on the boundary of S, if f is a differentiable function. This is called the maximum modulus theorem. The name of the theorem derives from the fact that the real-valued function $|f(z)|$ is called the *modulus* of $f(z)$, and we are concerned with the maximum that the modulus of $f(z)$ has as z varies over a set S.

We will first show that a differentiable function that is not constant on an open disk cannot have its maximum modulus at the center of the disk.

LEMMA 23.1

Let f be differentiable and not constant on an open disk D centered at z_0. Then, for some z in this disk,

$$|f(z)| > |f(z_0)|.$$

Proof   Suppose instead that $|f(z)| \leq |f(z_0)|$ for all z in D. We will derive a contradiction.

Let $\gamma(t) = z_0 + re^{it}$ for $0 \leq t \leq 2\pi$. Suppose r is small enough that this circle is contained in D. By Cauchy's integral theorem,

$$f(z_0) = \frac{1}{2\pi i} \oint_\gamma \frac{f(z)}{z - z_0} dz = \frac{1}{2\pi} \int_0^{2\pi} f(z_0 + re^{it}) dt.$$

Then

$$|f(z_0)| \leq \frac{1}{2\pi} \int_0^{2\pi} \left| f(z_0 + re^{it}) \right| dt.$$

But $z_0 + re^{it}$ is in D for $0 \leq t \leq 2\pi$, so $|f(z_0 + re^{it})| \leq |f(z_0)|$. Then

$$\frac{1}{2\pi} \int_0^{2\pi} \left| f(z_0 + re^{it}) \right| dt \leq \frac{1}{2\pi} \int_0^{2\pi} |f(z_0)| \, dt = |f(z_0)|.$$

The last two inequalities imply that

$$\frac{1}{2\pi} \int_0^{2\pi} \left| f(z_0 + re^{it}) \right| dt = |f(z_0)|.$$

But then

$$\frac{1}{2\pi} \int_0^{2\pi} \left(|f(z_0)| - \left| f(z_0 + re^{it}) \right| \right) dt = 0.$$

This integrand is continuous and nonnegative for $0 \leq t \leq 2\pi$. If it were positive for any t, then there would be some subinterval of $[0, 2\pi]$ on which the integrand would be positive, and then this integral would be positive, a contradiction. Therefore the integrand must be identically zero:

$$\left| f(z_0 + re^{it}) \right| = |f(z_0)| \quad \text{for } 0 \leq t \leq 2\pi.$$

This says that $|f(z)|$ has the constant value $|f(z_0)|$ on every circle about z_0 and contained in D. But every point in D is on some circle about z_0 and contained in D. Therefore $|f(z)| = |f(z_0)| =$ constant for all z in D. Then by Theorem 21.7, $f(z) =$ constant on D. This contradiction proves the lemma. ∎

We can now derive the maximum modulus theorem.

THEOREM 23.6 *Maximum Modulus Theorem*

Let S be a compact, connected set of complex numbers. Let f be continuous on S and differentiable at each interior point of S. Then $|f(z)|$ achieves its maximum value at a boundary point of S. Further, if f is not a constant function, then $|f(z)|$ does not achieve its maximum at an interior point of S.

Proof Because S is compact and f is continuous, we know from Theorem 21.3 that $|f(z)|$ achieves a maximum value at some (perhaps many) points of S. Let ζ be such a point. If ζ is an interior point, then there is an open disk D about ζ that contains only points of S. But then $|f(z)|$ achieves its maximum on this disk at its center. Now there are two cases.

Case 1 $f(z)$ is constant on this disk. By the identity theorem, $f(z)$ is constant on S. In this event $|f(z)|$ is constant on S.

Case 2 $f(z)$ is not constant on this disk. Then $|f(z)| \leq |f(\zeta)|$ for z in this disk, contradicting Lemma 23.1. In this case $|f(z)|$ cannot achieve a maximum in the interior of S, and so must achieve its maximum at a boundary point. ∎

EXAMPLE 23.8

Let $f(z) = \sin(z)$. We will determine the maximum value of $|f(z)|$ on the square $0 \leq x \leq \pi$, $0 \leq y \leq \pi$.

First, it is convenient to work with $|f(z)|^2$, since this will have its maximum at the same value of z that $|f(z)|$ does. Now

$$f(z) = \sin(z) = \sin(x)\cosh(y) + i\cos(x)\sinh(y),$$

so

$$|f(z)|^2 = \sin^2(x)\cosh^2(y) + \cos^2(x)\sinh^2(y).$$

By the maximum modulus theorem, $|f(z)|^2$ must have achieve its maximum value (for this square) on one of the sides of the square. Look at each side in turn.

On the bottom side, $y = 0$ and $0 \leq x \leq \pi$, so $|f(z)|^2 = \sin^2(x)$ achieves a maximum value of 1.

On the right side, $x = \pi$ and $0 \leq y \leq \pi$, so $|f(z)|^2 = \sinh^2(y)$ achieves a maximum value of $\sinh^2(\pi)$. This is because $\cos^2(\pi) = 1$ and $\sinh(y)$ is a strictly increasing function on $[0, \pi]$.

On the top side of the square, $y = \pi$ and $0 \le x \le \pi$. Now $|f(z)|^2 = \sin^2(x)\cosh^2(\pi) + \cos^2(x)\sinh^2(\pi)$. We need to know where this achieves its maximum value for $0 \le x \le \pi$. This is a problem in single-variable calculus. Let

$$g(x) = \sin^2(x)\cosh^2(\pi) + \cos^2(x)\sinh^2(\pi).$$

Then

$$g'(x) = 2\sin(x)\cos(x)\cosh^2(\pi) - 2\cos(x)\sin(x)\sinh^2(\pi)$$

$$= \sin(2x)[\cosh^2(\pi) - \sinh^2(\pi)] = \sin(2x).$$

This derivative is zero on $(0, \pi)$ at $x = \pi/2$, so this is the critical point of g. Further,

$$g\left(\frac{\pi}{2}\right) = \cosh^2(\pi).$$

At the ends of the interval, we have

$$g(0) = g(\pi) = \sinh^2(\pi) < \cosh^2(\pi).$$

Therefore, on the top side of the square, $|f(z)|^2$ achieves the maximum value of $\cosh^2(\pi)$.

Finally, on the left side of the square, $x = 0$ and $0 \le y \le \pi$, so $|f(z)|^2 = \sinh^2(y)$, with maximum $\sinh^2(\pi)$ on $0 \le y \le \pi$.

We conclude that, on this square, $|f(z)|^2$ has its maximum value of $\cosh^2(\pi)$, which is the maximum value of $|f(z)|^2$ on the boundary of the square. Therefore $|f(z)|$ has a maximum value of $\cosh(\pi)$ on this square. ■

SECTION 23.1   PROBLEMS

In each of Problems 1 through 12, find the Taylor series of the function about the point. Also determine the radius of convergence and open disk of convergence of the series.

1. $\cos(2z); z = 0$

2. $e^{-z}; z = -3i$

3. $\dfrac{1}{1 - z}; 4i$

4. $\sin(z^2); 0$

5. $\dfrac{1}{(1 - z)^2}; 0$

6. $\dfrac{1}{2 + z}; 1 - 8i$

7. $z^2 - 3z + i; 2 - i$

8. $1 + \dfrac{1}{2 + z^2}; i$

9. $(z - 9)^2; 1 + i$

10. $e^z - i\sin(z); 0$

11. $\sin(z + i); -i$

12. $\dfrac{3}{z - 4i}; -5$

13. Suppose f is differentiable in an open disk about zero, and satisfies $f''(z) = 2f(z) + 1$. Suppose $f(0) = 1$ and $f'(0) = i$. Find the Maclaurin expansion of $f(z)$.

14. Find the first three terms of the Maclaurin expansion of $\sin^2(z)$ in three ways as follows:

(a) First, compute the Taylor coefficients at 0.

(b) Find the first three terms of the product of the Maclaurin series for $\sin(z)$ with itself.

(c) Write $\sin^2(z)$ in terms of the exponential function and use the Maclaurin expansion of this function.

15. Show that

$$\sum_{n=0}^{\infty} \frac{1}{(n!)^2} z^{2n} = \frac{1}{2\pi} \int_0^{2\pi} e^{2z\cos(\theta)}\, d\theta.$$

Hint: First show that

$$\left(\frac{z^n}{n!}\right)^2 = \frac{1}{2\pi i} \oint_\Gamma \frac{z^n}{n! w^{n+1}} e^{zw}\, dw.$$

for $n = 0, 1, 2, \ldots$ and Γ the unit circle about the origin.

16. Find the maximum value of $|\cos(z)|$ on the square $0 \le x \le \pi, 0 \le y \le \pi$.

17. Find the maximum value of $|e^z|$ on the square $0 \le x \le 1, 0 \le y \le \pi$.

18. Find the maximum value of $|\sin(z)|$ on the rectangle $0 \le x \le 2\pi, 0 \le y \le 1$.

23.2   The Laurent Expansion

If f is differentiable in some disk about z_0, then $f(z)$ has a Taylor series representation about z_0.

If a function is not differentiable at z_0, it may have a different kind of series expansion about z_0, a Laurent expansion. This will have profound implications in analyzing properties of functions and in such applications as evaluating real and complex integrals.

First we need some terminology. The open set of points between two concentric circles is called an *annulus*. Typically an annulus is described by inequalities

$$r < |z - z_0| < R,$$

in which r is the radius of the inner circle and R the radius of the outer circle (Figure 23.7). We allow $r = 0$ in this inequality, in which case the annulus $0 < |z - z_0| < R$ is a *punctured disk* (open disk with the center removed).

We also allow $R = \infty$. The annulus $r < |z - z_0| < \infty$ consists of all points outside the inner circle of radius r. An annulus $0 < |z - z_0| < \infty$ consists of all complex z except z_0.

We can now state the main result on Laurent series.

THEOREM 23.7

Let $0 \le r < R \le \infty$. Suppose f is differentiable in the annulus $r < |z - z_0| < R$. Then, for each z in this annulus,

$$f(z) = \sum_{n=-\infty}^{\infty} c_n (z - z_0)^n,$$

where, for each integer n,

$$c_n = \frac{1}{2\pi i} \oint_\Gamma \frac{f(z)}{(z - z_0)^{n+1}} \, dz,$$

and Γ is any closed path about z_0 lying entirely in the annulus. ■

A typical such Γ is shown in Figure 23.8. The series in the theorem, which may include both positive and negative powers of $z - z_0$, is the *Laurent expansion*, or *Laurent series*, for $f(z)$ about z_0 in the given annulus. This expansion has the appearance

$$\cdots + \frac{c_{-2}}{(z - z_0)^2} + \frac{c_{-1}}{z - z_0} + c_0 + c_1 (z - z_0) + c_2 (z - z_0)^2 + \cdots .$$

The function need not be differentiable, or even defined, at z_0 or at other points within the inner circle of the annulus. The numbers c_n are the *Laurent coefficients* of f about z_0.

A Laurent series is a decomposition of $f(z)$ into a sum

$$f(z) = \sum_{n=-\infty}^{-1} c_n (z - z_0)^n + \sum_{n=0}^{\infty} c_n (z - z_0)^2 = \sum_{n=1}^{\infty} \frac{c_{-n}}{(z - z_0)^n} + \sum_{n=0}^{\infty} c_n (z - z_0)^n = h(z) + g(z).$$

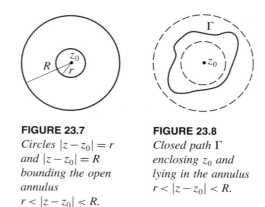

FIGURE 23.7
*Circles $|z - z_0| = r$
and $|z - z_0| = R$
bounding the open
annulus
$r < |z - z_0| < R$.*

FIGURE 23.8
*Closed path Γ
enclosing z_0 and
lying in the annulus
$r < |z - z_0| < R$.*

The part containing only nonnegative powers of $z - z_0$ defines a function $g(z)$ that is differentiable on $|z - z_0| < R$ (because this part is a Taylor expansion). The part containing only negative powers of $z - z_0$ defines a function $h(z)$ that is not defined at z_0. This part determines the behavior of $f(z)$ about a point z_0 where f is not differentiable.

A proof of the theorem is given on the website.

As with Taylor series, we rarely compute the coefficients in a Laurent expansion using this integral formula (quite the contrary, we will use one of these coefficients to evaluate integrals). Instead, we use known series and algebraic or analytic manipulations. This requires that we be assured that the Laurent expansion of a function in an annulus about a point is unique, and does not change with the method of derivation.

THEOREM 23.8

Let f be differentiable in an annulus $r < |z - z_0| < R$. Suppose, for z in this annulus,

$$f(z) = \sum_{n=-\infty}^{\infty} b_n (z - z_0)^n.$$

Then the $b_n's$ are the Laurent coefficients c_n of f, and this series is the Laurent expansion of $f(z)$ in this annulus.

Proof   Choose γ as a circle about z_0 in the annulus. Let k be any integer. Using Theorem 22.6, we get

$$2\pi i c_k = \oint_\gamma \frac{f(w)}{(w - z_0)^{k+1}} dw = \oint_\gamma \left(\sum_{n=-\infty}^{\infty} b_n (z - z_0)^n \right) \frac{1}{(w - z_0)^{k+1}} dw$$

$$= \sum_{n=-\infty}^{\infty} b_n \oint_\gamma \frac{1}{(w - z_0)^{k-n+1}} dw. \qquad (23.2)$$

Now, on γ, $w = z_0 + re^{it}$ for $0 \le t \le 2\pi$, with r the radius of γ. Then

$$\oint_\gamma \frac{1}{(w - z_0)^{k-n+1}} dw = \int_0^{2\pi} \frac{1}{r^{k-n+1}(e^{it})^{k-n+1}} ire^{it} dt$$

$$= \frac{i}{r^{k-n}} \int_0^{2\pi} e^{i(n-k)t} dt = \begin{cases} 0 & \text{if } k \ne n \\ 2\pi i & \text{if } k = n \end{cases}.$$

Thus in equation (23.2), all terms in the last vanish series except the term with $n = k$, and the equation reduces to

$$2\pi i c_k = 2\pi i b_k.$$

Hence for each integer k, $b_k = c_k$. ∎

Here are some examples of Laurent expansions.

EXAMPLE 23.9

$e^{1/z}$ is differentiable in the annulus $0 < |z| < \infty$, the plane with the origin removed. Since

$$e^z = \sum_{n=0}^{\infty} \frac{1}{n!} z^n,$$

then, in this annulus,

$$e^{1/z} = \sum_{n=0}^{\infty} \frac{1}{n!} \left(\frac{1}{z}\right)^n = 1 + \frac{1}{z} + \frac{1}{2}\frac{1}{z^2} + \frac{1}{6}\frac{1}{z^3} + \frac{1}{24}\frac{1}{z^4} + \cdots.$$

This is the Laurent expansion of $e^{1/z}$ about 0, and it converges for all nonzero z. This expansion contains a constant term and infinitely many negative integer powers of z, but no positive powers. ∎

EXAMPLE 23.10

We will find the Laurent expansion of $\cos(z)/z^5$ about zero. For all z,

$$\cos(z) = \sum_{n=0}^{\infty} \frac{(-1)^n}{(2n)!} z^{2n}.$$

For $z \neq 0$,

$$\frac{\cos(z)}{z^5} = \sum_{n=0}^{\infty} \frac{(-1)^n}{(2n)!} z^{2n-5} = \frac{1}{z^5} - \frac{1}{2}\frac{1}{z^3} + \frac{1}{24}\frac{1}{z} - \frac{1}{720}z + \frac{1}{40,320}z^3 - \cdots.$$

This is the Laurent expansion of $\cos(z)/z^5$ about 0. This expansion contains exactly three terms containing negative powers of z, and the remaining terms contain only positive powers. We can think of $\cos(z)/z^5 = h(z) + g(z)$, where

$$g(z) = -\frac{1}{720}z + \frac{1}{40,320}z^3 - \cdots$$

is a differentiable function (it is a power series about the origin), and

$$h(z) = \frac{1}{z^5} - \frac{1}{2}\frac{1}{z^3} + \frac{1}{24}\frac{1}{z}.$$

It is $h(z)$ that determines the behavior of $\cos(z)/z^5$ near the origin. ∎

EXAMPLE 23.11

Find the Laurent expansion of

$$\frac{1}{(z+1)(z-3i)}$$

about -1.

Use partial fractions to write

$$\frac{1}{(z+1)(z-3i)} = \frac{-1+3i}{10}\frac{1}{z+1} + \frac{1-3i}{10}\frac{1}{z-3i}.$$

$1/(z+1)$ is already expanded around -1, so concentrate on the last term:

$$\frac{1}{z-3i} = \frac{1}{-1-3i+(z+1)} = \frac{1}{-1-3i}\frac{1}{1-\frac{z+1}{1+3i}} = \frac{-1}{1+3i}\sum_{n=0}^{\infty}\left(\frac{z+1}{1+3i}\right)^n$$

$$= -\sum_{n=0}^{\infty}\frac{1}{(1+3i)^{n+1}}(z+1)^n.$$

This expansion is valid for $|(z+1)/(1+3i)| < 1$, or $|z+1| < \sqrt{10}$. The Laurent expansion of $1/(z+1)(z-3i)$ about -1 is

$$\frac{1}{(z+1)(z-3i)} = \frac{-1+3i}{10}\frac{1}{z+1} - \frac{1-3i}{10}\sum_{n=0}^{\infty}\frac{1}{(1+3i)^{n+1}}(z+1)^n,$$

and this representation is valid in the annulus $0 < |z+1| < \sqrt{10}$.

Notice that $\sqrt{10}$ is the distance from -1, the center of the Laurent expansion, to the other point, $3i$, at which the function is not differentiable. ▪

In the next chapter we will use the Laurent expansion to develop the powerful residue theorem, which has many applications, including the evalution of real and complex integrals.

SECTION 23.2 PROBLEMS

In each of Problems 1 through 10, write the Laurent expansion of the function in an annulus $0 < |z - z_0| < R$ about the point.

1. $\dfrac{2z}{1+z^2}; i$

2. $\dfrac{\sin(z)}{z^2}; 0$

3. $\dfrac{1-\cos(2z)}{z^2}; 0$

4. $z^2\cos(i/z); 0$

5. $\dfrac{z^2}{1-z}; 1$

6. $\dfrac{z^2+1}{2z-1}; 1/2$

7. $\dfrac{e^{z^2}}{z^2}; 0$

8. $\dfrac{\sin(4z)}{z}; 0$

9. $\dfrac{z+i}{z-i}; i$

10. $\sinh\left(\dfrac{1}{z^3}\right); 0$

CHAPTER **24**

SINGULARITIES THE RESIDUE THEOREM SOME
APPLICATIONS OF THE RESIDUE THEOREM THE
ARGUMENT PRINCIPLE AN INVERSION FORMULA
FOR THE LAPLACE TRANSFORM EVALUATION OF

Singularities and the Residue Theorem

As a prelude to the residue theorem, we will use the Laurent expansion to classify points at which a function is not differentiable.

24.1 Singularities

DEFINITION 24.1 *Isolated Singularity*

A complex function f has an isolated singularity at z_0 if f is differentiable in an annulus $0 < |z - z_0| < R$, but not at z_0 itself.

For example, $1/z$ has an isolated singularity at 0, and $\sin(z)/(z - \pi)$ has an isolated singularity at π.

We will now identify singularities as being of different types, depending on the terms appearing in the Laurent expansion of the function about the singularity.

DEFINITION 24.2 *Classification of Singularities*

Let f have an isolated singularity at z_0. Let the Laurent expansion of $f(z)$ in an annulus $0 < |z - z_0| < R$ be

$$f(z) = \sum_{n=-\infty}^{\infty} c_n (z - z_0)^n.$$

Then:

1. z_0 is a removable singularity of f if $c_n = 0$ for $n = -1, -2, \ldots$.
2. z_0 is a pole of order m (m a positive integer) if $c_{-m} \neq 0$ and $c_{-m-1} = c_{-m-2} = \cdots = 0$.
3. z_0 is an essential singularity of f if $c_{-n} \neq 0$ for infinitely many positive integers n.

These three types cover all the possibilities for an isolated singularity.

In the case of a removable singularity, the Laurent expansion has no negative powers of $z - z_0$, and is therefore

$$f(z) = \sum_{n=0}^{\infty} c_n (z - z_0)^n,$$

a power series about z_0. In this case we can assign $f(z_0)$ the value c_0 to obtain a function that is differentiable in the open disk $|z - z_0| < r$.

EXAMPLE 24.1

Let

$$f(z) = \frac{1 - \cos(z)}{z}$$

for $0 < |z| < \infty$. Since

$$\cos(z) = 1 - \frac{z^2}{2!} + \frac{z^4}{4!} - \frac{z^6}{6!} + \cdots$$

for all z, then

$$f(z) = \frac{1 - \cos(z)}{z} = \frac{z}{2!} - \frac{z^3}{4!} + \frac{z^5}{6!} = \sum_{n=1}^{\infty} \frac{(-1)^{n+1}}{(2n)!} z^{2n-1}$$

for $z \neq 0$. The series on the right is actually a power series, having the value 0 at $z = 0$. We can therefore define a new function

$$g(z) = \begin{cases} (1 - \cos(z))/z & \text{for } z \neq 0 \\ 0 & \text{for } z = 0 \end{cases}$$

which agrees with $f(z)$ for $z \neq 0$, but is defined at 0 in such a way as to be differentiable there, because $g(z)$ has a power series expansion about 0. Because it is possible to extend f to a function g that is differentiable at 0, we call 0 a removable singularity of f. ∎

Thus, a removable singularity is one that can be "removed" by appropriately assigning the function a value at the point.

EXAMPLE 24.2

$f(z) = \sin(z)/(z - \pi)$ has a removable singularity at π. To see this, first write the Laurent expansion of $f(z)$ in $0 < |z - \pi| < \infty$. An easy way to do this is to begin with

$$\sin(z - \pi) = \sin(z)\cos(\pi) - \cos(z)\sin(\pi) = -\sin(z),$$

so

$$\sin(z) = -\sin(z - \pi) = \sum_{n=0}^{\infty} \frac{(-1)^{n+1}}{(2n+1)!}(z - \pi)^{2n+1}.$$

Then, for $z \neq \pi$,

$$\frac{\sin(z)}{z - \pi} = \sum_{n=0}^{\infty} \frac{(-1)^{n+1}}{(2n+1)!}(z - \pi)^{2n} = -1 + \frac{1}{6}(z - \pi)^2 - \frac{1}{120}(z - \pi)^4 + \cdots.$$

Although $f(\pi)$ is not defined, the series on the right is defined for $z = \pi$, and is equal to -1 there. We therefore extend f to a differentiable function g defined over the entire plane by assigning the new function the value -1 when $z = \pi$:

$$g(z) = \begin{cases} f(z) & \text{for } z \neq \pi \\ -1 & \text{for } z = \pi \end{cases}.$$

This extension "removes" the singularity of f at π, since $f(z) = g(z)$ for $z \neq \pi$, and $g(\pi) = -1$. ∎

For f to have a pole at z_0, the Laurent expansion of f about z_0 must have terms with negative powers of $z - z_0$, but only finitely many such terms. If the pole has order m, then this Laurent expansion has the form

$$f(z) = \frac{c_{-m}}{(z - z_0)^m} + \frac{c_{-m+1}}{(z - z_0)^{m-1}} + \cdots + \frac{c_{-1}}{z - z_0} + \sum_{n=0}^{\infty} c_n(z - z_0)^n,$$

with $c_{-m} \neq 0$. This expansion is valid in some annulus $0 < |z - z_0| < R$.

EXAMPLE 24.3

Let $f(z) = 1/(z + i)$. This function is its own Laurent expansion about $-i$, and $c_{-1} = 1$, while all other coefficients are zero. Thus $-i$ is a pole of order 1 of f.

This singularity is not removable. There is no way to assign a value to $f(-i)$ so that the extended function is differentiable at $-i$. ∎

EXAMPLE 24.4

$g(z) = 1/(z + i)^3$, then g has a pole of order 3 at $-i$. Here the function is its own Laurent expansion about $-i$, and the coefficient of $1/(z + i)^3$ is nonzero, while all other coefficients are zero. ∎

DEFINITION 24.3 *Simple and Double Poles*

A pole of order 1 is called a simple pole. A pole of order 2 is a double pole.

EXAMPLE 24.5

Let

$$f(z) = \frac{\sin(z)}{z^3}.$$

For $z \neq 0$,

$$f(z) = \frac{1}{z^3} \sum_{n=0}^{\infty} \frac{(-1)^n}{(2n+1)!} z^{2n+1} = \sum_{n=0}^{\infty} \frac{(-1)^n}{(2n+1)!} z^{2n-2}$$

$$= \frac{1}{z^2} - \frac{1}{6} + \frac{1}{120} z^2 - \frac{1}{5,040} z^4 + \cdots .$$

Therefore f has a double pole at 0. ◼

EXAMPLE 24.6

$e^{1/z}$ is defined for all nonzero z, and, for $z \neq 0$,

$$e^{1/z} = \sum_{n=0}^{\infty} \frac{1}{n!} \frac{1}{z^n}.$$

Since this Laurent expansion has infinitely many negative powers of z, 0 is an essential singularity of $e^{1/z}$. ◼

We will discuss several results that are useful in identifying poles of a function.

THEOREM 24.1 *Condition for a Pole of Order m*

Let f be differentiable in the annulus $0 < |z - z_0| < R$. Then f has a pole of order m at z_0 if and only if

$$\lim_{z \to z_0} (z - z_0)^m f(z)$$

exists finite and is nonzero. ◼

Proof Expand $f(z)$ in a Laurent series in this annulus:

$$f(z) = \sum_{n=-\infty}^{\infty} c_n (z - z_0)^n \quad \text{for } 0 < |z - z_0| < R.$$

Suppose f has a pole of order m at z_0. Then $c_{-m} \neq 0$ and $c_{-m-1} = c_{-m-2} = \cdots = 0$, so the Laurent series is

$$f(z) = \sum_{n=-m}^{\infty} c_n (z - z_0)^n.$$

Then

$$(z-z_0)^m f(z) = \sum_{n=-m}^{\infty} c_n(z-z_0)^{n+m} = \sum_{n=0}^{\infty} c_{n-m}(z-z_0)^n$$

$$= c_{-m} + c_{-m+1}(z-z_0) + c_{-m+2}(z-z_0)^2 + \cdots .$$

Then

$$\lim_{z \to z_0} (z-z_0)^m f(z) = c_{-m} \neq 0.$$

Conversely, suppose $\lim_{z \to z_0} (z-z_0)^m f(z) = L \neq 0$. We want to show that f has a pole of order m at z_0.

Let $\epsilon > 0$. Because of this limit, there is a positive $\delta < R$ such that

$$|(z-z_0)^m f(z) - L| < \epsilon \quad \text{if } 0 < |z-z_0| < \delta.$$

Then, for such z,

$$|(z-z_0)^m f(z)| < |L| + \epsilon.$$

In particular, if $|z-z_0| = \delta$, then

$$\left|(z-z_0)^{-n-1} f(z)\right| < (|L|+\epsilon)|z-z_0|^{-n-m-1} = (|L|+\epsilon)\delta^{-n-m-1}.$$

The coefficients in the Laurent expansion of $f(z)$ about z_0 are given by

$$c_n = \frac{1}{2\pi i} \oint_\Gamma \frac{f(z)}{(z-z_0)^{n+1}} \, dz,$$

in which we can choose Γ to be circle of radius δ about z_0. Then

$$|c_n| \le \frac{1}{2\pi}(2\pi\delta)\max_{z \text{ on } \Gamma} \left|f(z)(z-z_0)^{-n-1}\right| < \delta(|L|+\epsilon)\delta^{-n-m-1} = (|L|+\epsilon)\delta^{-n-m}.$$

Now δ^{-n-m} can be made as small as we like by choosing δ small, if $n < -m$. We conclude that $|c_n| = 0$, hence $c_n = 0$, if $n < -m$. Thus the Laurent expansion of $f(z)$ about z_0 has the form

$$f(z) = \frac{c_{-m}}{(z-z_0)^m} + \frac{c_{-m+1}}{(z-z_0)^{m-1}} + \cdots + \frac{c_{-1}}{z-z_0} + \sum_{n=0}^{\infty} c_n(z-z_0)^n.$$

and therefore f has a pole of order m at z_0, as we wanted to show. ■

EXAMPLE 24.7

Look again at Example 24.3. Since

$$\lim_{z \to -i} (z+i)f(z) = \lim_{z \to -i} (z+i)\frac{1}{z+i} = 1 \neq 0,$$

f has a simple pole at $-i$.

In Example 24.4,

$$\lim_{z \to -i} (z+i)^3 g(z) = \lim_{z \to -i} (z+i)^3 \frac{1}{(z+i)^3} = 1 \neq 0,$$

so g has a pole of order 3 at $-i$.

In Example 24.5,

$$\lim_{z \to 0} z^2 \frac{\sin(z)}{z^3} = \lim_{z \to 0} \frac{\sin(z)}{z} = 1 \neq 0,$$

so $\sin(z)/z^3$ has a double pole at 0. It is a common error to think that this function has a pole of order 3 at zero, because the denominator has a zero of order 3 there. However,

$$\lim_{z \to 0} z^3 \frac{\sin(z)}{z^3} = \lim_{z \to 0} \sin(z) = 0,$$

so by Theorem 24.1, the function cannot have a third-order pole at 0. ■

If $f(z)$ is a quotient of functions, it is natural to look for poles at places where the denominator vanishes. Our first result along these lines deals with a quotient in which the denominator vanishes at z_0, but the numerator does not. Recall that $g(z)$ has a zero of order k at z_0 if $g(z_0) = \cdots = g^{(k-1)}(z_0) = 0$, but $g^{(k)}(z_0) \neq 0$. The order of the zero is the order of the lowest-order derivative that does not vanish at the point.

THEOREM 24.2

Let $f(z) = h(z)/g(z)$, where h and g are differentiable in some open disk about z_0. Suppose $h(z_0) \neq 0$, but g has a zero of order m at z_0. Then f has a pole of order m at z_0. ■

We leave a proof of this result to the student.

EXAMPLE 24.8

$$f(z) = \frac{1 + 4z^3}{\sin^6(z)}$$

has a pole of order 6 at 0, because the numerator does not vanish at 0 , and the denominator has a zero of order 6 at 0. By the same token, f has a pole of order 6 at $n\pi$ for any integer n. ■

Theorem 24.2 does not apply if the numerator also vanishes at z_0. The example $f(z) = \sin(z)/z^3$ is instructive. The numerator has a zero of order 1 at 0, and the denominator a zero of order 3 at 0, and we saw in Example 24.5 that the quotient has a pole of order 2. It would appear that the orders of the zeros of numerator and denominator subtract (or cancel) to give the order of a pole at the point. This is indeed the case.

THEOREM 24.3   *Poles of Quotients*

Let $f(z) = h(z)/g(z)$, and suppose h and g are differentiable in some open disk about z_0. Let h have a zero of order k at z_0 and g a zero of order m at z_0, with $m > k$. Then f has a pole of order $m - k$ at z_0. ■

A proof of this is left to the student. By allowing $k = 0$, this theorem includes the case that the numerator $h(z)$ has no zero at z_0.

EXAMPLE 24.9

Consider

$$f(z) = \frac{(z - 3\pi/2)^4}{\cos^7(z)}.$$

The numerator has a zero of order 4 at $3\pi/2$, and the denominator has a zero of order 7 there, so the quotient f has a pole of order 3 at $3\pi/2$. ■

EXAMPLE 24.10

Let $f(z) = \tan^3(z)/z^9$. The numerator has a zero of order 3 at 0, and the denominator has a zero of order 9 at 0. Therefore f has a pole of order 6 at 0. ■

There are also some useful results stated in terms of products, rather than quotients. We claim that the order of a pole of a product is the sum of the orders of the poles of the factors at a given point.

THEOREM 24.4   *Poles of Products*

Let f have a pole of order m at z_0 and let g have a pole of order n at z_0. Then fg has a pole of order $m + n$ at z_0. ■

EXAMPLE 24.11

Let

$$f(z) = \frac{1}{\cos^4(z)(z - \pi/2)^2}.$$

Here $f(z)$ is a product, which we write for emphasis as

$$f(z) = \left[\frac{1}{\cos^4(z)} \right] \left[\frac{1}{(z - \pi/2)^2} \right].$$

Now $1/\cos^4(z)$ has a pole of order 4 at $\pi/2$, and $1/(z - \pi/2)^2$ has a pole of order 2 there, so f has a pole of order 6 at $\pi/2$. f also has poles of order 4 (not 6) at $z = (2n + 1)\pi/2$ for n any nonzero integer other than -1. ■

We are now prepared to develop the powerful residue theorem.

SECTION 24.1   **PROBLEMS**

In each of Problems 1 through 12, determine all singularities of the function and classify each singularity as removable, a pole of a certain order, or an essential singularity.

1. $\cos(z)/z^2$

2. $\dfrac{4\sin(z + 2)}{(z + i)^2(z - i)}$

3. $e^{1/z}(z+2i)$

4. $\dfrac{\sin(z)}{z-\pi}$

5. $\dfrac{\cos(2z)}{(z-1)^2(1+z^2)}$

6. $\dfrac{z}{(z+1)^2}$

7. $\dfrac{z-i}{z^2+1}$

8. $\dfrac{\sin(z)}{\sinh(z)}$

9. $\dfrac{z}{z^4-1}$

10. $\tan(z)$

11. $1/\cos(z)$

12. $e^{1/z(z+1)}$

13. Let f be differentiable at z_0 and let g have a pole of order m at z_0. Let $f(z_0) \neq 0$. Prove that fg has a pole of order m at z_0.

14. Let h and g be differentiable at z_0, $g(z_0) \neq 0$, and h have a zero of order 2 at z_0. Prove that $g(z)/h(z)$ has a pole of order 2 at z_0.

15. Suppose h and g are differentiable at z_0 and $g(z_0) \neq 0$, while h has a zero of order 3 at z_0. Prove that $g(z)/h(z)$ has a pole of order 3 at z_0.

24.2 The Residue Theorem

To see a connection between Laurent series and the integral of a function, suppose f has a Laurent expansion

$$f(z) = \sum_{n=-\infty}^{\infty} c_n(z-z_0)^n$$

in some annulus $0 < |z-z_0| < R$. Let Γ be a closed path in this annulus and enclosing z_0. According to Theorem 23.6, the Laurent coefficients are given by an integral formula. In particular, the coefficient of $1/(z-z_0)$ is

$$c_{-1} = \frac{1}{2\pi i} \oint_{\Gamma} f(z)\,dz.$$

Therefore

$$\oint_{\Gamma} f(z)\,dz = 2\pi i c_{-1}. \tag{24.1}$$

Knowing this one coefficient in the Laurent expansion yields the value of this integral. This fact gives this coefficient a special importance, so we will give it a name.

DEFINITION 24.4 *Residue*

Let f have an isolated singularity at z_0, and Laurent expansion $f(z) = \sum_{n=-\infty}^{\infty} c_n(z-z_0)^n$ in some annulus $0 < |z-z_0| < R$. Then the coefficient c_{-1} is called the residue of f at z_0, and is denoted $\mathrm{Re}\,s(f, z_0)$.

We will now extend the idea behind equation (24.1) to include the case that Γ may enclose any finite number of points at which f is not differentiable.

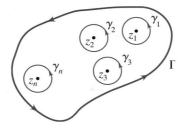

FIGURE 24.1

THEOREM 24.5 *Residue Theorem*

Let Γ be a closed path and let f be differentiable on Γ and all points enclosed by Γ, except for $z_1, \ldots, z_n$, which are all the isolated singularities of f enclosed by Γ. Then

$$\oint_{\Gamma} f(z)\,dz = 2\pi i \sum_{j=1}^{n} \mathrm{Re}\, s(f, z_j). \quad \blacksquare$$

In words, the value of this integral is $2\pi i$ times the sum of the residues of f at the singularities of f enclosed by Γ.

Proof Enclose each singularity z_j with a closed path γ_j (Figure 24.1) so that each γ_j is in the interior of Γ, encloses exactly one singularity, and does not intersect any other γ_k. By the extended deformation theorem,

$$\oint_{\Gamma} f(z)\,dz = \sum_{j=1}^{n} \oint_{\gamma_j} f(z)\,dz = 2\pi i \sum_{j=1}^{n} \mathrm{Re}\, s(f, z_j). \quad \blacksquare$$

The residue theorem is only as effective as our efficiency in evaluating residues of a function at singularities. If we had to actually write the Laurent expansion of f about each singularity to pick off the coefficient of the $1/(z - z_j)$ term, the theorem would be difficult to apply in many instances. What adds to its importance is that, at least for poles, there are efficient ways of calculating residues. We will now develop some of these.

THEOREM 24.6 *Residue at a Simple Pole*

If f has a simple pole at z_0, then

$$\mathrm{Re}\, s(f, z_0) = \lim_{z \to z_0} (z - z_0) f(z).$$

Proof If f has a simple pole at z_0, then its Laurent expansion about z_0 is

$$f(z) = \frac{c_{-1}}{z - z_0} + \sum_{n=0}^{\infty} c_n (z - z_0)^n$$

in some annulus $0 < |z - z_0| < R$. Then

$$(z - z_0) f(z) = c_{-1} + \sum_{n=0}^{\infty} c_n (z - z_0)^{n+1},$$

so

$$\lim_{z \to z_0} (z - z_0) f(z) = c_{-1} = \operatorname{Re} s(f, z_0). \quad \blacksquare$$

EXAMPLE 24.12

$f(z) = \sin(z)/z^2$ has a simple pole at 0, and

$$\operatorname{Re} s(f, 0) = \lim_{z \to 0} z \frac{\sin(z)}{z^2} = \lim_{z \to 0} \frac{\sin(z)}{z} = 1.$$

If Γ is any closed path in the plane enclosing the origin, then by the residue theorem,

$$\oint_{\Gamma} \frac{\sin(z)}{z^2} dz = 2\pi i \operatorname{Re} s(f, 0) = 2\pi i. \quad \blacksquare$$

EXAMPLE 24.13

Let

$$f(z) = \frac{z - 6i}{(z - 2)^2 (z + 4i)}.$$

Then f has a simple pole at $-4i$ and a double pole at 2. Theorem 24.6 will not help us with the residue of f at 2, but at the simple pole,

$$\operatorname{Re} s(f, -4i) = \lim_{z \to -4i} (z + 4i) \frac{z - 6i}{(z - 2)^2 (z + 4i)} = \lim_{z \to -4i} \frac{z - 6i}{(z - 2)^2} = \frac{-4i - 6i}{(-4i - 2)^2}$$

$$= -\frac{2}{5} + \frac{3}{10} i. \quad \blacksquare$$

Before looking at residues at poles of order greater than 1, the following version of Theorem 24.6 is sometimes handy.

COROLLARY 24.1

Let $f(z) = h(z)/g(z)$, where h is continuous at z_0 and $h(z_0) \neq 0$. Suppose g is differentiable at z_0 and has a simple zero there. Then f has a simple pole at z_0 and

$$\operatorname{Re} s(f, z_0) = \frac{h(z_0)}{g'(z_0)}. \quad \blacksquare$$

Proof f has a simple pole at z_0 by Theorem 24.2. By Theorem 24.6,

$$\operatorname{Re} s(f, z_0) = \lim_{z \to z_0} (z - z_0) \frac{h(z)}{g(z)} = \lim_{z \to z_0} \frac{h(z)}{((g(z) - g(z_0))/(z - z_0))} = \frac{h(z_0)}{g'(z_0)}. \quad \blacksquare$$

EXAMPLE 24.14

Let

$$f(z) = \frac{4iz - 1}{\sin(z)}.$$

Then f has a simple pole at π, and, by Corollary 24.1,

$$\mathrm{Re}\,s(f,\pi)=\frac{4i\pi-1}{\cos(\pi)}=1-4\pi i.$$

In fact, f has a simple pole at $n\pi$ for any integer n, and

$$\mathrm{Re}\,s(f,n\pi)=\frac{4in\pi-1}{\cos(n\pi)}=(-1)^n(-1+4n\pi i).\ \blacksquare$$

EXAMPLE 24.15

Evaluate

$$\oint_\Gamma \frac{4iz-1}{\sin(z)}\,dz$$

with Γ the closed path of Figure 24.2.

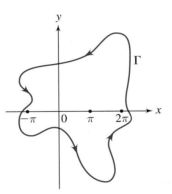

FIGURE 24.2 Γ *encloses only the singularities* $-\pi$, 0, π *and* 2π *of* $\frac{4iz-1}{\sin(z)}$.

Γ encloses the poles 0, π, 2π and $-\pi$, but no other singularities of f. By the residue theorem and Example 24.14,

$$\oint_\Gamma \frac{4iz-1}{\sin(z)}\,dz = 2\pi i[\mathrm{Re}\,s(f,0)+\mathrm{Re}\,s(f,\pi)+\mathrm{Re}\,s(f,2\pi)+\mathrm{Re}\,s(f,-\pi)]$$

$$= 2\pi i\,[-1+(1-4\pi i)+(-1+8\pi i)+(1+4\pi i)]=-16\pi^2.\ \blacksquare$$

Here is a formula for the residue of a function at a pole of order greater than 1.

THEOREM 24.7 *Residue at a Pole of Order m*

Let f have a pole of order m at z_0. Then

$$\mathrm{Re}\,s(f,z_0)=\frac{1}{(m-1)!}\lim_{z\to z_0}\frac{d^{m-1}}{dz^{m-1}}[(z-z_0)^m f(z)].\ \blacksquare$$

If $m = 1$ (simple pole), then $(m-1)! = 0! = 1$ by definition, and the $(m-1)$–order derivative is defined to be just the function itself. With these conventions, the conclusion of the theorem reduces to the result for residues at simple poles when $m = 1$.

Proof In some annulus about z_0,

$$f(z) = \frac{c_{-m}}{(z-z_0)^m} + \frac{c_{-m+1}}{(z-z_0)^{m-1}} + \cdots + \frac{c_{-1}}{z-z_0} + \sum_{n=0}^{\infty} c_n(z-z_0)^n.$$

It is c_{-1} we want. Write

$$(z-z_0)^m f(z) = c_{-m} + c_{-m+1}(z-z_0) + \cdots + c_{-1}(z-z_0)^{m-1} + \sum_{n=0}^{\infty} c_n(z-z_0)^{n+m}.$$

The right side of this equation is a power series about z_0, and can be differentiated any number of times within its open disk of convergence. Compute

$$\frac{d^{m-1}}{dz^{m-1}}[(z-z_0)^m f(z)]$$

$$= (m-1)!c_{-1} + \sum_{n=0}^{\infty}(n+m)(n+m-1)\cdots(n+1)(z-z_0)^{n+1}.$$

In the limit as $z \to z_0$, this equation yields

$$\lim_{z \to z_0} \frac{d^{m-1}}{dz^{m-1}}[(z-z_0)^m f(z)] = (m-1)!c_{-1} = (m-1)!\operatorname{Re} s(f, z_0). \ \blacksquare$$

EXAMPLE 24.16

Let

$$f(z) = \frac{\cos(z)}{(z+i)^3}.$$

Then f has a pole of order 3 at $-i$. By Theorem 24.7,

$$\operatorname{Re} s(f, -i) = \frac{1}{2!} \lim_{z \to -i} \frac{d^2}{dz^2}\left((z+i)^3 \frac{\cos(z)}{(z+i)^3}\right)$$

$$= \frac{1}{2} \lim_{z \to -i} \frac{d^2}{dz^2} \cos(z) = -\frac{1}{2}\cos(-i) = -\frac{1}{2}\cos(i). \ \blacksquare$$

Here are some examples of the residue theorem in evaluating complex integrals.

EXAMPLE 24.17

Let

$$f(z) = \frac{2iz - \cos(z)}{z^3 + z}.$$

We want to evaluate $\oint_{\Gamma} f(z)dz$, with Γ a closed path that does not pass through any singularity of f.

The singularities of f are simple poles at 0, i and $-i$. First compute the residue of f at each of these points. Here it is convenient to use Corollary 24.1:

$$\operatorname{Res}(f, 0) = \frac{-\cos(0)}{1} = -1,$$

$$\operatorname{Res}(f, i) = \frac{2i^2 - \cos(i)}{3(i)^2 + 1} = \frac{-2 - \cos(i)}{-2} = 1 + \frac{1}{2}\cos(i),$$

and

$$\operatorname{Res}(f, -i) = \frac{2i(-i) - \cos(-i)}{3(-i)^2 + 1} = -1 + \frac{1}{2}\cos(i).$$

Now consider cases.

1. If Γ does not enclose any of the singularities, then $\oint_\Gamma f(z)\,dz = 0$ by Cauchy's theorem.
2. If Γ encloses 0 but not i or $-i$, then

$$\oint_\Gamma f(z)\,dz = 2\pi i \operatorname{Res}(f, 0) = -2\pi i.$$

3. If Γ encloses i but not 0 or $-i$, then

$$\oint_\Gamma f(z)\,dz = 2\pi i \left(1 + \frac{1}{2}\cos(i)\right).$$

4. If Γ encloses $-i$ but not 0 or i, then

$$\oint_\Gamma f(z)\,dz = 2\pi i \left(-1 + \frac{1}{2}\cos(i)\right).$$

5. If Γ encloses 0 and i but not $-i$, then

$$\oint_\Gamma f(z)\,dz = 2\pi i \left(-1 + 1 + \frac{1}{2}\cos(i)\right) = \pi i \cos(i).$$

6. If Γ encloses 0 and $-i$ but not i, then

$$\oint_\Gamma f(z)\,dz = 2\pi i \left(-1 - 1 + \frac{1}{2}\cos(i)\right) = 2\pi i \left(-2 + \frac{1}{2}\cos(i)\right).$$

7. If Γ encloses i and $-i$ but not 0, then

$$\oint_\Gamma f(z)\,dz = 2\pi i \left(1 + \frac{1}{2}\cos(i) - 1 + \frac{1}{2}\cos(i)\right) = 2\pi i \cos(i).$$

8. If Γ encloses all three singularities, then

$$\oint_\Gamma f(z)\,dz = 2\pi i \left(-1 + 1 + \frac{1}{2}\cos(i) - 1 + \frac{1}{2}\cos(i)\right) = 2\pi i \left(-1 + \cos(i)\right). \ \blacksquare$$

EXAMPLE 24.18

Let

$$f(z) = \frac{\sin(z)}{z^2(z^2 + 4)}.$$

We want to evaluate $\oint_\Gamma f(z)\,dz$, where Γ is a closed path enclosing 0 and $2i$ but not $-2i$.

By Theorem 24.3, f has a simple pole at 0, not a double pole, because $\sin(z)$ has a simple zero at 0. f also has simple poles at $2i$ and $-2i$. Only the poles at 0 and $2i$ are of interest in using the residue theorem, because Γ does not enclose $-2i$.

Compute

$$\text{Re}\,s(f,0) = \lim_{z \to 0} z\, f(z) = \lim_{z \to 0} \frac{\sin(z)}{z} \frac{1}{z^2+4} = \frac{1}{4},$$

and

$$\text{Re}\,s(f,2i) = \lim_{z \to 2i}(z-2i)f(z) = \lim_{z \to 2i} \frac{\sin(z)}{z^2(z+2i)} = \frac{\sin(2i)}{(-4)(4i)} = \frac{i}{16}\sin(2i).$$

Then

$$\oint_\Gamma \frac{\sin(z)}{z^2(z^2+4)}\,dz = 2\pi i \left(\frac{1}{4} + \frac{i}{16}\sin(2i) \right). \ \blacksquare$$

EXAMPLE 24.19

We will evaluate

$$\oint_\Gamma e^{1/z}\,dz$$

for Γ any closed path not passing through the origin.

There are two cases. If Γ does not enclose the origin, then $\oint_\Gamma e^{1/z}\,dz = 0$ by Cauchy's theorem.

If Γ does enclose the origin, then use the residue theorem. We need $\text{Re}\,s(e^{1/z},0)$. As we found in Example 24.6, 0 is an essential singularity of $e^{1/z}$. There is no simple general formula for the residue of a function at an essential singularity. However,

$$e^{1/z} = \sum_{n=0}^{\infty} \frac{1}{n!}\frac{1}{z^n}$$

is the Laurent expansion of $e^{1/z}$ about 0, and the coefficient of $1/z$ is 1. Thus $\text{Re}\,s(e^{1/z},0) = 1$ and

$$\oint_\Gamma e^{1/z}\,dz = 2\pi i. \ \blacksquare$$

Next we will look at a variety of applications of the residue theorem.

SECTION 24.2   PROBLEMS

In each of Problems 1 through 16, use the residue theorem to evaluate the integral over the given path.

1. $\oint_\Gamma \dfrac{1+z^2}{(z-1)^2(z+2i)}\,dz$; Γ is the circle of radius 7 about $-i$

2. $\oint_\Gamma \dfrac{2z}{(z-i)^2}\,dz$; Γ is the circle of radius 3 about 1

3. $\oint_\Gamma (e^z/z)\,dz$; Γ is the circle of radius 2 about $-3i$

4. $\oint_\Gamma \dfrac{\cos(z)}{4+z^2}\,dz$; Γ is the square of side length 3 and sides parallel to the axes, centered at $-2i$

5. $\oint_\Gamma \dfrac{z+i}{z^2+6}\,dz$; Γ is the square of side length 8 and sides parallel to the axes, centered at the origin

6. $\oint_\Gamma \dfrac{z-i}{2z+1}\,dz$; Γ is the circle of radius 1 about the origin

7. $\oint_\Gamma \dfrac{z}{\sinh^2(z)}\,dz$; Γ is the circle of radius 1 about $\dfrac{1}{2}$

8. $\oint_\Gamma \dfrac{\cos(z)}{ze^z}\,dz$; Γ is the circle of radius $\dfrac{1}{2}$ about $\dfrac{i}{8}$

9. $\oint_\Gamma \dfrac{iz}{(z^2+9)(z-i)}\,dz$; Γ is the circle of radius 2 about $-3i$

10. $\oint_\Gamma e^{2/z^2}\,dz$; Γ is the square with sides parallel to the axes and of length 3, centered at $-i$

11. $\oint_\Gamma \dfrac{8z-4i+1}{z+4i}\,dz$; Γ is the circle of radius 2 about $-i$

12. $\oint_\Gamma \dfrac{z^2}{z-1+2i}\,dz$; Γ is the square of side length 4 and sides parallel to the axes, centered at $1-2i$

13. $\oint_\Gamma \coth(z)\,dz$; Γ is the circle of radius 2 about i

14. $\oint_\Gamma \dfrac{(1-z)^2}{z^3-8}\,dz$; Γ is the circle of radius 2 about 2

15. $\oint_\Gamma \dfrac{e^{2z}}{z(z-4i)}\,dz$; Γ is any closed path enclosing 0 and $4i$

16. $\oint_\Gamma \left(\dfrac{z}{z-1}\right)^2\,dz$; Γ is any closed path enclosing 1

17. With h and g as in Problem 14 of Section 24.1, show that

$$\mathrm{Re}\,s\left(\frac{g(z)}{h(z)}, z_0\right) = 2\frac{g''(z_0)}{h^{(3)}(z_0)} - \frac{2}{3}\frac{g'(z_0)h^{(4)}(z_0)}{[h^{(3)}(z_0)]^2}.$$

18. With h and g as in Problem 15 of Section 24.1, show that

$$\mathrm{Re}\,s\left(\frac{g(z)}{h(z)}, z_0\right) = 3\frac{g''(z_0)}{h'''(z_0)} - \frac{3}{10}\frac{g(z_0)h^{(5)}(z_0)}{(h'''(z_0))^2}$$
$$+9\left(\frac{g(z_0)h^{(4)}(z_0)}{24} - \frac{g'(z_0)h'''(z_0)}{6}\right)\frac{h^{(4)}(z_0)}{(h'''(z_0))^3}$$

19. Let g and h be differentiable at z_0. Suppose $g(z_0) \neq 0$ and let h have a zero of order k at z_0. Prove that $g(z)/h(z)$ has a pole of order k at z_0, and

$$\mathrm{Re}\,s\left(\frac{g(z)}{h(z)}, z_0\right) = \left(\frac{k!}{h^{(k)}(z_0)}\right)^k$$

$$\times \begin{vmatrix} H_k & 0 & 0 & \cdots & 0 & G_0 \\ H_{k+1} & H_k & 0 & \cdots & 0 & G_1 \\ H_{k+2} & H_{k+1} & H_k & \cdots & 0 & G_2 \\ \vdots & \vdots & \vdots & \vdots & \vdots & \vdots \\ H_{2k-1} & H_{2k-2} & H_{2k-3} & \cdots & H_{k+1} & G_{k-1} \end{vmatrix},$$

where

$$H_j = \frac{h^{(j)}(z_0)}{j!} \quad \text{and} \quad G_j = \frac{g^{(j)}(z_0)}{j!}.$$

24.3 Some Applications of the Residue Theorem

24.3.1 The Argument Principle

The argument principle is an integral formula for the difference between the number of zeros and the number of poles of a function (counting multiplicities) enclosed by a given closed path Γ.

THEOREM 24.8 *Argument Principle*

Let f be differentiable on a closed path Γ and at all points in the set G of points enclosed by Γ, except at possibly a finite number of poles of f in G. Let Z be the number of zeros of f in G, and P the number of poles of f in G, with each pole and zero counted k times if its multiplicity is k. Then,

$$\oint_\Gamma \frac{f'(z)}{f(z)}\,dz = Z - P.$$

Proof Observe first that the only points in G where f'/f might possibly have a singularity are the zeros and poles of f in G.

Now suppose that f has a zero of order k at z_0 in G. We will show that f'/f must have a simple pole at z_0, and that $\operatorname{Re} s(f'/f, z_0) = k$. To see this, first note that, because z_0 is a zero of order k,

$$f(z_0) = f'(z_0) = \cdots = f^{(k-1)}(z_0) = 0$$

while $f^{(k)}(z_0) \neq 0$. Then, in some open disk about z_0, the Taylor expansion of $f(z)$ is

$$f(z) = \sum_{n=k}^{\infty} c_n (z - z_0)^n = \sum_{n=0}^{\infty} c_{n+k}(z - z_0)^{n+k}$$

$$= (z - z_0)^k \sum_{n=0}^{\infty} c_{n+k}(z - z_0)^n = (z - z_0)^k g(z),$$

where g is differentiable at z_0 (because it has a Taylor expansion there) and $g(z_0) = c_k \neq 0$. Now, in some annulus $0 < |z - z_0| < R$

$$\frac{f'(z)}{f(z)} = \frac{k(z - z_0)^{k-1}g(z) + (z - z_0)^k g'(z)}{(z - z_0)^k g(z)} = \frac{k}{z - z_0} + \frac{g'(z)}{g(z_0)}.$$

Since $g'(z)/g(z)$ is differentiable at z_0, then $f'(z)/f(z)$ has a simple pole at z_0, and $\operatorname{Re} s(f'/f, z_0) = k$.

Next, suppose f has a pole of order m at z_1. In some annulus about z_0, $f(z)$ has Laurent expansion

$$f(z) = \sum_{n=-m}^{\infty} d_n (z - z_1)^n,$$

with $d_{-m} \neq 0$. Then

$$(z - z_1)^m f(z) = \sum_{n=-m}^{\infty} d_n (z - z_1)^{n+m} = \sum_{n=0}^{\infty} d_{n-m}(z - z_1)^n = h(z),$$

with h differentiable at z_1 and $h(z_1) = c_{-m} \neq 0$. Then $f(z) = (z - z_1)^{-m} h(z)$, so in some annulus about z_1,

$$\frac{f'(z)}{f(z)} = \frac{-m(z - z_1)^{-m-1}h(z) + (z - z_1)^{-m}h'(z)}{(z - z_1)^{-m}h(z)} = \frac{-m}{z - z_1} + \frac{h'(z)}{h(z)}.$$

Therefore f'/f has a simple pole at z_1, with $\operatorname{Re} s(f'/f, z_1) = -m$.

Therefore, the sum of the residues of $f'(z)/f(z)$ at singularities of this function in G counts the zeros of f in G, according to multiplicity, and the negative of the number of poles of f in G, again according to multiplicity. ■

EXAMPLE 24.20

We will evaluate $\oint_\Gamma \cot(z)\,dz$, with Γ the closed path of Figure 24.3.

Write

$$\cot(z) = \frac{\cos(z)}{\sin(z)} = \frac{f'(z)}{f(z)}$$

where $f(z) = \sin(z)$. Since f has five simple zeros and no poles enclosed by Γ, the argument principle yields

$$\oint_\Gamma \cot(z)\,dz = 2\pi i(5 - 0) = 10\pi i. \quad ■$$

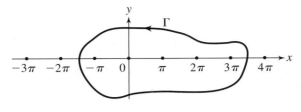

FIGURE 24.3

24.3.2   An Inversion Formula for the Laplace Transform

If f is a complex function defined at least for all z on $[0, \infty)$, the Laplace transform of f is

$$\mathfrak{L}[f](z) = \int_0^\infty e^{-zt} f(t)\, dt,$$

for all z such that this integral is defined and finite. If $\mathfrak{L}[f] = F$, then F is the Laplace transform of f, and f is an inverse Laplace transform of F. Sometimes we write $f = \mathfrak{L}^{-1}[f]$, although this requires additional conditions for uniqueness because there are in general many functions having a given F as their Laplace transform.

We will give a formula for $\mathfrak{L}^{-1}[f]$ in terms of the sum of the residues of $e^{zt} F(z)$ at the poles of f.

THEOREM 24.9   *Inverse Laplace Transform*

Let F be differentiable for all z except for a finite number of points $z_1, \ldots, z_n$, which are all poles of F. Suppose for some real σ, F is differentiable for all z with $\mathrm{Re}(z) > \sigma$. Suppose also that there are numbers M and R such that

$$|zF(z)| \le M \quad \text{for } |z| > R.$$

For $t \ge 0$, let

$$f(t) = \sum_{j=1}^n \mathrm{Re}\, s(e^{zt} F(z), z_j).$$

Then

$$\mathfrak{L}[f](z) = F(z) \quad \text{for } \mathrm{Re}(z) > \sigma. \quad \blacksquare$$

The condition that F is differentiable for $\mathrm{Re}(z) > \sigma$ means that $F'(z)$ for all z to the right of the vertical line $x = \sigma$. It is also assumed that $zF(z)$ is a bounded function for z outside some sufficiently large circle about the origin. For example, this condition is satisfied by any rational function (quotient of polynomials) in which the degree of the denominator exceeds that of the numerator.

EXAMPLE 24.21

Let $a > 0$. We want an inverse Laplace transform of $F(z) = 1/(a^2 + z^2)$.

This can be found in tables of Laplace transforms. To use the theorem, F has simple poles at $\pm ai$. Compute

$$\mathrm{Re}\, s\left(\frac{e^{zt}}{a^2 + z^2}, ai\right) = \frac{e^{ati}}{2ai}$$

and

$$\operatorname{Re} s\left(\frac{e^{zt}}{a^2 + z^2}, -ai\right) = \frac{e^{-ati}}{-2ai}.$$

An inverse Laplace transform of F is given by

$$f(t) = \frac{1}{2ai}\left(e^{ati} - e^{-ati}\right) = \frac{1}{a}\sin(at)$$

for $t \geq 0$. ∎

EXAMPLE 24.22

We want a function whose Laplace transform is

$$F(z) = \frac{1}{(z^2 - 4)(z - 1)^2}.$$

F has simple poles at ± 2 and a double pole at 1. Compute

$$\operatorname{Re} s\left(\frac{e^{zt}}{(z^2 - 4)(z - 1)^2}, 2\right) = \lim_{z \to 2} \frac{e^{zt}}{(z + 2)(z - 1)^2} = \frac{1}{4}e^{2t},$$

$$\operatorname{Re} s\left(\frac{e^{zt}}{(z^2 - 4)(z - 1)^2}, -2\right) = \lim_{z \to -2} \frac{e^{zt}}{(z - 2)(z - 1)^2} = -\frac{1}{36}e^{-2t},$$

and

$$\operatorname{Re} s\left(\frac{e^{zt}}{(z^2 - 4)(z - 1)^2}, 1\right) = \lim_{z \to 1} \frac{d}{dz}\left(\frac{e^{zt}}{z^2 - 4}\right)$$

$$= \lim_{z \to 1} e^{zt}\frac{tz^2 - 4t - 2z}{(z^2 - 4)^2} = -\frac{1}{3}te^t - \frac{2}{9}e^t.$$

An inverse Laplace transform of F is given by

$$f(t) = -\frac{1}{3}te^t - \frac{2}{9}e^t + \frac{1}{4}e^{2t} - \frac{1}{36}e^{-2t},$$

for $t > 2$ (since all poles of F occur on or to the left of the line $\operatorname{Re}(z) = 2$). ∎

In these sections we can see a theme developing. A variety of problems (zeros of functions, inverse Laplace transforms, others to be discussed) can be approached by integrating an appropriately chosen complex function over an appropriately chosen path. The function and path must be selected so that the integral gives us the quantity we want to calculate, perhaps after some limit process. We can then use the residue theorem to explicitly evaluate the integral. Depending on the problem, choosing the right function and the right path can be a nontrivial task, but at least this method provides an approach.

24.3.3 Evaluation of Real Integrals

We will illustrate the use of the residue theorem in evaluating several general classes of real integrals.

Integrals of $\int_0^{2\pi} K(\cos(\theta), \sin(\theta))d\theta$ Let $K(x, y)$ be a quotient of polynomials in x and y, for example,

$$\frac{x^3y - 2xy^2 + x - 2y}{x^4 + x^3}.$$

If we replace x with $\cos(\theta)$ and y with $\sin(\theta)$, we obtain a quotient involving sums of products of positive integer powers of $\cos(\theta)$ and $\sin(\theta)$. We are interested in evaluating integrals of the form

$$\int_0^{2\pi} K(\cos(\theta), \sin(\theta))d\theta.$$

The idea will be to show that this real integral is equal to an integral of a certain complex function over the unit circle. We then use the residue theorem to evaluate this complex integral, obtaining the value of the real integral.

To execute this strategy, let γ be the unit circle, oriented counterclockwise as usual. Parametrize γ by $\gamma(\theta) = e^{i\theta}$ for $0 \le \theta \le 2\pi$. On this curve, $z = e^{i\theta}$ and $\overline{z} = e^{-i\theta} = 1/z$, so

$$\cos(\theta) = \frac{1}{2}\left(e^{i\theta} + e^{-i\theta}\right) = \frac{1}{2}\left(z + \frac{1}{z}\right)$$

and

$$\sin(\theta) = \frac{1}{2i}\left(e^{i\theta} - e^{-i\theta}\right) = \frac{1}{2i}\left(z - \frac{1}{z}\right).$$

Further, on γ,

$$dz = ie^{i\theta}d\theta = izd\theta.$$

so

$$d\theta = \frac{1}{iz}dz.$$

Now we have

$$\oint_\gamma K\left(\frac{1}{2}\left(z + \frac{1}{z}\right), \frac{1}{2i}\left(z - \frac{1}{z}\right)\right)\frac{1}{iz}dz = \int_0^{2\pi} K(\cos(\theta), \sin(\theta))\frac{1}{ie^{i\theta}}ie^{i\theta}d\theta$$

$$= \int_0^{2\pi} K(\cos(\theta), \sin(\theta))d\theta.$$

This converts the real integral we want to evaluate into the integral of a complex function $f(z)$ over the unit circle, where

$$f(z) = K\left(\frac{1}{2}\left(z + \frac{1}{z}\right), \frac{1}{2i}\left(z - \frac{1}{z}\right)\right)\frac{1}{iz}.$$

Use the residue theorem to evaluate $\oint_\gamma f(z)dz$, obtaining

$$\int_0^{2\pi} K(\cos(\theta), \sin(\theta))d\theta = 2\pi i \sum_p \mathrm{Re}\,s(f, p). \tag{24.2}$$

The sum on the right is over all of the poles p of $f(z)$ enclosed by the unit circle. Poles occurring outside the unit circle are not included in the calculation. Finally, equation (24.2) assumes that $f(z)$ has no singularities on the unit circle.

The procedure for evaluating $\int_0^{2\pi} K(\cos(\theta), \sin(\theta))d\theta$, then, is to compute $f(z)$, determine its poles within the unit circle, evaluate the residues there, and apply equation (24.2). This is a very powerful method that often yields closed form evaluations of integrals for which standard techniques of integration from real calculus are inadequate.

EXAMPLE 24.23

We will evaluate

$$\int_0^{2\pi} \frac{\sin^2(\theta)}{2+\cos(\theta)} d\theta.$$

The function K in the above discussion is

$$K(x, y) = \frac{y^2}{2+x}.$$

The first step is to replace $x = \cos(\theta)$ with $(z+1/z)/2$ and $y = \sin(\theta)$ with $(z-1/z)/2i$, and then multiply by $1/iz$, to produce the complex function

$$f(z) = K\left(\frac{1}{2}\left(z+\frac{1}{z}\right), \frac{1}{2i}\left(z-\frac{1}{z}\right)\right)\frac{1}{iz}$$

$$= \frac{\left[\frac{1}{2i}\left(z-\frac{1}{z}\right)\right]^2}{2+\frac{1}{2}\left(z+\frac{1}{z}\right)}\frac{1}{iz} = \frac{i}{2}\frac{z^4-2z^2+1}{z^2(z^2+4z+1)}.$$

f has a double pole at 0 and simple poles at zeros of z^2+4z+1, which are $-2+\sqrt{3}$ and $-2-\sqrt{3}$. Of these two simple poles of f, the first is enclosed by γ and the second is not, so discard $-2-\sqrt{3}$. By equation (24.2),

$$\int_0^{2\pi} \frac{\sin^2(\theta)}{2+\cos(\theta)} d\theta = 2\pi i\left[\operatorname{Re} s(f, 0) + \operatorname{Re} s(f, -2+\sqrt{3})\right].$$

Now

$$\operatorname{Re} s(f, 0) = \lim_{z\to 0}\frac{d}{dz}\left[z^2 f(z)\right] = \lim_{z\to 0}\frac{d}{dz}\frac{i}{2}\frac{z^4-2z^2+1}{z^2+4z+1}$$

$$= \frac{i}{2}\lim_{z\to 0}\left(2\frac{z^5+6z^4-4z^2-3z+2z^3-2}{(z^2+4z+1)^2}\right) = -2i$$

and

$$\operatorname{Re} s(f, -2+\sqrt{3}) = \frac{i}{2}\left[\frac{z^4-2z^2+1}{2z(z^2+4z+1)+z^2(2z+4)}\right]_{z=-2+\sqrt{3}}$$

$$= \frac{i}{2}\frac{42-24\sqrt{3}}{-12+7\sqrt{3}}.$$

Then

$$\int_0^{2\pi} \frac{\sin^2(\theta)}{2+\cos(\theta)} d\theta = 2\pi i\left[-2i+\frac{i}{2}\frac{42-24\sqrt{3}}{-12+7\sqrt{3}}\right] = \frac{90-52\sqrt{3}}{12-7\sqrt{3}}\pi,$$

approximately 1.68357. ∎

In applying this method, if a complex number results, check the calculations, because a real integral must have a real value.

EXAMPLE 24.24

We will evaluate

$$\int_0^\pi \frac{1}{\alpha + \beta \cos(\theta)} d\theta,$$

where $0 < \beta < \alpha$.

Since the method we have developed deals with integrals over $[0, 2\pi]$, we must first decide how to accommodate an integral over $[0, \pi]$. Write

$$\int_0^{2\pi} \frac{1}{\alpha + \beta \cos(\theta)} d\theta = \int_0^\pi \frac{1}{\alpha + \beta \cos(\theta)} d\theta + \int_\pi^{2\pi} \frac{1}{\alpha + \beta \cos(\theta)} d\theta.$$

Let $w = 2\pi - \theta$ in the last integral to obtain

$$\int_\pi^{2\pi} \frac{1}{\alpha + \beta \cos(\theta)} d\theta = \int_\pi^0 \frac{1}{\alpha + \beta \cos(2\pi - w)} (-1) dw = \int_0^\pi \frac{1}{\alpha + \beta \cos(w)} dw.$$

Therefore

$$\int_0^\pi \frac{1}{\alpha + \beta \cos(\theta)} d\theta = \frac{1}{2} \int_0^{2\pi} \frac{1}{\alpha + \beta \cos(\theta)} d\theta,$$

and we can concentrate on the integral over $[0, 2\pi]$. First produce the function

$$f(z) = \frac{1}{\alpha + \frac{\beta}{2}\left(z + \frac{1}{z}\right)} \frac{1}{iz} = \frac{-2i}{\beta z^2 + 2\alpha z + \beta}.$$

f has simple poles at

$$z = \frac{-\alpha \pm \sqrt{\alpha^2 - \beta^2}}{\beta}.$$

Since $\alpha > \beta$, these numbers are real. Only one of them,

$$z_1 = \frac{-\alpha + \sqrt{\alpha^2 - \beta^2}}{\beta}$$

is enclosed by γ. The other is outside the unit disk and is irrelevant for our purposes. Then

$$\int_0^\pi \frac{1}{\alpha + \beta \cos(\theta)} d\theta = \frac{1}{2} \int_0^{2\pi} \frac{1}{\alpha + \beta \cos(\theta)} d\theta = \frac{1}{2} 2\pi i \operatorname{Res}(f, z_1)$$

$$= \pi i \frac{-2i}{2\beta z_1 + 2\alpha} = \frac{\pi}{\sqrt{\alpha^2 - \beta^2}}. \quad \blacksquare$$

Before continuing with other kinds of real integrals we can evaluate using the residue theorem, we will take a brief excursion and give another, perhaps surprising, proof of the fundamental theorem of algebra. This argument is originally due to N.C. Ankeny, and the version we give appeared in *Lion Hunting and Other Mathematical Pursuits*, by R.P. Boas (The Mathematical Association of America Dolciani Mathematical Expositions, Volume 15).

Let $p(z)$ be a nonconstant polynomial with complex coefficients. We want to show that, for some number z, $p(z) = 0$.

First, we may assume that $p(x)$ is real if x is real. To see why this is true, let

$$p(z) = a_0 + a_1 z + \cdots + a_n z^n,$$

where $a_n \neq 0$. Denote

$$\overline{p}(z) = \overline{a_0} + \overline{a_1}z + \cdots + \overline{a_n}z^n.$$

Then $q(z) = p(z)\overline{p}(z)$ is a nonconstant polynomial. Further, if $z = x$ is real, then $\overline{x} = x$ and

$$
\begin{aligned}
q(x) = p(x)\overline{p}(x) \\
&= (a_0 + a_1 x + \cdots + a_n x^n)\left(\overline{a_0} + \overline{a_1}x + \cdots + \overline{a_n}x^n\right) \\
&= (a_0 + a_1 x + \cdots + a_n x^n)\overline{\left(a_0 + a_1 x + \cdots + a_n x^n\right)} \\
&= |a_0 + a_1 x + \cdots + a_n x^n|^2
\end{aligned}
$$

is real. We could then use $q(z)$ in our argument in place of $p(z)$, since $q(z)$ is a polynomial with no zero if $p(z)$ has no zero. Thus suppose that $p(z) \neq 0$ for all z, and $p(x)$ is real if x is real.

Because $p(x)$ is continuous and never zero for real x, $p(x)$ must be strictly positive or strictly negative for all real x. But then

$$\int_0^{2\pi} \frac{1}{p(2\cos(\theta))}\,d\theta \neq 0.$$

But, by the method we have just discussed, with γ the unit circle, we conclude that

$$\int_0^{2\pi} \frac{1}{p(2\cos(\theta))}\,d\theta = \oint_\gamma \frac{1}{p(z+1/z)}\frac{1}{iz}\,dz = \frac{1}{i}\oint_\gamma \frac{z^{n-1}}{r(z)}\,dz \neq 0,$$

where

$$
\begin{aligned}
r(z) &= z^n p(z+1/z) \\
&= z^n\left[a_0 + a_1\left(z+\frac{1}{z}\right) + a_2\left(z+\frac{1}{z}\right)^2 + \cdots + a_n\left(z+\frac{1}{z}\right)^n\right] \\
&= z^n\left[a_0 + a_1\frac{z^2+1}{z} + a_2\frac{(z^2+1)^2}{z^2} + \cdots + a_n\frac{(z^2+1)^n}{z^n}\right].
\end{aligned}
$$

From this it is clear that $r(z)$ is a polynomial. If $r(\zeta) = 0$ for some $\zeta \neq 0$, then we would have $p(\zeta + 1/\zeta) = 0$, so $\zeta + 1/\zeta$ would be a zero of p, a contradiction. Further, $r(0) = a_n \neq 0$ because p has degree n. Therefore $r(z) \neq 0$ for all z, so $z^{n-1}/r(z)$ is a differentiable function for all z. But then, by Cauchy's theorem,

$$\frac{1}{i}\oint_\gamma \frac{z^{n-1}}{r(z)}\,dz = 0,$$

a contradiction. We conclude that $p(z) = 0$ for some number z, proving the fundamental theorem of algebra.

Evaluation of $\int_{-\infty}^{\infty}[p(x)/q(x)]dx$ We will now consider real integrals of the form

$$\int_{-\infty}^{\infty} \frac{p(x)}{q(x)}\,dx,$$

in which p and q are polynomials with real coefficients and no common factors, q has no real zeros, and the degree of q exceeds the degree of p by at least 2. These conditions are sufficient to ensure convergence of this improper integral.

As with the preceding class of integrals, the strategy is to devise a complex integral that is equal to this real integral, then evaluate the complex integral using the residue theorem. To

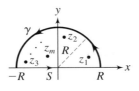

FIGURE 24.4

do this, first observe that $q(z)$ has real coefficients, so its zeros occur in complex conjugate pairs. Suppose the zeros of q are $z_1, \overline{z_1}, z_2, \overline{z_2}, \ldots, z_m, \overline{z_m}$, with each z_j in the upper half plane $\text{Im}(z) > 0$ and each $\overline{z_j}$ in the lower half plane $\text{Im}(z) < 0$. Let Γ be the curve shown in Figure 24.4, consisting of a semicircle γ of radius R and the segment S from $-R$ to R on the real axis, with R large enough that Γ encloses all the poles $z_1, \ldots, z_m$ of $p(z)/q(z)$ in the upper half plane. Then

$$\oint_\Gamma \frac{p(z)}{q(z)} dz = 2\pi i \sum_{j=1}^{m} \text{Re} \, s(p/q, z_j) = \int_S \frac{p(z)}{q(z)} dz + \int_\gamma \frac{p(z)}{q(z)} dz. \tag{24.3}$$

On S, $z = x$ for $-R \le x \le R$, so

$$\int_S \frac{p(z)}{q(z)} dz = \int_{-R}^{R} \frac{p(x)}{q(x)} dx.$$

Next consider the integral over γ. Since the degree of $q(z)$ exceeds that of $p(z)$ by at least 2,

$$\text{degree of } z^2 p(z) \le \text{degree of } q(z).$$

This means that, for sufficiently large R, $z^2 p(z)/q(z)$ is bounded for $|z| \ge R$. That is, for some number M,

$$\left| \frac{z^2 p(z)}{q(z)} \right| \le M \quad \text{for } |z| \ge R.$$

Then

$$\left| \frac{p(z)}{q(z)} \right| \le \frac{M}{|z|^2} \le \frac{M}{R^2} \quad \text{for } |z| \ge R,$$

so

$$\left| \int_\gamma \frac{p(z)}{q(z)} dz \right| \le \frac{M}{R^2} (\text{length of } \gamma)$$

$$= \frac{M}{R^2} (\pi R) = \frac{\pi M}{R} \to 0 \text{ as } R \to \infty.$$

Thus, in the limit as $R \to \infty$ in equation (24.3), the first integral on the right has limit $\int_{-\infty}^{\infty} (p(x)/q(x)) dx$, and the second integral has limit zero. In the limit as $R \to \infty$, equation (24.3) yields

$$\int_{-\infty}^{\infty} \frac{p(x)}{q(x)} dx = 2\pi i \sum_{j=1}^{m} \text{Re} \, s \left(\frac{p(z)}{q(z)}, z_j \right). \tag{24.4}$$

Equation (24.4) provides a general method for evaluating integrals of rational functions over the real line, under the assumptions made above. It is not necessary to repeat the derivation of this equation each time it is used—simply determine the zeros of $q(z)$ in the upper half-plane, evaluate the residue of p/q at each such zero (which is a pole of p/q whose order must be determined), and apply equation (24.4).

EXAMPLE 24.25

We will evaluate

$$\int_{-\infty}^{\infty} \frac{1}{x^6 + 64} dx.$$

Here $p(z) = 1$ and $q(z) = z^6 + 64$. The degree of q exceeds that of p by 6, and q has no real zeros. The zeros of $z^6 + 64$ are the sixth roots of -64. To find these, put -64 in polar form:

$$-64 = 64e^{i(\pi + 2n\pi)},$$

in which n can be any integer. The six sixth roots of -64 are

$$2e^{i(\pi + 2n\pi)/6} \text{ for } n = 0, 1, 2, 3, 4, 5.$$

The three roots in in the upper half-plane are

$$z_1 = 2e^{\pi i/6}, z_2 = 2e^{\pi i/2} = 2i, \quad \text{and} \quad z_3 = 2e^{5\pi i/6}.$$

We need the residue of $1/(z^6 + 64)$ at each of these simple poles. Corollary 24.1 is convenient to use here:

$$\mathrm{Re}\, s\left(\frac{1}{z^6 + 64}, 2e^{\pi i/6}\right) = \frac{1}{6(2e^{\pi i/6})^5} = \frac{1}{192} e^{-5\pi i/6},$$

$$\mathrm{Re}\, s\left(\frac{1}{z^6 + 64}, 2i\right) = \frac{1}{6(2i)^5} = -\frac{i}{192},$$

and

$$\mathrm{Re}\, s\left(\frac{1}{z^6 + 64}, 2e^{5\pi i/6}\right) = \frac{1}{6(2e^{5\pi i/6})^5} = \frac{1}{192} e^{-25\pi i/6} = \frac{1}{192} e^{-\pi i/6}.$$

Then

$$\int_{-\infty}^{\infty} \frac{1}{x^6 + 64} dx = \frac{2\pi i}{192} \left[e^{-5\pi i/6} - i + e^{-\pi i/6} \right]$$

$$= \frac{\pi i}{96} \left[\cos\left(\frac{5\pi}{6}\right) - i\sin\left(\frac{5\pi}{6}\right) - i + \cos\left(\frac{\pi}{6}\right) - i\sin\left(\frac{\pi}{6}\right) \right].$$

Now

$$\cos\left(\frac{5\pi}{6}\right) + \cos\left(\frac{\pi}{6}\right) = 0$$

and

$$\sin\left(\frac{5\pi}{6}\right) = \sin\left(\frac{\pi}{6}\right) = 1$$

so

$$\int_{-\infty}^{\infty} \frac{1}{x^6 + 64} dx = \frac{\pi i}{96}(-2i) = \frac{\pi}{48}. \quad ■$$

Integrals of $\int_{-\infty}^{\infty}[p(x)/q(x)]\cos(cx)dx$ ***and*** $\int_{-\infty}^{\infty}[p(x)/q(x)]\sin(cx)dx$ Suppose p and q are polynomials with real coefficients and no common factors, that the degree of q exceeds the degree of p by at least 2, and that q has no real zeros. We want to evaluate integrals

$$\int_{-\infty}^{\infty}\frac{p(x)}{q(x)}\cos(cx)dx \quad \text{and} \quad \int_{-\infty}^{\infty}\frac{p(x)}{q(x)}\sin(cx)dx,$$

in which c is any positive number.

Again, we proceed by looking for the integral of a suitably chosen complex function over a suitably chosen closed curve. Consider

$$\oint_{\Gamma}\frac{p(z)}{q(z)}e^{icz}dz,$$

where Γ is the closed path of the preceding subsection, enclosing all the zeros $z_1, \ldots, z_m$ of q lying in the upper half plane. Here is why this integral is promising. With Γ consisting of the semicircle γ and the segment S on the real axis, as before, then

$$\oint_{\Gamma}\frac{p(z)}{q(z)}e^{icz}dz = \int_{\gamma}\frac{p(z)}{q(z)}e^{icz}dz + \int_{-R}^{R}\frac{p(x)}{q(x)}e^{icx}dx$$

$$= \oint_{\gamma}\frac{p(z)}{q(z)}e^{icz}dz + \int_{-R}^{R}\frac{p(x)}{q(x)}\cos(cx)dx + i\int_{-R}^{R}\frac{p(x)}{q(x)}\sin(cx)dx$$

$$= 2\pi i\sum_{j=1}^{m}\text{Re}\,s\left(\frac{p(z)}{q(z)}e^{icz}, z_j\right).$$

As $R \to \infty$, one can show that $\int_{\gamma}[p(z)/q(z)]e^{icz}dz \to 0$, leaving

$$\int_{-\infty}^{\infty}\frac{p(x)}{q(x)}\cos(cx)dx + i\int_{-\infty}^{\infty}\frac{p(x)}{q(x)}\sin(cx)dx = 2\pi i\sum_{j=1}^{m}\text{Re}\,s\left(\frac{p(z)}{q(z)}e^{icz}, z_j\right). \tag{24.5}$$

The real part of the right side of equation (24.5) is $\int_{-\infty}^{\infty}[p(x)/q(x)]\cos(cx)dx$, and the imaginary part is $\int_{-\infty}^{\infty}[p(x)/q(x)]\sin(cx)dx$.

EXAMPLE 24.26

We will evaluate

$$\int_{-\infty}^{\infty}\frac{\cos(cx)}{(x^2+\alpha^2)(x^2+\beta^2)}dx,$$

in which c, α and β are positive numbers and $\alpha \neq \beta$.

The zeros of the denominator in the upper half plane are αi and βi, and these are simple poles of

$$f(z) = \frac{e^{icz}}{(z^2+\alpha^2)(z^2+\beta^2)}.$$

Compute

$$\text{Re}\,s(f, \alpha i) = \frac{e^{ic\alpha i}}{2\alpha i(\beta^2-\alpha^2)} = \frac{e^{-c\alpha}}{2\alpha i(\beta^2-\alpha^2)}$$

and

$$\text{Re}\,s(f, \beta i) = \frac{e^{-c\beta}}{2\beta i(\alpha^2-\beta^2)}.$$

Then

$$\int_{-\infty}^{\infty} \frac{\cos(cx)}{(x^2+\alpha^2)(x^2+\beta^2)} dx + i \int_{-\infty}^{\infty} \frac{\sin(cx)}{(x^2+\alpha^2)(x^2+\beta^2)} dx$$

$$= 2\pi i \left[\frac{e^{-c\alpha}}{2\alpha i(\beta^2-\alpha^2)} + \frac{e^{-c\beta}}{2\beta i(\alpha^2-\beta^2)} \right] = \frac{\pi}{\beta^2-\alpha^2} \left(\frac{e^{-c\alpha}}{\alpha} - \frac{e^{-c\beta}}{\beta} \right).$$

Separating real and imaginary parts, we have

$$\int_{-\infty}^{\infty} \frac{\cos(cx)}{(x^2+\alpha^2)(x^2+\beta^2)} dx = \frac{\pi}{\beta^2-\alpha^2} \left(\frac{e^{-c\alpha}}{\alpha} - \frac{e^{-c\beta}}{\beta} \right)$$

and

$$\int_{-\infty}^{\infty} \frac{\sin(cx)}{(x^2+\alpha^2)(x^2+\beta^2)} dx = 0.$$

The latter is obvious because the integrand is an odd function. ∎

Integrals Using Indented Contours Equation (24.4) enables us to evaluate certain improper integrals of quotients of polynomials, assuming that the denominator has no real zeros. We will extend this result to the case that the denominator has simple real zeros. Consider

$$\int_{-\infty}^{\infty} \frac{p(x)}{q(x)} dx$$

in which p and q are polynomials with real coefficients and no common factors, and the degree of q exceeds that of p by at least 2. Suppose q has complex zeros $z_1, \ldots, z_m$ in the upper half plane, as well as simple real zeros $t_1, \ldots, t_k$.

Let Γ be the path of Figure 24.5, including a semicircle γ of radius R about the origin, small semicircles γ_j of radius ϵ centered at each real zero t_j, and segments L_j along the real line connecting these semicircles as shown. We call such a path an indented path because of the small semicircles about the real zeros of $q(x)$. Let ϵ be small enough that no two of these semicircles intersects the other semicircles, and no z_j is enclosed by any γ_k with $j \neq k$. Also suppose R is large enough that Γ encloses each z_j. Note that each t_j is outside Γ.

By the residue theorem,

$$\oint_{\Gamma} \frac{p(z)}{q(z)} dz = 2\pi i \sum_{j=1}^{m} \text{Re}\, s \left(\frac{p(z)}{q(z)}, z_j \right)$$

$$= \int_{\gamma} \frac{p(z)}{q(z)} dz + \sum_{j=1}^{k} \int_{\gamma_j} \frac{p(z)}{q(z)} dz + \sum_{j=1}^{k+1} \int_{L_j} \frac{p(x)}{q(x)} dx. \qquad (24.6)$$

We want to investigate what happens in equation (24.6) when $R \to \infty$ and $\epsilon \to 0$.

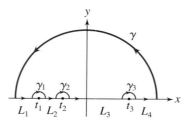

FIGURE 24.5

When $R \to \infty$, we claim that $\int_\gamma [p(z)/q(z)]dz \to 0$ by an argument like that we have done before. The sum of the residues at zeros of q is unchanged in this limit.

As $\epsilon \to 0$, the semicircles γ_j contract to t_j, and the segments L_j expand to cover the interval $[-R, R]$, and then the entire real line as $R \to \infty$. This means that, in equation (24.6)

$$\sum_{j=1}^{k+1} \int_{L_j} \frac{p(z)}{q(z)} dz \to \int_{-\infty}^{\infty} \frac{p(x)}{q(x)} dx$$

It is not yet clear what happens to each integral $\int_{\gamma_j} [p(z)/q(z)]dz$ in this process. We will show that each of these integrals approaches πi times the residue of $p(z)/q(z)$ at the real simple pole t_j.

To see this, write the Laurent expansion of $p(z)/q(z)$ about t_j:

$$\frac{p(z)}{q(z)} = \frac{c_{-1}}{z - t_j} + \sum_{s=0}^{\infty} c_s(z - t_j)^s = \frac{c_{-1}}{z - t_j} + g(z),$$

where g is differentiable at t_j. On γ_j, $z = t_j + \epsilon e^{it}$, where t varies from π to 0 (for counterclockwise orientation on Γ). Then

$$\int_{\gamma_j} \frac{p(z)}{q(z)} dz = c_{-1} \int_{\gamma_j} \frac{1}{z - t_j} dz + \int_{\gamma_j} g(z)dz$$

$$= c_{-1} \int_{\pi}^{0} \frac{1}{\epsilon e^{it}} i\epsilon e^{it} dt + \int_{\pi}^{0} g(t_j + \epsilon e^{it}) i\epsilon e^{it} dt$$

$$= -\pi i c_{-1} + i\epsilon \int_{\pi}^{0} g(t_j + \epsilon e^{it}) e^{it} dt$$

$$= -\pi i \operatorname{Res}\left(\frac{p(z)}{q(z)}, t_j\right) + i\epsilon \int_{\pi}^{0} g(t_j + \epsilon e^{it}) e^{it} dt.$$

Now $i\epsilon \int_{\pi}^{0} g(t_j + \epsilon e^{it}) e^{it} dt \to 0$ as $\epsilon \to 0$. Therefore

$$\int_{\gamma_j} \frac{p(z)}{q(z)} dz \to -\pi i \operatorname{Res}\left(\frac{p(z)}{q(z)}, t_j\right).$$

Therefore, as $R \to \infty$ and $\epsilon \to 0$ in equation (24.6), we get

$$2\pi i \sum_{j=1}^{\infty} \operatorname{Res}\left(\frac{p(z)}{q(z)}, z_j\right) = -\pi i \sum_{j=1}^{k} \operatorname{Res}\left(\frac{p(z)}{q(z)}, t_j\right) + \int_{-\infty}^{\infty} \frac{p(x)}{q(x)} dx,$$

hence

$$\int_{-\infty}^{\infty} \frac{p(x)}{q(x)} dx = \pi i \sum_{j=1}^{k} \operatorname{Res}\left(\frac{p(z)}{q(z)}, t_j\right) + 2\pi i \sum_{j=1}^{\infty} \operatorname{Res}\left(\frac{p(z)}{q(z)}, z_j\right). \tag{24.7}$$

In a sense, the simple poles of $p(z)/q(z)$ on the real line contribute "half residues", having been enclosed by semicircles instead of circles, while the poles in the upper half plane contribute "full residues" to this sum.

EXAMPLE 24.27

Evaluate

$$\int_{-\infty}^{\infty} \frac{3x+2}{x(x-4)(x^2+9)}.$$

Here

$$f(z) = \frac{3z+2}{z(z-4)(z^2+9)}.$$

The denominator has simple real zeros at 0 and 4, and simple complex zeros $-3i$ and $3i$. Only $3i$ is in the upper half plane. Compute the residues:

$$\mathrm{Re}\,s(f,0) = \lim_{z\to 0} z f(z) = \frac{2}{-36} = -\frac{1}{18},$$

$$\mathrm{Re}\,s(f,4) = \lim_{z\to 4}(z-4)f(z) = \frac{14}{100} = \frac{7}{50}$$

and

$$\mathrm{Re}\,s(f,3i) = \lim_{z\to 3i}(z-3i)f(z) = \frac{9i+2}{3i(3i-4)(6i)} = \frac{2+9i}{72-54i}.$$

Then

$$\int_{-\infty}^{\infty} \frac{3x+2}{x(x-4)(x^2+9)} = \pi i\left(-\frac{1}{18}+\frac{7}{50}\right) + 2\pi i\left(\frac{2+9i}{72-54i}\right) = -\frac{14}{75}\pi.$$

Integrals $\int_0^\infty x^a[p(x)/q(x)]dx$ Let $0 < a < 1$. We will consider integrals of the form

$$\int_0^\infty x^a \frac{p(x)}{q(x)}dx,$$

in which p and q are polynomials with real coefficients and no common factors, q has no positive zeros, and the degree of q exceeds the degree of p by at least 1. We also assume that either $q(0) \neq 0$, or $q(z)$ has a simple zero at the origin.

Let the nonzero zeros of q be $z_1, \ldots, z_m$. These are all the nonzero zeros of q, not just those in the upper half-plane. Since the coefficients of q are real, this list includes complex conjugate pairs.

Choose r small enough and R large enough that the closed path Γ shown in Figure 24.6 encloses $z_1, \ldots, z_m$. Γ consists of γ_R ("most" of the circle of radius R about 0), γ_r ("most" of the circle of radius r about 0), and the line segments L_1 and L_2 connecting γ_r and γ_R. We will eventually let $r \to 0$ and $R \to \infty$, but some work is required first.

We must agree on a meaning for z^a, since this symbol generally denotes a (possibly infinite) set of different numbers. Write $z = \rho e^{i\theta}$ for some θ in $[0, 2\pi)$, and define

$$z^a = \rho^a e^{ia\theta}.$$

As z approaches L_1,

$$f(z) = \frac{z^a p(z)}{q(z)} \to \frac{x^a p(x)}{q(x)},$$

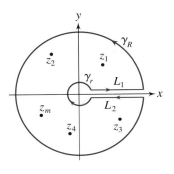

FIGURE 24.6

where $r < x < R$. But as z approaches L_2, the lower side of the positive real axis,

$$f(z) \to \frac{x^a e^{2\pi ai} p(x)}{q(x)}.$$

The reason for this is that the argument increases by 2π as z approaches the positive real axis from below, and then

$$z^a = \rho^a e^{i(\theta + 2\pi)a} = \rho^a e^{ia\theta} e^{2\pi ai}.$$

By the residue theorem,

$$\oint_\Gamma \frac{z^a p(z)}{q(z)} dz = 2\pi i \sum_{j=1}^m \text{Res}(f, z_j)$$

$$= \int_{\gamma_R} \frac{z^a p(z)}{q(z)} dz + \int_{\gamma_r} \frac{z^a p(z)}{q(z)} dz + \int_{L_1} \frac{x^a p(x)}{q(x)} dx + \int_{L_2} \frac{x^a e^{2\pi ai} p(x)}{q(x)} dx.$$

On L_1, x varies from r to R, while on L_2, x varies from R to r to maintain counterclockwise orientation on Γ. The last equation becomes

$$2\pi i \sum_{j=1}^m \text{Re } s(f, z_j) = \int_{\gamma_R} \frac{z^a p(z)}{q(z)} dz + \int_{\gamma_r} \frac{z^a p(z)}{q(z)} dz$$

$$+ \int_r^R \frac{x^a p(x)}{q(x)} dx + \int_R^r \frac{x^a e^{2\pi ai} p(x)}{q(x)} dx.$$

By making estimates on the two circular arcs, we can show that the first two integrals in the last equation tend to zero as $r \to 0$ and $R \to \infty$. In this limit, the last equation becomes

$$2\pi i \sum_{j=1}^m \text{Re } s(f, z_j) = \int_0^\infty \frac{x^a p(x)}{q(x)} dx + \int_\infty^0 \frac{x^a e^{2\pi ai} p(x)}{q(x)} dx.$$

From this we obtain

$$\int_0^\infty \frac{x^a p(x)}{q(x)} dx = \frac{2\pi i}{1 - e^{2\pi ai}} \sum_{j=1}^m \text{Re } s(f, z_j). \tag{24.8}$$

EXAMPLE 24.28

We will use equation (24.8) to evaluate

$$\int_0^\infty \frac{x^{1/3}}{x(x^2+1)} dx.$$

Here $p(z) = 1$, $a = \frac{1}{3}$ and $q(z) = z(1+z^2)$, with simple zeros at 0, i and $-i$. Compute

$$\mathrm{Re}\, s(z^{1/3}/q(z), i) = \frac{i^{1/3}}{2i^2} = \frac{(e^{\pi i/2})^{1/3}}{-2} = -\frac{1}{2} e^{\pi i/6}$$

and

$$\mathrm{Re}\, s(z^{1/3} q(z), -i) = \frac{(e^{3\pi i/2})^{1/3}}{-2} = -\frac{1}{2} e^{\pi i/2}.$$

Then

$$\int_0^\infty \frac{x^{1/3}}{x(x^2+1)} dx = \frac{2\pi i}{1 - e^{2\pi i/3}} \left(-\frac{1}{2}\right)\left(e^{\pi i/6} + e^{\pi i/2}\right)$$

$$= \frac{-\pi i}{1 + \frac{1}{2} - \frac{\sqrt{3}}{2}i} \left(\frac{\sqrt{3}}{2} + \frac{1}{2}i + i\right) = \pi. \ \blacksquare$$

Many other kinds of real integrals can be evaluated using complex integral techniques. Some of these require considerable ingenuity in seeking the right function to integrate over the path to get the result that is wanted.

The Cauchy Principal Value Since we have been dealing with improper integrals, we will mention the Cauchy principal value.

An integral

$$I = \int_{-\infty}^\infty g(x) dx$$

is defined to be

$$\lim_{r \to -\infty} \int_r^0 g(x) dx + \lim_{R \to \infty} \int_0^R g(x) dx,$$

if both of these integrals converge. These limits are independent of each other.

The *Cauchy principal value* of I is defined to be

$$CPV\left(\int_{-\infty}^\infty g(x) dx\right) = \lim_{R \to \infty} \int_{-R}^R g(x) dx.$$

This is a special case of the two independent limits defining I.

In the event that $\int_{-\infty}^\infty g(x) dx$ converges, certainly the value of I agrees with the Cauchy principal value of the integral. However, it is possible for an integral to have a finite CPV, but to diverge in the broader sense of the definition of I. This occurs with $\int_{-\infty}^\infty x dx$, which certainly diverges. However, this integral has Cauchy principal value 0, because for any positive R,

$$\int_{-R}^R x dx = 0.$$

In some of the examples we have discussed, we were actually computing Cauchy principal values, whenever we took a limit of $\int_{-R}^R g(x) dx$ as $R \to \infty$. In most cases the conditions imposed insured that the improper integral converged in the more general sense as well.

SECTION 24.3   PROBLEMS

1. Evaluate $\oint_\Gamma \dfrac{z}{1+z^2}\,dz$, with Γ the circle $|z| = 2$, first using the residue theorem, and then by the argument principle.

2. Evaluate $\oint_\Gamma \tan(z)\,dz$, with Γ the circle $|z| = \pi$, first by the residue theorem, and then by the argument principle.

3. Evaluate $\oint_\Gamma \dfrac{z+1}{z^2+2z+4}\,dz$, with Γ the circle $|z| = 1$, first by the residue theorem, and then by the argument principle.

4. Let $p(z) = (z-z_1)(z-z_2)\cdots(z-z_n)$, with $z_1, \ldots, z_n$ distinct complex numbers. Let Γ be a positively oriented closed path enclosing each of the $z_j's$. Prove that

$$\oint_\Gamma \frac{p'(z)}{p(z)}\,dz = 2\pi i n,$$

first by the residue theorem, and then by the argument principle.

In each of Problems 5 through 9, find an inverse Laplace transform of the function, using residues.

5. $\dfrac{z}{z^2+9}$

6. $\dfrac{1}{(z+3)^2}$

7. $\dfrac{1}{(z-2)^2(z+4)}$

8. $\dfrac{1}{(z^2+9)(z-2)^2}$

9. $(z+5)^{-3}$

In each of Problems 10 through 22, evaluate the integral.

10. $\displaystyle\int_0^{2\pi} \frac{1}{6+\sin(\theta)}\,d\theta$

11. $\displaystyle\int_0^{2\pi} \frac{1}{2-\cos(\theta)}\,d\theta$

12. $\displaystyle\int_{-\infty}^{\infty} \frac{1}{x^4+1}\,dx$

13. $\displaystyle\int_{-\infty}^{\infty} \frac{1}{x^6+1}\,dx$

14. $\displaystyle\int_{-\infty}^{\infty} \frac{1}{x^2-2x+6}\,dx$

15. $\displaystyle\int_{-\infty}^{\infty} \frac{x\sin(2x)}{x^4+16}\,dx$

16. $\displaystyle\int_0^{2\pi} \frac{2\sin(\theta)}{2+\sin^2(\theta)}\,d\theta$

17. $\displaystyle\int_{-\infty}^{\infty} \frac{1}{x(x+4)(x^2+16)}\,dx$

18. $\displaystyle\int_{-\infty}^{\infty} \frac{\sin(x)}{x^2-4x+5}\,dx$

19. $\displaystyle\int_{-\infty}^{\infty} \frac{\cos^2(x)}{(x^2+4)^2}\,dx$

20. $\displaystyle\int_0^{2\pi} \frac{\sin(\theta)+\cos(\theta)}{2-\cos(\theta)}\,d\theta$

21. $\displaystyle\int_{-\infty}^{\infty} \frac{1}{(x-4)(x^5+1)}\,dx$

22. $\displaystyle\int_0^{\infty} \frac{x^{3/4}}{x^4+1}\,dx$

23. Let α be a positive number. Show that

$$\int_{-\infty}^{\infty} \frac{\cos(\alpha x)}{x^2+1}\,dx = \pi e^{-\alpha}.$$

24. Let α and β be positive numbers. Show that

$$\int_{-\infty}^{\infty} \frac{\cos(\alpha x)}{x^2+\beta^2}\,dx = \frac{\pi}{2\beta^3}(1+\alpha\beta)e^{-\alpha\beta}.$$

25. Let α and β be distinct positive numbers. Show that

$$\int_0^{2\pi} \frac{1}{\alpha^2\cos^2(\theta)+\beta^2\sin^2(\theta)}\,d\theta = \frac{2\pi}{\alpha\beta}.$$

26. Let α be a positive number. Show that

$$\int_0^{\pi/2} \frac{1}{\alpha+\sin^2(\theta)}\,d\theta = \frac{\pi}{2\sqrt{\alpha(1+\alpha)}}.$$

27. Let β be a positive number. Show that

$$\int_0^{\infty} e^{-x^2}\cos(2\beta x)\,dx = \frac{\sqrt{\pi}}{2}e^{-\beta^2}.$$

Hint: Integrate e^{-z^2} about the rectangular path having corners at $\pm R$ and $R\pm\beta i$. Use Cauchy's theorem to evaluate this integral, set this equal to the sum of the integrals on the sides of the rectangle, and take the limit as $R \to \infty$. Assume the standard result that

$$\int_0^\infty e^{-x^2} dx = \frac{\sqrt{\pi}}{2}.$$

28. Derive *Fresnel's integrals*:

$$\int_0^\infty \cos(x^2)dx = \int_0^\infty \sin(x^2)dx = \frac{1}{2}\sqrt{\frac{\pi}{2}}.$$

Hint: Integrate e^{iz^2} over the closed path bounding the sector $0 \le x \le R$, $0 \le \theta \le \pi/4$, show in Figure 24.7. Use Cauchy's theorem to evaluate this integral, then evaluate it as the sum of integrals over the boundary segments of the sector. Show that the integral over the circular sector tends to zero as $R \to \infty$, and use the integrals over the straight segments to obtain Fresnel's integrals.

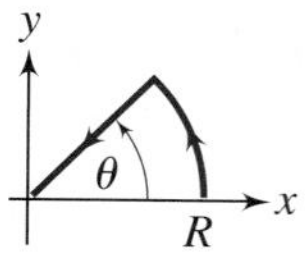

FIGURE 24.7

29. Let α and β be positive numbers. Show that

$$\int_0^\infty \frac{x \sin(\alpha x)}{x^4 + \beta^4} dx = \frac{\pi}{2\beta^2} e^{-\alpha\beta/\sqrt{2}} \sin\left(\frac{\alpha\beta}{\sqrt{2}}\right).$$

30. Let $0 < \beta < \alpha$. Show that

$$\int_0^\pi \frac{1}{(\alpha + \beta\cos(\theta))^2} d\theta = \frac{\alpha\pi}{(\alpha^2 - \beta^2)^{3/2}}.$$

CHAPTER 25

Conformal Mappings

In the calculus of real functions of a single real variable, we may gain some insight into the function's behavior by sketching its graph. For complex functions we cannot make the same kind of graph, since a complex variable $z = x + iy$ by itself has two variables. However, we can set $w = f(z)$ and make two copies of the complex plane, one for z and the other for image points w. As z traces out a path or varies over a set S in the z plane, we can plot image points $w = f(z)$ in the w plane, yielding a picture of how the function acts on this path or on points in S. The set of all image points $f(z)$ for z in S is denoted $f(S)$. When looked at in this way, a function is called a *mapping* or *transformation*. This idea is diagrammed in Figure 25.1.

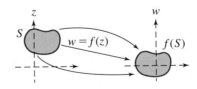

FIGURE 25.1

Thinking of a function as a mapping can be a powerful tool in solving certain kinds of problems, including the analysis of fluid motion and the solution of partial differential equations, particularly Dirichlet problems. We will develop some ideas about mappings, then turn to applications.

25.1 Functions as Mappings

First we need some terminology. Let f be a complex function and D a set of points in the plane on which $f(z)$ is defined. Let D^* also be a set of complex numbers.

DEFINITION 25.1

1. f maps D into D^* if $f(z)$ is in D^* for every z in D. In this event, we write $f: D \to D^*$.

2. f maps D onto D^* if $f(z)$ is in D^* for every z in D and, conversely, if w is in D^*, then there is some z in D such that $w = f(z)$. In this event, we call f an onto mapping.

Thus $f: D \to D^*$ is onto if every point of D^* is the image under f of some point in D.

EXAMPLE 25.1

Let $f(z) = iz$ for $|z| \leq 1$. Then f acts on points in the closed unit disk $D: |z| \leq 1$. If z is in D, then $|f(z)| = |iz| = |z| \leq 1$, so the image of any point in this disk is also in this disk. Here f maps D into D. (So $D^* = D$ in the definition).

This mapping is onto. If w is in D, then $z = w/i$ is also in D, and

$$f(z) = f(w/i) = i(w/i) = w.$$

Every point in the unit disk is the image of some point in this disk under this mapping.

We can envision this mapping geometrically. Since $i = e^{i\pi/2}$, if $z = re^{i\theta}$, then

$$f(z) = iz = re^{i\pi/2}e^{i\theta} = re^{i(\theta + \pi/2)},$$

so f takes z and adds $\pi/2$ to its argument. This rotates the line from the origin to z by $\pi/2$ radians counterclockwise. The action of f on z can be envisioned as in Figure 25.2. Since this function is simply a counterclockwise rotation by $\pi/2$ radians, it is clear why f maps the unit disk onto itself. ■

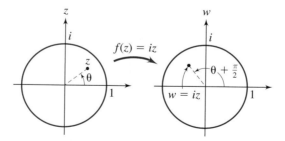

FIGURE 25.2   *The mapping $f(z) = iz$ for $|z| \leq 1$.*

Often we have the function f and the set D of complex numbers to which we want to apply this mapping. We then must analyze $f(z)$ to determine the image of D under the mapping. In effect, we are finding D^* so that f is a mapping of D onto D^*.

EXAMPLE 25.2

Let $f(z) = z^2$ for z in the wedge D shown in Figure 25.3. D consists of all complex numbers on or between the nonnegative real axis and the line $y = x$.

FIGURE 25.3 $w = z^2$ maps D one-to-one onto D^*.

In polar form $z = re^{i\theta}$ is in D if $0 \leq \theta \leq \pi/4$. Then $f(z) = z^2 = r^2 e^{2i\theta}$, so f has the effect of squaring the magnitude of z, and doubling its argument. If z has argument between 0 and $\pi/4$, then z^2 has argument between 0 and $\pi/2$. This spreads the wedge D out to cover the entire right quarter-plane, consisting of points on or between the nonnegative real and imaginary axes. If we call this right quarter plane D^*, then f maps D onto D^*. ∎

Some functions map more than one point to the same image. For example, $f(z) = \sin(z)$ maps all integer multiples of π to zero. If each image point is the unique target of exactly one number, then the mapping is called one-to-one.

DEFINITION 25.2

A mapping $f: D \rightarrow D^*$ is one-to-one if distinct points of D map to distinct points in D^*.

Thus f is one-to-one (or $1-1$) if $z_1 \neq z_2$ implies that $f(z_1) \neq f(z_2)$.

The notions of one-to-one and onto are independent of each other. A mapping may have one of these properties, or both, or neither. The mapping $f(z) = z^2$ of Example 25.2 maps the wedge $0 \leq \arg(z) \leq \pi/4$ in one-to-one fashion onto the right quarter plane. However, $f(z) = z^2$ does not map the entire complex plane to the complex plane in a one-to-one manner, since $f(-z) = f(z)$. This function does map the plane onto itself, since, given any complex number w, there is some z such that $f(z) = z^2 = w$.

EXAMPLE 25.3

Let $h(z) = z^2$ for all z. h maps the entire plane onto itself, but is not one-to-one.

If $z = x + iy$, then

$$h(z) = x^2 - y^2 + 2ixy = u + iv,$$

where $u = x^2 - y^2$ and $v = 2xy$. We will use this formulation to determine the image under f of a vertical line $x = a$. Any point on this line has the form $z = a + iy$, and maps to

$$h(a + iy) = u + iv = a^2 - y^2 + 2iay.$$

Points on the line $x = a$ map to points (u, v) with $u = a^2 - y^2$ and $v = 2ay$. Write $y = v/2a$ (assuming that $a \neq 0$) to obtain

$$u = a^2 - \frac{v^2}{4a^2},$$

or

$$v^2 = 4a^2(a^2 - u),$$

the equation of a parabola in the u, v plane. h maps vertical lines $x = a \neq 0$ to parabolas.

If $a = 0$, the vertical line $x = a$ is the imaginary axis, consisting of points $z = iy$. Now $h(z) = -y^2$, so h maps the imaginary axis in the x, y plane to the nonpositive part of the real axis in the u, v plane.

Figure 25.4 shows the parabolic image of a line $x = a \neq 0$. The larger a is, the more the parabola opens up to the left (intersects the v axis further from the origin). As a is chosen smaller, approaching 0, these parabolas become "flatter", approaching the nonpositive real axis in the u, v plane.

A horizontal line $y = b$ consists of points $z = x + ib$, which map to

$$h(z) = (x + ib)^2 = x^2 - b^2 + 2ixb = u + iv.$$

Now $u = x^2 - b^2$ and $v = 2xb$, so, for $b \neq 0$,

$$v^2 = 4b^2(b^2 + u).$$

A typical such parabola is shown in Figure 25.5, opening up to the right. These parabolas also open up more the larger b is. If $b = 0$, the line $y = b$ is the real axis in the z plane, and this maps to $h(x) = x^2$, giving the nonnegative real axis in the u, v plane as x takes on all real values. ∎

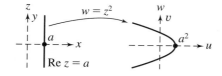

FIGURE 25.4 $w = z^2$ maps vertical lines to parabolas opening left.

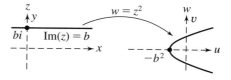

FIGURE 25.5 $w = z^2$ maps horizontal lines to parabolas opening right.

EXAMPLE 25.4

We will look at the exponential function $w = E(z) = e^z$ as a mapping. Write

$$w = u + iv = e^{x+iy} = e^x \cos(y) + ie^x \sin(y),$$

so

$$u = e^x \cos(y) \quad \text{and} \quad v = e^x \sin(y).$$

As a mapping of the entire plane to itself, E is not onto (no number maps to zero), and E is also not one-to-one (all points $z + 2n\pi i$ have the same image, for n any integer).

Consider a vertical line $x = a$ in the x, y plane. The image of this line consists of points $u + iv$ with

$$u = e^a \cos(y), \quad v = e^a \sin(y).$$

Then

$$u^2 + v^2 = e^{2a},$$

so the line $x = a$ maps to the circle of radius e^a about the origin in the u, v plane. Actually, as the point $z = a + iy$ moves along this vertical line, the image point $u + iv$ makes one complete circuit around the circle every time y varies over an interval of length 2π, since $\cos(y + 2n\pi) = \cos(y)$ and $\sin(y + 2n\pi) = \sin(y)$. We may therefore think of a vertical line as infinitely many intervals of length 2π strung together, and the exponential function wraps each segment once around the circle $u^2 + v^2 = e^{2a}$ (Figure 25.6).

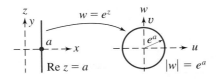

FIGURE 25.6 $w = e^z$ wraps a vertical line around a circle, covering the circle once for every interval of length 2π.

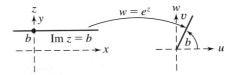

FIGURE 25.7 $w = e^z$ maps horizontal lines to half-rays from the origin.

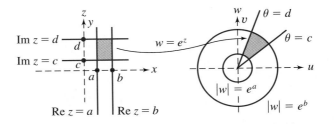

FIGURE 25.8 $w = e^z$ maps the rectangle shown to a wedge bounded by two half-rays and two circles.

The image of a point $z = x + ib$ on the horizontal line $y = b$ is a point $u + iv$ with

$$u = e^x \sin(b), \quad y = e^x \cos(b).$$

As x varies over the real line, e^x varies from 0 to ∞ over the positive real axis. The point $(e^x \sin(b), e^x \cos(b))$ moves along a half-line from the origin to infinity, making an angle b radians with the positive real axis (Figure 25.7). In polar coordinates this half-line is $\theta = b$.

Using these results, we can find the image of any rectangle in the x, y plane, having sides parallel to the axes. Let the rectangle have sides on the lines $x = a$, $x = b$, $y = c$ and $y = d$ (in the x, y plane in Figure 25.8). These lines map, respectively, to the circles

$$u^2 + v^2 = e^{2a}, \quad u^2 + v^2 = e^{2b}$$

and the half-lines

$$\theta = c \quad \text{and} \quad \theta = d.$$

The wedge in the u, v plane in Figure 25.8 is the image of the rectangle under this exponential mapping. ■

Given a mapping f and a domain D, here is a strategy that is often successful in determining $f(D)$. Suppose D has a boundary made up of curves $\gamma_1, \ldots, \gamma_n$. Find the images of these curves, $f(\gamma_1), \ldots, f(\gamma_n)$. These form curves in the $w-$ plane, bounding two sets, labeled I and II in Figure 25.9. $f(D)$ is one of these two sets. To determine which it is, choose a convenient point ζ in D and locate $f(\zeta)$. This set will be $f(D)$.

EXAMPLE 25.5

We will determine the image, under the mapping $w = f(z) = \sin(z)$, of the strip S consisting of all z with $-\pi/2 < \text{Re}(z) < \pi/2$ and $\text{Im}(z) > 0$. S is shown in Figure 25.10.

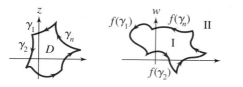

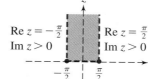

FIGURE 25.9

FIGURE 25.10 *Strip bounded by vertical lines* $x = -\pi/2$ *and* $x = \pi/2$ *and the x axis.*

The boundary of S consists of the segment $-\pi/2 \leq x \leq \pi/2$ on the real axis, together with the half-lines $x = -\pi/2$ and $x = \pi/2$ for $y \geq 0$. We will carry out the strategy of looking at images of the lines bounding S. First,

$$w = u + iv = \sin(x)\cosh(y) + i\cos(x)\sinh(y).$$

If $x = -\pi/2$, then

$$w = u + iv = -\cosh(y).$$

Since $0 \leq y < \infty$ on this part of the boundary of S, then $\cosh(y)$ varies from 1 to ∞. The image of the left vertical boundary of S is therefore the interval $(-\infty, -1]$ on the real axis in the u, v plane.

If $x = \pi/2$, a similar analysis shows that the image of the right vertical boundary of S is $[1, \infty)$ on the real axis in the u, v plane.

Finally, if $y = 0$, then

$$w = \sin(x).$$

As x varies from $-\pi/2$ to $\pi/2$, $\sin(x)$ varies from -1 to 1. Thus $[\pi/2, \pi/2]$ maps to $[-1, 1]$ in the u, v plane.

Figure 25.11 shows these results. The boundary of S maps onto the entire real axis in the u, v plane. This axis is the boundary of two sets in the w plane, the upper half-plane and the lower half-plane. Choose any convenient z in S, say $z = i$. Its image is

$$w = \sin(i) = i\sinh(1),$$

lying in the upper half-plane. Therefore the image of S is the upper half-plane.

Orientation plays a role in these mappings. Imagine walking along the boundary of S in a counterclockwise sense. This means that we start somewhere up the left boundary $x = -\pi/2$, walk down this line to the real axis, then turn left and walk along this axis to $x = \pi/2$, then turn left again and proceed up the right boundary line. Follow the movement of the image point $f(z)$

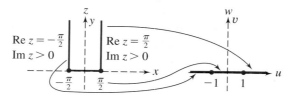

FIGURE 25.11 $w = \sin(z)$ *maps* $x = -\pi/2$, $y \geq 0$, *to* $u \leq -1$; $-\pi/2 \leq x \leq \pi/2$ *to* $-1 \leq u \leq 1$; *and* $x = \pi/2$, $y \geq 0$, *to* $u \geq 1$.

as z takes this route. As z moves down the line $x = -\pi/2$, $f(z) = \sin(z)$ begins somewhere to the left of -1 on the real axis in the w plane, and moves toward $w = -1$. As w turns the first corner and moves along the real axis in the z plane from $-\pi/2$ to $\pi/2$, $f(z)$ continues through -1 and proceeds along the real axis to $w = +1$. Finally, z turns upward and moves along the line $x = \pi/2$, and $f(z)$ moves through $w = 1$ and out the real axis in the w plane. As z traverses the boundary of the strip in a counterclockwise sense (interior of S to the left), $f(z)$ traverses the boundary of the upper half plane from left to right in a counterclockwise sense (interior of this plane to the left). ∎

In this example, as z moves over the boundary of D in a positive (counterclockwise) sense, $f(z)$ moves over the boundary of $f(D)$ in a positive sense. In the next section we will discuss mappings that preserve angles and sense of rotation.

SECTION 25.1   PROBLEMS

1. In each of (a) through (e), find the image of the given rectangle under the mapping $w = e^z$. Sketch the rectangle in the z plane and its image in the w plane.

   (a) $0 \le x \le \pi, 0 \le y \le \pi$

   (b) $-1 \le x \le 1, -\dfrac{\pi}{2} \le y \le \dfrac{\pi}{2}$

   (c) $0 \le x \le 1, 0 \le y \le \dfrac{\pi}{4}$

   (d) $1 \le x \le 2, 0 \le y \le \pi$

   (e) $-1 \le x \le 2, -\dfrac{\pi}{2} \le y \le \dfrac{\pi}{2}$

2. In each of (a) through (e), find the image of the rectangle under the mapping $w = \cos(z)$. Sketch the rectangle and its image in each case.

   (a) $0 \le x \le 1, 1 \le y \le 2$

   (b) $\dfrac{\pi}{2} \le x \le \pi, 1 \le y \le 3$

   (c) $0 \le x \le \pi, \dfrac{\pi}{2} \le y \le \pi$

   (d) $\pi \le x \le 2\pi, 1 \le y \le 2$

   (e) $0 \le x \le \dfrac{\pi}{2}, 0 \le y \le 1$

3. In each of (a) through (e), find the image of the rectangle under the mapping $w = 4\sin(z)$. Sketch the rectangle and its image in each case.

   (a) $0 \le x \le \dfrac{\pi}{2}, 0 \le y \le \dfrac{\pi}{2}$

   (b) $\dfrac{\pi}{4} \le x \le \dfrac{\pi}{2}, 0 \le y \le \dfrac{\pi}{4}$

   (c) $0 \le x \le 1, 0 \le y \le \dfrac{\pi}{6}$

   (d) $\dfrac{\pi}{2} \le x \le \dfrac{3\pi}{2}, 0 \le y \le \dfrac{\pi}{2}$

   (e) $1 \le x \le 2, 1 \le y \le 2$

4. Determine the image of the sector $\pi/4 \le \theta \le 5\pi/4$ under the mapping $w = z^2$. Sketch the sector and its image.

5. Determine the image of the sector $\pi/6 \le \theta \le \pi/3$, under the mapping $w = z^3$. Sketch the sector and its image.

6. Show that the mapping

$$w = \frac{1}{2}\left(z + \frac{1}{z}\right)$$

   maps the circle $|z| = r$ onto an ellipse with foci 1 and -1 in the w plane. Sketch a typical circle and its image.

7. Show that the mapping of Problem 6 maps a half-line $\theta = $ constant onto a hyperbola with foci ± 1 in the w plane. Sketch a typical half-line and its image.

8. Show that the mapping $w = 1/z$ maps every straight line to a circle or straight line, and every circle to a circle or straight line. Give an example of a circle that maps to a line, and a line that maps to a circle.

9. Determine the image of the infinite strip $0 \le \text{Im}(z) \le 2\pi$ under the mapping $w = e^z$.

10. Let D consist of all z in the rectangle having vertices $\pm \alpha i$ and $\pi \pm \alpha i$, with α a positive number.

   (a) Determine the image of D under the mapping $w = \cos(z)$. Sketch D and its image.

   (b) Determine the image of D under the mapping $w = \sin(z)$. Sketch this image.

   (c) Determine the image of D under the mapping $w = 2z^2$. Sketch this image.

25.2   **Conformal Mappings**

Let $f : D \to D^*$ be a mapping.

DEFINITION 25.3   *Angle Preserving Mapping*

We say that f preserves angles if, for any z_0 in D, if two smooth curves in D intersect at z_0, and the angle between these curves at z_0 is θ, then the images of these curves intersect at the same angle θ at $f(z_0)$.

This idea is illustrated in Figure 25.12. The images of γ_1 and γ_2 are curves $f(\gamma_1)$ and $f(\gamma_2)$ in D^*. Suppose γ_1 and γ_2 intersect at z_0, and that their tangents have an angle θ between them there. We require that the tangents to $f(\gamma_1)$ and $f(\gamma_2)$ intersect at $f(z_0)$ at the same angle. If this condition holds for all smooth curves passing through each point of D, then f is angle preserving on D.

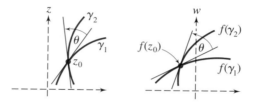

FIGURE 25.12   *Angle-preserving mapping.*

DEFINITION 25.4   *Orientation Preserving Mapping*

f preserves orientation if a counterclockwise rotation in D is mapped by f to a counterclockwise rotation in D^*.

This idea is illustrated in Figure 25.13. If L_1 and L_2 are lines through any point z_0 in D, and the sense of rotation from L_1 to L_2 is counterclockwise, then the sense of rotation from $f(L_1)$ to $f(L_2)$ through $f(z_0)$ in D^* must also be counterclockwise. Of course $f(L_1)$ and $f(L_2)$ need not be straight lines, but one can still consider a sense of rotation frrom the tangent to $f(L_1)$ to the tangent to $f(L_2)$ at $f(z_0)$. By contrast, Figure 25.14 illustrates a mapping that does not preserve orientation.

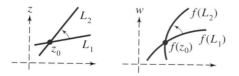

FIGURE 25.13   *Orientation-preserving mapping.*

FIGURE 25.14   *A nonorientation-preserving mapping.*

Preservation of angles and orientation are independent concepts. A mapping may preserve one but not the other. If $f: D \to D^*$ preserves both, we say that f is *conformal*.

DEFINITION 25.5   *Conformal Mapping*

$f: D \to D^*$ is a conformal mapping if f is angle preserving and orientation preserving.

The following theorem generates many examples of conformal mappings.

THEOREM 25.1

Let $f: D \to D^*$ be a differentiable function defined on a domain D. Suppose $f'(z) \neq 0$ for all z in D. Then f is conformal. ■

Thus, a differentiable function with a nonvanishing derivative on a domain (connected, open set) maps this set in such a way as to preserve both angles and orientation. We will sketch an argument showing why this is true. Let z_0 be in D and let γ be a smooth curve in D through z_0. Then $f(\gamma)$ is a smooth curve through $f(z_0)$ in D^* (Figure 25.15). If $w = f(z)$ and $w_0 = f(z_0)$, then

$$w - w_0 = \frac{f(z) - f(z_0)}{z - z_0}(z - z_0).$$

Now recall that argument behaves like a logarithm, in the sense that any argument of a product is a sum of arguments of the individual factors. Then

$$\arg(w - w_0) = \arg\left(\frac{f(z) - f(z_0)}{z - z_0}\right) + \arg(z - z_0). \tag{25.1}$$

In Figure 25.16, θ is the angle between the positive real axis and the line through z and z_0, and is an argument of $z - z_0$. The angle φ between the positive real axis and the line through w and w_0 in the w plane is an argument of $w - w_0$. In the limit as $z \to z_0$, equation (25.1) gives us

$$\varphi = \arg[f'(z_0)] + \theta.$$

It is here that we use the assumption that $f'(z_0) \neq 0$, because 0 has no argument.

If γ^* is another smooth curve through z_0, then by the same reasoning,

$$\varphi^* = \arg[f'(z_0)] + \theta^*.$$

Then

$$\varphi - \varphi^* = \theta - \theta^*,$$

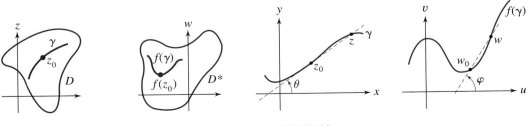

FIGURE 25.15   **FIGURE 25.16**

(to within integer multiples of 2π). But $\theta - \theta^*$ is the angle between the tangents to γ and γ^* at z_0, and $\varphi - \varphi^*$ is the angle between the tangents to $f(\gamma)$ and $f(\gamma^*)$ at $f(z_0)$. Therefore f preserves angles.

The last "equation" also implies that f preserves orientation, since the sense of rotation from γ to γ^* is the same as the sense of rotation from $f(\gamma)$ to $f(\gamma^*)$. A reversal of the sense of rotation would be implied if we had found that $\varphi - \varphi^* = \theta^* - \theta$. For example, $w = \sin(z)$ is differentiable, with a nonvanishing derivative, on the strip $-\pi/2 < \text{Re}(z) < \pi/2$, and so is a conformal mapping of this strip onto a set in the w plane.

A composition of conformal mappings is conformal. Suppose f maps D conformally onto D^*, and g maps D^* conformally onto D^{**}. Then $g \circ f$ maps D conformally onto D^{**} (Figure 25.17), because angles and orientation are preserved at each stage of the mapping.

We will now consider an important class of conformal mappings.

25.2.1 Linear Fractional Transformations

Often we have domains D and D^* (for example, representing areas of a fluid flow), and we want to produce a conformal mapping of D onto D^*. This can be a formidable task. Linear fractional transformations are relatively simple conformal mappings that will sometimes serve this purpose.

DEFINITION 25.6   *Linear Fractional Transformation*

A linear fractional transformation is a function

$$T(z) = \frac{az + b}{cz + d},$$

in which a, b, c and d are given complex numbers, and $ad - bc \neq 0$.

Other names for this kind of function are *Möbius transformation* and *bilinear transformation*. The function is defined except at $z = -d/c$, which is a simple pole of T. Further,

$$T'(z) = \frac{ad - bc}{(cz + d)^2},$$

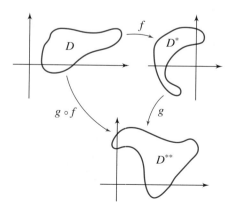

FIGURE 25.17 *A composition of conformal mappings is conformal.*

and this is nonzero if $z \neq -d/c$. T is therefore a conformal mapping of the plane with the point $z = -d/c$ removed.

The condition $ad - bc \neq 0$ ensures that T is one-to-one, hence invertible. If we set $w = (az+b)/(cz+d)$, then the inverse mapping is

$$z = \frac{dw - b}{-cw + a},$$

which is also a linear fractional transformation.

We will look at some special kinds of linear fractional transformations.

EXAMPLE 25.6

Let $w = T(z) = z + b$, with b constant. This is called a translation because T shifts z horizontally by $\mathrm{Re}(b)$ units and vertically by $\mathrm{Im}(z)$ units.

For example, if $T(z) = z + 2 - i$, then T takes z and moves it two units to the right and one unit down (Figure 25.18). We can see this with the following points and their images:

$$0 \to 2 - i, \quad 1 \to 3 - i, \quad i \to 2, \quad 4 + 3i \to 6 + 2i. \ \blacksquare$$

EXAMPLE 25.7

Let $w = T(z) = az$, with a a nonzero constant. This is called a rotation/magnitication. To see why, first observe that

$$|w| = |a|\,|z|.$$

If $|a| > 1$, this transformation lengthens a complex number, in the sense of lengthening the line from the origin to z. If $|a| < 1$ it shortens this distance. Thus the term magnification.

Now write the polar forms $z = re^{i\theta}$ and $a = Ae^{i\alpha}$. Then

$$T(z) = are^{i(\theta + \alpha)},$$

so the transformation adds α to the argument of any nonzero complex number. This rotates the number counterclockwise through an angle α. This is the reason for the term rotation.

The total effect of the transformation is therefore a scaling and a rotation. As a specific example, consider

$$w = (2 + 2i)z.$$

This will map

$$i \to -2 + 2i, 1 \to 2 + 2i, \quad \text{and} \quad 1 + i \to 4i,$$

as shown in Figure 25.19. As Figure 25.20 suggests, in general the image of z is obtained by multiplying the magnitude of z by $|2 + 2i| = \sqrt{8}$, and rotating the line from the origin to z counterclockwise through $\pi/4$ radians. $\blacksquare$

If $|a| = 1$, $T(z) = az$ is called a *pure rotation*, since in this case there is no magnification effect, just a rotation through an argument of a.

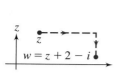

FIGURE 25.18

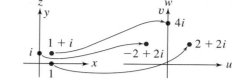

FIGURE 25.19

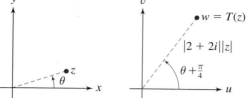

FIGURE 25.20 *The mapping* $T(z) = (2 + 2i)z$.

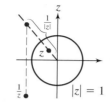

FIGURE 25.21
Image of z under an inversion.

EXAMPLE 25.8

Let $w = T(z) = 1/z$. This mapping is called an inversion. For $z \neq 0$,

$$|w| = \frac{1}{|z|}$$

and

$$\arg(w) = \arg(1) - \arg(z) = -\arg(z)$$

(within integer multiples of 2π). This means that we arrive at $T(z)$ by moving $1/|z|$ units from the origin along the line from 0 to z, and then reflecting this point across the real axis (Figure 25.21). This maps points inside the unit disk to the exterior of it, and points exterior to the interior, while points on the unit circle remain on the unit circle (but get moved around this circle, except for 1 and -1). For example, if $z = (1 + i)/\sqrt{2}$, then $1/z = (1 - i)/\sqrt{2}$ (Figure 25.22). ■

We will now show that translations, rotation/magnifications and inversions are the fundamental linear fractional transformations, in the sense that any such mapping can be achieved as a sequence of transformations of these three kinds. To see how to do this, begin with

$$T(z) = \frac{az + b}{cz + d}.$$

If $c = 0$, then

$$T(z) = \frac{a}{d}z + \frac{b}{d}$$

is a rotation/magnification followed by a translation:

$$z \underset{\text{rot/mag}}{\to} \frac{a}{d}z \underset{\text{trans}}{\to} \frac{a}{d}z + \frac{b}{d}.$$

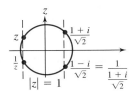

FIGURE 25.22 *Image of a point on the unit circle under an inversion.*

If $c \neq 0$, then T is the result of the following sequence:

$$z \underset{\text{rot/mag}}{\to} cz \underset{\text{trans}}{\to} cz + d \underset{\text{inv}}{\to} \frac{1}{cz + d}$$

$$\underset{\text{rot/mag}}{\to} \frac{bc - ad}{c} \frac{1}{cz + d} \underset{\text{trans}}{\to} \frac{bc - ad}{c} \frac{1}{cz + d} + \frac{a}{c} = \frac{az + b}{cz + d} = T(z).$$

This way of breaking a linear fractional transformation into simpler components has two purposes. First, we can analyze general properties of these transformations by analyzing the simpler component transformations. Perhaps more important, we sometimes use this sequence to build conformal mappings between given domains.

The following is a fundamental property of linear fractional transformations. We use the term line to mean straight line.

THEOREM 25.2

A linear fractional transformation maps any circle to a circle or line, and any line to a circle or line. ∎

Proof Because of the preceding discussion, we need to verify this only for translations, rotation/magnifications and inversions.

It is obvious geometrically that a translation maps a circle to a circle and a line to a line. Similarly, a rotation/magnification maps a circle to a circle and a line to a line.

Now we need to determine the effect of an inversion on a circle or line. Begin with the fact that any circle or line in the plane is the graph of an equation

$$A(x^2 + y^2) + Bx + Cy + R = 0,$$

in which A, B, C, and R are real numbers. This graph is a circle if $A \neq 0$ and a line if $A = 0$ and B and C are not both zero. With $z = x + iy$, this equation becomes

$$A|z|^2 + \frac{B}{2}(z + \bar{z}) + \frac{C}{2i}(z - \bar{z}) + R = 0.$$

Now let $w = 1/z$. The image in the w plane of this locus is the graph of

$$A\frac{1}{|w|^2} + \frac{B}{2}\left(\frac{1}{w} + \frac{1}{\bar{w}}\right) + \frac{C}{2i}\left(\frac{1}{w} - \frac{1}{\bar{w}}\right) + R = 0.$$

Multiply this equation by $w\bar{w}$ (the same as $|w|^2$) to get

$$R|w|^2 + \frac{B}{2}(w + \bar{w}) - \frac{C}{2i}(w - \bar{w}) + A = 0.$$

In the w plane, this is the equation of a circle if $R \neq 0$, and a line if $A = 0$ and B and C are not both zero. ∎

As the proof shows, translations and rotation/magnifications actually map circles to circles and lines to lines, while an inversion may map a circle to a circle or line, and a line to a circle or line.

EXAMPLE 25.9

Let $w = T(z) = i(z - 2) + 3$. This is the sequence

$$z \to z - 2 \to i(z - 2) \to i(z - 2) + 3 = w, \tag{25.2}$$

a translation by 2 to the left, followed by a counterclockwise rotation by $\pi/2$ radians (an argument of i is $\pi/2$), and then a translation by 3 to the right. Since this mapping does not involve an inversion, it maps circles to circles and lines to lines.

As a specific example, consider the circle K given by

$$(x - 2)^2 + y^2 = 9,$$

with radius 3 and center $(2, 0)$. Write this equation as

$$x^2 + y^2 - 4x - 5 = 0,$$

or

$$|z|^2 - 2(z + \bar{z}) - 5 = 0.$$

Solve $w = i(z - 2) + 3$ to get $z = -i(w - 3) + 2$ and substitute into the last equation to get

$$|i(w - 3) + 2|^2 - 2\left(-i(w - 3) + 2 + \overline{-i(w - 3) + 2}\right) - 5 = 0.$$

After some routine manipulation this gives us

$$|w|^2 - 3(w + \bar{w}) = 0.$$

With $w = u + iv$, this is

$$(u - 3)^2 + v^2 = 9,$$

a circle of radius 3 and center $(3, 0)$ in the $u, v-$ plane. This result could have been predicted geometrically from the sequence of elementary mappings 25.2, shown in stages in Figure 25.23. The sequence first moves the circle 2 units to the left, then (multiplication by i) rotates it by $\pi/2$ radians (which leaves the center and radius the same), and then translates it 3 units right. The result is a circle of radius 3 about $(3, 0)$. ∎

EXAMPLE 25.10

We will examine the effects of an inversion $w = 1/z$ on the vertical line $\text{Re}(z) = a \neq 0$. On this line, $z = a + iy$ and its image consists of points

$$w = \frac{1}{a + iy} = \frac{a}{a^2 + y^2} - \frac{y}{a^2 + y^2}i = u + iv.$$

It is routine to check that

$$\left(u - \frac{1}{2a}\right)^2 + v^2 = \frac{1}{4a^2},$$

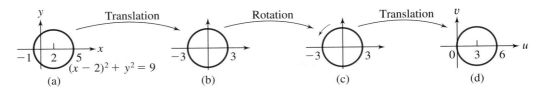

FIGURE 25.23

so the image of this vertical line is a circle in the u, v plane having center $(1/2a, 0)$ and radius $1/2a$. ∎

In preparation for constructing mappings between given domains, we will show that we can always produce a linear fractional transformation mapping three given points to three given points.

THEOREM 25.3 *Three Point Theorem*

Let z_1, z_2 and z_3 be three distinct points in the z plane, and w_1, w_2 and w_3 three distinct points in the w plane. Then there is a linear fractional transformation T of the z plane to the w plane such that

$$T(z_1) = w_1, T(z_2) = w_2 \quad \text{and} \quad T(z_3) = w_3. \ ∎$$

Proof Let $w = T(z)$ be the solution for w in terms of z and the six given points in the equation

$$(w_1 - w)(w_3 - w_2)(z_1 - z_2)(z_3 - z) = (z_1 - z)(z_3 - z_2)(w_1 - w_2)(w_3 - w). \tag{25.3}$$

Substitution of $z = z_j$ into this equation yields $w = w_j$ for $j = 1, 2, 3$. ∎

EXAMPLE 25.11

We will find a linear fractional transformation that maps

$$3 \to i, 1 - i \to 4 \quad \text{and} \quad 2 - i \to 6 + 2i.$$

Put

$$z_1 = 3, \quad z_2 = 1 - i, \quad z_3 = 2 - i$$

and

$$w_1 = i, \quad w_2 = 4, \quad w_3 = 6 + 2i$$

in equation (25.3) to get

$$(i - w)(2 + 2i)(2 + i)(2 - i - z) = (3 - z)(1)(i - 4)(6 + 2i - w).$$

Solve for w to get

$$w = T(z) = \frac{(20 + 4i)z - (68 + 16i)}{(6 + 5i)z - (22 + 7i)}.$$

Then each $T(z_j) = w_j$. ∎

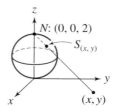

FIGURE 25.24
*Stereographic
projection
identifying the
complex sphere with
the extended
complex plane.*

One can show that specification of three points and their images uniquely determines a linear fractional transformation. In the last example, then, T is the only linear fractional transformation mapping the three given points to their given images.

When dealing with mappings, it is sometimes convenient to replace the complex plane with the complex sphere. To visualize how this is done, consider the three-dimensional coordinate system in Figure 25.24. A sphere of radius 1 is placed with its south pole at the origin and north pole at $(0, 0, 2)$. Think of the x, y plane as the complex plane. For any (x, y) in this plane, the line from $(0, 0, 2)$ to (x, y) intersects the sphere in exactly one point $S(x, y)$. This associates with each point on the sphere, except $(0, 0, 2)$, a unique point in the complex plane, and conversely. This mapping is called the *stereographic projection* of the sphere (minus its north pole) onto the plane. This punctured sphere is called the *complex sphere*. The point $(0, 0, 2)$ plays the role of a point at infinity. This is motivated by the fact that, as (x, y) is chosen further from the origin in the x, y plane, $S(x, y)$ moves closer to $(0, 0, 2)$ on the sphere. The point $(0, 0, 2)$ is not associated with any complex number, but gives a way of envisioning infinity as a point, something we cannot do in the plane. The *extended complex plane* (consisting of all complex numbers, together with infinity) is in a one-to-one correspondence with this sphere, including its north pole.

To get some feeling for the point at infinity, consider the line $y = x$ in the x, y plane. This consists of complex numbers $x + xi$. If we let $x \rightarrow \infty$, the point $(1 + i)x$ moves out this line indefinitely far away from the origin. The image of this line on the complex sphere is part of a great circle, and the image point $S(x, y)$ on the sphere approaches $(0, 0, 2)$ as $x \rightarrow \infty$. This enables us to think of $(1 + i)x$ as approaching a specific location we can point to in this limit process, instead of just going further from the origin.

In defining a linear fractional transformation, it is sometimes convenient to map one of the three given points in the last theorem to infinity. This can be done by deleting the factors in equation (25.3) involving w_3.

THEOREM 25.4

Let z_1, z_2, z_3 be three distinct complex numbers, and w_1, w_2 distinct complex numbers. Then there is a linear fractional transformation $w = T(z)$ that maps

$$T(z_1) = w_1, T(z_2) = w_2, \quad \text{and} \quad T(z_3) = \infty. \blacksquare$$

Proof Such a transformation is obtained by solving for w in the equation

$$(w_1 - w)(z_1 - z_2)(z_3 - z) = (z_1 - z)(w_1 - w_2)(z_3 - z_2). \blacksquare \quad (25.4)$$

EXAMPLE 25.12

We will find a linear fractional transformation mapping

$$i \to 4i, \quad 1 \to 3 - i, \quad 2 + i \to \infty.$$

Solve for w in the equation

$$(4i - w)(i - 1)(2 + i - z) = (i - z)(-3 + 5i)(1 + i)$$

to get

$$w = T(z) = \frac{(5 - i)z - 1 + 3i}{-z + 2 + i}. \quad \blacksquare$$

Some other properties of linear fractional transformations are pursued in the exercises. We now turn to the problem of constructing conformal mappings between given domains.

SECTION 25.2   PROBLEMS

In each of Problems 1 through 5, find a linear fractional transformation taking the given points to the indicated images.

1. $1 \to 1, 2 \to -i, 3 \to 1 + i$

2. $i \to i, 1 \to -i, 2 \to 0$

3. $1 \to 1 + i, 2i \to 3 - i, 4 \to \infty$

4. $-5 + 2i \to 1, 3i \to 0, -1 \to \infty$

5. $6 + i \to 2 - i, i \to 3i, 4 \to -i$

In each of Problems 6 through 12, find the image of the given circle or line under the linear fractional transformation.

6. $w = \dfrac{2i}{z}; \operatorname{Re}(z) = -4$

7. $w = 2iz - 4; \operatorname{Re}(z) = 5$

8. $w = \dfrac{z - i}{iz}; \dfrac{1}{2}(z + \overline{z}) + \dfrac{1}{2i}(z - \overline{z}) = 4$

9. $w = \dfrac{z - 1 + i}{2z + 1}; |z| = 4$

10. $w = 3z - i; |z - 4| = 3$

11. $w = \dfrac{2z - 5}{z + i}; z + \overline{z} - \dfrac{3}{2i}(z - \overline{z}) - 5 = 0$

12. $w = \dfrac{(1 + 3i)z - 2}{z}; |z - i| = 1$

13. Prove that the mapping $w = \overline{z}$ is not conformal.

14. Prove that the composition of two linear fractional transformations is a linear fractional transformation.

15. Prove that every linear fractional transformation has an inverse, and that this inverse is also a linear fractional transformation. (T^* is an inverse of T if $T \circ T^*$ and $T^* \circ T$ are both the identity mapping, taking each point to itself.)

16. Show that there is no linear fractional transformation mapping the open disk $|z| < 1$ onto the set of points bounded by the ellipse $u^2/4 + v^2 = 1/16$.

In Problems 17 and 18, the setting is the extended complex plane, which includes the point at infinity.

17. A point z_0 is a *fixed point* of a mapping f if $f(z_0) = z_0$. Suppose f is a linear fractional transformation that is neither a translation nor the identity mapping $f(z) = z$. Prove that f must have either one or two fixed points, but cannot have three. Why does this conclusion fail to hold for translations? How many fixed points can a translation have?

18. Let f be a linear fractional transformation with three fixed points. Prove that f is the identity mapping.

In each of Problems 19, 20 and 21, write the linear fractional transformation as the end result of a sequence of mappings, each of which is a translation, rotation/magnification or inversion.

19. $w = \dfrac{iz - 4}{z}$

20. $w = \dfrac{z - 4}{2z + i}$

21. $w = i(z + 6) - 2 + i$

22. $w = \dfrac{z - i}{z + 3 + i}$

25.3   Construction of Conformal Mappings Between Domains

A strategy for solving some kinds of problems (for example, Dirichlet problems) is to find the solution for a "simple" domain (for example, the unit disk), then map this domain conformally to the domain of interest. This mapping may carry the solution for the disk to a solution for the latter domain. Of course, this strategy is predicated on two steps: finding a domain for which we can solve the problem, and being able to map this domain to the domain for which we want the solution. We will now discuss the latter problem.

Although in practice it may be an imposing task to find a conformal mapping between given domains, the following result assures us that such a mapping exists, with one exception.

THEOREM 25.5   Riemann Mapping Theorem

Let D^* be a domain in the w plane, and assume that D^* is not the entire w plane. Then there exists a one-to-one conformal mapping of the unit disk $|z| < 1$ onto D^*. ∎

This powerful result implies the existence of a conformal mapping between given domains. Suppose we want to map D onto D^* (neither of which is the entire plane). Insert a third plane, the ζ plane, between the z plane and the w plane, as in Figure 25.25. By Riemann's theorem, there is a one-to-one conformal mapping g of the unit disk $|\zeta| < 1$ onto D^*. Similarly, there is a one-to-one conformal mapping f of $|\zeta| < 1$ onto D. Then $g \circ f^{-1}$ is a one-to-one conformal mapping of D onto D^*.

In theory, then, two domains, neither of which is the entire plane, can be mapped conformally in one-to-one fashion onto one another. This does not, however, make such mappings easy to find. In attempting to find such mappings, the following observation is useful.

A conformal mapping of a domain D onto a domain D^* will map the boundary of D to the boundary of D^*. We use this as follows. Suppose D is bounded by a path C (not necessarily closed) which separates the z plane into two domains, D and $\mathfrak{D}$. These are called *complementary domains*. Similarly, suppose D^* is bounded by a path C^* which separates the w plane into complementary domains D^* and $\mathfrak{D}^*$ (Figure 25.26). Try to find a conformal mapping f that sends points of C to points of C^*. This may be easier than trying to find a mapping of the entire domain. This mapping will then send D to either D^* or to $\mathfrak{D}^*$. To see which, choose a point z_0 in D and see whether $f(z_0)$ is in D^* or $\mathfrak{D}^*$. If $f(z_0)$ is in D^* (Figure 25.27(a)), then $f : D \to D^*$ and we have our conformal mapping. If $f(z_0)$ is in $\mathfrak{D}^*$ as in Figure 25.27(b), then $f : D \to \mathfrak{D}^*$. This is not yet the mapping we want, but sometimes we can take another step and use f to manufacture a conformal mapping from D to D^*.

We will now construct some conformal mappings, beginning with very simple ones and building up to more difficult problems.

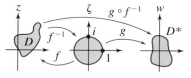

FIGURE 25.25 *Mapping D onto D* through the unit disk.*

FIGURE 25.26

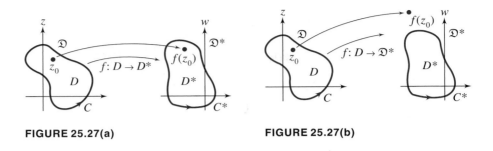

FIGURE 25.27(a)   **FIGURE 25.27(b)**

EXAMPLE 25.13

Suppose we want to map the unit disk $D : |z| < 1$ conformally onto the disk $D^* : |w| < 3$.

Clearly a magnification $w = f(z) = 3z$ will do this, because all we have to do is expand the unit disk to a disk of radius 3 (Figure 25.28). Notice that this mapping carries the boundary of D onto the boundary of D^*. ∎

EXAMPLE 25.14

Map the unit disk $D : |z| < 1$ conformally onto the domain $|w| > 3$.

Here we are mapping D to the complementary domain of the preceding example. We already know that $f(z) = 3z$ maps D conformally onto $|w| < 3$. Combine this map with an inversion, letting

$$g(z) = f(1/z) = \frac{3}{z}.$$

This maps $|z| < 1$ to $|w| > 3$ (Figure 25.29). Again, the boundary of the unit disk maps to the boundary of $|w| > 3$, which is the circle of radius 3 about the origin in the w plane. ∎

EXAMPLE 25.15

We will map the unit disk $D : |z| < 1$ onto the disk $D^* : |w - i| < 3$, of radius 3 and centered at i in the w plane.

Figure 25.30 suggests one way to construct this map. We want to expand the unit disk's radius by a factor of 3, then translate the resulting disk up one unit. Thus, map in steps:

$$z \rightarrow 3z \rightarrow 3z + i,$$

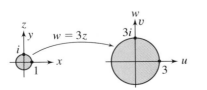

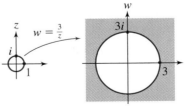

FIGURE 25.28 *Mapping of $|z| < 1$ onto $|w| < 3$.*

FIGURE 25.29 *Mapping of $|z| < 1$ onto $|w| > 3$.*

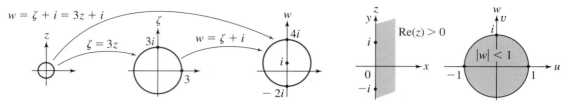

FIGURE 25.30 *Mapping of $|z| < 1$ onto $|w - i| < 3$.*   **FIGURE 25.31**

a magnification followed by a translation. The mapping is

$$w = f(z) = 3z + i.$$

This maps the unit circle $|z| = 1$ to the circle $|w - i| = 3$ because

$$|w - i| = |3z| = 3|z| = 3.$$

Further, the origin in the z plane (center of D) maps to i in the $w-$ plane, and i is the center of D^*, so $f: D \rightarrow D^*$. ■

EXAMPLE 25.16

Suppose we want to map the right half-plane $D: \operatorname{Re}(z) > 0$ onto the unit disk $D^*: |w| < 1$.

The domains are shown in Figure 25.31. The boundary of D is the imaginary axis $\operatorname{Re}(z) = 0$. We will map this to the boundary of the unit disk $|w| = 1$. To do this, pick three points on $\operatorname{Re}(z) = 0$, and three on $|w| = 1$, and use these to define a linear fractional transformation. There is a subtlety, however. To maintain positive orientation (counterclockwise on closed curves), choose three points in succession down the imaginary axis, so a person walking along these points sees the right half-plane on the left. Map these to points in order counterclockwise around $|w| = 1$.

For example, we can choose

$$z_1 = i, \quad z_2 = 0 \quad \text{and} \quad z_3 = -i$$

on the imaginary axis in the z plane, and map these in order to

$$w_1 = 1, \quad w_2 = i, \quad w_3 = -1.$$

From equation (25.3), we have

$$(1 - w)(-1 - i)(i)(-i - z) = (i - z)(-i)(1 - i)(-1 - w).$$

Solve for w:

$$w = T(z) = -i\left(\frac{z - 1}{z + 1}\right).$$

This conformal mapping must take the right half-plane to the interior or exterior of the unit disk in the w plane. To see which it is, pick a point in $\operatorname{Re}(z) > 0$, say $z = 1$. Since $T(1) = 0$ is in D^*, T maps the right half-plane to the unit disk $|w| < 1$ as we want. ■

EXAMPLE 25.17

Suppose we want to map the right half-plane to the exterior of the unit disk, the domain $|w| > 1$. We have $T: \operatorname{Re}(z) > 0 \rightarrow |w| < 1$ from the preceding example. If we follow this map (taking

Re$(z) > 0$ onto the unit disk) with an inversion (taking the unit disk to the exterior of the unit disk), we will have the map we want. Thus, with $T(z)$ as in the last example, let

$$f(z) = \frac{1}{T(z)} = i\left(\frac{z+1}{z-1}\right).$$

As a check, $1 + i$ is in the right half-plane, and

$$f(1+i) = i\left(\frac{2+i}{i}\right) = 2+i$$

is exterior to the unit disk in the w plane. ∎

EXAMPLE 25.18

We will map the right half-plane Re$(z) > 0$ conformally onto the disk $|w - i| < 3$.

We can do this as a composition of mappings we have already constructed. Put an intermediate ζ plane between the z and w planes (Figure 25.32). From Example 25.16, map Re$(z) > 0$ onto the unit disk $|\zeta| < 1$ by

$$\zeta = f(z) = -i\left(\frac{z-1}{z+1}\right).$$

Now use the mapping of Example 25.15 to send the unit disk $|\zeta| < 1$ onto the disk $|w - i| < 3$:

$$w = g(\zeta) = 3\zeta + i.$$

The composition $g \circ f$ is a conformal mapping of Re$(z) > 0$ onto $|w - i| < 3$:

$$w = (g \circ f)(z) = g(f(z)) = 3f(z) + i = 3\left[-i\left(\frac{z-1}{z+1}\right)\right] + i = \frac{2i(-z+2)}{z+1}. \quad ∎$$

EXAMPLE 25.19

We will map the infinite strip $S : -\pi/2 < \text{Im}(z) < \pi/2$ onto the unit disk $|w| < 1$.

Recall from Example 25.4 that the exponential function maps horizontal lines to half-lines from the origin. The boundary of S consists of two horizontal lines, Im$(z) = -\pi/2$ and Im$(z) = \pi/2$. On the lower boundary line, $z = x - i\pi/2$, so

$$e^z = e^x e^{-i\pi/2} = -ie^x,$$

which varies over the negative imaginary axis as x takes on all real values. On the upper boundary of S, $z = x + i\pi/2$, and

$$e^z = ie^x$$

varies over the positive part of the imaginary axis as x varies over the real line.

The imaginary axis forms the boundary of the right half-plane Re$(z) > 0$, as well as of the left half-plane Re$(w) < 0$ in the w plane. The mapping $w = e^z$ must map S to one of these complementary domains. However, this mapping sends 0 to 1, in the right half-plane, so the mapping $w = f(z) = e^z$ maps S to the right half-plane.

We want to map S onto the unit disk. But now we know a mapping of S onto the right half-plane, and we also know a mapping of the right half-plane onto the unit disk. All we have to do is put these together.

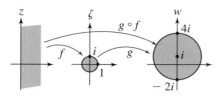

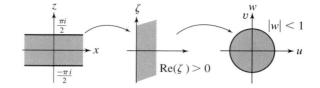

FIGURE 25.32 *Mapping of* $\text{Re}(z) > 0$ *onto* $|w - i| < 3$.

FIGURE 25.33 $|\text{Im}(z)| < \frac{\pi}{2} \rightarrow \text{Re}(\zeta) > 0 \rightarrow |w| < 1$ *yields a mapping of* $|\text{Im}(z)| < \frac{\pi}{2}$ *onto* $|w| < 1$.

In Figure 25.33, put a ζ plane between the z and w planes. Map

$$\zeta = f(z) = e^z$$

taking S onto the right half-plane $\text{Re}(\zeta) > 0$. Next map

$$w = g(\zeta) = -i\left(\frac{\zeta - 1}{\zeta + 1}\right),$$

taking the right half-plane $\text{Re}(\zeta) > 0$ onto the unit disk $|w| < 1$. Therefore, the function

$$w = (g \circ f)(z) = g(f(z))$$

$$= g(e^z) = -i\left(\frac{e^z - 1}{e^z + 1}\right)$$

is a conformal mapping of S onto $|w| < 1$. In terms of hyperbolic functions, this mapping can be written

$$w = -i\tanh(z/2). \quad \blacksquare$$

The conformal mapping of the last example is not a linear fractional transformation. These are convenient to use whenever possible. However, even when we know from the Riemann mapping theorem that a conformal mapping exists between two domains, we are not guaranteed that we can always find such a mapping in the form of a linear fractional transformation.

EXAMPLE 25.20

We will map the disk $|z| < 2$ onto the domain $D^* : u + v > 0$ in the u, v plane. These domains are shown in Figure 25.34.

Consider mappings we already have that relate to this problem. First, we can map $|z| < 2$ to $|\zeta| < 1$ by a simple magnification (multiply by $\frac{1}{2}$). But we also know a mapping from the unit disk to the right half-plane. Finally, we can obtain D^* from the right half-plane by a

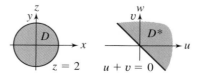

FIGURE 25.34

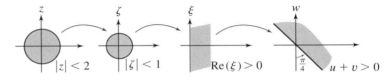

FIGURE 25.35

counterclockwise rotation through $\pi/4$ radians, an effect achieved by multiplying by $e^{i\pi/4}$. This suggests the strategy of constructing the mapping we want in the stages shown in Figure 25.35:

$$|z| < 2 \rightarrow |\zeta| < 1 \rightarrow \text{Re}(\xi) > 0 \rightarrow u + v > 0.$$

The first step is achieved by

$$\zeta = \frac{1}{2}z.$$

Next, use the inverse of the mapping from Example 25.16 and name the variables ζ and ξ to get

$$\xi = \frac{1 + i\zeta}{1 - i\zeta}.$$

This maps

$$|\zeta| < 1 \rightarrow \text{Re}(\xi) > 0.$$

Finally, perform the rotation:

$$w = e^{i\pi/4}\xi.$$

In sum,

$$w = e^{i\pi/4}\xi = e^{i\pi/4}\left(\frac{1 + i\zeta}{1 - i\zeta}\right) = e^{i\pi/4}\left(\frac{1 + i(z/2)}{1 - i(z/2)}\right) = \frac{2 + iz}{2 - iz}e^{i\pi/4}.$$

This maps the disk $|z| < 2$ conformally onto the half-plane $u + v > 0$. For example, 0 is in the disk, and

$$w(0) = e^{i\pi/4} = \frac{\sqrt{2}}{2}(1 + i)$$

is in $u + v > 0$. ∎

We will briefly discuss the Schwarz–Christoffel transformation, which may be used when a domain has a polygon as a boundary.

25.3.1 Schwarz–Christoffel Transformation

Suppose we want a conformal mapping of the upper half-plane $\mathfrak{H}$ to the interior $\mathfrak{P}$ of a polygon P, which could be a triangle, rectangle, pentagon or other polygon. A linear fractional transformation will not do this. However, the Schwarz–Christoffel transformation was constructed just for this purpose.

Let P have vertices $w_1, \ldots, w_n$ in the w plane (Figure 25.36). Let the exterior angles of P be $\pi\alpha_1, \ldots, \pi\alpha_n$. We claim that there are constants z_0, a and b, with $\text{Im}(z_0) > 0$, and real numbers $x_1, \ldots, x_n$ such that the function

$$f(z) = a \int_{z_0}^{z} (\xi - x_1)^{-\alpha_1}(\xi - x_2)^{-\alpha_2}\cdots(\xi - x_n)^{-\alpha_n}d\xi + b \tag{25.5}$$

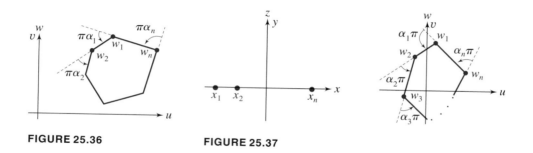

FIGURE 25.36   **FIGURE 25.37**

is a conformal mapping of $\mathfrak{H}$ onto $\mathfrak{P}$. This integral is taken over any path in $\mathfrak{H}$ from z_0 to z in $\mathfrak{H}$. The factors $(\xi - x_j)^{-\alpha_j}$ are defined using the complex logarithm obtained by taking the argument lying in $[0, 2\pi)$.

Any function of the form of equation (25.5) is called a *Schwarz–Christoffel transformation*. To see the idea behind this function, suppose each $x_j < x_{j+1}$. If z is in $\mathfrak{H}$, let

$$g(z) = a(z - x_1)^{-\alpha_1}(z - x_2)^{-\alpha_2} \cdots (z - x_n)^{-\alpha_n}.$$

Then $f'(z) = g(z)$ and

$$\arg[f'(z)] = \arg(z) - \alpha_1 \arg(z - x_1) - \cdots - \alpha_n \arg(z - x_n).$$

As we saw in the discussion of Theorem 25.1, $\arg[f'(z)]$ is the number of radians by which the mapping f rotates tangent lines, if $f'(z) \neq 0$.

Now imagine z moving from left to right along the real axis (Figure 25.37), which is the boundary of $\mathfrak{H}$. On $(-\infty, x_1)$, $f(z)$ moves along a straight line (no change in the angle). As z passes over x_1, however, $\arg[f'(z)]$ changes by $\alpha_1 \pi$. This angle remains fixed as z moves from x_1 toward x_2. As z passes over x_2, $\arg[f'(z)]$ changes by $\alpha_2 \pi$, then remains at this value until z reaches x_3, where $\arg[f'(z)]$ changes by $\alpha_3 \pi$, and so on. Thus $\arg[f'(z)]$ remains constant on intervals (x_{j-1}, x_j) and increases by $\alpha_j \pi$ as z passes over x_j. The net result is that the real axis is mapped to a polygon P^* having exterior angles $\alpha_1 \pi, \ldots, \alpha_n \pi$. These numbers are actually determined by $\alpha_1, \ldots, \alpha_{n-1}$, since

$$\sum_{j=1}^{n} \alpha_j \pi = 2\pi.$$

P^* has the same exterior angles as P but need not be the same as P because of its location and size. We may have to rotate, translate and/or magnify P^* to obtain P. These effects are achieved by choosing $x_1, \ldots, x_n$ to make P^* similar to P, and then choosing a (rotation/magnification) and b (translation) to obtain P.

If we choose $z_n = \infty$, then $z_1, \ldots, z_{n-1}, \infty$ are mapped to the vertices of P. In this case the Schwarz–Christoffel transformation is

$$f(z) = a \int_{z_0}^{z} (\xi - x_1)^{-\alpha_1}(\xi - x_2)^{-\alpha_2} \cdots (\xi - x_n)^{-\alpha_{n-1}} d\xi + b. \tag{25.6}$$

It can be shown that any conformal mapping of $\mathfrak{H}$ onto a polygon must have the form of a Schwarz–Christoffel transformation.

In practice a Schwarz–Christoffel transformation can be difficult or impossible to determine in closed form because of the integration.

EXAMPLE 25.21

We will map the upper half-plane $\mathfrak{H}$ onto a rectangle.

Choose $x_1 = 0$, $x_2 = 1$ and x_3 as any real number greater than 1. The Schwarz–Christoffel transformation of equation (25.6) has the form

$$f(z) = a \int_{z_0}^{z} \frac{1}{\sqrt{\xi(\xi - 1)(\xi - x_3)}}\, d\xi + b,$$

with a and b chosen to fit the dimensions of the rectangle and its orientation with respect to the axes. The radical appears because the exterior angles of a rectangle are all equal to $\pi/2$, so $\sum_{j=1}^{4} \alpha_j = 4\alpha_k = 2$. This integral is an elliptic integral and cannot be evaluated in closed form. ▪

EXAMPLE 25.22

We will map $\mathfrak{H}$ onto the strip $S : \operatorname{Im}(w) > 0$, $-c < \operatorname{Re}(w) < c$ in the w plane. Here c is a positive constant.

$\mathfrak{H}$ and the strip S are shown in Figure 25.38. To use the Schwarz–Christoffel transformation, we must think of S as a polygon with vertices $-c$, c and ∞. Choose $x_1 = -1$ to map to $-c$ and $x_2 = 1$ to map to c. Map ∞ to ∞. The exterior angles of the strip are $\pi/2$ and $\pi/2$, so $\alpha_1 = \alpha_2 = \frac{1}{2}$. The transformation has the form

$$w = f(z) = a \int_{z_0}^{z} (\xi + 1)^{-1/2}(\xi - 1)^{-1/2}\, d\xi + b.$$

We will choose $z_0 = 0$ and $b = 0$. Write

$$(\xi - 1)^{-1/2} = [-(1 - \xi)]^{-1/2} = -i(1 - \xi)^{-1/2}.$$

With $-ai = A$, we have

$$w = f(z) = A \int_{0}^{z} \frac{1}{(1 - \xi^2)^{1/2}}\, d\xi.$$

This integral is reminiscent of the real integral representation of the inverse sine function. Indeed, we can write

$$w = A \sin^{-1}(z),$$

by which we mean that

$$z = \sin\left(\frac{w}{A}\right).$$

To choose A so that -1 maps to $-c$ and 1 to c, we need

$$\sin\left(\frac{c}{A}\right) = 1.$$

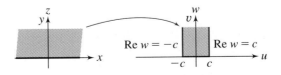

FIGURE 25.38

Thus choose $c/A = \pi/2$, or

$$A = \frac{2c}{\pi}.$$

The mapping is

$$w = \frac{2c}{\pi} \sin^{-1}(z).$$

If we choose $c = \pi/2$, this mapping is just $w = \sin^{-1}(z)$, mapping $\mathfrak{H}$ onto the strip $\text{Im}(w) > 0$, $-\pi/2 < \text{Re}(w) < \pi/2$. This is consistent with the result of Example 25.5. ∎

SECTION 25.3   PROBLEMS

In each of Problems 1 through 6, find a linear fractional transformation mapping the first domain onto the second.

1. $|z| < 3$ onto $|w - 1 + i| < 6$

2. $|z| < 3$ onto $|w - 1 + i| > 6$

3. $|z + 2i| < 1$ onto $|w - 3| > 2$

4. $\text{Re}(z) > 1$ onto $\text{Im}(w) > -1$

5. $\text{Re}(z) < 0$ onto $|w| < 4$

6. $\text{Im}(z) > -4$ onto $|w - i| > 2$

7. Find a conformal mapping of the upper half-plane $\text{Im}(z) > 0$ onto the wedge $0 < \arg(w) < \pi/3$.

8. Let $w = Log(z)$, in which the logarithm is given a unique value for each nonzero z by rectricting the argument of z to lie in $[0, 2\pi)$. Show that this mapping takes $\text{Im}(z) > 0$ onto the strip $0 < \text{Im}(w) < \pi$.

9. Show that the Schwarz–Christoffel transformation

$$f(z) = 2i \int_0^z (\xi + 1)^{-1/2}(\xi - 1)^{-1/2}\xi^{-1/2}d\xi$$

maps the upper half plane onto the rectangle with verticesl 0, c, $c + ic$ and ic, where $c = \Gamma\left(\frac{1}{2}\right)\Gamma\left(\frac{1}{4}\right)/\Gamma\left(\frac{3}{4}\right)$. Here Γ is the gamma function.

10. Define the *cross ratio* of z_1, z_2, z_3 and z_4 to be the image of z_1 under the linear fractional transformation that maps $z_2 \to 1$, $z_3 \to 0$, $z_4 \to \infty$. Denote this cross ratio as $[z_1, z_2, z_3, z_4]$. Suppose T is any linear fractional transformation. Show that T preserves the cross ratio. That is,

$$[z_1, z_2, z_3, z_4] = [Tz_1, Tz_2, Tz_3, Tz_4].$$

11. Prove that $[z_1, z_2, z_3, z_4]$ is the image of z_1 under the linear fractional transformation defined by

$$w = 1 - \frac{z_3 - z_4}{z_3 - z_2}\frac{z - z_2}{z - z_4}.$$

12. Prove that $[z_1, z_2, z_3, z_4]$ is real if and only if the $z_j's$ are on the same circle or straight line.

25.4   Harmonic Functions and the Dirichlet Problem

Given a set D of points in the plane, let ∂D denote the boundary of D. A Dirichlet problem for D is to find a solution of Laplace's equation

$$\frac{\partial^2 u}{\partial x^2} + \frac{\partial^2 u}{\partial y^2} = 0$$

for (x, y) in D, satisfying the boundary condition

$$u(x, y) = f(x, y) \quad \text{for } (x, y) \text{ in } \partial D.$$

Here f is a given function, usually assumed to be continuous on the boundary of D.

A function satisfying Laplace's equation in a set is said to be *harmonic* on that set. Thus the Dirichlet problem for a set is to find a function that is harmonic on that set, and satisfies given data on the boundary of the set.

Chapter 19 is devoted to solutions of Dirichlet problems using methods from real analysis. Our purpose here is to apply complex function methods to Dirichlet problems. The connection between a Dirichlet problem and complex function theory is given by the following.

THEOREM 25.6

Let D be an open set in the plane, and let $f(z) = u(x, y) + iv(x, y)$ be differentiable on D. Then u and v are harmonic on D. ∎

That is, the real and imaginary parts of a differentiable complex function are harmonic.

Proof   By the Cauchy–Riemann equations,

$$
\frac{\partial^2 u}{\partial x^2} + \frac{\partial^2 u}{\partial y^2} = \frac{\partial}{\partial x}\left(\frac{\partial u}{\partial x}\right) + \frac{\partial}{\partial y}\left(\frac{\partial u}{\partial y}\right)
$$

$$
= \frac{\partial}{\partial x}\left(\frac{\partial v}{\partial y}\right) + \frac{\partial}{\partial y}\left(-\frac{\partial v}{\partial x}\right) = \frac{\partial^2 v}{\partial x \partial y} - \frac{\partial^2 v}{\partial y \partial x} = 0.
$$

Therefore u is harmonic on D. The proof that v is harmonic is similar. ∎

Conversely, given a harmonic function u, there is a harmonic function v so that $f(z) = u(x, y) + iv(x, y)$ is differentiable. Such a v is called a *harmonic conjugate* for u.

THEOREM 25.7

Let u be harmonic on a domain D. Then, for some v, $u(x, y) + iv(x, y)$ defines a differentiable complex function for $z = x + iy$ in D. ∎

Proof   Let

$$
g(z) = \frac{\partial u}{\partial x} - i\frac{\partial u}{\partial y}
$$

for (x, y) in D. Using the Cauchy–Riemann equations and Theorem 21.6, we find that g is differentiable on D. Then, for some function G, $G'(z) = g(z)$ for z in D. Write

$$
G(z) = U(x, y) + iV(x, y).
$$

Now

$$
G'(z) = \frac{\partial U}{\partial x} - i\frac{\partial U}{\partial y} = g(z) = \frac{\partial u}{\partial x} - i\frac{\partial u}{\partial y}.
$$

Therefore

$$
\frac{\partial U}{\partial x} = \frac{\partial u}{\partial x} \quad \text{and} \quad \frac{\partial U}{\partial y} = \frac{\partial u}{\partial y}
$$

on D. Then, for some constant K,

$$
U(x, y) = u(x, y) + K.
$$

Let $f(z) = G(z) - K$. Then f is differentiable at all points of D. Further,

$$f(z) = G(z) - K = U(x, y) + iV(x, y) - K = u(x, y) + iv(x, y).$$

We may therefore choose $v(x, y) = V(x, y)$, proving the theorem. ∎

Given a harmonic function u, we will not be interested in actually producing a harmonic conjugate v. However, we will exploit the fact that there exists such a function to produce a differentiable complex function $f = u + iv$, given harmonic u. This enables us to apply complex function methods to Dirichlet problems. As a preliminary, we will derive two important properties of harmonic functions.

THEOREM 25.8 **Mean Value Property**

Let u be harmonic on a domain D. Let (x_0, y_0) be any point of D, and let C be a circle of radius r centered at (x_0, y_0), contained in D and enclosing only points of D. Then

$$u(x_0, y_0) = \frac{1}{2\pi} \int_0^{2\pi} u(x_0 + r\cos(\theta), y_0 + r\sin(\theta))d\theta. \quad ∎$$

As θ varies from 0 to 2π, $(x_0 + r\cos(\theta), y_0 + r\sin(\theta))$ moves once about the circle of radius r about (x_0, y_0). The conclusion of the theorem is called the mean value property because it states that the value of a harmonic function at the center of any circle in the domain is the average of its values on the circle.

Proof For some v, $f = u + iv$ is differentiable on D. Let $z_0 = x_0 + iy_0$. By Cauchy's integral formula,

$$u(x_0, y_0) + iv(x_0, y_0) = f(z_0) = \frac{1}{2\pi i} \oint_C \frac{f(z)}{z - z_0} dz$$

$$= \frac{1}{2\pi i} \int_0^{2\pi} \frac{f(z_0 + re^{i\theta})}{re^{i\theta}} ire^{i\theta} d\theta$$

$$= \frac{1}{2\pi} \int_0^{2\pi} u(x_0 + r\cos(\theta), y_0 + r\sin(\theta))d\theta$$

$$+ \frac{i}{2\pi} \int_0^{2\pi} v(x_0 + r\cos(\theta), y_0 + r\sin(\theta))d\theta.$$

By taking the real and imaginary part of both sides of this equation, we get the conclusion of the theorem. ∎

If D is a bounded domain, then the set $\overline{D}$ consisting of D, together with all boundary points of D, is called the closure of D. $\overline{D}$ is a closed and bounded, hence compact set. If $u(x, y)$ is continuous on $\overline{D}$, then $u(x, y)$ must achieve a maximum value on D. If u is also harmonic on D, we claim that this maximum must occur at a boundary point of D. This is reminiscent of the maximum modulus theorem, from which it follows.

THEOREM 25.9

Let D be a bounded domain. Suppose u is continuous on $\overline{D}$ and harmonic on D. Then $u(x, y)$ achieves its maximum value on D at a boundary point of D. ∎

Proof First produce v so that $f = u + iv$ is differentiable on D. Define

$$g(z) = e^{f(z)}$$

for all z in $\overline{D}$. Then g is differentiable on D. By the maximum modulus theorem, $|g(z)|$ achieves its maximum at a boundary point of D. But

$$|g(z)| = \left| e^{u(x,y)+iv(x,y)} \right| = e^{u(x,y)}.$$

Since $e^{u(x,y)}$ is a strictly increasing real function, $e^{u(x,y)}$ and $u(x, y)$ must achieve their maximum values at the same point. Therefore $u(x, y)$ must achieve its maximum at a boundary point of D. ∎

For example, $u(x, y) = x^2 - y^2$ is harmonic on the open unit disk $x^2 + y^2 < 1$, and continuous on its closure $x^2 + y^2 \leq 1$. This function must therefore achieve its maximum value for $x^2 + y^2 \leq 1$ at a boundary point of this disk, namely at a point for which $x^2 + y^2 = 1$. We find that this maximum value is 1, occurring at $(1, 0)$ and at $(-1, 0)$.

25.4.1 Solution of Dirichlet Problems by Conformal Mapping

We want to use conformal mappings to solve Dirichlet problems. The strategy is to first solve the Dirichlet problem for a disk. Once we have this, we can attempt to solve a Dirichlet problem for another domain D by constructing a conformal mapping between the unit disk and D, and applying this mapping to the solution we have for the disk.

In Section 19.3 we derived Poisson's integral formula for the solution of the Dirichlet problem for a disk, using Fourier methods. We will use complex function methods to obtain a form of this solution that is particularly suited to using with conformal mappings.

We want a function u that is harmonic on the disk $\widetilde{D} : |z| < 1$ and assumes given values $u(x, y) = g(x, y)$ on the boundary circle. Suppose u is harmonic on the slightly larger disk $|z| < 1 + \epsilon$. If v is a harmonic conjugate of u, then $f = u + iv$ is differentiable on this disk. We may, by adding a constant if necessary, choose v so that $v(0, 0) = 0$.

Expand f in a Maclaurin series

$$f(z) = \sum_{n=0}^{\infty} a_n z^n. \tag{25.7}$$

Then

$$u(x, y) = \mathrm{Re}(f(x+iy)) = \frac{1}{2}\left(f(z) + \overline{f(z)} \right)$$

$$= \frac{1}{2}\sum_{n=0}^{\infty} (a_n z^n + \overline{a_n}\overline{z}^n) = a_0 + \frac{1}{2}\sum_{n=1}^{\infty} (a_n z^n + \overline{a_n}\overline{z}^n).$$

Now let ζ be on the unit circle γ. Then $|\zeta|^2 = \zeta\overline{\zeta} = 1$, so $\overline{\zeta} = 1/\zeta$ and the series is

$$u(\zeta) = a_0 + \frac{1}{2}\sum_{n=1}^{\infty} (a_n \zeta^n + \overline{a_n}\zeta^{-n}).$$

Multiply this equation by $\zeta^m/2\pi i$ and integrate over γ. Within the open disk of convergence, the series and the integral can be interchanged. We get

$$\frac{1}{2\pi i}\oint_{\gamma} u(\zeta)\zeta^m \, d\zeta = \frac{a_0}{2\pi i}\oint_{\gamma} \zeta^m \, d\zeta + \frac{1}{2}\frac{1}{2\pi i}\sum_{n=1}^{\infty}\left(a_n \oint_{\gamma} \zeta^{n+m} \, d\zeta + \overline{a_n}\oint_{\gamma} \zeta^{-n+m} \, d\zeta \right). \tag{25.8}$$

Recall that

$$\oint_{\gamma} \zeta^k \, d\zeta = \begin{cases} 0 & \text{if } k \neq -1 \\ 2\pi i & \text{if } k = -1 \end{cases}.$$

Therefore, if $m = -1$ in equation (25.8), we have

$$\frac{1}{2\pi i}\oint_\gamma u(\zeta)\frac{1}{\zeta}d\zeta = a_0.$$

If $m = -n - 1$ with $n = 1, 2, 3, \ldots$, we obtain

$$\frac{1}{2\pi i}\oint_\gamma u(\zeta)\zeta^{-n-1} = \frac{1}{2}a_n.$$

Substitute these coefficients into equation (25.7) to get

$$f(z) = \sum_{n=0}^\infty a_n z^n = \frac{1}{2\pi i}\oint_\gamma u(\zeta)\frac{1}{\zeta}d\zeta + \sum_{n=1}^\infty \left(\frac{1}{\pi i}\oint_\gamma u(\zeta)\zeta^{-n-1}\right)d\zeta z^n$$

$$= \frac{1}{2\pi i}\oint_\gamma \left[1 + 2\sum_{n=1}^\infty \left(\frac{z}{\zeta}\right)^n\right]\frac{u(\zeta)}{\zeta}d\zeta.$$

Since $|z| < 1$ and $|\zeta| = 1$, then $|z/\zeta| < 1$ and the geometric series in this equation converges:

$$\sum_{n=1}^\infty \left(\frac{z}{\zeta}\right)^n = \frac{z/\zeta}{1 - z/\zeta} = \frac{z}{\zeta - z}.$$

Then

$$f(z) = \frac{1}{2\pi i}\oint_\gamma u(\zeta)\left[1 + \frac{2z}{\zeta - z}\right]\frac{1}{\zeta}d\zeta = \frac{1}{2\pi i}\oint_\gamma u(\zeta)\left(\frac{\zeta + z}{\zeta - z}\right)\frac{1}{\zeta}d\zeta.$$

If $u(\zeta) = g(\zeta)$, given values for u on the boundary of the unit disk, then, for $|z| < 1$,

$$u(x, y) = \text{Re}[f(z)] = \text{Re}\left(\frac{1}{2\pi i}\oint_\gamma g(\zeta)\left(\frac{\zeta + z}{\zeta - z}\right)\frac{1}{\zeta}d\zeta\right). \tag{25.9}$$

This is an integral formula for the solution of the Dirichlet problem for the unit disk. We leave it as an exercise for the student to retrieve the Poisson integral formula from this expression by putting $z = re^{i\theta}$ and $\zeta = e^{i\varphi}$.

Equation (25.9) is well suited to solving certain Dirichlet problems by conformal mappings. Suppose we know a differentiable, one-to-one conformal mapping $T : D \to \widetilde{D}$, where $\widetilde{D}$ is the unit disk $|w| < 1$ in the w plane. Assume that T maps C, the boundary of D, onto the unit circle $\widetilde{C}$ bounding $\widetilde{D}$, and that T^{-1} is also a differentiable conformal mapping.

To help follow the discussion, we will use ζ for an arbitrary point of $\widetilde{C}$, ξ for a point on C, and $(\widetilde{x}, \widetilde{y})$ for a point in the w plane (Figure 25.39).

Now consider a Dirichlet problem for D:

$$\frac{\partial^2 u}{\partial x^2} + \frac{\partial^2 u}{\partial y^2} = 0 \quad \text{for } (x, y) \text{ in } D,$$

$$u(x, y) = g(x, y) \quad \text{for } (x, y) \text{ in } C.$$

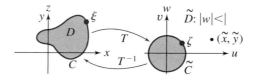

FIGURE 25.39

If $w = T(z)$, then $z = T^{-1}(w)$ and we define

$$\widetilde{g}(w) = g(T^{-1}(w)) = g(z).$$

In the w plane, we now have a Dirichlet problem for the unit disk:

$$\frac{\partial^2 \widetilde{u}}{\partial x^2} + \frac{\partial^2 \widetilde{u}}{\partial y^2} = 0 \quad \text{for } (\widetilde{x}, \widetilde{y}) \text{ in } \widetilde{D},$$

$$\widetilde{u}(\widetilde{x}, \widetilde{y}) = \widetilde{g}(\widetilde{x}, \widetilde{y}) \quad \text{for } (\widetilde{x}, \widetilde{y}) \text{ on } \widetilde{C}.$$

From equation (25.9) the solution of this problem for the unit disk is the real part of

$$\widetilde{f}(w) = \frac{1}{2\pi i} \oint_{\widetilde{C}} \widetilde{g}(\zeta) \left(\frac{\zeta + w}{\zeta - w} \right) \frac{1}{\zeta} d\zeta.$$

Finally, recall that T maps C onto $\widetilde{C}$, let $\zeta = T(\xi)$ for ξ on C to obtain

$$u(x, y) = \text{Re}[f(z)] = \text{Re} \left[\frac{1}{2\pi i} \int_C \widetilde{g}(T(\xi)) \left(\frac{T(\xi) + T(z)}{T(\xi) - T(z)} \right) \frac{1}{T(\xi)} T'(\xi) d\xi \right].$$

Since $\widetilde{g}(T(\xi)) = g(T^{-1}(T(\xi))) = g(\xi)$, we have the solution

$$u(x, y) = \text{Re}[f(z)] = \text{Re} \left[\frac{1}{2\pi i} \int_C g(\xi) \left(\frac{T(\xi) + T(z)}{T(\xi) - T(z)} \right) \frac{T'(\xi)}{T(\xi)} d\xi \right]. \tag{25.10}$$

This solves the Dirichlet problem for the original domain D.

To illustrate this technique, we will solve the Dirichlet problem for the right half plane:

$$\frac{\partial^2 u}{\partial x^2} + \frac{\partial^2 u}{\partial y^2} = 0 \quad \text{for } x > 0, -\infty < x < \infty,$$

$$u(0, y) = g(y) \quad \text{for } -\infty < y < \infty.$$

We need a conformal mapping from the right half plane to the unit disk. There are many such mappings. From Example 25.16, we can use

$$w = T(z) = -i \left(\frac{z - 1}{z + 1} \right).$$

Compute

$$T'(z) = \frac{-2i}{(z + 1)^2}.$$

From equation (25.10), the solution is the real part of

$$f(z) = \frac{1}{2\pi i} \int_C u(\xi) \left(\frac{-i(\xi - 1)/(\xi + 1) - i(z - 1)/(z + 1)}{-i(\xi - 1)/(\xi + 1) + i(z - 1)/(z + 1)} \right) \frac{1}{-i(\xi - 1)/(\xi + 1)} \frac{-2i}{(\xi + 1)^2} d\xi$$

$$= \frac{1}{\pi i} \int_C u(\xi) \left(\frac{\xi z - 1}{\xi - z} \right) \frac{1}{\xi^2 - 1} d\xi.$$

The boundary C of the right half plane is the imaginary axis, and is not a closed curve. Parametrize C as $\xi = (0, t) = it$, with t varying from $-\infty$ to ∞ for positive orientation on ∂D (as we walk down this axis, D is over our left shoulder). We get

$$f(z) = \frac{1}{\pi i} \int_\infty^{-\infty} u(0, t) \left(\frac{itz - 1}{it - z} \right) \left(\frac{-1}{1 + t^2} \right) i \, dt$$

$$= \frac{1}{\pi} \int_{-\infty}^\infty u(0, t) \left(\frac{itz - 1}{it - z} \right) \left(\frac{1}{1 + t^2} \right) dt.$$

The solution is the real part of this integral. Now t, $u(0, \xi)$ and $1/(1 + t^2)$ are real, so concentrate on the term containing i and $z = x + iy$:

$$\frac{itz - 1}{it - z} = \frac{itx - ty - 1}{it - x - iy} = \frac{itx - ty - 1}{it - x - iy} \frac{-it - x + iy}{-it - x + iy}$$

$$= \frac{tx(t - y) - itx^2 + ity(t - y) + txy + i(t - y) + x}{x^2 + (t - y)^2}.$$

The real part of this expression is

$$\frac{x(1 + t^2)}{x^2 + (t - y)^2}.$$

Therefore

$$u(x, y) = \text{Re}[f(z)] = \frac{1}{\pi} \int_{-\infty}^\infty u(0, t) \frac{x(1 + t^2)}{x^2 + (t - y)^2} \frac{1}{1 + t^2} dt$$

$$= \frac{1}{\pi} \int_{-\infty}^\infty g(t) \frac{x}{x^2 + (t - y)^2} dt.$$

This is an integral formula for the solution of the Dirichlet problem for the right half-plane.

SECTION 25.4 PROBLEMS

1. Using complex function methods, write an integral solution for the Dirichlet problem for the upper half-plane $\text{Im}(z) > 0$.

2. Using complex function methods, write an integral solution for the Dirichlet problem for the right quarter-plane $\text{Re}(z) > 0$, $\text{Im}(z) > 0$, if the boundary conditions are $u(x, 0) = f(x)$ and $u(0, y) = 0$.

3. Write an integral solution for the Dirichlet problem for the disk $|z - z_0| < R$.

4. Write a formula for the solution of the Dirichlet problem for the right half-plane if the boundary condition is given by

$$u(0, y) = \begin{cases} 1 & \text{for } -1 \le y \le 1 \\ 0 & \text{for } |y| > 1. \end{cases}$$

5. Write a formula for the solution of the Dirichlet problem for a unit disk if the boundary condition is given by $u(x, y) = x - y$ for (x, y) on the unit circle.

6. Write a formula for the solution of the Dirichlet problem for the unit disk if the boundary condition is given by

$$u(e^{i\theta}) = \begin{cases} 1 & \text{for } 0 \le \theta \le \pi/4 \\ 0 & \text{for } \pi/4 < \theta < 2\pi. \end{cases}$$

7. Write a formula for the solution of the Dirichlet problem for the strip $-1 < \text{Im}(z) < 1$, $\text{Re}(z) > 0$, if the boundary condition is given by

$$u(x, 1) = u(x, -1) = 0 \quad \text{for } 0 < x < \infty$$

$$u(0, y) = 1 - |y| \quad \text{for } -1 \le y \le 1.$$

8. Write an integral formula for the solution of the Dirichlet problem for the strip $-1 < \text{Re}(z) < 1$, $\text{Im}(z) > 0$ if the boundary condition is given by

$$u(x, 0) = 1 \quad \text{for } -1 < x < 1$$

$$u(-1, y) = u(1, y) = e^{-y} \quad \text{for } 0 < y < \infty.$$

25.5   Complex Function Models of Plane Fluid Flow

We will discuss how complex functions and integration are used in modeling and analyzing the flow of fluids.

Consider an incompressible fluid, such as water under normal conditions. Assume that we are given a velocity field $\mathbf{V}(x, y)$ in the plane. By assuming that the flow depends only on two variables, we are taking the flow to be the same in all planes parallel to the complex plane. Such a flow is called *plane-parallel*. This velocity vector is also assumed to be independent of time, a circumstance described by saying that the flow is *stationary*.

Write

$$\mathbf{V}(x, y) = u(x, y)\mathbf{i} + v(x, y)\mathbf{j}.$$

Since we can identify vectors and complex numbers, we will by a mild abuse of notation write the velocity vector as a complex function

$$V(z) = V(x + iy) = u(x, y) + iv(x, y).$$

Given $V(z)$, think of the complex plane as divided into two sets. The first is the domain D on which V is defined. The complement of D consists of all complex numbers not in D. Think of the complement as comprising channels confining the fluid to D, or as barriers through which the fluid cannot flow. This enables us to model fluid flow through a variety of configurations and around barriers of various shapes.

Suppose γ is a closed path in D. From vector analysis, if we parametrize γ by $x = x(s)$, $y = y(s)$, with s arc length along the path, then the vector $x'(s)\mathbf{i} + y'(s)\mathbf{j}$ is a unit tangent vector to γ, and

$$(u\mathbf{i} + v\mathbf{j}) \cdot \left(\frac{dx}{ds}\mathbf{i} + \frac{dy}{ds}\mathbf{j} \right) ds = u\,dx + v\,dy.$$

This is the dot product of the velocity with the tangent to a path trajectory, leading us to interpret

$$\oint_\gamma u\,dx + v\,dy$$

as a measure of the velocity of the fluid along γ. The value of this integral is called the *circulation* of the fluid along γ.

The vector $-y'(s)\mathbf{i} + x'(s)\mathbf{j}$ is a unit normal vector to γ, being perpendicular to the tangent vector (Figure 25.40). Therefore

$$-\oint_\gamma (u\mathbf{i} + v\mathbf{j}) \cdot \left(-\frac{dy}{dx}\mathbf{i} + \frac{dx}{ds}\mathbf{j} \right) ds = \oint_\gamma -v\,dx + u\,dy$$

is the negative of the integral of the normal component of the velocity along the path. When this integral is not zero, it is called the *flux* of the fluid across the path. This gives a measure

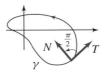

FIGURE 25.40

of fluid flowing across γ out from the region bounded by γ. When this flux is zero for every closed path in the domain of the fluid, the fluid is called *solenoidal*.

A point $z_0 = (x_0, y_0)$ is a vortex of the fluid if the circulation has a nonzero constant value on every closed path about z_0, in the interior of some punctured disk $0 < |z - z_0| < r$. The constant value of the circulation is the *strength of the vortex*.

If $\oint_\gamma -v\,dx + u\,dy$ has the same positive value k for all closed paths about z_0 in some punctured disk about z_0, then we call z_0 a source of strength k; if k is negative, z_0 is a sink of strength $|k|$.

The connection between the velocity field of a fluid and complex functions is provided by the following.

THEOREM 25.10

Let u and v be continuous with continuous first and second partial derivatives in a simply connected domain D. Suppose $u\mathbf{i} + v\mathbf{j}$ is irrotational and solenoidal in D. Then u and $-v$ satisfy the Cauchy-Riemann equations in D, and $f(z) = u(x, y) - iv(x, y)$ is a differentiable complex function on D.

Conversely, if u and $-v$ satisfy the Cauchy-Riemann equations on D, then $u\mathbf{i} + v\mathbf{j}$ defines an irrotational, solenoidal flow on D.

Proof   Let γ be any closed path in D. If M is the interior of γ, then every point in M is also in D by the assumption that D is simply connected. By Green's theorem,

$$\oint_\gamma u\,dx + v\,dy = \iint_M \left(\frac{\partial v}{\partial x} - \frac{\partial u}{\partial y} \right) dA = 0$$

because the flow is irrotational. But the flow is also solenoidal, so, again by Green's theorem,

$$\oint_\gamma -v\,dx + u\,dy = \iint_M \left(\frac{\partial u}{\partial x} + \frac{\partial v}{\partial y} \right) dA = 0.$$

Because M can be any set of points in D bounded by a closed path, the integrands in both of these double integrals must be zero throughout D, so

$$\frac{\partial u}{\partial x} = \frac{\partial}{\partial y}(-v) \quad \text{and} \quad \frac{\partial u}{\partial y} = -\frac{\partial}{\partial x}(-v).$$

By Theorem 21.6, $f(z) = u(x, y) - iv(x, y)$ is differentiable on D.

The converse follows by a similar argument. ∎

Theorem 25.9 provides some insight into irrotational, solenoidal flows. If the flow is irrotational, then

$$curl(u\mathbf{i} + v\mathbf{j}) = \left(\frac{\partial v}{\partial x} - \frac{\partial u}{\partial y} \right)\mathbf{k} = \mathbf{0},$$

as shown in the proof of the theorem. This curl is a vector normal to the plane of the flow. From the discussion of Section 12.5.2, the curl of $u\mathbf{i} + v\mathbf{j}$ is twice the angular velocity of the particle of fluid at (x, y). The fact that this curl is zero for an irrotational flow means that the fluid particles may experience translations and distortions in their motion, but no rotation. There is no swirling effect in the fluid.

If the flow is solenoidal, then

$$div(u\mathbf{i} + v\mathbf{j}) = \frac{\partial u}{\partial x} + \frac{\partial v}{\partial y} = 0.$$

A further connection between flows and complex functions is provided by the following.

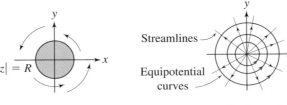

FIGURE 25.45 *Flow around a cylindrical barrier of radius R.*

FIGURE 25.46 *Equipotential curves and streamlines for the potential $f(z) = K \, Log(z)$.*

so

$$\varphi(x, y) = \frac{K}{2} \ln(x^2 + y^2) \quad \text{and} \quad \psi(x, y) = K\theta.$$

The equipotential curves are circles about the origin and the streamlines are half-lines emanating from the origin (Figure 25.46). As they must, these circles and lines form orthogonal families of curves. The velocity of this flow is

$$\overline{f'(z)} = \frac{K}{\overline{z}} = K\frac{x}{x^2 + y^2} + iK\frac{y}{x^2 + y^2} = u + iv.$$

Let γ be a circle of radius r about the origin. Now we find that

$$\oint_\gamma u\,dx + v\,dy = 0$$

and

$$\oint_\gamma -v\,dx + u\,dy = 2\pi K.$$

The origin is a source of strength $2\pi K$. We can think of particles of fluid streaming out from the origin, moving along straight lines with decreasing velocity as their distance from the origin increases. ∎

EXAMPLE 25.27

We will model flow around an elliptical barrier. From Example 25.25, the complex potential $f(z) = (iK/2\pi)Log(z)$ for $|z| > R$ models flow with circulation $-K$ about a cylindrical barrier of radius R about the origin. To model flow about an elliptical barrier, conformally map the circle $|z| = R$ to an ellipse. For this, consider the mapping

$$w = z + \frac{a^2}{z},$$

in which a is a positive constant. This is called a Joukowski transformation, and is used in analyzing fluid flow around airplane wings because of the different images of the circle that result by making different choices of a.

Let $z = x + iy$ and $w = X + iY$. We find that the circle $x^2 + y^2 = R^2$ is mapped to the ellipse

$$\frac{X^2}{1 + (a/R)^2} + \frac{Y^2}{1 - (a/R)^2} = R^2,$$

provided that $a \neq R$. This ellipse is shown in Figure 25.47. If $a = R$, the circle maps to $[-2a, 2a]$ on the real axis.

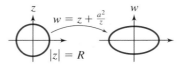

FIGURE 25.47 *Joukowski transformation mapping a circle to an ellipse.*

Solve for z in the Joukowski transformation. As a quadratic equation, this yields two solutions, and we choose

$$z = \frac{w + \sqrt{w^2 - 4a^2}}{2}.$$

Compose this mapping with the complex potential function for the circular barrier in Example 25.25 We get

$$F(w) = f(z(w)) = \frac{iK}{2\pi} Log \left(\frac{w + \sqrt{w^2 - 4a^2}}{2} \right).$$

This is the complex potential for flow in the w plane about an elliptical barrier if $R > a$, and about the flat plate $-2a \le X \le 2a$, $Y = 0$ if $R = a$. ∎

We will conclude this section with an application of complex integration to fluid flow. Suppose f is a complex potential for a flow about a barrier whose boundary is a closed path γ. Let the thrust of the fluid outside the barrier be the vector $A\mathbf{i} + B\mathbf{j}$. Then a theorem of Blasius asserts that

$$A - iB = \frac{1}{2}i\rho \oint_{\gamma} [f'(z)]^2 dz,$$

in which ρ is the constant density of the fluid. Further, the moment of the thrust about the origin is given by

$$Re \left(-\frac{1}{2}\rho \oint_{\gamma} z[f'(z)]^2 dz \right).$$

In practice, these integrals are usually evaluated using the residue theorem.

SECTION 25.5   PROBLEMS

1. Analyze the flow given by the complex potential $f(z) = az$, in which a is a nonzero complex constant. Sketch some equipotential curves and streamlines, determine the velocity, and whether the flow has any sources or sinks.

2. Analyze the flow having complex potential $f(z) = z^3$. Sketch some equipotential curves and streamlines.

3. Sketch some equipotential curves and streamlines for the flow having potential $f(z) = \cos(z)$.

4. Sketch some equipotential curves and streamlines for the flow having potential $f(z) = z + iz^2$.

5. Analyze the flow having potential $f(z) = KLog(z - z_0)$, in which K is a nonzero real constant and z_0 is a given complex number. Show that z_0 is a source for this flow if $K > 0$ and a sink if $K < 0$. Sketch some equipotential curves and streamlines of this flow.

6. Analyze the flow having potential $f(z) = KLog \left(\frac{z - a}{z - b} \right)$, where K is a nonzero real number and a and b are distinct complex numbers. Sketch some equipotential curves and streamlines for this flow.

7. Let $f(z) = k\left(z + \dfrac{1}{z}\right)$, with k a nonzero real constant. Sketch some equipotential curves and streamlines for this flow. Show that f models flow around the upper half of the unit circle.

8. Let

$$f(z) = \frac{m - ik}{2\pi} Log\left(\frac{z-a}{z-b}\right),$$

in which m and k are nonzero real numbers and a and b are distinct complex numbers. Show that this flow has a source or sink of strength m and a vortex of strength k at both a and b. (A point combining properties of a source (or sink) and a vortex is called a *spiral vortex*). Sketch some equipotential curves and streamlines for this flow.

9. Analyze the flow having potential

$$f(z) = k\left(z + \frac{1}{z}\right) + \frac{ib}{2\pi} Log(z),$$

in which k and b are nonzero real constants. Sketch some equipotential curves and streamlines for this flow.

10. Analyze the flow having potential

$$f(z) = iKa\sqrt{3}Log\left(\frac{2z - ia\sqrt{3}}{2z + ia\sqrt{3}}\right),$$

with K and a positive constants. Show that this potential models an irrotational flow around a cylinder $4x^2 + 4(y - a)^2 = a^2$ with a flat boundary along the y axis. Sketch some equipotential curves and streamlines for this flow.

11. Use Blasius's theorem to show that the force per unit width on the cylinder in Problem 10 has vertical component $2\sqrt{3}\pi \rho a K^2$, with ρ the constant density of the fluid.

PART 8

Probability and Statistics

CHAPTER 26
Counting and Probability

CHAPTER 27
Statistics

Few areas of expertise have as profound an influence on us as statistics. Manufactured products are tested for reliability by performing statistical analyses of random samples. Risk analysis is an application of statistics. Statistics determine costs and availability of insurance, whether a new drug will receive FDA approval for distribution, which television programs will be shown and when, boundaries of congressional districts in the United States, the distribution of some kinds of federal aid, public health programs, and on and on.

Professionals in business, medicine, science, engineering, and other areas use statistical analyses because they provide rigorous tools for analyzing information and drawing conclusions with measurable degrees of confidence.

Understanding and using ideas from statistics require some knowledge of probability, which in turn makes use of counting techniques. Based on this chain of dependence, we will begin this part with counting, followed by probability, and then statistics.

CHAPTER 26

Counting and Probability

Counting may sound simple enough. However, counting problems can be subtle. For example, how many lowercase, unordered nine-letter codes can be formed from the English alphabet if each vowel can be used no more than once? We will begin with techniques for solving the kinds of counting problems that we will encounter in statistics.

26.1   The Multiplication Principle

Suppose we have some process that proceeds in n independent stages. Independent means that the outcome of one stage is not influenced by the outcome of the others. How many different ways can the entire process be carried out?

As a simple example, suppose we are designing a car (the process), and we have four door designs and six fender designs. Door and fender selection are the two stages. How many different cars can we design from these choices, if each door looks good with each fender, and two cars are different if they differ in either a fender, a door, or both?

This problem is easily solved. With the first door, we can use any of six fenders for six possibilities. With the second door, we can choose any of six fenders for six more cars. Similarly, there are six fenders that can go with the third door and six with the fourth. The total number of car possibilities is

$$6+6+6+6=24.$$

Or, since there are six fenders with each of four doors, the number of cars is

$$4 \cdot 6 = 24.$$

To take a slightly more complicated example, suppose we have four doors, six fender styles, and nine hood shapes. Now how many cars can be formed? Since we can form 24 cars from the doors and fenders, and each can go with one of the hoods, there are $24 \cdot 9 = 216$ cars that can be made in this way. The answer in this case is $4 \cdot 6 \cdot 9$.

These examples suggest a general principle.

The Multiplication Principle Suppose a process consists of n independent stages, or steps. Suppose stage j can be done in s_j ways. Then the total number of ways of carrying out the process is the product

$$s_1 s_2 \ldots s_n.$$

One way to look at this result is to envision n boxes, in each of which any of a certain number of objects (or choices) can be put.

$$s_1 \ s_2 \ s_3 \ldots s_{n-1} \ s_n.$$

The total number of ways of picking one object from each box is the product of the number of objects in each box.

EXAMPLE 26.1

A person flips a coin nine times. How many outcomes are there?

We want to count something, namely the number of outcomes. However, before we count something, we should be clear on what we are counting. What is an outcome?

An outcome here is the result of nine flips, hence will be a string of nine symbols, with the *j*th symbol an H (if toss j came up a head) or a T (if toss j was a tail). A typical outcome might be

$$T\ H\ H\ T\ H\ H\ H\ T\ H.$$

The number of outcomes is the number of different nine letter strings, with each letter a T or an H. Think of nine empty boxes. There are two possible results we can put in the first box, namely T or H. There are also two for the second, and so on. Further, these flips are independent. The result of any flip does not influence the result of any other flip. The total number of possible outcomes of nine flips is therefore two multiplied by itself nine times, or 2^9, which equals 512. This is an application of the multiplication principle, with $n = 9$ and each $s_j = 2$.

Similarly, the number of possible outcomes with thirty flips is

$$2^{30} = 1,073,741,824. \ \blacksquare$$

EXAMPLE 26.2

A game consists of flipping a coin four times, then rolling five dice. What is the number of outcomes?

Here the activity or experiment has nine stages. The first four are all coin tosses, each with two possible outcomes. The last five are dice tosses, each with six outcomes. The number of possible outcomes is $2 \cdot 2 \cdot 2 \cdot 2 \cdot 6 \cdot 6 \cdot 6 \cdot 6 \cdot 6$, or $2^4 6^5$, which equals $124,416$. In the formalism of the multiplication principle, $n = 9$ and $s_1 = s_2 = s_3 = s_4 = 2$, while $s_5 = s_6 = s_7 = s_8 = s_9 = 6$. $\blacksquare$

EXAMPLE 26.3

We want to form identification codes by choosing seven integers from 1 through 9, inclusive. How many ways can this be done?

This problem has a wrinkle to it. If we choose the seven integers with replacement (that is, each can be any integer from 1 through 9, inclusively), then the total number of outcomes is 9^7, or $4,782,969$.

If, however, the seven integers are chosen without replacement, then every time we pick one it is used up, and we cannot choose it again. This means that there are nine choices for the first integer picked, but only eight for the second, seven for the third, and so on. Now the number of possible outcomes is

$$9 \cdot 8 \cdot 7 \cdot 6 \cdot 5 \cdot 4 \cdot 3,$$

or $181,440$. ■

SECTION 26.1   PROBLEMS

1. A game consists of flipping a coin seven times and rolling a die five times.

   (a) What is a typical outcome?

   (b) How many possible outcomes are there of this game?

2. A room has forty chests of drawers, and each chest has six drawers. A worker is assigned the task of inspecting each drawer in each chest. If each chest and each drawer take one second, how many seconds will it take the worker to complete this task?

3. A game consists of rolling ten dice, then choosing an integer falling between 7 and 21, inclusively. How many different outcomes are there to this game?

4. A man's outfit for the day consists of a pair of shoes, a pair of trousers, a shirt, tie, jacket, sweater (but not both), and coat and a hat. He has seven pairs of shoes, twelve pairs of trousers, fifteen shirts, ten ties, three jackets, four sweaters, two coats and four hats. How many different outfits are possible, assuming that all the pairings making up an outfit are compatible (so, for example, any shirt looks good with any sweater)?

   How does the answer change, if at all, if an outfit consists of a pair of shoes, a pair of trousers, a shirt, tie, jacket and/or sweater, and a coat and/or hat?

5. ID codes for a company's employees are to be formed as strings of six symbols. Each of the first three symbols can be any of the integers 1, 3 , 7, or 9, and each of the last three can be any of the letters *A*, *C* , *D*,

E or *K*. The company has 3, 300 employees. Determine whether it is possible to assign each employee a different code in this way.

6. A factory produces tops for coffee tables. For each top, any of six colored panels are selected, then any of fifteen designer patterns is stamped on the selected panel. Finally, the underside of the panel is given any of four different finishes. How many different coffee table tops can be produced in this way?

7. A woman can fill out a set of golf clubs by choosing any one of seven putters, any one of fifteen drivers, any one of eight wedges, and any one of seventeen irons. How many different sets are there?

8. A carnival game consists of a large wheel with the numbers 1 through 50 spaced equally around the perimeter. A pointer is pivoted at the center and is spun by the operator, eventually coming to land on one of the numbers. The counter is spun four times. What does an outcome of these four spins look like, and how many different possible outcomes are there?

9. A committee of four is to be formed on the city council. The first member must be chosen from among seven residents of south side, the second from among eleven residents of city center, the third from among six residents of the park area, and the fourth from among fourteen residents of north beach. How many different committes can be formed?

10. Six coins are each flipped twenty times. What does an outcome look like, and how many different outcomes are there?

26.2 Permutations

Suppose we have a collection of objects, and we want to arrange or list them in some order. How many ways are there to do this?

This question has an important but simple answer. Think of having n boxes.. We can put any of the numbers $1, 2, \ldots, n$ object in the first box, so there are n ways to fill this box. With one object chosen, there are $n - 1$ ways to fill the second box, then $n - 2$ ways to pick an object for the third box, and so on. Continue in this way. For the third from the last box, there are three remaining objects to choose from. For the next to last, there are two to choose from. Finally, there is only one object left, and that goes into the last box. By the multiplication principle, the total number of ways of making these choices is

$$n \cdot (n - 1) \cdot (n - 2) \ldots 3 \cdot 2 \cdot 1,$$

which is the product of the integers from 1 through n. Our conclusion is:

The number of ways of ordering n objects is the product of the integers from 1 *through n, inclusive.*

An ordering of objects is called a *permutation* of these objects. Thus, the number of permutations of three objects is 6, the number of permutations of four objects is 24, and the number of permutations of n objects is $1 \cdot 2 \cdot 3 \ldots n$. This product occurs frequently in counting and other contexts (for example, coefficients in Taylor expansions), and is denoted $n!$ (read "n factorial"). In this language:

The number of permutations on n objects is n!

Here is a short list of factorials:

n	$n!$
1	1
2	2
3	6
4	24
5	120
6	720
10	3,628,800
15	1.3077×10^{12}
20	2.4329×10^{18}
30	2.6525×10^{32}
50	3.0414×10^{64}

Factorials grow at an extremely rapid rate, 10! is already well over three million.

EXAMPLE 26.4

A lottery entry involves choosing any ordering of the objects a, b, c, d, e, and then any ordering of the objects A, B, C, D. How many possible outcomes are there in this lottery?

Think of the game as consisting of two stages, the first choosing any ordering of a, b, c, d, e, the second choosing an ordering of A, B, C, D. There are $5! = 120$ ways of doing the first step, and $4! = 24$ ways of doing the second step. Further, the two steps are independent.

By the multiplication principle, there are $120 \cdot 24 = 2880$ possible outcomes. For example, one outcome is

$$b, c, a, d, e, B, A, D, C.$$

Suppose we require that a be in the first position, and A in the last. How many outcomes are possible with this requirement?

Think of nine boxes, with a already placed in the first and A in the last:

$$a \ldots A.$$

In the second through fifth places, there can be any arrangement of b, c, d and e. There are 4! such arrangements. In the sixth through eighth places, there can be any arrangement of B, C and D. There are $3! = 6$ such arrangements. There are therefore

$$4!3! = (24)(6) = 144$$

outcomes. ∎

EXAMPLE 26.5

Suppose we are playing a poker game in which each hand has seven cards, but the order in which the cards is played is important. A particular player is dealt a jack, a king, a four, a two, a ten, a seven and a queen. How many different ordered hands can the player form?

Since there are seven different cards, there are

$$7! = 5040$$

different orderings. This is the number of different hands that can be formed. The actual value of the cards is irrelevant information in reaching this conclusion. Given any seven different cards, there are 5040 orderings of them. ∎

SECTION 26.2   *PROBLEMS*

1. How many ways can the first nine letters of the alphabet be arranged in different orders?

2. How many different codes can be formed from the lower case letters of the English alphabet, if a code consists of seventeen distinct letters, with different orders counting as different codes?

3. An ID number for each employee in a certain company consists of a string of nine numbers, consisting of an arrangements of the integers 1 through 9. How many different ID numbers can be formed?

4. Suppose we have five symbols available, and these are %, $, #, * and &. One plan is to form passwords by using different orderings of these five symbols. A second plan is to use ordered strings chosen from these five symbols, in which any symbol can be used one or more times. How many different passwords are possible under each plan?

5. (a) How many arrangements are there of the objects a, b, c, d, f, g, h?

   (b) How many arrangements are there if we insist on using only those beginning with a?

   (c) How many arrangements are there if a must be first and g fifth in the list?

6. We want to form ID numbers by using n distinct symbols and allowing any order for their arrangement. How large must n be to accommodate $20,000$ people? How many for $1,000,000$ people?

7. Letters a through f are to be arranged in a three by two pattern, with one symbol in each location. For example,

   $d\ a$

   $b\ f$

   $c\ e$

is one such pattern. How many patterns can be formed in this way?

8. Bowling pins are traditionally arranged in a triangle of fifteen identical pins. Suppose we decide to number the pins 1 through 15. How many different arrangements are there of these pins?

9. A lottery is run as follows. Twelve slips of paper are placed in a bowl. Each slip has a different symbol on it. A player makes an ordered list of these twelve symbols, and wins if they are drawn from the bowl in this order. How many possible different outcomes are there of this lottery?

10. The letters *a* through *l* are to be arranged in some order. How many arrangements are there that have *a* in the second place, *d* in the fifth place and *k* in the seventh place?

11. How many ways are there of choosing, with order, the even integers out of the integers 1 through 12?

12. We have seen that *n*! increases at a fast pace as *n* is chosen larger. Because factorials arise in many contexts, there are formulas that can be used to approximate *n*! when *n* is large, but which can be computed in fewer steps than it takes to compute *n*! as the product of the integers from 1 through *n*. Stirling's formula states that

$$n! \approx \left(\frac{n}{e}\right)^n \sqrt{2\pi n},$$

with accuracy improving as *n* is chosen larger. To test this supposition, make a three column table, having values of *n* for $n = 1, 2, \ldots 20$ in the first column. In the second column, compute *n*!, and in the third column, the Stirling approximation. Compute the percentage error in the approximation in each case.

26.3   Choosing *r* Objects from *n* Objects

Suppose we have *n* objects, and we want to choose *r* of them, with $1 \leq r \leq n$. How many ways are there to do this? The answer depends on whether or not we take order into account. First consider the case that we do.

26.3.1   *r* Objects from *n* Objects, with Order

Given *n* objects, how many ways are there to make an ordered list of *r* of these objects?

Using the multiplication principle, it is not difficult to derive a general formula for this number.

THEOREM 26.1

Let *r* and *n* be positive integers, with $1 \leq r \leq n$. Then, the number of ways of picking *r* objects from *n* objects, taking order into account, is

$$\frac{n!}{(n-r)!}. \quad \blacksquare$$

To understand this conclusion, envision *r* boxes. There are *n* choices of objects to put in box 1, leaving $n-1$ choices for box 2, then $n-2$ for box 3, and so on, until finally there are $n-r+1$ objects left from which to pick one for box *r*. By the multiplication principle, the number of ways of making these choices of *r* objects from the given *n* objects is the product

$$n(n-1)(n-2)\ldots(n-r+1).$$

This product is

$$(n-r+1)\ldots n = \frac{1\cdot 2\cdots (n-r-1)(n-r)(n-r+1)\cdots\cdot n}{1\cdot 2\cdots (n-r)}$$

$$= \frac{n!}{(n-r)!}.$$

This number is often denoted $_nP_r$, which is an abbreviation for "the number of permutations of r objects chosen from n objects." Thus,

$$_nP_r = \frac{n!}{(n-r)!}.$$

For example, if $n = 4$ and $r = 2$, then

$$_4P_2 = \frac{4!}{2!} = 4\cdot 3 = 12.$$

This is the number of ways of choosing two ordered objects from four objects.

As a convenience, define $0! = 1$. In the present context, this makes sense. Suppose, for example, we want to compute $_6P_6$. This is the number of ways of choosing six ordered objects from six objects. But this is exactly the number of permutations of six objects, which we know equals 6! Now compute

$$_6P_6 = \frac{6!}{(6-6)!} = \frac{6!}{0!} = 6!.$$

EXAMPLE 26.6

An election is being held and there are eight nominations for three offices. A ballot consists of three lines. The name filled in first receives one vote for president, the second name receives one vote for vice president, and the third name receives one vote for janitor. No name can be duplicated on any ballot. How many different ballots are possible in this election?

Obviously the order in which candidate names are listed is significant here. The number of ballots is the number of ways of choosing three from eight, with order:

$$_8P_3 = \frac{8!}{5!} = 6\cdot 7\cdot 8 = 336. \ \blacksquare$$

EXAMPLE 26.7

An ID code is to consist of eight different lowercase letters of the English alphabet, written in some order, together with an ordered string of any five distinct integers, chosen from 1 through 9, inclusively. How many different codes are there?

There are $_{26}P_8$ ways of choosing eight of the 26 letters of the alphabet, with order, and $_9P_5$ ways of choosing five of the integers 1 through 9, with order. By the multiplication principle, the number of codes is

$$(_{26}P_8)(_9P_5) = \frac{26!}{18!}\frac{9!}{4!}$$

$$= 19\cdot 20\ldots 26\cdot 5\cdot 6\ldots 9 = 9.5242(10)^{14}. \ \blacksquare$$

26.3.2   *r* Objects from *n* Objects, without Order

Sometimes we want the number of ways of choosing *r* objects out of *n* objects, but the order in which the selected objects are listed does not matter. This number is denoted $_nC_r$, and is called the number of *combinations* of *r* objects chosen from *n* objects. Whenever the word " combination" is used, order is not taken into account. When " permutation" is used, order is a factor.

We already know how to compute $_nC_r$. Given *n* and *r*, $_nP_r$ differs from $_nC_r$ only in taking the orderings into account. There are *r*! ways of ordering any *r* of the *n* objects. Therefore each combination of *r* of the *n* objects counted in $_nC_r$ gives rise to *r*! different orderings of these objects, and these are all included in the number $_nP_r$. This means that

$$_nP_r = r!\,_nC_r.$$

Therefore,

$$_nC_r = \frac{1}{r!}\,_nP_r = \frac{n!}{r!(n-r)!}.$$

For example, suppose we want to choose two objects out of four. If order is taken into account, then there are twelve possibilities, since

$$_4P_2 = \frac{4!}{2!} = 12.$$

Explicitly, the possible choices are

$$ab, ac, ad, bc, bd, cd, ba, ca, da, cb, db, dc.$$

If order is not to be taken into account, then *ab* and *ba* are counted as one choice. Similarly, *ac* and *ca* are the same, and so on. There are six distinct choices (without order) of two of these four letters, and they are

$$ab, ac, ad, bc, bd, cd$$

Without having this explicit list, we could still know that there are six such combinations by computing

$$_4C_2 = \frac{4!}{2!2!} = \frac{3 \cdot 4}{2} = 6.$$

EXAMPLE 26.8

Elections are being held to form a committee to consist of four club members. There are seven nominations. A ballot consists of a list of four of the nominees, without regard to order, because the committee has no hierarchy. How many different ballots are there?

Discount ordering and look for combinations, not permutations, of four members chosen from the seven nominees. The number of these combinations is

$$_7C_4 = \frac{7!}{4!3!} = \frac{2 \cdot 3 \cdot 4 \cdot 5 \cdot 6 \cdot 7}{2 \cdot 3 \cdot 4 \cdot 2 \cdot 3} = 35. \ \blacksquare$$

EXAMPLE 26.9

Consider a poker game in which seven cards are dealt face down. Bets are placed after all hands have been dealt, at which time each player has seven cards making up the hand. What is the total number of possible hands?

Assume a standard 52 card deck. Then the number of hands is the number of ways of choosing seven from 52 cards, without regard to order:

$$_{52}C_7 = \frac{52!}{7!(52-7)!} = \frac{52!}{7!45!}$$

$$= \frac{46 \cdot 47 \cdot 48 \cdot 49 \cdot 50 \cdot 51 \cdot 52}{2 \cdot 3 \cdot 4 \cdot 5 \cdot 6 \cdot 7} = 133,784,560.$$

Order does not matter here, because bets are made only after each player receives all seven cards, and nothing would change if the same seven cards were dealt in a different order.

Now suppose each player is dealt one card face up, and then each player is dealt one card face down, at which time bets are made. Then each player is dealt one more card face down, followed by another round of betting. This continues until each player has seven cards (so six are face down, and there are six rounds of betting).

Notice the difference between this and the first game. In the first game, the player only cares about which seven cards have been dealt, and the order made no difference. In the second game, order matters. If a queen is dealt first to a player (for all to see) and a second queen is dealt as the second card (for only the player to see), the player might bet in the early rounds differently than if the second queen is dealt in the last round. And opponents might bet differently if both queens had been dealt face down. Now order is vital to betting strategy. With order, the number of possible hands is

$$_{52}P_7 = \frac{52!}{45!} = 46 \cdot 47 \cdot 48 \cdot 49 \cdot 50 \cdot 51 \cdot 52 = 674,274,182,400.$$

It is routine to check that this is 7! times $_{52}C_7$. ■

Often $_nC_r$ is written $\binom{n}{r}$. For example,

$$\binom{6}{2} = \frac{6!}{2!4!} = 15$$

and

$$\binom{5}{2} = \frac{5!}{2!3!} = 10.$$

This notation is often seen in connection with binomial expansions. If x and y are numbers, and n is a positive integer, then

$$(x+y)^n = \sum_{k=0}^{n} \binom{n}{k} x^k y^{n-k}.$$

Because of their appearance as coefficients in a binomial expansion, the numbers $\binom{n}{k}$ are called *binomial coefficients*. The coefficient of x^k (which is the same as the coefficient of x^{n-k}) is the number of ways of choosing k objects from n objects, disregarding the order of the choice. This makes sense, because if we choose k from n objects, then we have automatically also chosen $n-k$ of the n objects.

26.3.3 Tree Diagrams

In working with permutations and combinations, it is often handy to use a systematic device called a *tree diagram*. An illustration will clarify what this is.

Consider strings of symbols of length 5, using either an *H* or a *T* in each place. For example,

$$HHTHT \quad \text{and} \quad HTTTT$$

are two such strings. There are $2^5 = 32$ strings.

Now, suppose we want the number of strings having exactly two *T*'s (and therefore three *H*'s). Think of a string of five boxes. We want to pick out two to put *T* in, the rest automatically getting an *H*. There are $_5C_3 = 10$ ways of doing this. Order is irrelevant here because, once we pick two boxes, we put an identical *T* in each, then an identical *H* in the other three.

None of this involves a new idea. But now suppose we want to actually list all ten of these strings. Here is a systematic way to do this. Put a dot on a piece of paper to represent a starting point. Next, place two dots to the right (or left, if you prefer), one for *H* and the other for *T*, with a line (or edge, or branch) from the starting dot to each of these. So far the diagram displays the outcomes of the first flip. Next draw two lines, ending in dots for *H* and *T*, from each of the first *H* and *T* dots. The diagram so far, Figure 26.1, shows outcomes of the first two flips. Continue, putting two lines from each of the four end dots drawn so far, with each line ending with an *H* or a *T* dot (Figure 26.2). The pattern is obvious, and we carry out two more steps (two lines from each *H* or *T*, then repeat once more), until strings of five edges form along each path from the starting dot to the the right-most dots (Figure 26.3). The resulting configuration is called a *tree diagram*, and it is useful for reading information about

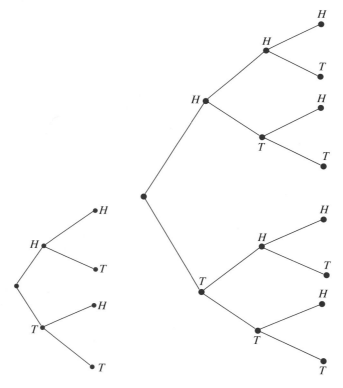

FIGURE 26.1
Outcomes of the first two coin flips.

FIGURE 26.2 *Outcomes of the first three coin flips.*

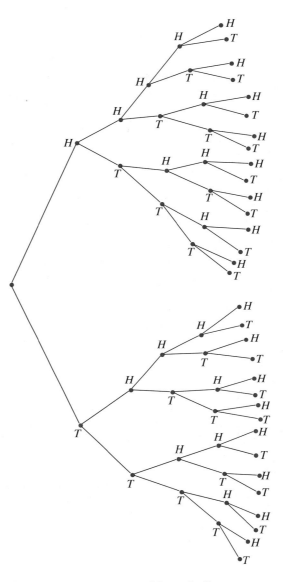

FIGURE 26.3 *Outcomes of five coin flips.*

the strings. Each path of five edges, from the starting dot to an end dot on the right, details one complete sequence of five flips of the coin. By following various paths, we can, for example, easily pick out exactly those having two *T's* and three *H's*:

$$HHHTT, HHTHT, HHTTH, HTHHT, HTHTH, HTTHH,$$

$$THHHT, THHTH, THTHH, TTHHH.$$

Although we knew without the tree diagram that there would be ten of these outcomes, the tree diagram is a systematic way of listing them all, if that is needed.

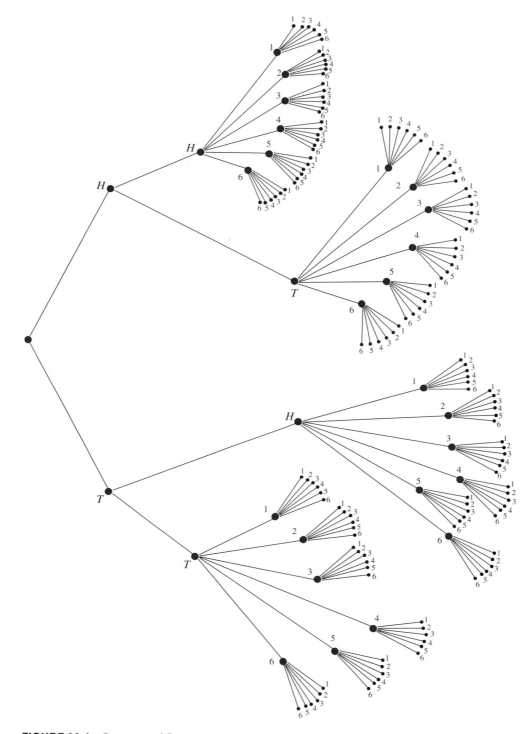

FIGURE 26.4   *Outcomes of flipping two coins or one coin twice), then rolling two dice (or one die twice).*

EXAMPLE 26.10

A game consists of flipping two coins, then rolling two dice. An outcome will consist of a string of length four, the first two symbols recording the results of the coin flips (*H* or *T*) and the last two the numbers that come up on the dice (1 through 6). There are $2 \cdot 2 \cdot 6 \cdot 6$ (or 72) outcomes.

Figure 26.4 shows a tree diagram for this game. By following all of the paths from the left starting dot to the end dots on the right, we can read all of the outcomes explicitly. For example, all of the outcomes in which the two dice come up both 3, or both 4, or one 3 and one 4, can be easily read from the diagram:

$$HH33, HT33, TH33, TT33,$$

$$HH44, HT44, TH44, TT44,$$

$$HH34, HT34, TH34, TT34,$$

$$HH43, HT43, TH43, TT43. \blacksquare$$

SECTION 26.3   *PROBLEMS*

1. Seven members of an audience of 25 people are to be chosen to win a prize. The first name drawn will win half of the planet, the second name drawn will win an airplane, the third name drawn a new house, and so on down to the last name drawn, which will win fifty cents worth of merchandise at the nearest drug store. How many different possible outcomes are there of this drawing?

2. There are five positions open on the board of a swimming club, and sixteen people are eligible for election to the board. A ballot consists of a list of names of five of the eligible members, with order being important because new board members are assigned positions of decreasing importance, depending on how far down the list a person is selected. How many different ballots are possible in this election?

3. A car dealer has a lottery. First, 22 names are selected at random from a data base of past customers. Six of these names will be winners. The first name chosen can go through the lot and pick any car. The second person can do the same, but perhaps the best car has already been chosen by the first person. The third person also goes through the lot, taking third pick, and so on. How many different possibilities are there for lists of people to go through the lot and make choices?

4. A game consists of choosing and listing, in order, three numbers from the integers 1, 2, . . . , 20.

(a) How many different choices are there?

(b) What percentage of these begins with the number 4? Would this answer change if the first number is 17 instead of 4?

(c) What percentage of these choices ends with the number 9? Would this number be the same if the last number were 11 instead of 9?

(d) How many choices are there if the first number must be 3 and the last number 15?

5. How many different ways can a ten card hand be dealt from a standard 52 card deck, if the order in which the cards are dealt is unimportant? What is the number if the order of the deal is significant?

6. How many different nine man lineups can be formed from a roster of 17 players, if order of selection is not a factor? How many can be formed if order makes a difference?

7. How many different ways can four drumsticks be chosen from a barrel containing twenty drumsticks, if order of selection does not matter?

8. A company is selecting twelve of its forty employees to lay off. How many different ways can such a selection be made, if the order of choice is unimportant?

9. A carnival game begins with the contestant drawing five cards from a standard deck. Contrast the number

of different ways this can be done if order is important, with the number of different hands that can be
drawn if order does not count.

10. How many different ways can a seven person committee be selected from a group of seventeen people,
(a) if the order of selection is important, and (b) if the
order does not matter?

11. Let n and k be integers with $0 \le k \le n$. Show that

$$\binom{n}{k} = \binom{n}{n-k}.$$

12. Five coins are tossed.

(a) Draw a tree diagram for this experiment.

(b) List all outcomes in which the second and third
coins are heads.

(c) List all outcomes in which the first coin comes
up heads and the fourth, tails.

(d) List all outcomes in which two coins come up
heads and two come up tails.

13. Three dice are rolled.

(a) Draw a tree diagram for this experiment.

(b) List all outcomes in which the sum of the dice is
even.

(c) List all outcomes in which the first and third die
are odd.

(d) List all outcomes in which the first die comes up
2 or 5, and the last die is 3, 4 or 6.

14. Two coins are tossed and then and two dice are
rolled.

(a) Draw a tree diagram for this experiment.

(b) List all outcomes having a head on the first coin
and the sum of the dice is odd.

(c) List all outcomes in which the first die is a 1
or 5.

(d) List all outcomes in which both coins come up
tails and the second die is 1, 3 or 4.

26.4   Events and Sample Spaces

In this section we begin to establish a framework within which we will be able to compute
probabilities of certain kinds of events.

In order to isolate the essential issues, begin with a simple probability problem that we can
all solve. Flip an honest coin. What is the probability that it comes up heads? Everyone knows
that this probability is 1/2. Although this probability is sometimes stated as 50%, we prefer to
specify any probability as a number from 0 to 1 inclusive.

Why is this obvious? Perhaps without explicit verbalization, 1/2 seems natural for this
probability because a head is one of two equally likely outcomes, heads or tails. Formally,

$$\text{Probability (head)} = \frac{\text{number of ways the coin can come up heads}}{\text{total number of possible outcomes of one flip}} = \frac{1}{2}.$$

Try this reasoning on a similar but slightly more complicated problem. Roll a single
die. What is the probability that it comes up 3? It is common to guess that this probability
must be 1/6. Why? There are six possible outcomes (six faces on the die), and they are all
equally likely (honest die), so 3 will likely come up one in six times, for a probability of 1/6.
Again,

$$\text{Probability (rolling 3)} = \frac{\text{number of ways 3 can come up}}{\text{total number of possible outcomes of one roll}} = \frac{1}{6}.$$

Notice a common thread in both of these probabilities. In each, we performed an experiment
(flip a coin, roll a die), and there were certain outcomes. The probability of an outcome was the
number of ways this outcome could occur, divided by the total number of possible outcomes.

These simple examples are useful in suggesting an approach that will enable us to handle
more complicated probability questions.

The fundamental setting for any question in probability is an *experiment*, by which we mean simply something that is done. It could be a coin flip, a roll of a die, pulling an item from a production line, picking twelve cards from a deck, choosing a marble from a jar, guessing a lottery number, choosing a patient in a clinical trial, or almost any other action that has a finite number of outcomes. We will not consider experiments with infinitely many outcomes.

We assume that each experiment we deal with has known outcomes. The number of outcomes may be very large, so we do not want to have to actually make a list to compute a probability. But we do need to know what the outcomes are and at least be able to describe them all by some rule or rules. We will also have to be able to count them. For example, suppose an experiment is to choose an integer at least as large as 1 and no larger than ten hundred billion. This experiment has ten hundred billion possible outcomes, namely all of the integers in the specified range. It would take us a long time to actually write these all down in a list, and there is no need to do this. The important thing is that we know all the outcomes, what they look like, and how many there are.

DEFINITION 26.1   Sample Space

The set of all outcomes of an experiment is called its *sample space*.

EXAMPLE 26.11

An experiment is to flip two coins. Now there are four possible outcomes. If the sample space is called Q, then

$$Q = \{HH, TT, HT, TH\}.$$

These are all the outcomes. Notice that TH and HT are separate outcomes. There are two ways we can get a head and a tail—a head on the first coin and tail on the second or a head on the second coin and tail on the first. ■

EXAMPLE 26.12

Roll two dice. How may outcomes are there?

We can record the result of rolling two dice as a pair (a, b), where a is the number that comes up on the first die, and b is the number on the second die. There are six choices for a, and six for b, so by the multiplication principle, there are $6 \cdot 6 = 36$ outcomes. If we list them explicitly, the sample space W is

$$W = \{(1, 1), (1, 2), (1, 3), (1, 4), (1, 5), (1, 6),$$
$$(2, 1), (2, 2), (2, 3), (2, 4), (2, 5), (2, 6),$$
$$(3, 1), (3, 2), (3, 3), (3, 4), (3, 5), (3, 6),$$
$$(4, 1), (4, 2), (4, 3), (4, 4), (4, 5), (4, 6),$$
$$(5, 1), (5, 2), (5, 3), (5, 4), (5, 5), (5, 6),$$
$$(6, 1), (6, 2), (6, 3), (6, 4), (6, 5), (6, 6)\}. ■$$

EXAMPLE 26.13

An experiment consists of choosing (without replacement) five different letters of the English alphabet and writing them in some order. What are the outcomes, and how many outcomes are there?

Suppose we use only lowercase letters. Then there are 26 letters from which to choose five. Order counts because of the way the experiment was defined. Thus there are

$$_{26}P_5 = \frac{26!}{21!} = 22 \cdot 23 \cdot 24 \cdot 25 \cdot 26 = 7,893,600.$$

outcomes, each of which is a string of different letters (because the letters were chosen without replacement). Typical outcomes are $acdfg$ and $gdfac$. We know what an outcome looks like, and how many there are. ∎

Once we understand the concepts of an experiment and the resulting sample space, we can define an *event* for an experiment.

DEFINITION 26.2   *Event*

An *event* for an experiment is a set of outcomes.

The rationale for this definition is that we sometimes want the probability of something that is more complicated than a single outcome, and consists of several outcomes specified in some way.

EXAMPLE 26.14

Flip three coins. A natural way to record an outcome of this experiment is as a 3-character string of H's and T's. Since each flip has two possible outcomes, there are $2^3 = 8$ outcomes. This is a small enough number that we can actually write out the sample space explicitly:

$$S = \{HHH, HHT, HTH, HTT, TTT, TTH, THT, THH\}.$$

An event in this experiment is any collection of outcomes.

The entire sample space S is an event. Another is

$$E_1 = \{HHH, TTT, HTH\}.$$

Another event is

$$E_2 = \{HHH, TTT\}.$$

This is the event that all three flips come up the same. Still another event is

$$E_3 = \{HTT, THT, TTH\},$$

the event that there is exactly one head. ∎

EXAMPLE 26.15

Consider the experiment of rolling two dice. The sample space W consists of 36 outcomes, each of the form (a, b), where a and b can independently be any integer from 1 through 6, inclusively. Suppose we are interested in the event E that the sum of the numbers that come up on the dice is 5. E consists of all outcomes (a, b) with $a + b = 5$:

$$E = \{(1, 4), (2, 3), (3, 2), (4, 1)\}.$$

These are all the ways the dice can total 5.

Suppose we want the event B consisting of all the ways we can roll a total of 2. This is the event

$$B = \{(1, 1)\}.$$

There is only one way to roll a total of 2. We have the intuition that it is less likely to roll a total of 2 than a total of 5, because there is only one way to roll 2, but four ways to roll 5. ■

It will be useful to have an *empty event*. This event is denoted ∅, and consists of no outcomes. To illustrate, in the last example, the event that the dice total 13 is empty, containing no outcomes, since this can never happen.

We are now ready to compute probabilities. In doing this, we emphasize a crucial point, the difference between an outcome and an event. An outcome is something that occurs when the experiment is performed. An event is a collection of one or more outcomes (or even perhaps no outcomes). Outcomes are the building blocks of events.

SECTION 26.4   PROBLEMS

In each of Problems 1 through 10, an experiment is described. Describe a typical outcome, and count the number of outcomes. Determine the number of outcomes in each of the events defined for each experiment. It is not necessary to list all of the outcomes of an event explicitly.

1. Roll four dice. Event A consists of all outcomes in which the dice total 9. Event B consists of all outcomes in which each die comes up 1 or 2.

2. Draw seven cards from a standard 52 card deck, with order of the draw having no importance. Event W consists of all hands having only cards numbered 2 or 3. Event K consists of all hands having only kings and/or aces. Event M consists of all hands with exactly one ace.

3. Pick four distinct lowercase letters from the English alphabet, without regard to order. Event A consists of the outcomes having an a and a z. Event W consists of the outcomes having only letters between a and g, inclusively.

4. Pick five distinct lowercase letters from the English alphabet, taking order into account. Event I consists of all outcomes beginning with zk. Event W consists of all outcomes having third letter e. Event P consists of all outcomes with $chjk$ as the last four letters.

5. Flip three coins and then roll three dice. Event C consists of all outcomes with three heads and the dice totalling 15. Event D consists of all outcomes with at least two heads and the dice totalling at least 15. Event E consists of all outcomes with exactly one head and only a five or six showing on the each die.

6. Pick an integer from 0 through 10 inclusive, then three letters from the English alphabet. M is the event that the number chosen is even. K is the event that the number is 3, 5 or 7, and one of the letters is w.

7. Five dice are rolled. U is the event that the dice total at least 28. K is the event that the dice total no more than 7.

8. Twenty three coins are flipped. R is the event that at least twenty heads come up. Q is the event that the last nineteen flips all came up heads.

9. Sixteen cards are drawn (without regard to order) from a standard 52-card deck. Y is the event that every card drawn was a face card or ace. M is the event that four jacks, four kings and three aces were drawn (together with other cards).

10. A ten sided polygon has its sides numbered $1, \ldots, 10$. Four sides are selected at random. Y is the event that the sides total exactly 14. P is the event that sides 2, 3 and 7 were picked.

26.5   The Probability of an Event

Suppose some experiment has taken place, and we focus on a certain event. We want to assign a number, between 0 and 1, to this event in such a way as to give a measure of the likelihood, or probability, that this event will occur if we perform this experiment. In this scheme, probability 0 means that the event cannot occur, probability 1 means that it is certain, and numbers strictly between 0 and 1 are assigned to events that are possible, but not certain. Further, these numbers must be assigned so that larger probabilities correspond in a reasonable way to "more likely" events.

To calculate the probability of an event, the following must be in place.

1. There must be an experiment and a sample space $S = \{o_1, o_2, \ldots, o_N\}$ with finitely many outcomes. We call o_j the jth outcome.

2. For each outcome o_j, there must be given, or determined, a number $\Pr(o_j)$, with $0 < \Pr(o_j) < 1$. $\Pr(o_j)$ is called the *probability* of o_j.

3. The sum of the probabilities of all the outcomes must equal 1:

$$\Pr(o_1) + \Pr(o_2) + \cdots + \Pr(o_N) = 1.$$

The function Pr, operating on the outcomes, is called a *probability function*, or *probability measure*, for this experiment.

When we have a probability function, the probability of an event E is denoted $\Pr(E)$, and is defined to be the sum of the probabilities of the outcomes in E:

$$\Pr(E) = \text{sum of probabilities of outcomes in the event } E.$$

For example if $E = \{o_3, o_7, o_{10}\}$, then

$$\Pr(E) = \Pr(o_3) + \Pr(o_7) + \Pr(o_{10}),$$

in which each of the probabilities of outcomes on the right is assumed known.

The probability of the empty event, $\emptyset$, is defined to be zero, and the probability of the entire sample space (which is an event), is one:

$$\Pr(\emptyset) = 0, \Pr(S) = 1.$$

The fact that $\Pr(S) = 1$ is a necessary consequence of Property 3 of the probability function. S is itself an event containing all of the outcomes, and the probability of this event is by definition the sum of the probilities of all the outcomes in S, which must equal one.

Finding a probability function for an experiment is now the central issue in computing probabilities of events.

EXAMPLE 26.16

Consider a single coin flip. We do not need all of this machinery for such a simple experiment, but it is instructive to see how it works here.

This experiment is to flip a coin once. There are two outcomes, which we call H and T, so the sample space is $S = \{H, T\}$. Here $o_1 = H$ and $o_2 = T$ and the number of outcomes is $N = 2$.

We need to assign a probability to each outcome. If the coin is honest, then we expect a head to have the same likelihood of coming up a tail, so we set

$$\Pr(H) = \Pr(T) = \frac{1}{2}.$$

This is consistent with Property 3, since the sum of the probabilities of all the outcomes is one:

$$\Pr(H) + \Pr(T) = \frac{1}{2} + \frac{1}{2} = 1.$$

In this experiment, there are only four events, namely the empty event $\varnothing$, $\{H\}$ consisting of just H, $\{T\}$ consisting of just T, and $\{H, T\}$, which is the entire sample space. ∎

EXAMPLE 26.17

We will redo the last example with a twist. Suppose the coin is dishonest, and on any flip, a head is twice as likely as a tail. If $o_1 = H$ and $o_2 = T$, then

$$\Pr(o_1) = 2\Pr(o_2).$$

Now, to be a probability measure, we require that

$$\Pr(o_1) + \Pr(o_2) = 1.$$

These equations imply that

$$\Pr(H) = \frac{2}{3} \quad \text{and} \quad \Pr(T) = \frac{1}{3}.$$

This is a legitimate probability function for this experiment, but it is different from that of the preceding example because the coin is dishonest in a known way. ∎

We will now move to more complicated experiments, beginning with a class of special probability problems having equally likely outcomes.

Suppose an experiment has N outcomes $o_1, \ldots, o_N$, and each is equally likely:

$$\Pr(o_1) = \Pr(o_2) = \cdots = \Pr(o_N).$$

Since

$$\Pr(o_1) + \Pr(o_2) + \cdots + \Pr(o_N) = N\Pr(o_1) = 1,$$

then necessarily

$$\Pr(o_1) = \frac{1}{N}.$$

Because all the outcomes are equally likely, then

$$\Pr(o_j) = \frac{1}{N} \quad \text{for } j = 1, 2, \ldots, N.$$

Such an experiment is called an *equally likely outcome experiment*. We also say that the sample space is an *equally likely sample space*.

In such a case, if an event has k outcomes in it, then the probability of this event is the sum of the probabilities of the outcomes in the event, which is $1/N$ added to itself k times, or k/N.

We will record these results for future use.

THEOREM 26.2

In an equally likely outcome experiment with N outcomes, the probability of each outcome is $1/N$. Further, if an event E has k outcomes, then

$$\Pr(E) = \frac{k}{N}. \ \blacksquare$$

Another, sometimes useful, way of writing this result is that, in an equally likely outcome experiment,

Probability of an Event E

$$= \frac{\text{the number of outcomes in } E}{\text{the total number of outcomes of the experiment}}$$

$$= \frac{\text{the number of ways the event can occur}}{\text{the total number of outcomes of the experiment}}. \tag{26.1}$$

This reduces many probability calculations to counting problems.

EXAMPLE 26.18

Flip three coins. What is the probability of getting exactly two heads?

There are $2^3 = 8$ outcomes, each equally likely. The probability of any one outcome is $1/8$. The event E of getting exactly two heads is

$$E = \{(H, H, T), (H, T, H), (T, H, H)\},$$

containing three outcomes. The probability of getting exactly three heads is therefore

$$\Pr(E) = \frac{3}{8}. \ \blacksquare$$

EXAMPLE 26.19

Three dice are rolled. What is the probability that the dice total 17?

Each outcome is a triple (a, b, c), with a the number that came up on the first die, b that on the second, and c the number on the third die. Assuming honest dice, all outcomes are equally likely. There are $N = 6^3 = 216$ outcomes. The event E we are interested in (dice total 17) is

$$E = \{(6, 6, 5), (6, 5, 6), (5, 6, 6)\}.$$

There are $k = 3$ outcomes in E. By equation (26.1), $\Pr(E) = 3/216$. $\blacksquare$

EXAMPLE 26.20

An experiment consists of flipping 25 honest coins. What is the probability that exactly seven coins come up heads?

This is an equally likely outcome experiment. We need the number of outcomes, and the number of outcomes in which there are exactly seven heads.

Since there are 25 flips, each with two possible outcomes, the experiment has $2^{25} = 33,554,432$ outcomes.

The event E we are interested in is that exactly seven tosses yield H (so the other 18 are all tails). The number of outcomes having exactly seven H's is the number of ways of choosing seven out of 25 without regard to order, and this number is

$$_{25}C_7 = \frac{25!}{7!(25-7)!} = \frac{25!}{7!18!} = 480,700.$$

Now we have both the numerator and denominator in equation (26.1), and

$$\Pr(E) = \frac{480,700}{33,554,432} \approx 0.0143.$$

What is the probability of coming up with at least 22 heads? Let F be this event. The key phrase here is "at least." We obtain at least 22 heads if we roll exactly 22 heads, or exactly 23, or exactly 24, or all 25 heads. These are all different outcomes comprising parts of event F.

We will count all of these outcomes:

Number of outcomes with at least 22 heads

$= $ number of outcomes with exactly 22 heads

$+$ number of outcomes with exactly 23 heads

$+$ number of outcomes with exactly 24 heads

$+$ number of outcomes with exactly 25 heads

$= {}_{25}C_{22} + {}_{25}C_{23} + {}_{25}C_{24} + {}_{25}C_{25}$

$= \dfrac{25!}{3!22!} + \dfrac{25!}{2!23!} + \dfrac{25!}{1!24!} + \dfrac{25!}{25!} = 2626.$

From equation (26.1),

$$\Pr(F) = \frac{2626}{33,554,432} \approx 0.000078.$$

As intuition might suggest, this event is not one to bet on. ■

EXAMPLE 26.21

Suppose a person is dealt five cards, without regard to order, from a standard deck. What is the probability that the hand has four aces in it?

The total number of outcomes is the number of ways of choosing five cards from 52, disregarding order. This number is $_{52}C_5 = \frac{52!}{5!47!} = 2,598,960.$

This is the denominator in equation (26.1). Now we need the numerator. How many unordered five-card poker hands have exactly four aces? If four of the cards are aces, the fifth card can be any of the remaining 48 cards. Therefore the probability of being dealt four aces is

$$\Pr(\text{four aces}) = \frac{48}{2,598,960},$$

which is approximately 0.000018. This is why, in westerns, a gambler showing four aces usually gets shot. ■

We will consider experiments in which not all outcomes have the same probability when we have more machinery to deal with them efficiently.

SECTION 26.5 PROBLEMS

1. Suppose five honest coins are flipped.

   (a) Find the probability of getting exactly two heads.

   (b) Find the probability of getting at least two heads.

2. Roll four dice.

   (a) What is the probability that exactly two 4's come up?

   (b) What is the probability that exactly three 4's come up?

   (c) What is the probability that at least two 4's come up?

   (d) What is the probability that the dice total 22?

3. Two cards are selected from a standard deck. The order of the draw is unimportant.

   (a) What is the probability that both cards were kings?

   (b) What is the probability that neither card was an ace or face card?

4. Four letters are selected from the English alphabet (only lowercase is used). The order of the selection is recorded.

   (a) What is the probability that the first letter was q?

   (b) What is the probability that a and b are two of the letters?

   (c) What is the probability that the letters are a, b, d, z, in this order?

5. Eight bowling balls are in a bin. Two are defective, having been manufactured as cubes instead of the traditional spherical shape. A person uses a remote gripping device to pick three of the balls out of the bin, sight unseen. The order of the choice is unimportant.

   (a) What is the probability that none of the balls chosen was defective?

   (b) What is the probability that exactly one defective ball was taken?

   (c) What is the probability that both defective balls were taken?

6. Seven pyramid-shaped (tetrahedron) dice are tossed. The faces on each pyramid are numbered 1 through 4.

   (a) What is the probability that all seven dice came up 3?

   (b) What is the probability that five dice came up 1, and two came up 4?

   (c) What is the probability that the sum of the numbers that came up is 26?

   (d) What is the probability that the sum of the numbers that came up is at least 26?

7. Twenty balls in an urn are numbered 1 through 20. A blindfolded contestant draws five balls from the urn, with the order of the draw recorded.

   (a) What is the probability that balls 1, 2, 3, 4, and 5 were drawn (in this order)?

   (b) What is the probability that the number 3 ball was selected?

   (c) What is the probability that an even-numbered ball was drawn?

8. Seven drawers in a desk contain a 50-cent piece, while two other drawers contain a thousand dollar bill. A person is allowed to choose three drawers at random. The order of the draw is unimportant.

   (a) What is the probability that the person gets at least $1,000?

   (b) What is the probability that the person ends up with less than one dollar?

   (c) What is the probability that the payoff is $1.50?

9. Five cards are drawn, without regard to order, from a standard deck.

   (a) What is the probability that the hand contains at exactly one jack and exactly one king?

   (b) What is the probability that the hand contains at least two aces?

10. Twenty integers are chosen at random, and without regard to order, from the integers 0 to 100, inclusively.

   (a) What is the probability that all of the numbers chosen are larger than 79?

   (b) What is the probability that one of the numbers is 5?

26.6   **Complementary Events**

If E is an event for some experiment, then E consists of certain outcomes. The outcomes that are not in E form the *complement* of E, denoted E^C. This is another event.

Notice that the complement of E^C is E again:

$$(E^C)^C = E.$$

We may think of E^C as the event "E does not occur".

The outcomes in E, together with those in E^C, are all of the outcomes. Further, E and E^C have no outcomes in common. If we listed all of the outcomes in E, and then all those in E^C, we would list all the outcomes in the sample space S, with no repetitions. This means that

$$\Pr(S) = \Pr(E) + \Pr(E^C) = 1.$$

Another way of looking at this equation is that, for any event E, it is certain (probability 1) that either E occurs, or E does not occur (which is the same as E^C occurs). If we write this equation in a slightly different way, we obtain the following.

***Principle of Complementarity*:**

$$\Pr(E) = 1 - \Pr(E^C).$$

This equation holds for $E = S$ as well, since then $E^C = \emptyset$, so $\Pr(E) = \Pr(S) = 1$ and $\Pr(E^C) = \Pr(\emptyset) = 0$.

The principle of complementarity is useful because it offers us the choice of computing $\Pr(E)$ or $\Pr(E^C)$, and one might be easier than the other.

EXAMPLE 26.22

Roll three dice. There are $6^3 = 216$ outcomes. Consider the event E that the dice come up with a total of at least 5. Compute $\Pr(E)$.

One way to do this is by using equation (26.1):

$$\Pr(E) = \frac{\text{number of outcomes in } E}{216}.$$

Counting the number of outcomes in E is certainly possible, but it will be tedious. E contains all outcomes with the dice summing to 5 or more, meaning that the dice can total 5, 6, 7, 8, ..., 18. We would have to count the number of ways each of these totals can occur.

However, look at E^C, which consists of all tosses of the three dice in which the total is 4 or less. There are many fewer such outcomes, making them easier to count. The only way the dice can total 4 is to come up 2, 1, 1 or 1, 2, 1 or 1, 1, 2 (three ways). The only way they can total less than 4 is to total 3, which can happen only one way (they all come up 1). Therefore E^C has exactly four outcomes in it, so

$$\Pr(E^C) = \frac{4}{216} = \frac{1}{54}$$

and by the principle of complementarity,

$$\Pr(E) = 1 - \frac{1}{54} = \frac{53}{54} \approx 0.98.$$

Rolling a total of at least 5 with three dice is not certain, but it is very likely. ■

1. Seven dice are rolled. What is the probability that at least two of them come up 4?

2. Fourteen coins are tossed. What is the probability that at least three come up heads?

3. Five cards are drawn from a standard deck, without regard to order. What is the probability that at least one is a face card, an ace, or numbered 4 or higher?

4. Two coins are tossed and five dice are rolled. What is the probability that two heads and at least one 4 come up?

5. Four numbers are chosen at random and without regard to order from among the integers from 1 through 55, inclusively. What is the probability that at least one number is greater than 4?

6. Six dice are rolled. What is the probability that they total at least 11?

7. Here is the famous *Birthday Problem*. Suppose N people are in a room. What is the probability that at least two have the same birthday?

26.7 Conditional Probability

Probability depends in subtle ways on how much is known. Here is an illustration of this.

Suppose we pick a card at random from a deck of 52 cards. What is the probability that we chose a diamond? Since one fourth of the cards are diamonds, the probability of choosing a diamond is 1/4.

However, suppose, as the card was drawn, it flashed for an instant in front of a mirror and we saw that the card's suit is red. We immediately know that the card must be a diamond or heart. This narrows our choice down to one suit out two, not four, so the probability of a diamond is now 1/2. The additional knowledge that the suit was red has changed the sample space, which now consists of only those outcomes that are consistent with the additional information that the card chosen was red.

Which is correct, 1/4 or 1/2? The answer is both are right, because these numbers are different probabilities. The first is a straightforward probability of picking a particular suit of card from the entire deck. The second is a conditional probability, in which we not only pick a card, but also have additional information that eliminates certain outcomes as possibilities, hence reduces the sample space.

To put all of this on a firm footing that we can work with, suppose an experiment leads to outcomes and a sample space S. Single out a particular event U, having positive probability. (This will be the additional information of the conditional probability). If E is any event, define $E \cap U$ to be the event consisting of outcomes common to E and to U. For example, if

$$E = \{a, b, c, d, e, f, g, h\} \quad \text{and} \quad U = \{k, g, h, a, w, z\}$$

then

$$E \cap U = \{a, g, h\}.$$

This is also an event. $E \cap U$ is read "E intersect U," or "the intersection of E and U," or, in the probability context, "E and U." Notice that $E \cap U = U \cap E$, since the act of taking all outcomes common to E and U does not depend on the order in which E and U are written.

It is possible that there are no outcomes common to E and U, in which case $E \cap U = \emptyset$, the empty event.

Now imagine that the experiment is performed, but that, by some means (such as the mirror in the card experiment), we know that U occurs. The conditional probability of E, knowing U, is denoted $\Pr(E \mid U)$ and is computed as

$$\Pr(E \mid U) = \frac{\Pr(E \cap U)}{\Pr(U)}. \tag{26.2}$$

By taking the probability of $E \cap U$ in the numerator, we are factoring in the information that U is assumed known, so we only look at outcomes in E that are also in U. In the denominator, we have the probability of U computed with respect to the original sample space of the experiment. In effect, we are considering only outcomes of E that are in U, and thinking of U as the new sample space.

We will redo the card example to illustrate these ideas and how equation (26.2) works.

EXAMPLE 26.23

Pick a card out of a 52-card deck. What is the probability that a diamond is chosen? Since 13 of the 52 cards are diamonds,

$$\Pr(E) = \frac{13}{52} = \frac{1}{4}.$$

Now let U be the event that the card is a diamond or heart. This is the information flashed in the mirror. In this example $E \cap U = E$, because every event in E (card is a diamond) is already in U (card is a diamond or heart). Further, U consists of exactly half of the cards, so $\Pr(U) = 1/2$ (in the original experiment). Then

$$\Pr(E \mid U) = \frac{\Pr(E \cap U)}{\Pr(U)} = \frac{\Pr(E)}{\Pr(U)} = \frac{1/4}{1/2} = \frac{1}{2},$$

consistent with intuition. Knowing that the card is a diamond or heart, the probability of picking a diamond is $1/2$. ∎

EXAMPLE 26.24

Toss three dice. What is the probability of rolling a total of 5?

This is not a conditional probability, but we need this result for the conditional probability we will consider. The sample space consists of triples (a, b, c), in which each letter can be any integer from 1 through 6 inclusive. There are $6^3 = 216$ outcomes. The outcomes in which the dice total 5 are

$$(1, 1, 3), (1, 3, 1), (3, 1, 1), (1, 2, 2), (2, 1, 2), (2, 2, 1),$$

six in number. These constitute the event E: Roll a total of 5. Then

$$\Pr(E) = \frac{6}{216} = \frac{1}{36}.$$

Now suppose a person sitting on the side knows that two dice are loaded, and must always come up 2. This means that at least two dice must come up 2 on any roll of all three dice. Let U consist of all outcomes

$$(x, 2, 2), (2, x, 2), \quad \text{and} \quad (2, 2, x),$$

in which x (for the honest die) can be any of 1, 2, 3, 4, 5, or 6. There are 16 such outcomes (note that when $x = 2$ all three triples are the same $(2, 2, 2)$), so

$$\Pr(U) = \frac{16}{216} = \frac{2}{27}.$$

Now

$$E \cap U = \{1, 2, 2), (2, 1, 2), (2, 2, 1)\},$$

the outcomes common to E and U. There are three such outcomes, so

$$\Pr(E \cap U) = \frac{3}{216} = \frac{1}{72}.$$

The conditional probability that E will happen, knowing that U happens, is

$$\Pr(E \mid U) = \frac{\Pr(E \cap U)}{\Pr(U)} = \frac{1/72}{2/27} = \frac{3}{16}.$$

This is the probability that the dice will sum to 5, as far as the person who knows about the two loaded dice is concerned.

Notice that the probability of E (dice sum to 5) is only 1/36. However, to the person who knows that two dice always come up 2, the probability of the dice summing to 5 is considerably improved to 3/16. Knowing that two dice always come up 2 changes the sample space by eliminating certain outcomes. ■

Examine equation (26.2) more closely. By using equation (26.1) twice, we can write

$$\Pr(E \cap U) = \frac{\text{number of outcomes common to } E \text{ and } U}{\text{number of outcomes in } S}$$

and

$$\Pr(U) = \frac{\text{number of outcomes in } U}{\text{number of outcomes in } S}.$$

From these equations a conditional probability can be computed as

$$\Pr(E \mid U) = \frac{\Pr(E \cap U)}{\Pr(U)}$$

$$= \frac{\dfrac{\text{number of outcomes common to } E \text{ and } U}{\text{number of outcomes in } S}}{\dfrac{\text{number of outcomes in } U}{\text{number of outcomes in } S}}$$

$$= \frac{\text{number of outcomes common to } E \text{ and } U}{\text{number of outcomes in } U}. \tag{26.3}$$

This is exactly the result we would get by equation (26.1) if we used the fact that U is known to alter the experiment, thinking of U as the new sample space, and counting only those outcomes in E that are also in U. There is nothing in equation (26.3) that is not already in equation (26.2), but it makes explicit the cancellations carried out in the last example to compute a conditional probability.

EXAMPLE 26.25

Four coins are tossed. Two of them fall within view of an observer, who sees that they are both heads. What is the probability, to this observer, that exactly three of the coins come up heads?

The experiment is to toss four coins. An outcome consists of a string *abcd* of four letters, each of which is either an *H* or a *T*. The event *E* we are interested in consists of all such strings with exactly three *H's*. *E* has four outcomes in it:

$$E = \{THHH, HTHH, HHTH, HHHT\}.$$

Let *U* be the event that at least two heads have come up, since this is what the observer knows when he or she sees two heads. Then *U* consists of all of the outcomes with exactly two heads, or exactly three heads, or exactly four heads. The number of these outcomes is

$$_4C_2 + {_4C_3} + {_4C_4} = 6 + 4 + 1 = 11.$$

Further, every outcome in *E* is also in *U*, so the number of outcomes common to *E* and *U* is four, the number of outcomes in *E*. By equation (26.3), the conditional probability that *E* happens, knowing that *U* happens, is

$$\Pr(E \mid U) = \frac{\text{number of outcomes common to } E \text{ and } U}{\text{number of outcomes in } U} = \frac{4}{11}.$$

The knowledge that at least two heads must come up makes the outcome of exactly three heads more likely than it would be without this information. ∎

SECTION 26.7   PROBLEMS

1. Two coins are flipped.

   (a) What is the probability that the first one came up heads?

   (b) What is the probability that the first one came up heads, if we know that at least one came up heads?

2. Four coins are flipped.

   (a) What is the probability that exactly three came up heads?

   (b) What is the probability that exactly three come up heads, if we saw that one came up tails?

3. Four coins are flipped.

   (a) What is the probability that at least three came up tails?

   (b) What is the probability that at least three came up tails, if we saw two coins land tails?

4. Six cards are dealt from a standard deck without regard to order.

   (a) What is the probability that exactly two face cards were dealt?

   (b) What is the probability that exactly two face cards were dealt, if we know that a king was dealt?

5. What is the probability that four rolls of the dice total exactly 19? What is the probability of totaling exactly 19 if we know that one die came up 1?

6. What is the probability that two rolled dice sum to at least 9, if we know that one die came up even?

7. What is the probability that a five-card poker hand (unordered) has four aces, if we know that a four of spades was dealt?

8. What is the probability that a toss of seven coins will produce at least five heads, if we know that four of them came up heads?

9. Calculate the probability that four dice will all come up odd. What is this probability if we know that one came up 1 and another came up 5? What is the probability if we know that the second die came up 6?

10. Suppose *A* and *B* are events. Denote *A* ∪ *B* as the event containing all outcomes in *A* and all those in *B*. For example, if $A = \{a, b, c, d\}$ and $B = \{c, d, e, f\}$, then $A \cup B = \{a, b, c, d, e, f\}$. Show that

    $$\Pr(A \cup B) = \Pr(A) + \Pr(B) - \Pr(A \cap B).$$

    Conclude that, if *A* and *B* have no outcomes in common, then $\Pr(A \cup B) = \Pr(A) + \Pr(B)$. However, give an example to show that this equality fails to hold if *A* and *B* have outcomes in common.

26.8 Independent Events

Informally, two events are independent if the knowledge that one occurs implies no information about the probability of the other occurring. This can be stated in terms of conditional probability.

DEFINITION 26.3

Events E and U are *independent* if

$$\Pr(E \mid U) = \Pr(E) \text{ or } \Pr(U \mid E) = \Pr(U).$$

If E and U are not independent, then we say that they are dependent.

EXAMPLE 26.26

Consider the simple experiment of flipping one coin once. The sample space is $S = \{H, T\}$, and the nonempty events are $\{H\}$, $\{T\}$ and $\{H, T\}$. We claim that the events $E = \{H\}$ and $U = \{T\}$ are dependent. The reason for this is that $E \cap U = \emptyset$, so $\Pr(E \cap U) = 0$, forcing $\Pr(E \mid U) = 0$ (equation (26.2)). However, $\Pr(E) = 1/2$, so

$$\Pr(E \mid U) \neq \Pr(E).$$

Similarly, $U \cap E = \emptyset$, so $\Pr(U \mid E) = 0$, but $\Pr(U) = 1/2$, so

$$\Pr(U \mid E) \neq \Pr(U).$$

Therefore U and E are not independent.

Although we have formally verified that E and U are not independent, the dependence of these events in this experiment is obvious. In one coin flip, if we know that one of the events $\{H\}$ or $\{T\}$ occurs, then we know that the other does not. ∎

EXAMPLE 26.27

Draw two cards from a deck by first drawing one card, then drawing a second card (without replacement). The outcomes are pairs (a, b), in which a is the first card drawn, and b the second. Order makes a difference here, since, for example, if a king of hearts is drawn first, then b could not be a king of hearts. The card drawn first influences the possibilities for the card drawn second. The sample space S consists of all pairs (a, b) with a and b cards, but $a \neq b$. There are $52 \cdot 51 = 2652$ outcomes in S.

Consider the events

$$E: \text{a king is drawn first,}$$

and

$$U: \text{a jack, queen, king or ace is drawn second.}$$

Events in E are pairs (a, b) with $a = $ king and b any card different from that drawn for a. There are four ways of drawing a king, and after this, 51 ways of drawing the second card, so there are $4 \cdot 51 = 204$ events in E. Then

$$\Pr(E) = \frac{204}{2652}.$$

How many outcomes are in U? U will consist of all pairs (a, b), in which a and b are both drawn from the jacks, queens, kings and aces, together with all pairs (a, b) with only b drawn from the jacks, queens, kings or aces. In the first category, there are 16 possibilities for a and after that 15 for b, for $15 \cdot 16 = 240$ possible outcomes. In the second category with only b a jack, queen, king or ace, there are 36 choices for a and 16 for b, for a total of $36 \cdot 16 = 576$ outcomes. Therefore U has $240 + 576 = 816$ outcomes.

To compute the conditional probability $\Pr(E \mid U)$, we need to look at $E \cap U$. This event consists of all outcomes (a, b) with a a king, and b drawn from the jacks, queens, kings and aces. There are four choices for a, and then 15 for b, so $E \cap U$ has $4 \cdot 15 = 60$ outcomes in it. Then

$$\Pr(E \mid U) = \frac{\text{number of outcomes common to } E \text{ and } U}{\text{number of outcomes in } U}$$

$$= \frac{60}{816}.$$

Since $204/2652 \neq 60/816$, then

$$\Pr(E) \neq \Pr(E \mid U).$$

Similarly, it is routine to check that $\Pr(U) = 816/2652$ and $\Pr(U \mid E) = 60/204$, so

$$\Pr(U) \neq \Pr(U \mid E).$$

This means that E and U are not independent, and are therefore dependent.

This makes sense intuitively. If we know U, then we know that a jack, queen, king, or ace was drawn second. This changes the probability that a king was drawn first. ∎

EXAMPLE 26.28

We will repeat the experiment of the preceding example, but this time with replacement. That is, draw a card, record the result, then replace the card in the deck, shuffle, and draw again.

Now the sample space S consists of all pairs (a, b) with a and b possibly the same card. There are $52 \cdot 52 = 2,704$ outcomes in S.

Let E and U be the events of the preceding example. Now E consists of outcomes (a, b), with a a king (four possibilities), but b can be any card (52 possibilities). There are now $4 \cdot 52 = 208$ outcomes in E, different from the preceding example because this experiment is different. Now

$$\Pr(E) = \frac{208}{2704}.$$

This happens to be the same probability of this event in the previous experiment. Now there are more outcomes, but also more ways E can happen.

Now consider pairs (a, b) in U. There are 52 possible choices for a, and 16 for b, for a total of $52 \cdot 16 = 832$ outcomes in U.

Finally, the outcomes common to E and U are the outcomes (a, b) with a a king and b a jack, queen, king or ace. There are four ways to choose a, and (with replacement) 16 cards from which to draw b, for $4 \cdot 16 = 64$ outcomes common to E and U. Therefore

$$\Pr(E \mid U) = \frac{\text{number of outcomes common to } E \text{ and } U}{\text{number of outcomes in } U}$$

$$= \frac{64}{832} = \Pr(E).$$

The probability of E occurring is the same as the probability of E occurring, knowing that U occurs. Events E and U are therefore independent. Again, this makes sense intuitively. Because we are drawing with replacement, knowing that a face card was drawn second does not tell us anything about the first card drawn. ▓

26.8.1 The Product Rule

Equation (26.2) can be written

$$\Pr(E \cap U) = \Pr(E \mid U) \Pr(U). \tag{26.4}$$

This equation is called the *product rule*, and it is particularly useful in the context of independent events. If E and U are independent, then $\Pr(E \mid U) = \Pr(E)$ or $\Pr(U \mid E) = \Pr(U)$.

If $\Pr(E \mid U) = \Pr(E)$, then the product rule becomes

$$\Pr(E \cap U) = \Pr(E) \Pr(U).$$

If $\Pr(U \mid E) = \Pr(U)$, we can use the fact that $E \cap U = U \cap E$ and use the product rule to write

$$\Pr(E \cap U) = \Pr(U \cap E) = \Pr(U \mid E) \Pr(E) = \Pr(U) \Pr(E).$$

In either event, then, if E and U are independent, then

$$\Pr(E \cap U) = \Pr(E) \Pr(U).$$

Conversely, suppose E and U are events, and $\Pr(E \cap U) = \Pr(E) \Pr(U)$. Then by the product rule,

$$\Pr(E \cap U) = \Pr(E) \Pr(U) = \Pr(U) \Pr(E \mid U),$$

so

$$\Pr(E \mid U) = \Pr(E)$$

and therefore E and U are independent.

We can summarize these conclusions as follows.

THEOREM 26.3

Events E and U are independent if and only if

$$\Pr(E \cap U) = \Pr(E) \Pr(U). \blacksquare \tag{26.5}$$

This result is used in two ways. First, it provides another way of determining whether or not two two events are independent. Equation (26.5) is sometimes easier to check than the two conditions in the definition of independence. Second, equation (26.5) provides an often convenient way of computing the probability of an event $E \cap U$, consisting of outcomes common to E and U, as a product of the individual probabilities of E and U.

Keep in mind, however, that the product rule applies only when E and U are independent. In this case, equation (26.5) reads "the probability of E and U is the product of the probability of E with the probability of U.

EXAMPLE 26.29

Suppose the probability of having a boy is 0.49, and that of having a girl, 0.51. A family has four children. What is the probability that exactly three of them are boys?

Here the experiment is to have four children. An outcome is a string of four letters, for example, *gbbg* for girl, boy, boy, girl. The event E that we are interested in is that the family has three boys and one girl:

$$E = \{bbbg, bbgb, bgbb, gbbb\}.$$

The probability of any one of these is the product of the probabilities of each letter, g or b. The reason for this is that, in looking at four births $\alpha\beta\gamma\delta$, any of these letters can be a g or a b independent of what the others are. Therefore

$$\text{Pr}(bbbg) = (0.49)(0.49)(0.49)(0.51) = 0.06$$

$$= \text{Pr}(bbgb) = \text{Pr}(bgbb) = \text{Pr}(gbbb).$$

The probability of E is the sum of the probabilities of each outcome in E:

$$\text{Pr}(E) = 0.06 + 0.06 + 0.06 + 0.06 = 0.24.$$

This probability is based on the information that girls are slightly more probable than boys in individual births. If boys and girls were equally likely (each probability $1/2$), then we would proceed as follows. E has four outcomes in it, and the sample space has $2^4 = 16$ outcomes. Now the probability of E is $4/16 = 0.25$. ∎

SECTION 26.8   *PROBLEMS*

1. Four coins are flipped. E is the event that exactly one coin comes up heads. U is the event that at least three coins come up tails. Determine whether E and U are independent.

2. Two cards are drawn from a standard deck, without replacement. E is the event that both cards are aces. U is the event that one card is a diamond and the other is a spade. Determine whether these events are independent.

3. Two dice are rolled. E is the event that the dice total more than 11. U is the event that at least one die comes up an even number. Determine whether these events are independent.

4. A family has six children. E is the event that at least three are girls. U is the event that at least two are girls. Determine whether these events are independent.

5. An experiment consists of flipping two coins and then rolling two dice. E is the event that at least one coin comes up heads. U is the event that at least one die comes up 6. Determine whether these events are independent.

6. An experiment consists of picking two cards from a standard deck, with replacement. E is the event that the first card drawn was a king. U is the event that the second card drawn was an ace. Determine whether E and U are independent.

7. Two cards are dealt from an honest deck, without replacement. E is the event that the first card dealt was a jack of diamonds. U is the event that the second card was a club or spade. Determine whether these events are independent.

8. Four coins are flipped. E is the event that the first coin comes up heads. U is the event that the last coin comes up tails. Determine whether these events are independent.

9. Suppose a coin has been shaved so that the probability of tossing a head is 0.40. This coin is flipped

four times. What is the probability of getting at least two heads. What is the probability of getting exactly two heads?

10. A dishonest die comes up only 1, 4 or 6. This die is rolled three times. What is the probability that the total is 5?

11. A jar contains twenty marbles, eight red, eight blue and four green. The probability of drawing a blue marble is twice that of drawing a green, and three times that of drawing a red. What is the probability of drawing exactly two red marbles if three marbles are drawn at random, without replacement?

26.9   Tree Diagrams in Computing Probabilities

Tree diagrams, in conjunction with the product rule, often provide a convenient way of computing certain probabilities in which the experiment can be broken down into a sequence of steps.

EXAMPLE 26.30

A cabinet has two drawers, labeled left and right. In the left drawer are three envelopes, e_1, e_2, and e_3, and in the right drawer are four vouchers, v_1 through v_4. A drawer is chosen at random, then an object is selected at random from that drawer. What is the probability that the object drawn is v_3?

We may think of this experiment as proceeding in two stages, each of which is an experiment in its own right:

Experiment 1—choose a drawer.

Experiment 2—choose an object from a drawer.

The tree diagram of Figure 26.5 displays the sequence of experiments. First, there is a probability of 1/2 of choosing either drawer, hence the numbers on the first two branches of the tree. There is a probability of 1/3 of choosing any of the envelopes, if drawer one was chosen. There is a probability of 1/4 of choosing any of the vouchers, if drawer two was chosen. The branches from each drawer to the last outcomes are conditional probabilities, since, for example, we can only pick an envelope if drawer one was chosen. This is where the product rule for probabilities comes in.

To find the probability of choosing voucher v_3 first follow the lower branch to drawer two, with probability 1/2, then the branch from drawer two to v_3, which has conditional probability 1/4. The product of these two numbers gives the probability of choosing v_3:

$$\Pr(v_3) = \Pr(\text{drawer two}) \Pr(v_3 \mid \text{knowing drawer two was selected})$$

$$= \frac{1}{2} \cdot \frac{1}{4} = \frac{1}{8}.$$

As we might expect by symmetry, the probability of choosing any envelope is the same (namely $\frac{1}{2} \cdot \frac{1}{3} = \frac{1}{6}$), and the probability of choosing any voucher is the same ($\frac{1}{2} \cdot \frac{1}{4} = \frac{1}{8}$). Notice that the probabilities of all of the outcomes sum to one, as they must:

$$3\left(\frac{1}{6}\right) + 4\left(\frac{1}{8}\right) = 1. \ \blacksquare$$

The tree diagram is actually taking us through a sequence of conditional probabilities. The first stage of the experiment is to choose a drawer, but after this, the choice of envelope or voucher is a conditional probability, based on the choice of the drawer. In this example, there

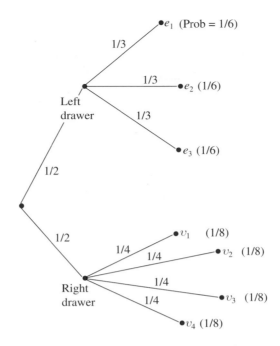

FIGURE 26.5 *Probabilities of outcomes of choosing a drawer, then an envelope or voucher.*

were only two stages to the experiment, but more stages could be accommodated by continuing the tree with more edges from each stage to the next one. For the probability of any final outcome o, first identify each path leading to o. On each such path, multiply the probabilities on each branch of the path, and then add these results.

EXAMPLE 26.31

A room contains three urns.

One urn has two baskets. One basket holds an envelope containing a $1 bill, an envelope containing $50 and an envelope containing $100. The other basket has three envelopes, one containing a quarter, one a half dollar and one a silver dollar.

The second urn has two baskets. One basket holds an envelope containing nothing and an envelope containing $1,000, while the second basket has three envelopes, containing $.50, $1, and $500.

The third urn contains four baskets. The first basket has four envelopes, three holding nothing and the fourth, $200. The second basket has two envelopes, one with nothing and one with $300. The third basket has three envelopes, with, respectively, $1, $50, and $500. The fourth basket contains two envelopes, with $100 and $500.

A person gets to choose one urn, then from it, one basket, and from it, one envelope. Determine the outcomes and the probability of each.

This is an example of a problem that takes longer to state than to solve. Figure 26.6 shows a tree diagram for this experiment. By following paths to each payoff, as many times as it occurs as an end result, we obtain the following probabilities:

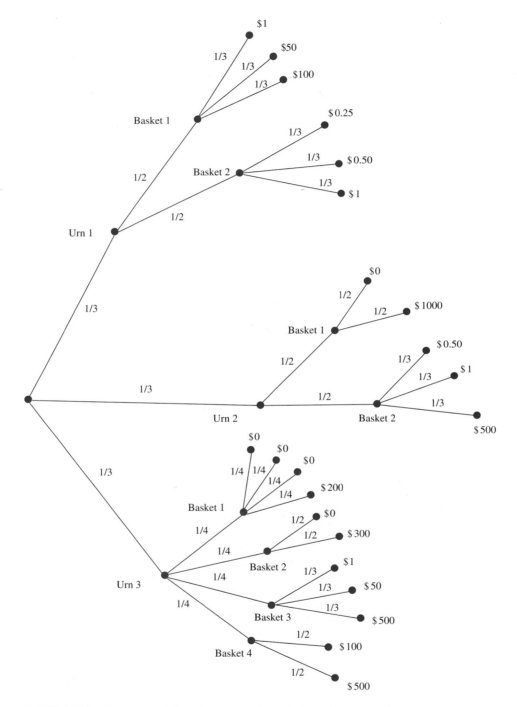

FIGURE 26.6 *Outcomes of choosing an urn, then a basket, then an envelope.*

$$\Pr(\$0) = \frac{1}{3}\frac{1}{2}\frac{1}{2} + 3\left(\frac{1}{3}\frac{1}{4}\frac{1}{4}\right) + \frac{1}{3}\frac{1}{4}\frac{1}{2} = \frac{3}{16},$$

$$\Pr(\$0.25) = \frac{1}{3}\frac{1}{2}\frac{1}{3} = \frac{1}{18},$$

$$\Pr(\$0.50) = \frac{1}{3}\frac{1}{2}\frac{1}{3} + \frac{1}{3}\frac{1}{2}\frac{1}{3} = \frac{1}{9},$$

$$\Pr(\$1) = \frac{1}{3}\frac{1}{2}\frac{1}{3} + \frac{1}{3}\frac{1}{2}\frac{1}{3} + \frac{1}{3}\frac{1}{2}\frac{1}{3} + \frac{1}{3}\frac{1}{4}\frac{1}{3} = \frac{7}{36},$$

$$\Pr(\$50) = \frac{1}{3}\frac{1}{2}\frac{1}{3} + \frac{1}{3}\frac{1}{4}\frac{1}{3} = \frac{1}{12},$$

$$\Pr(\$100) = \frac{1}{3}\frac{1}{2}\frac{1}{3} + \frac{1}{3}\frac{1}{4}\frac{1}{2} = \frac{7}{72},$$

$$\Pr(\$200) = \frac{1}{3}\frac{1}{4}\frac{1}{4} = \frac{1}{48},$$

$$\Pr(\$300) = \frac{1}{3}\frac{1}{4}\frac{1}{2} = \frac{1}{24},$$

$$\Pr(\$500) = \frac{1}{3}\frac{1}{2}\frac{1}{3} + \frac{1}{3}\frac{1}{4}\frac{1}{3} + \frac{1}{3}\frac{1}{4}\frac{1}{2} = \frac{1}{8},$$

$$\Pr(\$1,000) = \frac{1}{3}\frac{1}{2}\frac{1}{2} = \frac{1}{12}.$$

Again, these probabilities of all the outcomes must sum to 1. ∎

SECTION 26.9   *PROBLEMS*

1. A cabinet has four drawers. Two of the drawers each contain two envelopes, each containing $10, one drawer contains one envelope with $5 and one envelope with $50, and one drawer contains one empty envelope and one envelope with $1,200. A person can choose any drawer, and from that drawer, any one envelope. What are the outcomes and their probabilities?

2. A room has three urns in it. One urn has two compartments, one with nothing in it, and one with a key which can open any of four safes. One safe has diamonds, one has stocks, one has cash, and one has a Cracker Jacks whistle of sentimental value to the owner of the urns. The other two urns each have three compartments. One of these urns has two empty compartments and one filled with Confederate currency. The third urn has one compartment filled with expensive perfume, one filled with stock certificates, and the third with the deed to a mansion. A person can pick an urn and any compartment and, if the key comes up, any one of the safes. What are the outcomes and their probabilities?

3. A wealthy sultan has six automobile sheds which look identical from the outside. Each shed contains a number of identical containers, with each container closed, but holding one vehicle. One shed has two identical Fords and a Chevrolet (in their containers). A second shed has a VW Beetle (circa 1952) and a Porsche. A third shed has a Lamborghini and a very nice tricycle. A fourth shed has two Mercedes SUVs and a Honda Civic. A fifth shed has a World War I tank (partially destroyed in battle) and a Porsche. And the sixth shed has three mountain bicycles and a mint condition Stanley Steamer. A person can pick a shed, and then any container in that shed. What are the outcomes and their probabilities?

4. A traveler can choose to fly in a Piper Cub that seats one passenger, a company jet seating eight passengers,

or a jumbo jet seating seven hundred passengers. The traveler can pick any plane and any passenger seat on that plane. What is the probability that the traveler picks an odd numbered seat on the jumbo jet?

5. A person can choose any of five houses, each of which has four upstairs bedrooms. In one of the houses, three bedrooms are empty and one contains an antique chair worth $50,000. In another house, two bedrooms are empty and one contains $1,000, and one contains a newly minted nickel. In a third house, each bedroom contains $500. And in the last two houses, two bedrooms contain $1,500 each, one contains $20, and one contains a person-eating lion which has not been fed recently. If the person is to pick a house and then a bedroom, what are the outcomes and their probabilities?

26.10 Bayes' Theorem

Bayes' Theorem is named for the Reverend Thomas Bayes (1702–1761), although it only appeared in print after his death. It enables us to determine the conditional probability of E, knowing U, if we know the individual probabilities of E and $U \cap E$ (which is the event U and E) as well as the conditional probabilities of U knowing E and U knowing E^C.

The rule is as close as we normally come in mathematics to "getting something for nothing," and its derivation appears at first to be just a simplistic sequence of substitutions. If done in the right order, however, a very useful formula results.

Begin with an experiment, and consider events E and U. Recall that $E \cap U = U \cap E$. Now

$$\text{Probability of } E, \text{ Assuming } U = \Pr(E \mid U)$$

$$= \frac{\Pr(E \cap U)}{\Pr(U)}$$

$$= \frac{\Pr(U \cap E)}{\Pr(U)}$$

$$= \frac{\Pr(U \mid E) \Pr(E)}{\Pr(U)}, \tag{26.6}$$

in which we used the product rule (equation (26.4)) in the numerator to go from the next to last line to the last line.

Now consider Figure 26.7, in which U and E are shown as typical sets of outcomes (events). We can split the outcomes in U into two kinds: those that are also in E, hence in $U \cap E$, and those that are not in E, hence are in $U \cap E^C$. Furthermore, $U \cap E$ and $U \cap E^C$ have no outcomes in common. Therefore

$$\Pr(U) = \Pr(U \cap E) + \Pr(U \cap E^C).$$

Now apply the product rule (26.4) to each of the probabilities on the right to obtain

$$\Pr(U) = \Pr(U \mid E) \Pr(E) + \Pr(U \mid E^C) \Pr(E^C).$$

Substitute this result into the denominator on the right in equation (26.6) to get

$$\Pr(E \mid U) = \frac{\Pr(U \mid E) \Pr(E)}{\Pr(U \mid E) \Pr(E) + \Pr(U \mid E^C) \Pr(E^C)}. \tag{26.7}$$

Equation (26.7) is known as *Bayes' Theorem*, although it is actually a special case of a more general result to be stated shortly (equation (26.8)). The theorem enables us to determine the conditional probability of E, knowing U, if we know: the probability of E, the probability of E^C, the probability of U knowing E, and the probability of U knowing E^C.

The tree diagram in Figure 26.8 shows points representing the events E and E^C, which together contain all the outcomes. Outcome U is given. From point E (the case that E occurs),

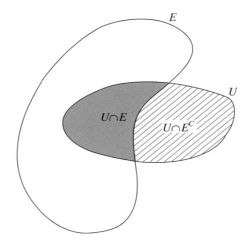

FIGURE 26.7 *U consists of outcomes in U and in E ($U \cap E$) and outcomes in U that are not in E ($U \cap E^C$).*

the two conditional events, $U \mid E$ and $U^C \mid E$ are shown. And from vertex E^C, the case that E does not occur, the two conditional events, $U \mid E^C$ and $U^C \mid E^C$ are shown. Four of the branches are labeled with probabilities. The numerator in Bayes' Theorem is the product of the probabilities on branches 1 and 2. The denominator is the sum of this product, and the product of the probabilities on branches 3 and 4. The paths ending in conditional probabilities involving U^C are not relevant in computing $\Pr(E \mid U)$ in this way.

Bayes' Theorem is all about drawing probability inferences from certain kinds of available information. Here is a typical application of the theorem.

EXAMPLE 26.32

A factory produces wombles. Suppose, over a given day, the probability of producing a defective womble is 0.04. Suppose the probability that a defective womble will result in injury to a womble user is 0.02, while the probability that a womble user is injured through no fault in the product is 0.06. A lawsuit is in progress, in which the plaintiff has been injured and wishes a settlement from the company. The defense attorney wants some measure of whether a womble was to blame. The defense therefore wants to know the probability that the product was defective, if it is known that an injury occurred.

Let U be the event that injury occurs, and let E be the event that a defective womble was produced. From the given information,

$$\Pr(E) = 0.04, \quad \Pr(U \mid E) = 0.02, \quad \text{and} \quad \Pr(U \mid E^C) = 0.06.$$

We want to determine $\Pr(E \mid U)$.

Figure 26.9 shows the three probabilities just listed, together with the probability $\Pr(E^C) = 1 - 0.04 = 0.96$ which we infer from the principle of complementarity.

We now have all the terms occurring on the right side of Bayes' Theorem, so

$$\Pr(E \mid U) = \frac{\Pr(U \mid E)\,\Pr(E)}{\Pr(U \mid E)\,\Pr(E) + \Pr(U \mid E^C)\,\Pr(E^C)}$$

$$= \frac{(0.02)(0.04)}{(0.02)(0.04) + (0.06)(0.96)} \approx 0.0137. \quad \blacksquare$$

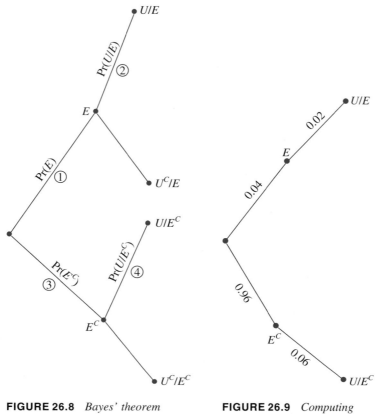

FIGURE 26.8 *Bayes' theorem (simplest case).*

FIGURE 26.9 *Computing probabilities of a defective womble, knowing that an injury occurred.*

In Figure 26.8, points for $U^C \mid E$ and $U^C \mid E^C$ were included for completeness, although paths to these two points were not used in Bayes' Theorem. In Figure 26.9, only the points representing events used in Bayes' Theorem are included.

There is a more general form of Bayes' Theorem in which the single event E is replaced by k events $E_1, \ldots, E_k$. Now we find that

$$\Pr(E_j \mid U) = \frac{\Pr(E_j)\,\Pr(U \mid E_j)}{\Pr(E_1)\,\Pr(U \mid E_1) + \Pr(E_2)\,\Pr(U \mid E_2) + \cdots + \Pr(E_k)\,\Pr(U \mid E_k)} \tag{26.8}$$

for $j = 1, \ldots, k$. Figure 26.10 illustrates this conclusion. Like Figure 26.9, this tree diagram contains only paths needed for terms in equation (26.8).

EXAMPLE 26.33

An airplane manufacturing company receives shipments of parts from five companies. The following table gives the percent of the total parts needs filled by each company, and the probability for each company that a part is defective (data taken over some period of time). A defective part is found. What is the probability that it came from Company 4?

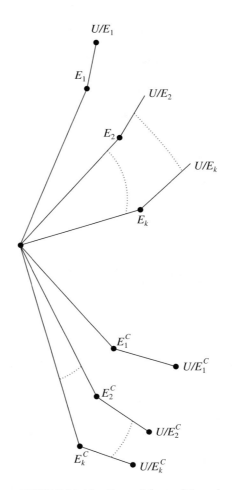

FIGURE 26.10 *General form of Bayes'
theorem.*

Company	Supplied	Probability of Defect
1	15	.03
2	2	.04
3	4	.01
4	48	.02
5	27	.08

Imagine a part has been chosen from the parts inventory. Let E_j be the event that the part came from company j, for $j = 1, 2, 3, 4, 5$. Let U be the event that the part is defective. We want to compute $\Pr(E_4 \mid U)$. From equation (26.8) we have enough information to do this:

$$\Pr(E_4 \mid U) = \frac{\Pr(E_4)\Pr(U \mid E_4)}{\Pr(E_1)\Pr(U \mid E_1) + \Pr(E_2)\Pr(U \mid E_2) + \cdots + \Pr(E_5)\Pr(U \mid E_5)}$$

$$= \frac{(0.48)(0.02)}{(0.15)(0.03) + (0.02)(0.04) + (0.04)(0.04) + (0.48)(0.02) + (0.27)(0.08)}$$

$$= 0.25,$$

rounded to two decimal places. Notice that the percent supplied by each company (Column 2 of the table) is converted to decimals in thinking of these percents as probabilities.

Just for comparison, consider the probability that the defective part came from the next largest supplier, Company 5. The denominator in applying equation (26.8) is the same as that used for Company 4, and we need only recompute the numerator:

$$\Pr(E_5 \mid U) = \frac{(0.27)(0.08)}{(0.15)(0.03) + (0.02)(0.04) + (0.04)(0.04) + (0.48)(0.02) + (0.27)(0.08)}$$

$$= 0.57,$$

to two decimal places. The disparity is due to the fact that, while Company 5 supplies a little more than half the parts Company 4 does, it has four times the failure rate on its parts. ∎

SECTION 26.10 PROBLEMS

1. A company hires people in four different groupings to install automobile carpet. The company has found that people with at least ten years experience generally produce products that are defective 1% of the time; people with five to ten years of experience, 3% of the time; people with one to five years experience, 5.7% of the time; and people with less than one year, 11.3% of the time. Of the total workforce preparing carpet, those with ten or more years comprise 45% of the total; those with five to ten years, 37%; those with one to five years, 7%; and those with less than one year, 11%. For each of these categories, calculate the probability that a defective installation was done by a worker in that group.

2. Suppose 37% of a company's computer keyboards are manufactured in Los Angeles, and 63% in Detroit. Suppose 2% of the keyboards made in Los Angeles have some problem, and 5.3% of those made in Detroit are defective. Calculate the probability that a given defective keyboard was manufactured in Los Angeles, and also the probability that it came from Detroit.

3. A drug trial performed with seriously ill patients produces the following data:

	Adult Men	Adult Women	Boys	Girls
Survived at least two years	257	320	104	152
Survived less than one year	619	471	51	38

(a) If a patient is selected randomly from this pool, what is the probability of choosing an adult male, if we are told that the person survived at least two more years?

(b) What is the probability of choosing a girl if we are told that the person survived less than one year?

4. A certain herb is grown in three places on Earth. It is known that this herb has medicinal value in treating certain illnesses, but that sometimes it is fatal. In the accompanying table, column two gives the percent of the total herb production of the world that is grown in that location, and the third column gives a percent of the herb from that location that is fatal.

	% of Total	Percent Fatal
Lower Amazon	62	14
Sub-Saharan Africa	25	6
Newark, New Jersey	13	1/2

For each location, calculate the probability that a sample of the herb came from that location, if it was found to be fatal.

5. Target pistols are manufactured in six cities. The following table gives the percent of the total production that comes from each city, together with the probability that the gun explodes upon firing.

	% of Total	Probability of Exploding
City 1	15	.02
City 2	7	.01
City 3	21	.06
City 4	4	.02
City 5	9	.03
City 6	44	.09

Suppose a gun explodes. Calculate, for each city, the probability that the gun came from there.

26.11   Expected Value

For anyone visiting a carnival or gambling casino, the expected value of a game or experiment is a very useful number to be able to compute. Here is an example to illustrate the idea.

EXAMPLE 26.34

A carnival game has a large wheel with the numbers 1 through 50 equally spaced around the outer rim. It costs $1 to bet on which number will end up at the top when the wheel is spun and allowed to come to rest. A winner receives $25. Is this a profitable game to play?

In view of the payoff, which is twenty-five times the cost of making a bet, it apparently is believed that such a game is a winning proposition for the player. At least, the game is popular and seems to draw a lot of players. On the other hand, we should be suspicious, since the carnival is a profit-making enterprise and the owners of the game must be making money or they would change the game. Who is right?

We will answer this question by trying to define a sense of how much we should expect to win or lose each time we play. On one spin of the wheel, there are fifty equally likely outcomes, assuming an honest wheel (a reasonable assumption, since the player can bet on any number). On any number we pick, the probability of winning is $1/50$, and the probability of losing is $49/50$. Since winning pays $25 and losing costs $1, compute

$$\frac{1}{50}(\$25) - \frac{49}{50}(\$1) = -\$0.48.$$

This is the expected value of this game from the player's perspective. A player should expect on average to lose (because of the negative sign) forty-eight cents on each spin. Therefore the "house" expects to win this much on each spin, with each player. Although the game owner will occasionally make payouts, the owner stands on average to make nearly a half dollar per player per game. ∎

Thought of in a slightly different way, the player will on average win $25 , for $1/50$, or 2% of the time, and lose $1 for $49/50$, or 98% of the time. Although the winning payoff is many times the loss on each game, a person will most likely lose so many more times than he or she wins that on average each person will contribute forty-eight cents to the carnival for each game.

In general, we obtain the *expected value of an experiment* by multiplying the probability of each outcome by the value of that outcome, with a plus sign for value gained, and a negative sign for value lost, and adding the results. Thus, the expected value has a perspective, since a loss for one person may be a win for another. Of course, the concept of expected value assumes that each outcome has been given a value or payoff of some kind.

EXAMPLE 26.35

Twelve coins are flipped. We win $8 every time at least eight heads come up, and lose $2 otherwise, with no significance placed on the order of the coins. What is the expected value of this game?

The number of ways of obtaining at least eight heads is the sum of the number of ways of obtaining exactly eight, nine, ten, eleven or twelve heads. This number is

$$\binom{12}{8} + \binom{12}{9} + \binom{12}{10} + \binom{12}{11} + \binom{12}{12}$$

$$= 495 + 220 + 66 + 12 + 1 = 794.$$

Since there are 2^{12} outcomes, the probability of obtaining eight or more heads is

$$\text{Pr(eight or more heads)} = \frac{794}{4096}.$$

The probability of this not occurring is

$$\text{Pr(fewer than eight heads)} = 1 - \frac{794}{4096} = \frac{3302}{4096}.$$

The expected value of this game is

$$\frac{794}{4096}(8) - \frac{3302}{4096}(2) = -\frac{252}{4096},$$

or about -0.0615 dollars. On average, the owner expects to make slightly over six cents on each game. ▪

EXAMPLE 26.36

Based on performance over the past thirty years, a salesman estimates the following probabilities for commissions on sales over the coming year: 0.25 probability of getting $400 from shoe sales, 0.15 probability of getting $200 from trouser sales, 0.35 probability of getting $600 from sport jacket sales, 0.20 probability of getting $1,000 from sales of complete golf outfits, and 0.05 probability of getting $300 from sales of derby hats. He wants to calculate his expected commission to estimate his income for tax purposes.

The information is most easily read by making a table:

Commission	400	200	600	1000	300
Probability	0.25	0.15	0.35	0.20	0.05

Notice that the probabilities add up to 1, since presumably all possibilities for commission income have been included. The expected commission income is

$$400(0.25) + 200(0.15) + 600(0.35) + 1000(0.20) + 300(0.05) = 555$$

dollars. ▪

SECTION 26.11   PROBLEMS

1. A game consists of flipping seven coins, without regard to order. If at least three heads come up, the player wins $5. If not, the player loses $9. What is the player's expected value for this game?

2. Five dice are tossed. If at least three come up 5 or 6, the house pays $50. If not, the house wins $4. What is the player's expected value?

3. Six cards are dealt from a standard deck, without regard to order. If one or more aces comes up, the player wins $45. Otherwise he or she loses $30. What is the player's expected value?

4. Nine coins are flipped. If seven or more come up tails, the player wins $50. Otherwise the player loses $3. What is the player's expected value?

5. Twenty marbles, labeled 1 through 20, are in a jar. A game consists of reaching in blind and pulling out three marbles. If at least two are even, the player wins $3. Otherwise, the player loses $7. What is the player's expected value?

6. Sixteen dice are rolled, and unordered results are recorded. If at least five sixes come up, the player wins $70, otherwise the player pays $4. What is the player's expected value?

7. Seven hats are in a closet. Four are black and three are red. A person reaches in and pulls out four hats, without regard to order. If at least two are red, the player wins $10. Otherwise the player loses $5. What is the player's expected value?

8. Six coins are flipped, then four dice are rolled. If four heads or a total of at least 24 on the dice result, the player wins $25. Otherwise the player loses $3. What is the expected value of this game?

CHAPTER 27

Statistics

With this background on counting and probability, we can begin to look at some of the ideas behind statistics.

27.1 Measures of Center and Variation

Many processes generate numbers, in tables of data, graphs, or some other format. Such numbers are called *data*. A *statistic* is a measure that assists in the analysis of data in order to extract information and draw conclusions from the data.

In this section we will discuss two kinds of elementary statistics. The first kind are measures of center, attempting to quantify in some sense the "middle" or "center" of a data set. The second kind of measure attempts to quantify the "spread" of the data, giving a sense of how the numbers vary from each other.

27.1.1 Measures of Center

Suppose we have N numbers, $A_1, A_2, \ldots, A_N$, not necessarily all distinct.

DEFINITION 27.1 *Mean or Average*

The *mean*, or *average*, of numbers $A_1, A_2, \ldots, A_N$ is their sum, divided by N:

$$\text{Mean of } A_1, A_2, \ldots, A_N = \frac{A_1 + A_2 + \cdots + A_N}{N}.$$

This number is often denoted $\bar{x}$. Sometimes the Greek letter μ (mu) is also used.

EXAMPLE 27.1

The mean of the numbers 16, −25, 27, 12, 15 and 31 is

$$\bar{x} = \frac{16 - 25 + 27 + 12 + 15 + 31}{6} = \frac{38}{3}. \ \blacksquare$$

As this example shows, the mean of a set of numbers need not be one of the numbers in the set.

In computing means, some numbers may occur more than once in the data list. For example, in a list of daily high temperatures in a city over a thirty year period, some temperatures may be repeated. These are still listed because they accurately record the data of interest.

The mean of a data set is a statistic that provides what is in a sense a "balance point" for the data. Consider a standard 12 inch ruler, and suppose the data set consists of the numbers 2, 3, 3.5, 4, 8, 11 and 11.5. Imagine a one gram weight placed at each of these points on the ruler, as in Figure 27.1. At what point should a fulcrum be placed so that the ruler balances? The answer is, it should be placed at the mean of the data set, which is

$$\bar{x} = \frac{2 + 3 + 3.5 + 4 + 8 + 11 + 11.5}{7} = 6.1429,$$

just past the half-way mark on the ruler. In this way the mean behaves like the center of mass of the data.

Mean is a useful statistic, but it must be treated with care.

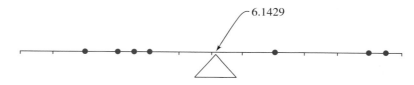

FIGURE 27.1 *The mean is the balance point for the data set.*

EXAMPLE 27.2

Last year there were eight graduates of a very prestigious electrical engineering progam. Upon graduation, they all received good job offers with starting salaries listed below:

Person	Starting Salary
Jones	$80,000
Smith	$85,000
Connolly	$78,000
Andrews	$90,000
Finch	$80,000
Hatton	$87,000
Douglas	$92,000
Seagram	$6,000,000

The average starting salary is $\bar{x} = \$824,000$. This is very misleading. The first seven graduates listed certainly did very well, but nothing like this. What the data do not reveal is that Seagram hit 200 home runs in 250 at bats in college and could pitch every other day, either right handed or left handed, with a 153 mile per hour fast ball and a curve ball that breaks at an angle of $3\pi/4$ radians. ■

In this data set, Seagram would be called an *outlier*, which is a point very far removed from all of the others. Outliers skew the mean and invite false conclusions if care is not taken. In some analyses of (fairly large) data sets, the highest and lowest numbers are dropped before computing a mean. For example, in some figure skating scoring systems, the high and low scores are deleted and the other scores averaged.

A different measure of center is given by the *median*. This number locates the "middle" of a data set, without taking into account the actual magnitude of the numbers themselves.

DEFINITION 27.2 Median

Suppose we are given an ordered data set $A_1, A_2, \ldots, A_N$, in which $A_j \leq A_{j+1}$ for $j = 1, \ldots, N-1$. The median of this set is a number M having the property that half of numbers in the data set are $\leq M$, and half of the numbers are $\geq M$.

The mean gives a center of gravity (weighted center) of the data set, taking the magnitude and sign of each number into account. By contrast, the median gives a geometric center (actual middle of the list), and only assumes that the numbers are written in nondecreasing order, without other regard to their magnitude. Like the mean, the median may or may not itself be a number in the data set. It is easy to verify that if:

$$N \text{ is odd, then } M = A_{(N+1)/2}$$

and

$$N \text{ is even, then } M = \frac{A_{N/2} + A_{(N/2)+1}}{2}.$$

In the case that N is odd, one number, namely $A_{(N+1)/2}$, is at the exact center of the ordered list, so in this case the median is a number in the list. When N is even, the median is the average of entry $N/2$ and entry $(N/2)+1$ in the list, counting from the left, and may or may not be a number in the list.

EXAMPLE 27.3

Find the median of the data set

$$-4, 16, 1, 2, 2, 3, 7, 5, 15, -4, 2, 1, 1, 3, 9, 8.$$

First order (or sort) the list:

$$-4, -4, 1, 1, 1, 2, 2, 2, 3, 3, 5, 7, 8, 9, 15, 16.$$

Here $N = 16$, so

$$M = \frac{A_8 + A_9}{2} = \frac{2+3}{2} = 2.5.$$

In this case the median is not in the set. There are eight numbers in the data set to the left of 2.5, and eight numbers to the right:

$$\underbrace{-4, -4, 1, 1, 1, 2, 2, 2} \; [M = 2.5] \; \underbrace{3, 3, 5, 7, 8, 9, 15, 16.} \; ■$$

EXAMPLE 27.4

Consider the data set

$$-4, 16, 1, 2, 2, 3, 7, 5, 15, -4, 2, 1, 1, 3, 9, 8, 1.$$

As an ordered list, this is

$$-4, -4, 1, 1, 1, 1, 2, 2, 2, 3, 3, 5, 7, 8, 9, 15, 16,$$

with $N = 17$ numbers, an odd number. If we denote these numbers $B_1, \ldots, B_{17}$, the median is

$$M = B_{(N+1)/2} = B_9 = 2.$$

and we can write

$$\underbrace{-4, -4, 1, 1, 1, 1, 2, 2}\, [M = 2] \, \underbrace{3, 3, 5, 7, 8, 9, 15, 16}.$$

The median is 2, but it is the third 2 from the left in the ordered list, not one of the other 2's. In this case the median is a number in the list. ∎

Data is frequently given by a *frequency table*, particularly if N is large. This is a table that gives each number according to its frequency in the list, saving the trouble of writing the number down as many times as it is repeated.

EXAMPLE 27.5

Data (already ordered) is given in the frequency table

Data Point	-3	-1	4	7	12	17
Frequency	5	2	12	6	12	21

The data has -3 listed five times, -1 two times, and so on. The sum of the frequencies is $N = 58$, and this is the number of data points. The mean is

$$\mu = \frac{(-3)(5) + (-1)(2) + 4(12) + 7(6) + 12(12) + 17(21)}{58} = \frac{287}{29},$$

approximately 9.897.

Because the number of data points is even, the median is $(A_{29} + A_{30})/2$. Counting the frequencies from the left, the 29th number in the ordered list occurs in the group of twelve 12's, and equals 12. The 30th number is also 12, so the median is 12. ∎

27.1.2   Measures of Variation

Measures of variation are indicators of how "spread out" the data is, as opposed to where a "center" might be located. The simplest measure of variation is the *range*.

DEFINITION 27.3   *Range*

The range of a data set is the difference between the largest number in the set and the smallest number in the set.

EXAMPLE 27.6

In the data set $-4, -4, 1, 1, 1, 1, 2, 2, 2, 3, 3, 5, 7, 8, 9, 15, 16$, the range is $16 - (-4) = 20$. If these numbers are marked on the number line, the number at the left is twenty units from the number at the right of the list. ▪

Note that the data set need not be ordered to compute the range. However, if the set is large, it is certainly easier to locate the largest and smallest numbers if the list is ordered.

Another measure of variation is the *standard deviation*, which considers variations of data points from the mean of the data.

DEFINITION 27.4 Standard Deviation

Let $A_1, \ldots, A_N$ be numbers in a data set, having mean $\overline{x}$.

1. If these numbers represent a sample within a (generally much) larger population, then the standard deviation of this sample is

$$s = \sqrt{\frac{1}{N-1} \sum_{j=1}^{N} (A_j - \overline{x})^2}.$$

2. If these numbers represent the entire population, or total set of items under consideration, then the standard deviation is

$$\sigma = \sqrt{\frac{1}{N} \sum_{j=1}^{N} (A_j - \overline{x})^2}.$$

For example, an x-ray unit might take data at 4000 points. The readings at these points would be the entire population of data, and σ would be used for a standard deviation. It might be useful, however, to periodically take samples of 30 of these points, for which we would use the standard deviation s.

The numbers s^2 and σ^2 (squares of the standard deviation) are called the *variance* of the data, and are used in some contexts.

The standard deviation of $A_1, \ldots, A_N$ is zero if and only if each $A_j = \overline{x}$. In this case the data points are all the same and there is no deviation from the mean. However, if one or more A_j has a large difference from the mean, then the standard deviation will be correspondingly large. A large standard deviation indicates data that are "spread out", while a small standard deviation corresponds to data that are clustered together, hence all lie fairly close to the mean. Of course, the idea of variation from the mean makes no sense if there is only one number, so $N > 1$ is assumed in defining the standard deviation s.

It is a routine exercise in algebra to show that

$$s = \sqrt{\frac{N \sum_{j=1}^{N} A_j^2 - \left(\sum_{j=1}^{N} A_j\right)^2}{N(N-1)}}.$$

Some statisticians use $1/N$ in place of $1/(N-1)$ in defining s. We will use $1/(N-1)$ because, for a given s, if $\bar{x}$ is known, then any $N-1$ of the data points determine the remaining one.

EXAMPLE 27.7

Consider the data set consisting of the numbers 1.1, 1.3, 1.6, 2, 2.1, 2.2, 2.4 and 2.5. These numbers are all fairly close together, with a range of only $2.5-1.1 = 1.4$. The mean of these numbers is

$$\bar{x} = \frac{1.1+1.3+1.6+2+2.1+2.2+2.4+3.5}{8} = 2.025.$$

For the standard deviation, first compute the sum of the squares of the differences of the numbers from the mean:

$$(1.1-2.025)^2 + (1.3-2.025)^2 + (1.6-2.025)^2 + (2-2.025)^2$$
$$(2.1-2.025)^2 + (2.2-2.025)^2 + (2.4-2.025)^2 + (2.5-2.025)^2$$
$$= 1.9650.$$

The standard deviation is

$$s = \sqrt{\frac{1.9650}{7}} = 0.5298,$$

to four decimal places. This small standard deviation is due to the fact that these numbers are fairly close to one another with not much spread. ■

Contrast this standard deviation with a similar calculation for the following data set, which is more "spread out."

EXAMPLE 27.8

Consider the data set 1.1, 4.6, 9.2, 15.7 and 28. The range is 26.9. Routine calculations give $\bar{x} = 11.72$ and $\sigma = 9.4943$. The large standard deviation reflects the fact that the numbers in the data set are spread out. Greater spread would result in a larger standard deviation. For example, if 1.1 were replaced by -12.7, making the range 40.70, then the mean of the new data set is 8.96, and the standard deviation is $s = \sqrt{481.19/4} \approx 10.968$. ■

Figures 27.2 and 27.3 show scatter plots of the data in Examples 27.7 and 27.8, respectively, giving a visual sense of the connection between spread of the data and standard deviation.

As another example of the idea of s as a spread, we would expect the standard deviation of the data set of electrical engineering starting salaries to be very large. A routine calculation shows that this standard deviation is approximately 2,091,400, all due to the outlier Seagram.

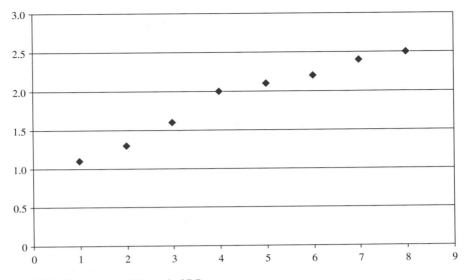

FIGURE 27.2   *Data of Example 27.7.*

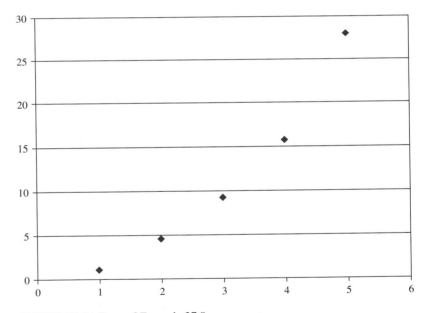

FIGURE 27.3   *Data of Example 27.8.*

SECTION 27.1   *PROBLEMS*

1. Sometimes the range of a data set is used to make a rough estimate of the standard deviation, according to the rule

$$s \approx \frac{1}{4} \text{ (largest number in the list } - \text{ smallest number).}$$

Compute s, then try this estimate for the following data sets:

(a) $-5, -2, -1.5, 0, 0, 1, 1, 1, 2, 7, 9, 11.6$

(b) $7, 1, -4, 2, 2, 1, 4, 1, 1, 2, 6, 3$

(c) $5, -2, -10, 5, 2, 2, 5, 3, 5$

2. Compute the mean, median, and standard deviation s for each of the data sets:

(a) $-4, -6, 2.5, 3, 8, 5, -3, -4, 8, 3, 2.2$

(b) $1, 1, 1, -1, 2, 3, -1, 4, 2$

(c) $3, -4, 2, 1.5, -4, -4, 2, 1, 7$

(d) $9.3, 9.5, 9.7, 10, 8.4, 8.7, 8.8, 8.8, 4.1$

(e) $-16, -14, -10, 0, 0, 1, 1, 3, 5, 7$

3. Data are given by the following frequency table:

Data point	−3	−1	0	1	3	4
Frequency	4	2	6	4	12	3

Find the mean, median, and standard deviation s for this data set.

4. Data are given by the following frequency table:

Data point	−12	−9.7	−8	−7.6	−5.1	4
Frequency	4	2	6	4	12	3

Find the mean, median, and standard deviation s for this data set.

27.2   Random Variables and Probability Distributions

A *random variable* on an experiment is a function that assigns a real number to each outcome of the experiment, based in some specified way on the random outcomes of the experiment. If X is such a random variable, then $X(o)$ is a real number for each outcome o of the experiment.

EXAMPLE 27.9

Consider the experiment of flipping three coins. Each outcome is a string of three letters, each an H or T. If o is an outcome, let

$$X(o) = \text{number of heads in } o.$$

X assigns a number to each outcome. In this example, for any outcome o, $X(o)$ must be one of the numbers 0, 1, 2, or 3.

The outcomes of this experiment are

$$o_1 = HHH, \quad o_2 = HHT, \quad o_3 = HTH, \quad o_4 = THH,$$
$$o_5 = HTT, \quad o_6 = THT, \quad o_7 = TTH, \quad o_8 = TTT,$$

and

$$X(o_1) = 3, \quad X(o_2) = X(o_3) = X(o_4) = 2,$$
$$X(o_5) = X(o_6) = X(o_7) = 1, \quad \text{and} \quad X(o_8) = 0.$$

For any repetition of this experiment, any outcome may occur, hence X is a random variable. ■

EXAMPLE 27.10

Consider the experiment of flipping six coins, but repeating these six flips fifteen times. An outcome consists of a list of fifteen strings of six letters each, each letter being an H or T. If o is an outcome, let $X(o)$ equal the total number of tails that came up in the fifteen repetitions of six flips. $X(o)$ can be any number from 0 through 90, inclusively and X is a random variable, because for any fifteen repetitions of the six flips, the outcome is random. ■

DEFINITION 27.5 **Probability Distribution**

A probability distribution on a random variable X is a function P which assigns a probability $P(x)$ to each value x that the random variable can assume.

If $\sum_x$ denotes a summation over all values x that the random variable can assume, then a probability distribution must satisfy

$$\sum_x P(x) = 1$$

and

$$0 \le P(x) \le 1 \text{ for each outcome } x.$$

Both of these requirements are consistent with our understanding of a probability function. The only new wrinkle is that now we have a probability function not on the outcomes themselves, but on the values of the random variable X. The probability $P(X(o))$ is the probability, not of the outcome o itself, but of $X(o)$, the value of the random variable at o. We are using P for this probability distribution, to distinguish it from a probability Pr that may be defined directly on the outcomes of the experiment. $\Pr(o)$ is the probability that the outcome o occurs, and $P(x)$ is the probability that the random variable assumes the value x. We could therefore write $\sum_x P(x)$ as $\sum_o P(X(o))$, the first sum being over the values x that X takes on, and the second sum over the outcomes o of the experiment.

EXAMPLE 27.11

Flip three coins. There are $2^3 = 8$ outcomes $(o_1, \ldots, o_8)$, each with probability $\Pr(o_j) = 1/8$.

Define a random variable X as follows. For each outcome o_j, let $X(o_j) =$ number of tails in o_j. Then X has the following values:

$$X(HHH) = 0, \quad X(HHT) = X(HTH) = X(THH) = 1,$$

$$X(TTH) = X(THT) = X(HTT) = 2, \quad X(TTT) = 3.$$

There are four values this probability distribution can assume, namely 0, 1, 2, and 3. A probability distribution on X is given by assigning a probability to each value X can assume. In this example, assign

$$P(0) = \frac{1}{8}, \quad P(1) = \frac{3}{8},$$

$$P(2) = \frac{3}{8} \quad \text{and} \quad P(3) = \frac{1}{8}.$$

The probability function Pr acts on the outcomes of the experiment, and every outcome is equally likely. The probability distribution P acts on the values of the random variable, giving a probability for each value of the random variable to occur. Not all values that the random variable assumes are equally likely. Three of the eight outcomes outcomes have two tails, so $P(2) = 3/8$ and so on. ∎

The mean and standard deviation for a random variable are defined as follows.

DEFINITION 27.6 *Mean and Standard Deviation*

Let X be a Random Variable. Suppose X has probability distribution P.

1. The mean of X is the number μ defined by

$$\mu = \sum_x x P(x).$$

2. The standard deviation of X is denoted σ, and is defined by

$$\sigma = \sqrt{\sum_x (x - \mu)^2 P(x)}.$$

The sum $\sum_x$ is over all values that the random variable can assume.

The expression for μ is reminiscent of the expected value of an experiment or game. Each term of the sum for μ is the product of a payoff x and the probability that the random variable achieves this value.

As a special case, if the numerical values of X are $x_1, x_2, \ldots, x_N$ and if X is equally likely to achieve each of these values, then $P(x_j) = 1/N$ and the formula for μ becomes

$$\mu = \sum_{j=1}^{N} x_j \left(\frac{1}{N}\right) = \frac{1}{N} \sum_{j=1}^{N} x_j = \overline{x} = \text{ mean of the data set } x_1, \ldots, x_N.$$

Further, in this case

$$\sigma = \sqrt{\sum_{j=1}^{n} (x_j - \mu)^2 / N} = \sqrt{\frac{\sum_{j=1}^{N} (x_j - \overline{x})^2}{N}},$$

the familiar formula for the standard deviation of a population.

It is a routine calculation to show that

$$\sigma = \sqrt{\sum_x [x^2 P(x)] - \mu^2}.$$

EXAMPLE 27.12

If we flip four coins, there are $2^4 = 16$ outcomes:

$$o_1 = HHHH, \quad o_2 = TTTT, \quad o_3 = THHH, \quad o_4 = HTHH,$$
$$o_5 = HHTH, \quad o_6 = HHHT, \quad o_7 = HTHT, \quad o_8 = HHTT,$$
$$o_9 = HTTH, \quad o_{10} = THHT, \quad o_{11} = THTH, \quad o_{12} = TTHH,$$
$$o_{13} = HTTT, \quad o_{14} = THTT, \quad o_{15} = TTHT, \quad o_{16} = TTTH.$$

Define a random variable X by letting $X(o)$ equal the number of tails in the outcome o. From the list of outcomes, we have:

$$X(o_1) = 0, \quad X(o_2) = 4,$$
$$X(o_3) = X(o_4) = X(o_5) = X(o_6) = 1,$$
$$X(o_7) = X(o_8) = X(o_9)$$
$$= X(o_{10}) = X(o_{11}) = X(o_{12}) = 2,$$

and

$$X(o_{13}) = X(o_{14}) = X(o_{15}) = X(o_{16}) = 3.$$

X can take on five numerical values. We can assign a probability to each numerical value of X by defining

$$P(0) = P(4) = \frac{1}{16},$$
$$P(1) = \frac{4}{16}, \quad P(2) = \frac{6}{16}, \quad \text{and} \quad P(3) = \frac{4}{16}.$$

For example, the value 3 (for three tails) occurs four times out of the sixteen outcomes of the experiment, so its probability of occurring as a numerical value of X is 4/16. Notice that these probabilities sum to 1.

The mean of X is

$$\mu = \sum_x x P(x)$$
$$= 0 \left(\frac{1}{16} \right) + 4 \left(\frac{1}{16} \right) + (1) \left(\frac{4}{16} \right) + (2) \left(\frac{6}{16} \right) + (3) \left(\frac{4}{16} \right) = 2.$$

On average, with four flips, we expect to see two tails.

The standard deviation for X is

$$\sigma = \sum_x (x - \mu)^2 P(x)$$
$$= (0 - 2)^2 \left(\frac{1}{16} \right) + (4 - 2)^2 \left(\frac{1}{16} \right) + (1 - 2)^2 \left(\frac{4}{16} \right)$$
$$+ (2 - 2)^2 \left(\frac{6}{16} \right) + (3 - 2)^2 \left(\frac{4}{16} \right) = 1. \ \blacksquare$$

Random variables are not restricted to have only finitely many outcomes. For example, if the experiment is to pick a positive integer k, and $X(k) = k$, then X is a random variable which assumes infinitely many values. This leads to the following definition, which includes a subtlety involving orders of infinity.

DEFINITION 27.7 *Random Variables*

A discrete random variable is one that assumes either a finite or countable number of values.

A continuous random variable is one that assumes an uncountable infinity of values.

An infinite set is called *countable* if it can be put into one-to-one correspondence with the set of positive integers. For example, suppose E consists of all powers 2^n, with n a positive integer. The correspondence $n \leftrightarrow 2^n$, for n any positive integer, matches each positive integer with a unique number in E, and conversely. E is therefore countable, or countably infinite.

An infinite set that cannot be put into one-to-one correspondence with the positive integers is said to be *uncountable*, or *uncountably infinite*. The real numbers form an uncountable set, because it can be shown that there is no one-to-one match between the positive integers and the real numbers. The real numbers have a higher order of infinity than the positive integers, even though both sets are infinite.

As an example of a continuous random variable, suppose the experiment is to choose a number (not necessarily an integer) between 0 and 1 inclusive. There are uncountably many such numbers. If $X(k) = k$ for $0 \leq k \leq 1$, then X is continuous because the number of values X can assume is uncountably infinite.

SECTION 27.2   PROBLEMS

1. Suppose two dice are rolled. If o is an outcome, let $X(o) =$ the sum of the numbers on the dice. Determine the probability distribution of X, as well as the mean and standard deviation for X.

2. Four coins are tossed. If o is an outcome, let

$$X(o) = \begin{cases} 1 \text{ if two or more tails come up} \\ 3 \text{ otherwise.} \end{cases}$$

Determine the probability distribution of X, and its mean and standard deviation.

3. A wheel having the numbers 1 through 20 equally spaced about its circumference, is spun, and the number that is on top when the wheel comes to rest is recorded. If o is an outcome, let $X(o) =$ the number of factors in the prime factorization of o. For example, if 7 comes up, then $X(7) = 1$ because 7 is prime. But $X(15) = 2$ because $15 = 3(5)$, and $X(12) = 3$ because $12 = 2(2)(3)$. By convention, 1 is not prime and has no prime factors. Determine the probability distribution of X, and the mean and standard deviation of X.

4. Suppose two dice are rolled. If o is an outcome, and the two dice show different numbers, let $X(o)$ be the quotient of the larger number divided by the smaller. If o is an outcome in which both dice come up the same, let $X(o)$ be this common value. Determine the probability distribution of X, and its mean and standard deviation.

5. Two cards are picked in succession (without replacement) from a standard deck. If o is an outcome, let $X(o)$ equal the sum of the numbers on the cards if both cards are numbered; $X(o) = 11$ if exactly one card is a jack, queen, king or ace; and $X(o) = 12$ if two of the cards are in the jack, queen, king, ace group. Determine the probability distribution for X, as well as its mean and standard deviation.

6. An experiment is to choose any integer from 1 to 30, inclusively. If o is an outcome, let $X(o) = 1$ if o is divisible by 2, $X(o) = 2$ if o is divisible by 3 but not 2, and $X(o) = \pi$ otherwise. Determine the probability distribution of X, and its mean and standard deviation.

27.3   The Binomial and Poisson Distributions

Not every distribution that can be defined is interesting. However, the binomial and Poisson distributions have important applications. This section is devoted to these two distributions.

27.3.1   The Binomial Distribution

The binomial distribution is used in a very specific setting. Suppose we have some experiment or procedure that involves a fixed number of trials (repetitions). For example, in flipping a coin fifty times, the experiment consists of the fifty flips, and each flip is a trial. Assume that the following conditions are satisfied.

1. Each trial must have exactly two outcomes. These might be called A and B, or S (success) and F (failure), or H and T (for a coin), or some other designation.

2. The trials are independent. The outcome of one trial is unaffected by the outcome of any other trial.

3. For each trial, the probabilities remain constant. For example, with coin tosses, each toss might have $1/2$ probability for a head, and $1/2$ for a tail, and these probabilities do not change as more trials are performed.

Now suppose N trials are carried out, and the result of each trial is S or F. Define $X(k) =$ the number of times S comes up exactly k times in the N trials. Then X is a random variable, taking on the values $0, 1, \ldots, N$. Suppose S has probability p on any one trial, meaning that F has probability $q = 1 - p$. Then the probability distribution P of X is the *binomial distribution*

$$P(x) = \binom{N}{x} p^x q^{N-x} \text{ for } x = 0, 1, \ldots, N. \tag{27.1}$$

Recall that $\binom{N}{x}$ or $_N C_x$ is the number of ways of choosing x objects from N objects without regard to order and is given by

$$\binom{N}{x} = \frac{N!}{x!(N-x)!}.$$

To see why equation (27.1) holds, consider the probability of getting S exactly x times in the N trials. Imagine picking x boxes out of N boxes, without regard to order. There are $\binom{N}{x}$ ways of doing this. For each such way, the probability of that way occurring is $p^x q^{N-x}$, because S comes up x times, each with probability p, and therefore F comes up $N - x$ times, each with probability q. Therefore the probability of getting S exactly x times is

$$P(x) = (\text{number of ways this outcome occurs}) \cdot (\text{probability of each occurrence})$$

$$= \binom{N}{x} p^x q^{N-x}.$$

Notice that this is the term having p to the x power in the binomial expansion $(p + q)^N$. Since $p + q = 1$,

$$\sum_x P(x) = \sum_{x=0}^{N} \binom{N}{x} p^x q^{N-x} = (p + q)^N = 1^N = 1,$$

as is required for the probability distribution of a random variable.

EXAMPLE 27.13

A district attorney is deciding on strategy for considering a plea bargain. The D.A. knows that jurors make a correct vote for guilt or innocence about 79% of the time. There are twelve jurors, who vote independently, and it takes a vote of at least ten to convict. What is the probability that at least ten jurors will reach a correct decision?

We want the probability of at least ten out of twelve votes being correct (as decided by the evidence and presentation). Let $N = 12$, $p = 0.79$ and $q = 1 - 0.79 = 0.21$. Since at least ten jurors means exactly ten, exactly eleven or exactly twelve, compute

$$P(10) + P(11) + P(12) = \binom{12}{10}(0.79)^{10}(0.21)^2 + \binom{12}{11}(0.79)^{11}(0.21) + \binom{12}{12}(0.79)^{12}$$

$$= \frac{12 \cdot 11}{2}(0.79)^{10}(0.21)^2 + (12)(0.79)^{11}(0.21) + (0.79)^{12}$$

$$\approx 0.523.$$

This is the probability that at least ten jurors reach a correct decision.

As another example, the probability that exactly eight jurors reach a correct decision is

$$P(8) = \binom{12}{8}(0.79)^8(0.21)^4 \approx 0.146. \quad \blacksquare$$

For a binomial probability distribution, the mean and standard deviation have a particularly simple form.

THEOREM 27.1

For a binomial probability distribution on N trials,

$$\mu = Np \quad \text{and} \quad \sigma = \sqrt{Npq}. \quad \blacksquare$$

These are routine computations. For the mean, write

$$\mu = \sum_{k=0}^{N} k \binom{N}{k} p^k q^{N-k} = \sum_{k=1}^{N} k \binom{N}{k} p^k q^{N-k}$$

$$= \sum_{k=1}^{N} N \binom{N-1}{k-1} p^k q^{N-k},$$

because

$$k \binom{N}{k} = \frac{kN!}{k!(N-k)!} = N \frac{(N-1)!}{(k-1)!(N-k)!}$$

$$= N \binom{N-1}{k-1}.$$

Now change the summation index to $m = k - 1$ to write

$$\mu = \sum_{k=1}^{N} N \binom{N-1}{k-1} p^k q^{N-k} = \sum_{m=0}^{N-1} N \binom{N-1}{m} p^{m+1} q^{N-1-m}$$

$$= Np \sum_{k=0}^{N-1} \binom{N-1}{m} p^m q^{N-1-m} = Np(p+q)^{N-1} = Np$$

because $p + q = 1$. A similar calculation verifies that $\sigma = \sqrt{Npq}$.

EXAMPLE 27.14

An assembly line produces automatic veebles. It has been found that the probability that a veeble is defective (fails to veebulate) is 0.02. If 40 veebles are selected at random, what is the probability that no more than three are defective?

Let $N = 40$ and $p = 0.02$, so $q = 0.98$. The random variable X is defined by $X(x) =$ number of veebles that are defective, for $x = 0, 1, \ldots, 40$. The probability distribution is binomial, and $P(x) =$ probability that x of the forty veebles are defective. If no more than three are defective, then none, one, two or three could be defective. We want to know

$$P(0) + P(1) + P(2) + P(3) = \binom{40}{0} p^0 q^{40} + \binom{40}{1} pq^{39} + \binom{40}{2} p^2 q^{38} + \binom{40}{3} p^3 q^{37}$$

$$= (0.98)^{40} + 40(0.02)(0.98)^{39}$$

$$+ 20(39)(0.02)^2(0.98)^{38} + 20(13)(38)(0.02)^3(0.98)^{37}$$

$$\approx 0.992.$$

This probability makes sense intuitively. The probability of one veeble being defective is quite small, so it should be very likely that fewer than four are defective.

The mean of this probability distribution is

$$\mu = Np = 40(0.02) = 0.8.$$

The standard deviation is

$$\sigma = \sqrt{Npq} = \sqrt{40(0.02)(0.98)} \approx 0.885. \quad \blacksquare$$

27.3.2 The Poisson Distribution

Suppose we have some specific interval or segment in mind. This could be an interval in time, or, in terms of a space unit, some segment such as a length, distance, area, or something else. We are often interested in the occurrence of some event falling within this interval or segment.

Let $X(x) =$ the number of times x occurs in the given interval. Then X is a random variable, assuming that the occurrence of falling or not falling in the interval is a random event. The probability that the event falls in the interval x times can be shown to have the form

$$P(x) = \frac{\mu^x e^{-\mu}}{x!}, \tag{27.2}$$

in which μ is a ratio of certain occurrences per interval, according to the setting of the problem. P is a probability distribution on the random variable X, and is called the *Poisson distribution*.

The binomial distribution is discrete, and in fact finite, since it deals with the probability of some event occurring a certain number of times out of a given number. By contrast, the Poisson distribution is not finite, since it can take on values $0, 1, 2, \ldots$.

In the Poisson distribution, it is assumed that the occurrences under consideration are independent of each other, and are uniformly distributed over the interval of interest. The occurrences are therefore not allowed to cluster in one particular part of the interval.

EXAMPLE 27.15

A game consists of tossing darts onto a large flat mat that has been divided into 450 blocks of 6 square inches each. In one session, 370 darts were thrown. Suppose we want the probability that one block was hit exactly twice or exactly four times.

We will use the Poisson distribution because the game involves an event (dart hitting the floor) occurring over an interval, which in this case is a 6-square-inch block of the floor. First, compute

$$\mu = \frac{370}{450} = 0.822$$

darts per block. Let $P(x) = \mu^x e^{-\mu}/x!$ for $x = 0, 1, 2, \ldots$. We want the probability of a block being hit exactly two or exactly four times. Thus, compute

$$P(2) + P(4) = \frac{(0.822)^2 e^{-0.822}}{2!} + \frac{(0.822)^4 e^{-0.822}}{4!} \approx 0.157.$$

Since $450(0.157) = 70.65$, we would expect on average that 71 blocks will be hit exactly two or four times.

For contrast, suppose only 80 darts were thrown. Now take

$$\mu = \frac{80}{450} = 0.178,$$

so

$$P(2) + P(4) = \frac{(0.178)^2 e^{-0.178}}{2!} + \frac{(0.178)^4 e^{-0.178}}{4!} = 0.0133.$$

Since $450(0.0133) = 5.985$, we would expect six of the blocks to be hit exactly two or four times if 80 darts are thrown. ■

It is possible to show that the mean of the Poisson distribution (27.2) is μ, and the standard deviation is $\sigma = \sqrt{\mu}$.

SECTION 27.3   PROBLEMS

Binomial Distribution

1. In each of (a) through (f), a number N of trials is performed, each with probability p of success. Use a binomial distribution to compute the probability of x successes for the given values.

   (a) $N = 8, p = 0.43, x = 2$

   (b) $N = 4, p = 0.7, x = 3$

   (c) $N = 6, p = 0.5, x = 3$

   (d) $N = 10, p = 0.6, 2 \le x \le 5$

   (e) $N = 8, p = 0.4, x \ge 7$

   (f) $N = 10, p = 0.58, 2 \le x \le 4$

   (g) $N = 10, p = 0.35, x = 3$ or $x = 7$

   (h) $N = 7, p = 0.24, x = 1$ or $x = 3$ or $x = 5$

2. A professor gives a test consisting of six multiple choice questions, each offering four answers from which to choose. A student who knows less than nothing takes the test by the method of random choice, simply guessing on each question.

   (a) What is the probability that the student gets exactly one question right?

   (b) What is the probability of getting exactly two right?

   (c) What is the probability of getting four or five right?

   (d) What is the probability of getting all six questions right?

3. In Problem 2, change the number of choices for each question to three. Now answer questions (a) through (d).

4. In Problem 2, keep the number of choices given with each question at four, but suppose now there are ten questions. Answer the questions posed in Problem 2, and also determine the probability of getting five, six, or seven questions correct.

5. An auto manufacturer purchases starting mechanisms from an independent contractor. Every week, a quality control officer pulls one hundred starters out of the shipment from the contractor and inspects each. A starter is either defective or not, with no range in

between. If two or fewer are defective, the total ship-ment of the week is accepted. Otherwise it is returned to the contractor. Further, it is known that overall the starter company has a 3.2% rate of production of de-fective products. What is the probability that the next shipment will be accepted?

6. In a clinical trial, it was found that 7% of those in the control group (who did not receive the drug) ex-perienced a particular side effect commonly associated with this drug. Suppose the same 7% rate was found in those taking the drug in the trial. Find the probability that among the 1000 subjects taking the drug exactly 92 exhibited the side effect.

Poisson Distribution

7. For $\mu = 1.3$, plot points of the Poisson distribution cor-responding to $x = 0, 1, 2, \ldots, 8$. Draw a smooth curve through these points. This will gives some sense of the fact that a Poisson distribution has an approximately bell-shaped curve although here $x \geq 0$ and the curve is not an exact bell curve.

8. Assuming a Poisson distribution, determine $P(x)$ for each of the following.

   (a) $\mu = 0.9, x = 6$

   (b) $\mu = 0.85, x = 10$

   (c) $\mu = 0.92, x = 4$

   (d) $\mu = 0.87, x = 8$

   (e) $\mu = 0.94, 1 \leq x \leq 5$

   (f) $\mu = 0.64, 3 \leq x \leq 5$

   (g) $\mu = 0.75, x = 3$ or $x = 8$

   (h) $\mu = 0.97, x = 1$ or $x = 3$ or $x = 10$

9. In a splatter test conducted over a full day, a car wind-shield is subdivided into 320 pieces, and it is found that 295 were hit by some material kicked up from the road by other cars. Assuming a Poisson distribution, determine

   (a) the probability that some piece is hit three times

   (b) the probability that some piece is hit from two to five times, inclusively

10. A new computer chip has one million microdots etched on its surface. In the manufacturing process, 997, 850 dots are imprinted with information. Assuming a Pois-son distribution, determine the probability that the pro-cess will incorrectly etch exactly three information packets on the same dot.

11. A golf driving range subdivides the area between 100 and 300 yards from the tee into 500 regions. In one four hour period, 476 balls were driven into this area. Assuming a Poisson distribution, compute the prob-ability that any region was hit 3 times. What is the probability that a region was hit from two to six times, inclusive?

12. A gaming machine randomly selects a positive in-teger each time fifty cents is inserted. A trained cocker spaniel always bets on 15. The probability of 15 coming up is 1/24. The spaniel plays the game 100 times. Assuming a Poisson distribution, find the probability

   (a) of winning 7 times

   (b) of winning 3 times

   (c) of not winning even once

27.4   A Coin Tossing Experiment, Normally Distributed Data, and the Bell Curve

Here is a simple but instructive experiment. Flip a coin twelve times and record the number of heads.

If we perform this experiment once, some number of heads from 0 to 12, inclusively, will come up. We would be surprised to see no heads or twelve heads, but this is not impossible. An outcome of, say, five, six or seven heads would not cause much reaction.

Repeat the experiment (12 flips) a few times, recording the number of heads each time. On any given set of 12 flips, we can get any number of heads from 0 to 12, inclusive.

Now suppose we conduct *N* sets of 12 flips. Record the number of heads on each set of 12 flips. Is there any pattern that becomes apparent in carrying out large numbers of repetitions of 12 flips?

Since in any repetition the number of heads can be any integer from 0 through 12, we might at first guess that there is not. However, a perhaps surprising regularity begins to occur if we look not just at outcomes, but at *frequencies of outcomes*. Instead of making a list of the number of heads in each repetition, count, over all the repetitions, the *frequency* of the occurrence of any given number of heads. For example, suppose we run 50 repetitions of 12 flips. If five heads occur in exactly 15 of these repetitions, we say that 5 has a frequency of 15. If eight heads occur in exactly 12 of the repetitions, then 8 has a frequency of 12. In this way, we can look at the frequency of each outcome over all the repetitions.

To illustrate, below are the results of $N = 21$ repetitions of the 12 coin flips, recording the number of heads on each set. (If you carry out your own 21 sets, you may get different outcomes). The first set of twelve flips had four heads, the seventh set eight heads, the thirteenth had six heads, and so on. Exactly three of the sets had four heads, so four heads has frequency 3. Similarly, 8 heads occur six times in row two of Table 27.1, so 8 heads has a frequency of 6, and 9 heads has a frequency of 3, and so on. Table 27.2 is a frequency table, summarizing the results of Table 27.1 in terms of frequencies:

It is convenient to display this frequency table in a graph of number of heads (horizontal) against frequency (vertical). The resulting bar graph is shown in Figure 27.4.

This bar graph, based on only 21 repetitions, does not suggest any pattern. However, Figures 27.5 through 27.9 show, in turn, frequency graphs for 86, 254, 469, 920 and, finally,

TABLE 27.1

Set of Twelve Flips	1	2	3	4	5	6	7	8	9	10	11	12	13	14	15	16	17	18	19	20	21
Number of Heads	4	6	9	8	5	6	8	6	8	9	8	6	6	8	8	6	3	9	4	4	6

TABLE 27.2

Number of Heads	0	1	2	3	4	5	6	7	8	9	10	11	12
Frequency of this Number in 21 Trials	0	0	0	1	3	1	7	0	6	3	0	0	0

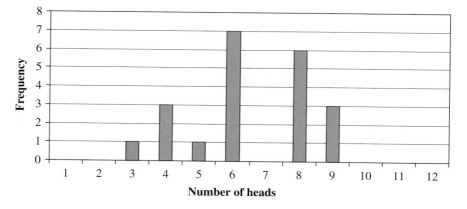

FIGURE 27.4 *12 coin flips, 21 repetitions.*

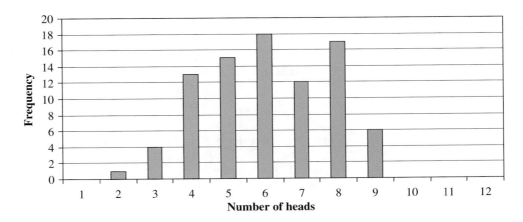

FIGURE 27.5   *12 coin flips, 86 repetitions.*

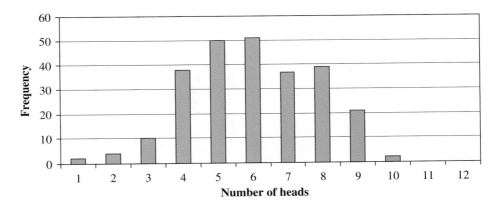

FIGURE 27.6   *12 coin flips, 254 repetitions.*

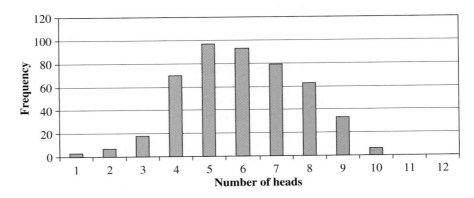

FIGURE 27.7   *12 coin flips, 469 repetitions.*

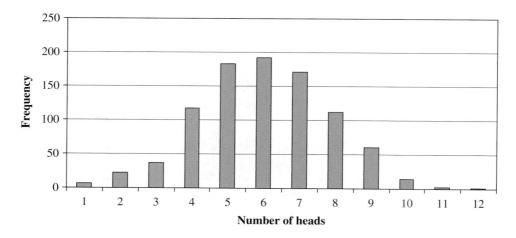

FIGURE 27.8   *12 coin flips, 920 repetitions.*

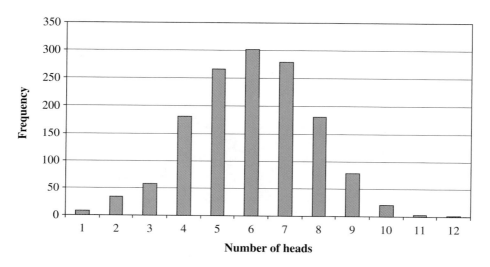

FIGURE 27.9   *12 coin flips, 1414 repetitions.*

1414 repetitions of the 12 flips. Figure 27.10 shows a summary of the bar charts of Figures 27.5 through 27.9, except that, instead of bars, we have drawn a curve through the tops of the bars. The bottom curve is for 86 repetitions of the 12 flips, the next for 254 repetitions, and so on through 469, 920, and—the highest curve—1414 repetitions. Notice that, as the number of repetitions increases, the frequency graphs in figure 27.10 approach a bell curve. We will give a more careful characterization of bell curves shortly, but for now, this is a curve having the general appearance of the graph of Figure 27.11.

The fact that the frequency charts approach a bell-shaped curve as N increases is characterized by saying that the data of these trials are *normally distributed*. Normal distribution means that there is a bell curve which can be fit (approximately) to the data. We will see that such a bell curve contains a great deal of information about probabilities of the experiment. Part of our task will be to see how to extract this information.

There are many other normally distributed data sets whose graphs approximate bell curves. For example, Table 27.3 gives score ranges on a standardized test that is administered nationally, and the percentage of the students taking the test who scored in each range that year.

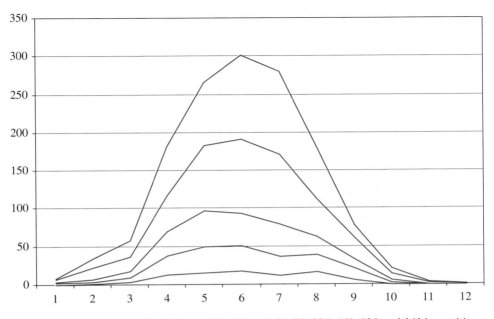

FIGURE 27.10 *Line graphs of frequencies of heads for 86, 254, 469, 920 and 1414 repetitions.*

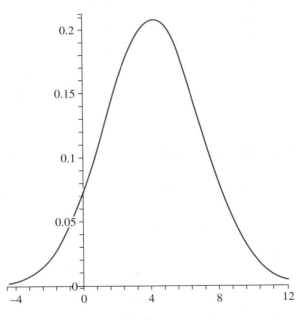

FIGURE 27.11 *Typical bell curve.*

This data is graphed as a bar chart in Figure 27.12 (a). If a curve is drawn through the tops of the bars, as in Figure 27.12 (b), an approximately bell-shaped curve results.

We have now seen two examples of curves we have referred to as "bell curves". Here is a definition of this term.

TABLE 27.3

Range	Percent of Students in this Range
200–240	0.9
250–290	1.8
300–340	4.6
350–390	8.9
400–440	13.5
450–490	17.6
500–540	17.5
550–590	14.3
600–640	10.6
650–690	6.4
700–740	2.5
750–800	1.4

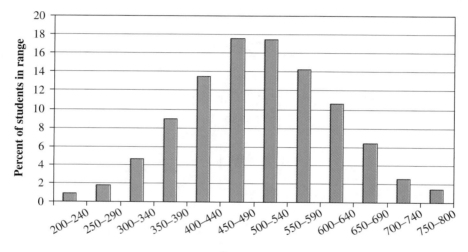

FIGURE 27.12(a)   *Standardized test scores.*

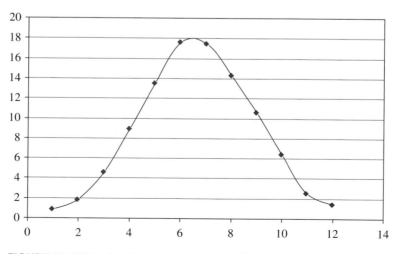

FIGURE 27.12(b)   *Standardized test scores bell curve.*

DEFINITION 27.8   Bell Curve

A bell curve is the graph of an exponential function

$$y = \frac{1}{\sqrt{2\pi}\sigma} e^{-(x-\mu)^2/2\sigma^2},$$

in which σ is any positive number and μ is any number.

Figure 27.13 shows graphs of three bell curves drawn on the same axes for comparison. All curves have $\mu = 6$, and the choices for σ are 3.5, 4 and 4.5.

The following are some important properties shared by every bell curve.

1. The curve lies entirely above the horizontal axis and and has a single maximum point at $x = \mu$.
2. The curve is symmetric about the vertical line $x = \mu$.
3. The curve is asymptotic to the horizontal axis as $x \to \infty$ and as $x \to -\infty$.
4. The curve has exactly two points of inflection.
5. The area bounded by the bell curve and the x-axis is 1:

$$\frac{1}{\sqrt{2\pi}\sigma} \int_{-\infty}^{\infty} e^{-(x-\mu)^2/2\sigma^2} dx = 1.$$

We will see that σ is actually a standard deviation, and μ is a median.

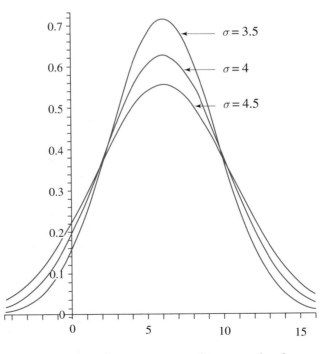

FIGURE 27.13 *Bell curves corresponding to $\mu = 6$ and σ equal to 3.5, 4 and 4.5.*

It is Property 5 which makes possible the following connection between a bell curve and probability.

THEOREM 27.2

Suppose the bell curve $y = \frac{1}{\sqrt{2\pi}\sigma} e^{-(x-\mu)^2/2\sigma^2}$ is the graph of a continuous random variable X. Then,

1. If $a < b$, and $P(a \leq x \leq b)$ denotes the probability that an observed data value $X(x)$ falls within $[a, b]$, then

$$P(a \leq x \leq b) = \frac{1}{\sqrt{2\pi}\sigma} \int_a^b e^{-(x-\mu)^2/2\sigma^2}\, dx.$$

(See the shaded portion of Figure 27.14.)

2. If $P(x \geq a)$ denotes the probability that an observed data value $X(x)$ is at least as large as a, then

$$P(x \geq a) = \frac{1}{\sqrt{2\pi}\sigma} \int_a^\infty e^{-(x-\mu)^2/2\sigma^2}\, dx.$$

(See the shaded portion of Figure 27.15.)

3. If $P(x \leq b)$ denotes the probability that an observed data value $X(x)$ is no larger than b, then

$$P(x \leq b) = \frac{1}{\sqrt{2\pi}\sigma} \int_{-\infty}^b e^{-(x-\mu)^2/2\sigma^2}\, dx.$$

(See the shaded part of Figure 27.16.) ∎

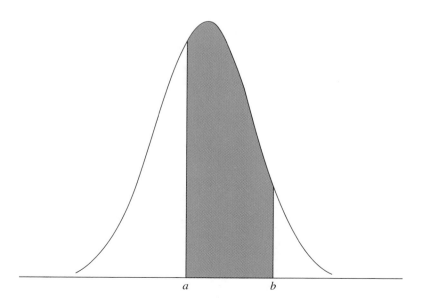

FIGURE 27.14   *Shaded area equals $P(a \leq x \leq b)$.*

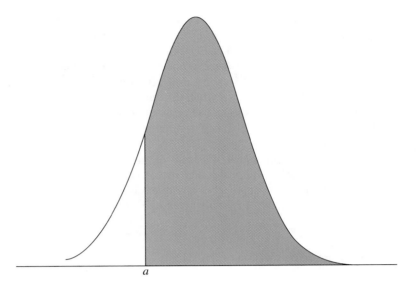

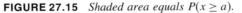

FIGURE 27.15 *Shaded area equals $P(x \geq a)$.*

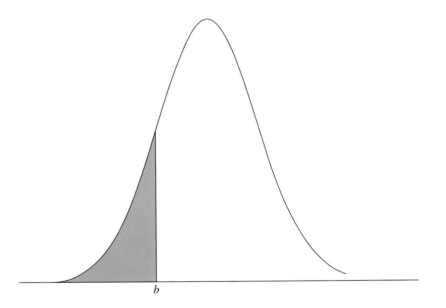

FIGURE 27.16 *Shaded area equals $P(x \leq b)$.*

A few years ago these integrals would be approximated using tables constructed for this purpose. Now, however, the integrals are quickly approximated by mathematics computation software, such as MAPLE or MATHEMATICA.

Now we must make the significant leap from a continuous random variable to a discrete random variable, since the latter are what are often generated by experiments or procedures that we actually carry out.

We have seen two examples (coin flips and/standardized test scores) in which the data approximated a bell curve. Such data, which are often values of a discrete random variable, are said to be *normally distributed*. We will now show how the mean and standard deviation of normally distributed data can be used to associate the data with a particular bell curve (by specifying the constants μ and σ), and then how conclusions about the probability of certain outcomes related to the data can be drawn from the curve, using the theorem.

Suppose we carry out some set of trials (such as flipping a coin, or inspecting items for defects, or determining whether a drug has beneficial results), and each trial has exactly two possible outcomes, which we will call A and B, or success and failure, or some other bimodal designation. Suppose also the outcomes of separate trials are independent of each other. We therefore have a binomial random variable which we will call X, where $X(x) =$ number of times A occurs in x.

Let the probability that A occurs in any trial be p. (For an honest coin flip, $p = 1/2$.) By complementarity the probability that B occurs is $q = 1 - p$. The frequency of A after N trials, as N increases, approaches a normal distribution given by a bell curve. The mean of the frequencies of any set of N trials given by this bell curve is

$$\mu = Np,$$

and the standard deviation of this data is

$$\sigma = \sqrt{Np(1 - p)}.$$

The bell curve, or normal curve, associated with these trials is the graph of

$$y = \frac{1}{\sqrt{2\pi}\sigma} e^{-(x-\mu)^2/2\sigma^2} \tag{27.3}$$

Now suppose we pick an interval of values on the x-axis, and we want the probability that $X(x)$ falls within this interval (that is, that A occurs between a and b times, inclusive, in x). Here we must be careful. The graph of the continuous bell curve from equation (27.3) is only approximated by the graph of the discrete random variable. We must therefore make an adjustment in relating area under this curve to a probability. This is done by what is called a *continuity adjustment* in the limits of integration, effected by adding $1/2$ to the upper limit of integration, and subtracting $1/2$ from the lower limit. This is described in the following theorem.

THEOREM 27.3

---

1. Let $a \leq x \leq b$. Assume that the random variable X has a binomial distribution. Then $P(a \leq x \leq b)$, denote the probability that an observed data value $X(x)$ falls within $[a, b]$, is given by

$$P(a \leq x \leq b) \approx \int_{a-1/2}^{b+1/2} \frac{1}{\sqrt{2\pi}\sigma} e^{-(x-\mu)^2/2\sigma^2} \, dx.$$

2. $P(x \geq a) =$ probability that the observed value is at least as large as a

$$\approx \int_{a-1/2}^{\infty} \frac{1}{\sqrt{2\pi}\sigma} e^{-(x-\mu)^2/2\sigma^2} \, dx.$$

3. $P(x \leq b) =$ probability that the observed value is no larger than b

$$\approx \int_{-\infty}^{b+1/2} \frac{1}{\sqrt{2\pi}\sigma} e^{-(x-\mu)^2/2\sigma^2} \, dx. \quad \blacksquare$$

Keep in mind that this continuity adjustment in the limits of integration applies only to the bell curve approximation of a binomial distribution.

The reason these conclusions are stated as approximations is that we are approximating the discrete random variable X by a continuous bell curve (chosen with μ and σ determined by X), and also the limits of integration include a continuity adjustment which is itself an approximation.

We will illustrate how the theorem is used to extract numerical information about events in an experiment.

EXAMPLE 27.16

Flip a coin 12 times. Previously we performed many repetitions of the 12 flips, charting the frequencies of the occurrences of heads.

Here $N = 12$, and the probability of obtaining a head on any one flip of the coin is $p = 1/2$, assuming an honest coin. The only other outcome of any coin toss is a tail, which has probability $q = 1 - 1/2 = 1/2$. The mean of the (approximately) normally distributed data is

$$\mu = Np = (12)\frac{1}{2} = 6,$$

not a surprising result. Ideally, if we flip a coin 12 times, we expect on average to obtain 6 heads, although in a specific run of 12 flips we might get any number of heads from 0 through 12.

The standard deviation is

$$\sigma = \sqrt{Npq} = \sqrt{12\left(\frac{1}{2}\right)\left(\frac{1}{2}\right)} = \sqrt{3}.$$

The bell curve for this experiment is

$$y = \frac{1}{\sqrt{2\pi}\sigma}e^{-(x-\mu)^2/2\sigma^2}$$

$$= \frac{1}{\sqrt{2\pi}\sqrt{3}}e^{-(x-6)^2/6} = \frac{1}{\sqrt{6\pi}}e^{-(x-6)^2/6}.$$

A graph of this curve is shown in Figure 27.17. The maximum occurs at $x = 6$, and this line is also the axis of symmetry.

Suppose we want to compute the probability that the number of heads that comes up falls between, say, 4 and 8. Taking care to use the continuity adjustment, this probability is

$$P(4 \leq x \leq 8) \approx \frac{1}{\sqrt{6\pi}}\int_{3.5}^{8.5} e^{-(x-6)^2/6}dx \approx 0.85109.$$

The probability is approximately 0.85 that a head will come up 4, 5, 6, 7 or 8 times. Figure 27.18 shows this probability as an area under the approximating normal curve.

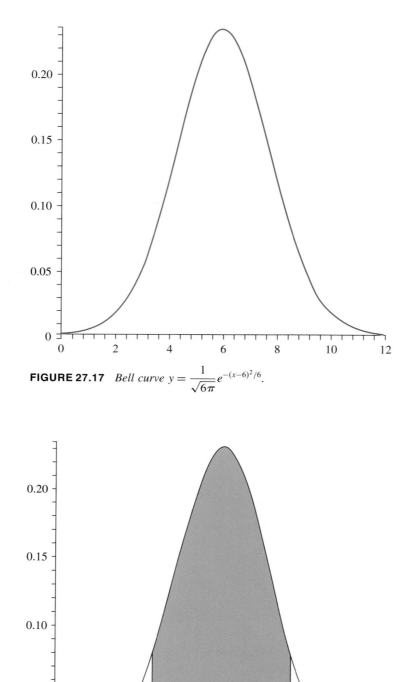

FIGURE 27.17 *Bell curve* $y = \dfrac{1}{\sqrt{6\pi}} e^{-(x-6)^2/6}$.

FIGURE 27.18 $P(4 \le x \le 8)$, *with the continuity adjustment.*

In this example we can compute $P(4 \leq x \leq 8)$ exactly using a binomial distribution for comparison:

$$P(4) + P(5) + P(6) + P(7) + P(8)$$

$$= \binom{12}{4}\left(\frac{1}{2}\right)^4\left(\frac{1}{2}\right)^8 + \binom{12}{5}\left(\frac{1}{2}\right)^5\left(\frac{1}{2}\right)^7 + \binom{12}{6}\left(\frac{1}{2}\right)^6\left(\frac{1}{2}\right)^6$$

$$+ \binom{12}{7}\left(\frac{1}{2}\right)^7\left(\frac{1}{2}\right)^5 + \binom{12}{8}\left(\frac{1}{2}\right)^8\left(\frac{1}{2}\right)^4$$

$$= \frac{1}{2^{12}}\left(\binom{12}{4} + \binom{12}{5} + \binom{12}{6} + \binom{12}{7} + \binom{12}{8}\right)$$

$$= \frac{1}{2^{12}}(495 + 792 + 924 + 792 + 495) = 0.854,$$

differing from the approximation by about three thousandths. If we left out the continuity adjustment, we would compute $P(4 \leq x \leq 8)$ as

$$\frac{1}{\sqrt{6\pi}}\int_4^8 e^{-(x-6)^2/6}dx,$$

which is approximately $0.751\,79$. We know that this is incorrect because we have computed $P(4 \leq x \leq 8)$ exactly in this case using a binomial distribution.

What is the probability that the number of heads will be 10 or more? This is

$$P(x \geq 10) \approx \frac{1}{\sqrt{6\pi}}\int_{10-1/2}^{\infty} e^{-(x-6)^2/6}dx \approx 0.02165.$$

As we might expect, getting 10 or more heads in 12 flips is very unlikely. This probability is represented by the shaded area in Figure 27.19.

What is the probability of getting from 0 to 6 heads, inclusive? This is the area of the shaded region in Figure 27.20, and is given by

$$P(x \leq 6) \approx \frac{1}{\sqrt{6\pi}}\int_{-\infty}^{6+1/2} e^{-(x-6)^2/6}dx \approx 0.61359.$$

It is a common error to think that $P(x \leq 6)$ should be $1/2$. However, there are seven ways the number of heads can be 6 or less, but only six ways it can be more than 6. This probability also dramatizes the need for the continuity adjustment. The area under this bell curve, for $x \leq 6$, is indeed half the total area bounded by the curve, or $1/2$. However, the probability $P(x \leq 6)$ is not $1/2$. The apparent discrepancy is due to the fact that this bell curve is only an approximation to the data of the experiment.

Finally, what is the probability that there will be exactly 7 heads? This probability is

$$P(x = 7) = \frac{1}{\sqrt{6\pi}}\int_{7-1/2}^{7+1/2} e^{-(x-6)^2/6}dx \approx 0.193.$$

Again, this is a probability we can compute without a bell curve as

$$P(7) = \binom{12}{7}\left(\frac{1}{2}\right)^7\left(\frac{1}{2}\right)^5 = 0.193\cdots. \quad \blacksquare$$

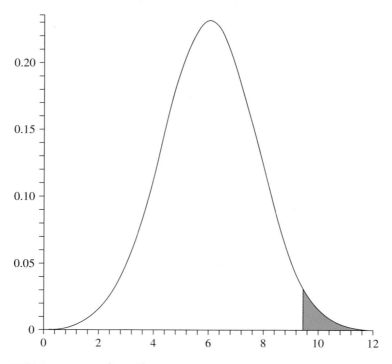

FIGURE 27.19 *P(x ≥ 10), with the continuity adjustment.*

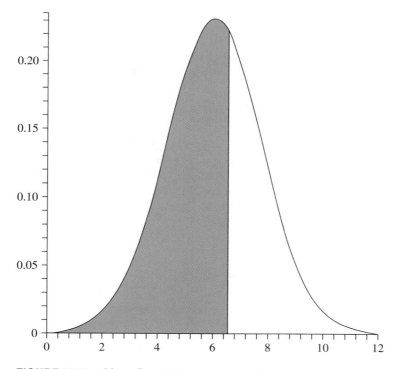

FIGURE 27.20 *P(x ≤ 6), with the continuity adjustment.*

EXAMPLE 27.17

Suppose we roll a die 50 times. We are interested in the frequency of having 4 come up.

Think of each roll or trial as having two outcomes of interest, either 4 or not 4. Since there are six faces on the die, the probability of getting a 4 on one roll is $p = 1/6$, while the probability of getting not 4 is 5/6. Since $N = 50$ for fifty trials, the mean of the normally distributed data is

$$\mu = (50)\frac{1}{6} = \frac{25}{3},$$

approximately 8.33. The standard deviation is

$$\sigma = \sqrt{50\left(\frac{1}{6}\right)\left(\frac{5}{6}\right)} = \sqrt{\frac{250}{36}} = \frac{5}{6}\sqrt{10},$$

approximately 2.64. The bell curve associated with these trials is the graph of

$$y = \frac{1}{\sqrt{2\pi}\sigma}e^{-(x-\mu)^2/2\sigma^2} = \frac{1}{\sqrt{2\pi}\left(\frac{5}{6}\sqrt{10}\right)}e^{-9(x-25/3)^2/125}$$

$$= \frac{6}{5\sqrt{20\pi}}e^{-9(x-25/3)^2/125}.$$

Suppose, for example, we want the probability that, on fifty rolls of the die, the number of times 4 comes up is between 2 and 15, inclusively. This probability is (approximately) the

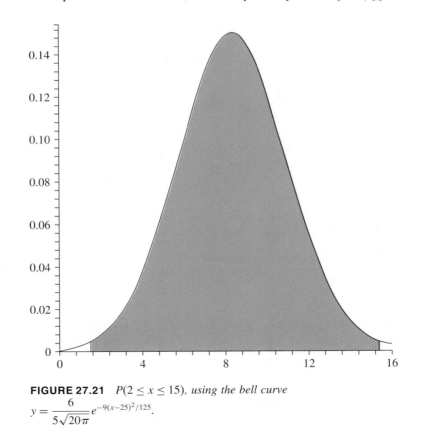

FIGURE 27.21 $P(2 \le x \le 15)$, *using the bell curve*

$$y = \frac{6}{5\sqrt{20\pi}}e^{-9(x-25)^2/125}.$$

shaded area under the bell curve shown in Figure 27.21. This area appears to be nearly all of the area under the curve, so we expect $P(2 \leq x \leq 15)$ to be close to 1. Compute

$$P(2 \leq x \leq 15) \approx \frac{6}{5\sqrt{20\pi}} \int_{2-1/2}^{15+1/2} e^{-9(x-25/3)^2/125} dx \approx 0.99198.$$

Suppose we want the probability that the number of 4's that come up in fifty rolls is 47 or 48. The area between the bell curve and the horizontal axis for x between 47 and 48 is nearly 0. In fact, it is so small that it doesn't show up on the graph (in the scale of the drawing). This means that, although 47 or 48 4s are not impossible in fifty rolls, it is extremely unlikely that either of these number of 4s will come up. To check this intuition, compute

$$P(47 \leq x \leq 48) \approx \frac{6}{5\sqrt{20\pi}} \int_{47-1/2}^{48+1/2} e^{-9(x-25/3)^2/125} dx$$

$$\approx 7.7325(10^{-48}). \ \blacksquare$$

EXAMPLE 27.18

Suppose an airline finds (by analyzing past flight information) that its planes fly an average of 1500 miles per month per passenger, with a standard deviation of 90 miles. Suppose we want the probability that a typical passenger flies between 1400 and 1600 miles per month.

Under the assumption that the data is normally distributed, we have $\mu = 1500$ and $\sigma = 90$, and these determine the appropriate bell curve for this study:

$$y = \frac{1}{\sqrt{2\pi}\sigma} e^{-(x-\mu)^2/2\sigma^2} = \frac{1}{90\sqrt{2\pi}} e^{-(x-1500)^2/16200}.$$

The probability that a typical passenger flies between 1400 and 1600 miles per month is approximately

$$P(1400 \leq x \leq 1600) \approx \frac{1}{90\sqrt{2\pi}} \int_{1400-1/2}^{1600+1/2} e^{-(x-1500)^2/16200} dx$$

$$\approx 0.735\,86. \ \blacksquare$$

27.4.1 The Standard Bell Curve

The bell curve corresponding to $\mu = 0$ and $\sigma = 1$ is the graph of

$$y = \frac{1}{\sqrt{2\pi}} e^{-z^2/2}. \tag{27.4}$$

The graph is shown in Figure 27.22, with the horizontal axis as the line of symmetry. This curve is called the *standard* or *normal bell curve*. It is routine to use z as the variable in this context, and statisticians often refer to values on the horizontal axis as *z-scores*.

One reason for having a standard bell curve is that it provides a reference point from which to compile certain information in tables. To illustrate one case where this is useful, suppose we have in mind a particular area under the standardized bell curve. For example, we may have a particular target probability that we are aiming for, and we want to know a value $z = z_0$ so

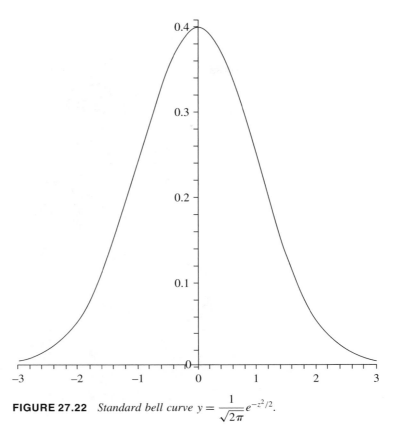

FIGURE 27.22 *Standard bell curve* $y = \dfrac{1}{\sqrt{2\pi}} e^{-z^2/2}.$

that the area under the curve, to the left of z_0, gives that probability. If the probability we are aiming for is k, then we need to solve

$$\frac{1}{\sqrt{2\pi}} \int_{-\infty}^{z_0} e^{-z^2/2} dz = k$$

for z_0, a highly nontrivial task. Table 27.4 gives some commonly used probabilities, and the value of z_0 such that that the area to the left of z_0 under the standard bell curve gives this probability.

For example,

$$\frac{1}{\sqrt{2\pi}} \int_{-\infty}^{1.645} e^{-z^2/2} dz = 0.95002$$

TABLE 27.4

Area to the Left of z_0	z_0
0.99	2.33
0.95	1.645
0.90	1.29
0.85	1.04
0.80	0.84
0.75	0.67

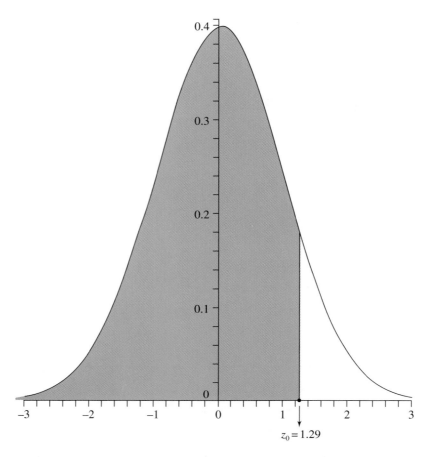

FIGURE 27.23   *Area under the standard bell curve to the left of $z_0 = 1.29$ is approximately 0.90.*

and

$$\frac{1}{\sqrt{2\pi}} \int_{-\infty}^{1.29} e^{-z^2/2} dz = 0.90147.$$

The last integral is illustrated in Figure 27.23.

27.4.2   The 68, 95, 99.7 Rule

Suppose we have some experiment that involves a fixed number of trials. For example, in flipping a coin fifty times, the experiment consists of the fifty flips, each of which is a trial. Let the probability of the result of a trial that we are interested in (such as heads for a coin toss) be p. Compute the mean $\mu = Np$ and standard deviation $\sigma = \sqrt{Np(1-p)}$. Define the random variable $X(x) =$ number of occurrences of the trial result of interest in outcome x. Then the bell curve associated with X is

$$y = \frac{1}{\sqrt{2\pi}\sigma} e^{-(x-\mu)^2/2\sigma^2}. \tag{27.5}$$

It is routine to check (solve $y''(x) = 0$) that this curve has two points of inflection, namely $x = \mu + \sigma$ and $x = \mu - \sigma$. The points of inflection are therefore one standard deviation to the left and right of the mean, hence to the left and right of the bell curve's axis of symmetry. Moving one, two or three standard deviations to the left or right of the mean is particularly significant, according to the following rule.

The* 68, 95, 99.7 *Rule

> The area under the bell curve between $\mu - \sigma$ and $\mu + \sigma$ is approximately 68% of the total area.
>
> The area under bell curve between $\mu - 2\sigma$ and $\mu + 2\sigma$ is approximately 95% of the total area.
>
> The area under bell curve between $\mu - 3\sigma$ and $\mu + 3\sigma$ is approximately 99.7% of the total area.

In terms of probabilities:

> The probability that the outcome falls between $\mu - \sigma$ and $\mu + \sigma$ is approximately 0.68.
>
> The probability that the outcome falls between $\mu - 2\sigma$ and $\mu + 2\sigma$ is approximately 0.95.
>
> The probability that the outcome falls between $\mu - 3\sigma$ and $\mu + 3\sigma$ is approximately 0.997.
>
> The probability that an outcome falls to the left of $\mu - 3\sigma$ or to the right of $\mu + 3\sigma$ is $1 - 0.997 = 0.003$. Hence it is nearly certain that any outcome of the experiment will fall within three standard deviations of the mean.

EXAMPLE 27.19

Suppose we have a dishonest coin, and the probability of a head on any toss is $p = 0.8$. Flip the coin 1000 times. Compute $\mu = 1000(0.8) = 800$ and

$$\sigma = \sqrt{1000(0.8)(0.2)} = 12.65.$$

Now $\mu - \sigma = 787.35$ and $\mu + \sigma = 812.65$, so in the thousand flips, there is a probability of about .68 of seeing between 787 and 813 heads. There is a probability of about .95 of seeing between 774 and 826 heads, and a probability of about .997 of seeing between 762 and 838 heads. ∎

SECTION 27.4   PROBLEMS

1. Roll a die 90 times. We are interested in the outcome that a 6 comes up.

(a) Determine μ and σ for this experiment.

(b) Write the equation of the corresponding bell curve and graph the curve.
Determine the probability that a 6 comes up:

(c) between 30 and 60 times

(d) between 2 and 80 times

(e) at least 35 times

(f) fewer than 20 times

(g) exactly 45 times

2. A coin is flipped 100 times.

(a) Determine μ and σ for this experiment.

(b) Write the equation of the appropriate bell curve and graph the curve.
Determine the probability that a head comes up:

(c) between 20 and 40 times

(d) between 10 and 50 times

(e) between 45 and 55 times

(f) at least 30 times

(g) fewer than 60 times

(h) exactly 55 times

3. In a certain kingdom, babies are born with a probability of 0.48 for boys and 0.52 for girls. In a particular year, it is expected that 350 children will be born. We are interested in the outcome that a newborn child was a girl.

(a) Determine μ and σ for this experiment.

(b) Write the equation of the bell curve and graph the curve.

Determine the probability that:

(c) at least 220 of the babies will be girls

(d) at least 150 of the babies will be girls

(e) the number of girl babies will fall between 120 and 250

(f) the number of girl babies will be exactly 180

4. It is known that, when a stratigather is produced by a certain company, it may be either left handed or right handed. The probability that a particular stratigather will be right handed is 0.58, and that it will be left handed, 0.42. A thousand stratigathers are picked at random. Compute the probability

(a) That at least 400 of these are right handed.

(b) That between 400 and 600 are right handed.

(c) That no more than 450 are right handed.

(d) That exactly 520 are right handed.

5. A bus company finds that its buses drive an average of 700 miles per month for each passenger with a standard deviation of 65 miles. Assume that the data consisting of the number of miles flown per passenger per month

is normally distributed. Determine the probability that a typical passenger rides between 250 and 600 miles per month. What is the probability that the passenger rides between 600 and 900 miles per month?

6. An auto rental firm finds that its cars travel an average of 940 miles for each rental, with a standard deviation of 76 miles. Find the probability that a customer who rents the car drives it between 750 and 1000 miles. What is the probability that the car is driven between 300 and 500 miles?

7. In a recent year in the American League, hitters averaged .247, with a standard deviation of .021. Determine the probability that a hitter averaged between .245 and 270. What is the probability that a hitter averaged over .260? What is the probability that a batter averages .300 or more?

8. A coin has a probability of 0.42 of coming up heads if it is flipped. The coin is flipped 2000 times.

(a) Determine a and b so that there is a probability of about 0.68 of seeing between a and b heads.

(b) Determine a and b so that there is a probability of about 0.95 of seeing between a and b heads.

(c) Determine a and b so that there is a probability of about 0.99 of seeing between a and b heads.

9. An honest die is rolled, and we are interested in the outcome that the number that comes up is even. A total of 550 tosses are made.

(a) Determine a and b so that there is a probability of about 0.68 of seeing between a and b even tosses.

(b) Determine a and b so that there is a probability of about 0.95 of seeing between a and b even tosses.

(c) Determine a and b so that there is a probability of about 0.99 of seeing between a and b even tosses.

27.5   Sampling Distributions and the Central Limit Theorem

We now have some facts and information about data sets and how certain statistics can be extracted from them. We now move toward addressing a fundamental problem of statistics.

In statistical studies, the term *population* refers to the set of all the objects under study. For example, if we are studying airplane parts coming off a factory production line in a certain time period, then the population would consist of all the parts produced in that time.

Suppose we want to measure the success of some process (such as manufacturing) by estimating how many defective products are produced. An obvious strategy is to sample the product to try to infer from the sample a measure of how many products are defective in the entire population. How can we do this in a reasonable and efficient manner? Clearly the answer lies somewhere between the extremes of inspecting every item (probably costly and inefficient), and inspecting only none or one (of questionable value). How do we decide how many items to sample, and what confidence can we have in conclusions drawn from samples? In particular, can we tie the number of samples to a predetermined level of confidence, so that we can set the sample size to achieve this confidence level?

To approach this important issue, let us agree that, in taking a sample from a collection of objects, we will sample *with replacement*. This means that, if we pick an object and make some measurement on it, then we replace this object back in the population before picking another object to test. This way each sample is chosen from the entire population.

One reason for doing this is that usually very large numbers of objects are involved, so sampling with or without replacement makes little numerical difference. In addition, sampling with replacement ensures that the selection of each sample object is independent from the selection of any other, since all objects are chosen from the entire set of objects. This is a considerable simplification.

We also will agree that sample size is fixed at some number n throughout the discussion. Thus, all samples in a given study are taken with replacement, and have the same sample size.

When we take samples involving numerical quantities, each sample will have a mean (mean of the numbers in the sample). The *sampling distribution of the mean* is the probability distribution of the means of the samples, assuming that all the samples have the same size. We also may compute other statistics from the samples, such as medians of the samples and standard deviations of the samples, and average these.

EXAMPLE 27.20

A contractor looks at the number of buildings his company has completed over the past five years, and the numbers are 1, 4, 6, 8 and 9. These numbers constitute the population under consideration. Samples of size two are taken, with replacement. Of course in reality, we would not take samples of two out of five, but this example has the sole purpose of illustrating the discussion.

With replacement, there are $5^2 = 25$ samples of two of the numbers. The samples are listed in Table 27.5, together with each sample mean and sample standard deviation.

If we average all fifty numbers contained in the samples, we find that this mean is 5.6. Column 2 of the table contains the mean of each sample, which in this case is an average of just two numbers for each sample. If the means $\overline{x}$ for each sample x are averaged (that is, average the numbers in column two), we find that this sample mean is also 5.6. This is not a coincidence. The mean of all the numbers in the samples is the same as the average of all the sample means. We say that this sample statistic (mean of the samples) targets the population parameter (mean of all the items appearing in the samples).

The sampling distribution of the mean is the probability distribution of the sample means (which are in Column 2). There are 25 samples, and, for example, the number 5 occurs four times as an average of samples, so $P(5) = 4/25$. Similarly, the number 3.5 occurs twice as an average of samples, so $P(3.5) = 2/25$. The entire sample distribution is:

$$P(1) = 1/25, \; P(2.5) = P(3.5) = P(4.5) = 2/25, \; P(5) = 4/25,$$

$$P(4) = 1/25, \; P(6) = 3/25, \; P(6.5) = P(7) = P(7.5) = 2/25,$$

$$P(8) = 1/25, \; P(8) = 2/25, \; P(9) = 1/25.$$

As required, these probabilities sum to 1.

If we compute the mean of the sample standard deviations (Column 3), we get 2.2368. However, if we compute the standard deviation of the fifty items in the samples, we get 2.8705. The standard deviation of the samples is not targeted by the mean of the sample standard deviations. ∎

TABLE 27.5

Sample x	Sample Mean $\bar{x}$	Sample Standard Deviation
1,1	1	0
1,4	2.5	2.1213
1,6	3.5	3.5355
1,8	4.5	4.3012
1,9	5	5.6569
4,1	2.5	2.1213
4,4	4	0
4,6	5	1.4142
4,8	6	2.8284
4,9	6.5	3.5355
6,1	3.5	3.5355
6,4	5	1.4142
6,6	6	0
6,8	7	1.4142
6,9	7.5	2.1213
8,1	4.5	4.9497
8,4	6	2.8284
8,6	7	1.4142
8,8	8	0
8,9	8.5	0.7071
9,1	5	5.6569
9,4	6.5	3.5355
9,6	7.5	2.1213
9,8	8.5	0.7071
9,9	9	0

In making inferences about a population by observing samples, the sample distribution of a proportion often plays a role. Suppose a sample of n objects from the population has k of one type of object. Then the *sample proportion of that sample for that item* is k/n. The *sampling distribution of the population*, with respect to that item, is the probability distribution of the sample proportions for that item.

EXAMPLE 27.21

Suppose, in trying to determine quality of manufacture of a product, ten samples of 20 items each are taken off the line (with replacement). Table 27.6 shows the data and the sample ratios (number defective divided by sample size):

The sample ratio for each sample (with regard to defective items) is the number of defective items in the sample, divided by $n = 20$. Since $1/20$ occurs four times out of ten as a sample ratio, $P(1/20) = 4/10 = 0.4$. In this way we compute the sampling distribution of this proportion:

$$P(1/20) = 0.4, \quad P(0) = 0.4, \quad P(1/10) = 0.2. \quad \blacksquare$$

We now have the vocabulary to state the important central limit theorem, which relates a distribution of the original population itself to a distribution of the sample means.

TABLE 27.6

Sample	Number Defective	Sample Ratio
1	1	1/20
2	0	0
3	2	1/10
4	0	0
5	0	0
6	1	1/20
7	2	1/10
8	1	1/20
9	1	1/20
10	0	0

THEOREM 27.4   Central Limit Theorem

Suppose a random variable X has mean μ and standard deviation σ. Then the distribution of sample means will approach a normal distribution as the sample size increases, regardless of whether or not the original population distribution is normally distributed. Further,

1. The mean of all the sample means equals μ.

2. The standard deviation of all sample means is approximately $\sigma/\sqrt{n}$, where n is the sample size. This approximation can be improved by increasing n. ■

The first conclusion can be phrased: the mean of the samples equals the mean of the population. The second conclusion justifies the sense in which we can approximate the standard deviation of the total population using the standard deviation of the sample means.

The central limit theorem justifies the approximation of a distribution by a normal distribution. Even when the original random variable does not have a normal distribution, the sample means will approach a normal distribution. As a rule of thumb (that is, true except for "pathological" cases), we can safely approximate the sample means distribution by a normal distribution if $n > 30$.

The following example illustrates the idea of the central limit theorem, and emphasizes the crucial difference that must be understood between the distribution of the original random variable, and the distribution of the sample means.

EXAMPLE 27.22

Imagine that forty samples of six numbers each have been drawn, with replacement, from the integers 0 through 9, inclusive. Table 27.7 shows the samples and the sample means.

The sample column has forty entries of six numbers each, hence a total of 240 numbers (the population), each an integer from 0 through 9, inclusively. The random variable X is defined by $X(k)$ = number of occurrences of k in this set of 240 numbers. Figure 27.24 shows a graph of these values of $X(k)$. Clearly this is not a normal distribution, nor should we expect it to be.

Figure 27.25 shows a graph of the distribution of the sample means. This distribution is not normal, because $n = 6$ is too small. However, if n were chosen larger, the sample means would more closely approximately a true normal distribution.

TABLE 27.7

Sample	Sample Mean	Sample	Sample Mean
289186	5.66	188635	5.16
957888	7.5	405396	4.5
231332	2.33	148235	3.83
767099	6.33	332674	4.16
686505	5	962669	6.33
859901	5.33	445186	4.66
063159	4	637269	5.50
501547	3.66	521802	3
855909	6	040848	4
161078	3.83	358298	5.83
809973	6	568735	5.60
290800	3.16	630761	3.83
925079	5.33	607495	5.16
732111	2.5	188965	6.16
795556	6.16	201037	2.16
145776	5	749018	4.83
276535	4.66	180629	4.33
605812	3.66	291554	4.33
633966	5.50	958087	6.16
747358	5.60	799365	6.5

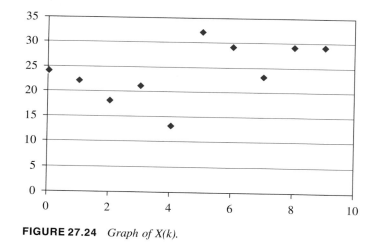

FIGURE 27.24 *Graph of X(k).*

It is routine to compute the mean of the population, obtaining

$$\mu = \frac{387}{80}.$$

A similar routine calculation shows that the mean of the sample means is also 387/80, as expected.

The standard deviation of the population is found to be

$$\sigma = \frac{\sqrt{492,159}}{240},$$

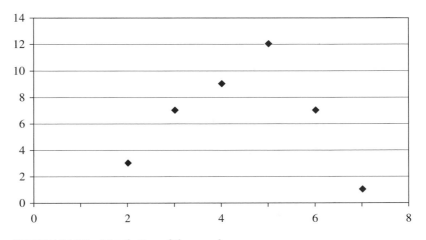

FIGURE 27.25 *Distribution of the sample means.*

which is approximately 2.9231. The standard deviation of the sample means is

$$\sigma_{\text{means}} = \frac{\sqrt{86,919}}{240},$$

or approximately 1.2284. If we compute $\sigma/\sqrt{n}$, which is $\sigma/\sqrt{6}$ for this example, we get 1.1933. According to the central limit theorem, this should approximate σ_{means}, and indeed this number is within 0.035 of σ_{means}. Even with a small n, this approximation is good to about three hundredths in this example. ■

EXAMPLE 27.23

The headmaster of an exclusive private high school is interested in the probability that all twenty two of his seniors will score at least 670 out of 900 on a standardized test used by colleges in making admission decisions about applicants. The national average on this test is 640, with a standard deviation of 120.

Think of taking samples of size $n = 22$ from the national pool of students taking this test, and use the approximately distributed sample means to draw conclusions about this sample. For the entire population, $\mu = 640$ and $\sigma = 120$. For the sample means,

$$\mu_{\text{means}} = \mu = 640$$

and

$$\sigma_{\text{means}} = \frac{120}{\sqrt{22}}.$$

The bell curve for the sample means is the graph of

$$y = \frac{1}{\sqrt{2\pi}(120/\sqrt{22})} e^{-(x-640)^2/2(120/\sqrt{22})^2}$$

$$= \frac{\sqrt{11}}{120\sqrt{\pi}} e^{-11(x-640)^2/14400}.$$

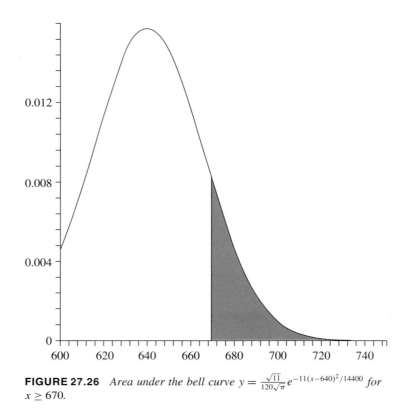

FIGURE 27.26 *Area under the bell curve* $y = \frac{\sqrt{11}}{120\sqrt{\pi}} e^{-11(x-640)^2/14400}$ *for* $x \geq 670.$

We want the area under this bell curve for $x \geq 670$. This area is shown in Figure 27.26, and is approximately equal to

$$\frac{\sqrt{11}}{120\sqrt{\pi}} \int_{670}^{900} e^{-11(x-640)^2/14400} dx,$$

or 0.120 48. Perhaps on average, the headmaster can expect the entire class to score this high once in ten years, although it also could happen two years in a row, or never in this headmaster's tenure.

What is the probability that all twenty-two students of the students score between 640 and 700? This is

$$\frac{\sqrt{11}}{120\sqrt{\pi}} \int_{640}^{700} e^{-11(x-640)^2/14400} dx,$$

or 0.490 49, very close to one half.

What is the probability that ten of the students score better than 660? Now use $n = 10$ in forming the samples, so the bell curve is

$$y = \frac{\sqrt{5}}{120\sqrt{\pi}} e^{-5(x-640)^2/14400},$$

and the probability we want is

$$\frac{\sqrt{5}}{120\sqrt{\pi}} \int_{660}^{900} e^{-5(x-640)^2/14400} dx,$$

which is 0.299 08, about 3/10. ■

SECTION 27.5   PROBLEMS

1. Thirty samples are taken of five digit numbers. Each of these numbers has been drawn, with replacement, from the integers 3 through 9, inclusive. The samples are given in the following table:

Sample	Sample	Sample	Sample	Sample
74974	78365	94489	84937	33933
76693	57733	58438	59786	58393
43856	86934	96649	88533	48576
85994	43865	67339	59643	58834
36496	59378	47937	75488	84938
48659	43958	48896	69537	78953

(a) Compute the sample means, the mean of the sample means, and the mean of the population.

(b) Compute the standard deviation of the population and the standard deviation of the sample means, and verify that $\sigma_{means} \approx \sigma/\sqrt{n}$ for the appropriate choice of n.

2. Thirty samples are taken of seven digit numbers. Each of these digits has been drawn, with replacement, from the integers 0 through 9, inclusive. The samples are given in the following table:

Sample	Sample	Sample	Sample	Sample
9388204	7939720	5773902	1912038	1749823
8902817	3022850	5492018	4491002	4910292
7921082	5910293	9017839	4491029	4019283
8019283	4911029	3019402	5616209	9201898
5501829	3371932	0002910	3611390	4092179
4039112	9571120	9912118	8401938	7109032

(a) Compute the sample means, the mean of the sample means, and the mean of the population.

(b) Compute the standard deviation of the population and the standard deviation of the sample means, and verify that $\sigma_{means} \approx \sigma/\sqrt{n}$ for the appropriate choice of n.

3. A recruiter for a government agency wants his candidates to be successful on a test administered by the agency to prospective employees. He would like his group of thirty recruits to score at least 700 out of the possible 950. Over the time this test has been administered, the average score has been 670, with a standard deviation of 105.

(a) Estimate the probability that all thirty of the recruits will score in the 700–750 range.

(b) Estimate the probability that all the recruits will score at least 670.

(c) The recruiter gets a bonus if seven of the candidates score 800 or higher. Should the recruiter look forward to a bonus?

4. A uniform maker has a large order from a new branch of the military. On average, the pants legs are 31 inches, with a standard deviation of 3.2 inches. Suppose six new recruits are chosen at random.

(a) Find the probability that their mean length is at least 29 inches.

(b) Find the probability that their length is in the 29–33 inch range.

(c) Find the probability that their length is no greater than 32 inches.

5. A state uses standard braces for its highway bridges. The braces can handle a mean pressure of 5000 pounds per square inch, with a standard deviation of 800. Suppose twenty braces are tested at random throughout the state.

(a) What is the probability that their mean pressure tolerance is at least 4800 pounds per square inch?

(b) What is the probability that their mean pressure tolerance falls in the 4700–5100 range?

(c) What is the probability that their mean pressure tolerance is not less than 4500 pounds per square inch?

6. A product coming off an assembly line has been found to weigh on average 17 pounds, with a standard deviation of 1.8. Thirty samples are chosen at random from the line.

(a) What is the probability that these samples will weigh on average between 16.8 and 17.2 pounds?

(b) What is the probability that they weigh on average at least 16.7 pounds?

(c) Find the probability that they do not weigh on average less than 17.2 pounds.

27.6   Confidence Intervals and Estimating Population Proportion

If we somehow know that exactly five of every thousand cars coming out of a plant are defective, then there is no need to take samples, and we do not need statistics. The need for statistical analysis arises when we do not have perfect knowledge of the outcome of some process, as is usually the case in real-world scenarios. In this section we will focus on how to estimate (make an educated guess about) certain statistics, such as the mean and standard deviation of a population. We also want to be able to determine a confidence interval, which is a set of values measuring, in a sense we will define, ranges of accuracy to be expected of our estimates.

Throughout this section we will have some population proportion p. We are examining some question or process which has exactly two outcomes, called success and failure. We form random samples of size n, and consider the sample proportions $\tilde{p} = x/n$, where n is the size of the sample, and x is the number of successes in the sample. This number is between 0 and 1 and may be thought of as a probability. The complementary probability is $\tilde{q} = 1 - \tilde{p}$. As a typical example, we might draw samples of 900 trout from a stream over a day, and find that 47% are male. The sample size here is $n = 900$, and the sample proportion is $\tilde{p} = 0.47$.

We also assume that there is a fixed number of independent trials, and that the resulting distribution can be approximated by a normal distribution.

In making estimates of various statistics or numbers associated with the population, we will use the notion of a *confidence interval*, which is an interval of values used to estimate the statistic. The corresponding *confidence level* of the estimate is the ratio of the times that this interval actually does contain the statistic of interest, taken over a large number of repetitions or samples. This confidence level is routinely denoted as $1 - \alpha$.

The most common confidence levels, expressed as percents, are 90%, 95%, or 99%. Below 90% is often unacceptable as a worthwhile measure of accuracy of the estimate. Associate with 90% the probability 0.9, so $\alpha = 0.1$ and $1 - \alpha = 0.9$. Similarly, for 95%, use $\alpha = 0.05$, so $1 - \alpha = 0.95$. And for 99%, use $\alpha = 0.01$, so $1 - \alpha = 0.99$.

If, for example, we are using 95% as a confidence level to estimate the population proportion p, and this determines (in a way we will describe) an interval $a < p < b$, then we say we are 95% confident that the true value of p, as estimated, falls between a and b.

When these percentages are written decimals, we may think of them as probabilities, or areas bounded by the standard bell curve, which is the graph of

$$y = \frac{1}{\sqrt{2\pi}} e^{-z^2/2}.$$

Part of this graph is shown in Figure 27.27. For a given α, there is a point Z such that the area under the graph to the right of Z and to the left of $-Z$ is α, hence the area between $-Z$ and Z is $1 - \alpha$. This number Z, which depends on α, is denoted $z_{\alpha/2}$. The use of $\alpha/2$ in the subscript is a reminder that the bell graph has two tails (to the left of $-z_{\alpha/2}$ and to the right of $z_{\alpha/2}$), having total area α, so the area under just one tail is $\alpha/2$. The number $z_{\alpha/2}$ is called a *critical value*, separating those sample proportions (between $-z_{\alpha/2}$ and $z_{\alpha/2}$) that are likely from those that are unlikely (in the right or left tails of the bell curve).

Table 27.8 gives the critical values corresponding to confidence levels of 85%, 90%, 95%, and 99%. These percents are written as decimals 0.85, 0.90, 0.95, and 0.99 to have interpretations as areas. For example, the area under the standard bell curve between $-z_{\alpha/2}$ and $z_{\alpha/2}$ for $\alpha = 0.15$ is

$$\frac{1}{\sqrt{2\pi}} \int_{-1.44}^{1.44} e^{-z^2/2} dz = 0.85013,$$

corresponding to 85% of the sample proportions falling in this interval. We may also think of 0.85 as the probability that a sample proportion falls between -1.44 and 1.44 for this standard curve.

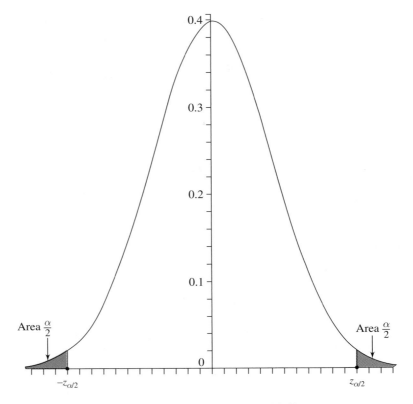

FIGURE 27.27 *Critical point $z_{\alpha/2}$ for the standard bell curve.*

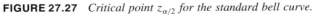

TABLE 27.8

Confidence Level (As a Decimal)	α	$z_{\alpha/2}$
0.85	0.15	1.44
0.90	0.10	1.645
0.95	0.05	1.96
0.99	0.01	2.575

From previous results, we can write

$$\mu = np \text{ and } \sigma = \sqrt{npq}.$$

Since these results are for n trials, we can write the mean of the sample proportions as

$$\mu = \frac{np}{n} = p$$

and the standard deviations of the sample proportions as

$$\sigma = \frac{\sqrt{npq}}{n} = \sqrt{\frac{pq}{n}}.$$

In general, we do not know p (or q), and we want to estimate these values from $\widetilde{p}$ and $\widetilde{q}$. Replace p by $\widetilde{p}$ and q by $\widetilde{q}$ in the expression for σ to obtain $\sqrt{\widetilde{p}\widetilde{q}/n}$. The probability is $1 - \alpha$

that a sample proportion will differ from the actual population proportion (which we want to estimate) by no more than $z_{\alpha/2}\sqrt{\widetilde{pq}/n}$. This leads us to define the maximum error of the estimate to be

$$\epsilon = z_{\alpha/2}\sqrt{\frac{\widetilde{pq}}{n}}, \tag{27.6}$$

or

$$\epsilon = z_{\alpha/2}\sqrt{\frac{\widetilde{p}(1-\widetilde{p})}{n}}.$$

The confidence level associated with this α is

$$\widetilde{p} - \epsilon < p < \widetilde{p} + \epsilon.$$

EXAMPLE 27.24

Suppose samples of 900 fish are drawn from a stream each day. Suppose on a particular day, it is found that 47% were male. Here $n = 900$ and $\widetilde{p} = 0.47$. Based on the information we have, 0.47 is the best estimate we can make for $\widetilde{p}$, the proportion of the total fish population that is male.

Suppose we want the maximum error associated with a 95% confidence level. For a 95% confidence level, $\alpha = 0.05$ and we read from Table 27.8 the critical value $z_{\alpha/2} = 1.96$. The maximum error is

$$\epsilon = (1.96)\sqrt{\frac{(0.47)(0.53)}{900}} = 0.0326078.$$

Generally, we round maximum error calculations to three decimal places, so take $\epsilon = 0.033$. The confidence interval is

$$0.47 - 0.033 < p < 0.47 + 0.033,$$

or

$$0.437 < p < 0.503.$$

There is a probability of $1 - \alpha$ (or 0.95) that the actual population proportion falls in this interval. ■

Often, we want to determine the size of the sample we need to estimate some statistic with a certain level of confidence. To do this for the population proportion, begin with the expression (27.6) for the maximum error and solve for n to get

$$n = \frac{(z_{\alpha/2})^2\widetilde{pq}}{\epsilon^2}. \tag{27.7}$$

Use this to estimate the size n that should be used to estimate p with a confidence interval $\widetilde{p} - \epsilon < p < \widetilde{p} + \epsilon$, assuming that $\widetilde{p}$ is known. Of course, usually equation (27.7) will not yield an integer, so in practice take n to be the smallest integer larger than $(z_{\alpha/2})^2\widetilde{pq}/\epsilon^2$. For example, if the right side of equation (27.7) is 956.24, then choose $n = 957$.

In many practical situations that occur, we do not know $\widetilde{p}$. If this is the case, replace $\widetilde{pq}$ in equation (27.7) with 0.25 to write

$$n = \frac{(0.25)(z_{\alpha/2})^2}{\epsilon^2}.$$

The rationale for this is that 0.25 is the largest value that $\widetilde{p}\widetilde{q}$ can assume, occuring when $\widetilde{p} = \widetilde{q} = 0.5$.

EXAMPLE 27.25

A member of a United Nations team wants to survey the population of a certain country to determine the commonality of households having at least two telephones. She wants to be 90% confident of her results, and to be in error by no more than 3%. How many households should she survey?

Here we take 0.90 to be the confidence level that is wanted, and $\epsilon = 0.03$. There is no information about $\widetilde{p}$, so compute

$$\frac{(0.25)(z_{\alpha/2})^2}{\epsilon^2}.$$

For a 90% confidence level, Table 27.8 gives $z_{\alpha/2} = 1.645$. Thus compute

$$\frac{(0.25)(1.645)^2}{(0.03)^2} = 751.67.$$

She should do a random survey of 752 households.

Suppose, from another recent study, it is estimated that $\widetilde{p} = 0.32$. Now use equation (27.7) and compute

$$\frac{(1.645)^2(0.32)(0.68)}{(0.03)^2} = 654.26.$$

This estimate tells us to survey 655 households. This, however, assumes that the "recent study" was recent enough that the number of two-telephone households might not have changed much. If, for example, this study was done ten years ago, we might play safe and go with 752 households in the survey.

Suppose we wanted a 95% instead of 90% confidence level, assuming no information about $\widetilde{p}$. Now we would use $\alpha = 0.05$ and $z_{\alpha/2} = 1.96$. Compute

$$\frac{(0.25)(1.96)^2}{(0.03)^2} = 1067.11,$$

so she should survey 1068 households. It is not surprising that more households need to be included in the survey to increase the confidence level. ∎

SECTION 27.6 *PROBLEMS*

1. A parachute assembly and packing plant produces thousands of parachutes each month. One month, 1200 are inspected and it is found that 0.2% have a defect.

(a) Find an estimate with a 99% confidence interval of the proportion of parachutes produced in a month that are defective.

(b) Redo (a), except with a 95% confidence level.

(c) Redo (a), with a 90% confidence level.

(d) Suppose only 800 parachutes are inspected instead of 1200, and it is still found that 0.2% are defective. Now determine an estimate with a 95% confidence interval of the proportion of parachutes produced in a month that are defective. How has decreasing the size of the sample affected the confidence interval?

2. A drug being tested for a certain condition appears to have side effects. In a large clinical trial conducted nationally, 750 patients who took the drug are selected

at random, and it is found that 22% developed skin rashes.

(a) Determine an estimate with a 99% confidence interval of the proportion of the entire patient population that will be expected to develop a skin rash.

(b) Redo (a) for a 95% confidence interval.

3. A survey taken over a week has inspected 200 fish in a lake and found that 87 were man-eating guppies.

(a) Determine an estimate with a 95% confidence interval of the proportion of the fish population of the lake that are man-eating guppies.

(b) Determine an estimate with an 85% confidence interval of the proportion of the fish population that are man-eating guppies.

4. A plant produces packaged chicken for distribution to grocery stores throughout the midwest. In a sample of 100 packages of chicken taken over one work day, it is found that seven contain the blue virus, which has no other effect on the person who consumes the chicken than to turn their skin permanently light blue.

(a) Determine an estimate with a 99% confidence interval of the proportion of one day's chicken packages that contain the virus.

(b) Determine an estimate with a 90% confidence interval of the proportion of one day's chicken packages that contain the virus.

5. A marketing executive wants to survey a city to determine how many people have purchased his company's product over the past twelve months.

(a) Suppose he wants a 95% confidence level in the results of the survey with an error of no more than 2%. How many people should he survey?

(b) How many people should he survey if, in (a), he is willing to allow the error to be no more than 5%?

(c) Suppose, in the previous year's study, it was found that $\widetilde{p} = 0.37$. Now make an estimate of how many people he should survey for a 95% confidence level and an error of no more than 2%.

(d) Suppose another person in marketing notes an economic trend suggesting that a better estimate for $\widetilde{p}$ is 0.32. How will this affect the conclusion of (c) about the number of people to be surveyed?

6. A public health official is charged with completing an annual survey of a county population, checking for incidents of a certain viral infection over the past year.

(a) Suppose she wants a 99% confidence level in the results of the survey with an error of no more than 3%. How many people should she survey?

(b) How many people should she survey if, in (a), she is willing to settle for a 95% confidence level?

(c) Suppose, in the previous year's study, it was found that $\widetilde{p} = 0.12$. Make an estimate of how many people she should survey for a 99% confidence level and an error of no more than 2%.

7. A professional pollster is charged with taking a survey throughout a large state, in order to estimate the number of qualified voters who favor the Freeload Party candidate.

(a) Suppose he wants an 85% confidence level in the results of the survey with an error of no more than 7%. How many people should he survey?

(b) How many people should he survey if, in (a), he is willing to allow the error to be no more than 12%?

(c) Suppose, in the previous election, it was found that $\widetilde{p} = 0.06$. Now make an estimate of how many people he should survey, for an 85% confidence level and an error of no more than 7%.

27.7   Estimating Population Mean and the Student *t* Distribution

This section follows the theme of the preceding one, except there we wanted to estimate population proportion, and now we are concerned with estimating the population mean μ. We assume the same setting of random independent samples of uniform size, and a distribution that can be approximated as a normal distribution.

Let $\overline{x}$ be the sample mean of sample x. As noted previously, in the absence of more definitive information, it is reasonable to estimate the population mean as the sample mean.

The issue now is to develop a concept of maximum error enabling us to state confidence intervals. Previously we saw that, if σ is the standard deviation of the population, then $\sigma/\sqrt{n}$ is the standard deviation of the sample means, with n the sample size as usual. In the preceding section, equation (27.6) gave the maximum error in the estimate of the population proportion. The adaptation of this to maximum error in the estimate of the population mean is

$$\epsilon = z_{\alpha/2} \frac{\sigma}{\sqrt{n}}. \tag{27.8}$$

We will still use ϵ for this maximum error, taking from context whether we are referring to population proportion or mean. The corresponding confidence interval in estimating μ from $\overline{x}$ is

$$\overline{x} - \epsilon < \mu < \overline{x} + \epsilon.$$

If we solve equation (27.8) for n, we get

$$n = \left(\frac{\sigma z_{\alpha/2}}{\epsilon}\right)^2.$$

The right side of this equation is used to estimate the size of samples that should be taken to have a maximum error of ϵ and a confidence level determined by the critical point $z_{\alpha/2}$.

EXAMPLE 27.26

Suppose a study of blood pressure is being planned. Sample groups of size $n = 210$ are to be used, and a 99% confidence level is sought. It is known from many studies that $\sigma = 0.82$, and the sample mean is $\overline{x} = 127$. We want to estimate the population mean and the confidence interval.

From Table 27.8, choose $z_{\alpha/2} = 2.575$. Then

$$\epsilon = (2.575)\frac{0.82}{\sqrt{210}} = 0.14571,$$

so

$$\overline{x} - 0.14571 < \mu < \overline{x} + 0.14571,$$

or

$$126.85 < \mu < 127.15.$$

Suppose we go back to the planning stages, and imagine that we have not yet decided on the number of samples to take. We want n so that we have a 95% confidence level. For 95%, use $z_{\alpha/2} = 1.96$. We need some information about the maximum error. Suppose we want $\epsilon = 0.2$. Now estimate

$$n = \left(\frac{(0.82)(1.96)}{0.2}\right)^2 = 64.577,$$

so use $n = 65$ as sample size. ∎

This example assumed the ideal condition that we had information about σ. Often, perhaps usually, we do not know σ. In such a case, it is common practice to use the student t distribution instead of the normal distribution. Assuming that the population is approximately normal, the *student t distribution*, or just *t distribution*, is defined by

$$t(x) = \frac{\overline{x} - \mu}{s/\sqrt{n}}.$$

Because of the appearance of n in this definition, there is a different t distribution for each positive integer n. Each is bell-shaped in general appearance, but is not a normal distribution.

As n increases, the corresponding t distributions approach the standard normal curve (Figure 27.28). As with the standard bell curve, $t_{\alpha/2}$ is that number such that the area under the t distribution to the right of $t_{\alpha/2}$ and to the left of $-t_{\alpha/2}$, is α, hence the area between $-t_{\alpha/2}$ and $t_{\alpha/2}$ is $1-\alpha$ (Figure 27.29).

In determining $t_{\alpha/2}$, n plays an important role, since the distribution is different for each n. In the present context, with estimation of population mean as the objective, note that the mean $\bar{x}$ of each sample x is a sum of n numbers, divided by n. If $\bar{x}$ is known, any $n-1$ of these numbers can be chosen as having any values, and the nth number is then determined. We therefore say that $t_{\alpha/2}$ has $n-1$ *degrees of freedom*. In a table of critical points for t distributions, there will be a row or column associated with the number of degrees of freedom, and from this $t_{\alpha/2}$ can be read for given values of α and n.

In practice, we use t-critical points just as we used z-critical points previously. Now, given n and α, which in turn is determined by a confidence level that is stated, define the maximum error ϵ_t as

$$\epsilon_t = t_{\alpha/2}\frac{s}{\sqrt{n}}.$$

The corresponding confidence level is

$$\bar{x} - \epsilon_t < \mu < \bar{x} + \epsilon_t.$$

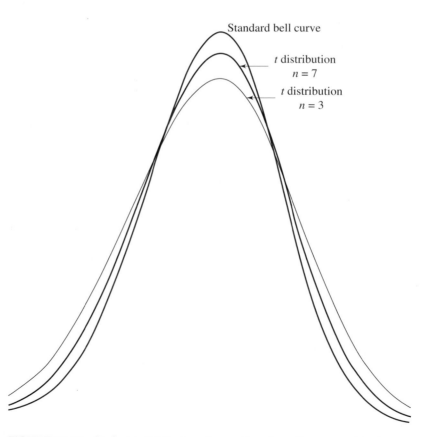

FIGURE 27.28 *Student t distributions for $n=3$ and $n=7$, compared to the standard bell curve.*

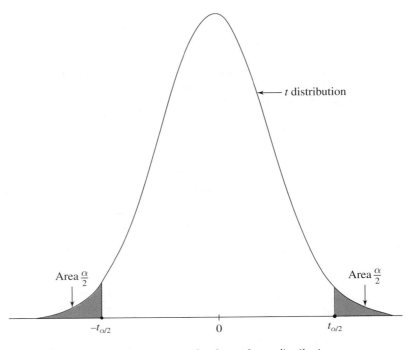

FIGURE 27.29 *Critical point* $-t_{\alpha/2}$ *for the student t distribution.*

EXAMPLE 27.27

An international gymnastics oversight committee is checking blood levels of athletes for the performance enhancing chemical hyperjump. Random samples of 35 gymnasts are taken, and it is known that the sample mean is $\bar{x} = 0.4$ milligrams. We want to construct the maximum error if a confidence level of 99% is needed, and then find the associated confidence interval about the population mean.

For a 99% confidence level, $\alpha = 0.01$. With $n = 35$, the number of degrees of freedom is 34, and we find from a standard table that $t_{\alpha/2} = 2.728$. Suppose from the sample we compute the standard deviation $s = 0.03$. Now compute the maximum error:

$$\epsilon_t = (2.728)\frac{0.03}{\sqrt{35}} = 0.013833.$$

The confidence interval is

$$0.4 - 0.013833 < \mu < 0.4 + 0.013833,$$

or

$$0.386 < \mu < 0.414,$$

to three decimal places. ▪

1. (a) Suppose a study of blood concentration of a certain protein is being done. Groups of 350 patients are sampled. It is known from parallel studies that $\sigma = 1.04$, and the sample means are $\bar{x} = 72$. For a 99% confidence level, estimate the population mean and the confidence interval.

   (b) Suppose in (a), the sample size has not yet been determined, but n should be chosen to have a 99% confidence level and an error of no more than 0.2. Estimate the sample size that should be used.

2. (a) Samples of size 50 are being drawn from a company's production line. It has been found that $\bar{x} = 119$, and $\sigma = 0.7$. If a 95% confidence level is wanted, estimate the population mean and determine the confidence interval.

   (b) Suppose in (a), the sample size has not yet been determined, but n should be chosen to have a 99% confidence level and an error of no more than 0.2. Estimate the sample size that should be used.

3. (a) Samples of 100 patients are being drawn randomly from a clinical trial. If it is estimated that $\sigma = 2.4$ and $\bar{x} = 106$, estimate the population mean and confidence interval for a 95% confidence level.

   (b) Suppose in (a) that the sample size has not been set, but n must be chosen to have a 99% confidence level with an error no more than 0.1. Estimate the sample size that should be used.

4. Random samples of 50 lawnmower motors are taken from a plant each week, checking for a certain amount of contaminant in the fuel line. Assume that $\bar{x} = 0.8$ and $s = 0.05$. Use the t-distribution to construct a 95% confidence interval in estimating the population mean. *Hint*: A table estimates the critical value here as 2.009.

5. Random samples of 75 students are drawn from the senior year population of a large city public school system in studying absences per month. With $\bar{x} = 3$ and $s = 0.7$, construct a 95% confidence interval in estimating the population mean. *Hint*: The critical value is approximately 1.992.

6. Random samples of fish of size 200 are taken from fishing waters near a certain island, checking for irregularities in gill structure. With $\bar{x} = 7$ and $s = 0.01$, construct a 95% confidence interval in estimating the population mean. *Hint*: The critical value is approximately 1.971.

27.8   Correlation and Regression

In this section, we are concerned with a collection of n data pairs (x_i, y_i), which we can plot as points in the plane We say that a *correlation* exists between the x values and the y values when there is some specific relationship between them. Although there are many different kinds of correlations, we will be concerned here with linear correlations, and whether a linear correlation exists between a given data set of points. A *linear correlation* exists when the points (x_i, y_i) are approximately distributed about a straight line in the plane. Figure 27.30 shows a data set with a linear correlation, while there is no such correlation in the data set of Figure 27.31. The data set of Figure 27.30 would be said to have a positive linear correlation (between x and y values), while the data set of Figure 27.32 has a negative linear correlation. These characterizations depend on the slope of the line that is approximately along the points.

Define the number

$$c = \frac{\sum_{i=1}^{n}(x_i - \bar{x})(y_i - \bar{y})}{(n-1)s_x s_y} \tag{27.9}$$

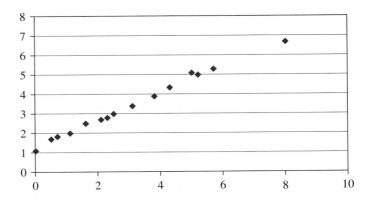

FIGURE 27.30 *Data with a positive linear correlation.*

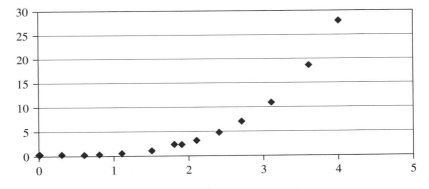

FIGURE 27.31 *Data with no significant linear correlation.*

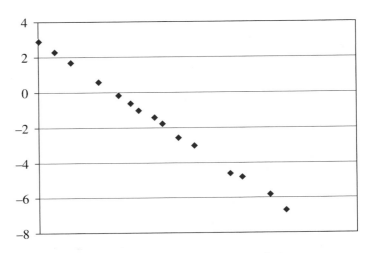

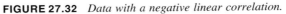

FIGURE 27.32 *Data with a negative linear correlation.*

to be the *linear correlation coefficient* of the data. As usual,

$$\overline{x} = \frac{1}{n} \sum_{i=1}^{n} x_i$$

is the mean of the x_i's, and $\overline{y}$ is the mean of the y_i's. Sometimes $(\overline{x}, \overline{y})$ is called the *centroid* of the data. The term s_x is the standard deviation of $x_1, \ldots, x_n$, while s_y is the standard deviation of $y_1, \ldots, y_n$. It is routine to carry out the algebra to show that

$$c = \frac{n \sum_{i=1}^{n} x_i y_i - \left(\sum_{i=1}^{n} x_i\right) \left(\sum_{i=1}^{n} y_i\right)}{\sqrt{n \left(\sum_{i=1}^{n} x_i^2\right) - \left(\sum_{i=1}^{n} x_i\right)^2} \sqrt{n \left(\sum_{i=1}^{n} y_i^2\right) - \left(\sum_{i=1}^{n} y_i\right)^2}}.$$

While this expression for c may appear more complicated that in equation (27.9), it is more explicit in the sense that it involves only the data points themselves, and not their means or standard deviations.

It is routine to check that $-1 \leq c \leq 1$. Further, if the points lie on a line, say $y_i = ax_i$ for $i = 1, \ldots, n$, then $c = 1$. In general, if c is near 1 or -1, we say that there is a *significant linear correlation* between the x_is and y_is. If c is near 0, we say that there is *no significant linear correlation* between the x_is and the y_is. Although this is vague, we will firm up this idea shortly.

The linear correlation coefficient is used in connection with tables of values. Table 27.9 shows a typical part of such a table.

This table has been constructed for a 95% ($\alpha = 0.05$) confidence level. Corresponding to the number n of samples, the critical value has this significance. If $|c|$ is greater than the critical value, then there is a $1 - 0.05$ (or 0.95) probability (confidence) that there is a significant correlation between the x_i's and the y_i's. For example, with $n = 15$ points, if $|c| > 0.514$, there is a $1 - 0.05 = 0.95$ probability that there is a significant linear correlation between the points. If $n = 50$ and $|c| > 0.279$, there is a 0.95 probability that there is a significant linear correlation.

If $|c|$ is less than or equal to the critical value, then there is only a 0.05 probability of a linear correlation between the x_i's and y_i's.

Notice that, as the number of sample points increases, we can infer significant linear correlations with smaller values of $|c|$, while, if n is small (and therefore provide less information), it takes a larger $|c|$ to draw this inference.

TABLE 27.9

n	Critical value of c for $\alpha = 0.05$
10	0.632
15	0.514
20	0.444
25	0.396
30	0.361
35	0.335
40	0.312
45	0.294
50	0.279
60	0.254
80	0.220
100	0.196

EXAMPLE 27.28

The following table gives gold medal heights in the pole vault for the Olympics, from some years extending from 1932 through 1996. Heights are in feet.

Year	Height	Year	Height
1932	14.15	1972	18.04
1936	14.27	1976	18.04
1948	14.10	1980	18.96
1952	14.92	1984	18.85
1956	14.96	1988	19.77
1960	15.42	1992	19.02
1964	16.73	1996	19.42
1968	17.71		

We will investigate this data set for a significant linear correlation, or absence of one. A scatter graph of the data is shown in Figure 27.33. The x-values are the years and the y-values are the heights. We find that $\bar{x} = 1966.9333$, $\bar{y} = 16.9573$, $s_x = 19.6813$, and $s_y = 2.1138$. A routine computation yields $c = 0.9546$. From Table 27.9 with $n = 15$, because $c > 0.514$, we infer that there is a .95 probability that there is a significant linear correlation between x- and y-values. This is intuitively apparent from Figure 27.33. ∎

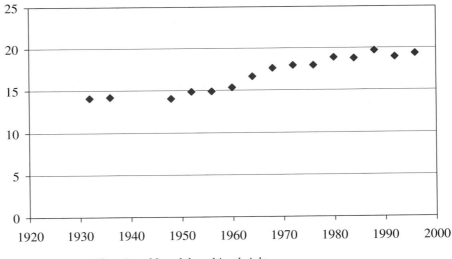

FIGURE 27.33 *Olympic gold medal vaulting heights.*

EXAMPLE 27.29

Consider the following data set:

x_i	0	0.5	1.0	1.5	2.0	2.5	3.0	3.5	4.0
y_i	1	2.12	6.24	2.44	11.58	3.72	1.04	25.63	2.63

Figure 27.34 shows a scatter graph of this data. There does not appear to be a significant linear correlation. To check this intuition, we find that $c = 0.3884153476$. Table 27.9 does not have

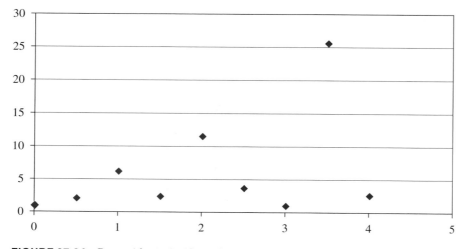

FIGURE 27.34 *Data with no significant linear correlation.*

a critical value corresponding to $n = 9$, so we will use the value for $n = 10$ as a best estimate. This critical value is 0.632. Since $|c| < 0.632$, there is only a 0.05 probability that there is a significant linear correlation between the x-values and the y-values. ∎

Correlation must not be confused with causality. Just because two sets of data have a significant linear correlation, does not imply that the x-values cause the y-values. There may or may not be such a cause and effect relationship. In the case of pole vaulting heights, it is hard to believe that the year is a cause of the height achieved in the pole vault. The fact that the heights increase with passing years is due to a complex set of factors, probably including conditioning of the athletes, improvements in vaulting technique, and changes in materials from which vaulting poles were made.

To understand the idea of regression, consider again the data shown in Figure 27.33. We found that there was a significant linear correlation between x-values and y-values. This suggests that the data, plotted as points in the plane, form an "approximate" straight line. It is possible to determine a straight line L which is a best fit to the data. This line is called the *regression line* for the data. It is defined to be the best least squares fit to the data, in the sense of minimizing the sum of the squares of the vertical distances between the y_is and the respective y-values on the line corresponding to the x_is.

If we write the equation of the regression line as $y = a + bx$, then the standard least squares method yields

$$a = \frac{\left(\sum_{i=1}^{n} y_i\right)\left(\sum_{i=1}^{n} x_i^2\right) - \left(\sum_{i=1}^{n} x_i\right)\left(\sum_{i=1}^{n} x_i y_i\right)}{n\left(\sum_{i=1}^{n} x_i^2\right) - \left(\sum_{i=1}^{n} x_i\right)^2} \tag{27.10}$$

and

$$b = \frac{n\sum_{i=1}^{n} x_i y_i - \left(\sum_{i=1}^{n} x_i\right)\left(\sum_{i=1}^{n} y_i\right)}{n\left(\sum_{i=1}^{n} x_i^2\right) - \left(\sum_{i=1}^{n} x_i\right)^2}. \tag{27.11}$$

We can also compute a from the expression

$$a = \overline{y} - b\overline{x}, \tag{27.12}$$

if we have computed the means of the x_i's and the y_i's.

EXAMPLE 27.30

We will determine the regression line for the heights of Olympic pole vaults. Use equations (27.11) and (27.12) to compute a and b, obtaining

$$a = -185.637 \text{ and } b = 0.103.$$

The regression line for this data has equation

$$y = -185.637 + 0.103x.$$

Figure 27.35 again shows the data (as in Figure 27.33), along with the regression line.

The data ends at 1996. If we use the regression line to try to project ahead to 2008, we get

$$y = -185.637 + 0.103(2008) = 21.187 \text{ ft}.$$

This would require an extraordinary effort. But we learn a more dramatic lesson if we use the line to project to the 3000 Olympics. Now we get

$$y = -185.637 + 0.103(3000) = 123.36 \text{ ft}.$$

No one would believe this. The point is that the regression line in this example has positive slope, and it will return as large as value of y as we want by putting in a sufficiently large value of x. However, there are clearly limits to how high a human being can vault. We do not know what this limit is, but 124 feet seems too high. ■

As this example shows, we must not use a regression line to attempt to project conclusions about y-values that are "too far" outside the data set from which the line was derived. The further out of touch we get from the data, the less reliable our projected conclusions are.

There is a very useful interpretation that can be made for the square of the linear correlation coefficient c. Suppose we have sample points $(x_1, y_1), \ldots, (x_n, y_n)$, and there is a significant linear correlation between the x_i's and the y_i's. The regression line is $y = a + bx$, with a and b from equations (27.10) or (27.12), and (27.11). For a given x_i, write $(y_r)_i = a + bx_i$ to distinguish between y_i and the y-coordinate of the point on the regression line corresponding to x_i.

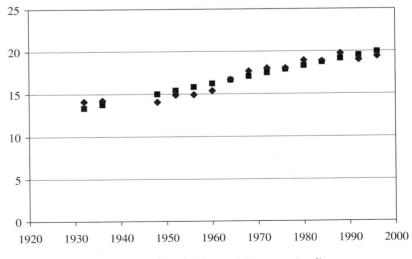

FIGURE 27.35   *Olympic vaulting heights and the regression line.*

If we think of the regression line as defining a sense of how the data "should" arrange itself, we can look to the regression line to "explain" the y-values. That is, think of $(y_r)_i$ as the number that should go with x_i, and y_i as the number that actually does go with x_i in the sample. This makes it reasonable to attempt to compute the ratio of differences of the data from the mean that are explained by the regression line, to the total differences of the data from the mean.

We can quantify these ideas as follows. Interpret

$$\sum_{i=1}^{n} (y_i - \bar{y})$$

as the total deviation of the y_is from their mean. Further,

$$\sum_{i=1}^{n} ((y_r)_i - \bar{y})$$

is the deviation of regression line y-values from the mean of the y_i's. Think of this as a deviation explained by the regression line. The ratio we are interested in, which we will temporarily call k, is therefore

$$k = \frac{\sum_{i=1}^{n} ((y_r)_i - \bar{y})}{\sum_{i=1}^{n} (y_i - \bar{y})}.$$

Next,

$$\sum_{i=1}^{n} (y_i - (y_r)_i)$$

is the deviation of the regression line values from the actual y-values. Think of this as the deviation for which the regression line presents no rationale. Now observe that

$$\sum_{i=1}^{n} (y_i - \bar{y}) = \sum_{i=1}^{n} ((y_r)_i - \bar{y}) + \sum_{i=1}^{n} (y_i - (y_r)_i).$$

Therefore,

$$k = \frac{\sum_{i=1}^{n} ((y_r)_i - \bar{y})}{\sum_{i=1}^{n} ((y_r)_i - \bar{y}) + \sum_{i=1}^{n} (y_i - (y_r)_i)}$$

$$= \frac{\text{differences of } y_i\text{s from the mean explained by the regression line}}{\text{total differences of } y_i\text{'s from the mean}}.$$

Now comes what may be a surprise. If the algebra is carried out, we find that $k = c^2$. Thus c enables us to detect a significant linear correlation, and c^2 gives a measure of how well the deviations of the y_i's from the norm are explained by the regression line.

EXAMPLE 27.31

A state compiles statistics on deer hunters and deaths in the deer population each year. For a period of ten years, these are given by the following table:

Number of Hunters	168	172	194	204	230	270	295	320	390	402
Deaths in Deer Population	28	30	36	39	42	50	46	57	61	62

We find that $\bar{x} = 255.50$, $\bar{y} = 45.10$, $s_x = 97.961$, and $s_y = 12.28$. A routine computation yields $c = 0.8488$. With $n = 10$ in Table 27.9, the critical value is 0.632. Because $c > 0.632$, there is

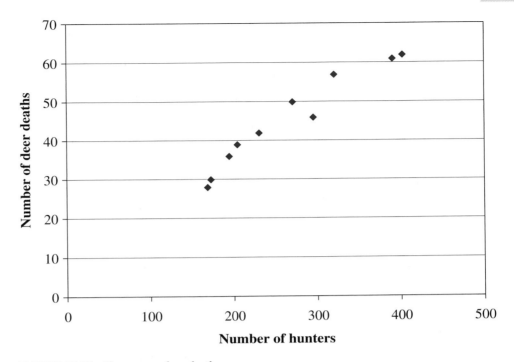

FIGURE 27.36   *Hunters vs. deer deaths.*

a .95 probability that there is a significant linear correlation between x- and y-values. A scatter plot of these values is given in Figure 27.36.

Now we ask: How many of the deaths in the deer population are explained by the number of hunters? We expect some deer to be killed by hunters, and some to die from other causes. Compute

$$c^2 = (0.8488)^2 = 0.7201.$$

We conclude that 72% of the deer deaths can be explained by the regression line, which means that 72% can be explained by the presence of the hunters. The other 28% must be accounted for by other factors. ∎

Finally, we would like to develop a kind of confidence interval for predictions based on a regression line. In the present context, such an interval will be called a *prediction interval*. Begin with the *spread of the error of the estimate*, which is analogous to standard deviation in the sense that it measures the spread of the sample points about the regression line. This spread of the error of the estimate is denoted S_r and is defined by

$$S_r = \sqrt{\frac{\sum_{i=1}^{n}(y_i - (y_r)_i)^2}{n-2}}.$$

It is routine to verify that

$$S_r = \sqrt{\frac{\sum_{i=1}^{n} y_i^2 - a\sum_{i=1}^{n} y_i - b\sum_{i=1}^{n} x_i y_i}{n-2}},$$

with a and b given by equations (27.10) and (27.11) (or (27.12)), respectively.

Next, analogous to the process developed for confidence intervals, define the maximum error ϵ_r for a given x-value (which is in the x-population, but need not be one of the actual sample values x_i) to be

$$\epsilon_r = t_{\alpha/2} S_r \sqrt{1 + \frac{1}{n} + \frac{n(x - \bar{x})^2}{n\left(\sum_{i=1}^{n} x_i^2\right) - \left(\sum_{i=1}^{n} x_i\right)^2}}.$$

Here $t_{\alpha/2}$ is a critical point of the Student t-distribution corresponding to a confidence level α. We have usually taken $\alpha = 0.05$ to have a 95% confidence level in the conclusion. The number $t_{\alpha/2}$ must be determined from a table. The difference between the current and previous use is that previously, in estimating population mean, we had $n - 1$ degrees of freedom, and now we have $n - 2$. This information must be used in order to reference the value of $t_{\alpha/2}$ from a table of critical values for the t-distribution.

Now, for a given x, we define the prediction interval for the corresponding y to be

$$y_x - \epsilon_r < y < y_x + \epsilon_r,$$

where $y_x = a + bx$, the y-value given by the equation of the regression line for the given value of x.

EXAMPLE 27.32

Consider again the hunters and deaths in the deer population given over a ten year period. Suppose we want to estimate how many deer kills would correspond to $x = 350$ hunters.

It is routine to compute the equation of the regression line, obtaining $y = 8.4509 + 0.1386x$. We have stated that $\bar{x} = 255.50$. We need to compute $(y_r)_i = a + bx_i$ for $i = 1, \ldots, 10$. These values are:

x_i	168	172	194	204	230	270	295	320	390	402
$(y_r)_i = a + bx_i$	31.7357	32.2901	35.3393	36.7253	40.3289	45.8729	49.3379	52.8029	62.5049	64.1681

Compute

$$\sum_{i=1}^{10} (y_i - (y_r)_i)^2 = 80.3589$$

and

$$S_r = \sqrt{\frac{\sum_{i=1}^{10} (y_i - (y_r)_i)^2}{8}} = 3.1694.$$

Then

$$\epsilon_r = (2.306)(3.1694)\sqrt{1 + \frac{1}{10} + \frac{10(350 - 255.50)}{10(765989) - (2645)^2}}$$

$$= 7.6703.$$

Finally, compute $y_x = a + bx = 8.4509 + 0.1386(350) = 59.961$, the y-value on the regression line corresponding to $x = 350$.

The prediction interval is $y_x - \epsilon_r < y < y_x + \epsilon_r$, or

$$59.961 - 7.6703 < y < 59.961 + 7.6703.$$

In the present context, we will use two decimal places and write the prediction interval as

$$52.29 < y < 67.63.$$

The meaning of this interval is that, for a hunter population of 350, the predicted (by the regression line) number of deer deaths is 59.96 (or 60) , and we have a confidence level of 95% (because of the way we chose the critical value $t_{\alpha/2}$) that the actual number is between 52 and 68. ▨

Again, we can change the confidence level from 95% to another value by making the appropriate change in the choice of $t_{\alpha/2}$.

SECTION 27.8   PROBLEMS

For each of Problems 1 through 8, draw a scatter plot of the data, compute c and determine whether or not there is a significant linear correlation between the x_i's and the y_i's. If there is not, the problem is completed. If there is, determine the equation of the regression line, and, for each given x-value, determine the y-value predicted by the regression line, as well as the corresponding prediction interval with a 95% confidence level.

1.

x_i	0.98	1.3	2.1	2.8	3.6	5.2	5.8	7.3	9.7	13.6
y_i	3.91	4.10	4.81	5.07	6.21	7.15	7.66	9.04	10.84	14.26

$x = 0.4, 6.2,$ and 15.1.

2.

x_i	0.2	0.9	1.4	1.9	2.6	3.4	4.2	6.8	10	15.9
y_i	2.8	0.93	−0.61	−2.1	−3.9	−6.5	−8.9	−16.1	−27.2	−42.41

$x = 5.2, 8.6,$ and 17.8.

3.

x_i	1.9	2.5	5.4	8.91	10.5	17.3	18.9	21.7	25.3	34.7
y_i	−1.4	4.2	3.15	−5.6	10.7	11.2	−6.8	−15.3	2.7	9.4

$x = 0, 9.2,$ and 38.8.

4.

x_i	4.8	5.8	7.3	9.5	15.3	19.5	27.4	32.6	36.3	41.9
y_i	34.8	41.1	47.2	57.1	76.9	98.6	133.8	148.4	164.9	197.5

$x = 2.9, 29$ and 46.

5.

x_i	3	3.4	3.8	4.2	5.9	7.5	12.3	21.8	29.8	35.3
y_i	1	1.3	1.9	2.28	3.82	5.42	9.0	19.1	24.9	28.7

$x = 0.6, 3.0, 39.0,$ and 42.1.

6.

x_i	3.7	3.9	4.2	4.6	4.8	5.2	5.7	6.3	6.5	6.9
y_i	−1.2	3.9	−5.6	3.8	−12.9	4.2	−27.2	4.8	−18.6	15.9

$x = 3.5, 4.7,$ and 7.3.

7.

x_i	0	2.5	6.1	8.3	9.8	11.6	15.3	17.2
y_i	−3.1	1.22	7.2	10.37	12.9	15.85	20.7	25.2

	19.5	22.9	25.5	29.6	32.2	36.2	40.8
	28.19	32.7	38.6	43.92	46.8	56.2	61.9

$x = -4, 11.1, 30.1,$ and 66.7.

8.

x_i	0	1.3	1.9	2.3	2.5	2.8	3.1	4.8
y_i	3	0.5	−0.84	−1.74	−1.90	−2.73	−3.0	−6.9

	5.4	7.4	12.9	15.3	19.4	22.5	25.9
	−7.4	−12.32	−24.8	−27.6	−35.9	−43.7	−48.5

$x = 1.5, 4.3, 13,$ and 32.

9. A basketball coach is attempting to evaluate the impact of an expensive player on the team's won/loss record. He considers the following table, which gives number of games per season in which the player has seen at least twenty five minutes of floor time, together with wins over the season.

x_i: Games	62	58	59	73	69	75	72	81	46	79
y_i: Wins	47	46	47	56	55	62	55	63	38	64

(a) Show that there is a significant linear correlation between games in which the player participated, and team wins.

(b) Write the equation of the regression line.

(c) Estimate the percentage of wins (in games the player played in) that are explained by this player's floor presence.

(d) Predict with a 95% confidence level how many games the team will win next season if this player is in 85 games. Write the prediction interval for this estimate.

10. A drug is being tested. One purpose of the test is to demonstrate the efficacy of the drug, but another is to measure incidence of a certain side effect (lowered body temperature). The following table gives numbers of randomly chosen patients in ten states, together with the number exhibiting the side effect:

x_i: Patients	5,000	5,500	4,200	10,000	8,000	5,700
y_i: Side Effect	160	167	135	305	235	183
	6,900	8,800	12,500	6,000		
	221	265	394	190		

(a) Show that there is a significant linear correlation between number of patients and incidents of this side effect.

(b) Determine the equation of the regression line.

(c) Estimate the percentage of patients that will have this side effect in a patient population of 17,000.

(d) Predict with a 95% confidence level how many patients out of a population of 17,500 will exhibit this side effect. Write the prediction interval for this estimate.

11. Over a period of ten years, the number of times a certain individual has visited New York each year has been recorded. Records have also been kept of the number of incidents of major jewelry thefts in the city for each year in this period. The numbers are as follows:

x_i: Visits	17	12	15	22	14	9	18	21	10	13
y_i: Thefts	6	5	6	8	5	3	7	8	5	5

(a) Show that there is a significant linear correlation between number of visits and the number of thefts.

(b) Determine the equation of the regression line.

(c) Estimate the percentage of thefts that are explained by this person's number of visits to the city each year.

(d) Predict with a 95% confidence level how many thefts are likely to occur if this person visits New York 25 times next year. Write the prediction interval for this estimate.

12. A city is experimenting with an additive to the water with the objective of decreasing tooth decay. Over a ten year period, records have been kept on pounds of the chemical put into the water system and the number of children twelve or under who were cavity free that year.

x_i: Additive (pounds)	410	500	475	390	470
y_i: Cavity free	3550	4412	4119	3420	4090
	525	480	510	590	600
	4598	4203	4452	5143	5259

(a) Show that there is a significant linear correlation between number of pounds of the chemical, and the number of children who were cavity free.

(b) Determine the equation of the regression line.

(c) Estimate the percentage of children who were cavity free that is explained by the chemical added to the water supply.

(d) Predict with a 95% confidence level how many children are likely to be cavity free if 650 pounds are used. Write the prediction interval for this estimate.

Answers and Solutions to Selected Problems

CHAPTER 1

Section 1.1

1. Yes, since $2\varphi\varphi' = 2(\sqrt{x-1})\left(\dfrac{1}{2\sqrt{x-1}}\right) = 1$ for $x > 1$.   **3.** Yes   **5.** Yes

7. $\dfrac{d}{dx}(y^2 + xy - 2x^2 - 3x - 2y) = (y - 4x - 3) + (2y + x - 2)y' = 0$

13. $y = 3 - e^{-x}$ **15.** $y = 2\sin^2(x) - 2$

17. Direction field for $y' = x + y$; solution satisfying $y(2) = 2$

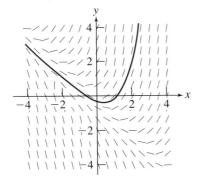

19. Direction field for $y' = xy$; solution satisfying $y(0) = 2$

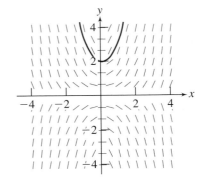

21. Direction field for $y' = \sin(y)$; solution satisfying $y(1) = \pi/2$

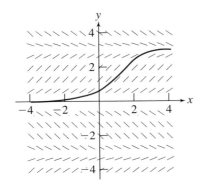

23. Direction field for $y' = y\sin(x) - 3x^2$; solution satisfying $y(0) = 1$

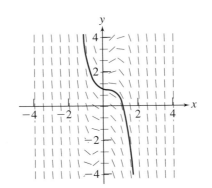

25. Direction field for $y' - y\cos(x) = 1 - x^2$; solution satisfying $y(2) = 2$

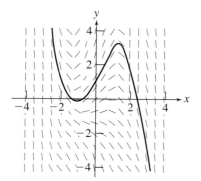

27. *Hint:* The lineal element to the solution curve through (x_0, z) has equation $y = [q(x_0) - p(x_0)z](x - x_0) + z$.

Section 1.2

1. $2x^2 = y^3 + c$ **3.** Not separable   **5.** $y = \dfrac{1}{1 - cx}$; also $y = 0$ **7.** $\sec(y) = Ax$ **9.** Not separable

11. $\frac{1}{2}y^2 - y + \ln(y + 1) = \ln(x) - 2$ **13.** $(\ln(y))^2 = 3x^2 - 3$ **15.** $3y\sin(3y) + \cos(3y) = 9x^2 - 5$

17. 45°F   **19.** $V = \left[V_0^{1/3} + k\left(\dfrac{4\pi}{3}\right)^{1/3} t\right]^3$; V_0 = initial volume   **21.** 8.57 kg   **23.** $\frac{1}{2}\sqrt{\pi}e^{-6}$

25. $3888\sqrt{2}$ s, or approximately 91 min, 39 s   **27.** (a) 576 s   (b) 489 s (approximate)   **29.** No

Section 1.3

1. $y = cx^3 + 2x^3 \ln|x|$ **3.** $y = \frac{1}{2}x - \frac{1}{4} + ce^{-2x}$ **5.** $y = 4x^2 + 4x + 2 + ce^{2x}$

7. $y = e^{-x}\displaystyle\int\left(\dfrac{x-1}{x^2}\right)e^x\,dx + ce^{-x}$ **9.** $y = x^2 - x - 2$ **11.** $y = x + 1 + 4(x + 1)^{-2}$ **13.** $y = \frac{2}{3}e^{4x} - \frac{11}{3}e^x$

15. $y = -2x^2 + cx$

17. $A_1(t) = 50 - 30e^{-t/20}$, $A_2(t) = 75 + 90e^{-t/20} - 75e^{-t/30}$; $A_2(t)$ has its minimum value of $\frac{5450}{81}$ pounds at $60\ln\left(\frac{9}{5}\right)$ minutes.

Section 1.4

1. $2xy^2 + e^{xy} + y^2 = c$ **3.** Not exact   **5.** $y^3 + xy + \ln|x| = c$ **7.** $\cosh(x)\sinh(y) = c$

9. $3xy^4 - x = 47$ **11.** $x\sin(2y - x) = \dfrac{\pi}{24}$ **13.** Not exact   **15.** $\alpha = -3$; $x^2y^3 - 3xy - 3y^2 = c$

17. $\dfrac{\partial}{\partial x}(\varphi + c) = \dfrac{\partial \varphi}{\partial x} = M$ and $\dfrac{\partial}{\partial y}(\varphi + c) = \dfrac{\partial \varphi}{\partial y} = N$

Section 1.5

1. $\dfrac{1}{M}\left(\dfrac{\partial N}{\partial x} - \dfrac{\partial M}{\partial y}\right)$ is independent of x.

3. (a) $\dfrac{\partial M}{\partial y} = 1$, $\dfrac{\partial N}{\partial x} = -1$, so this equation is not exact.   (b) $\mu(x) = \dfrac{1}{x^2}$ (c) $\nu(y) = \dfrac{1}{y^2}$

     (d) $\eta(x, y) = x^a y^b$ for all a and b satisfying $a + b = -2$

5. e^{3y}; $xe^{3y} - e^y = c$ **7.** x^2y; $x^4y^2 + 2x^3y^3 = c$ **9.** $\dfrac{1}{y+1}$; $x^2y = c$ or $y = -1$

11. $e^{-3x}y^{-4}$; $y^3 - 1 = ky^3e^{3x}$ **13.** $\dfrac{1}{x}$; $y = 4 - \ln|x|$ **15.** x; $x^2(y^3 - 2) = -9$ **17.** $\dfrac{1}{y}$; $y = 4e^{-x^2/3}$

19. e^x; $e^x\sin(x - y) = \frac{1}{2}$ **21.** $\dfrac{\partial}{\partial y}(c\mu M) = c\dfrac{\partial}{\partial y}(\mu M) = c\dfrac{\partial}{\partial x}(\mu N) = \dfrac{\partial}{\partial x}(c\mu N)$

Section 1.6

1. $y = x + \dfrac{x}{c - \ln|x|}$ **3.** $y = 1/(1 + e^{x^2/2})$ **5.** $y\ln|y| - x = cy$ **7.** $xy - x^2 - y^2 = c$

9. $y = x^{-1}\left(c - \frac{7}{5}x^{-5/4}\right)^{4/7}$ **11.** $y = 2 + \dfrac{2}{cx^2 - 1}$ **13.** $y = \dfrac{2e^x}{ce^{2x} - 1}$ **15.** $h = \dfrac{ce - br}{ae - bd},\ k = \dfrac{ar - dc}{ae - bd}$

17. $3(x-2)^2 - 2(x-2)(y+3) - (y+3)^2 = c$ **19.** $(2x + y - 3)^2 = c(y - x + 3)$

21. $(x - y + 3)^2 = 2x + c$ **23.** $3(x - 2y) - 8\ln|x - 2y + 4| = x + c$

25. Let the dog start at $(A, 0)$, and suppose the man walks upward into the upper half-plane. The dog's path is along the graph of $y = -\sqrt{A}\sqrt{A - x} + \dfrac{1}{3\sqrt{A}}(A - x)^{3/2} + \dfrac{2}{3}A$, and the dog catches the man at $(A, 2A/3)$ at time $t = 2A/3v$ units.

27. (a) $r = a - \dfrac{v\theta}{\omega}$, a spiral   (b) $\dfrac{a\omega}{2\pi v}$ revolution

(c) Distance $= \dfrac{1}{2}\left[\dfrac{a\omega}{v^2}\sqrt{v^2 + a^2\omega^2} + \ln\left(\dfrac{a\omega + \sqrt{v^2 + a^2\omega^2}}{v}\right)\right]$

Section 1.7

1. Velocity $= \dfrac{8}{9}\sqrt{\dfrac{1358}{3}}$, about 18.91 ft/s   **3.** Velocity $= 8\sqrt{30}$, about 43.82 ft/s

5. Velocity $= 12\sqrt{5}$, about 26.84 ft/s; time $= \frac{\sqrt{3}}{2}\ln(6 + \sqrt{35})$, about 2.15 s

7. Time $= \dfrac{\sqrt{3}}{8}\displaystyle\int_{10}^{40}\dfrac{x}{\sqrt{x^3 - 100}}\,dx$, about 1.7117 seconds   **9.** Velocity $= 2\sqrt{210}$, about 28.98 ft/s

11. Max height $= 342.25$ ft; object hits the ground at 148 ft/s, 4.75 s after drop

13. $v(t) = 32 - 32e^{-t}$ for $0 \le t \le 4$, $v(t) = 8(1 + ke^{-8t})/(1 - ke^{-8t})$ ft/s for $t \ge 4$, with $k = e^{32}(3e^4 - 4)/(5e^4 - 4)$; $\lim_{t \to \infty} v(t) = 8$ ft/s; $s(t) = 32(t + e^{-t} - 1)$ for $0 \le t \le 4$, $s(t) = 8t + 2\ln(1 - ke^{-8t}) + 64 + 32e^{-4} - 2\ln(2e^4/(5e^4 - 4))$ for $t \ge 4$

15. 17.5 ft/s   **17.** $t = 2\sqrt{R/g}$, where $R =$ radius of the circle

19. $V_C = 76$ V when $t = \ln(20)/2$; $i(\frac{1}{2}\ln(20)) = 16\,\mu$A   **21.** $i_1(0+) = i_2(0+) = 3/20$ amp; $i_3(0+) = 0$

23. (a) $q(t) = EC + (q_0 - EC)e^{-t/RC}$ (b) EC (d) $-RC\ln\left(\dfrac{0.01\,EC}{q_0 - EC}\right)$

25. $y = c - \frac{3}{4}\ln|x|$ **27.** $x^2 + 2y^2 - 4y = c$ **29.** $y^2(\ln(y^2) - 1) + 2x^2 = c$

Section 1.8

7. (b) $y = 2 - e^{-x}$ (c) $y_n = 1 + x - \dfrac{1}{2}x^2 + \dfrac{1}{6}x^3 - \dfrac{1}{24}x^4 + \cdots + \dfrac{(-1)^{n+1}}{n!}x^n$

(d) $y = 2 - \displaystyle\sum_{n=0}^{\infty}\dfrac{(-1)^n}{n!}x^n = 1 + x - \dfrac{1}{2}x^2 + \dfrac{1}{6}x^3 - \dfrac{1}{24}x^4 + \cdots + \dfrac{(-1)^{n+1}}{n!}x^n + \cdots$

9. (b) $y = \frac{7}{3} + \frac{2}{3}x^3$ (c) $y_0 = 3,\ y_1 = \frac{7}{3} + \frac{2}{3}x^3 = y_2 = y_3 = \cdots = y_n$

(d) $y = 3 + 2(x - 1) + 2(x - 1)^2 + \frac{2}{3}(x - 1)^3 = y_1$

CHAPTER 2

Section 2.2

1. $y = \cosh(2x)$ **3.** $y = \frac{12}{5}e^{-3x} - \frac{7}{5}e^{-8x}$ **5.** $y = 2x^4 - 4x^4\ln|x|$

7. y_1 and y_2 are solutions of $x^2y'' - 4xy' + 6y = 0$. We must write this equation as $y'' - \dfrac{4}{x}y' + \dfrac{6}{x^2}y = 0$ to have the form to which the theorem applies, and then we must have $x \ne 0$. On an interval not containing 0, the Wronskian of these solutions is nonzero.

9. $y'' - y' - 2y = 0$ has solutions $y_1 = e^{-x}$ and $y_2 = e^{2x}$, but $y_1 y_2 = e^x$ is not a solution. Many other examples also work.
11. *Hint:* Recall that at a relative extremum x_0, $y'(x_0) = 0$.   **13.** *Hint:* Consider $W(x_0)$.

Section 2.3

1. $y = c_1 \cos(2x) + c_2 \sin(2x)$ **3.** $y = c_1 e^{5x} + c_2 x e^{5x}$ **5.** $y = c_1 x^2 + c_2 x^2 \ln|x|$ **7.** $y = c_1 x^4 + c_2 x^{-2}$

9. $y = c_1 \left(\dfrac{\cos(x)}{\sqrt{x}} \right) + c_2 \left(\dfrac{\sin(x)}{\sqrt{x}} \right)$ **11.** $y = c_1 e^{-ax} + c_2 x e^{-ax}$

13. (a) $y^4 = c_1 x + c_2$ (b) $(y-1)e^y = c_1 x + c_2$ or $y = c_3$ (c) $y = c_1 e^{c_1 x}/(c_2 - e^{c_1 x})$ or $y = 1/(c_3 - x)$
(d) $y = \ln|\sec(x + c_1)| + c_2$ (e) $y = \ln|c_1 x + c_2|$

Section 2.4

1. $y = c_1 e^{-2x} + c_2 e^{3x}$ **3.** $y = e^{-3x}[c_1 + c_2 x]$ **5.** $y = e^{-5x}[c_1 \cos(x) + c_2 \sin(x)]$

7. $y = e^{-3x/2}[c_1 \cos(3\sqrt{7}x/2) + c_2 \sin(3\sqrt{7}x/2)]$ **9.** $y = e^{7x}(c_1 + c_2 x)$ **11.** $y = e^{-2x}(c_1 \cos(\sqrt{5}x) + c_2 \sin(\sqrt{5}x))$

13. $y = 5 - 2e^{-3x}$ **15.** $y(x) = 0$

17. $y = \frac{9}{7} e^{3(x-2)} + \frac{5}{7} e^{-4(x-2)}$ **19.** $y = e^{x-1}(29 - 17x)$

21. $y = e^{(x+2)/2} \left[\cos\left(\frac{\sqrt{15}}{2}(x+2) \right) + \frac{5}{\sqrt{15}} \sin\left(\frac{\sqrt{15}}{2}(x+2) \right) \right]$

23. (a) $\psi(x) = e^{ax}[c + (d - ac)x]$ (b) $\psi_\epsilon(x) = \dfrac{1}{2\epsilon} e^{ax}[(d - ac + \epsilon c)e^{\epsilon x} + (ac - d + \epsilon c)e^{-\epsilon x}]$
(c) $\lim_{\epsilon \to 0} \psi_\epsilon(x) = \psi(x)$ (use l'Hôpital's rule)

Section 2.5

1. $y = c_1 x^2 + c_2 x^{-3}$ **3.** $y = c_1 \cos(2\ln(x)) + c_2 \sin(2\ln(x))$ **5.** $y = c_1 x^4 + c_2 x^{-4}$

7. $y = c_1 x^{-2} + c_2 x^{-3}$ **9.** $y = x^{-12}(c_1 + c_2 \ln(x))$ **11.** $y = x^{3/2}[c_1 \cos(\sqrt{39}\ln(x)/2) + c_2 \sin(\sqrt{39}\ln(x)/2)]$

13. $y = x^{-2}(3\cos(4\ln(-x)) - 2\sin(4\ln(-x)))$ **15.** $y = -3 + 2x^2$

17. $y = -x^{-3}\cos(2\ln(-x))$

19. $y = -4x^{-12}(1 + 12\ln(x))$ **21.** $y = \frac{11}{4}x^2 + \frac{17}{4}x^{-2}$

Section 2.6

1. $y = c_1 \cos(x) + c_2 \sin(x) - \cos(x)\ln|\sec(x) + \tan(x)|$

3. $y = c_1 \cos(3x) + c_2 \sin(3x) + 4x\sin(3x) + \frac{4}{3}\ln|\cos(3x)|\cos(3x)$ **5.** $y = c_1 e^x + c_2 e^{2x} - e^{2x}\cos(e^{-x})$

7. $y = c_1 e^{2x} + c_2 e^{-x} - x^2 + x - 4$ **9.** $y = e^x[c_1 \cos(3x) + c_2 \sin(3x)] + 2x^2 + x - 1$ **11.** $y = c_1 e^{2x} + c_2 e^{4x} + e^x$

13. $y = c_1 e^x + c_2 e^{2x} + 3\cos(x) + \sin(x)$ **15.** $y = e^{2x}[c_1 \cos(3x) + c_2 \sin(3x)] + \frac{1}{3}e^{2x} - \frac{1}{2}e^{3x}$

17. $y = c_1 e^{2x} + c_2 e^{-x} + \frac{1}{3}x e^{2x}$

19. $y = c_1 e^{2x} + c_2 e^{-3x} - \frac{1}{6}x - \frac{1}{36}$ **21.** $y = c_1 x^2 + c_2 x^4 + x$

23. $y = c_1 \cos(2\ln(x)) + c_2 \sin(2\ln(x)) - \frac{1}{4}\cos(2\ln(x))\ln(x)$ **25.** $y = c_1 e^{2x} + c_2 x e^{2x} + e^{3x} - \frac{1}{4}$

27. $y = \frac{7}{4}e^{2x} - \frac{3}{4}e^{-2x} - \frac{7}{4}x e^{2x} - \frac{1}{4}x$

29. $y = \frac{3}{8}e^{-2x} - \frac{19}{120}e^{-6x} + \frac{1}{5}e^{-x} + \frac{7}{12}$ **31.** $y = 2e^{4x} + 2e^{-2x} - 2e^{-x} - e^{2x}$

33. $y = -\frac{17}{4}e^{2x} + \frac{55}{13}e^{3x} + \frac{1}{52}\cos(2x) - \frac{5}{52}\sin(2x)$

35. $y = \frac{1}{11}e^{4(x+1)}\left[(55 - e)\cosh(\sqrt{14}(x+1)) + \frac{1}{\sqrt{14}}(5e - 198)\sinh(\sqrt{14}(x+1))\right] + \frac{1}{11}e^{-x}$

37. $y = 4e^{-x} - \sin^2(x) - 2$ **39.** $y = 2x^3 + x^{-2} - 2x^2$ **41.** $y = x - x^2 + 3\cos(\ln(x)) + \sin(\ln(x))$

Section 2.7

1. $y = e^{-2t}[5\cosh(\sqrt{2}t) + \frac{10}{\sqrt{2}}\sinh(\sqrt{2}t)]$;
$y = \frac{5}{\sqrt{2}}e^{-2t}\sinh(\sqrt{2}t)$ (graphed below)

3. $y = \frac{5}{2}e^{-t}[2\cos(2t) + \sin(2t)]$;
$y = \frac{5}{2}e^{-t}\sin(2t)$ (graphed below)

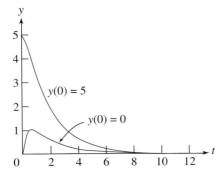

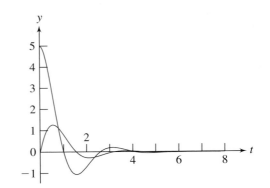

5. $y = \frac{A}{\sqrt{2}}e^{-2t}\sinh(\sqrt{2}t)$ (graphed below)

7. $y = Ate^{-2t}$ (graphed below)

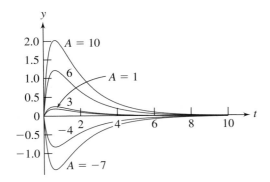

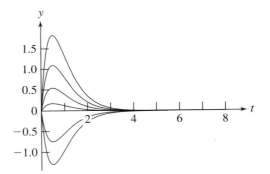

9. $y = \frac{A}{2}e^{-t}\sin(2t)$ (graphed below)

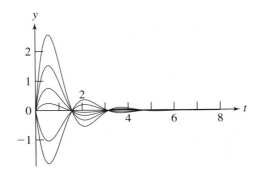

11. $y = \frac{1}{60}(57e^{-8t} - 52e^{-3t})$ down positive

13. At most once; no condition on only $y(0)$ is enough, as one needs to specify $y'(0)$ also.

15. Increasing C decreases the frequency **17.** *Hint:* Show that $(m/k)^2 = (d/a)^2$ **19.** $\dfrac{A}{2m\omega_0} t \sin(\omega_0 t)$

21. (a) $y = \frac{1}{373}\left[e^{-3t}\left(2266\cosh(\sqrt{7}t) + \frac{6582}{\sqrt{7}}\sinh(\sqrt{7}t)\right) - 28\cos(3t) + 72\sin(3t)\right]$

(b) $y = \frac{1}{373}\left[e^{-3t}\left(28\cosh(\sqrt{7}t) + \frac{2106}{\sqrt{7}}\sinh(\sqrt{7}t)\right) - 28\cos(3t) + 72\sin(3t)\right]$

These functions are graphed below.

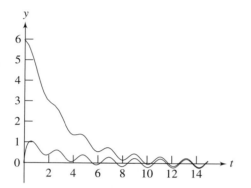

23. (a) $y = \frac{1}{15}\left[e^{-t/2}\left(98\cos(\sqrt{11}t/2) + \frac{74}{\sqrt{11}}\sin(\sqrt{11}t/2)\right) - 8\cos(3t) + 4\sin(3t)\right]$

(b) $y = \frac{1}{15}\left[e^{-t/2}\left(8\cos(\sqrt{11}t/2) + \frac{164}{\sqrt{11}}\sin(\sqrt{11}t/2)\right) - 8\cos(3t) + 4\sin(3t)\right]$

These functions are graphed below.

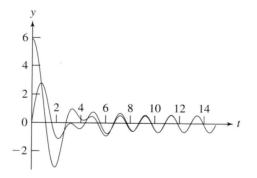

25. $i(t) = .015e^{-0.0625t} - 5.4 \times 10^{-7}e^{-3333.27t} + 0.015\cos(20t) - 0.00043\sin(20t)$

27. $i(t) = 0.0001633e^{-t} + 0.00161e^{-0.3177t} + 0.000023e^{-t}\cos(6t) - 0.000183e^{-t}\sin(6t)$

CHAPTER 3

Section 3.1

1. $\dfrac{1}{s-1} - \dfrac{1}{s+1}$ **3.** $\dfrac{16s}{(s^2+4)^2}$ **5.** $\dfrac{1}{s^2} - \dfrac{s}{s^2+25}$ **7.** $\dfrac{2}{s^3} + \dfrac{8}{s^2} + \dfrac{16}{s}$ **9.** $\dfrac{6}{s^4} - \dfrac{3}{s^2} + \dfrac{s}{s^2+16}$ **11.** $-2e^{-16t}$

13. $2\cos(4t) - \frac{5}{4}\sin(4t)$ **15.** $3e^{7t} + t$ **17.** $e^{4t} - 6te^{4t}$ **23.** $\dfrac{5}{s(1+e^{-3s})}$

25. From the graph, $f(t) = 0$ if $0 < t \leq 5$, and $f(t) = 5$ if $5 < t \leq 10$, and $f(t) = 0$ if $10 < t \leq 25$. Further, $f(t+25) = f(t)$, so f is periodic of period $T = 25$. Thus $\pounds[f](s) = \dfrac{5e^{-5s}(1 - e^{-5s})}{s(1 - e^{-25s})}$.

27. $\dfrac{E\omega}{s^2 + \omega^2} \dfrac{1}{1 - e^{-\pi s/\omega}}$ **29.** $f(t) = h$ if $0 < t \leq a$ and $f(t) = 0$ if $a < t \leq 2a$. Further, $f(t+2a) = f(t)$, so f is periodic of period $2a$, and $L[f](s) = \dfrac{h}{s(1 + e^{-as})}$.

Section 3.2

1. $y = \frac{1}{4} - \frac{13}{4}e^{-4t}$ **3.** $y = -\frac{4}{17}e^{-4t} + \frac{4}{17}\cos(t) + \frac{1}{17}\sin(t)$ **5.** $y = -\frac{1}{4} + \frac{1}{2}t + \frac{17}{4}e^{2t}$

7. $y = \frac{22}{25}e^{2t} - \frac{13}{5}te^{2t} + \frac{3}{25}\cos(t) - \frac{4}{25}\sin(t)$ **9.** $y = \frac{1}{16} + \frac{1}{16}t - \frac{33}{16}\cos(4t) + \frac{15}{64}\sin(4t)$

Section 3.3

1. $\dfrac{6}{(s+2)^4} - \dfrac{3}{(s+2)^2} + \dfrac{2}{s+2}$ **3.** $\dfrac{1}{s}(1 - e^{-7s}) + \dfrac{s}{s^2+1}\cos(7)e^{-7s} - \dfrac{1}{s^2+1}\sin(7)e^{-7s}$

5. $\dfrac{1}{s^2} - \dfrac{11}{s}e^{-3s} - \dfrac{4}{s^2}e^{-3s}$ **7.** $\dfrac{1}{s+1} - \dfrac{2}{(s+1)^3} + \dfrac{1}{(s+1)^2+1}$ **9.** $\dfrac{s}{s^2+1} + \left(\dfrac{2}{s} - \dfrac{s}{s^2+1} - \dfrac{1}{s^2+1}\right)e^{-2\pi s}$

11. $\dfrac{s^2 + 4s - 5}{(s^2 + 4s + 13)^2}$ **13.** $\dfrac{1}{s^2} - \dfrac{2}{s} - \left(\dfrac{1}{s^2} + \dfrac{15}{s}\right)e^{-16s}$ **15.** $\dfrac{24}{(s+5)^5} + \dfrac{4}{(s+5)^3} + \dfrac{1}{(s+5)^2}$ **17.** $e^{2t}\sin(t)$

19. $\cos(3(t-2))H(t-2)$ **21.** $\frac{1}{\sqrt{2}}e^{-3t}\sinh(\sqrt{2}t)$ **23.** $e^{-3t}\cosh(2\sqrt{2}t) - \frac{1}{2\sqrt{2}}e^{-3t}\sinh(2\sqrt{2}t)$

25. $\frac{1}{16}[1 - \cos(4(t-21))]H(t-21)$ **27.** $y = \cos(2t) + \frac{3}{4}[1 - \cos(2(t-4))]H(t-4)$

29. $y = [-\frac{1}{4} + \frac{1}{12}e^{2(t-6)} + \frac{1}{6}e^{-(t-6)}\cos(\sqrt{3}(t-4))]H(t-6)$

31. $y = -\frac{1}{4} + \frac{2}{5}e^t - \frac{3}{20}\cos(2t) - \frac{1}{5}\sin(2t) + [-\frac{1}{4} + \frac{2}{5}e^{t-5} + \frac{3}{20}\cos(2(t-5)) - \frac{1}{5}\sin(2(t-5))]H(t-5)$

33. $E_{\text{out}} = 5e^{-4t} + 10[(1 - e^{-4(t-5)})H(t-5)]$ **35.** $i(t) = \dfrac{k}{R}(1 - e^{-Rt/L}) - \dfrac{k}{R}(1 - e^{-R(t-5)/L})H(t-5)$

37. $\pounds[KH(t-a) - KH(t-b)](s) = \dfrac{K}{s}e^{-as} - \dfrac{K}{s}e^{-bs}$

39. $\pounds\left[h\left(\dfrac{t-a}{b-a}\right)H(t-a) + h\left(\dfrac{c-t}{c-b} - \dfrac{t-a}{b-a}\right)H(t-b) - h\left(\dfrac{c-t}{c-b}\right)H(t-c)\right]$

$= \dfrac{h}{b-a}\dfrac{e^{-as}}{s^2} - \dfrac{h(c-a)}{(c-b)(b-a)}\dfrac{e^{-bs}}{s^2} + \dfrac{h}{c-b}\dfrac{e^{-cs}}{s^2}$

Section 3.4

1. $\frac{1}{16}[\sinh(2t) - \sin(2t)]$ **3.** $\dfrac{\cos(at) - \cos(bt)}{(b-a)(b+a)}$ if $b^2 \neq a^2$; $\dfrac{t\sin(at)}{2a}$ if $b^2 = a^2$

5. $\dfrac{1}{a^4}[1 - \cos(at)] - \dfrac{1}{2a^3}t\sin(at)$ **7.** $\left(\frac{1}{2} - \frac{1}{2}e^{-2(t-4)}\right)H(t-4)$ **9.** $y(t) = e^{3t} * f(t) - e^{2t} * f(t)$

11. $y(t) = \frac{1}{4}e^{6t} * f(t) - \frac{1}{4}e^{2t} * f(t) + 2e^{6t} - 5e^{2t}$ **13.** $y(t) = \frac{1}{3}\sin(3t) * f(t) - \cos(3t) + \frac{1}{3}\sin(3t)$

15. $y(t) = \frac{4}{3}e^t - \frac{1}{4}e^{2t} - \frac{1}{12}e^{-2t} - \frac{1}{3}e^t * f(t) + \frac{1}{4}e^{2t} * f(t) + \frac{1}{12}e^{-2t} * f(t)$ **17.** $f(t) = \frac{1}{2}e^{-2t} - \frac{3}{2}$

19. $f(t) = \cosh(t)$ **21.** $f(t) = 3 + \frac{2}{5}\sqrt{15}e^{t/2}\sin(\sqrt{15}t/2)$ **23.** $f(t) = \frac{1}{4}e^{-2t} + \frac{3}{4}e^{-6t}$

Section 3.5

1. $y = 3[e^{-2(t-2)} - e^{-3(t-2)}]H(t-2) - 4[e^{-2(t-5)} - e^{-3(t-5)}]H(t-5)$ **3.** $y = 6(e^{-2t} - e^{-t} + te^{-t})$

5. $\varphi(t) = (B+9)e^{-2t} - (B+6)e^{-3t}$; $\varphi(0) = 3$, $\varphi'(0) = B$ **7.** $3/\pi$ **9.** 4

11. $E_{\text{out}} = 10e^{-4(t-2)}H(t-2) - 10e^{-4(t-3)}H(t-3)$ **13.** 0 if $t < a$; $f(t-a)$ if $t \geq a$

15. $y(t) = \sqrt{\dfrac{m}{k}}v_0 \sin\left(\sqrt{\dfrac{k}{m}}t\right)$

Section 3.6

1. $x(t) = -2 + 2e^{t/2} - t$, $y(t) = -1 + e^{t/2} - t$ **3.** $x(t) = \frac{4}{9} + \frac{1}{3}t - \frac{4}{9}e^{3t/4}$, $y(t) = -\frac{2}{3} + \frac{2}{3}e^{3t/4}$

5. $x(t) = \frac{3}{4} - \frac{3}{4}e^{2t/3} + \frac{1}{2}t^2 + \frac{1}{2}t$, $y(t) = -\frac{3}{2}e^{2t/3} + t + \frac{3}{2}$ **7.** $x(t) = e^{-t}\cos(t) + t - 1$, $y(t) = e^{-t}\sin(t) + t^2 - t$

9. $x(t) = 1 - e^{-t} - 2te^{-t}$, $y(t) = 1 - e^{-t}$

11. $y_1(t) = \frac{1}{2}e^t + \frac{1}{2}e^{-t} - 1 - t$, $y_2(t) = -\frac{1}{4}t^2 - \frac{1}{2}t$, $y_3(t) = -\frac{1}{6}e^t + \frac{1}{6}e^{-t} - \frac{1}{3}t$

13. $i_1(t) = \frac{1}{5}(1 - \frac{1}{2}e^{-t/2}) - \frac{2}{85}[e^{-(t-4)/2} - \cos(2(t-4)) + \frac{9}{2}\sin(2(t-4))]H(t-4)$, and
$i_2(t) = \frac{1}{10}e^{-t/2} + \frac{2}{85}[e^{-(t-4)/2} - \cos(2(t-4)) - 4\sin(2(t-4))]H(t-4)$

15. $x_1(t) = \frac{5}{36} - \frac{1}{20}\cos(2t) - \frac{4}{45}\cos(3t) - [\frac{5}{36} - \frac{1}{20}\cos(2(t-2)) - \frac{4}{45}\cos(3(t-2))]H(t-2)$, and
$x_2(t) = \frac{1}{18} - \frac{1}{10}\cos(2t) + \frac{2}{45}\cos(3t) - [\frac{1}{18} - \frac{1}{10}\cos(2(t-2)) + \frac{2}{45}\cos(3(t-2))]H(t-2)$

17. $m_1 y_1'' = k(y_2 - y_1)$, $m_2 y_2'' = -k(y_2 - y_1)$; $y_1(0) = y_1'(0) = y_2'(0) = 0$; $y_2(0) = d$. Then $(m_1 s^2 + k)Y_1 - kY_2 = 0$ and
$(m_2 s^2 + k)Y_2 - kY_1 = m_2 ds$. Replace Y_2 with $\frac{m_1 s^2 + k}{k} Y_1$ in the second equation to get
$$Y_1(s) = \frac{kd}{m_1 s[s^2 + k((m_1 + m_2)/m_1 m_2)]}.$$ The quadratic term in the denominator indicates that the objects will
oscillate with period $2\pi\sqrt{\dfrac{m_1 m_2}{k(m_1 + m_2)}}$.

19. $i_1 = [\frac{1}{10}e^{-(t-1)} + \frac{3}{20}e^{-(t-1)/6}]H(t-1)$, $i_2 = [-\frac{1}{10}e^{-(t-1)} + \frac{1}{10}e^{-(t-1)/6}]H(t-1)$

21. $x_1(t) = 9e^{-t/100} + e^{-3t/50} + 3[e^{-(t-3)/100} - e^{-3(t-3)/50}]H(t-3)$;
$x_2(t) = 6e^{-t/100} - e^{-3t/50} + [2e^{-(t-3)/100} + 3e^{-3(t-3)/50}]H(t-3)$

Section 3.7

1. $y = -1 + ce^{-2/t}$ **3.** $y = 7t^2$ **5.** $y = ct^2 e^{-t}$ **7.** $y = 4$ **9.** $y = 3t^2/2$

CHAPTER 4

Section 4.1

1. $y = -2 - \frac{1}{3}x^3 + \frac{1}{12}x^4 - \frac{1}{60}x^5 - \frac{1}{120}x^6 + \cdots$ **3.** $y = 3 + \frac{5}{2}(x-1)^2 + \frac{5}{6}(x-1)^3 + \frac{5}{24}(x-1)^4 + \frac{1}{6}(x-1)^5 + \cdots$

5. $y = 7 + 3(x-1) - 2(x-1)^2 - (x-1)^3 + (x-1)^4 + \cdots$ **7.** $y = -3 + x + 4x^2 + \frac{7}{6}x^3 + \frac{1}{3}x^4 + \cdots$

9. $y = 1 + x - \dfrac{1}{4}x^2 + \dfrac{1}{4}x^3 + \dfrac{1}{32}x^4 + \cdots$

11. $y = a_0[1 - \frac{1}{2}x^2 + \frac{1}{6}x^4 - \frac{31}{720}x^6 + \frac{379}{40320}x^8] - [\frac{1}{2}x^2 - \frac{1}{8}x^4 + \frac{5}{144}x^6 - \frac{43}{5760}x^8 + \frac{1741}{1209600}x^{10} + \cdots]$

13. $y = x - 1 + A\left[1 - \dfrac{1}{2}x^2 + \dfrac{1}{4(2!)}x^4 - \dfrac{1}{8(3!)}x^6 + \dfrac{1}{16(4!)}x^8 + \cdots\right]$;

$y = x - 1 + A\displaystyle\sum_{n=0}^{\infty}(-1)^n \dfrac{1}{n!2^n}x^{2n} = x - 1 + (A+1)e^{-x^2/2}$

15. $a_{n+2} = -\dfrac{a_{n-1}}{(n+1)(n+2)}$ for $n \geq 1$; $(a_1 = 0)$ $y_1 = 1 - \frac{1}{6}x^3 + \frac{1}{180}x^6 - \frac{1}{12960}x^9 + \frac{1}{1710720}x^{12} - \cdots$; $(a_0 = 0)$
$y_2 = x - \frac{1}{12}x^4 + \frac{1}{504}x^7 - \frac{1}{45360}x^{10} + \frac{1}{7076160}x^{13} - \cdots$

17. $y = a_0\left[1 + \frac{1}{4(5)}x^5 + \frac{1}{4(5)(9)(10)}x^{10} + \frac{1}{4(5)(9)(10)(14)(15)}x^{15} + \cdots\right] + a_1\left[x + \frac{1}{5(6)}x^6 + \frac{1}{5(6)(10)(11)}x^{11} + \right.$
$\left. \frac{1}{5(6)(10)(11)(15)(16)}x^{16} + \cdots\right] + \frac{1}{2}x^2 + \frac{1}{2(6)(7)}x^7 + \frac{1}{2(6)(7)(11)(12)}x^{12} + \frac{1}{2(6)(7)(11)(12)(16)(17)}x^{17} + \cdots$

19. $y = a_0\left[1 + \dfrac{1}{12}x^4 - \dfrac{1}{60}x^5 + \dfrac{1}{360}x^6 - \dfrac{1}{2520}x^7 + \cdots\right] + a_1\left[x - \dfrac{1}{2}x^2 + \dfrac{1}{6}x^3 - \dfrac{1}{24}x^4 + \dfrac{7}{120}x^5 - \cdots\right]$

21. $y = a\left[1 - \frac{1}{2(3)}x^3 + \frac{1}{2(3)(5)(6)}x^6 - \frac{1}{2(3)(5)(6)(8)(9)}x^9 + \cdots\right] + b\left[x - \frac{1}{3(4)}x^4 + \frac{1}{3(4)(6)(7)}x^7 - \frac{1}{(3)(4)(6)(7)(9)(10)}x^{10} + \cdots\right]$

23. $y = 2 - 3e^{-x} = -1 + 3x - \dfrac{3}{2}x^2 + \dfrac{3x^3}{3!} - \dfrac{1}{8}x^4 + \cdots$

25. $y = \frac{1}{5} + \frac{1}{5}e^{2x}[32\sin(x) - 6\cos(x)] = -1 + 4x + 11x^2 + \frac{34}{3}x^3 + \frac{27}{4}x^4 + \cdots$

Section 4.2

1. a_0 arbitrary, $a_1 = 1, 2a_2 - a_0 = -1, a_n = \dfrac{1}{n}a_{n-2}$ for $n \geq 3$,

$$y = a_0 + (a_0 - 1)\left[\tfrac{1}{2}x^2 + \tfrac{1}{2(4)}x^4 + \tfrac{1}{2(4)(6)}x^6 + \tfrac{1}{2(4)(6)(8)}x^8 + \cdots\right] + x + \tfrac{1}{3}x^3 + \tfrac{1}{3(5)}x^5 + \tfrac{1}{3(5)(7)}x^7 + \tfrac{1}{3(5)(7)(9)}x^9 + \cdots$$

3. a_0 arbitrary, $a_1 + a_0 = 0, 2a_2 + a_1 = 1, a_{n+1} = \dfrac{1}{n+1}(-a_n + a_{n-2})$ for $n \geq 2$;

$$y = a_0\left[1 - x + \tfrac{1}{2!}x^2 + \tfrac{1}{3!}x^3 - \tfrac{7}{4!}x^4 + \cdots\right] + \tfrac{1}{2!}x^2 - \tfrac{1}{3!}x^3 + \tfrac{1}{4!}x^4 + \tfrac{11}{5!}x^5 - \tfrac{31}{6!}x^6 + \cdots$$

5. a_0, a_1 arbitrary, $a_2 = \tfrac{1}{2}(3 - a_0), a_{n+2} = \dfrac{(n-1)}{(n+1)(n+2)}a_n$ for $n \geq 1$;

$$y = a_0 + a_1 x + (3 - a_0)\left[\tfrac{1}{2!}x^2 + \tfrac{1}{4!}x^4 + \tfrac{3}{6!}x^6 + \tfrac{3(5)}{8!}x^8 + \tfrac{3(5)(7)}{10!}x^{10} + \cdots\right]$$

7. a_0, a_1 arbitrary, $a_2 + a_0 = 0, 6a_3 + 2a_1 = 1, a_{n+2} = \dfrac{(n-1)a_{n-1} - 2a_n}{(n+1)(n+2)}$ for $n \geq 2$;

$$y = a_0 + a_1 x - a_0 x^2 + \left(\tfrac{1}{6} - \tfrac{1}{3}a_1\right)x^3 + \left(\tfrac{1}{6}a_0 + \tfrac{1}{12}a_1\right)x^4 + \cdots$$

9. a_0, a_1 arbitrary, $2a_2 + a_1 + 2a_0 = 1, 6a_3 + 2a_2 + a_1 = 0$;

$$a_{n+2} = \dfrac{(n-2)a_n - (n+1)a_{n+1}}{(n+1)(n+2)} \text{ for } n \geq 3,$$

$$y(x) = a_0 + a_1 x + \left(\tfrac{1}{2} - a_0 - \tfrac{1}{2}a_1\right)x^2 + \left(\tfrac{1}{3}a_0 - \tfrac{1}{6}\right)x^3 - \left(\tfrac{1}{24} + \tfrac{1}{12}a_0\right)x^4 + \cdots$$

11. a_0 arbitrary, $a_1 = 1, a_{2k} = -\tfrac{1}{2k}a_{2k-2}$ for $k \geq 1$; $a_{2k+1} = \dfrac{-a_{2k-1} + (1/(2k)!)(-1)^k}{2k+1}$ for $k \geq 1$;

$$y = a_0\left[1 - \tfrac{1}{2}x^2 + \tfrac{1}{2(4)}x^4 - \tfrac{1}{2(4)(6)}x^6 + \cdots\right] + x - \tfrac{1}{2!}x^3 + \tfrac{13}{5!}x^5 - \cdots$$

Section 4.3

1. 0, regular, 3, regular   **3.** 0, regular, 2, regular   **5.** 0, irregular, 2, regular

7. $4r^2 - 2r = 0$; $c_n = \dfrac{1}{2(n+r)(2n+2r-1)}c_{n-1}$ for $n \geq 1$; $y_1 = \displaystyle\sum_{n=0}^{\infty} \dfrac{1}{(2n+1)!}x^{n+1/2}$, $y_2 = \displaystyle\sum_{n=0}^{\infty} \dfrac{1}{(2n)!}x^n$

9. $9r^2 - 9r + 2 = 0$; $c_n = \dfrac{-4}{9(n+r)(n+r-1)+2}c_{n-1}$ for $n \geq 1$;

$$y_1 = x^{2/3}\left[1 - \tfrac{4}{3(4)}x + \tfrac{4^2}{3(4)(6)(7)}x^2 - \tfrac{4^3}{3(4)(6)(7)(9)(10)}x^3 + \tfrac{4^4}{3(4)(6)(7)(9)(10)(12)(13)}x^4 - \tfrac{4^5}{3(4)(6)(7)(9)(10)(12)(13)(15)(16)}x^6 + \cdots\right]$$

$$= x^{2/3} + \sum_{n=1}^{\infty} \dfrac{2(5)(8)\cdots(3n-1)(-1)^n 4^n}{(3n+1)!}x^{n+2/3}; \quad y_2 = x^{1/3} + \sum_{n=1}^{\infty} \dfrac{1(4)(7)\cdots(3n-2)(-1)^n 4^n}{(3n)!}x^{n+1/3}$$

11. $2r^2 - r = 0$; $c_n = \dfrac{-2(n+r-1)}{(n+r)(2n+2r-1)}c_{n-1}$ for $n \geq 1$;

$$y_1 = x^{1/2} + \sum_{n=1}^{\infty} \dfrac{(-1)^n(2n+3)}{3(n!)}x^{n+1/2}; \quad y_2 = 1 + \sum_{n=1}^{\infty} \dfrac{(-1)^n 2^n(n+1)}{1(3)(5)\cdots(2n-1)}x^n$$

13. $2r^2 - r - 1 = 0$; $c_1 = -\dfrac{2}{2r+3}c_0$; $c_n = \dfrac{2c_{n-2} - 2(n+r-1)c_{n-1}}{2(n+r)^2 - (n+r) - 1}$ for $n \geq 2$;

$$y_1 = x - \tfrac{2}{1!(5)}x^2 + \tfrac{18}{2!(5)(7)}x^3 - \tfrac{164}{3!(5)(7)(9)}x^4 + \tfrac{2284}{4!(5)(7)(9)(11)}x^5 - \tfrac{37272}{5!(5)(7)(9)(11)(13)}x^6 + \cdots;$$

$$y_2 = x^{-1/2} - x^{1/2} + \tfrac{3}{2}x^{3/2} - \tfrac{13}{3!(3)}x^{5/2} + \tfrac{119}{4!(3)(5)}x^{7/2} - \tfrac{1353}{5!(3)(5)(7)}x^{9/2} + \cdots$$

15. $9r^2 - 4 = 0$; $(9r^2 + 18r + 5)c_1 = 0$; $c_n = \dfrac{-9}{9(n+r)^2 - 4}c_{n-2}$ for $n \geq 2$;

$$y_1 = x^{2/3} - \tfrac{3}{2^2 1!(5)}x^{8/3} + \tfrac{3^2}{2^4 2!(5)(8)}x^{14/3} - \tfrac{3^3}{2^6 3!(5)(8)(11)}x^{20/3}$$

$$+ \tfrac{3^4}{2^8 4!(5)(8)(11)(14)}x^{26/3} - \tfrac{3^5}{2^{10} 5!(5)(8)(11)(14)(17)}x^{32/3} + \cdots;$$

$$y_2 = x^{-2/3} - \tfrac{3}{2^2 1!(1)}x^{4/3} + \tfrac{3^2}{2^4 2!(1)(4)}x^{10/3} - \tfrac{3^3}{2^6 3!(1)(4)(7)}x^{16/3}$$

$$+ \tfrac{3^4}{2^8 4!(1)(4)(7)(10)}x^{22/3} - \tfrac{3^5}{2^{10} 5!(1)(4)(7)(10)(13)}x^{28/3} + \cdots$$

Section 4.4

1. $y_1 = c_0(x - 1)$, $\ y_2 = c_0^*[(x-1)\ln(x) - 3x + \frac{1}{4}x^2 + \frac{1}{36}x^3 + \frac{1}{288}x^4 + \frac{1}{2400}x^5 + \cdots]$

3. $y_1 = c_0[x^4 + 2x^5 + 3x^6 + 4x^7 + 5x^8 + \cdots] = c_0 \dfrac{x^4}{(x-1)^2}$, $\ y_2 = c_0^* \dfrac{3 - 4x}{(x-1)^2}$

5. $y_1 = c_0\left[x^{1/2} - \dfrac{1}{2\cdot 1!3}x^{3/2} + \dfrac{1}{2^2 2!3(5)}x^{5/2} - \dfrac{1}{2^3 3!3(5)(7)}x^{7/2} + \dfrac{1}{2^4 4!3(5)(7)(9)}x^{9/2} + \cdots\right]$,

$\quad y_2 = c_0^*\left[1 - \dfrac{1}{2}x + \dfrac{1}{2^2 2!3}x^2 - \dfrac{1}{2^3 3!3(5)}x^3 + \dfrac{1}{2^4 4!3(5)(7)}x^4 - \cdots\right]$

7. $y_1 = c_0[x^2 + \frac{1}{3!}x^4 + \frac{1}{5!}x^6 + \frac{1}{7!}x^8 + \frac{1}{9!}x^{10} + \cdots]$, $y_2 = c_0^*[x - x^2 + \frac{1}{2!}x^3 - \frac{1}{3!}x^4 + \frac{1}{4!}x^5 - \cdots]$

9. $y_1 = c_0(1 - x)$; $y_2 = c_0^*[1 + \frac{1}{2}(x - 1)\ln((x-2)/x))]$

11. (a) $25r^2 + 15r - 4 = 0$, with roots $r_1 = \frac{1}{5}$, $r_2 = -\frac{4}{5}$

  (b) $y_1 = \sum\limits_{n=0}^{\infty} c_n x^{n+1/5}$, $c_0 \neq 0$, and $y_2 = ky_1(x)\ln(x) + \sum\limits_{n=0}^{\infty} c_n^* x^{n-4/5}$

13. (a) $48r^2 - 20r - 8 = 0$, with roots $r_1 = \frac{2}{3}$, $r_2 = -\frac{1}{4}$

  (b) $y_1 = \sum\limits_{n=0}^{\infty} c_n x^{n+2/3}$ with $c_0 \neq 0$, $y_2 = \sum\limits_{n=0}^{\infty} c_n^* x^{n-1/4}$ with $c_0^* \neq 0$

15. (a) $4r^2 - 10r = 0$, with roots $r_1 = \frac{5}{2}$, $r_2 = 0$ (b) $y_1 = \sum\limits_{n=0}^{\infty} c_n x^{n+5/2}$ with, $c_0 \neq 0$, $\ y_2 = \sum\limits_{n=0}^{\infty} c_n^* x^n$ with $c_0^* \neq 0$

CHAPTER 5

Section 5.1

In Problems 1 through 6, approximate solutions were computed by Euler's method with $h = 0.2$, then $h = 0.1$ and $h = 0.05$.

1. Solution of $y' = y\sin(x)$; $y(0) = 1$ on $[0, 4]$

x	$h = 0.2$	$h = 0.1$	$h = 0.05$	*Exact Solution Value*
0	1	1	1	1
0.2	1	1.009098344	1.011503107	1.02013342
0.4	1.03973387	1.06048863	1.07118496	1.08213832
0.6	1.12071215	1.15460844	1.17239843	1.19084648
0.8	1.24727249	1.29838437	1.32567276	1.35431161
1	1.42622019	1.50052665	1.54082744	1.58359518
1.2	1.66624478	1.77177248	1.82981081	1.89201471
1.4	1.97684583	2.12354101	2.205173	2.29339409
1.6	2.36646226	2.56550146	2.67726796	2.79882454
1.8	2.83955291	3.10178429	3.24991245	3.41167064
2	3.39261128	3.72595725	3.91473574	4.12121011
2.2	4.00958982	4.41563127	4.64536355	4.89640429
2.4	4.65793762	5.12853123	5.39367649	5.68251387
2.6	5.28719068	5.90260482	6.09104775	6.403782
2.8	5.83230149	6.36250556	6.65682772	6.97423289
3	6.22305187	6.73296375	7.01389293	7.31547887
3.2	6.39869129	6.85637053	7.10744867	7.37646684
3.4	6.32398766	6.70882212	6.92043335	6.14775408
3.6	6.0007799	6.30806368	6.47904791	6.66425664
3.8	5.46968635	5.70948505	5.8457521	5.99525134
4	4.80035219	4.99149302	5.10259695	5.22598669

3. Solution of $y = 3xy$; $y(0) = 5$ on $[0, 4]$

x	$h = 0.2$	$h = 0.1$	$h = 0.05$	*Exact*
0	5	5	5	5
0.2	5	5.15	5.22810641	5.30918274
0.4	5.6	5.90531	6.14480554	6.35624575

0.6	6.944	7.66399928	8.09129921	8.58003432
0.8	9/44384	10.9426582	11.8990307	13.0584824
1	13.9768832	17.2324981	19.4849022	22.4084454
1.2	22.3630131	29.7949892	35.4287514	43.3556883
1.4	38.4643826	56.3244477	71.3385803	94.5792316
1.6	70.774464	115.972038	158.672557	232.627372
1.8	138.717949	259.17431	388.901099	645.121012
2	288.533335	626.631648	1047.95246	2017.14397
2.2	634.773337	1634.25534	3097.73286	7111.2827
2.4	1472.67414	4584.73992	10024.1822	28266.6493
2.6	3593.32491	13800.0672	35439.1284	126682.333
2.8	9198.91176	44461.0564	136620.046	640137.266
3	24653.0835	152981.603	573253.363	3647081.85
3.2	69028.6339	560983.536	2613461.49	23427893.9
3.4	201563.611	2188060.18	12923807.1	169682214
3.6	612753.378	9060757.21	69209615.8	$1.38565379(10^9)$
3.8	1936300.68	39765851.2	400745113	$1,27581728(10^{10})$
4	6351066,22	184664659	$2,50522053(10^9)$	$1,32445611(10^{11})$

5. Solution of $y' = y - \cos(x)$; $y(1) = -2$ on $[1, 5]$

x	$h = 0.2$	$h = 0.1$	$h = 0.05$	*Exact*
1	−2	−2	−2	−2
1.2	−2.50806046	−2.52479287	−2.53395265	−2.54372206
1.4	−3.0821441	−3.1216086	−3.14338517	−3.16674525
1.6	−3.73256636	−3.80291652	−3.84303839	−3.88424161
1.8	−4.47323972	−4.58543259	−4.6482934	−4.71647511
2	−5.32244724	−5.49105224	−5.58620527	−5.68995512
2.2	−6.30370733	−6.54791245	−6.68669139	−6.838775
2.4	−7.44674857	−7.79161134	−7.98890878	−8.20617878
2.6	−8.78861954	−9.26662206	−9.54186557	−9.84641081
2.8	−10.3749657	−11.0279477	−11.4063233	−11.826918
3	−12.2615144	−13.1430765	−13.6570618	−14.2309923
3.2	−14.5158187	−15.6943098	−16.3855953	−17.1609616
3.4	−17.2193235	−18.7815545	−19.7034487	−20.7420636
3.6	−20.4698286	−22.5256874	−23.7461298	−25.127167
3.8	−24.2844426	−27.0726284	−28.6779576	−30.5025422
4	−29.1031376	−32.5982807	−34.6979486	−37.0949271
4.2	−34.7930364	−39.3145364	−42.046999	−45.1801881
4.4	−41.6536915	−47.4765804	−51.0166552	−55.0939413
4.6	−49.9228433	−57.3917761	−61.9598251	−67.2445787
4.8	−59.8849815	−69.4304735	−75.3038559	−82.1292389
5	−71.8794775	−84.03149	−91.5664948	−100.35338

7. 2.70481383; this approximation is too small because $y''(x) > 0$.

9. A drag coefficient of 0.3 gives $y(40) \approx 238.75$ feet. A drag coefficient of 0.8 gives $y(40) \approx 351.5$ feet.

11. With $h = 0.1$ we get $y(40) \approx 342.6$ feet, so drums will likely rupture on impact.

Section 5.2

In Problems 1 through 9, the approximate solutions were computed using $h = 0.1$ by the modified Euler, Taylor and RK4 methods.

1. Solution of $y' = \sin(x + y)$; $y(0) = 2$ on $[0, 4]$.

x	Modified Euler	Taylor	RK4
0	2	2	2
0.2	2.16260835	2.16331964	2.16257799
0.4	2.27764497	2.27864781	2.27783452
0.6	2.34149618	2.34249201	2.34198641
0.8	2.35864818	2.35950334	2.35938954
1.0	2.33660171	2.33728697	2.33750216
1.2	2.28294468	2.28347612	2.28392071

x	Modified Euler	Taylor	RK4
1.4	2.20420589	2.20461236	2.2.0519759
1.6	2.10562833	2.2.10593799	2.106598
1.8	1.99129888	2.99153503	2.99222519
2.0	1.86436976	1.86455048	1.8652422
2.2	1.72727096	1.72740984	1.72808569
2.4	1.58188451	1.58199169	1.58264163
2.6	1.42967893	1.42976193	1.4303807
2.8	1.27181015	1.27187458	1.27245995
3.0	1.10919644	1.10924652	1.10979812
3.2	0.942574127	0.942613018	0.94313596
3.4	0.772538925	0.772569046	0.773056001
3.6	0.599577036	0.599600237	0.60057301
3.8	0.424088544	0.424106255	0.424535308
4.0	0.246405248	0.24641858	0.24682153

3. Solution of $y' = \cos(y) + e^{-x}$; $y(0) = 1$ on $[0., 4]$

x	Modified Euler	Taylor	RK4
0	1	1	1
0.2	1.26402944	1.26403233	1.26466198
0.4	1.45281544	1.45269679	1.45391187
0.6	1.58349547	1.1.58325838	1.58485267
0.8	1.67072292	1.67040421	1.67218108
1.0	1.72600007	1.7256358	1.7274517
1.2	1.75807746	1.75769492	1.75945615
1.4	1.77354268	1.77316065	1.77481079
1.6	1.77733578	1.77696658	1.7784748
1.8	1.7731483	1.77279968	1.77415235
2.0	1.7637228	1.76339926	1.76459409
2.2	1.75107799	1.75078179	1.75182385
2.4	1.73668018	1.73641198	1.73731088
2.6	1.72157515	1.72133454	1.72210246
2.8	1.7064905	1.7062763	1.70692664
3.0	1.69191512	1.69172569	1.69227208
3.2	1.67816081	1.67799425	1.6784499
3.4	1.6650987	1.66526414	1.66564147
3.6	1.65375148	1.65362453	1.65393488
3.8	1.64320934	1.64309917	1.64335274
4.0	1.63384681	1.63382381	1.63387303

5. Solution of $y' = -y + e^{-x}$; $y(0) = 4$ on $[0, 4]$

x	Modified Euler	Taylor	RK4
0	4	4	4
0.2	3.43920787	3.43898537	3.43866949
0.4	2.95033866	2.94997425	2.94940876
0.6	2.5257356	2.52528799	2.52453424
0.8	2.1581561	2.15766738	2.15677984
1.0	1.84087289	1.84037264	1.83939807
1.2	1.56772495	1.56723338	1.56621078
1.4	1.33313308	1.33266345	1.33162448
1.6	1.13209122	1.13165172	1.13062135
1.8	0.960142926	0.959737036	0.958734358
2.0	0.813341791	0.812973396	0.812012458
2.2	0.688221511	0.687889673	0.686980287
2.4	0.581743491	0.581447053	0.58059555
2.6	0.491259275	0.4909963	0.49020621
2.8	0.414468233	0.414236234	0.413508964
3.0	0.349378445	0.349174974	0.348509965
3.2	0.294270343	0.294092618	0.293488305
3.4	0.247663405	0.247508773	0.246962588
3.6	0.208285963	0.20815189	0.207660638
3.8	0.175048125	0.174932237	0.174492328
4.0	0.14701764	0.146917746	0.146525383

11. Solution of $y' = -\frac{y}{x} + x$; $y(1) = 1$ on $[1, 5]$

x	Euler	Modified Euler	Improved Euler	Exact
1.0	1	1	1	1
1.2	1.01909091	1.03616507	1.03583333	1.03555556
1.4	1.10307692	1.13040682	1.13	1.12952381
1.6	1.23666667	1.27101358	1.270625	1.27
1.8	1.41176471	1.45144731	1.45111111	1.45037037
2.0	1.62368421	1.66777308	1.6675	1.6666667
2.2	1.86952381	1.9174816	1.91727273	1.91636364
2.4	2.1473913	2.19889755	2.19875	2.19777778
2.6	2.456	2.51085981	2.51076923	2.50974359
2.8	2.79444445	2.85253832	2.8525	2.85142858
3.0	3.16206897	3.223324	3.22333334	3.22222223
3.2	3.5583871	3.62275978	3.6228125	3.62166667
3.4	3.9830303	4.050496	4.05058824	4.04941177
3.6	4.43571428	4.50626061	4.50638889	4.50518519
3.8	4.91621621	4.98983879	4.99	4.98877194
4.0	5.42435897	5.50105862	5.50125	5.50000001
4.2	5.95999999	6.03978091	6.03999999	6.03873016
4.4	6.52302235	6.6.60589176	6.60613636	6.60484849
4.6	7.11333332	7.19929706	7.19956521	7.19826087
3.8	7.73085105	7.81991837	7.82020832	7.81888889
5.0	8.37551019	8.46768981	8.46799999	8.46666667

Section 5.3

In Problems 1 through 5, approximate solutions were computed using $h = 0.1$ and the Taylor, modified Euler, RK4 and Adams-Bashforth-Moulton methods.

1. Solution of $y' = 4y^2 - x$; $y(3) = 0$ on $[3, 7]$

x	Taylor	Modified Euler	RK4	Adams-Bashforth-Moulton
3.0	0	0	0	0
3.2	−0.54950962	−0.535839146	−0.53549231	−0.535492931
3.4	−0.806871572	−0.798461491	−0.806778016	−0.80455223
3.6	−0903569977	−0.900545864	−0.907274543	−0.905024282
3,8	−0.950052097	−0.949091031	−0.952253424	−0.952144216
4.0	−0.981689238	−0.981381742	−0.982583	−0.982752774
4.2	−1.00868179	−1.00856977	−1.00898001	−1.00908338
4.4	−1.03393561	−1.03388121	−1.03403163	−1.03408442
4.6	−1.05828751	−1.05825061	−1.05831574	−1.05832243
4.8	−1.08199512	−1.0819642	−1.08200303	−1.0820113
5.0	−1.10515444	−1.10512619	−1.10515651	−1.10515675
5.2	−1.1278152	−1.1277886	−1.12781558	−1.12781814
5.4	−1.1500123	−1.14998697	−1.15001214	−1.15001326
5.6	−1.17177457	−1.17175035	−1.17177421	−1.17177585
5.8	−1.19312738	−1.19310414	−1.1931269	−1.19312833
6.0	−1.21409353	−1.21407118	−1.21409298	−1.21409441
6.2	−1.23469371	−1.23467218	−1.23469309	−1.23469455
6.4	−1.25494679	−1.25492601	−1.25494612	−1.25494751
6.6	−1.27487005	−1.27487995	−1.27486934	−1.26487076
6.8	−1.29447936	−1.29445989	−1.29447861	−1.29447997
7.0	−1.31378934	−1.31377045	−1.31378855	−1.31378993

3. Solution of $y' = x^2 + 4y$; $y(0) = -2$ on $[0, 4]$

x	Taylor	Modified Euler	RK4	Adams-Bashforth-Moulton
0	−2	−2	−2	−2
0.2	−4.3786	−4.37798	−4.44723874	−4.44723874
0.4	−9.56702144	−9.56504339	−9.87011722	−9.86993267
0.6	−20.8862678	−20.8813151	−21.8900872	−21.8887964
0.8	−45.6106649	−45.5991965	−48.5658508	−48.561028
1.0	−99.6738964	−99.648156	−107.830182	−107.815098

x	Taylor	Modified Euler	RK4	Adams-Bashforth-Moulton
1.2	−217.977103	−217.920101	−239.588317	−239.545057
1.4	−476.967742	−476.842265	−532.640112	−532.522265
1.6	−1044.09633	−1043.82086	−1184.58908	−1184.2788
1.8	−2286.14646	−2285.54246	−2635.15604	−264.35871
2.0	−5006.52093	−5005.19732	−5862.83785	−5860.82572
2.2	−10964.9933	−10962.0934	−13045.0526	−13040.0457
2.4	−24016.1713	−24009.8188	−29027.1396	−29014.8203
2.6	−52603.1881	−52589.273	−64591.2795	−64561.245
2.8	−115219.882	−115189.402	−143730.717	−143658.051
3.0	−252375.158	−252308.393	−319836.86	−319662.181
3.2	−552799.719	−552653.478	−711719.918	−711302.336
3.4	−1210489.3	−1210528.97	−1583764.49	−1582771.01
3.6	−2652240.7	−2651539.05	−3524297.25	−3521943.51
3.8	−5809463.99	−5807927.1	−7842502.92	−7836947.07
4.0	−12725045.4	−12721679	−17451668.8	−17438597.6

5. Solution of $y' = 4x^3 - xy + \cos(y)$; $y(0) = 4$ on $[0, 4]$

x	Taylor	Modified Euler	RK4	Adams-Bashforth-Moulton
0	4	4	4	4
0.2	3.7794333	3.78043259	3.77999805	3.77999805
0.4	3.4063912	3.41050545	3.41104815	3.4110294
0.6	2.98742511	2.99596552	2.99802794	2.99786651
0.8	2.67888513	2.69113585	2.69319067	2.69290979
1.0	2.61904369	2.63355977	2.63372362	2.63352302
1.2	2.90467175	2.9211945	2.91895169	2.91894526
1.4	3.62976051	3.65076771	3.64732119	3.64756467
1.6	4.97054479	4.99929765	4.99555968	4.99474741
1.8	7.06207082	7.07183105	7.05743353	7.05537836
2.0	9.37312564	9.38527061	9.37941313	9.3863398
2.2	12.2268713	12.2600988	12.2487484	12.2388627
2.4	15.6095086	15.6111703	15.605291	15.6243401
2.6	19.4141045	19.4310567	19.408775	19.377544
2.8	23.4681005	23.5044464	23.5079285	23.5176327
3.0	28.1280137	28.1104867	28.1077469	28.1137305
3.2	33.10814	33.0802212	33.052868	32.9831436
3.4	38.2813467	38.3144963	38.2882438	38.2409524
3.6	43.7987621	43.8554581	43.8484638	43.8459653
3.8	49.6967946	49.746549	49.7487578	49.7574115
4.0	55.936434	55.9835947	55.9845424	55.9910457

7. Solution of $y' = 2xy - y^3$; $y(0) = 2$ on $[0, 4]$

x	h = 0.2	h = 0.1
0	2	2
0.2	1.22921715	1.27928486
0.4	1.07091936	1.08638842
0.6	1.04836859	1.05688972
0.8	1.01157152	1.10836346
1.0	1.14419902	1.21475378
1.2	1.31901324	1.35628443
1.4	1.49026217	1.51174278
1.6	1.65343971	1.66272411
1.8	1.7992031	1.79992887
2.0	1.92265942	1.92272594
2.2	2.02954279	2.03410264
2.4	2.1312142	2.13707792
2.6	2.23463857	2.23374303
2.8	2.23692569	2.32542008
3.0	2.42896574	2.41296935
3.2	2.50245762	2.49699181
3.4	2.55106451	2.57793593
3.6	2.55394614	2.65615241
3.8	2.38180227	2.7319243
4.0	2.10320803	2.80548524

CHAPTER 6

Section 6.1

1. $(2+\sqrt{2})\mathbf{i}+3\mathbf{j}$; $(2-\sqrt{2})\mathbf{i}-9\mathbf{j}+10\mathbf{k}$; $\sqrt{38}$; $\sqrt{63}$; $4\mathbf{i}-6\mathbf{j}+10\mathbf{k}$; $3\sqrt{2}\mathbf{i}+18\mathbf{j}-15\mathbf{k}$
3. $3\mathbf{i}-\mathbf{k}$; $\mathbf{i}-10\mathbf{j}+\mathbf{k}$; $\sqrt{29}$; $3\sqrt{3}$; $4\mathbf{i}-10\mathbf{j}$; $3\mathbf{i}+15\mathbf{j}-3\mathbf{k}$
5. $3\mathbf{i}-\mathbf{j}+3\mathbf{k}$; $-\mathbf{i}+3\mathbf{j}-\mathbf{k}$; $\sqrt{3}$; $2\sqrt{3}$; $2\mathbf{i}+2\mathbf{j}+2\mathbf{k}$; $6\mathbf{i}-6\mathbf{j}+6\mathbf{k}$
7. $\mathbf{F}+\mathbf{G}=3\mathbf{i}-2\mathbf{j}$ $\qquad$ $\mathbf{F}-\mathbf{G}=\mathbf{i}$ $\qquad$ 9. $\mathbf{F}+\mathbf{G}=2\mathbf{i}-5\mathbf{j}$ $\qquad$ $\mathbf{F}-\mathbf{G}=\mathbf{j}$

11. $\alpha\mathbf{F}=-\frac{1}{2}\mathbf{i}-\frac{1}{2}\mathbf{j}$ $\qquad$ 13. $\alpha\mathbf{F}=12\mathbf{j}$ $\qquad$ 15. $\alpha\mathbf{F}=-9\mathbf{i}+6\mathbf{j}$

17. $x=3+6t, y=-t, z=0; -\infty<t<\infty$ $\qquad$ 19. $x=0, y=1+t, z=3+2t; -\infty<t<\infty$
21. $x=2+3t, y=-3-9t, z=6+2t; -\infty<t<\infty$ $\qquad$ 23. $\mathbf{F}=3\mathbf{i}+3\sqrt{3}\mathbf{j}$ $\qquad$ 25. $\mathbf{F}=\frac{15}{\sqrt{2}}\mathbf{i}-\frac{15}{\sqrt{2}}\mathbf{j}$

Section 6.2

1. $\mathbf{F}\cdot\mathbf{G}=2$; $\cos(\theta)=2/\sqrt{14}$; not orthogonal; $|\mathbf{F}\cdot\mathbf{G}|=2<\sqrt{14}=\|\mathbf{F}\|\,\|\mathbf{G}\|$
3. -23; $-23/\sqrt{29}\sqrt{41}$; not orthogonal; $23<\sqrt{29}\sqrt{41}$ $\quad$ 5. -18; $-9/10$; not orthogonal; $18<\sqrt{10}\sqrt{40}=20$
7. $3x-y+4z=4$ $\quad$ 9. $4x-3y+2z=25$ $\quad$ 11. $7x+6y-5z=-26$ $\quad$ 13. $112/11\sqrt{105}$
15. $113/5\sqrt{590}$ $\quad$ 17. $\mathbf{F}=\mathbf{O}$ $\quad$ 19. *Hint:* $|\mathbf{F}\cdot\mathbf{U}|=\|\mathbf{F}\|\cos(\theta)$, which is a maximum when $\cos(\theta)=1$.

Section 6.3

In Problems 1 through 5, the value is given in order for $\mathbf{F}\times\mathbf{G}$, $\cos(\theta)$, $\sin(\theta)$, and the common value of $\|\mathbf{F}\|\,\|\mathbf{G}\|\sin(\theta)$ and $\|\mathbf{F}\times\mathbf{G}\|$.

1. $8\mathbf{i}+2\mathbf{j}+12\mathbf{k}$; $-4/\sqrt{69}$; $\sqrt{53}/\sqrt{69}$; $2\sqrt{53}$ $\quad$ 3. $-8\mathbf{i}-12\mathbf{j}-5\mathbf{k}$; $-12/\sqrt{29}\sqrt{13}$; $\sqrt{233}/\sqrt{29}\sqrt{13}$; $\sqrt{233}$
5. $18\mathbf{i}+50\mathbf{j}-60\mathbf{k}$; $62/5\sqrt{2}\sqrt{109}$; $\sqrt{1606}/5\sqrt{2}\sqrt{109}$; $2\sqrt{1606}$
7. Not collinear; $x-2y+z=3$
9. Not collinear; $2x-11y+z=0$ $\quad$ 11. Not collinear; $29x+37y-12z=30$ $\quad$ 13. $7\sqrt{2}$ $\quad$ 15. $2\sqrt{209}$ $\quad$ 17. 92
19. 98 $\quad$ 21. 22 $\quad$ 23. $\mathbf{i}-\mathbf{j}+2\mathbf{k}$ $\quad$ 25. $7\mathbf{i}+\mathbf{j}-7\mathbf{k}$
27. $\mathbf{F}\times(\mathbf{G}+\mathbf{H})=\begin{vmatrix} \mathbf{i} & \mathbf{j} & \mathbf{k} \\ f_1 & f_2 & f_3 \\ g_1+h_1 & g_2+h_2 & g_3+h_3 \end{vmatrix}=\begin{vmatrix} \mathbf{i} & \mathbf{j} & \mathbf{k} \\ f_1 & f_2 & f_3 \\ g_1 & g_2 & g_3 \end{vmatrix}+\begin{vmatrix} \mathbf{i} & \mathbf{j} & \mathbf{k} \\ f_1 & f_2 & f_3 \\ h_1 & h_2 & h_3 \end{vmatrix}=(\mathbf{F}\times\mathbf{G})+(\mathbf{F}\times\mathbf{H})$

31. $[\mathbf{F}, \mathbf{G}, \mathbf{H}] = (a_1\mathbf{i} + b_1\mathbf{j} + c_1\mathbf{k}) \cdot \begin{vmatrix} \mathbf{i} & \mathbf{j} & \mathbf{k} \\ a_2 & b_2 & c_2 \\ a_3 & b_3 & c_3 \end{vmatrix} = a_1(b_2c_3 - c_2b_3) + b_1(c_2a_3 - a_2c_3) + c_1(a_2b_3 - b_2a_3)$

$$= \begin{vmatrix} a_1 & b_1 & c_1 \\ a_2 & b_2 & c_2 \\ a_3 & b_3 & c_3 \end{vmatrix}$$

Section 6.4

In Problems 1 through 5, we give in order the sum of the two vectors, their dot product, and the cosine of the angle between them.

1. $5\mathbf{e}_1 + 5\mathbf{e}_2 + 6\mathbf{e}_3 + 5\mathbf{e}_4 + \mathbf{e}_5; 0; 0$ **3.** $17\mathbf{e}_1 - 4\mathbf{e}_2 + 3\mathbf{e}_3 + 6\mathbf{e}_4; 24; 6/\sqrt{30}\sqrt{17}$

5. $6\mathbf{e}_1 + 7\mathbf{e}_2 - 6\mathbf{e}_3 - 2\mathbf{e}_5 - \mathbf{e}_6 + 11\mathbf{e}_7 + 4\mathbf{e}_8; -94; -47/\sqrt{37}\sqrt{303}$ **7.** S is a subspace of R^5.

9. S is not a subspace of R^6. **11.** S is a subspace of R^4. **13.** S is a subspace of R^4.

15. $\|\mathbf{F} + \mathbf{G}\|^2 + \|\mathbf{F} - \mathbf{G}\|^2 = (\mathbf{F} + \mathbf{G}) \cdot (\mathbf{F} + \mathbf{G}) + (\mathbf{F} - \mathbf{G}) \cdot (\mathbf{F} - \mathbf{G})$
$= \mathbf{F} \cdot \mathbf{F} + 2\mathbf{F} \cdot \mathbf{G} + \mathbf{G} \cdot \mathbf{G} + \mathbf{F} \cdot \mathbf{F} - 2\mathbf{F} \cdot \mathbf{G} + \mathbf{G} \cdot \mathbf{G}$
$= 2\mathbf{F} \cdot \mathbf{F} + 2\mathbf{G} \cdot \mathbf{G} = 2(\|\mathbf{F}\|^2 + \|\mathbf{G}\|^2)$

17. Using part of the calculation from Problem 15, $\|\mathbf{F} + \mathbf{G}\|^2 = \|\mathbf{F}\|^2 + 2\mathbf{F} \cdot \mathbf{G} + \|\mathbf{G}\|^2$. If also $\|\mathbf{F} + \mathbf{G}\|^2 = \|\mathbf{F}\|^2 + \|\mathbf{G}\|^2$, then $\mathbf{F} \cdot \mathbf{G} = 0$ and the vectors are orthogonal.

Section 6.5

1. Independent **3.** Independent **5.** Dependent **7.** Dependent **9.** Independent **13.** Dependent; $[\mathbf{F}, \mathbf{G}, \mathbf{H}] = 0$
15. Independent; $[\mathbf{F}, \mathbf{G}, \mathbf{H}] = -44 \neq 0$ **17.** A basic consists of $(1, 0, 0, -1)$ and $(0, 1, -1, 0)$; the dimension is 2.
19. A basis consists of $(1, 0, -2)$ and $(0, 1, 1)$; the dimension is 2.
21. A basis consists of $(1, 0, 0, 0)$, $(0, 0, 1, 0)$ and $(0, 0, 0, 1)$; the dimension is 3.
23. A basis consists of $(1, 4)$; the dimension is 1.

CHAPTER 7

Section 7.1

1. $\begin{pmatrix} 14 & -2 & 6 \\ 10 & -5 & -6 \\ -26 & -43 & -8 \end{pmatrix}$ **3.** $\begin{pmatrix} 2 + 2x - x^2 & -12x + (1 - x)(x + e^x + 2\cos(x)) \\ 4 + 2x + 2e^x + 2xe^x & -22 - 2x + e^{2x} + 2e^x\cos(x) \end{pmatrix}$

5. $\begin{pmatrix} -36 & 0 & 68 & 196 & 20 \\ 128 & -40 & -36 & -8 & 72 \end{pmatrix}$ **7.** $\mathbf{AB} = \begin{pmatrix} -10 & -34 & -16 & -30 & -14 \\ 10 & -2 & -11 & -8 & -45 \\ -5 & 1 & 15 & 61 & -63 \end{pmatrix}$; $\mathbf{BA}$ is not defined.

9. $\mathbf{AB} = (115)$; $\mathbf{BA} = \begin{pmatrix} 3 & -18 & -6 & -42 & 66 \\ -2 & 12 & 4 & 28 & -44 \\ -6 & 36 & 12 & 84 & -132 \\ 0 & 0 & 0 & 0 & 0 \\ 4 & -24 & -8 & -56 & 88 \end{pmatrix}$.

11. $\mathbf{AB}$ is not defined; $\mathbf{BA} = \begin{pmatrix} 410 & 36 & -56 & 227 \\ 17 & 253 & 40 & -1 \end{pmatrix}$.

13. $\mathbf{AB}$ is not defined; $\mathbf{BA} = (-16 \ -13 \ -5)$. **15.** $\mathbf{AB} = \begin{pmatrix} 39 & -84 & 21 \\ -23 & 38 & 3 \end{pmatrix}$; $\mathbf{BA}$ is not defined.

17. $\mathbf{AB}$ is 14×14; $\mathbf{BA}$ is 21×21. **19.** $\mathbf{AB}$ is not defined; $\mathbf{BA}$ is 4×2. **21.** $\mathbf{AB}$ is not defined; $\mathbf{BA}$ is 7×6.

23. $\mathbf{A}^3 = \begin{pmatrix} 2 & 7 & 7 & 4 & 4 \\ 7 & 8 & 9 & 9 & 9 \\ 7 & 9 & 8 & 9 & 9 \\ 4 & 9 & 9 & 6 & 7 \\ 4 & 9 & 9 & 7 & 6 \end{pmatrix}$ and $\mathbf{A}^4 = \begin{pmatrix} 14 & 17 & 17 & 18 & 18 \\ 17 & 34 & 33 & 26 & 26 \\ 17 & 33 & 34 & 26 & 26 \\ 18 & 26 & 26 & 25 & 24 \\ 18 & 26 & 26 & 24 & 25 \end{pmatrix}$.

The number of distinct $v_1 - v_4$ walks of length 3 is $(\mathbf{A}^3)_{14}$, or 4; the number of $v_1 - v_4$ walks of length 4 is $(\mathbf{A}^4)_{14} = 18$.
The number of distinct $v_2 - v_3$ walks of length 3 is $(\mathbf{A}^3)_{23} = 9$; the number of distinct $v_2 - v_4$ walks of length 4 is 26.

25. $\mathbf{A}^2 = \begin{pmatrix} 4 & 2 & 3 & 3 & 2 \\ 2 & 3 & 2 & 2 & 3 \\ 3 & 2 & 4 & 3 & 2 \\ 3 & 2 & 3 & 4 & 2 \\ 2 & 3 & 2 & 2 & 3 \end{pmatrix}$, $\mathbf{A}^3 = \begin{pmatrix} 10 & 10 & 11 & 11 & 10 \\ 10 & 6 & 10 & 10 & 6 \\ 11 & 10 & 10 & 11 & 10 \\ 11 & 10 & 11 & 10 & 10 \\ 10 & 6 & 10 & 10 & 6 \end{pmatrix}$, and $\mathbf{A}^4 = \begin{pmatrix} 42 & 32 & 41 & 41 & 32 \\ 32 & 30 & 32 & 32 & 30 \\ 41 & 32 & 42 & 41 & 32 \\ 41 & 32 & 41 & 42 & 32 \\ 32 & 30 & 32 & 32 & 30 \end{pmatrix}$.

The number of distinct $v_4 - v_5$ walks of length 2 is 2, the number of $v_2 - v_3$ walks of length 3 is 10, the number of $v_1 - v_2$ walks of length 4 is 32, and the number of $v_4 - v_5$ walks of length 4 is 32.

Section 7.2

In Problems 1 through 7, the first matrix is $\Omega\mathbf{A}$, the second is Ω.

1. $\begin{pmatrix} -2 & 1 & 4 & 2 \\ 0 & \sqrt{3} & 16\sqrt{3} & 3\sqrt{3} \\ 1 & -2 & 4 & 8 \end{pmatrix}$, $\begin{pmatrix} 1 & 0 & 0 \\ 0 & \sqrt{3} & 0 \\ 0 & 0 & 1 \end{pmatrix}$

3. $\begin{pmatrix} 40 & 5 & -15 \\ -2+2\sqrt{13} & 14+9\sqrt{13} & 6+5\sqrt{13} \\ 2 & 9 & 5 \end{pmatrix}$, $\begin{pmatrix} 0 & 5 & 0 \\ 1 & 0 & \sqrt{13} \\ 0 & 0 & 1 \end{pmatrix}$

5. $\begin{pmatrix} 30 & 120 \\ -3+2\sqrt{3} & 15+8\sqrt{3} \end{pmatrix}$, $\begin{pmatrix} 0 & 15 \\ 1 & \sqrt{3} \end{pmatrix}$ **7.** $\begin{pmatrix} -1 & 0 & 3 & 0 \\ -36 & 28 & -20 & 28 \\ -13 & 3 & 44 & 9 \end{pmatrix}$; $\begin{pmatrix} 1 & 0 & 0 \\ 0 & 0 & 4 \\ 14 & 1 & 0 \end{pmatrix}$

Section 7.3

In Problems 1 through 11, the reduced matrix $\mathbf{A}_R$ is given first, then a matrix Ω such that $\Omega\mathbf{A} = \mathbf{A}_R$.

1. $\begin{pmatrix} 1 & 0 & 5 \\ 0 & 1 & 2 \\ 0 & 0 & 0 \end{pmatrix}$, $\begin{pmatrix} 1 & 1 & 0 \\ 0 & 1 & 0 \\ 0 & 0 & 1 \end{pmatrix}$ **3.** $\begin{pmatrix} 1 & -4 & -1 & 0 \\ 0 & 0 & 0 & 1 \\ 0 & 0 & 0 & 0 \\ 0 & 0 & 0 & 0 \end{pmatrix}$, $\begin{pmatrix} -1 & 0 & 0 & 1 \\ 0 & 0 & 0 & 1 \\ 0 & 0 & 1 & 0 \\ 0 & 1 & 0 & 0 \end{pmatrix}$ **5.** $\begin{pmatrix} 1 & 0 \\ 0 & 1 \\ 0 & 0 \\ 0 & 0 \end{pmatrix}$, $\begin{pmatrix} 0 & 0 & 1 & -3 \\ 0 & 0 & 0 & 1 \\ 1 & 0 & -6 & 17 \\ 0 & 1 & 0 & 0 \end{pmatrix}$

7. $\begin{pmatrix} 1 & 0 & 0 \\ 0 & 1 & 0 \\ 0 & 0 & 1 \end{pmatrix}$, $\frac{1}{270}\begin{pmatrix} -8 & -2 & 38 \\ 37 & 43 & -7 \\ 19 & -29 & 11 \end{pmatrix}$ **9.** $\begin{pmatrix} 1 & 0 & 0 & 0 \\ 0 & 1 & \frac{3}{2} & \frac{1}{2} \end{pmatrix}$, $\begin{pmatrix} 0 & 1 \\ \frac{1}{2} & \frac{1}{2} \end{pmatrix}$ **11.** $\begin{pmatrix} 1 & 0 & 0 \\ 0 & 1 & 0 \\ 0 & 0 & 1 \end{pmatrix}$, $\begin{pmatrix} 0 & \frac{1}{2} & -1 \\ 0 & 0 & 1 \\ -\frac{1}{7} & \frac{2}{7} & -\frac{3}{7} \end{pmatrix}$

Section 7.4

In Problems 1 through 13, first the reduced matrix is given, then its rank, a basis for its row space (as row vectors), the dimension of the row space, a basis for the column space (as column vectors) and the dimension of the column space.

1. $\begin{pmatrix} 1 & 0 & -\frac{3}{5} \\ 0 & 1 & \frac{3}{5} \end{pmatrix}$; 2; $(-4, 1, 3), (2, 2, 0)$; 2; $\begin{pmatrix} -4 \\ 2 \end{pmatrix}, \begin{pmatrix} 1 \\ 2 \end{pmatrix}$; 2   **3.** $\begin{pmatrix} 1 & 0 \\ 0 & 1 \\ 0 & 0 \end{pmatrix}$; 2; $(-3, 1), (2, 2)$; 2; $\begin{pmatrix} -3 \\ 2 \\ 4 \end{pmatrix}, \begin{pmatrix} 1 \\ 2 \\ -3 \end{pmatrix}$; 2

5. $\begin{pmatrix} 1 & 0 & -\frac{1}{4} & \frac{1}{2} \\ 0 & 1 & -\frac{5}{4} & \frac{1}{2} \end{pmatrix}$; 2; $(8, -4, 3, 2), (1, -1, 1, 0)$; 2; $\begin{pmatrix} 8 \\ 1 \end{pmatrix}, \begin{pmatrix} -4 \\ -1 \end{pmatrix}$; 2

7. $\begin{pmatrix} 1 & 0 & 0 \\ 0 & 1 & 0 \\ 0 & 0 & 1 \\ 0 & 0 & 0 \end{pmatrix}$; 3; $(2, 2, 1), (1, -1, 3), (0, 0, 1)$; 3; $\begin{pmatrix} 2 \\ 1 \\ 0 \\ 4 \end{pmatrix}, \begin{pmatrix} 2 \\ -1 \\ 0 \\ 0 \end{pmatrix}, \begin{pmatrix} 1 \\ 3 \\ 1 \\ 7 \end{pmatrix}$; 3

9. $\begin{pmatrix} 1 & 0 & 0 \\ 0 & 1 & 0 \\ 0 & 0 & 1 \end{pmatrix}$; 3; $(0, 4, 3), (6, 1, 0), (2, 2, 2)$; 3; $\begin{pmatrix} 0 \\ 6 \\ 2 \end{pmatrix}, \begin{pmatrix} 4 \\ 1 \\ 2 \end{pmatrix}, \begin{pmatrix} 3 \\ 0 \\ 2 \end{pmatrix}$; 3

11. $\begin{pmatrix} 1 & 0 & 0 \\ 0 & 1 & 0 \\ 0 & 0 & 1 \end{pmatrix}$; 3; $(-3, 2, 2), (1, 0, 5), (0, 0, 2)$; 3; $\begin{pmatrix} -3 \\ 1 \\ 0 \end{pmatrix}, \begin{pmatrix} 2 \\ 0 \\ 0 \end{pmatrix}, \begin{pmatrix} 2 \\ 5 \\ 2 \end{pmatrix}$; 3

13. $\begin{pmatrix} 1 & 0 & -11 \\ 0 & 1 & -3 \\ 0 & 0 & 0 \end{pmatrix}$; 2; $(-2, 5, 7), (0, 1, -3)$; 2; $\begin{pmatrix} -2 \\ 0 \\ -4 \end{pmatrix}; \begin{pmatrix} 5 \\ 1 \\ 11 \end{pmatrix}$; 2

Section 7.5

1. $\alpha\begin{pmatrix}-1\\1\\1\\0\end{pmatrix}+\beta\begin{pmatrix}1\\-1\\0\\1\end{pmatrix}$

3. $\alpha\begin{pmatrix}0\\0\\0\end{pmatrix}$ (only the trivial solution)

5. $\alpha\begin{pmatrix}-\frac{9}{4}\\-\frac{7}{4}\\-\frac{5}{8}\\\frac{13}{8}\\1\end{pmatrix}$

7. $\alpha\begin{pmatrix}-\frac{5}{6}\\-\frac{2}{3}\\-\frac{8}{3}\\-\frac{2}{3}\\1\\0\end{pmatrix}+\beta\begin{pmatrix}-\frac{5}{9}\\-\frac{10}{9}\\-\frac{13}{9}\\-\frac{1}{9}\\0\\1\end{pmatrix}$

9. $\alpha\begin{pmatrix}\frac{5}{14}\\\frac{11}{7}\\\frac{6}{7}\\1\end{pmatrix}$

11. $\alpha\begin{pmatrix}1\\1\\0\\1\\1\\0\\0\end{pmatrix}+\beta\begin{pmatrix}-2\\-\frac{3}{2}\\\frac{2}{3}\\-\frac{4}{3}\\0\\1\\0\end{pmatrix}+\gamma\begin{pmatrix}0\\\frac{1}{2}\\-3\\0\\0\\0\\1\end{pmatrix}$

Section 7.6

1. 2 3. 0 5. 1 7. 2 9. 1 11. 3

13. Yes, provided that $rank(\mathbf{A}) <$ number of unknowns in the system.

Section 7.7

In each of Problems 1 through 13, the unique or general solution is given, whichever applies, or it is noted that the system has no solution.

1. $\begin{pmatrix}1\\\frac{1}{2}\\4\end{pmatrix}$

3. $\alpha\begin{pmatrix}1\\1\\\frac{3}{2}\\1\\0\\0\end{pmatrix}+\beta\begin{pmatrix}0\\0\\\frac{1}{2}\\0\\1\\0\end{pmatrix}+\gamma\begin{pmatrix}-\frac{17}{2}\\-6\\-\frac{51}{4}\\0\\0\\1\end{pmatrix}+\begin{pmatrix}\frac{9}{2}\\3\\\frac{25}{4}\\0\\0\\0\end{pmatrix}$

5. $\alpha\begin{pmatrix}2\\2\\7\\\frac{3}{2}\\1\\0\end{pmatrix}+\beta\begin{pmatrix}-2\\-1\\-\frac{9}{2}\\-\frac{3}{4}\\0\\1\end{pmatrix}+\begin{pmatrix}-4\\-4\\-38\\-\frac{11}{2}\\0\\0\end{pmatrix}$

7. $\alpha\begin{pmatrix}-\frac{1}{2}\\-1\\3\\1\\0\end{pmatrix}+\beta\begin{pmatrix}-\frac{3}{4}\\1\\-2\\0\\1\end{pmatrix}+\begin{pmatrix}\frac{9}{8}\\2\\0\\0\\0\end{pmatrix}$

9. $\alpha\begin{pmatrix}-1\\1\\0\\0\\0\\0\end{pmatrix}+\beta\begin{pmatrix}1\\0\\0\\1\\0\\0\end{pmatrix}+\gamma\begin{pmatrix}-\frac{3}{14}\\0\\\frac{3}{14}\\0\\1\\0\end{pmatrix}+\delta\begin{pmatrix}-1\\0\\0\\0\\1\\0\end{pmatrix}+\epsilon\begin{pmatrix}\frac{1}{14}\\0\\-\frac{1}{14}\\0\\0\\1\end{pmatrix}+\begin{pmatrix}-\frac{29}{7}\\0\\\frac{1}{7}\\0\\0\\0\end{pmatrix}$

11. $\alpha\begin{pmatrix}-\frac{19}{15}\\3\\\frac{67}{15}\\1\end{pmatrix}+\begin{pmatrix}\frac{22}{15}\\-5\\-\frac{121}{15}\\0\end{pmatrix}$

13. $\begin{pmatrix}\frac{16}{57}\\\frac{99}{57}\\\frac{23}{57}\end{pmatrix}$

15. $\mathbf{AX}=\mathbf{B}$ has a solution if and only if $rank(\mathbf{A})=rank([\mathbf{A}:\mathbf{B}])$. Since $\mathbf{A}_R$ is a reduced matrix, this occurs only if the last $n-r$ rows of $\mathbf{B}$ are zero rows, hence $b_{r+1}=b_{r+2}=\cdots=b_n=0$.

Section 7.8

1. $\frac{1}{5}\begin{pmatrix}-1&2\\2&1\end{pmatrix}$

3. $\frac{1}{12}\begin{pmatrix}-2&2\\1&5\end{pmatrix}$

5. $\frac{1}{12}\begin{pmatrix}3&-2\\-3&6\end{pmatrix}$

7. $\frac{1}{31}\begin{pmatrix}-6&11&2\\3&10&-1\\1&-7&10\end{pmatrix}$

9. $\frac{1}{12}\begin{pmatrix}-6&6&0\\3&9&-2\\-3&3&2\end{pmatrix}$

11. $\dfrac{1}{11}\begin{pmatrix} -23 \\ -75 \\ -9 \\ 14 \end{pmatrix}$ **13.** $\dfrac{1}{7}\begin{pmatrix} 22 \\ 27 \\ 30 \end{pmatrix}$ **15.** $\dfrac{1}{5}\begin{pmatrix} -21 \\ 14 \\ 0 \end{pmatrix}$

CHAPTER 8

Section 8.1

1. 1, 2, 3 (the identity permutation) is even, as are 2, 3, 1 and 3, 1, 2; the permutations 1, 3, 2 and 2, 1, 3 and 3, 2, 1 are odd.

Section 8.2

1. -3 **3.** -62

Section 8.3

1. $\det(\mathbf{B}) = \sum_p (-1)^{sgn(p)} b_{1p(1)} b_{2p(2)} \dots b_{np(n)} = \sum_p (-1)^{sgn(p)} (\alpha a_{1p(1)})(\alpha a_{2p(2)}) \dots (\alpha a_{np(n)})$

$= (\alpha)^n \sum_p (-1)^{sgn(p)} a_{1p(1)} a_{2p(2)} \dots a_{np(n)} = \alpha^n \det(\mathbf{A})$

3. Using the result of Problem 1, $\det(\mathbf{A}) = (-\mathbf{A}^t) = (-1)^n \det(\mathbf{A}^t) = (-1)^n \det(\mathbf{A})$. If n is odd, then $(-1)^n = -1$, so $\det(\mathbf{A}) = -\det(\mathbf{A})$, hence $\det(\mathbf{A}) = 0$.

Section 8.4

1. -22 **3.** -14 **5.** -2247 **7.** -122 **9.** -72

Section 8.5

1. 32 **3.** 3 **5.** -773 **7.** -152 **9.** 1693

13. $1 = \det(\mathbf{I}_n) = \det(\mathbf{A}\mathbf{A}^{-1}) = \det(\mathbf{A}) \det(\mathbf{A}^{-1}) = \det(\mathbf{A}) \det(\mathbf{A}^t) = [\det(\mathbf{A})]^2$, hence $\det(\mathbf{A}) = \pm 1$.

Section 8.6

1. 2240 **3.** -1440

Section 8.7

1. $\dfrac{1}{13}\begin{pmatrix} 6 & 1 \\ -1 & 2 \end{pmatrix}$ **3.** $\dfrac{1}{5}\begin{pmatrix} -4 & 1 \\ 1 & 1 \end{pmatrix}$ **5.** $\dfrac{1}{32}\begin{pmatrix} 5 & 3 & 1 \\ -8 & -24 & 24 \\ -2 & -14 & 6 \end{pmatrix}$ **7.** $\dfrac{1}{29}\begin{pmatrix} -1 & 25 & -21 \\ -8 & -3 & 6 \\ -1 & -4 & 8 \end{pmatrix}$

9. $\dfrac{1}{378}\begin{pmatrix} 210 & -42 & 42 & 0 \\ 899 & -124 & 223 & -135 \\ 275 & -64 & 109 & -27 \\ -601 & 122 & -131 & 81 \end{pmatrix}$

Section 8.8

1. $x_1 = -11/47, x_2 = -100/47$ **3.** $x_1 = -1/2, x_2 = -19/22, x_3 = 2/11$ **5.** $x_1 = 5/6, x_2 = -10/3, x_3 = -5/6$

7. $x_1 = -86, x_2 = -109/2, x_3 = -43/2, x_4 = 37/2$ **9.** $x_1 = 11/31, x_2 = -409/93, x_3 = -1/93, x_4 = 116/93$

Section 8.9

1. 21 **3.** 61 **5.** 61

CHAPTER 9

Section 9.1

In the following, when an eigenvalue is listed twice in succession, this eigenvalue has multiplicity 2, but does not have two linearly independent eigenvectors (hence only one eigenvector is listed for such an eigenvalue). In Problems 1–15, MAPLE code for the Gerschgorin circles is included.

1. $1 + \sqrt{6}, \begin{pmatrix} \sqrt{6}/2 \\ 1 \end{pmatrix}; 1 - \sqrt{6}, \begin{pmatrix} -\sqrt{6}/2 \\ 1 \end{pmatrix}$

```
plot({[1+(3)*sin(t),3*cos(t), t=-Pi..Pi],[1+(2)*sin(t),2*cos(t), t=-Pi..Pi]},
scaling=CONSTRAINED); # and plot POINTS at  (1,0)
```

3. $-5, \begin{pmatrix} 7 \\ -1 \end{pmatrix}; 2, \begin{pmatrix} 0 \\ 1 \end{pmatrix}$

```
plot({[2+sin(t),cos(t), t=-Pi..Pi]},
scaling=CONSTRAINED); # and plot POINTS at  (-5,0) and (2,0)
```

5. $\frac{1}{2}(3 + \sqrt{47}i), \begin{pmatrix} -1+\sqrt{47}i \\ 4 \end{pmatrix}; \frac{1}{2}(3 - \sqrt{47}i), \begin{pmatrix} -1-\sqrt{47}i \\ 4 \end{pmatrix}$

```
plot({[1+ (6)*sin(t),6*cos(t), t=-Pi..Pi],[2+ (2)*sin(t),2*cos(t), t=-Pi..Pi]},
scaling=CONSTRAINED); # and plot POINTS at (1,0) and (2,0)
```

7. $0, \begin{pmatrix} 0 \\ 1 \\ 0 \end{pmatrix}; 2, \begin{pmatrix} 2 \\ 1 \\ 0 \end{pmatrix}; 3, \begin{pmatrix} 0 \\ 2 \\ 3 \end{pmatrix}$

```
plot({[3*sin(t),3*cos(t), t=-Pi..Pi]},
scaling=CONSTRAINED); # and plot POINTS at  (2,0), (0,0) and (3,0)
```

9. $0, 0, \begin{pmatrix} 1 \\ 0 \\ 3 \end{pmatrix}; -3, \begin{pmatrix} 1 \\ 0 \\ 0 \end{pmatrix}$

```
plot({[-3+(2)*sin(2),2*cos(t),t=-Pi..Pi],[sin(t),cos(t),t=-Pi..Pi]},
scaling=CONSTRAINED); # and plot
POINTS at  (-3,0) and (0,0)
```

11. $2, 2, \begin{pmatrix} 0 \\ 0 \\ 1 \end{pmatrix}; -14, \begin{pmatrix} -16 \\ 0 \\ 1 \end{pmatrix}$

```
plot({[-14+sin(t),cos(t),t=-Pi..Pi],[2+sin(t),cos(t),t=-Pi..Pi]},
scaling=CONSTRAINED); # and plot
POINTS at  (-14,0) and (2,0)
```

13. $0, \begin{pmatrix} 14 \\ 7 \\ 10 \end{pmatrix}; 1, \begin{pmatrix} 6 \\ 0 \\ 5 \end{pmatrix}; 7, \begin{pmatrix} 0 \\ 0 \\ 1 \end{pmatrix}$

```
plot({[1+(2)*sin(t),2*cos(t),t=-Pi..Pi],[7+(5)*sin(t),5*cos(t),t=-Pi..Pi]},
scaling=CONSTRAINED); # and
plot POINTS at  (1,0), (0,0) and (7,0)
```

15. $1, \begin{pmatrix} -2 \\ -11 \\ 0 \\ 1 \end{pmatrix}; 2, \begin{pmatrix} 0 \\ 0 \\ 1 \\ 0 \end{pmatrix}; \frac{1}{2}(-1+\sqrt{53}), \begin{pmatrix} -7+\sqrt{53} \\ 0 \\ 0 \\ 2 \end{pmatrix}; \frac{1}{2}(-1-\sqrt{53}), \begin{pmatrix} -7-\sqrt{53} \\ 0 \\ 0 \\ 2 \end{pmatrix}$

```
plot({[-4+(2)*sin(t),2*cos(t),t=-Pi..Pi],[3+sin(t),cos(t),t=-Pi..Pi]},
scaling=CONSTRAINED); # and plot
POINTS at  (-4,0), (1,0), (2,0) and (3,0)
```

17. The characteristic polynomial is $|\lambda \mathbf{I}_2 - \mathbf{A}| = \lambda^2 - (\alpha + \gamma)\lambda + \alpha\gamma - \beta^2$. Now $(\alpha + \gamma)^2 - 4(\alpha\gamma - \beta^2) = (\alpha - \gamma)^2 + 4\beta^2 \geq 0$, so the eigenvalues are real.

19. Suppose $\mathbf{AE} = \lambda\mathbf{E}$ and $\mathbf{E} \neq \mathbf{O}$. Then $\mathbf{A}^2\mathbf{E} = \mathbf{A}(\mathbf{AE}) = \mathbf{A}(\lambda\mathbf{E}) = \lambda(\mathbf{AE}) = \lambda^2\mathbf{E}$, so λ^2 is an eigenvalue of $\mathbf{A}^2$ with eigenvector $\mathbf{E}$. The same idea holds for $k > 2$.

21. The constant term of $p_{\mathbf{A}}(\lambda) = |\lambda\mathbf{I}_n - \mathbf{A}|$ is found by setting $\lambda = 0$, yielding $|-\mathbf{A}|$, which equals $(-1)^n|\mathbf{A}|$. 0 can be an eigenvalue of $\mathbf{A}$ if and only if this constant term is zero, which occurs exactly when $|\mathbf{A}| = 0$, and this occurs exactly when $\mathbf{A}$ is singular.

Section 9.2

1. $\dfrac{1}{8}\begin{pmatrix} 3+\sqrt{7}i & 3-\sqrt{7}i \\ -8 & -8 \end{pmatrix}$ **3.** Not diagonalizable   **5.** $\begin{pmatrix} 0 & 5 & 0 \\ 1 & 1 & -\frac{3}{2} \\ 0 & 0 & 1 \end{pmatrix}$ **7.** Not diagonalizable

9. $\begin{pmatrix} 1 & 0 & 0 & 0 \\ 0 & 1 & \frac{2-3\sqrt{3}}{41} & \frac{2+3\sqrt{5}}{41} \\ 0 & 0 & \frac{-1+\sqrt{5}}{2} & \frac{-1-\sqrt{5}}{2} \\ 0 & 0 & 1 & 1 \end{pmatrix}$

11. *Hint:* $\mathbf{A}^2$ has n linearly independent eigenvectors $\mathbf{X}_1, \ldots, \mathbf{X}_n$ with associated eigenvalues $\lambda_1, \ldots, \lambda_n$. Thus $(\mathbf{A}^2 - \lambda_j\mathbf{I}_n)\mathbf{X}_j = (\mathbf{A} - \sqrt{\lambda_j}\mathbf{I}_n)(\mathbf{A} + \sqrt{\lambda_j}\mathbf{I}_n)\mathbf{X}_j = \mathbf{O}$. Now show that either $(\mathbf{A} - \sqrt{\lambda_j}\mathbf{I}_n)\mathbf{X}_j = \mathbf{O}$ or $(\mathbf{A} + \sqrt{\lambda_j}\mathbf{I}_n)\mathbf{X}_j = \mathbf{O}$.

13. $\begin{pmatrix} 1 & 0 \\ \frac{1}{4}(1 - 5^{18}) & 5^{18} \end{pmatrix}$ **15.** $\begin{pmatrix} 0 & 2^{22} \\ 2^{21} & 0 \end{pmatrix}$

Section 9.3

1. $0, \begin{pmatrix} 1 \\ 2 \end{pmatrix}; \ 5, \begin{pmatrix} -2 \\ 1 \end{pmatrix}; \ \dfrac{1}{\sqrt{5}}\begin{pmatrix} 1 & -2 \\ 2 & 1 \end{pmatrix}$ **3.** $5 + \sqrt{2}, \begin{pmatrix} 1+\sqrt{2} \\ 1 \end{pmatrix}; \ 5 - \sqrt{2}, \begin{pmatrix} 1-\sqrt{2} \\ 1 \end{pmatrix}; \ \begin{pmatrix} \frac{1+\sqrt{2}}{\sqrt{4+2\sqrt{2}}} & \frac{1-\sqrt{2}}{\sqrt{4-2\sqrt{2}}} \\ \frac{1}{\sqrt{4+2\sqrt{2}}} & \frac{1}{\sqrt{4-2\sqrt{2}}} \end{pmatrix}$

5. $3, \begin{pmatrix} 0 \\ 0 \\ 1 \end{pmatrix}; \ -1 + \sqrt{2}, \begin{pmatrix} 1+\sqrt{2} \\ 1 \\ 0 \end{pmatrix}; \ -1 - \sqrt{2}, \begin{pmatrix} 1-\sqrt{2} \\ 1 \\ 0 \end{pmatrix}; \ \begin{pmatrix} 0 & \frac{1+\sqrt{2}}{\sqrt{4+2\sqrt{2}}} & \frac{1-\sqrt{2}}{\sqrt{4-2\sqrt{2}}} \\ 0 & \frac{1}{\sqrt{4+2\sqrt{2}}} & \frac{1}{\sqrt{4-2\sqrt{2}}} \\ 1 & 0 & 0 \end{pmatrix}$

7. $0, \begin{pmatrix} 0 \\ 1 \\ 0 \end{pmatrix}; \ \dfrac{1}{2}(5+\sqrt{41}), \begin{pmatrix} 5+\sqrt{41} \\ 0 \\ 4 \end{pmatrix}; \ \dfrac{1}{2}(5-\sqrt{41}), \begin{pmatrix} 5-\sqrt{41} \\ 0 \\ 4 \end{pmatrix}; \ \begin{pmatrix} 0 & \frac{5+\sqrt{41}}{\sqrt{82+10\sqrt{41}}} & \frac{5-\sqrt{41}}{\sqrt{82-10\sqrt{41}}} \\ 1 & 0 & 0 \\ 0 & \frac{4}{\sqrt{82+10\sqrt{41}}} & \frac{4}{\sqrt{82-10\sqrt{41}}} \end{pmatrix}$

9. $0, \begin{pmatrix} 1 \\ 0 \\ 0 \end{pmatrix}; \ \dfrac{1}{2}(1+\sqrt{17}), \begin{pmatrix} 0 \\ -1-\sqrt{17} \\ 4 \end{pmatrix}; \ \dfrac{1}{2}(1-\sqrt{17}), \begin{pmatrix} 0 \\ -1+\sqrt{17} \\ 4 \end{pmatrix}; \ \begin{pmatrix} 1 & 0 & 0 \\ 0 & -\frac{1+\sqrt{17}}{\sqrt{34+2\sqrt{17}}} & -\frac{1-\sqrt{17}}{\sqrt{34-2\sqrt{17}}} \\ 0 & \frac{4}{\sqrt{34+2\sqrt{17}}} & \frac{4}{\sqrt{34+2\sqrt{17}}} \end{pmatrix}$

11. $0, \begin{pmatrix} 1 \\ 0 \\ 0 \\ 0 \end{pmatrix}; \ 0, \begin{pmatrix} 0 \\ 0 \\ 0 \\ 1 \end{pmatrix}; \ -1, \begin{pmatrix} 0 \\ 1 \\ 1 \\ 0 \end{pmatrix}; \ 3, \begin{pmatrix} 0 \\ -1 \\ 1 \\ 0 \end{pmatrix}; \ \begin{pmatrix} 1 & 0 & 0 & 0 \\ 0 & 0 & \frac{1}{\sqrt{2}} & -\frac{1}{\sqrt{2}} \\ 0 & 0 & \frac{1}{\sqrt{2}} & \frac{1}{\sqrt{2}} \\ 0 & 1 & 0 & 0 \end{pmatrix}$

Section 9.4

1. $\begin{pmatrix} 1 & 1 \\ 1 & 6 \end{pmatrix}$ **3.** $\begin{pmatrix} 1 & -2 \\ -2 & 1 \end{pmatrix}$ **5.** $\begin{pmatrix} -1 & 0 & -\frac{1}{2} & -1 \\ 0 & 0 & 2 & \frac{3}{2} \\ -\frac{1}{2} & 2 & 0 & 0 \\ -1 & \frac{3}{2} & 0 & 1 \end{pmatrix}$ **7.** $(-1+2\sqrt{5})y_1^2 + (-1-2\sqrt{5})y_2^2$

9. $(2+\sqrt{29})y_1^2 + (2-\sqrt{29})y_2^2$ **11.** $(2+\sqrt{13})y_1^2 + (2-\sqrt{13})y_2^2$ **13.** $-y_1^2 + y_2^2 + 2y_3^2$

15. $\frac{1}{2}\sqrt{61}y_1^2 - \frac{1}{2}\sqrt{16}y_2^2 = 5$; hyperbola   **17.** $5y_1^2 - 5y_2^2 = 8$; hyperbola   **19.** $-2x_1^2 + 2x_1x_2 + 6x_2^2$

21. $6x_1^2 + 2x_1x_2 - 14x_1x_3 + 2x_2^2 + x_3^2$

Section 9.5

1. None of these; 2, 2, $\begin{pmatrix} i \\ 1 \end{pmatrix}$; not diagonalizable

3. Skew-hermitian; 0, $\begin{pmatrix} 1 \\ 0 \\ \frac{1+i}{2} \end{pmatrix}$; $\sqrt{3}i$, $\begin{pmatrix} 1 \\ \sqrt{3}i \\ -1-i \end{pmatrix}$; $-\sqrt{3}i$, $\begin{pmatrix} 1 \\ -\sqrt{3}i \\ -1-i \end{pmatrix}$; $\begin{pmatrix} 1 & 1 & 1 \\ 0 & \sqrt{3}i & -\sqrt{3}i \\ \frac{1+i}{2} & -1-i & -1-i \end{pmatrix}$

5. Hermitian; eigenvalues satisfy $\lambda^3 - 3\lambda^2 - 5\lambda + 3 = 0$. Eigenvalues and corresponding eigenvectors are, approximately,

4.051374, $\begin{pmatrix} 1 \\ 0.525687 \\ -0.129755i \end{pmatrix}$; 0.482696, $\begin{pmatrix} 1 \\ -1.258652 \\ 2.607546i \end{pmatrix}$; -1.53407, $\begin{pmatrix} 1 \\ -2.267035 \\ -1.477791i \end{pmatrix}$;

$\begin{pmatrix} 1 & 1 & 1 \\ 0.525687 & -1.258652 & -2.267035 \\ -0.129755i & 2.607546i & -1.47791i \end{pmatrix}$

7. Skew-hermitian; eigenvalues satisfy $\lambda^3 - i\lambda^2 + 5\lambda - 4i = 0$. Eigenvalues and eigenvectors are, approximately,

$-2.164248i$, $\begin{pmatrix} -i \\ -3.164248 \\ 2.924109 \end{pmatrix}$; $0.772866i$, $\begin{pmatrix} i \\ 0.227134 \\ 0.587772 \end{pmatrix}$; $2.391382i$, $\begin{pmatrix} i \\ -1.391382 \\ -1.163664 \end{pmatrix}$;

$\begin{pmatrix} -i & i & i \\ -3.164248 & 0.227134 & -1.391382 \\ 2.924109 & 0.587772 & -1.163664 \end{pmatrix}$

9. Hermitian; 0, $\begin{pmatrix} 0 \\ i \\ 1 \end{pmatrix}$; $4 + 3\sqrt{2}$, $\begin{pmatrix} 4+3\sqrt{2} \\ -1 \\ -i \end{pmatrix}$; $4 - 3\sqrt{2}$, $\begin{pmatrix} 4-3\sqrt{2} \\ -1 \\ -i \end{pmatrix}$; $\begin{pmatrix} 0 & 4+3\sqrt{2} & 4-3\sqrt{2} \\ i & -1 & -1 \\ 1 & -i & -i \end{pmatrix}$

CHAPTER 10

Section 10.1

1. $\Omega(t) = \begin{pmatrix} -e^{2t} & 3e^{6t} \\ e^{2t} & e^{6t} \end{pmatrix}$; $x_1(t) = -3e^{2t} + 3e^{6t}$, $x_2(t) = 3e^{2t} + e^{6t}$

3. $\Omega(t) = \begin{pmatrix} 4e^{(1+2\sqrt{3})t} & 4e^{(1-2\sqrt{3})t} \\ (-1+\sqrt{3})e^{(1+2\sqrt{3})t} & (-1-\sqrt{3})e^{(1-2\sqrt{3})t} \end{pmatrix}$; $x_1(t) = \left(1 + \frac{5}{3}\sqrt{3}\right)e^{(1+2\sqrt{3})t} + \left(1 - \frac{5}{3}\sqrt{3}\right)e^{(1-2\sqrt{3})t}$,

$x_2(t) = \left(1 - \frac{1}{6}\sqrt{3}\right)e^{(1+2\sqrt{3})t} + \left(1 + \frac{1}{6}\sqrt{3}\right)e^{(1-2\sqrt{3})t}$

5. $\Omega(t) = \begin{pmatrix} e^t & 0 & e^{-3t} \\ 0 & e^t & 3e^{-3t} \\ -e^t & e^t & e^{-3t} \end{pmatrix}$; $x_1(t) = 10e^t - 9e^{-3t}$, $x_2(t) = 24e^t - 27e^{-3t}$, $x_3(t) = 14e^t - 9e^{-3t}$

Section 10.2

1. $\Omega(t) = \begin{pmatrix} 7e^{3t} & 0 \\ 5e^{3t} & e^{-4t} \end{pmatrix}$ is a fundamental matrix; general solution is $\mathbf{X}(t) = \Omega(t)\mathbf{C} = \begin{pmatrix} 7c_1 e^{3t} \\ 5c_1 e^{3t} + c_2 e^{-4t} \end{pmatrix}$.

3. $\Omega(t) = \begin{pmatrix} 1 & e^{2t} \\ -1 & e^{2t} \end{pmatrix}$; $\mathbf{X}(t) = \Omega(t)\mathbf{C} = \begin{pmatrix} c_1 + c_2 e^{2t} \\ -c_1 + c_2 e^{2t} \end{pmatrix}$

5. $\Omega(t) = \begin{pmatrix} 1 & 2e^{3t} & -e^{-4t} \\ 6 & 3e^{3t} & 2e^{-4t} \\ -13 & -2e^{3t} & e^{-4t} \end{pmatrix}$; $\mathbf{X}(t) = \begin{pmatrix} c_1 + 2c_2 e^{3t} - c_3 e^{-4t} \\ 6c_1 + 3c_2 e^{3t} + 2c_3 e^{-4t} \\ -13c_1 - 2c_2 e^{3t} + c_3 e^{-4t} \end{pmatrix}$

7. $\Omega(t) = \begin{pmatrix} 2e^{4t} & e^{-3t} \\ -3e^{4t} & 2e^{-3t} \end{pmatrix}$ is a fundamental matrix; the solution of the initial value problem is

$\mathbf{X}(t) = \begin{pmatrix} 6e^{4t} - 5e^{-3t} \\ -9e^{4t} - 10e^{-3t} \end{pmatrix}$.

9. $\Omega(t) = \begin{pmatrix} 0 & e^{2t} & 3e^{3t} \\ 1 & e^{2t} & e^{3t} \\ 1 & 0 & e^{3t} \end{pmatrix}$; $\mathbf{X}(t) = \begin{pmatrix} 4e^{2t} - 3e^{3t} \\ 2 + 4e^{2t} - e^{3t} \\ 2 - e^{3t} \end{pmatrix}$ **11.** $\Omega(t) = \begin{pmatrix} 3e^{-t} & 0 & e^{4t} \\ -5e^{-t} & -e^{2t} & 0 \\ 0 & e^{2t} & 0 \end{pmatrix}$; $\mathbf{X}(t) = \begin{pmatrix} -\frac{6}{5}e^{-t} + \frac{51}{5}e^{4t} \\ 2e^{-t} - 3e^{2t} \\ 3e^{2t} \end{pmatrix}$

13. $\begin{pmatrix} c_1 t^8 + c_2 t^2 \\ c_1 t^8 - 2c_2 t^2 \end{pmatrix}$ **15.** $\Omega(t) = \begin{pmatrix} 2e^{2t}\cos(2t) & 2e^{2t}\sin(2t) \\ e^{2t}\sin(2t) & -e^{2t}\cos(2t) \end{pmatrix}$ **17.** $\begin{pmatrix} 5e^t\cos(t) & 5e^t\sin(t) \\ e^t[2\cos(t) + \sin(t)] & e^t[2\sin(t) - \cos(t)] \end{pmatrix}$

19. $\begin{pmatrix} 0 & e^{-t}\cos(2t) & e^{-t}\sin(2t) \\ 0 & e^{-t}[\cos(2t) - 2\sin(2t)] & e^{-t}[\sin(2t) + 2\cos(2t)] \\ e^{-2t} & 3e^{-t}\cos(2t) & 3e^{-t}\sin(2t) \end{pmatrix}$ **21.** $\begin{pmatrix} 2\cos(t) - 14\sin(t) \\ 10\cos(t) - 20\sin(t) \end{pmatrix}$

23. $\begin{pmatrix} 2e^t + 5e^t[\cos(t) + \sin(t)] \\ 2e^t + e^t[2\cos(t) + 6\sin(t)] \\ 2e^t + e^t[\cos(t) + 3\sin(t)] \end{pmatrix}$ **25.** $\Omega(t) = \begin{pmatrix} e^{3t} & 2te^{3t} \\ 0 & e^{3t} \end{pmatrix}$; general solution $\mathbf{X}(t) = \begin{pmatrix} c_1 e^{3t} + 2c_2 te^{3t} \\ c_2 e^{3t} \end{pmatrix}$

27. $\begin{pmatrix} e^{2t} & 3e^{5t} & 27te^{5t} \\ 0 & 3e^{5t} & (3+27t)e^{5t} \\ 0 & -e^{5t} & (2-9t)e^{5t} \end{pmatrix}$; $\mathbf{X}(t) = \begin{pmatrix} c_1 e^{2t} + [3c_2 + 27c_3 t]e^{5t} \\ [3c_2 + (3+27t)c_3]e^{5t} \\ [-c_2 + (2-9t)c_3]e^{5t} \end{pmatrix}$

29. $\begin{pmatrix} 2 & 3e^{3t} & e^t & 0 \\ 0 & 2e^{3t} & 0 & -2e^t \\ 1 & 2^{3t} & 0 & -2e^t \\ 0 & 0 & 0 & e^t \end{pmatrix}$; $\mathbf{X}(t) = \begin{pmatrix} 2c_1 + 3c_2 e^{3t} + c_3 e^t \\ 2c_2 e^{3t} - 2c_4 e^t \\ c_1 + 2c_2 e^{3t} - 2c_4 e^t \\ c_4 e^t \end{pmatrix}$ **31.** $\mathbf{X}(t) = \begin{pmatrix} (5 + 2t)e^{6t} \\ (3 + 2t)e^{6t} \end{pmatrix}$

33. $\mathbf{X}(t) = \begin{pmatrix} -e^{2t} + (1 + 22t)e^{-4t} \\ -6e^{2t} + 10e^{-4t} \\ 12e^{-4t} \end{pmatrix}$ **35.** $\mathbf{X}(t) = \begin{pmatrix} 2\cos(t) + 6\sin(t) \\ -2\cos(t) + 4\sin(t) \\ (1 - 9t)e^{2t} \\ (4 - 9t)e^{2t} \end{pmatrix}$ **37.** $\mathbf{X}(t) = \begin{pmatrix} 3c_1 e^{2t} + c_2 e^{6t} \\ -c_1 e^{2t} + c_2 e^{6t} \end{pmatrix}$

39. $\mathbf{X}(t) = \begin{pmatrix} c_1 e^t + 5c_2 e^{7t} \\ -c_1 e^t + c_2 e^{7t} \end{pmatrix}$ **41.** $e^{\mathbf{A}t} = \begin{pmatrix} e^{3t} & 2te^{3t} \\ 0 & e^{3t} \end{pmatrix}$

43. $e^{\mathbf{A}t} = \begin{pmatrix} (1 - 2t)e^{4t} & -4te^{4t} \\ te^{4t} & (1 + 2t)e^{4t} \end{pmatrix}$ **45.** $e^{\mathbf{A}t} = \begin{pmatrix} e^{2t} & (\frac{2}{3} + 3t)e^{5t} - \frac{2}{3}e^{2t} & (-1 + 9t)e^{5t} + e^{2t} \\ 0 & (1 + 3t)e^{5t} & 9te^{5t} \\ 0 & -te^{5t} & (1 - 3t)e^{5t} \end{pmatrix}$

Section 10.3

1. $\mathbf{X}(t) = \begin{pmatrix} [c_1(1 + 2t) + 2c_2 t + t^2]e^{3t} \\ [-2c_1 t + (1 - 2t)c_2 + t - t^2]e^{3t} + \frac{3}{2}e^t \end{pmatrix}$ **3.** $\mathbf{X}(t) = \begin{pmatrix} [c_1 + (1 + t)c_2 + 2t + t^2 - t^3]e^{6t} \\ [c_1 + c_2 t + 4t^2 - t^3]e^{6t} \end{pmatrix}$

5. $\mathbf{X}(t) = \begin{pmatrix} c_2 e^t \\ (1 - 2c_2)e^t + (c_3 - 9c_4)e^{3t} \\ 2c_4 e^{3t} \\ (c_1 - 5c_2 t + 1 + 3t)e^t + c_3 e^{3t} \end{pmatrix}$ **7.** $\mathbf{X}(t) = \begin{pmatrix} (-1 - 14t)e^t \\ (3 - 14t)e^t \end{pmatrix}$

9. $\mathbf{X}(t) = \begin{pmatrix} (6 + 12t + \frac{1}{2}t^2)e^{-2t} \\ (2 + 12t + \frac{1}{2}t^2)e^{-2t} \\ (3 + 38t + 66t^2 + \frac{13}{6}t^3)e^{-2t} \end{pmatrix}$ **11.** $\Omega(t)\Omega^{-1}(0) = \begin{pmatrix} \frac{2}{5}e^t + \frac{3}{5}e^{6t} & -\frac{2}{5}e^t + \frac{2}{5}e^{6t} \\ -\frac{3}{5}e^t + \frac{3}{5}e^{6t} & \frac{3}{5}e^t + \frac{2}{5}e^{6t} \end{pmatrix}$ is a transition matrix.

13. $\begin{pmatrix} -e^{-3t} + 2e^t & e^{-3t} - e^t & -e^{-3t} + e^t \\ -3e^{-3t} + 3e^t & 3e^{-3t} - 2e^t & -3e^{-3t} + 3e^t \\ -e^{-3t} + e^t & e^{-3t} - e^t & -e^{-3t} + 2e^t \end{pmatrix}$ **15.** $\mathbf{X}(t) = \begin{pmatrix} 3c_1 e^{2t} + c_2 e^{6t} - 4e^{3t} - \frac{10}{3} \\ -c_1 e^{2t} + c_2 e^{6t} + \frac{2}{3} \end{pmatrix}$

17. $\mathbf{X}(t) = \begin{pmatrix} c_1 e^t + 5c_2 e^{7t} + \frac{68}{145}\cos(3t) - \frac{54}{145}\sin(3t) + \frac{40}{7} \\ -c_1 e^t + c_2 e^{7t} + \frac{2}{145}\cos(3t) + \frac{24}{145}\sin(3t) - \frac{48}{7} \end{pmatrix}$ **19.** $\mathbf{X}(t) = \begin{pmatrix} 2 + 4(1+t)e^{2t} \\ -2 + 2(1+2t)e^{2t} \end{pmatrix}$

21. $\mathbf{X}(t) = \begin{pmatrix} 10\cos(t) + \frac{5}{2}t\sin(t) - 5t\cos(t) \\ 5\cos(t) + \frac{5}{2}\sin(t) - \frac{5}{2}t\cos(t) \end{pmatrix}$ **23.** $\mathbf{X}(t) = \begin{pmatrix} -\frac{1}{4}e^{2t} + (2+2t)e^t - \frac{3}{4} - \frac{1}{2}t \\ e^{2t} + (2+2t)e^t - 1 - t \\ -\frac{5}{4}e^{2t} + 2te^t - \frac{3}{4} - \frac{1}{2}t \end{pmatrix}$

CHAPTER 11

Section 11.1

1. a gives the initial value of θ (hence initial displacement); b gives the initial rate of change of θ with respect to time. There are no restrictions (at least mathematically) on a and b.

3. Yes

Section 11.2

1. $\mathbf{X}(t) = \begin{pmatrix} -c_1\cos(t) - c_2\sin(t) \\ (4c_1 - c_2)\cos(t) + (c_1 + 4c_2)\sin(t) \end{pmatrix}$;

a phase portrait is shown below.

3. $\mathbf{X}(t) = \begin{pmatrix} c_1 e^{-3t} + 7c_2 e^{2t} \\ c_1 e^{-3t} + 2c_2 e^{2t} \end{pmatrix}$;

a phase portrait is shown below.

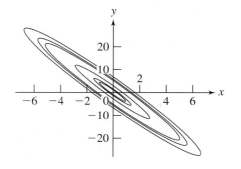

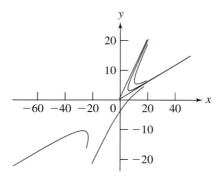

5. $\mathbf{X}(t) = \begin{pmatrix} c_1 e^{5t} + 2c_2 e^{4t} \\ c_2 e^{4t} \end{pmatrix}$;

a phase portrait is shown below.

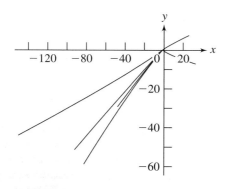

7. $\dfrac{dy}{dx} = -\dfrac{4x}{9y}$; $4x^2 + 9y^2 = c$; integral curves are ellipses with center $(0, 0)$.

9. $\dfrac{dy}{dx} = \dfrac{x-1}{y+2}$; $(x-1)^2 - (y+2)^2 = c$; integral curves are hyperbolas with center $(1, -2)$.

11. $\dfrac{dy}{dx} = \dfrac{x+y}{x}$; $y = x \ln|cx|$

13. These systems have the same graphs of trajectories, but with opposite orientations.

Section 11.3

1. eigenvalues $-2, -2$; improper nodal sink (phase portrait given below)

3. $\pm 2i$, center (phase portrait given below)

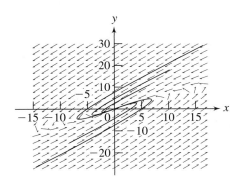

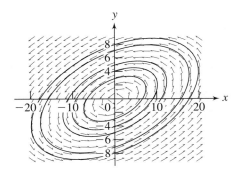

5. $4 \pm 5i$; spiral point (phase portrait given below)

7. $3, 3$; improper nodal source (phase portrait given below)

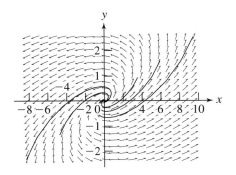

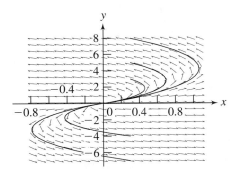

9. $-2 \pm \sqrt{3}i$; spiral point (phase portrait given below)

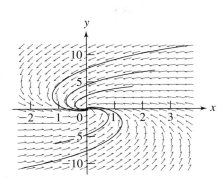

Section 11.4

1. stable and asymptotically stable improper node **3.** stable but not asymptotically stable center
5. unstable spiral point **7.** unstable improper node **9.** stable and asymptotically stable spiral point

Section 11.5

1. $(0, 0)$ is an unstable spiral point; $(-3/2, 3/4)$ is an unstable saddle point (phase portrait given below).

3. $(0, 0)$ is an unstable saddle point; $(-5, -5)$ is an asymptotically stable nodal sink (phase portrait given below).

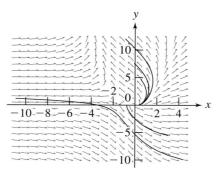

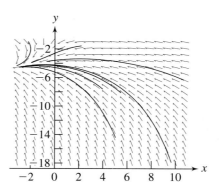

5. $(0, 0)$ is a center of the linear system, and may be a center or spiral point of the nonlinear system; $(1/2, -1/8)$ and $(-1/2, 1/8)$ are unstable saddle points (phase portrait given below).

7. $(0, 0)$ is an asymptotically stable node or spiral point (phase portrait given below).

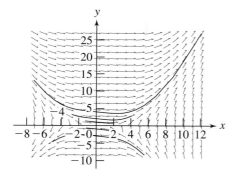

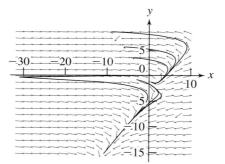

9. $(0, 0)$ is an unstable saddle point; $(3/8, 3/2)$ is an asymptotically stable spiral point.

Section 11.6

1. stable **3.** asymptotically stable **5.** unstable **7.** unstable

Section 11.7

1. $\dfrac{\partial f}{\partial x} + \dfrac{\partial g}{\partial y} = 3 + 4x^2 - 2\sin(x) \geq 1 + 4x^2 > 0$ **3.** $\dfrac{\partial f}{\partial x} + \dfrac{\partial g}{\partial y} = \cosh(x) - 1 + 15e^{3y} > 0$

7. $\dfrac{dr}{dt} = 0, \dfrac{d\theta}{dt} = r^2 - 1$; trajectories are the origin (a critical point), all points on the circle $r = 1$ (each is a critical point), and the closed circles $r = a \neq 1$. Each closed trajectory $r = a \neq 1$ is a stable limit cycle.

9. $\dfrac{dr}{dt} = r(1 - r^2)(4 - r^2)(9 - r^2)$, $\dfrac{d\theta}{dt} = -1$; trajectories are the origin (a critical point), and the circles $r = 1$, $r = 2$, and $r = 3$ are each closed trajectories. The circles $r = 1$ and $r = 3$ are asymptotically stable limit cycles, and $r = 2$ is an unstable limit cycle.

11. $xx' + yy' = (x^2 + y^2)[4 - (x^2 + 9y^2)]$. The ellipse $x^2 + 9y^2 = 4$ is a closed trajectory, and the annular region $\frac{4}{9} \le r^2 \le 4$ has the stated property.

13. The ellipse $4x^2 + y^2 = 4$ is a limit cycle; the region defined by $1 \le r^2 \le 4$ has the stated property.

15. No; $\dfrac{dr}{dt} = r(1 + r^2) > 0$ for $r > 0$.   17. No; $\dfrac{dy}{dt} > 0$ and the system has no critical points, hence no trajectory.

19. No; $\dfrac{\partial f}{\partial x} + \dfrac{\partial g}{\partial y} > 0$ 21. $x^4 + 2y^2 = C$ is a closed trajectory for all positive C.

23. Apply Lienard's theorem with $p(x) = x^2 - 1$ and $q(x) = 2x + \sin(x)$.

25. $x^4 + 2y^2 = C$ are closed trajectories for each positive C.

27. $\ln(1 + x^2) + y^2 = C$ are closed trajectories for each positive C.

CHAPTER 12

Section 12.1

1. $\dfrac{d}{dt}[f(t)\mathbf{F}(t)] = -12\sin(3t)\mathbf{i} + 12t[2\cos(3t) - 3t\sin(3t)]\mathbf{j} + 8[\cos(3t) - 3t\sin(3t)]\mathbf{k}$

3. $\dfrac{d}{dt}[\mathbf{F}(t) \times \mathbf{G}(t)] = [1 - 4\sin(t)]\mathbf{i} - 2t\mathbf{j} - [\cos(t) - t\sin(t)]\mathbf{k}$

5. $\dfrac{d}{dt}[f(t)\mathbf{F}(t)] = (1 - 8t^3)\mathbf{i} + [6t^2\cosh(t) - (1 - 2t^3)\sinh(t)]\mathbf{j} + [-6t^2 e^t + e^t(1 - 2t^3)]\mathbf{k}$

7. $\dfrac{d}{dt}[\mathbf{F}(t) \times \mathbf{G}(t)] = te^t(2 + t)[\mathbf{j} - \mathbf{k}]$

9. position: $\mathbf{F}(t) = \sin(t)\mathbf{i} + \cos(t)\mathbf{j} + 45t\mathbf{k}$; tangent: $\mathbf{F}'(t) = \cos(t)\mathbf{i} - \sin(t)\mathbf{j} + 45\mathbf{k}$; length: $s(t) = \sqrt{2026}\,t$;
position: $\mathbf{G}(s) = \mathbf{F}(t(s)) = \sin\left(\dfrac{s}{\sqrt{2026}}\right)\mathbf{i} + \cos\left(\dfrac{s}{\sqrt{2026}}\right)\mathbf{j} + \dfrac{45s}{\sqrt{2026}}\mathbf{k}$

11. position: $\mathbf{F}(t) = 2t^2\mathbf{i} + 3t^2\mathbf{j} + 4t^2\mathbf{k} = t^2(2\mathbf{i} + 3\mathbf{j} + 4\mathbf{k})$; tangent: $\mathbf{F}'(t) = 2t(2\mathbf{i} + 3\mathbf{j} + 4\mathbf{k})$; length: $s(t) = \sqrt{29}(t^2 - 1)$;
position: $\mathbf{G}(s) = \left(1 + \dfrac{s}{\sqrt{29}}\right)(2\mathbf{i} + 3\mathbf{j} + 4\mathbf{k})$

Section 12.2

1. $\mathbf{v}(t) = 3\mathbf{i} + 2t\mathbf{k}$, $v(t) = \sqrt{9 + 4t^2}$, $\mathbf{a}(t) = 2\mathbf{k}$, $a_T = \dfrac{4t}{\sqrt{9 + 4t^2}}$, $a_N = \dfrac{6}{\sqrt{9 + 4t^2}}$, $\kappa = \dfrac{6}{(9 + 4t^2)^{3/2}}$,
$\mathbf{T} = \dfrac{1}{\sqrt{9 + 4t^2}}[3\mathbf{i} + 2t\mathbf{k}]$, $\mathbf{N} = \dfrac{1}{\sqrt{9 + 4t^2}}[-2t\mathbf{i} + 3\mathbf{k}]$, $\mathbf{B} = -\mathbf{j}$

3. $\mathbf{v} = 2\mathbf{i} - 2\mathbf{j} + \mathbf{k}$, $v = 3$, $\mathbf{a} = \mathbf{O}$, $a_T = a_N = \kappa = 0$, $\mathbf{T} = \frac{1}{3}(2\mathbf{i} - 2\mathbf{j} + \mathbf{k})$, $\mathbf{N} = \dfrac{1}{\sqrt{2}}(\mathbf{i} + \mathbf{j})$ (or any unit vector perpendicular to $\mathbf{T}$), $\mathbf{B} = \frac{1}{6}\sqrt{2}(-\mathbf{i} + \mathbf{j} + 4\mathbf{k})$

5. $\mathbf{v} = -3e^{-t}(\mathbf{i} + \mathbf{j} - 2\mathbf{k})$, $v = 3\sqrt{6}e^{-t}$, $\mathbf{a} = 3e^{-t}(\mathbf{i} + \mathbf{j} - 2\mathbf{k})$, $a_T = -3\sqrt{6}e^{-t}$,
$a_N = 0$, $\kappa = 0$, $\mathbf{T} = \dfrac{1}{\sqrt{6}}(-\mathbf{i} - \mathbf{j} + 2\mathbf{k})$, $\mathbf{N} = \dfrac{1}{\sqrt{2}}(\mathbf{i} - \mathbf{j})$, or any unit vector perpendicular to $\mathbf{T}$, $\mathbf{B} = \dfrac{1}{\sqrt{3}}(\mathbf{i} + \mathbf{j} + \mathbf{k})$

7. $\mathbf{v} = 2\cosh(t)\mathbf{j} - 2\sinh(t)\mathbf{k}$, $v = 2\sqrt{\cosh(2t)}$, $\mathbf{a} = 2\sinh(t)\mathbf{j} - 2\cosh(t)\mathbf{k}$,
$a_T = \dfrac{2\sinh(2t)}{\sqrt{\cosh(2t)}}$, $a_N = \dfrac{2}{\sqrt{\cosh(2t)}}$, $\kappa = \dfrac{1}{2[\cosh(2t)]^{3/2}}$,
$\mathbf{T} = \dfrac{1}{\sqrt{\cosh(2t)}}[\cosh(t)\mathbf{j} - \sinh(t)\mathbf{k}]$, $\mathbf{N} = \dfrac{1}{\sqrt{\cosh(2t)}}[-\sinh(t)\mathbf{j} - \cosh(t)\mathbf{k}]$, $\mathbf{B} = -\mathbf{i}$

9. $\mathbf{v} = 2t(\alpha\mathbf{i}+\beta\mathbf{j}+\gamma\mathbf{k})$, $v = 2|t|\sqrt{\alpha^2+\beta^2+\gamma^2}$, $\mathbf{a} = 2(\alpha\mathbf{i}+\beta\mathbf{j}+\gamma\mathbf{k})$, $\alpha_T = 2sgn(t)\sqrt{\alpha^2+\beta^2+\gamma^2}$, where $sgn(t)$ equals
1 if $t \geq 0$ and -1 if $t < 0$, $a_N = \kappa = 0$, $\mathbf{T} = \dfrac{1}{\sqrt{\alpha^2+\beta^2+\gamma^2}}(\alpha\mathbf{i}+\beta\mathbf{j}+\gamma\mathbf{k})$, $\mathbf{N}$ is any unit vector perpendicular to
$\mathbf{T}$, and $\mathbf{B} = \mathbf{T} \times \mathbf{N}$.

Section 12.3

1. $\dfrac{\partial \mathbf{G}}{\partial x} = 3\mathbf{i} - 4y\mathbf{j}$, $\dfrac{\partial \mathbf{G}}{\partial y} = -4x\mathbf{j}$ **3.** $\dfrac{\partial \mathbf{G}}{\partial x} = 2y\mathbf{i} - \sin(x)\mathbf{j}$, $\dfrac{\partial \mathbf{G}}{\partial y} = 2x\mathbf{i}$

5. $\dfrac{\partial \mathbf{G}}{\partial x} = 6x\mathbf{i} + \mathbf{j}$, $\dfrac{\partial \mathbf{G}}{\partial y} = -2\mathbf{j}$ **7.** $\dfrac{\partial \mathbf{F}}{\partial x} = -4z^2\sin(x)\mathbf{i} - 3x^2yz\mathbf{j} + 3x^2y\mathbf{k}$, $\dfrac{\partial \mathbf{F}}{\partial y} = -x^3z\mathbf{j} + x^3\mathbf{k}$, $\dfrac{\partial \mathbf{F}}{\partial z} = 8z\cos(x)\mathbf{i} - x^3y\mathbf{j}$

9. $\dfrac{\partial \mathbf{F}}{\partial x} = -yz^4\cos(xy)\mathbf{i} + 3y^4z\mathbf{j} - \sinh(z-x)\mathbf{k}$, $\dfrac{\partial \mathbf{F}}{\partial y} = -xz^4\cos(xy)\mathbf{i} + 12xy^3z\mathbf{j}$,

$\dfrac{\partial \mathbf{F}}{\partial z} = -4z^3\sin(xy)\mathbf{i} + 3xy^4\mathbf{j} + \sinh(z-x)\mathbf{k}$

11. $x = x$, $y = \dfrac{1}{x+c}$, $z = e^{x+k}$; $x = x$, $y = \dfrac{1}{x-1}$, $z = e^{x-2}$
13. $x = x$, $y = e^x(x-1) + c$, $x^2 = -2z + k$; $x = x$, $y = e^x(x-1) - e^2$, $z = \frac{1}{2}(12 - x^2)$
15. $x = c$, $y = y$, $2e^z = k - \sin(y)$; $x = 3$, $y = y$, $z = \ln(1 + \frac{1}{4}\sqrt{2} - \frac{1}{2}\sin(y))$
17. Take any constant $\mathbf{F}$, say $\mathbf{F} = \mathbf{i}+\mathbf{j}+\mathbf{k}$.   **23.** This is impossible.

Section 12.4

1. $yz\mathbf{i} + xz\mathbf{j} + xy\mathbf{k}$; $\mathbf{i}+\mathbf{j}+\mathbf{k}$; $\sqrt{3}$ and $-\sqrt{3}$
3. $(2y+e^z)\mathbf{i} + 2x\mathbf{j} + xe^z\mathbf{k}$; $(2+e^6)\mathbf{i} - 4\mathbf{j} - 2e^6\mathbf{k}$, $\sqrt{20+4e^6+5e^{12}}$ and $-\sqrt{20+4e^6+5e^{12}}$
5. $2y\sinh(2xy)\mathbf{i} + 2x\sinh(2xy)\mathbf{j} - \cosh(z)\mathbf{k}$; $-\cosh(1)\mathbf{k}$; $\cosh(1)$ and $-\cosh(1)$
7. $\dfrac{1}{\sqrt{3}}(8y^2 - z + 16xy - x)$ **9.** $\dfrac{1}{\sqrt{5}}(2x^2z^3 + 3x^2yz^2)$
11. $x+y+\sqrt{2}z = 4$; $x = y = 1+2t$, $z = \sqrt{2}(1+2t)$ **13.** $x = y$; $x = 1+2t$, $y = 1-2t$, $z = 0$
15. $x = 1$; $x = 1+2t$, $y = \pi$, $z = 1$ **17.** $\cos^{-1}(45/\sqrt{10653}) \approx 1.11966$ rad
19. $\cos^{-1}(1/\sqrt{2})$, or $\pi/4$ rad   **21.** Level surfaces are planes $x+z = k$. The streamlines of $\nabla\varphi$ are parallel to $\nabla\varphi$.

Section 12.5

In 1, 3, and 5, $\nabla \cdot \mathbf{F}$ is given first, then $\nabla \times \mathbf{F}$.
1. 4, $\mathbf{O}$ **3.** $2y + xe^y + 2$; $(e^y - 2x)\mathbf{k}$ **5.** $2(x+y+z)$; $\mathbf{O}$
In 7, 9, and 11, $\nabla\varphi$ is given.
7. $\mathbf{i}-\mathbf{j}+4z\mathbf{k}$ **9.** $-6x^2yz^2\mathbf{i} - 2x^3z^2\mathbf{j} - 4x^3yz\mathbf{k}$
11. $[\cos(x+y+z) - x\sin(x+y+z)]\mathbf{i} - x\sin(x+y+z)\mathbf{j} - x\sin(x+y+z)\mathbf{k}$
13. $\nabla\cdot(\varphi\mathbf{F}) = \nabla\varphi\cdot\mathbf{F} + \varphi\nabla\cdot\mathbf{F}$; $\nabla\times(\varphi\mathbf{F}) = \nabla\varphi\times\mathbf{F} + \varphi\nabla\times\mathbf{F}$
15. *Hint:* Let $\mathbf{F} = f_1\mathbf{i}+f_2\mathbf{j}+f_3\mathbf{k}$ and $\mathbf{G} = g_1\mathbf{i}+g_2\mathbf{j}+g_3\mathbf{k}$ and compute both sides of the proposed identity.

CHAPTER 13

Section 13.1

1. 0 **3.** $\frac{26}{3}\sqrt{2}$ **5.** $\sin(3) - \frac{81}{2}$ **7.** 0 **9.** $-\frac{422}{5}$ **11.** $48\sqrt{2}$ **13.** $-12e^4 + 4e^2$
15. $\sqrt{14}[\cos(1) - \cos(3)]$ **17.** $-\frac{27}{2}$

Section 13.2

1. -8 **3.** -12 **5.** -40 **7.** 512π **9.** 0 **11.** $\frac{95}{4}$

Section 13.2.1

1. 0   **3.** 2π if C encloses the origin, 0 if C does not.   **5.** 0

Section 13.3

1. Conservative; $\varphi(x, y) = xy^3 - 4y$.   **3.** Conservative; $\varphi(x, y) = 8x^2 + 2y - \frac{1}{3}y^3$.

5. Conservative; $\varphi(x, y) = \ln(x^2 + y^2)$.   **7.** Conservative; $\varphi(x, y) = e^y \sin(2x) - \frac{1}{2}y^2$.

9. -27 **11.** $5 + \ln(3/2)$ **13.** -5 **15.** $e^3 - 24e - 9e^{-1}$

Section 13.4

1. $125\sqrt{2}$ **3.** $\frac{\pi}{6}[(29)^{3/2} - 27]$ **5.** $\frac{28\pi}{3}\sqrt{2}$ **7.** $\frac{9}{8}[\ln(4 + \sqrt{17} + 4\sqrt{17})]$ **9.** $-10\sqrt{3}$

Section 13.5

1. $\frac{49}{12}$; $\left(\frac{12}{35}, \frac{33}{35}, \frac{24}{35}\right)$ **3.** $9\pi\sqrt{2}$; $(0, 0, 2)$ **5.** 78π; $\left(0, 0, \frac{27}{13}\right)$ **7.** 32

Section 13.6

1. *Hint:* Apply Green's theorem to $\oint_c -\varphi \dfrac{\partial \psi}{\partial y}\, dx + \varphi \dfrac{\partial \psi}{\partial x}\, dy$.

3. *Hint:* The unit tangent to C is $x'(s)\mathbf{i} + y'(s)\mathbf{j}$. Show that the unit outer normal is $\mathbf{N} = y'(s)\mathbf{i} - x'(s)\mathbf{j}$. Then $D_{\mathbf{N}}\varphi(x, y) = \nabla\varphi \cdot \mathbf{N} = \dfrac{\partial \varphi}{\partial x}\dfrac{dy}{ds} - \dfrac{\partial \varphi}{\partial y}\dfrac{dx}{ds}$. But then $D_{\mathbf{N}}\varphi(x, y)\,ds = -\dfrac{\partial \varphi}{\partial y}\, dx + \dfrac{\partial \varphi}{\partial x}\, dy$. Now apply Green's theorem to $\oint_c -\dfrac{\partial \varphi}{\partial y}\, dx + \dfrac{\partial \varphi}{\partial x}\, dy$.

Section 13.7

1. $\frac{256}{3}\pi$ **3.** 0   **5.** $\frac{8}{3}\pi$ **7.** 2π **9.** 0 because $\nabla \cdot (\nabla \times \mathbf{F}) = 0$.

Section 13.8

1. -8π **3.** -16π **5.** $-\frac{32}{3}$ **7.** -108 **9.** $\varphi(x, y) = x - 2y + z$ **11.** Not conservative.   **13.** Not conservative.

15. -403 **17.** $2e^{-2}$ **19.** 71

CHAPTER 14

Section 14.1

1. Graphs of the second, third, and fourth partial sums are shown below.

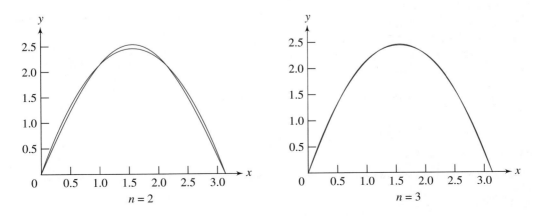

$n = 2$ $n = 3$

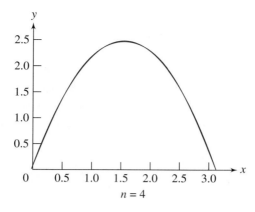

$n = 4$

Section 14.2

1. 4   **3.** $\dfrac{1}{\pi}\sinh(\pi) + \dfrac{2}{\pi}\sinh(\pi)\displaystyle\sum_{n=1}^{\infty}\dfrac{(-1)^n}{n^2+1}\cos(n\pi x)$ **5.** $\dfrac{16}{\pi}\displaystyle\sum_{n=1}^{\infty}\dfrac{1}{2n-1}\sin((2n-1)x)$

7. $\dfrac{13}{3} + \displaystyle\sum_{n=1}^{\infty}(-1)^n\left[\dfrac{16}{n^2\pi^2}\cos\left(\dfrac{n\pi x}{2}\right) + \dfrac{4}{n\pi}\sin\left(\dfrac{n\pi x}{2}\right)\right]$ **9.** $\dfrac{3}{2} + \dfrac{2}{\pi}\displaystyle\sum_{n=1}^{\infty}\dfrac{1}{2n-1}\sin((2n-1)x)$

11. $\dfrac{1}{3}\sin(3) + 6\sin(3)\displaystyle\sum_{n=1}^{\infty}\dfrac{(-1)^n}{n^2\pi^2-9}\cos\left(\dfrac{n\pi x}{3}\right)$ **13.** The Fourier coefficients of f and g are the same.

Section 14.3

1. The Fourier series is $\dfrac{11}{18} + \displaystyle\sum_{n=1}^{\infty}\left\{\dfrac{1}{n\pi}\left[4\sin\left(\dfrac{2n\pi}{3}\right) - \sin\left(\dfrac{n\pi}{3}\right)\right] + \dfrac{6}{n^2\pi^2}\left[\cos\left(\dfrac{2n\pi}{3}\right) - \cos\left(\dfrac{n\pi}{3}\right) + 2(-1)^n\right] + \right.$

$\left. \dfrac{18}{n^3\pi^3}\sin\left(\dfrac{n\pi}{3}\right)\right\}\cos\left(\dfrac{n\pi x}{3}\right) + \displaystyle\sum_{n=1}^{\infty}\left\{\dfrac{1}{n\pi}\left[4\cos\left(\dfrac{2n\pi}{3}\right) + \cos\left(\dfrac{n\pi}{3}\right) - 15(-1)^n\right] - \dfrac{6}{n^2\pi^2}\left[\sin\left(\dfrac{2n\pi}{3}\right) + \sin\left(\dfrac{n\pi}{3}\right)\right]\right.$

$\left. -\dfrac{18}{n^3\pi^3}\left[\cos\left(\dfrac{n\pi}{3}\right) - (-1)^n\right]\right\}\sin\left(\dfrac{n\pi x}{3}\right)$; this series converges to $\frac{3}{2}$ if $x=3$ or if $x=-3$, to $2x$ if $-3<x<-2$, to -2 if $x=-2$, to 0 if $-2<x<1$, to $\frac{1}{2}$ if $x=1$, and to x^2 if $1<x<3$.

3. Let $\alpha_n = n\pi/3$. The Fourier series is $\dfrac{11}{3}\sinh(3) - 2\cosh(3) + \displaystyle\sum_{n=1}^{\infty}(-1)^n\left\{\sinh(3)\left[\dfrac{1}{1+\alpha_n^2} + \dfrac{4(1-3\alpha_n^2)}{3(1+\alpha_n^2)^3}\right] + \right.$

$\left.\dfrac{4(\alpha_n^2-1)\cosh(3)}{(1+\alpha_n^2)^2}\right\}\cos(\alpha_n x) + \displaystyle\sum_{n=1}^{\infty}(-1)^n\left\{\sinh(3)\left[\dfrac{6\alpha_n}{1+\alpha_n^2} + \dfrac{4\alpha_n(\alpha_n^2-3)}{3(1+\alpha_n^2)^2}\right] - \dfrac{8\alpha_n\cosh(3)}{(1+\alpha_n^2)^2}\right\}\sin(\alpha_n x)$; this

converges to $18\cosh(3)$ if $x=-3$ or $x=3$, and to $x^2 e^{-x}$ if $-3<x<3$.

5. $\dfrac{6+\pi^2}{6} + 2\displaystyle\sum_{n=1}^{\infty}\dfrac{(-1)^n}{n^2}\cos(nx) + \dfrac{1}{\pi}\displaystyle\sum_{n=1}^{\infty}\left[\left(\dfrac{2}{n^3}+\dfrac{2}{n}\right)(1-(-1)^n) + \dfrac{\pi^2}{n}(-1)^n\right]\sin(nx)$; this converges to $\frac{1}{2}(\pi^2+2)$ for $x=\pi$ or $x=-\pi$, to x^2 if $-\pi<x<0$, to 1 if $x=0$, and to 2 if $0<x<\pi$.

7. $\dfrac{4}{\pi}\displaystyle\sum_{n=1}^{\infty}\dfrac{1}{2n-1}\sin\left(\dfrac{(2n-1)\pi x}{4}\right)$; converges to -1 if $-4<x<0$, to 0 if $x=-4$, 0 or 4, and to 1 if $0<x<4$.

9. $\dfrac{1-e^{-\pi}}{\pi} + \dfrac{2}{\pi}\displaystyle\sum_{n=1}^{\infty}\dfrac{1-(-1)^n e^{-\pi}}{n^2+1}\cos(nx)$; converges to $e^{-|x|}$ for $-\pi \le x \le \pi$.

12. $-\pi^2/12$

Section 14.4

1. cosine series: 4 (this function is its own Fourier cosine expansion), converging to 4 for $0 \le x \le 3$; sine series: $\dfrac{16}{\pi}\displaystyle\sum_{n=1}^{\infty}\dfrac{1}{2n-1}\sin\left(\dfrac{(2n-1)\pi x}{3}\right)$, converging to 0 if $x=0$ or $x=3$, and to 4 for $0<x<3$

3. cosine series: $\dfrac{1}{2}\cos(x) - \dfrac{2}{\pi}\sum_{n=1}^{\infty}\dfrac{(-1)^n(2n-1)}{(2n-3)(2n+1)}\cos\left(\dfrac{(2n-1)x}{2}\right)$, converging to 0 if $0 \le x < \pi$ or $x = 2\pi$, to $-\dfrac{1}{2}$

if $x = \pi$, and to $\cos(x)$ if $\pi < x < 2\pi$; sine series: $\dfrac{2}{\pi}\sum_{n=1}^{\infty}\dfrac{(-1)^n(2n-1)}{(2n-3)(2n+1)}\sin\left(\dfrac{(2n-1)x}{2}\right) - \dfrac{2}{\pi}\sum_{n=2}^{\infty}\dfrac{n}{n-1}\sin(nx)$,

converging to 0 if $0 \le x < \pi$ or $x = 2\pi$, to $-\dfrac{1}{2}$ if $x = \pi$, and to $\cos(x)$ if $\pi < x < 2\pi$

5. cosine series: $\dfrac{4}{3} + \dfrac{16}{\pi^2}\sum_{n=1}^{\infty}\dfrac{(-1)^n}{n^2}\cos\left(\dfrac{n\pi x}{2}\right)$, converging to x^2 for $0 \le x \le 2$; sine series:

$-\dfrac{8}{\pi}\sum_{n=1}^{\infty}\left[\dfrac{(-1)^n}{n} + \dfrac{2(1-(-1)^n)}{n^3\pi^2}\right]\sin\left(\dfrac{n\pi x}{2}\right)$, converging to x^2 for $0 \le x < 2$ and to 0 for $x = 2$

7. cosine series: $\dfrac{1}{2} + \sum_{n=1}^{\infty}\left[\dfrac{4}{n\pi}\sin\left(\dfrac{2n\pi}{3}\right) + \dfrac{12}{n^2\pi^2}\cos\left(\dfrac{2n\pi}{3}\right) - \dfrac{6}{n^2\pi^2}(1+(-1)^n)\right]\cos\left(\dfrac{n\pi x}{3}\right)$, converging to x if

$0 \le x < 2$, to 1 if $x = 2$, and to $2 - x$ if $2 < x \le 3$; sine series:

$\sum_{n=1}^{\infty}\left[\dfrac{12}{n^2\pi^2}\sin\left(\dfrac{2n\pi}{3}\right) - \dfrac{4}{n\pi}\cos\left(\dfrac{2n\pi}{3}\right) + \dfrac{2}{n\pi}(-1)^n\right]\sin\left(\dfrac{n\pi x}{3}\right)$, converging to x if $0 \le x < 2$, to 1 if $x = 2$, to

$2 - x$ if $2 < x < 3$, and to 0 if $x = 3$

9. cosine series: $\dfrac{5}{6} + \dfrac{16}{\pi^2}\sum_{n=1}^{\infty}\left[\dfrac{1}{n^2}\cos\left(\dfrac{n\pi}{4}\right) - \dfrac{4}{n^3\pi}\sin\left(\dfrac{n\pi}{4}\right)\right]\cos\left(\dfrac{n\pi x}{4}\right)$, converging to x^2 if $0 \le x \le 1$, and to 1 if

$1 < x \le 4$; sine series: $\sum_{n=1}^{\infty}\left[\dfrac{16}{n^2\pi^2}\sin\left(\dfrac{n\pi}{4}\right) + \dfrac{64}{n^3\pi^3}\left(\cos\left(\dfrac{n\pi}{4}\right) - 1\right) - \dfrac{2(-1)^n}{n\pi}\right]\sin\left(\dfrac{n\pi x}{4}\right)$, converging to x^2 if

$0 \le x \le 1$, to 1 if $1 < x \le 4$, and to 0 if $x = 4$

11. Let $g(x) = \dfrac{1}{2}(f(x) + f(-x))$ and $h(x) = \dfrac{1}{2}(f(x) - f(-x))$. Then g is even and h is odd, and $f(x) = g(x) + h(x)$.

13. $\dfrac{1}{2} - \dfrac{\pi}{4}$

Section 14.5

3. (a) The Fourier series of f on $[-\pi, \pi]$ is $\dfrac{1}{4}\pi + \sum_{n=1}^{\infty}\left[\dfrac{(-1)^n - 1}{\pi n^2}\cos(nx) + \dfrac{(-1)^{n+1}}{n}\sin(nx)\right]$. This series converges

to 0 for $-\pi < x < 0$, to x for $0 < x < \pi$, and to $\dfrac{1}{2}(f(0+) + f(0-))$, or 0, at $x = 0$.

(b) f is continuous, hence piecewise continuous on $[-\pi, \pi]$. By Theorem 14.5, its Fourier series can be integrated term-by-term to yield the integral of the sum of the Fourier series.

(c) First, $\displaystyle\int_{-\pi}^{x} f(t)\,dt = \begin{cases} 0 & \text{if } -\pi \le x \le 0 \\ \frac{1}{2}x^2 & \text{if } 0 < x \le \pi \end{cases}$.

This function is represented by the series obtained by integrating the Fourier series term-by-term from $-\pi$ to x to

obtain: $\dfrac{1}{4}x\pi + \dfrac{1}{4}\pi^2 + \sum_{n=1}^{\infty}\left[\dfrac{(-1)^n - 1}{\pi n^2}\dfrac{1}{n}\sin(nx) + \dfrac{(-1)^{n+1}}{n}\dfrac{1}{n}(-\cos(nx) + (-1)^n)\right]$.

5. (a) For $-\pi \le x \le \pi$, $x\sin(x) = \pi - \dfrac{1}{2}\pi\cos(x) + 2\pi\sum_{n=2}^{\infty}\dfrac{(-1)^{n+1}}{n^2-1}\cos(nx)$.

(b) f is continuous with continuous first and second derivatives on $[-\pi, \pi]$, and $f(-\pi) = f(\pi)$. Theorem 14.6 gives

us $x\cos(x) + \sin(x) = \dfrac{1}{2}\pi\sin(x) + 2\pi\sum_{n=2}^{\infty}\dfrac{(-1)^n}{n^2-1}n\sin(nx)$ for $-\pi < x < \pi$.

(c) The Fourier series of $x\cos(x) + \sin(x)$ on $[-\pi, \pi]$ is $\dfrac{1}{2}\pi\sin(x) + \sum_{n=2}^{\infty}2n(-1)^n\pi\dfrac{1}{n^2-1}\sin(nx)$.

Section 14.6

3. *Hint:* Write the definition of $f'(x+p)$ and use the periodicity of f.   **5.** $1 - \dfrac{2}{\pi}\sum_{n=1}^{\infty}\dfrac{1}{n}\cos\left(n\pi x - \dfrac{\pi}{2}\right)$

7. $16 + \dfrac{48}{\pi^2}\sum_{n=1}^{\infty}\dfrac{1}{\pi^2}\sqrt{1+n^2\pi^2}\cos\left(\dfrac{n\pi x}{2} + \tan^{-1}(n\pi)\right)$ **9.** $\dfrac{8}{\pi}\sum_{n=1}^{\infty}\dfrac{n}{4n^2-1}\cos\left(2n\pi x - \dfrac{\pi}{2}\right)$

11. $\dfrac{2}{\pi}\sum_{n=1}^{\infty}\dfrac{1}{n}\cos\left(n\pi x + \dfrac{\pi}{2}(-1)^n\right)$ **13.** $\dfrac{3}{2} + \dfrac{2}{\pi}\sum_{n=1}^{\infty}\dfrac{1}{2n-1}\cos\left(\dfrac{(2n-1)\pi x}{2} + \dfrac{\pi}{2}(1-(-1)^n)\right)$

15. $i(t) = \sum\limits_{n=1}^{\infty} \dfrac{120(-1)^{n+1}(10-n^2)\pi}{n^2[100n^2+(10-n^2)^2]}\cos(nt) + \dfrac{1200(-1)^{n+1}\pi}{n[100n^2+(10-n^2)^2]}\sin(nt)$

Section 14.7

1. $3 + \dfrac{3i}{\pi}\sum\limits_{n=-\infty,n\neq0}^{\infty}\dfrac{1}{n}e^{2n\pi ix/3}$ **3.** $\dfrac{3}{4} - \dfrac{1}{2\pi}\sum\limits_{n=-\infty,n\neq0}^{\infty}\dfrac{1}{n}\left[\sin\left(\dfrac{n\pi}{2}\right) + i\left(\cos\left(\dfrac{n\pi}{2}\right)-1\right)\right]e^{n\pi ix/2}$

5. $\dfrac{1}{2} + \dfrac{3i}{\pi}\sum\limits_{n=-\infty,n\neq0}^{\infty}\dfrac{1}{2n-1}e^{(2n-1)\pi ix/2}$ **7.** $\dfrac{1}{2} - \dfrac{2}{\pi^2}\sum\limits_{n=-\infty,n\neq0}^{\infty}\dfrac{1}{(2n-1)^2}e^{(2n-1)\pi ix}$

9. $f(x) = \dfrac{5}{3} + \dfrac{5}{\pi}\sum\limits_{n=-\infty,n\neq0}^{\infty}\dfrac{1}{n}\sin\left(\dfrac{n\pi}{3}\right)e^{n\pi ix/6}$ and $g(x) = \dfrac{5}{3} + \dfrac{5i}{\pi}\sum\limits_{n=-\infty,n\neq0}^{\infty}\dfrac{1}{n}\left\{\left[\cos\left(\dfrac{2n\pi}{3}\right)-1\right] - \right.$

$\left. i\sin\left(\dfrac{2n\pi}{3}\right)\right\}e^{n\pi ix/6}$. f and g have the same frequency spectra but different phase spectra.

CHAPTER 15

Section 15.1

1. $\displaystyle\int_0^{\infty}\left[\dfrac{2\sin(\pi\omega)}{\pi\omega^2} - \dfrac{2\cos(\pi\omega)}{\omega}\right]\sin(\omega x)\,d\omega$, converging to $-\dfrac{\pi}{2}$ if $x=-\pi$, to x for $-\pi < x < \pi$, to $\dfrac{\pi}{2}$ if $x=\pi$, and to 0 if $|x| > \pi$.

3. $\displaystyle\int_0^{\infty}\left(\dfrac{2}{\pi\omega}(1-\cos(\pi\omega))\right)\sin(\omega x)\,d\omega$, converging to $-\dfrac{1}{2}$ if $x=-\pi$, to -1 if $-\pi < x < 0$, to $x=0$ if $x=0$, to 1 if $0 < x < \pi$, to $\dfrac{1}{2}$ if $x=\pi$, and to 0 if $|x| > \pi$.

5. $\displaystyle\int_0^{\infty}\dfrac{1}{\pi\omega^3}[400\omega\cos(100\omega) + (20,000\omega^2 - 4)\sin(100\omega)]\cos(\omega x)\,d\omega$, converging to x^2 if $-100 < x < 100$, to 5000 if $x = \pm100$, and to 0 if $|x| > 100$.

7. $\displaystyle\int_0^{\infty}\dfrac{2}{\pi(\omega^2-1)}[-\sin(\pi\omega)\sin(2\pi\omega)\cos(\omega x) - \cos(\pi\omega)\sin(2\pi\omega)\sin(\omega x)]\,d\omega$, converging to $\sin(x)$ if $-3\pi \leq x \leq \pi$, and to 0 if $x < -3\pi$ or $x > \pi$.

9. $\displaystyle\int_0^{\infty}\dfrac{2}{\pi(1+\omega^2)}\cos(\omega x)\,d\omega$, converging to $e^{-|x|}$ for all real x.

Section 15.2

1. sine integral: $\displaystyle\int_0^{\infty}\dfrac{4}{\pi\omega^3}[10\omega\sin(10\omega) - (50\omega^2-1)\cos(10\omega) - 1]\sin(\omega x)\,d\omega$;

cosine integral: $\displaystyle\int_0^{\infty}\dfrac{4}{\pi\omega^3}[10\omega\cos(10\omega) - (50\omega^2-1)\sin(10\omega)]\cos(\omega x)\,d\omega$; both integrals converge to x^2 for $0 \leq x < 10$, to 50 if $x = 10$, and to 0 for $x > 10$.

3. sine integral: $\displaystyle\int_0^{\infty}\dfrac{2}{\pi\omega}[1+\cos(\omega) - 2\cos(4\omega)]\sin(\omega x)\,d\omega$; cosine integral: $\displaystyle\int_0^{\infty}\dfrac{2}{\pi\omega}[2\sin(4\omega) - \sin(\omega)]\cos(\omega x)\,d\omega$;

both integrals converge to 1 for $0 < x < 1$, to $\dfrac{3}{2}$ for $x=1$, to 2 for $1 < x < 4$, to 1 for $x=4$, and to 0 for $x > 4$. The cosine integral converges to 1 at $x=0$, while the sine integral converges to 0 at $x=0$.

5. sine integral: $\displaystyle\int_0^{\infty}\left\{\dfrac{2}{\pi\omega}[1+(1-2\pi)\cos(\pi\omega) - 2\cos(3\pi\omega)] + \dfrac{4}{\pi\omega^2}\sin(\pi\omega)\right\}\sin(\omega x)\,d\omega$; cosine integral:

$\displaystyle\int_0^{\infty}\left\{\dfrac{2}{\pi\omega}[(2\pi-1)\sin(\pi\omega) + 2\sin(3\pi\omega)] + \dfrac{4}{\pi\omega^2}[\cos(\pi\omega) - 1]\right\}\cos(\omega x)\,d\omega$; both integrals converge to $1+2x$ for $0 < x < \pi$, to $\dfrac{1}{2}(3+2\pi)$ for $x=\pi$, to 2 for $\pi < x < 3\pi$, to 1 for $x = 3\pi$, and to 0 for $x > 3\pi$. The sine integral converges to 0 for $x=0$, while the cosine integral converges to 1 for $x=0$.

7. sine integral: $\displaystyle\int_0^{\infty}\dfrac{2}{\pi}\left(\dfrac{\omega^3}{4+\omega^4}\right)\sin(\omega x)\,d\omega$; cosine integral: $\displaystyle\int_0^{\infty}\dfrac{2}{\pi}\left(\dfrac{2+\omega^2}{4+\omega^4}\right)\cos(\omega x)\,d\omega$; both integrals converge to $e^{-x}\cos(x)$ for $x > 0$. The cosine integral converges to 1 for $x=0$, and the sine integral converges to 0 for $x=0$.

9. sine integral: $\int_0^\infty \dfrac{2k}{\pi\omega}[1-\cos(c\omega)]\sin(\omega x)d\omega$; cosine integral: $\int_0^\infty \dfrac{2k}{\pi\omega}\sin(c\omega)\cos(\omega x)d\omega$; both integrals converge to k for $0<x<c$, to $\frac{1}{2}k$ for $x=c$, and to 0 for $x>c$. The cosine integral converges to k for $x=0$, and the sine integral to 0 for $x=0$.

11. For all x, $\int_0^\infty e^{-\omega}\cos(\omega x)d\omega = \dfrac{1}{1+x^2}$ and $\int_0^\infty e^{-\omega}\sin(\omega x)d\omega = \dfrac{x}{1+x^2}$.

Section 15.3

1. $\dfrac{i}{\pi}\int_{-\infty}^{\infty}\left(-2\omega\dfrac{(1-\omega^2)^2}{((1-\omega^2)^2+4\omega^2)^2}-8\dfrac{\omega^3}{((1-\omega^2)^2+4\omega^2)^2}\right)e^{i\omega x}d\omega$; converging to $xe^{-|x|}$ for all real x.

3. $i\int_{-\infty}^{\infty}\left(\dfrac{\sin(5\omega)}{\omega^2-\pi^2}\right)e^{i\omega x}d\omega$; converging to $\sin(\pi x)$ for $-5<x<5$, and to 0 for $|x|\ge 5$.

5. $\dfrac{1}{\pi}\int_{-\infty}^{\infty}\left[-e^{-1}\dfrac{\omega}{\omega^2+1}\sin(\omega)+e^{-1}\dfrac{1}{\omega^2+1}\cos(\omega)+\dfrac{i}{\omega^2}[\omega\cos(\omega)-\sin(\omega)]\right]e^{i\omega x}d\omega$; converging to x for $-1<x<1$, to $\frac{1}{2}(1+e^{-1})$ for $x=1$, to $\frac{1}{2}(-1+e^{-1})$ for $x=-1$, and to $e^{-|x|}$ for $|x|>1$.

7. $\dfrac{1}{2\pi}\int_{-\infty}^{\infty}\left[-\dfrac{\cos(\pi\omega/2)}{\omega^2-1}+i\dfrac{\sin(\pi\omega/2)-\omega}{\omega^2-1}+\dfrac{1-\omega\sin(\pi\omega/2)}{\omega^2-1}+i\dfrac{\omega}{\omega^2-1}\cos(\pi\omega/2)\right]e^{i\omega x}d\omega$; converging to $\cos(x)$ for $0<x<\pi/2$, to $\sin(x)$ for $-\pi/2<x<0$, to 0 for $|x|>\pi/2$, to $\frac{1}{2}$ at $x=0$, to $-\frac{1}{2}$ at $x=-\pi/2$, and to 0 at $x=\pi/2$.

9. $\dfrac{2i}{\omega}[\cos(\omega)-1]$ **11.** $-\dfrac{10}{\omega}e^{-2\omega i}\sin(\omega)$ **13.** $\dfrac{4}{1+4i\omega}e^{-(1+4i\omega)k/4}$ **15.** $\pi e^{-|\omega|}$ **17.** $\dfrac{24}{16+\omega^2}e^{2i\omega}$

19. $18\sqrt{\dfrac{2}{\pi}}e^{-8t^2}e^{-4it}$ **21.** $H(t+2)e^{-10-(5-3i)t}$ **23.** $H(t)[2e^{-3t}-e^{-2t}]$

Section 15.4

1. $\pi i[H(-\omega)e^{3\omega}-H(\omega)e^{-3\omega}]$ **3.** $\dfrac{26}{(2+i\omega)^2}$ **5.** $\dfrac{i\omega}{3+i\omega}-1$ **7.** $\dfrac{5\pi}{3}e^{-2i(\omega-3)}e^{-3|\omega-3|}$ **9.** $H(t)te^{-t}$

11. $\frac{1}{4}[1-e^{-2(t+3)}]H(t+3)-\frac{1}{4}[1-e^{-2(t-3)}]H(t-3)$ **13.** $\dfrac{3}{2\pi}e^{-4it}\left[\dfrac{1}{9+(t+2)^2}+\dfrac{1}{9+(t-2)^2}\right]$

17. 3π **19.** $\dfrac{1}{\omega^3}[50\omega^2\sin(5\omega)+20\omega\cos(5\omega)-4\sin(5\omega)]$, $t_C=0$, $t_R=\dfrac{25}{3}$

21. $e^{-4}\sin(4\omega)\dfrac{\omega}{\omega^2+1}-\dfrac{e^{-4}\cos(4\omega)-1}{\omega^2+1}+i\left([e^{-4}\cos(4\omega)-1]\dfrac{\omega}{\omega^2+1}+e^{-4}\dfrac{\sin(4\omega)}{\omega^2+1}\right)$, $t_C=2$, $t_R=\dfrac{4}{3}$

23. $-\dfrac{2}{\omega^3}[-8\omega^2\sin(2\omega)-4\omega\cos(2\omega)+2\sin(2\omega)]+2i\dfrac{1}{\omega^3}[8\omega^2\cos(2\omega)-4\omega\sin(2\omega)]$, $t_C=0$, $t_R=\dfrac{4}{3}$

Section 15.5

1. $\hat{f}_C(\omega)=\dfrac{1}{1+\omega^2}$, $\hat{f}_s(\omega)=\dfrac{\omega}{1+\omega^2}$

3. $\hat{f}_C(\omega)=\dfrac{1}{2}\left[\dfrac{\sin(K(1-\omega))}{1-\omega}+\dfrac{\sin(K(1+\omega))}{1+\omega}\right]$

$\hat{f}_s(\omega)=\dfrac{\omega}{\omega^2-1}-\dfrac{1}{2}\left[\dfrac{\cos(K(1+\omega))}{1+\omega}-\dfrac{\cos(K(1-\omega))}{1-\omega}\right]$

5. $\hat{f}_C(\omega)=\dfrac{1}{2}\left[\dfrac{1}{1+(1+\omega)^2}+\dfrac{1}{1+(1-\omega)^2}\right]$

$\hat{f}_s(\omega)=\dfrac{1}{2}\left[\dfrac{1+\omega}{1+(1+\omega)^2}-\dfrac{1-\omega}{1+(1-\omega)^2}\right]$

7. Sufficient conditions are: f'' and $f^{(3)}$ continuous on $[0,\infty)$; $f^{(4)}$ piecewise continuous on $[0,L]$ for every positive L; and $f(t)\to 0$, $f'(t)\to 0$, $f''(t)\to 0$; and $f^{(3)}(t)\to 0$ as $t\to\infty$. Also needed are $\int_0^\infty |f(t)|dt$ and $\int_0^\infty |f''(t)|dt$ convergent.

Section 15.6

1. $\dfrac{K}{n}[1-(-1)^n]$ for $n = 1, 2, \ldots$ **3.** $-\dfrac{2}{n^3}+(-1)^n\left(\dfrac{2}{n^3}-\dfrac{\pi^2}{n}\right)$ for $n = 1, 2, \ldots$

5. $\dfrac{(-1)^n n \sin(a\pi)}{a^2 - n^2}$ for $n = 1, 2, \ldots$ if a is not an integer; if $a = m$, a positive integer, then $\tilde{f}_S(n) = \begin{cases} 0 & \text{if } n \neq m \\ \pi/2 & \text{if } n = m \end{cases}$.

7. $\dfrac{n}{n^2+1}[1-(-1)^n e^{-\pi}]$ for $n = 1, 2, \ldots$ **9.** $\tilde{f}_C(n) = \begin{cases} \pi^2/2 & \text{if } n = 0 \\ [(-1)^n - 1]/n^2 & \text{if } n = 1, 2, \ldots \end{cases}$.

11. $\tilde{f}_C(0) = \dfrac{1}{4}\pi^4$, $\tilde{f}_C(n) = \dfrac{6}{n^4}+(-1)^n\left(\dfrac{3\pi^2}{n^2}-\dfrac{6}{n^4}\right)$ if $n = 1, 2, \ldots$.

13. $\dfrac{a}{a^2-n^2}[1-(-1)^n]\cos(a\pi)$ for $n = 0, 1, 2, \ldots$, if a is not an integer.

15. Write $\tilde{f}_S'(n) = \displaystyle\int_0^\pi f'(x)\sin(nx)\,dx$ and integrate by parts.

Section 15.7

1. $\mathbb{D}[u](0) = \displaystyle\sum_{j=0}^5 \cos(j) \approx -.23582$, $\mathbb{D}[u](1) = \displaystyle\sum_{j=0}^5 \cos(j)e^{-\pi ij/3} \approx 2.9369 - .42794i$,

$\mathbb{D}[u](2) = \displaystyle\sum_{j=0}^5 \cos(j)e^{-2\pi ij/3} \approx .13292 - 1.6579 \times 10^{-2}i$, $\mathbb{D}[u](3) = \displaystyle\sum_{j=0}^5 \cos(j)e^{-\pi ij} \approx 9.6238 \times 10^{-2}$,

$\mathbb{D}[u](4) = \displaystyle\sum_{j=0}^5 \cos(j)e^{-4\pi ij/3} \approx .13292 + 1.6579 \times 10^{-2}i$, $\mathbb{D}[u](-1) = \displaystyle\sum_{j=0}^5 \cos(j)e^{\pi ij/3} \approx 2.9369 + .42794i$,

$\mathbb{D}[u](-2) = \displaystyle\sum_{j=0}^5 \cos(j)e^{2\pi ij/3} \approx .13292 + 1.6579 \times 10^{-2}i$, $\mathbb{D}[u](-3) = \displaystyle\sum_{j=0}^5 \cos(j)e^{\pi ij} \approx 9.6238 \times 10^{-2}$,

$\mathbb{D}[u](-4) = \displaystyle\sum_{j=0}^5 \cos(j)e^{4\pi ij/3} \approx .13292 - 1.6579 \times 10^{-2}i$

3. $\mathbb{D}[u](0) = \displaystyle\sum_{j=0}^5 \dfrac{1}{j+1} = 2.45$, $\mathbb{D}[u](1) = \displaystyle\sum_{j=0}^5 \dfrac{1}{j+1}e^{-\pi ij/3} \approx .81667 - .40415i$, $\mathbb{D}[u](2) \approx .65 - .17321i$,

$\mathbb{D}[u](3) \approx .61667$, $\mathbb{D}[u](4) \approx .65 + .17321i$, $\mathbb{D}[u](-1) \approx .81667 + .40415i$, $\mathbb{D}[u](-2) \approx .65 + .17321i$,
$\mathbb{D}[u](-3) \approx .61667$, $\mathbb{D}[u](-4) \approx .65 - .17321i$

5. $\mathbb{D}[u](0) = 55$, $\mathbb{D}[u](1) \approx -6.0 + 31.177i$, $\mathbb{D}[u](2) \approx -14.0 + 10.392i$, $\mathbb{D}[u](3) = 15$, $\mathbb{D}[u](4) \approx -14.0 - 10.392i$,
$\mathbb{D}[u](-1) \approx -6.0 - 31.177i$, $\mathbb{D}[u](-2) \approx -14.0 - 10.392i$, $\mathbb{D}[u](-3) \approx -15$, $\mathbb{D}[u](-4) \approx -14.0 + 10.392i$

7. The inverse is $\{u_j\}_{j=0}^5$, where $u_0 = \dfrac{1}{6}\displaystyle\sum_{k=0}^5 (1+i)^k \approx -1.3333 + .16667i$, $u_1 = \dfrac{1}{6}\displaystyle\sum_{k=0}^5 (1+i)^k e^{\pi ik/3} \approx -.42703$
$+ .54904i$, $u_2 \approx -1.6346 \times 10^{-2} + .561i$, $u_3 \approx .33333 + .5i$, $u_4 \approx .84968 + .27233i$, and $u_5 \approx 1.5937 - 2.049i$

9. $u_0 = \dfrac{1}{7}\displaystyle\sum_{k=0}^6 e^{-ik} \approx .10348 + 1.4751 \times 10^{-2}i$, $u_1 = \dfrac{1}{7}\displaystyle\sum_{k=0}^6 e^{-ik}e^{2\pi ik/7} \approx .93331 - .29609i$,

$u_2 \approx -9.4163 \times 10^{-2} + 8.8785 \times 10^{-2}i$, $u_3 \approx -2.3947 \times 10^{-2} + 6.2482 \times 10^{-2}i$,
$u_4 \approx 4.3074 \times 10^{-3} + 5.1899 \times 10^{-2}i$, $u_5 \approx 2.5788 \times 10^{-2} + 4.3852 \times 10^{-2}i$, $u_6 \approx 5.1222 \times 10^{-2} + 3.4325 \times 10^{-2}i$

11. $u_0 \approx -.1039$, $u_1 \approx .42051 + .29456i$, $u_2 \approx .13143 + 3.1205 \times 10^{-2}i$,
$u_3 \approx .13143 - 3.1205 \times 10^{-2}i$, $u_4 \approx .42051 - .29456i$

13. The Fourier coefficients are $d_k = \dfrac{1}{2}\displaystyle\int_0^2 \cos(\xi)e^{-\pi ki\xi}\,d\xi = -\dfrac{1}{2}\dfrac{\sin(2)}{\pi^2 k^2 - 1} + \dfrac{k\pi i}{2}\dfrac{\cos(2)-1}{\pi^2 k^2 - 1}$. For the DFT

approximation, choose $N = 128$, and approximate d_k by $f_k = \dfrac{1}{128}\displaystyle\sum_{j=0}^{127} \cos(j/64)e^{-\pi ijk/64}$.

Then
$d_0 = \dfrac{1}{2}\sin(2) \approx 0.45465$, $f_0 \approx 0.46017$
$d_1 \approx -5.1259 \times 10^{-2} - .2508i$ and $f_1 \approx -4.5737 \times 10^{-2} - .25075i$
$d_2 \approx -1.1816 \times 10^{-2} - .11562i$ and $f_2 \approx -6.2931 \times 10^{-3} - .11553i$
$d_3 \approx -5.1767 \times 10^{-3} - 7.5984 \times 10^{-2}i$ and $f_3 \approx 3.4589 \times 10^{-4} - 7.5849 \times 10^{-2}i$

$d_{-1} \approx -5.1259 \times 10^{-2} + .2508i$ and $f_{-1} \approx -4.5737 \times 10^{-2} + .25075i$

$d_{-2} \approx -1.1816 \times 10^{-2} + .11562i$, $f_{-2} \approx -6.2931 \times 10^{-3} + .11553i$

$d_{-3} \approx -5.1767 \times 10^{-3} + 7.5984 \times 10^{-2}i$, $f_{-3} \approx 3.4589 \times 10^{-4} + 7.5849 \times 10^{-2}i$

15. Now, $d_k = \int_0^1 \xi^2 e^{-2\pi k i \xi} d\xi = \dfrac{1}{2\pi^2 k^2} + i \dfrac{1}{2\pi k}$ if $k \neq 0$, and $d_0 = \frac{1}{3}$. The DFT approximation is

$$f_k = \frac{1}{128} \sum_{j=0}^{127} \left(\frac{j}{128} \right)^2 e^{-\pi i j k/64}.$$

$d_0 = \frac{1}{3}$, $f_0 \approx .32944$

$d_1 \approx 5.0661 \times 10^{-2} + .15915i$, $f_1 \approx 4.6765 \times 10^{-2} + .15912i$

$d_2 \approx 1.2665 \times 10^{-2} + 7.9577 \times 10^{-2}i$, $f_2 \approx 8.7691 \times 10^{-3} + 7.9514 \times 10^{-2}i$

$d_3 \approx 5.629 \times 10^{-3} + 5.3052 \times 10^{-2}i$, $f_3 \approx 1.7329 \times 10^{-3} + 5.2956 \times 10^{-2}i$

$d_{-1} \approx 5.0661 \times 10^{-2} - .15915i$, $f_{-1} \approx 4.6765 \times 10^{-2} - .15912i$

$d_{-2} \approx 1.2665 \times 10^{-2} - 7.9577 \times 10^{-2}i$, $f_{-2} \approx 8.7691 \times 10^{-3} - 7.9514 \times 10^{-2}i$

$d_{-3} \approx 5.629 \times 10^{-3} - 5.3052 \times 10^{-2}i$, $f_{-3} \approx 1.7329 \times 10^{-3} - 5.2956 \times 10^{-2}i$

Section 15.8

1. The complex Fourier series is $2 + \displaystyle\sum_{k=-\infty, k\neq 0}^{\infty} \frac{i}{\pi k} e^{\pi i k t}$, so $S_{10}\left(\frac{1}{8}\right) = 1.0207 + 1.6653 \times 10^{-16}i$. Approximate

$$S_{10}\left(\frac{1}{8}\right) \approx \frac{1}{128} \sum_{k=-0}^{127} V_k e^{\pi i k/8}, \text{ which is } 1.0552 + 10^{-14}i;$$

$|1.0207 + 1.6653 \times 10^{-16}i - (1.0552 - 2.0983 \times 10^{-16}i)| = 0.003452.$

3. The complex Fourier series is $\displaystyle\sum_{\substack{k=-\infty \\ k\neq \pm 1}}^{\infty} \left[-\frac{1}{2} \frac{\sin(2)}{\pi^2 k^2 - 1} + \frac{i}{2} k\pi \frac{\cos(2)-1}{\pi^2 k^2 - 1} \right] e^{\pi i k t}$. Then

$$S_{10}\left(\frac{1}{8}\right) = 1.0672 - 3.4694 \times 10^{-18}i. \text{ Approximate } S_{10}\left(\frac{1}{8}\right) \approx \frac{1}{128} \sum_{k=0}^{127} V_k e^{\pi i k/8}, \text{ which works out to}$$

$1.0428 + 3.8025 \times 10^{-15}i; |1.0672 - 3.4694 \times 10^{-18}i - (1.0428 + 3.8025 \times 10^{-15}i)| = 0.002440.$

5. The complex Fourier series is $\dfrac{1}{4} + \displaystyle\sum_{k=-\infty, k\neq 0}^{\infty} \left(\frac{3}{4} \frac{1}{\pi^2 k^2} + \frac{i}{4} \frac{2k^2\pi^2 - 3}{\pi^3 k^3} \right) e^{2k\pi i t}$, and

$$S_{10}\left(\tfrac{1}{4}\right) = -7.2901 \times 10^{-4} + 1.0408 \times 10^{-17}i. \text{ Approximate } S_{10}\left(\tfrac{1}{4}\right) \approx \frac{1}{128} \sum_{k=0}^{127} V_k e^{\pi k i/2}, \text{ which works out to}$$

$3.4826 \times 10^{-3} + 9.1593 \times 10^{-16}i; |-7.2901 \times 10^{-4} + 1.0408 \times 10^{-17}i - (3.4826 \times 10^{-3} + 9.1593 \times 10^{-16}i)|$

$\approx 0.004212.$

7. $0.14386 - 0.12455i$ **9.** $-6.5056 \times 10^{-3} - 2.191 \times 10^{-3}i$.

In the graphs associated with Problems 11 and 13, the series 1 points are the actual values computed from the transform, and the series two points are the DFT approximations. In all cases the approximations can be improved by choosing N larger.

11. $\hat{f}(\omega) = \dfrac{2\omega\sin(2\omega) + \cos(2\omega) - \omega\sin(\omega) - \cos(\omega)}{\omega^2} + i\dfrac{2\omega\cos(2\omega) - \sin(2\omega) - \omega\cos(\omega) + \sin(\omega)}{\omega^2}$. Note: in the sum of equation (15.24), $11 \leq j \leq 20$ because $f(t)$ is zero outside the interval $[1,2]$. Generate the following table using $L = 4$:

k	$\hat{f}(k/4)$	DFT $\hat{f}(k/4)$	$\left|\hat{f}(k/4)\right|$	$\left|\text{DFT } \hat{f}(k/4)\right|$
1	$1.3845 - 0.5673i$	$1.3764 - 0.5714i$	1.4962	1.4903
2	$1.0579 - 1.0421i$	$1.0445 - 1.048i$	1.485	1.4796
3	$0.5761 - 1.3488i$	$0.5558 - 1.3521i$	1.4667	1.4619
4	$0.2068 - 1.4404i$	$-.0573 - 1.4372i$	1.4406	1.4383
5	$-0.5162 - 1.3098i$	$-0.5453 - 1.2959i$	1.4078	1.406
6	$-0.9483 - 0.9865i$	$-0.9749 - 0.9602i$	1.3684	1.3684
7	$-1.2108 - 0.5325i$	$-1.2288 - 0.4945i$	1.3227	1.3247
8	$-1.2708 - 0.0295i$	$-1.2751 + .0170i$	1.2711	1.2752
9	$-1.1323 + 0.4386i$	$-1.1194 + 0.4866i$	1.2143	1.2206
10	$-0.8329 + 0.7966i$	$-0.8026 + 0.8393i$	1.1525	1.1613
11	$-0.4359 + 0.9953i$	$-0.3909 + 1.0258i$	1.0866	1.0978
12	$-0.0166 + 1.0168i$	$.0374 + 1.0299i$	1.0169	1.0306

The plots below compare the (a) real parts, (b) imaginary parts, and (c) absolute values, of $\hat{f}(k/4)$ and the DFT approximations.

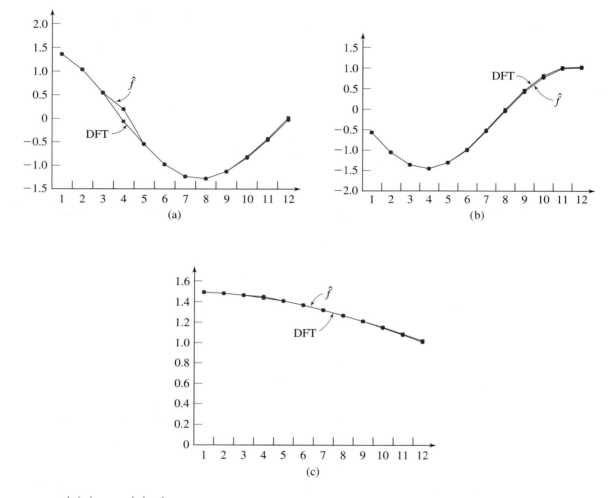

(a)

(b)

(c)

13. $\hat{f}(\omega) = \dfrac{\sin(\omega)}{\omega} + i\dfrac{\cos(\omega) - 1}{\omega}$. With $L = 4$ we obtain the following table (with j summing from 0 to 10 in equation (15.24)):

k	$\hat{f}(k/4)$	DFT $\hat{f}(k/4)$	$\left\|\hat{f}(k/4)\right\|$	$\left\|\text{DFT } \hat{f}(k/4)\right\|$
1	$.9896 - .1244i$	$1.0686 - .1318i$	.99739	1.0767
2	$.9589 - .2448i$	$1.035 - .25925i$	.98965	1.067
3	$.9089 - .3577i$	$.98047 - .37821i$	.97675	1.0509
4	$.8415 - .4597i$	$.90716 - .48489i$	.95888	1.0286
5	$.7592 - .5477i$	$.81791 - .57604i$	.93614	1.0004
6	$.6650 - .6195i$	$.71616 - .64909i$	.90885	.96654
7	$.5623 - .6733i$	$.60574 - .70222i$	.87722	.92738
8	$.4546 - .7081i$	$.49076 - .73447i$	.84147	.88334
9	$.3458 - .7236i$	$.37537 - .74574i$	.80198	.83488
10	$.2394 - .7205i$	$.26362 - .73678i$	.75923	.78252
11	$.1388 - .6997i$	$.15924 - .70914i$	.71333	.7268
12	$.0470 - .6633i$	$.0655 - .66506i$	.66496	.66828

The plots below compare the (a) real parts, (b) imaginary parts, and (c) absolute values, of $\hat{f}(k/4)$ and the DFT approximations.

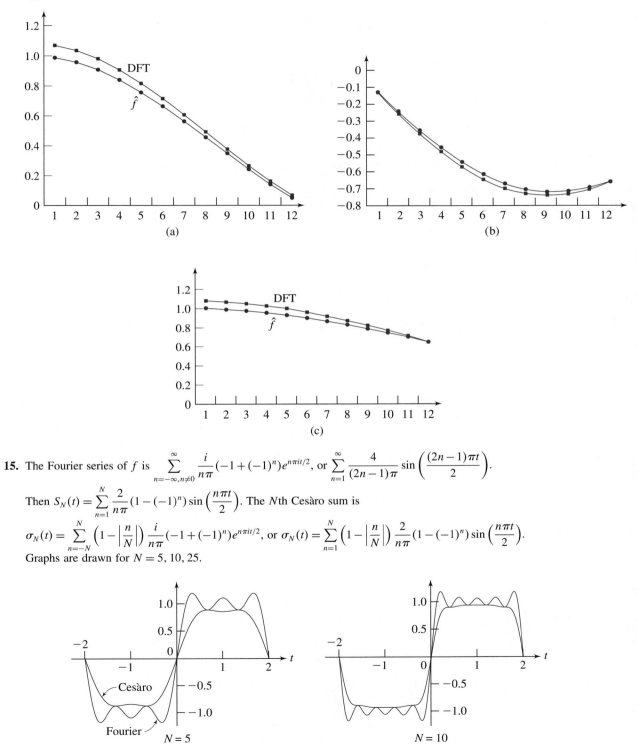

(a)

(b)

(c)

15. The Fourier series of f is $\displaystyle\sum_{n=-\infty,n\neq 0}^{\infty} \frac{i}{n\pi}(-1+(-1)^n)e^{n\pi it/2}$, or $\displaystyle\sum_{n=1}^{\infty} \frac{4}{(2n-1)\pi}\sin\left(\frac{(2n-1)\pi t}{2}\right)$.

Then $\displaystyle S_N(t)=\sum_{n=1}^{N}\frac{2}{n\pi}(1-(-1)^n)\sin\left(\frac{n\pi t}{2}\right)$. The Nth Cesàro sum is

$$\sigma_N(t)=\sum_{n=-N}^{N}\left(1-\left|\frac{n}{N}\right|\right)\frac{i}{n\pi}(-1+(-1)^n)e^{n\pi it/2}, \text{ or } \sigma_N(t)=\sum_{n=1}^{N}\left(1-\left|\frac{n}{N}\right|\right)\frac{2}{n\pi}(1-(-1)^n)\sin\left(\frac{n\pi t}{2}\right).$$

Graphs are drawn for $N=5,10,25$.

$N=5$

$N=10$

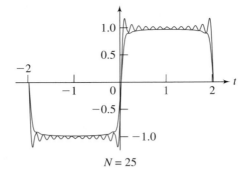

$N = 25$

17. $S_N(t) = \displaystyle\sum_{n=-N, n\neq 0}^{N} \frac{i}{n\pi}((-1)^n - \cos(n\pi/2))e^{n\pi it} = \sum_{n=1}^{N} \frac{2}{n\pi}(\cos(n\pi/2) - (-1)^n)\sin(n\pi t)$, $\sigma_N(t) =$

$\displaystyle\sum_{n=-N, n\neq 0}^{N} \left(1 - \left|\frac{n}{N}\right|\right)\frac{i}{n\pi}((-1)^n - \cos(n\pi/2))e^{n\pi it} = \sum_{n=1}^{N} \left(1 - \left|\frac{n}{N}\right|\right)\frac{2}{n\pi}(\cos(n\pi/2) - (-1)^n)\sin(n\pi t)$

Graphs are drawn for $N = 5, 10, 25$.

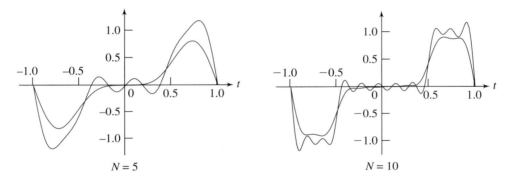

$N = 5$ $N = 10$

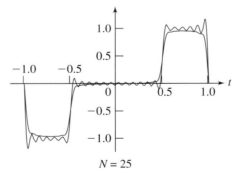

$N = 25$

19. $S_N(t) = \dfrac{17}{4} + \displaystyle\sum_{n=-N, n\neq 0}^{N} \left(\frac{1}{2}\frac{1-(-1)^n}{n^2\pi^2} + \frac{i}{n\pi}\left(1 - \frac{1}{2}(-1)^n + \frac{7}{2}((-1)^n - 1)\right)\right)e^{n\pi it}$

$= \dfrac{17}{4} + \displaystyle\sum_{n=1}^{N} \frac{1-(-1)^n}{n^2\pi^2}\cos(n\pi t) - \frac{2}{n\pi}\left(-\frac{5}{2} + 3(-1)^n\right)\sin(n\pi t),$

$\sigma_N(t) = \dfrac{17}{4} + \displaystyle\sum_{n=-N, n\neq 0}^{N} \left(1 - \left|\frac{n}{N}\right|\right)\left[\frac{1}{2}\frac{1-(-1)^n}{n^2\pi^2} + \frac{i}{n\pi}\left(1 - \frac{1}{2}(-1)^n + \frac{7}{2}[(-1)^n - 1]\right)\right]e^{n\pi it}$

$= \dfrac{17}{4} + \displaystyle\sum_{n=1}^{N} \left(1 - \left|\frac{n}{N}\right|\right)\left[\frac{1-(-1)^n}{n^2\pi^2}\cos(n\pi t) - \frac{2}{n\pi}\left(-\frac{5}{2} + 3(-1)^n\right)\sin(n\pi t)\right]$

Graphs are drawn for $N = 5, 10, 25$ (see next page).

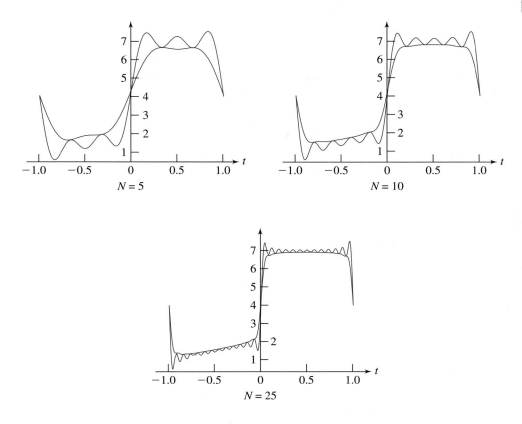

$N = 5$ $N = 10$

$N = 25$

21. $S_N(t) = 1 + \displaystyle\sum_{n=-N, n\neq 0}^{N} \frac{i}{n\pi}(3(-1)^n - 1)e^{n\pi it/2} = 1 + \sum_{n=1}^{N} \frac{-2}{n\pi}(3(-1)^n - 1)\sin(n\pi t/2)$, $\sigma_N(t) =$

$1 + \displaystyle\sum_{n=1}^{N} \frac{-2}{n\pi}\left(1 - \left|\frac{n}{N}\right|\right)(3(-1)^n - 1)\sin(n\pi t/2)$

Hamming filtered partial sum: $H_N(t) = 1 + \displaystyle\sum_{n=1}^{N} \frac{-2}{n\pi}(0.54 + 0.46\cos(\pi n/N))(3(-1)^n - 1)\sin(n\pi t/2)$

Gauss filtered partial sum: $G_N(t) = 1 + \displaystyle\sum_{n=1}^{N} -\frac{2}{n\pi}e^{-a\pi^2 n^2/N^2}(3(-1)^n - 1)\sin(n\pi t/2)$

Graphs are drawn for $N = 5, 10, 25$, with $a = \dfrac{1}{2}$ in the Gauss filter.

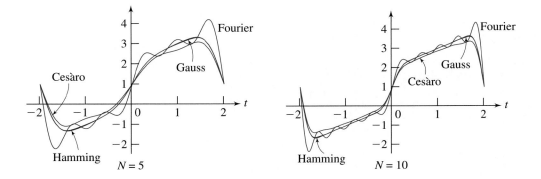

$N = 5$ $N = 10$

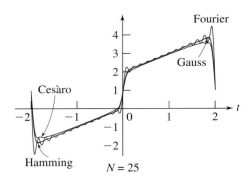

Section 15.9

1. Power spectrum of $y(t) = 4\sin(80\pi t) - \sin(20\pi t)$

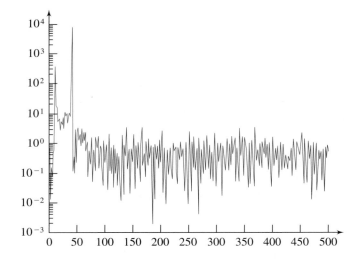

3. Power spectrum of $y(t) = 3\cos(90\pi t) - \sin(30\pi t)$

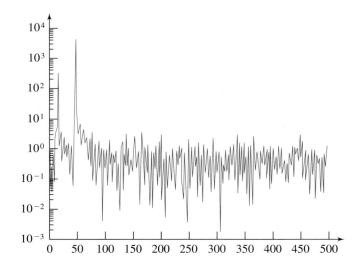

5. Corrupted signal of $y(t) = \cos(30\pi t) + \cos(70\pi t) + \cos(140\pi t)$

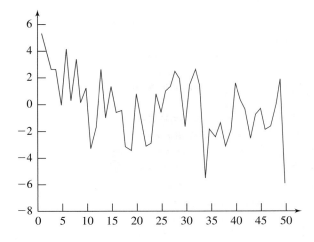

Frequency components of the corrupted signal

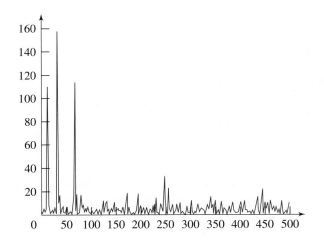

7. Corrupted signal of $y(t) = \cos(20\pi t) + \sin(140\pi t) + \cos(240\pi t)$

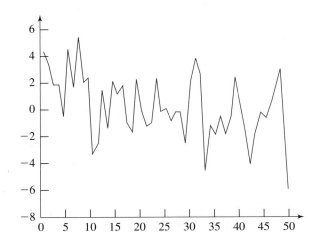

Frequency components of the corrupted signal

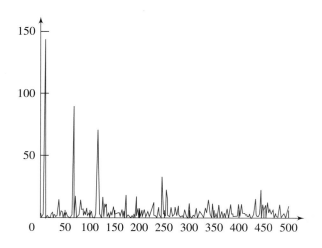

CHAPTER 16

Section 16.1

3. We will illustrate for $P_3(x)$. By Rodrigues's formula,
$$P_3(x) = \frac{1}{2^3 3!} \frac{d^3}{dx^3}((x^2-1)^3) = \frac{1}{48}(120x^3 - 72x) = \frac{1}{2}(5x^3 - 3x).$$

5. For example, with $n=3$ we have $\left[\frac{3}{2}\right] = 1$ and $\sum_{k=0}^{1}(-1)^k \frac{(6-2k)!}{8k!(3-k)!(3-2k)!}x^{3-2k} =$
$$\frac{6!}{8(3!)(3!)}x^3 - \frac{4!}{8(2!)(1!)}x = \frac{5}{2}x^3 - \frac{3}{2}x = P_3(x).$$

7. Substitute $Q(x) = P_n(x)u(x)$ in Legendre's equation. After cancellations because $P_n(x)$ is one solution, we obtain
$$u'' + \left(2\frac{P_n'}{P_n} - \frac{2x}{1-x^2}\right)u' = 0.$$ Let $v = u'$ to write $\frac{v'(x)}{v(x)} = -2\frac{P_n'(x)}{P_n(x)} + \frac{2x}{1-x^2}$. Integrate to obtain
$$\ln(v(x)) = -2\ln(P_n(x)) - \ln(1-x^2), \text{ so } v(x) = \frac{1}{P_n(x)^2(1-x^2)}.$$ Then $u(x) = \int \frac{1}{P_n(x)^2(1-x^2)}dx$ and
$Q(x) = P_n(x)u(x)$.

13. For $-1 < x < 1$, $\sin(\pi x/2) = \frac{12}{\pi^2}x + 168\frac{\pi^2-10}{\pi^4}\frac{1}{2}(5x^3-3x) + 660\frac{-112\pi^2+\pi^4+1008}{\pi^6}\frac{1}{8}(63x^5 - 70x^3 + 15x) + \cdots.$
In the graph, the sum of these terms is indistinguishable from the function.

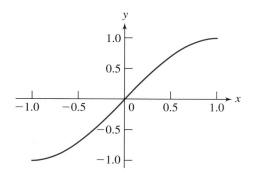

15. For $-1 < x < 1$, $\sin^2(x) = \left[-\frac{1}{2}\cos(1)\sin(1) + \frac{1}{2} \right] + \left[-\frac{5}{8}\cos(1)\sin(1) + \frac{15}{8} - \frac{15}{4}\cos^2(1) \right]\frac{1}{2}(3x^2 - 1) +$

$\left[\frac{531}{32}\cos(1)\sin(1) - \frac{585}{32} + \frac{585}{16}\cos^2(1) \right]\frac{1}{8}(35x^4 - 30x^2 + 3) + \cdots$. In the graph, the sum of these terms is indistinguishable from the function.

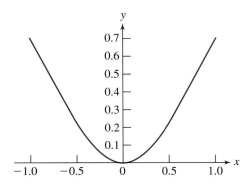

17. For $-1 < x < 0$ and for $0 < x < 1$, $f(x) = \frac{3}{2}x - \frac{7}{8}\frac{1}{2}(5x^3 - 3x) + \frac{11}{16}\frac{1}{8}(63x^5 - 70x^3 + 15x) + \cdots$. The graph below shows the function and the sum of these three terms of the Fourier–Legendre expansion.

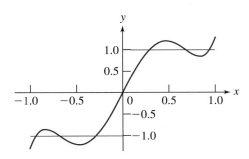

Note that in 13 and 15, just the first three terms of the eigenfunction expansion approximate the function so closely that the two graphs are virtually indistinguishable. In 17, it is clear that we must include more terms of the eigenfunction expansion to reasonably approximate $f(x)$.

Section 16.2

1. Let $y = x^a J_\nu(bx^c)$ and compute $y' = ax^{a-1}J_\nu(bx^c) + x^a bcx^{c-1}J'_\nu(bx^c)$ and
$Y'' = a(a-1)x^{a-2}J_\nu(bx^c) + [2ax^{a-1}bcx^{c-1} + x^a bc(c-1)x^{c-2}]J'_\nu(bx^c) + x^a b^2 c^2 x^{2c-2}J''_\nu(bx^c)$. Substitute these into the differential equation and simplify to get $c^2 x^{a-2}\{(bx^c)^2 J''_\nu(bx^c) + bx^c J'_\nu(bx^c) + [(bx^c)^2 - \nu^2]J_\nu(bx^c)\} = 0$.

3. $y = c_1 J_{1/3}(x_2) + c_2 J_{-1/3}(x^2)$ **5.** $y = c_1 x^{-1}J_{3/4}(2x^2) + c_2 x^{-1}J_{-3/4}(2x^2)$

7. $y = c_1 x^4 J_{3/4}(2x^3) + c_2 x^4 J_{-3/4}(2x^3)$ **9.** $y = c_1 x^{-2}J_{1/2}(3x^3) + c_2 x^{-2}J_{-1/2}(3x^3)$

11. $y_1 = c_1 J_3(\sqrt{x}) + c_2 Y_3(\sqrt{x})$ **13.** $y = c_1 J_4(2x^{1/3}) + c_2 Y_4(2x^{1/3})$

15. $y = c_1 x^{2/3}J_{1/2}(x) + c_2 x^{2/3}J_{-1/2}(x)$

17. Substitute into the differential equation and use the face that $J_{1/3}(z)$ satisfies $z^2 J''_{1/3} + zJ'_{1/3} + \left(z^2 - \frac{1}{9}\right)J_{1/3} = 0$.

19. $y = c_1 x J_2(x) + c_2 x Y_2(x)$ **21.** $y = c_1 x^2 J_2(\sqrt{x}) + c_2 x^2 Y_2(\sqrt{x})$

29. (a) The sum of the first five terms of the Fourier–Bessel expansion is
$\approx 1.67411 J_2(5.135x) - 0.77750 J_2(8.417x) + 0.8281 J_2(11.620x) - 0.6201 J_2(14.796x) + 0.6281 J_2(17.960x)$. From the graphs of x and the first five terms of this expansion, more terms would have to be included to achieve reasonable accuracy.

(c) The sum of the first five terms of the Fourier–Bessel expansion is $0.85529 J_2(5.135x) - 0.21338 J_2(8.417x)$ $+ 0.35122 J_2(11.620x) - 0.20338 J_2(14.796x) + 0.025800 J_2(17.960x)$. As the graphs indicate, more terms are needed to reasonably approximate the function by the partial sum of the Fourier–Bessel expansion.

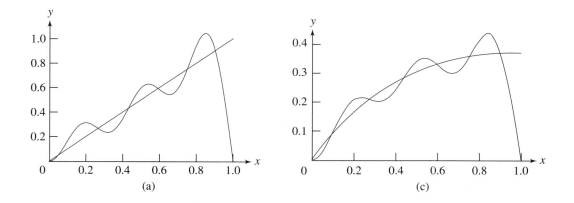

(a)   (c)

Section 16.3

1. regular problem on $[0, L]$; eigenvalues $\left(\dfrac{2n-1}{2L}\pi\right)^2$ for $n = 1, 2, \ldots$; eigenfunctions nonzero constant multiples of $\sin\left(\dfrac{2n-1}{2L}\pi x\right)$

3. regular on $[0, 4]$; $\left(\dfrac{2n-1}{2}\dfrac{\pi}{4}\right)^2$; $\cos\left(\dfrac{2n-1}{2}\dfrac{\pi}{4}x\right)$

5. periodic on $[-3\pi, 3\pi]$; 0 is an eigenvalue with eigenfunction 1; for $n = 1, 2, \ldots, \dfrac{1}{9}n^2$ is an eigenvalue with eigenfunction $a_n \cos(nx/3) + b_n \sin(nx/3)$, not both a_n and b_n zero

7. regular on $[0, 1]$; eigenvalues are positive solutions of $\tan(\sqrt{\lambda}) = \dfrac{1}{2}\sqrt{\lambda}$. There are infinitely many such solutions, of which the first four are approximately 0.43, 10.84, 40.47, and 89.82. Corresponding to an eigenvalue λ_n, eigenfunctions have the form $2\sqrt{\lambda}\cos(\sqrt{\lambda_n}x) + \sin(\sqrt{\lambda}x)$.

9. regular on $[0, \pi]$; $1 + n^2$ for $n = 1, 2, \ldots$; $e^{-x}\sin(nx)$ for $n = 1, 2, \ldots$

11. regular on $[1, e^3]$; $1 + \dfrac{n^2\pi^2}{9}$ for $n = 1, 2, \ldots$; $x^{-1}\sin\left(\dfrac{n\pi}{3}\ln(x)\right)$ for $n = 1, 2, \ldots$

13. For $0 < x < 1, 1 - x = \displaystyle\sum_{n=1}^{\infty} \dfrac{2}{n\pi}\sin(n\pi x)$. The tenth partial sum of the series is compared to the function in the graph.

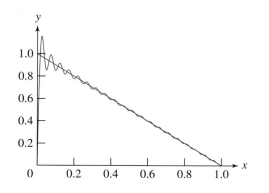

15. The expansion is $\displaystyle\sum_{n=1}^{\infty} \frac{4}{\pi} \frac{\sqrt{2}\cos(n\pi/2) - \sqrt{2}\sin(n\pi/2) - (-1)^n}{2n-1} \cos\left(\frac{2n-1}{8}\pi x\right)$. This converges to -1 for $0 < x < 2$

and 1 for $2 < x < 4$, and to 0 if $x = 2$. The tenth partial sum of the series is compared to the function in the graph.

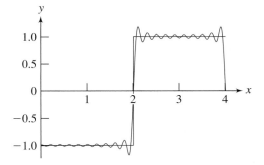

17. For $-3\pi < x < 3\pi$, $x^2 = 3\pi^2 + 36\displaystyle\sum_{n=1}^{\infty} \frac{(-1)^n}{n^2} \cos(nx/3)$. The tenth partial sum of the series is compared to the

function in the graph.

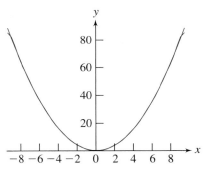

19. Normalized eigenfunctions are $\varphi_n(x) = \dfrac{1}{\sqrt{2}} \cos\left(\dfrac{2n-1}{8}\pi x\right)$. Now, $(f \cdot \varphi_n) = \displaystyle\int_0^4 x(4-x) \dfrac{1}{\sqrt{2}} \cos\left(\dfrac{2n-1}{8}\pi x\right) dx =$

$-128\sqrt{2}\dfrac{4(-1)^n + (2n-1)\pi}{\pi^3(2n-1)^3}$, so $\displaystyle\sum_{n=1}^{\infty}\left((128\sqrt{2})\dfrac{4(-1)^n + (2n-1)\pi}{\pi^3(2n-1)^3}\right)^2 \le f \cdot f = \int_0^4 x^2(4-x)^2 dx = \dfrac{512}{15}$,

or $\displaystyle\sum_{n=1}^{\infty}\left(\dfrac{4(-1)^n + (2n-1)\pi}{\pi^3(2n-1)^3}\right)^2 \le \dfrac{512}{15(128\sqrt{2})^2} = \dfrac{1}{960}$.

Section 16.4

3. The interval on which $\sigma_{1,3}(t)$ is nonzero is disjoint from the interval on which $\sigma_{-2,1}(t)$ is nonzero, so $\sigma_{1,3}(t)\sigma_{-2,1}(t)$ is identically zero, hence $\int_{-\infty}^{\infty} \sigma_{1,3}(t)\sigma_{-2,1}(t)dt = 0$. Graphs of $\sigma_{1,3}(t)$ and $\sigma_{-2,1}(t)$ are shown below.

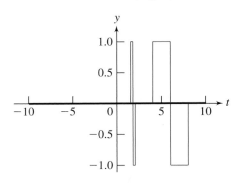

5. A graph of $\psi(2t - 3)$ is shown below.

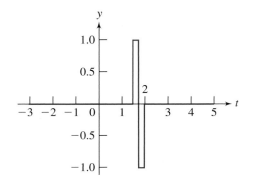

7. The Fourier series of $f(t)$ on $[-16, 16]$ is

$$\sum_{n=1}^{\infty} \left[\frac{4}{n\pi} \left(-2\sin\left(\frac{3n\pi}{4}\right) + \sin\left(\frac{n\pi}{2}\right) \right) - \frac{6}{n\pi} \left(\sin\left(\frac{n\pi}{8}\right) - 2\sin\left(\frac{3n\pi}{16}\right) + \right.$$

$$\left. \sin\left(\frac{n\pi}{4}\right) \right) \right] \cos\left(\frac{n\pi t}{16}\right) + \left[-\frac{4}{n\pi} \left(-\cos(n\pi) + 2\cos\left(\frac{3n\pi}{4}\right) - \cos\left(\frac{n\pi}{2}\right) \right) + \frac{6}{n\pi} \left(\cos\left(\frac{n\pi}{8}\right) - 2\cos\left(\frac{3n\pi}{16}\right) + \right.$$

$$\left. \cos\left(\frac{n\pi}{4}\right) \right) \right] \sin\left(\frac{n\pi t}{16}\right).$$ The graph below compares the function with the fiftieth partial sum of its Fourier series.

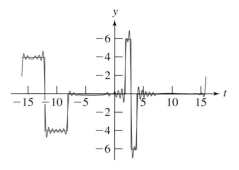

9. The Fourier series of $f(t)$ on $[-16, 16]$ is $\sum_{n=1}^{\infty} \frac{1}{n\pi} \left[-14\sin\left(\frac{n\pi}{2}\right) - 8\sin\left(\frac{n\pi}{4}\right) + 16\sin\left(\frac{3n\pi}{8}\right) \right] \cos\left(\frac{n\pi t}{16}\right) +$

$\frac{1}{n\pi} \left[3(-1)^n + 2\cos\left(\frac{n\pi}{2}\right) + 3 + 8\cos\left(\frac{n\pi}{4}\right) - 16\cos\left(\frac{3n\pi}{8}\right) \right] \sin\left(\frac{n\pi t}{16}\right).$ The graph below compares the function with the fiftieth partial sum of its Fourier series.

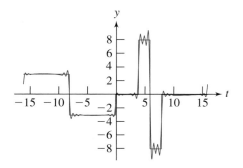

CHAPTER 17

Section 17.1

1. Compute $\dfrac{\partial^2 y}{\partial x^2} = -\dfrac{n^2\pi^2}{L^2}\sin(n\pi x/L)\cos(n\pi ct/L)$ and $\dfrac{\partial^2 y^2}{\partial t} = -\dfrac{n^2\pi^2 c^2}{L^2}\sin(n\pi x/L)\cos(n\pi ct/L)$.

3. Compute $\dfrac{\partial^2 y}{\partial x^2} = \dfrac{1}{2}[f''(x+ct)+f''(x-ct)]$ and $\dfrac{\partial^2 y}{\partial t^2} = \dfrac{1}{2}c^2[f''(x+ct)+f''(x-ct)]$.

5. The problem for the displacement function $z(x, y, t)$ is $\dfrac{\partial^2 z}{\partial t^2} = c^2\left(\dfrac{\partial^2 z}{\partial x^2}+\dfrac{\partial^2 z}{\partial y^2}\right)$ for $0 < x < a, 0 < y < b$,

$$z(x, y, 0) = f(x, y), \frac{\partial z}{\partial t}(x, y, 0) = 0 \text{ for } 0 < x < a, 0 < y < b,$$

$$z(0, y, t) = z(a, y, t) = z(x, 0, t) = z(x, b, t) = 0.$$

Section 17.2

1. $y(x, t) = \displaystyle\sum_{n=1}^{\infty} \dfrac{16(-1)^n}{(2n-1)^3\pi^3 c}\sin\left(\dfrac{(2n-1)\pi x}{2}\right)\sin\left(\dfrac{(2n-1)\pi ct}{2}\right) + \displaystyle\sum_{n=1}^{\infty}\dfrac{2(-1)^n}{n^2\pi^2 c}\sin(n\pi x)\sin(n\pi ct)$

3. $y(x, t) = \displaystyle\sum_{n=1}^{\infty}\dfrac{108}{(2n-1)^4\pi^4}\sin\left(\dfrac{(2n-1)\pi x}{3}\right)\sin\left(\dfrac{2(2n-1)\pi t}{3}\right)$

5. $y(x, t) = \displaystyle\sum_{n=1}^{\infty}\dfrac{24}{(2n-1)^2\pi}(-1)^{n+1}\sin\left(\dfrac{(2n-1)x}{2}\right)\cos\left((2n-1)\sqrt{2}t\right)$

7. $y(x, t) = \displaystyle\sum_{n=1}^{\infty}\dfrac{-32}{(2n-1)^3\pi^3}\sin\left(\dfrac{(2n-1)\pi x}{2}\right)\cos\left(\dfrac{3(2n-1)\pi t}{2}\right)$

$\quad + \displaystyle\sum_{n=1}^{\infty}\dfrac{4}{n^2\pi^2}\sin\left(\dfrac{n\pi x}{2}\right)\left[\cos\left(\dfrac{n\pi}{4}\right)-\cos\left(\dfrac{n\pi}{2}\right)\right]\sin\left(\dfrac{3n\pi t}{2}\right)$

9. Let $Y(x, t) = y(x, t) + h(x)$ and substitute into the problem to choose $h(x) = \frac{1}{9}x^3 - \frac{4}{9}x$. The problem for Y becomes

$$\frac{\partial^2 Y}{\partial t^2} = 3\frac{\partial^2 Y}{\partial x^2},$$

$$Y(0, t) = Y(2, t) = 0,$$

$$Y(x, 0) = \frac{1}{9}x^3 - \frac{4}{9}x, \frac{\partial Y}{\partial t}(x, 0) = 0.$$

We find that $Y(x, t) = \displaystyle\sum_{n=1}^{\infty}\dfrac{32}{3n^3\pi^3}(-1)^n\sin\left(\dfrac{n\pi x}{2}\right)\cos\left(\dfrac{n\pi\sqrt{3}t}{2}\right)$, and then $y(x, t) = Y(x, t) - h(x)$.

11. Let $Y(x, t) = y(x, t) + h(x)$ and choose $h(x) = \cos(x) - 1$. The problem for Y is

$$\frac{\partial^2 Y}{\partial t^2} = \frac{\partial^2 Y}{\partial x^2},$$

$$Y(0, t) = Y(2\pi, t) = 0,$$

$$Y(x, 0) = \cos(x) - 1, \frac{\partial Y}{\partial t}(x, 0) = 0.$$

This problem has solution $Y(x, t) = \displaystyle\sum_{n=1}^{\infty}\dfrac{16}{\pi}\dfrac{1}{(2n-1)[(2n-1)^2 - 4]}\sin\left(\dfrac{(2n-1)x}{2}\right)\cos\left(\dfrac{(2n-1)t}{2}\right)$, and then $y(x, t) = Y(x, t) + 1 - \cos(x)$.

13. $u(x, t) = e^{-At/2}\displaystyle\sum_{n=1}^{\infty}C_n\sin\left(\dfrac{n\pi x}{L}\right)\left[\dfrac{1}{AL}r_n\cos\left(\dfrac{r_n t}{2L}\right)+\sin\left(\dfrac{r_n t}{2L}\right)\right]$, where $C_n = \dfrac{2A}{r_n}\displaystyle\int_0^L f(x)\sin\left(\dfrac{n\pi x}{L}\right)dx$ and $r_n = \sqrt{4(BL^2 + n^2\pi^2 c^2) - A^2 L^2}$

15. (a) The solution with the forcing term is $y_f(x, t) = \sum_{n=1}^{\infty} \frac{64}{\pi^3} \left(\frac{2}{(2n-1)^3} - \frac{1}{9} \frac{1}{(2n-1)[(2n-1)^2 - 16]} \right) \sin\left(\frac{n\pi x}{4}\right)$

$\cos\left(\frac{3(2n-1)\pi t}{4}\right) + \frac{1}{9\pi^2}[\cos(\pi x) - 1]$.

(b) Without the forcing term, the solution is $y(x, t) = \sum_{n=1}^{\infty} \frac{128}{\pi^3 (2n-1)^3} \sin\left(\frac{(2n-1)\pi x}{4}\right) \cos\left(\frac{3(2n-1)\pi t}{4}\right)$.

Both solutions are graphed together for times $t = 0.5, 0.6, 4.9,$ and 9.8, using the same axes to allow comparison.

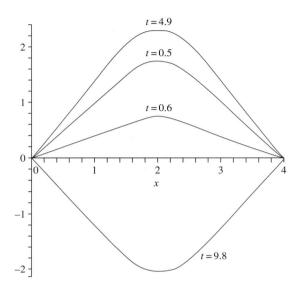

17. $y_{j,1} = 0.25$ for $j = 1, 2, \ldots, 19$
   $y_{1,2} = 0.08438$, $y_{j,2} = 0.05$ for $j = 2, 3, \ldots, 19$
   $y_{1,3} = 0.13634$, $y_{2,3} = 0.077149$, $y_{j,3} = 0.075$ for $j = 3, 4, \ldots, 19$
   $y_{1,4} = 0.17608$, $y_{2,4} = 0.10786$, $y_{3,4} = 0.10013$, $y_{j,4} = 0.1$ for $j = 4, 5, \ldots, 19$
   $y_{1,5} = 0.20055$, $y_{2,5} = 0.14235$, $y_{3,5} = 0.12574$, $y_{4,5} = 0.12501$
   $y_{j,5} = 0.125$ for $j = 5, 6, \ldots, 19$

19. We give $y_{j,k}$ for $j = 1, 2, \ldots, 9$, first for $k = -1$, then $k = 0, 1, \ldots, 5$.
   $y_{j,-1}$: $0.08075, 0.127, 0.14475, 0.14, 0.11875, 0.087, 0.05075, 0.016, -0.01125$
   $y_{j,0}$: $0.081, 0.128, 0.147, 0.144, 0.125, 0.096, 0.063, 0.032, 0.009$
   $y_{j,1}$: $0.079125, 0.1735, 0.14788, 0.147, 0.13063, 0.10475, 0.075375, 0.0485, 0.030125$
   $y_{j,2}$: $0.0057813, 00.2115, 0.77078, 0.14903, 0.13567, 0.11328, 0.087906, 0.065531, 0.050516$
   $y_{j,3}$: $-0.055066, 0.27160, 1.3199, 0.18908, 0.14015, 0.12162, 0.10062, 0.083022, 0.068688$
   $y_{j,4}$: $-0.092055, 0.3768, 1.7328, 0.29675, 0.14653, 0.12981, 0.11355, 0.10072, 0.083463$
   $y_{j,5}$: $-0.093987, 0.53745, 1.9712, 0.48652, 0.16125, 0.13803, 0.12669, 0.11814, 0.0941$

Section 17.3

1. $y(x, t) = \int_0^{\infty} \frac{10}{\pi(25 + \omega^2)} \cos(\omega x) \cos(12\omega t) d\omega$ **3.** $y(x, t) = \int_0^{\infty} \frac{-1}{2\pi\omega} \frac{\sin(\pi\omega)}{\omega^2 - 1} \sin(\omega x) \sin(4\omega t) d\omega$

5. $y(x, t) = \int_0^{\infty} \left[\left(\frac{1}{3\pi\omega} e^{-2} \frac{2\cos(\omega) - \omega\sin(\omega)}{4 + \omega^2} \right) \cos(\omega x) + \left(\frac{1}{3\pi\omega} e^{-2} \frac{\omega\cos(\omega) + 2\sin(\omega)}{4 + \omega^2} \right) \sin(\omega x) \right] \sin(3\omega t) d\omega$

7. $y(x, t) = \int_0^{\infty} \frac{2}{\pi} \frac{2 - \omega\sin(\omega) - 2\cos(\omega)}{\omega^3} \sin(\omega x) \cos(3\omega t) d\omega$

9. $y(x, t) = \int_0^\infty \frac{1}{\pi\omega} \frac{\sin(\pi\omega/2) - \sin(5\pi\omega/2)}{\omega^2 - 1} \sin(\omega x) \sin(2\omega t) d\omega$

11. $y(x, t) = \int_0^\infty -\frac{3}{7\pi\omega^5} [16\omega \cos^3(\omega) - 12\omega \cos(\omega) + 12\omega^2 \sin(\omega) \cos^2(\omega) - 3\omega^2 \sin(\omega) - 8 \sin(\omega) \cos^2(\omega)$
$+ 2 \sin(\omega) + 2\omega] \sin(\omega x) \sin(14\omega t) d\omega$

13. $y(x, t) = At + (1 - A) \left(t - \frac{x}{c}\right) H \left(t - \frac{x}{c}\right)$

Section 17.4

1. Characteristics are lines $x - t = k_1, x + t = k_2$;
$$y(x, t) = \frac{1}{2} \left[(x - t)^2 + (x + t)^2\right] + \frac{1}{2} \int_{x-t}^{x+t} -\xi \, d\xi = x^2 + t^2 - xt$$

3. Characteristics are $x - 7t = k_1, x + 7t = k_2$;
$$y(x, t) = \frac{1}{2} [\cos(\pi(x - 7t)) + \cos(\pi(x + 7t))] + t - x^2 t - \frac{49}{3} t^3$$

5. Characteristics are $x - 14t = k_1, x + 14t = k_2$;
$y(x, t) = \frac{1}{2} [e^{x-14t} + e^{x+14t}] + xt$

7. $y(x, t) = x + \frac{1}{8} (e^{-x+4t} - e^{-x-4t}) + \frac{1}{2} xt^2 + \frac{1}{6} t^3$

9. $y(x, t) = x^2 + 64t^2 - x + \frac{1}{32} (\sin(2(x + 8t)) - \sin(2(x - 8t))) + \frac{1}{12} t^4 x$

11. $y(x, t) = \frac{1}{2} [\cosh(x - 3t) + \cosh(x + 3t)] + t + \frac{1}{4} xt^4$

In each of 13, 15, and 17, the graphs show a progression of the motion as a sum of forward and backward waves.

13.

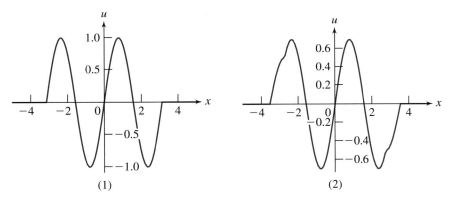

(1)   (2)

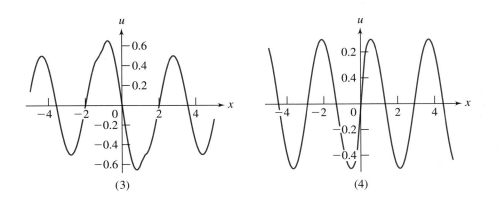

(3)   (4)

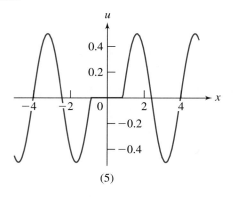

(5)

15.

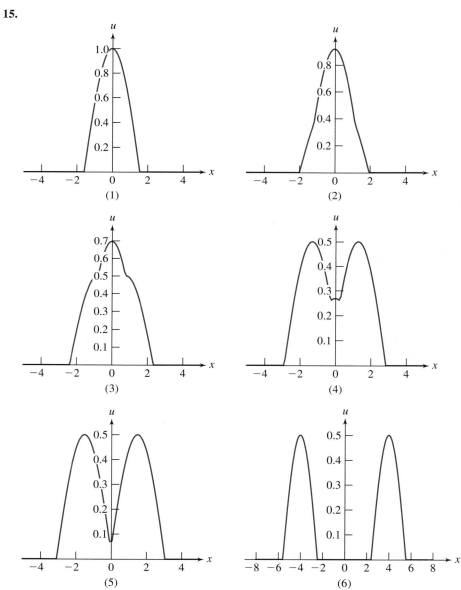

(1)

(2)

(3)

(4)

(5)

(6)

17.

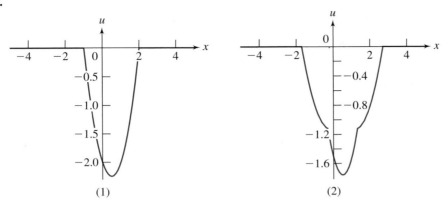

(1)   (2)

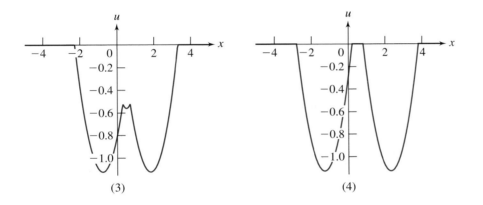

(3)   (4)

Section 17.5

1. We find that (approximately) $a_1 = \dfrac{2 \int_0^1 x J_0(2.405x)\,dx}{[J_1(2.405)]^2} = 2\dfrac{0.1057}{0.2695} = 0.78442$, $a_2 = 0.04112$, $a_3 = -8.1366$, $a_4 = -375.2$, $a_5 = -6470.9$. The fifth partial sum of the series gives the approximation $z(r,t) \approx$
$0.78442 J_0(2.405r)\cos(2.405t) + 0.04112 J_0(5.520r)\cos(5.520t) - 8.1366 J_0(8.654r)\cos(8.654t) -$
$375.2 J_0(11.792r)\cos(11.792t) - 6470.9 J_0(14.931r)\cos(14.931t)$.
The graph below shows $z(r,t)$ at various times.

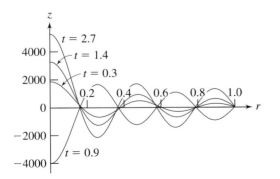

3. Approximately, $z(r, t) \approx 1.2534 J_0(2.405r) \cos(2.405t) - 0.88824 J_0(5.520r) \cos(5.520t) - 24.89 J_0(8.654r) \cos(8.654t) - 1133.6 J_0(11.792r) \cos(11.792t) - 19523 J_0(14.931r) \cos(14.931t)$. The graph below shows $z(r, t)$ at selected times.

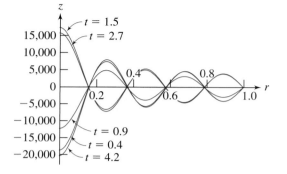

Section 17.6

1. Compute

$$\frac{1}{2}\alpha_0(r) = \frac{1}{2\pi} \int_{-\pi}^{\pi} (4 - r^2) \sin^2(\theta) d\theta = \frac{1}{2}(4 - r^2)$$

$$\alpha_n(r) = \frac{4 - r^2}{\pi} \int_{-\pi}^{\pi} \sin^2(\theta) \cos(n\theta) d\theta = \begin{cases} 0 & \text{if } n \neq 2 \\ \dfrac{4 - r^2}{\pi} \left(-\dfrac{1}{2}\pi\right) & \text{if } n = 2 \end{cases}$$

$$\beta_n(r) = \frac{4 - r^2}{\pi} \int_{-\pi}^{\pi} \sin^2(\theta) \sin(n\theta) d\theta = 0.$$

Thus, $\quad z(r, \theta, t) = \displaystyle\sum_{k=1}^{\infty} \frac{2}{[J_1(j_{0k})]^2} \left(\int_0^1 \xi(1 - \xi^2) J_0(j_{0k}\xi) d\xi \right) J_0\left(\frac{1}{2} j_{0k} r\right) \cos(j_{0k} t)$

$$+ \sum_{k=1}^{\infty} \frac{4}{[J_3(j_{2k})]^2} \left(\int_0^1 \xi(\xi^2 - 1) J_2(j_{2k}\xi) d\xi \right) J_2\left(\frac{1}{2} j_{2k} r\right) \cos(2\theta) \cos(j_{2k} t)$$

$$+ \sum_{p=1}^{\infty} \sin(p\theta) \sum_{q=1}^{\infty} \frac{4(-1)^{p+1}}{p j_{pq} [J_{p+1}(j_{pq})]^2} \int_0^1 \xi J_p(j_{pq}\xi) d\xi) J_\theta\left(\frac{1}{2} j_{pq} r\right) \sin(j_{pq} t)$$

$$\approx 1.1081 J_0(1.2025r) \cos(2.40483t) - 0.13975 J_0(2.760r) \cos(5.52008t)$$

$$+ 0.4555 J_0(4.3270r) \cos(8.65373t) - 0.02105 J_0(5.8960r) \cos(11.7915t)$$

$$+ 0.01165 J_0(7.4655r) \cos(14.43092t) + \cdots - 2.9777 J_2(2.5675r) \cos(2\theta) \cos(5.1356t)$$

$$- 1.4035 J_2(4.2085r) \cos(2\theta) \cos(8.41724t) - 1.1405 J_2(5.8100r) \cos(2\theta) \cos(11.6198t)$$

$$- 0.83271 J_2(7.398r) \cos(2\theta) \cos(14.7960t) - \cdots .$$

Section 17.7

1. $z(x, y, t) = \dfrac{1}{\pi} \displaystyle\sum_{n=1}^{\infty} \left[\dfrac{8(-1)^{n+1} \pi^2}{n} + \dfrac{16}{n^3}[(-1)^n - 1] \right] \sin\left(\dfrac{nx}{2}\right) \sin(y) \cos\left(\dfrac{1}{2}\sqrt{n^2 + 4t}\right)$

3. $z(x, y, t) = \sum\limits_{n=1}^{\infty} \sum\limits_{m=1}^{\infty} \left[\dfrac{16}{\pi^2(2n-1)(2m-1)\sqrt{(2n-1)^2+(2m-1)^2}} \right] \cos\left(\dfrac{(2n-1)x}{2}\right) \sin\left(\dfrac{(2m-1)x}{2}\right)$

$\times \sin\left(\sqrt{(2n-1)^2+(2m-1)^2}\, t\right)$

CHAPTER 18

Section 18.1

1. $\dfrac{\partial u}{\partial t} = k \dfrac{\partial^2 u}{\partial x^2}$ for $0 < x < L, t > 0$; $u(0, t) = \dfrac{\partial u}{\partial x}(L, t) = 0$ for $t \geq 0$; $u(x, 0) = f(x)$ for $0 \leq x \leq L$.

3. $\dfrac{\partial u}{\partial t} = k \dfrac{\partial^2 u}{\partial x^2}$ for $0 < x < L, t > 0$; $\dfrac{\partial u}{\partial x}(0, t) = 0$ and $u(L, t) = \beta(t)$ for $t \geq 0$; $u(x, 0) = f(x)$ for $0 \leq x \leq L$.

Section 18.2

In these solutions, $\exp(A) = e^A$.

1. $u(x, t) = \sum\limits_{n=1}^{\infty} \dfrac{8L^2}{(2n-1)^3 \pi^3} \sin\left(\dfrac{(2n-1)\pi x}{L}\right) \exp\left(\dfrac{-(2n-1)^2 \pi^2 kt}{L^2}\right)$

3. $u(x, t) = \sum\limits_{n=1}^{\infty} \dfrac{-16L}{(2n-1)\pi[(2n-1)^2-4]} \sin\left(\dfrac{(2n-1)\pi x}{L}\right) \exp\left(\dfrac{-3(2n-1)^2 \pi^2 t}{L^2}\right)$

5. $u(x, t) = \dfrac{2}{3}\pi^2 - \sum\limits_{n=1}^{\infty} \dfrac{4}{n^2} \cos(nx)e^{-4n^2 t}$

7. $u(x, t) = \dfrac{1}{6}(1 - e^{-6}) + \sum\limits_{n=1}^{\infty} 12\left(\dfrac{1-e^{-6}(-1)^n}{36+n^2\pi^2}\right) \cos\left(\dfrac{n\pi x}{6}\right) e^{-n^2\pi^2 t/18}$

9. $u(x, t) = \sum\limits_{n=1}^{\infty} \dfrac{4B}{(2n-1)\pi} \sin\left(\dfrac{(2n-1)\pi x}{2L}\right) \exp\left(\dfrac{-(2n-1)^2 \pi^2 kt}{4L^2}\right)$

11. Substitute $e^{\alpha x + \beta t}v(x, t)$ into the partial differential equation and solve for α and β so that $v_1 = kv_{xx}$. We get $\alpha = -A/2$ and $\beta = k(B - A^2/4)$.

13. Let $u(x, t) = e^{-3x-9t}v(x, t)$. Then $v_t = v_{xx}$, $v(0, t) = v(4, t) = 0$, and $v(x, 0) = e^{3x}$. Then $v(x, t) = $

$\sum\limits_{n=1}^{\infty} \left(2n\pi \dfrac{1-e^{12}(-1)^n}{144+n^2\pi^2}\right) \sin\left(\dfrac{n\pi x}{4}\right) e^{-n^2\pi^2 t/16}$. Graphs of the solution are shown for times $t = 0.003, 0.02, 0.08$, and 1.3.

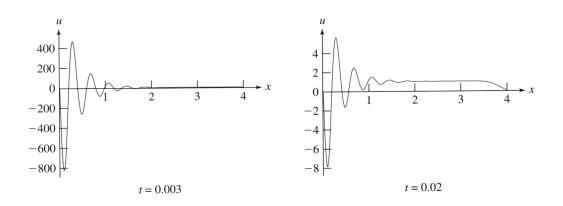

$t = 0.003$ $t = 0.02$

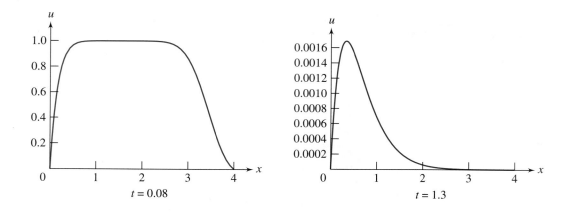

$t = 0.08$ $t = 1.3$

15. Let $u(x, t) = v(x, t) + f(x)$ and choose $f(x) = 3x + 2$ to have $v_t = 16v_{xx}$, $v(0, t) = v(1, t) = 0$, and
$u(x, 0) = x^2 - f(x)$. Then $v(x, t) = \sum_{n=1}^{\infty} 2 \left(\dfrac{4n^2 \pi^2 (-1)^n + 2(-1)^n - 2 - 2n^2 \pi^2}{n^3 \pi^3} \right) \sin(n\pi x) e^{-16n^2 \pi^2 t}$ and
$u(x, t) = v(x, t) + 3x + 2$. Graphs of the solution for times $t = 0.005, 0.009$, and 0.01.

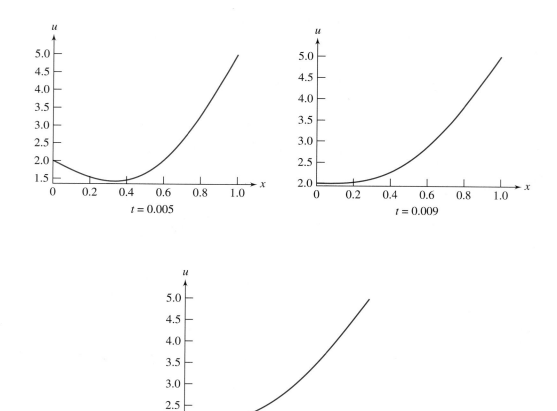

$t = 0.005$ $t = 0.009$

$t = 0.01$

17. Let $u(x, t) = e^{-At}w(x, t)$. Then $w_t = 4w_{xx}$, $w(0, t) = w(9, t) = 0$, and $w(x, 0) = 3x$. Obtain

$$w(x, t) = \sum_{n=1}^{\infty} \frac{54(-1)^{n+1}}{n\pi} \sin\left(\frac{n\pi x}{9}\right) e^{-4n^2\pi^2 t/81}.$$ The graphs compare solutions at times $t = 0.008, 0.04$, and 0.6 for

$A = \frac{1}{4}$, 1, and 3.

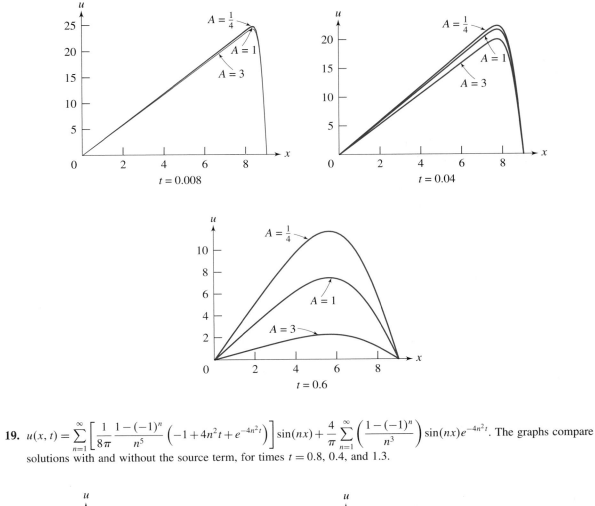

19. $u(x, t) = \sum_{n=1}^{\infty} \left[\frac{1}{8\pi} \frac{1-(-1)^n}{n^5} \left(-1 + 4n^2 t + e^{-4n^2 t}\right) \right] \sin(nx) + \frac{4}{\pi} \sum_{n=1}^{\infty} \left(\frac{1-(-1)^n}{n^3} \right) \sin(nx) e^{-4n^2 t}$. The graphs compare

solutions with and without the source term, for times $t = 0.8, 0.4$, and 1.3.

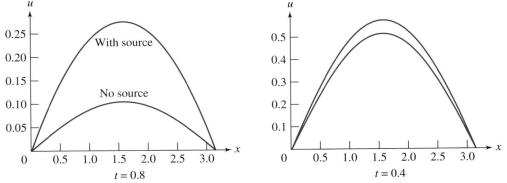

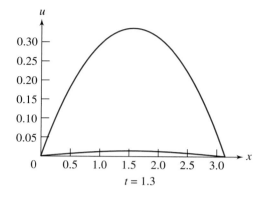

$t = 1.3$

21. $u(x, t) = \displaystyle\sum_{n=1}^{\infty} \frac{50}{n^3 \pi^3} \frac{1 - (\cos 5)(-1)^n}{n^2 \pi^2 - 25} \left(-25 + n^2 \pi^2 t + 25 e^{-n^2 \pi^2 t/25} \right) \sin\left(\frac{n \pi x}{5} \right)$

$+ \displaystyle\sum_{n=1}^{\infty} \left(-250 \frac{4(-1)^n + 2}{n^3 \pi^3} \right) \sin\left(\frac{n \pi x}{5} \right) e^{-n^2 \pi^2 t/25}$. The graphs compare solutions with and without the source term, for

times $t = 0.7$, 1.5, 2.6, and 4.2.

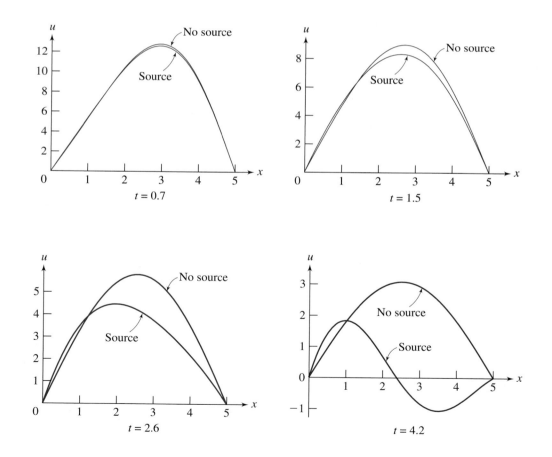

23. $u(x, t) = \sum_{n=1}^{\infty} \frac{27(-1)^{n+1}}{128} \left(\frac{16n^2 \pi^2 t + 9e^{-16n^2 \pi^2 t/9} - 9}{n^5 \pi^5} \right) \sin\left(\frac{n\pi x}{3} \right) + 2K \sum_{n=1}^{\infty} \left(\frac{1 - (-1)^n}{n\pi} \right) \sin\left(\frac{n\pi x}{3} \right) e^{-16n^2 \pi^2 t/9}.$

The graphs show the solution with and without the source term, at times $t = 0.05$ and 0.2, with $K = \frac{1}{2}$.

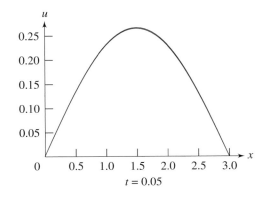

$t = 0.05$

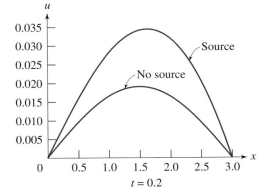

$t = 0.2$

25. In the following, $j = 1, 2, \ldots, 9.$
$u_{j,0}$: 0.009, 0.032, 0.063, 0.096, 0.125, 0.144
0.147. 0.128, 0.081
$u_{j,1}$: 0.0125, 0.034, 0.0635, 0.095, 0.1225
0.14, 0.1415, 0.121, 0.0725
$u_{j,2}$: 0.01475, 0.064125, 0.089, 0.094, 0.1195
0.136, 0.136, 0.114, 0.0665
$u_{j,3}$: 0.023381, 0.058, 0.084031, 0.099125, 0.11725
0.13188, 0.1305, 0.10763, 0.06175

27. In the following, $j = 1, 2, \ldots, 9.$
$u_{j,0}$: 0.098769, 0.19021, 0.2673, 0.32361, 0.35355
0.35267, 0.31779, 0.24721, 0.14079
$u_{j,1}$: 0.096937, 0.18622, 0.26211, 0.31702, 0.34585
0.34417, 0.30887, 0.23825, 0.13220
$u_{j,2}$: 0.095124, 0.18307, 0.25697, 0.3105, 0.33822
0.33577, 0.30004, 0.22939, 0.12566
$u_{j,3}$: 0.09330, 0.17956, 0.25188, 0.30405, 0.33062
0.32745, 0.29131, 0.22112, 0.12018

Section 18.3

1. $u(x, t) = \frac{1}{\pi} \int_0^{\infty} \frac{8}{(16 + \omega^2)} \cos(\omega x) e^{-\omega^2 kt} d\omega$

3. $u(x, t) = \int_0^{\infty} \left[\left(\frac{8}{\pi} \cos(\omega) \frac{\cos^3(\omega) - \cos(\omega) + 4\omega \sin(\omega) \cos^2(\omega) - 2\omega \sin(\omega)}{\omega^2} \right) \cos(\omega x) \right.$
$\left. - \left(\frac{4}{\pi} \frac{-2\sin(\omega) \cos^3(\omega) + \sin(\omega) \cos(\omega) + 8\omega \cos^4(\omega) - 8\omega \cos^2(\omega) + \omega}{\omega^2} \right) \sin(\omega x) \right] e^{-\omega^2 kt} d\omega$

5. $u(x, t) = \frac{2}{\pi} \int_0^{\infty} \frac{\omega}{\alpha^2 + \omega^2} \sin(\omega x) e^{-\omega^2 kt} d\omega$

7. $u(x, t) = \frac{2}{\pi} \int_0^{\infty} \frac{1 - \cos(h\omega)}{\omega} \sin(\omega x) e^{-\omega^2 kt} d\omega$

9. $u(x, t) = \frac{4}{\pi} \int_0^{\infty} \frac{\omega}{(1 + \omega^2)^2} \sin(\omega x) e^{-\omega^2 t} e^{-t^2/2} d\omega$

11. $u(x, t) = \int_0^{t} 2(t - \tau) \mathrm{erfc}\left(\frac{x}{2\sqrt{k\tau}} \right) d\tau$, in which erfc is the complementary error function.

Section 18.4

1. $U(r,t) = \sum_{n=1}^{\infty} \dfrac{2}{[J_1(j_n)]^2} \left(\int_0^1 \xi^2 J_0(j_n\xi)\,d\xi \right) J_0(j_n r)e^{-j_n^2 t}$; the fifth partial sum, with approximate values inserted, is

$U(r,t) \approx .8170 J_0(2.405r)e^{-5.785t} - 1.1394 J_0(5.520r)e^{-30.47t} + 0.7983 J_0(8.654r)e^{-74.89t} - 0.747 J_0(11.792r)e^{-139.04t} + 0.6315 J_0(14.931r)e^{-222.93t}$. A graph of this function is shown for times $t = 0.003, 0.009, 0.04,$ and 0.7.

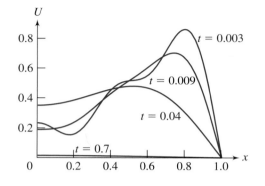

3. $U(r,t) = \sum_{n=1}^{\infty} \dfrac{2}{[J_1(j_n)]^2} \left(\int_0^1 \xi(9-\xi^2)J_0(j_n\xi)\,d\xi \right) J_0\!\left(\dfrac{j_n}{3}r\right)e^{-j_n^2 t/18}$; the fifth partial sum, with approximate values inserted, is $U(r,t) \approx 9.9722 J_0(2.405r/3)e^{-5.78t/18} - 1.258 J_0(5.520r/3)e^{-30.47t/18} + 0.4093 J_0(8.654r/3)e^{-74.89t/18} - 0.1889 J_0(11.792r/3)e^{-139.04t/18} + 0.1048 J_0(14.931r/3)e^{-222.93t/18}$. A graph of this partial sum is shown for times $t = 0.003, 0.009, 0.08,$ and 0.4.

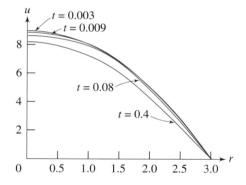

Section 18.5

1. $u(x,y,t) = \sum_{n=1}^{\infty}\sum_{m=1}^{\infty} b_{nm} \sin\!\left(\dfrac{n\pi x}{L}\right)\sin\!\left(\dfrac{m\pi y}{K}\right)e^{-\beta_{nm}kt}$, where $\beta_{nm} = \left(\dfrac{n^2}{L^2} + \dfrac{m^2}{K^2}\right)\pi^2$ and

$\beta_{nm} = \dfrac{4}{LK}\int_0^K\int_0^L f(x,y)\sin(n\pi x/L)\sin(m\pi y/K)\,dx\,dy$.

3. $u(x,y) = \sum_{m=1}^{\infty} \dfrac{4}{\pi}\dfrac{8(-1)^{m+1}m}{(2m+1)^2(2m-1)^2}\sin(x)\sin(my)e^{-(1+m^2)t}$.

CHAPTER 19

Section 19.1

1. $\nabla^2(f+g) = (f+g)_{xx} + (f+g)_{yy} = (f_{xx}+f_{yy}) + (g_{xx}+g_{yy}) = \nabla^2 f + \nabla^2 g$ and
$\nabla^2(\alpha f) = (\alpha f)_{xx} + (\alpha f)_{yy} = \alpha(f_{xx}+f_{yy}) = \alpha\nabla^2 f$.

3. Compute $\dfrac{\partial}{\partial x}\ln(x^2+y^2) = \dfrac{2x}{x^2+y^2}$ and $\dfrac{\partial}{\partial x}\left(\dfrac{2x}{x^2+y^2}\right) = 2\dfrac{y^2-x^2}{(x^2+y^2)^2}$.

Similarly, $\dfrac{\partial^2}{\partial y^2}\left(\dfrac{2x}{x^2+y^2}\right) = 2\dfrac{x^2-y^2}{(x^2+y^2)^2}$. Then $\nabla^2\ln(x^2+y^2) = 0$, provided that $x^2+y^2 \neq 0$.

5. Recall that, in polar coordinates, Laplace's equations is $\dfrac{\partial^2 u}{\partial r^2} + \dfrac{1}{r}\dfrac{\partial u}{\partial r} + \dfrac{1}{r^2}\dfrac{\partial^2 u}{\partial \theta^2} = 0$. It is routine to verify by substitution that the given functions are harmonic.

Section 19.2

1. $u(x,y) = \dfrac{-1}{\sinh(\pi^2)}\sin(\pi x)\sin h(\pi(y-\pi)))$

3. $u(x,y) = \displaystyle\sum_{n=1}^{\infty} \dfrac{32}{\pi^2\sinh(4n\pi)}\dfrac{n(-1)^{n+1}}{(2n-1)^2(2n+1)^2}\sin(n\pi x)\sinh(n\pi y)$

5. $u(x,y) = \dfrac{1}{\sinh(\pi^2)}\sin(\pi x)\sinh(\pi y) + \displaystyle\sum_{n=1,n\neq 2}^{\infty} 16n\dfrac{(-1)^n-1}{\pi^2(n-2)^2(n+2)}\dfrac{1}{\sinh(n\pi^2/2)}\sin\left(\dfrac{n\pi x}{2}\right)\sinh\left(\dfrac{n\pi y}{2}\right)$

$+ \dfrac{1}{\sinh(2)}\sin(y)\sinh(x)$

7. $u(x,y) = \displaystyle\sum_{n=1}^{\infty} c_n\sin\left(\dfrac{(2n-1)\pi x}{2a}\right)\sinh\left(\dfrac{(2n-1)\pi y}{2a}\right)$,

where $c_n = \dfrac{2}{a\sinh[(2n-1)\pi b/2a]}\displaystyle\int_0^a f(x)\sin\left(\dfrac{(2n-1)\pi x}{2a}\right)dx$.

9. $u(x,y) = \dfrac{-1}{\sinh(4\pi)}\sin(\pi y)\sinh(\pi(x-4)) + \displaystyle\sum_{n=1}^{\infty} \dfrac{2}{\sinh(4n\pi)}\left(2\dfrac{1-(-1)^n}{\pi^3 n^3}\right)\sin(n\pi y)\sinh(n\pi x)$

Section 19.3

1. $u(r,\theta) = 1$ 3. $u(r,\theta) = \dfrac{1}{3}\pi^2 + \displaystyle\sum_{n=1}^{\infty}\left(\dfrac{r}{2}\right)^n 2(-1)^n\dfrac{1}{n^2}[2\cos(n\theta) + n\sin(n\theta)]$

5. $u(r,\theta) = \dfrac{1}{\pi}\sinh(\pi) + \dfrac{1}{\pi}\displaystyle\sum_{n=1}^{\infty}\left(\dfrac{r}{4}\right)^n\dfrac{e^{-\pi}(-1)^n}{n^2+1}[-\cos(n\theta) - n\sin(n\theta) + e^{2\pi}\cos(n\theta) + e^{2\pi}n\sin(n\theta)]$

7. $u(r,\theta) = 1 + \displaystyle\sum_{n=1}^{\infty}\left(\dfrac{r}{8}\right)^n\left(\dfrac{2}{n^3}\right)[n^2\pi^2(-1)^n\sin(n\theta) - 6(-1)^n\sin(n\theta)]$

9. In polar coordinates, the problem is $\nabla^2 U(r,\theta) = 0$ for $r < 4$, $U(4,\theta) = 16\cos^2(\theta)$. This has solution $U(r,\theta) = 8 + r^2(\cos^2\theta - \tfrac{1}{2})$. In rectangular coordinates, the solution is $u(x,y) = \tfrac{1}{2}(x^2-y^2) + 8$.

11. In polar coordinates, the solution is $U(r,\theta) = r^2(2\cos^2\theta - 1)$, so $u(x,y) = x^2 - y^2$.

Section 19.4

1. $u\left(\dfrac{1}{2},\pi\right) = \dfrac{3}{8\pi}\displaystyle\int_0^{2\pi}\dfrac{\xi}{5/4 - \cos(\xi-\pi)}d\xi = 9.8696/\pi$; $u\left(\dfrac{3}{4},\pi/3\right) \approx 4.813941647/\pi$,
$u(0.2,\pi/4) \approx 8.843875590/\pi$

3. $u(4,\pi) \approx 155.25/\pi$, $u(12,3\pi/2) \approx 302/\pi$, $u(8,\pi/4) \approx 111.56/\pi$, $u(7,0) \approx 248.51/\pi$

5. With $u(r,\theta) = r^n\sin(n\theta)$, compute $u(R/2,\pi/2) = \dfrac{R^n}{2^n}\sin(n\pi/2) = \dfrac{1}{2\pi}\displaystyle\int_0^{2\pi}\dfrac{R^2-R^2/4}{R^2+R^2/4 - R^2\cos(\xi-\pi/2)}$
$R^n\sin(n\xi)d\xi$. Upon dividing out common powers of R and solving for the integral, we obtain
$\dfrac{1}{2^n}\dfrac{2\pi}{3}\sin(n\pi/2) = \displaystyle\int_0^{2\pi}\dfrac{\sin(n\xi)}{5 - 4\sin(\xi)}d\xi$.

7. $\dfrac{\pi}{3(2^{n-1})}\cos\left(\dfrac{n\pi}{2}\right) = \displaystyle\int_0^{2\pi}\dfrac{1}{5-4\sin(\xi)}\cos(n\xi)d\xi$, $\dfrac{\pi}{3(2^{n-1})}(-1)^n = \displaystyle\int_0^{2\pi}\dfrac{1}{5+4\cos(\xi)}\cos(n\xi)d\xi$

Section 19.5

1. $u(x, y) = \dfrac{1}{\pi}\left[\arctan\left(\dfrac{4-x}{y}\right) - \arctan\left(\dfrac{4+x}{y}\right)\right]$ for $-\infty < x < \infty,\ y > 0$

3. $u(x, y) = \dfrac{y}{\pi}\displaystyle\int_0^\infty \left(\dfrac{1}{y^2+(\xi-x)^2} - \dfrac{1}{y^2+(\xi+x)^2}\right) e^{-\xi}\cos(\xi)d\xi$

5. $u(x, y) = \dfrac{2}{\pi}\displaystyle\int_0^\infty \left(\int_0^\infty f(\xi)\sin(\omega\xi)d\xi\right)\sin(\omega x)e^{-\omega y}d\omega + \dfrac{2}{\pi}\int_0^\infty\left(\int_0^\infty g(\xi)\sin(\omega\xi)d\xi\right)\sin(\omega y)e^{-\omega x}d\omega$

7. $u(x, y) = Be^{-y}\sin(x) + \displaystyle\sum_{n=1}^\infty \dfrac{2}{\pi}\dfrac{h}{n^3}(1-(-1)^n)(1-e^{-ny})\sin(nx)$

9. Using a finite Fourier sine transform in x, we get $u(x, y) = \dfrac{2}{\pi}\displaystyle\sum_{n=1}^\infty\left[\left(-\dfrac{4}{n}+6\dfrac{(-1)^n}{n}\right)e^{-ny} - 2\dfrac{(-1)^n}{n}\right]\sin(nx).$

11. $u(x, y) = \dfrac{2}{\pi}\displaystyle\int_0^\infty\left(\dfrac{\omega}{1+\omega^2}\right)\sin(\omega y)e^{-\omega x}d\omega$

13. $u(x, y) = \dfrac{y}{\pi}\displaystyle\int_4^8 \dfrac{A}{y^2+(\xi-x)^2}d\xi = \dfrac{A}{\pi}\left[-\arctan\left(\dfrac{x-8}{y}\right) + \arctan\left(\dfrac{x-4}{y}\right)\right]$

Section 19.6

1. $u(x, y, z) = \displaystyle\sum_{n=1}^\infty\sum_{m=1}^\infty \dfrac{4(-1)^{n+m}}{nm\pi^2\sinh\left(\pi\sqrt{n^2+m^2}\right)}\sin(n\pi x)\sin(m\pi y)\sinh(\pi\sqrt{n^2+m^2}z)$

3. $u(x, y, z) = \displaystyle\sum_{n=1}^\infty\sum_{m=1}^\infty\left[\dfrac{16}{\pi^2(2n-1)(2m-1)\sinh(2\pi\sqrt{(2m-1)^2+\pi^2(2n-1)^2})}\right.$

$\left.\times \sin((2n-1)\pi x)\sin((2m-1)z)\sinh(\sqrt{(2m-1)^2+\pi^2(2n-1)^2}\,y)\right]$

$+\displaystyle\sum_{n=1}^\infty\sum_{m=1}^\infty\left[\dfrac{16}{\pi^2(2n-1)(2m-1)}\dfrac{1}{\sinh\left(\pi\sqrt{\dfrac{(2m-1)^2}{4}+\pi^2(2n-1)^2}\right)}\right.$

$\left.\times \sin((2n-1)\pi x)\sin\left(\dfrac{(2m-1)y}{2}\right)\sinh\left(\sqrt{\dfrac{(2m-1)^2}{4}+\pi^2(2n-1)^2}z\right)\right]$

Section 19.7

1. $u(\rho, \varphi) = \displaystyle\sum_{n=0}^\infty \dfrac{(2n+1)A}{2}\left(\int_{-1}^1 (\arccos(\xi))^2 P_n(\xi)d\xi\right)\left(\dfrac{\rho}{R}\right)^n P_n(\cos(\varphi))$

$\approx 2.9348A - 3.7011A\left(\dfrac{\rho}{R}\right)P_1(\cos(\varphi)) + 1.1111A\left(\dfrac{\rho}{R}\right)^2 P_2(\cos(\varphi))$

$-0.5397A\left(\dfrac{\rho}{R}\right)^3 P_3(\cos(\varphi)) + 0.3200A\left(\dfrac{\rho}{R}\right)^4 P_4(\cos(\varphi)) - 0.2120\left(\dfrac{\rho}{R}\right)^5 P_5(\cos(\varphi)) + \cdots$

3. $u(\rho, \varphi) \approx 6.0784 - 9.8602\left(\dfrac{\rho}{R}\right)P_1(\cos(\varphi)) + 5.2360\left(\dfrac{\rho}{R}\right)^2 P_2(\cos(\varphi))$

$-2.4044\left(\dfrac{\rho}{R}\right)^3 P_3(\cos(\varphi)) + 1.5080\left(\dfrac{\rho}{R}\right)^4 P_4(\cos(\varphi)) - 0.9783\left(\dfrac{\rho}{R}\right)^5 P_5(\cos\varphi) + \cdots$

5. $u(\rho, \varphi) = \dfrac{1}{R_2-R_1}(T_1R_1)\left[\dfrac{1}{\rho}R_2 - 1\right]$

7. $u(\rho, \varphi) = \sum_{n=1}^{\infty} a_{2n-1}\rho^{2n-1}P_{2n-1}(\cos(\varphi))$, where $a_{2n-1} = \dfrac{\int_0^1 AP_{2n-1}(x)dx}{R^{2n-1}\int_0^1 (P_{2n-1}(x))^2 dx} = \dfrac{(4n-1)A}{R^{2n-1}}\int_0^1 P_{2n-1}(x)dx.$

9. $u(\rho, \varphi) = \sum_{n=1}^{\infty} a_{2n-1}\rho^{2n-1}P_{2n-1}(\cos(\varphi))$, where $a_{2n-1} = \dfrac{4n-1}{R^{2n-1}}\int_0^1 f(\arccos(x))P_{2n-1}(x)dx.$

Section 19.8

1. Since $\int_0^1 4\cos(\pi x)dx = 0$, a solution may exist. We find $u(x, y) = \dfrac{4}{-\pi\sinh(\pi)}\cos(\pi x)\cosh(\pi(1-y)) + C.$

3. Since $\int_0^\pi \cos(3x)dx = \int_0^\pi (6x - 3\pi)dx = 0$, a solution may exist. We find $u(x, y) =$
$\dfrac{1}{-3\sinh(3\pi)}\cos(3x)\cosh(3(\pi - y)) + \sum_{n=1}^{\infty}\dfrac{12}{\pi}\dfrac{(-1)^n - 1}{n^3\sinh(n\pi)}\cos(nx)\cosh(ny) + C.$

5. $u(x, y) = \sum_{n=1}^{\infty} 2\left(\dfrac{n^2\pi^2(-1)^n + 6(1-(-1)^n)}{n^4\pi^4\sinh(\pi)}\right)\sin(n\pi y)\cosh(n\pi(1-x))$

7. $u(r, \theta) = \dfrac{1}{2}a_0 + \dfrac{R}{2}\left(\dfrac{r}{R}\right)^2 (2\cos^2\theta - 1)$

9. $u(x, y) = \dfrac{1}{2\pi}\int_{-\infty}^{\infty}\ln(y^2 + (\xi - x)^2)e^{-|\xi|}\sin(\xi)d\xi + c$

11. $u(x, y) = \int_0^{\infty} a_\omega\cos(\omega x)e^{-\omega y}d\omega + c$, with $a_\omega = -\dfrac{2}{\pi\omega}\int_0^{\infty} f(\xi)\cos(\omega\xi)d\xi$

CHAPTER 20

Section 20.1

1. $26 - 18i$ **3.** $\frac{1}{65}(1 + 18i)$ **5.** $4 + 228i$ **7.** $6 - i$ **9.** $\frac{1}{4225}(-1632 + 2024i)$

11. $i^{4n} = ((i^2)^2)^n = 1^n = 1$; $i^{4n+1} = ii^{4n} = i$, since $i^{4n} = 1$; $i^{4n+2} = i^{4n}(i^2) = -1$; $i^{4n+3} = i^{4n}i^2i = -i$

13. $a^2 - b^2 + b + 1$; $2ab - a$ **17.** $\dfrac{\pi}{2} + 2n\pi$ **19.** $\pi - \tan^{-1}\left(\frac{2}{3}\right) + 2n\pi$ **21.** $\pi + 2n\pi$

23. $2\sqrt{2}[\cos(3\pi/4) + i\sin(3\pi/4)]$ **25.** $\sqrt{29}\left[\cos\left(-\tan^{-1}\left(\frac{2}{5}\right)\right) + i\sin\left(-\tan^{-1}\left(\frac{2}{5}\right)\right)\right]$

27. $\sqrt{65}\left[\cos\left(\tan^{-1}\left(\frac{1}{8}\right)\right) + i\sin\left(\tan^{-1}\left(\frac{1}{8}\right)\right)\right]$

29. *Hint*: If $|z| = 1$, then $z\bar{z} = 1$ and $\left|\dfrac{z-w}{1-\bar{z}w}\right| = \left|\dfrac{z-w}{z\bar{z} - w\bar{z}}\right| = \dfrac{1}{|\bar{z}|}\left|\dfrac{z-w}{z-w}\right| = 1.$

Section 20.2

1. Circle of radius 9 with center $(8, -4)$ **3.** Circle of radius $\frac{1}{2}\sqrt{65}$ with center $(0, -\frac{1}{2})$

5. The real axis for $x \le 0$ **7.** The line $y = x + 2$

9. The line $8x + 10y + 27 = 0$ **11.** The half-plane $3x + y + 2 > 0$

13. K is the closed half-plane $2x + 8y + 15 \ge 0$; every point of K is a limit point of K, and there are no other limit points; boundary points of K are those points on the line $2x + 8y + 15 = 0$; K is closed but not compact (because K is not bounded).

15. M consists of all points below the line $y = 7$; limit points are points of M and points on the line $y = 7$; boundary points are points $x + 7i$; M is open; M is not compact.

17. U consists of all points $x + iy$ with $1 < x \le 3$; limit points are points of U and points on the line $x = 1$; boundary points are points on the lines $x = 1$ and $x = 3$; U is neither open nor closed; U is not compact (neither closed nor bounded).

19. W consists of all $x = iy$ with $x > y^2$. These are points (x, y) inside and to the right of the parabola $x = y^2$. This set is open, and not compact. Limit points are all points of W and points on the parabola; boundary points are the points on the parabola.

21. $1 + 2i$ **23.** $2 - i$ **25.** -1 **27.** $\frac{3}{2}i$

29. If n is even, say $n = 2m$, then $i^{2n} = i^{4m} = 1$, so $\{1\}$ is one convergent subsequence; if $n = 2m + 1$, then $i^{2n} = i^{4m}i^2 = i^2 = -1$, so $\{-1\}$ is another convergent subsequence. There are others.

CHAPTER 21

Section 21.1

1. $u = x$, $v = y - 1$; Cauchy–Riemann equations hold at all points; f is differentiable for all complex z.
3. $u = \sqrt{x^2 + y^2}$, $v = 0$; nowhere; nowhere
5. $u = 0$, $v = x^2 + y^2$; the Cauchy–Riemann equations hold at $(0, 0)$; nowhere
7. $u = 1$, y/x; nowhere; nowhere   **9.** $u = x^2 - y^2$, $v = -2xy$; $(0,0)$; nowhere
11. $u = -4x + \dfrac{x}{x^2 + y^2}$, $v = -4y - \dfrac{y}{x^2 + y^2}$; Cauchy–Riemann equations hold for all nonzero z; differentiable for $z \neq 0$

Section 21.2

1. 2; $|z + 3i| < 2$ **3.** 1; $|z - 1 + 3i| < 1$ **5.** 2; $|z + 8i| < 2$ **7.** 1; $|z + 6 + 2i| < 1$
9. No; i is closer to $2i$ than 0 is, so if the series converged at 0 it would have to converge at i.
11. c_{n+1}/c_n is either 2 or $\frac{1}{2}$, depending on whether n is odd or even, so c_{n+1}/c_n has no limit. However, $\lim\limits_{n \to \infty} |c_n|^{1/n} = 1$,

so the radius of convergence is 1 by the nth root test applied to $\sum\limits_{n=0}^{\infty} |c_n z^n|$.

Section 21.3

1. $\cos(1) + i\sin(1)$ **3.** $\cos(3)\cosh(2) - i\sin(3)\sinh(2)$ **5.** $e^5\cos(2) + ie^5\sin(2)$
7. $\frac{1}{2}[1 - \cos(2)\cosh(2)] + \frac{1}{2}i\sin(2)\sinh(2)$ **9.** i **11.** $u = e^{x^2 - y^2}\cos(2xy)$, $v = e^{x^2 - y^2}\sin(2xy)$
13. $u = \dfrac{\sin(x)\cos(x)}{\cos^2\cosh^2(y) + \sin^2(x)\sinh^2(y)}$, $v = \dfrac{\cosh(y)\sinh(y)}{\cos^2(x)\cosh^2(y) + \sin^2(x)\sinh^2(y)}$
15. $\sin^2(z) + \cos^2(z) = \left(\dfrac{1}{2i}(e^{iz} - e^{-iz})\right)^2 + \left(\dfrac{1}{2}(e^{iz} + e^{-iz})\right)^2 = 1$
17. $z = \ln(2) + i\left(\dfrac{\pi}{2} + 2n\pi\right)$, n any integer   **19.** $z = \ln(2) + (2n + 1)\pi i$, n any integer

Section 21.4

1. $\ln(4) + \dfrac{4n - 1}{2}\pi i$, $\ln(4) + \dfrac{3}{2}\pi i$ **3.** $\ln(5) + (2n + 1)\pi i$, $\ln(5) + \pi i$
5. $\ln(\sqrt{85}) + \left[(2n + 1)\pi + \tan^{-1}\left(-\frac{2}{9}\right)\right]i$, $\ln(\sqrt{85}) + \left(\pi + \tan^{-1}\left(-\frac{2}{9}\right)\right)i$
7. *Hint:* In polar form, $\dfrac{z}{w} = \left|\dfrac{z}{w}\right|e^{i(\arg(z) - \arg(w))}$.

Section 21.5

1. $ie^{-(2n\pi + \pi/2)}$ **3.** $e^{-(2n\pi + \pi/2)}$ **5.** $e^{3(2n\pi + 3\pi/4)}\left[\cos\left(\dfrac{3\ln(2)}{2}\right) - i\sin\left(\dfrac{3\ln(2)}{2}\right)\right]$
7. $\cos\left(\dfrac{\pi}{8} + \dfrac{n\pi}{2}\right) + i\sin\left(\dfrac{\pi}{8} + \dfrac{n\pi}{2}\right)$ **9.** $16e^{(2n+1)\pi}[\cos(\ln(4)) - i\sin(\ln(4))]$
11. $2\left[\cos\left(\dfrac{(2n + 1)\pi}{4}\right) + i\sin\left(\dfrac{(2n + 1)\pi}{4}\right)\right]$ **13.** $\cos(n\pi/3) + i\sin(n\pi/3)$

15. The nth roots of unity are $\omega_k = e^{2k\pi i/n}$ for $k = 0, 1, \ldots, n - 1$. Now use the fact that for $z \neq 1$, $\sum\limits_{k=0}^{n-1} z^k = \dfrac{z^n - 1}{z - 1}$, with $z = e^{2\pi i/n}$.

CHAPTER 22

Section 22.1

The graph of the curves in Problems 1,3,5,7, and 9 are shown below.

1. initial point $6 - 2i$, terminal point $2 - 2i$; simple and not closed; tangent $\Gamma'(t) = 2ie^{it} = -2\sin(t)\mathbf{i} + 2\cos(t)\mathbf{j}$

3. $1 + i, 3 + 9i$; simple and not closed; $\Gamma'(t) = 1 + 2ti = \mathbf{i} + 2t\mathbf{j}$

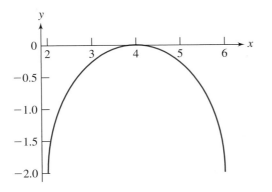

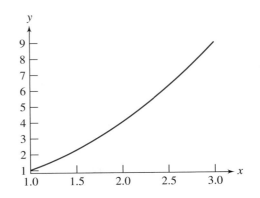

5. $3, 3$; closed but not simple; $\Theta'(t) = -3\sin(t) + 5\cos(t)i = -3\sin(t)\mathbf{i} + 5\cos(t)\mathbf{j}$

7. $-2 - 4i, 4 - 16i$; simple and not closed; $\Psi'(t) = 1 - ti = \mathbf{i} - t\mathbf{j}$

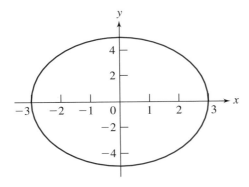

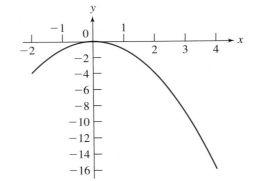

9. $1, \cos(2) - 2\sin(4)i$; simple and not closed; $\Gamma'(t) = -\sin(t) - 4\cos(2t)i = -\sin(t)\mathbf{i} - 4\cos(2t)\mathbf{j}$

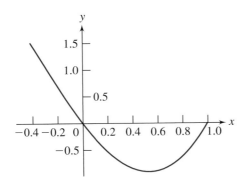

Section 22.2

1. $8 - 2i$ **3.** $\frac{3}{2}(1+i)$ **5.** $\frac{1}{2}(-13+4i)$ **7.** $-\frac{1}{2}[\cosh(8) - \cosh(2)]$

9. $-\frac{1}{2}[e^{-1}(\cos(2) + i\sin(2)) - e(\cos(2) - i\sin(2))]$ **11.** $10 + 210i$ **13.** $\frac{25}{2}i$ **15.** $\frac{2}{3}(1+i)$ **16.** $1/\sqrt{z}$ (or any larger number)

Section 22.3

1. 0   **3.** 0   **5.** $2\pi i$ **7.** 0   **9.** 0   **11.** $4\pi i$

Section 22.4

1. $32\pi i$ **3.** $2\pi i(-8 + 7i)$ **5.** $-2\pi e^2(\cos(1) - i\sin(1))$ **7.** $\pi i(6\cos(12) - 36\sin(12))$

9. $-512\pi(1 - 2i)\cos(256)$ **11.** $-\frac{13}{2} - 39i$ **13.** 2π

CHAPTER 23

Section 23.1

1. $\displaystyle\sum_{n=0}^{\infty} \frac{(-1)^n}{(2n)!} 2^{2n} z^{2n}$; $|z| < \infty$ (that is, the series converges for all complex z)

3. $\displaystyle\sum_{n=0}^{\infty} \frac{1}{(1 - 4i)^{n+1}}(z - 4i)^n$; $|z - 4i| < \sqrt{17}$ **5.** $\displaystyle\sum_{n=0}^{\infty}(n+1)z^n$; $|z| < 1$

7. $-3 + (1 - 2i)(z - 2 + i) + (z - 2 + i)^2$; $|z| < \infty$ **9.** $63 - 16i + (-16 + 2i)(z - 1 - i) + (z - 1 - i)^2$; $|z| < \infty$

11. $\displaystyle\sum_{n=0}^{\infty} \frac{(-1)^n}{(2n+1)!}(z+i)^{2n+1}$; $|z| < \infty$

13. $1 + iz + \displaystyle\sum_{n=1}^{\infty}\left(\frac{2^n + 2^{n-1}}{(2n)!}z^{2n} + i\frac{2^n}{(2n+1)!}z^{2n+1}\right)$; $|z| < \infty$

15. Fix z and think of w as the variable. Define $f(w) = e^{zw}$. Then $f^{(n)}(w) = z^n e^{zw}$. By Cauchy's integral formula,

$f^{(n)}(0) = z^n = \dfrac{n!}{2\pi i}\displaystyle\int_\Gamma \frac{e^{zw}}{w^{n+1}}\,dw$, with Γ the unit circle about the origin. Then $\dfrac{z^n}{n!} = \dfrac{1}{2\pi i}\displaystyle\int_\Gamma \frac{e^{zw}}{w^{n+1}}\,dw$, so

$\left(\dfrac{z^n}{n!}\right)^2 = \dfrac{1}{2\pi i}\displaystyle\int_\Gamma \frac{z^n}{n!\,w^{n+1}}e^{zw}\,dw$. Then $\displaystyle\sum_{n=0}^{\infty}\left(\frac{z^n}{n!}\right)^2 = \dfrac{1}{2\pi i}\displaystyle\sum_{n=0}^{\infty}\int_\Gamma \frac{z^n}{n!\,w^{n+1}}e^{zw}\,dw = \dfrac{1}{2\pi i}\displaystyle\int_\Gamma\left(\sum_{n=0}^{\infty}\frac{1}{n!}\left(\frac{z}{w}\right)^n\right)\frac{e^{zw}}{w}\,dw$

$= \dfrac{1}{2\pi i}\displaystyle\int_\Gamma e^{z(w+1/w)}\frac{1}{w}\,dw$. Now let $w = e^{i\theta}$ on Γ to derive the result.

17. The maximum must occur at a boundary point of the rectangle. Consider each side. On the left vertical side, $x = 0$ and $|e^z| = |e^{iy}| = 1$. On the right vertical side, $|e^z| = e^1|e^{iy}| = e$ has maximum e. On the lower horizontal side, $|e^z| = e^x$ for $0 \le x \le 1$, with maximum e. On the upper horizontal side, $|e^z| = e^x$ has maximum e. Thus the maximum of $|e^z|$ on this rectangle is e.

Section 23.2

1. $\dfrac{1}{z - i} + \displaystyle\sum_{n=0}^{\infty} \frac{(-1)^n}{(2i)^{n+1}}(z - i)^n$, for $0 < |z - i| < 2$ **3.** $\displaystyle\sum_{n=1}^{\infty} \frac{(-1)^{n+1}4^n}{(2n)!}z^{2n-2}$; $|z| < \infty$

5. $-\dfrac{1}{z - 1} - 2 - (z - 1)$; $0 < |z - 1| < \infty$ **7.** $\dfrac{1}{z^2} + \displaystyle\sum_{n=0}^{\infty} \frac{z^{2n}}{(n+1)!}$; $0 < |z| < \infty$ **9.** $1 + \dfrac{2i}{z - i}$; $0 < |z - i| < \infty$

CHAPTER 24

Section 24.1

1. pole of order 2 at $z = 0$ **3.** essential singularity at $z = 0$ **5.** simple poles at i and $-i$, pole of order 2 at 1

7. simple pole at $-i$, removable singularity at i **9.** simple poles at $1, -1, i,$ and $-i$ **11.** simple poles at $\dfrac{(2n+1)}{2}\pi$

13. f has a Taylor expansion $f(z) = \sum\limits_{n=0}^{\infty} a_n(z - z_0)^n$ in some open disk about z_0, and g has a Laurent expansion of the

form $g(z) = \dfrac{b_{-1}}{z - z_0} + \sum\limits_{n=0}^{\infty} b_n(z - z_0)^n$ in some annulus $0 < |z - z_0| < r$. Then fg has an expansion of the form

$\dfrac{b_{-1}a_0}{z - z_0} + \sum\limits_{n=0}^{\infty} c_n(z - z_0)^n$ in this annulus, and $b_{-1}a_0 \neq 0$ because $b_{-1} \neq 0$ and $a_0 = f(z_0) \neq 0$.

15. Write $h(z) = (z - z_0)^3 q(z)$, where q is analytic at z_0 and $q(z_0) \neq 0$. Then $\dfrac{g(z)}{h(z)} = \dfrac{1}{(z - z_0)^3} \dfrac{g(z)}{q(z)}$ in some annulus

$0 < |z - z_0| < r$. Now g/q is analytic at z_0, and so has Taylor expansion $g(z)/q(z) = \sum\limits_{n=0}^{\infty} c_n(z - z_0)^n$ in some disk

about z_0. Further, $c_0 \neq 0$ because $q(z_0) \neq 0$ and $g(z_0) \neq 0$. Then, in some annulus about z_0,

$\dfrac{g(z)}{h(z)} = \dfrac{c_0}{(z - z_0)^3} + \sum\limits_{n=1}^{\infty} c_n(z - z_0)^{n-2}$.

Section 24.2

1. The residue at 1 is $\frac{1}{25}(16 - 12i)$, and at $-2i$, $\frac{1}{25}(9 + 12i)$; the value of the integral is therefore $2\pi i$.

3. 0   **5.** $2\pi i$ **7.** $2\pi i$ **9.** $-\pi i/4$ **11.** 0   **13.** $2\pi i$ **15.** $\dfrac{\pi}{2}(e^{8i} - 1)$

18. Write $g(z) = \sum\limits_{n=0}^{\infty} a_n(z - z_0)^n$ and $h(z) = \sum\limits_{n=3}^{\infty} b_n(z - z_0)^n$, with $a_0 \neq 0$ and $b_3 \neq 0$. From Problem 15, Section 24.1,

$\dfrac{g(z)}{h(z)} = \sum\limits_{n=-3}^{\infty} d_n(z - z_0)^n$, with $d_{-3} \neq 0$. Write $g(z) = \sum\limits_{n=0}^{\infty} a_n(z - z_0)^n = \left(\sum\limits_{n=3}^{\infty} b_n(z - z_0)^n \right) \left(\sum\limits_{n=-3}^{\infty} d_n(z - z_0)^n \right)$ and

equate the coefficient of $(z - z_0)^n$ on the left with the coefficient of $(z - z_0)^n$ in the product on the right. We get $a_0 = d_{-3}b_3, a_1 = d_{-3}b_4 + d_{-2}b_3, a_2 = d_{-3}b_5 + d_{-2}b_4 + d_{-1}b_3$. Use these to solve for d_{-1} in terms of coefficients $a_0, a_1, a_2, b_1, \ldots, b_4$ and use the fact that $a_n = \dfrac{1}{n!}g^{(n)}(z_0), b_n = \dfrac{1}{n!}h^{(n)}(z_0)$.

Section 24.3

1. $2\pi i$ **3.** 0

5. $\cos(3t)$ **7.** $\frac{1}{36}e^{-4t} - \frac{1}{36}e^{2t} + \frac{1}{6}te^{2t}$ **9.** $\frac{1}{2}t^2 e^{-5t}$

11. $2\pi/\sqrt{3}$ **13.** $2\pi/3$ **15.** $\frac{1}{4}\pi e^{-2\sqrt{2}}\sin(2\sqrt{2})$ **17.** $-\pi/128$ **19.** $\dfrac{\pi}{32}(1 + 5e^{-4})$

21. $-\dfrac{16\pi}{5}\sin\left(\dfrac{3\pi}{5}\right)\dfrac{17\cos(\pi/5) + 16\cos(3\pi/5)}{289 + 168\cos(2\pi/5) + 136\cos(4\pi/5) + 32\cos(6\pi/5)}$

23. $\operatorname{Re} s(e^{i\alpha z}/(z^2 + 1), i) = -\frac{1}{2}ie^{-\alpha}$, so $\displaystyle\int_{-\infty}^{\infty} \dfrac{\cos(\alpha x)}{x^2 + 1}\,dx = 2\pi i\left(-\dfrac{1}{2}ie^{-\alpha}\right) = \pi e^{-\alpha}$.

25. With the trigonometric substitutions, we obtain $-4i\displaystyle\int_{\Gamma} \dfrac{z}{(\alpha^2 - \beta^2)z^2 + 2(\alpha^2 + \beta^2)z + (\alpha^2 - \beta^2)}\,dz$, with Γ the unit

circle. The two poles within the unit disk are $z = \pm\sqrt{\dfrac{\beta - \alpha}{\beta + \alpha}}$, and the residue at each is $-i/2\alpha\beta$. Therefore, the value

of the integral is $2\pi i(-i/\alpha\beta)$, or $2\pi/\alpha\beta$.

27. By Cauchy's theorem, $\int_{\Gamma} e^{-z^2}\,dz = 0$, where Γ is the rectangular path. Writing the integral over each piece of the

boundary (starting on the bottom and going counterclockwise), we have $\displaystyle\int_{-R}^{R} e^{-x^2}\,dx + \int_{0}^{\beta} e^{-(R+it)^2}i\,dt +$

$\displaystyle\int_{R}^{-R} e^{-(x+\beta i)^2}\,dx + \int_{\beta}^{0} e^{-(-R+it)^2}i\,dt = 0$. Let $R \to \infty$. The second integral is $e^{-R^2}\displaystyle\int_{0}^{\beta} e^{t^2}e^{-2iRt}\,dt$, and this goes to

zero as $R \to \infty$. Similarly, the fourth integral has limit zero. The first and third integrals give $\displaystyle\int_{-\infty}^{\infty} e^{-x^2}\,dx -$

$\displaystyle\int_{-\infty}^{\infty} e^{-x^2}e^{\beta^2}e^{-2\beta i x}\,dx = 0$. Then $\sqrt{\pi} = e^{\beta^2}\displaystyle\int_{-\infty}^{\infty} e^{-x^2}\cos(2\beta x)\,dx + ie^{-\beta^2}\displaystyle\int_{-\infty}^{\infty} e^{-x^2}\sin(2\beta x)\,dx$. The last integral is zero

because the integrand is odd. Finally, write $\sqrt{\pi} = 2e^{\beta^2}\int_{0}^{\infty} e^{x^2}\cos(2\beta x)\,dx$, since this integrand is even. Now solve

for the integral.

28. By Cauchy's theorem, $\int_\Gamma e^{iz^2}\,dz = 0$. Now integrate over each piece of Γ, going counterclockwise and beginning

with the segment $[0, R]$: $\int_0^R e^{ix^2}\,dx + \int_0^{\pi/4} e^{iR^2 e^{2i\xi}} Rie^{i\xi}\,d\xi + \int_R^0 e^{i(re^{i\pi/4})^2} e^{i\pi/4}\,dr = 0$. The second integral tends to

zero as $R \to \infty$, and in the limit the last equation becomes

$\int_0^\infty [\cos(x^2) + i\sin(x^2)]\,dx = \dfrac{\sqrt{2}}{2}(1+i)\int_0^\infty e^{-r^2}\,dr = \dfrac{\sqrt{2}}{2}(1+i)\dfrac{1}{2}\pi$. Equate the real part of each side and the

imaginary part of each side to evaluate Fresnel's integrals.

30. $\int_0^{2\pi} \dfrac{1}{(\alpha + \beta\cos(\theta))^2}\,d\theta = \int_\Gamma \dfrac{1}{\left(\alpha + \dfrac{\beta}{2}\left(z + \dfrac{1}{z}\right)\right)^2}\dfrac{1}{iz}\,dz = -4i\int_\Gamma \dfrac{z}{(\beta z^2 + 2\alpha z + \beta)^2}\,dz$. The integrand has double

poles at $\dfrac{1}{\beta}(-\alpha \pm \sqrt{\alpha^2 - \beta^2})$, but only $\dfrac{1}{\beta}(-\alpha + \sqrt{\alpha^2 - \beta^2})$ is enclosed by the unit circle Γ. Compute

$\mathrm{Re}\,s\left(\dfrac{-4iz}{(\beta z^2 + 2\alpha z + \beta)^2}, \dfrac{1}{\beta}(-\alpha + \sqrt{\alpha^2 - \beta^2})\right) = -\dfrac{\alpha i}{(\alpha^2 - \beta^2)^{3/2}}$. Then $\int_0^{2\pi} \dfrac{1}{(\alpha + \beta\cos(\theta))^2}\,d\theta = \dfrac{2\pi\alpha}{(\alpha^2 - \beta^2)^{3/2}}$.

Finally, check that $\int_0^{2\pi} \dfrac{1}{(\alpha + \beta\cos(\theta))^2}\,d\theta = 2\int_0^\pi \dfrac{1}{(\alpha + \beta\cos(\theta))^2}\,d\theta$.

CHAPTER 25

Section 25.1

1. The images are given by the following diagrams.

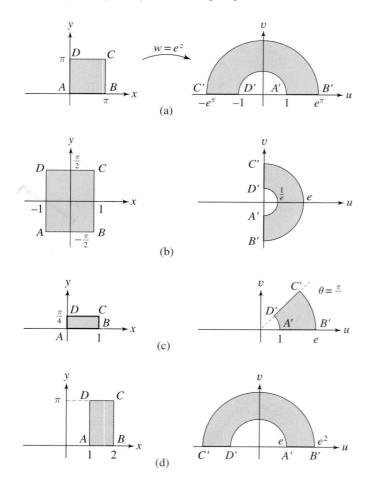

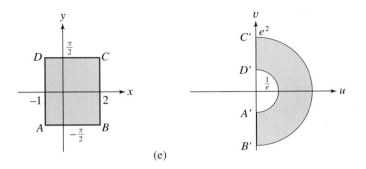

(e)

3. The images are given by the following diagrams.

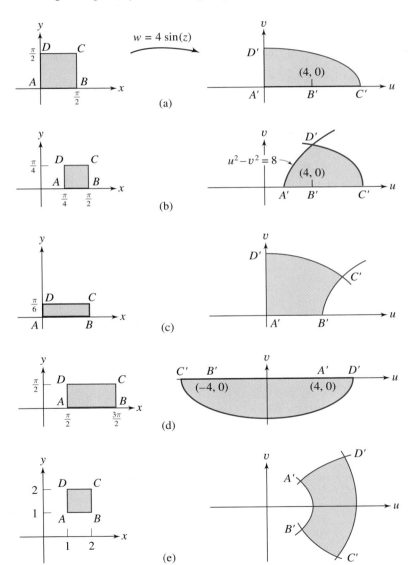

5. The sector consisting of all w with an argument in $[\pi/2, \pi]$.

7. *Hint:* Put $z = re^{i\theta}$ and obtain $u = \dfrac{1}{2}\left(r + \dfrac{1}{r}\right)\cos(k)$, $v = \dfrac{1}{2}\left(r - \dfrac{1}{r}\right)\sin(k)$, where the half-line is $\theta = k$.

9. The entire w plane with the origin excluded.

Section 25.2

1. $w = \dfrac{3 + 8i - (1 + 4i)z}{4 + 7i - (2 + 3i)z}$ **3.** $w = \dfrac{16 - 16i + (-7 + 13i)z}{4 - 8i + (-1 + 2i)z}$ **5.** $w = \dfrac{4 - 75i + (3 + 22i)z}{-21 + 4i + (2 + 3i)z}$

7. $v = 10$ **9.** $(u - \dfrac{11}{21})^2 + (v + \dfrac{1}{63})^2 = \dfrac{208}{3969}$ **11.** $(u - 1)^2 + (v + \dfrac{19}{4})^2 = \dfrac{377}{16}$

13. $w = \bar{z}$ reverses orientation.

15. If $w = \dfrac{az + b}{cz + d}$ and $ad - bc \neq 0$, then $z = -\dfrac{dw - b}{cw - a}$ is also a linear fractional transformation.

17. *Hint:* Show that $z = \dfrac{az + b}{cz + d}$ has either one or two solutions, depending on whether or not c is zero. A translation has no fixed point.

In each of Problems 19 and 21, there are many solutions, of which one is given here.

19. $z \to \dfrac{1}{z} \to -4\dfrac{1}{z} \to -4\dfrac{1}{z} + i = w$ **21.** $z \to iz \to iz - (2 - 7i) = w$

Section 25.3

In Problems 1, 3 and 5, there are many mappings having the stated property. We give one such mapping in each case.

1. $w = 2z + 1 - i$ **3.** $w = \dfrac{3z + 2 + 6i}{z + 2i}$ **5.** $w = \dfrac{-4i(z + 1)}{z - 1}$ **7.** $w = z^{1/3}$

9. *Hint:* Evaluate $f(1), f(-1), f(0)$, and $f(\infty)$ and then use the result that $\displaystyle\int_0^1 t^{m-1}(1 - t)^{n-1}\,dt = \dfrac{\Gamma(m)\Gamma(n)}{\Gamma(m + n)}$ for positive integers m and n.

Section 25.4

1. $u(x, y) = \dfrac{y}{\pi}\displaystyle\int_{-\infty}^{\infty} \dfrac{g(t)}{(t - x)^2 + y^2}\,dt$, where $u(x, 0) = g(x)$.

3. $u(x, y) = \dfrac{1}{2\pi}\displaystyle\int_0^{2\pi} g(x_0 + R\cos(t), y_0 + R\sin(t))$
$$\times \left[\dfrac{R^2 - (x - x_0)^2 - (y - y_0)^2}{R^2 + (x - x_0)^2 + (y - y_0)^2 - 2R(x - x_0)\cos(t) - 2R(y - y_0)\sin(t)}\right] dt$$

5. $u(r\cos(\theta), r\sin(\theta)) = \dfrac{1}{2\pi}\displaystyle\int_0^{2\pi} \dfrac{[r\cos(t) - r\sin(t)](1 - r^2)}{1 + r^2 - 2r\cos(t - \theta)}\,dt$

7. $u(x, y) = \dfrac{1}{8}\displaystyle\int_{-1}^1 \dfrac{(1 - |t|)\cos(\pi t/2)}{1 + \sin^2(\pi t/2)}$
$$\times \left[\dfrac{4\sinh(\pi x/2)\cos(\pi y/2)[1 + \sin^2(\pi t/2)] + \sinh(\pi x)\sin(\pi y)[1 - \sin(\pi t/2)]}{\sinh^2(\pi x/2) + \sin^2(\pi y/2) - 2\cosh(\pi x/2)\sin(\pi y/2)\sin(\pi t/2) + \sin^2(\pi t/2)}\right] dt$$

Section 25.5

1. With $a = Ke^{i\theta}$, equipotential curves are $\varphi(x, y) = K[x\cos(\theta) - y\sin(\theta)] = $ constant. These are lines of the form $y = \cot(\theta)x + b$. Streamlines are $\psi(x, y) = K[y\cos(\theta) + x\sin(\theta)] = $ constant, which are lines $y = -\tan(\theta)x + b$. Velocity $= \overline{f'(z)} = Ke^{-i\theta}$. There are no sources or sinks.

3. $\varphi(x, y) = \cos(x)\cosh(y)$, $\psi(x, y) = -\sin(x)\sinh(y)$. Equipotential curves are graphs of $y = \cosh^{-1}(K/\cos(x))$, streamlines are graphs of $y = \sinh^{-1}(C/\sin(x))$.

5. $\varphi(x, y) = K\ln|z - z_0|$, $\psi(x, y) = K\arg(z - z_0)$. Equipotential curves are circles $|z - z_0| = r$ and streamlines are rays emanating from z_0; $\displaystyle\int_C -v\,dx + u\,dv = 2\pi K$, with C the circle of radius r about z_0.

7. $f(z) = k\left[x + \dfrac{x}{x^2 + y^2} + i\left(y - \dfrac{y}{x^2 + y^2}\right)\right]$. Equipotential curves are graphs of $x + \dfrac{x}{x^2 + y^2} = c$, streamlines are graphs

of $y - \dfrac{y}{x^2 + y^2} = d$.

9. Equipotential curves are graphs of $K\left[x + \dfrac{x}{x^2 + y^2}\right] - \dfrac{b}{2\pi}\arg(z) = c$. Streamlines are graphs of

$k\left[y - \dfrac{y}{x^2 + y^2}\right] + \dfrac{b}{4\pi}\ln|z| = d$. Stagnation points occur where $f'(z) = k\left(1 - \dfrac{1}{z^2}\right) + \dfrac{ib}{2\pi z} = 0$, or

$z = -\dfrac{ib}{4k\pi} \pm \sqrt{1 - \dfrac{b^2}{16\pi^2 k^2}}$.

CHAPTER 26

Section 26.1

1. (a) abcdefghijkl, where each of the letters a, ..., g can be either an H (for heads) or T (for tails), and each of the symbols h, ..., l can be any of the integers from 1 through 6 inclusive. (b) $2^7 6^5$

3. $6^{10}(15)$ **5.** There are $4^3 5^3 = 8{,}000$ outcomes, more than enough.   **7.** $7(15)(8)(17)$, or $14{,}280$

9. $7(11)(6)(14)$, or $6{,}468$

Section 26.2

1. $9!$ **3.** $9!$

5. (a) $7!$ (b) $6!$ (c) $5!$

7. $6!$ **9.** $12!$ **11.** $6!$

Section 26.3

1. $_{25}P_7$, or $2{,}422{,}728{,}000$ **3.** $_{22}P_6$, or $53{,}721{,}360$

5. $_{52}P_{10}$, or $5.7408(10^{16})$ if order counts; $_{52}C_{10}$, or $158{,}200{,}024{,}220$ if order is unimportant

7. $_{20}C_4$, or $4{,}845$ **9.** with order: $_{52}P_5$, or $311{,}875{,}200$; without order, $_{52}C_5$, or $2{,}598{,}960$

Section 26.4

1. Typical outcome: a, b, c, d, where each letter can be any of the integers 1, 2, 3, 4, 5, 6. There are 6^4 outcomes. A has 40 outcomes in it, and B has 16 outcomes.

3. Typical outcome: $\alpha, \beta, \gamma, \delta$, with α, β, γ and δ four distinct letters (English) alphabet. There are $_{26}C_4$ outcomes. A has $_{24}C_2$ outcomes, and W has $_7C_4$ outcomes.

5. Typical outcome: a, b, c, d, e, f, where each of a, b and c can be H or T, and each of d, e and f can be any 1, 2, 3, 4, 5, 6. There are $2^3 6^3$ outcomes.
C has 10 outcomes, D has 80 outcomes, E has 24 outcomes.

7. Typical outcome: a, b, c, d, e, in which each letter can be any of 1, 2, 3, 4, 5, 6.
U has 21 outcomes, K has 21 outcomes.

9. Typical outcome: $a, b, \ldots, p$, with each letter a distinct card; there are $_{52}C_{16}$ outcomes.
Y has one outcome, M has $4(_{40}C_5)$ outcomes.

Section 26.5

1. (a) 5/16 (b) 13/16   **3.** (a) 1/221 (b) 105/221   **5.** (a) 5/14 (b) 15/28 (c) 9/28

7. (a) 1/1860480 (b) 1/4 (c) 1271/1292   **9.** (a) 1892/23205 (b) 2257/54145

Section 26.6

1. $1 - ((7.5^6 + 5^7)/6^7)$, about 0.3302   **3.** $1 - {_8C_5}/{_{52}C_5}$, about 0.9998   **5.** $1 - 1/341, 055$

7. For n people, the probability of at least two having the same birthday is $1 - \dfrac{(365)(364)\cdots(365 - n + 1)}{365^n}$, assuming a 365-day year.

Section 26.7

1. (a) 1/2 (b) 2/3   **3.** (a) 5/16 (b) 5/11   **5.** (a) 56/1296 (b) 4/671   **7.** 1/249,900   **9.** 1/16, 1/4, 0

Section 26.8

1. dependent   **3.** dependent
5. independent   **7.** dependent
9. at least two heads, 0.4864, exactly two heads, 0.3456
11. probability of drawing exactly two reds is $108/11^3$

Section 26.9

1. $\Pr(10) = 1/2$, $\Pr(5) = \Pr(50) = \Pr(0) = \Pr(1200) = 1/8$
3. $\Pr(\text{Ford}) = 1/9$, $\Pr(\text{Chevy}) = 1/18$, $\Pr(\text{Porsche}) = 1/6$, $\Pr(\text{VW}) = 1/12$, $\Pr(\text{Lamborghini}) = 1/12$, $\Pr(\text{tricycle}) = 1/12$, $\Pr(\text{Honda}) = 1/18$, $\Pr(\text{Mercedes}) = 1/9$, $\Pr(\text{tank}) = 1/12$, $\Pr(\text{Steamer}) = 1/24$, $\Pr(\text{bike}) = 1/8$
5. $\Pr(0) = 1/4$, $\Pr(50,000) = 1/20$, $\Pr(.05) = \Pr(1000) = 1/20$
$\Pr(500) = \Pr(1500) = 1/5$, $\Pr(20) = \Pr(\text{lion}) = 1/10$

Section 26.10

1. $\Pr(\geq 10 \text{ years}|\text{item defective}) = 0.14$,
$\Pr(5\text{–}10 \text{ years}|\text{item defective}) = 0.35$,
$\Pr(1\text{–}5 \text{ years}|\text{item defective}) = 0.12$,
$\Pr(<1 \text{ year}|\text{item defective}) = 0.039$
3. $\Pr(\text{adult male}|\text{survived} \geq 2 \text{ years} = 0.039$
$\Pr(\text{girl}|\text{survived} <1 \text{ year} = 0.032$
5. $\Pr(\text{City 1}|\text{gun explodes}) = 0.05$
$\Pr(\text{City 2}|\text{gun explodes}) = 0.012$
$\Pr(\text{City 3}|\text{gun explodes}) = 0.212$
$\Pr(\text{City 4}|\text{gun explodes}) = 0.014$
$\Pr(\text{City 5}|\text{gun explodes}) = 0.045$
$\Pr(\text{City 6}|\text{gun explodes}) = 0.666$

Section 26.11

1. win $1.82 per game   **3.** lose $0.23 per game
5. lose $2 per game   **7.** win $4.43 per game

CHAPTER 27

Section 27.1

1. (a) $s = 4.809$, approximation yields 4.15
(c) $s = 4.9497$, approximation yields 3.75
3. $\bar{x} = 1.2258$ median $= 1$, $s = 8.6872$

Section 27.2

1. $P(2) = 1/36 = P(12)$, $P(3) = P(11) = 2/36$, $P(4) = P(10) = 3/36$, $P(5) = P(9) = 4/36$, $P(6) = P(8) = 5/36$, $P(7) = 6/36$, $\mu = 7$, $\sigma = 2.4152$
3. $P(0) = 1/20$, $P(1) = 8/20$, $P(2) = 6/20$, $P(3) = 4/20$, $P(4) = 1/20$, $\mu = 1.8$, $\sigma = 0.98$
5. $\Pr(4) = 6/1326$, $\Pr(5) = 16/1326$, $\Pr(6) = 22/1326$, $\Pr(7) = 32/1326$, $\Pr(8) = 38/1326$, $\Pr(9) = 48/1326$,
$\Pr(10) = 54/1326$, $\Pr(11) = 640/1326$, $\Pr(12) = 190/1326$, $\Pr(13) = 64/1326$, $\Pr(14) = 54/1326$, $\Pr(15) = 48/1326$,
$\Pr(16) = 38/1326$, $\Pr(17) = 32/1326$, $\Pr(18) = 22/1326$, $\Pr(19) = 16/1326$, $\Pr(20) = 6/1326$,
$\mu = 11.566$, $\sigma = 2.33$

Section 27.3

1. (a) 0.178 (c) 0.313 (e) 0.0085 (g) 0.273
3. (a) 0.263 (b) 0.329 (c) 0.099 (d) 0.0014

5. 0.376

9. (a) 0.052 (b) 0.23519

11. For three hits, 0.055. For two to six hits, 0.24653.

Section 27.4

1. (a) $\mu = 15$, $\sigma = 5/\sqrt{2}$ (b) $y = \dfrac{1}{5\sqrt{\pi}}e^{-(x-15)^2/25}$ (c) $2.055(10^{-5})$ (d) 0.999 (e) $1.7396(10^{-8})$

3. (a) $\mu = 168$, $\sigma = 9.3467$ (b) $y = \dfrac{1}{(9.3467)\sqrt{2\pi}}e^{-(x-162)^2/174.72}$ (c) $3.0087(10^{-5})$ (d) 0.99974 (e) ≈ 1

5. probability of between 250 and 600 miles is 0.0417
probability of between 600 and 900 miles is 0.979

7. probability of between .245 and .270 is 0.539
probability of over .260 is 0.35162
probability of .300 or over is 0.01135

9. (a) $a = 263$, $b = 287$ (b) $a = 251$, $b = 299$ (c) $a = 239$, $b = 311$

Section 27.5

1. mean of the sample means = population mean = 5.97, standard deviation of the population = $\sigma = 2.1446$, standard deviation of the sample means = 0.6629, $\sigma/\sqrt{5} = 0.959$

3. (a) 0.059 (b) 0.5 (c) 0.00053 (bonus extremely unlikely)

5. (a) 0.868 (b) 0.665 (c) 0.997

Section 27.6

1. (a) $0.01 < p < 0.03$ (b) $0.012 < p < 0.028$ (c) $0.013 < p < 0.027$

3. (a) $0.366 < p < 0.504$ (b) $0.385 < p < 0.485$

5. (a) 2,401 (b) 384 (c) 2215.9

7. (a) 105.8 (b) 36 (c) 24

Section 27.7

1. (a) $71.86 < \mu < 72.14$ (b) 180

3. (a) $105.33 < \mu < 106.47$ (b) 3,819

5. $2.839 < \mu < 3.161$

Section 27.8

1. $c = 0.99895$, significant linear correlation regression line: $y = 3.0196 + 0.81813x$
$y(0.4) = 3.3469$; $2.9297 < y < 3.7641$
$y(6.2) = 8.092$; $7.701 < y < 8.4830$
$y(15.1) = 15.373$; $14.879 < y < 15.687$

3. $c = 0.042039$ – no significant linear correlation exists.

5. $c = 0.99845$, significant linear correlation regression line: $y = -1.3931 + 0.87678x$
$y(0.6) = -0.86703$; $-2.5493 < y < 0.81527$
$y(3) = 1.2372$; $-0.4168 < y < 2.8912$
$y(39) = 32.801$; $30.848 < y < 34.754$
$y(42.1) = 35.519$; $33.488 < y < 37.55$

7. $c = 0.99919$, significant linear correlation regression line: $y = -2.8232 + 1.5892x$
$y(-4) = -9.18$; $-11.339 < y < -7.0212$
$y(11.1) = 14.817$; $12.838 < y < 16.796$
$y(30.1) = 45.012$; $43 < y < 47.024$
$y(66.7) = 103.18$; $100.41 < y < 105.95$

9. (a) $c = 0.98198$, hence a significant linear correlation.
   (b) $y = 1.375 + 0.7704x$
   (c) 96% of these wins are accounted for by this player's presence.
   (d) 67 wins projected, with $62 < y < 72$.

11. (a) $c = 0.95235$, significant linear correlation.
    (b) $y = 0.71719 + 0.33661x$
    (c) 91%
    (d) 9 thefts, with $7.64 < y < 10.62$

Index

Guide to Notation

The following symbols and notation are used throughout this text. Each symbol is paired with a section in which it is defined or used. Standard symbols, such as notation for integrals and sums, are not included.

$W[f,g]$ Wronskian of f and g (2.2)

$\mathcal{L}[f]$ Laplace transform of f (3.1)

$\mathcal{L}[f](s)$ Laplace transform of f evaluated at s (3.1)

$\mathcal{L}^{-1}[F]$ inverse Laplace transform of F

$H(t)$ Heaviside function   (3.3.2)

$\delta(t)$ Dirac delta function   (3.5)

(a, b, c) vector with three components   (6.1)

$\|\mathbf{v}\|$ norm (magnitude) of a vector $\mathbf{v}$ (6.1)

$\mathbf{F} \cdot \mathbf{G}$ dot product of $\mathbf{F}$ and $\mathbf{G}$ (6.2)

$\mathbf{F} \times \mathbf{G}$ cross product of $\mathbf{F}$ and $\mathbf{G}$ (6.3)

R^n n-space; set of all n-vectors   (6.4)

$[a_{ij}]$ matrix whose i, j element is a_{ij} (7.1)

$\mathbf{O}_{n,m}$ $n \times m$ zero matrix   (7.1.3)

$\mathbf{I}_n$ $n \times n$ identity matrix   (7.1.3)

$\mathbf{A}^t$ transpose of $\mathbf{A}$ (7.1.3)

$\mathbf{A}_R$ reduced row echelon form of A (7.3)

$rank(\mathbf{A})$ rank of $\mathbf{A}$ (7.4)

$[\mathbf{A}\vdots\mathbf{B}]$ augmented matrix   (7.7.2)

$\mathbf{A}^{-1}$ inverse of $\mathbf{A}$ (7.9)

$|\mathbf{A}|$ or $\det(\mathbf{A})$ determinant of $\mathbf{A}$ (8.2)

$\mathbf{A}_{ij}$ often denotes the minor of the i, j element of A (9.1)

$p_{\mathbf{A}}(\lambda)$ characteristic polynomial of A (9.1)

Ω In the context of a system $\mathbf{X}' = \mathbf{AX}$, denotes a fundamental matrix (10.1); in the context of the fast Fourier transform, denotes the set of nth roots of unity   (15.9.1)

$\mathbf{T}$ often denotes a unit tangent vector to a curve   (12.1)

κ curvature   (12.2)

$\mathbf{N}$ often denotes a normal (or unit normal) to a curve   (12.2)

∇ del operator   (12.5)

$\nabla\varphi$ or $grad(\varphi)$ gradient of φ (12.4)

$D_{\mathbf{u}}\varphi(P)$ directional derivative of φ in the direction of $\mathbf{u}$, evaluated at P (12.4)

$\int_C f dx + g dy + h dz$ line integral over C (13.1)

$\int_C \mathbf{F} \cdot d\mathbf{R}$ another notation for $\int_C f dx + g dy + h dz$, with $\mathbf{F} = f\mathbf{i} + g\mathbf{j} + h\mathbf{k}$ (13.1)

$\int_C f(x, y, z) ds$ line integral of f with respect to arc length   (13.1.1)

$\dfrac{\partial(f, g)}{\partial(u, v)}$ Jacobian of f and g with respect to u and v (13.4.1)

$\iint_\Sigma f(x, y, z) d\sigma$ surface integral of f over a surface Σ (13.4.4)

$f(x_0-), f(x_0+)$ left and right limits, respectively, of f at x_0 (14.3)

$f'_{\mathcal{L}}(x_0), f'_{\mathcal{R}}(x_0)$ left and right derivatives (respectively) of f at x_0 (14.3.2)

$\Im[f]$, or $\hat{f}$ Fourier transform of f (15.3)

$\Im^{-1}[f]$ inverse Fourier transform of f (15.3)

$\Im_{win}[f]$ windowed Fourier transform of f (15.4.6)

$\Im_{win,t_0}[f]$ windowed Fourier transform of shifted f (15.4.6)

$\Im_C[f]$, or $\hat{f}_C(\omega)$ Fourier cosine transform of f (15.5)

$\Im_S[f]$, or $\hat{f}_S(\omega)$ Fourier sine transform of f (15.5)

$\mathfrak{C}[f]$ or $\widetilde{f}_C(n)$ finite Fourier cosine transform of f (15.6)

$\mathfrak{S}[f]$ or $\widetilde{f}_S(n)$ finite Fourier sine transform of f (15.6)

$\mathbb{D}[u]$ discrete N-point Fourier transform (DFT) of $\{u_j\}$ (15.7)

$\sigma_N(t)$ in the context of Fourier series, denotes the Nth Cesàro sum of f (15.8.2)

$Z(t)$ in the context of filtering, denotes a filter function   (15.8.2)

$L^2(R)$ space of square integrable functions defined on the real line   (16.5.2)

$P_n(x)$ n^{th} Legendre polynomial   (16.1)

$T_n(x)$ n^{th} Chebyschev polynomial   (16.4.1)

$L_n(x)$ · n^{th} Laguerre polynomial   (16.4.2)

$H_n(x)$ n^{th} Hermite polynomial   (16.4.3)

$\Gamma(x)$ gamma function   (16.2.1)

$J_n(x)$ Bessel function of the first kind of order n (16.2.2)

$Y_n(x)$ Bessel function of the second kind of order n (16.2.3)

γ sometimes used to denote Euler's constant   (16.2.3)

$I_0(x),\ K_0(x)$ modified Bessel functions of the first and second kinds, respectively, of order zero   (16.2.4)

$\chi_{[0,1]}$ characteristic function of $[0, 1]$ (16.5.2)

$\sigma_{m,n}(t) = \psi(2^m t - n)$ functions used in constructing Haar wavelets   (16.5.2)

$\psi_{m,n}(t)$ Haar wavelets   (16.5.2)

$\nabla^2(u)$ Laplacian of u (13.7.2, 19.1)

$\mathrm{Re}(z)$ real part of z (20.1)

$\mathrm{Im}(z)$ imaginary part of z (20.1)

$\bar{z}$ complex conjugate of z (20.1.2)

$|z|$ magnitude (modulus) of z (20.1.2)

$\arg(z)$ argument of z (20.1.5)

$\int_\Gamma f(z)dz$ integral of a complex function f over a curve Γ (22.2)

$\mathrm{Re}\,s(f, z_0)$ residue of f at z_0 (24.2)

$f : D \to D^*$ f is a mapping from D into D^* (25.1)

$_nP_r = n!/(n-r)!$ (26.3)

$_nC_r = n!/(r!(n-r)!)$ (26.3)

$\begin{pmatrix} n \\ r \end{pmatrix}$ alternate notation for $_nC_r$ (26.3)

$\mathrm{Pr}(E)$ probability of an event E (26.5)

E^C complement of event E (26.6)

$\mathrm{Pr}(E \mid U)$ conditional probability of E, assuming U (26.7)

$\bar{x}$ or μ often used for mean or average   (27.1)

s or σ in the context of statistics, usually denotes standard deviation   (27.1)

$z_{\alpha/2}$ with reference to a bell curve, usually denotes a critical value   (27.6)

$t_{\alpha/2}$ with reference to a Student t-distribution, usually denotes a critical value   (27.7)